FIRST MULTICOLOUR

Theory of Machines

[A Textbook for the Students of B.E. / B.Tech.,
U.P.S.C. (Engg. Services); Section 'B' of A.M.I.E. (I)]

(S. I. UNITS)

R.S. KHURMI
J.K. GUPTA

EURASIA PUBLISHING HOUSE (PVT.) LTD.

S Chand And Company Limited

(ISO 9001 Certified Company)

Head Office: D-92, Sector–2, Noida – 201301, U.P. (India), Ph. 91-120-4682700

Registered Office: A-27, 2nd Floor, Mohan Co-operative Industrial Estate, New Delhi – 110 044, Phone: 011-49731800

www.schandpublishing.com; e-mail: info@schandpublishing.com

Marketing Offices:

Chennai : Ph: 23632120; chennai@schandpublishing.com
Guwahati : Ph: 2738811, 2735640; guwahati@schandpublishing.com
Hyderabad : Ph: 40186018; hyderabad@schandpublishing.com
Jalandhar : Ph: 4645630; jalandhar@schandpublishing.com
Kolkata : Ph: 23357458, 23353914; kolkata@schandpublishing.com
Lucknow : Ph: 4003633; lucknow@schandpublishing.com
Mumbai : Ph: 25000297; mumbai@schandpublishing.com
Patna : Ph: 2260011; patna@schandpublishing.com

S. CHAND'S Seal of Trust

In our endeavour to protect you against counterfeit/fake books, we have pasted a hologram over the cover of this book. The hologram displays full visible effect, emboss effect, relief effect, mirror lens effect, pearl effect, motion effect, animated text, kinetic effect, concealed effect, micro structure, multicolour small text 'S.CHAND', nanotext '50 micron' ORIGINAL' 'S.CHAND', mirror strip '6.5 mm', mirror lens 3 mm with text 'SC', microtext 'OK', scratch strip '7 mm', color sparkling effect under scratch and QR code size 10 mm x 10 mm, etc.

A fake hologram does not display ALL these effects.

First Edition 1976
Subsequent Editions and Reprints 1977, 78, 79, 80, 81, 83, 84, 85, 86, 87, 88, 89, 90, 91, 93 (Twice), 94, 95, 96, 97, 98, 99, 2000, 2001, 2002, 2003, 2004 (Twice), 2005, First Multicolour Revised & Updated Edition 2005; Reprints 2006, 2007, 2008, 2009, 2010 (Twice), 2011 (Twice), 2012, 2013, 2014 (Twice), 2015 (Twice), 2016 (Twice), 2017 (Twice) 2018 (Twice), 2019

Reprint 2022 (Twice)

ISBN: 978-81-219-2524-2   **Product Code:** H3TOM62TOMH10ENAN0XO

PRINTED IN INDIA

By Vikas Publishing House Private Limited, Plot 20/4, Site-IV, Industrial Area Sahibabad, Ghaziabad – 201 010 and Published by S Chand And Company Limited, A-27, 2nd Floor, Mohan Co-operative Industrial Estate, New Delhi – 110 044.

Preface to the Fourteenth Revised Edition

We feel satisfied in presenting the new edition of this popular treatise. The favourable and warm reception which the previous editions and reprints of this book have enjoyed all over India and abroad, is a matter of great satisfaction for us.

The present multicolour edition has been thoroughly revised and brought up-to-date. Multicolour pictures have been added to enhance the content value and to give the students an idea of what he will be dealing in reality, and to bridge the gap between theory and practice. The mistakes which had crept in, have been eliminated. We wish to express our sincere thanks to numerous professors and students, both at home and abroad, for sending their valuable suggestions and recommending the book to their students and friends. We hope, that they will continue to patronise this book in the future also.

Our grateful thanks are due to the Editorial staff of S. Chand & Company Ltd., especially to Mr. E.J. Jawahardatham and Mr. Rupesh Gupta, for their help in conversion of the book into multicolour edition.

Any errors, omissions and suggestions, for the improvement of this volume brought to our notice, will be thankfully acknowledged and incorporated in the next edition.

R.S. KHURMI
J.K. GUPTA

Preface to the First Edition

We take an opportunity to present this standard treatise entitled as "Theory of Machines" to the students of Degree, Diploma and A.M.I.E. (I) classes in M.K.S. and S.I. units. The object of this book is to present the subject matter in a most concise, compact, to-the-point and lucid manner.

While writing the book, we have continuously kept in mind the examination requirements of the students preparing for U.P.S.C. (Engg. Services) and A.M.I.E. (I) examinations. In order to make this volume more useful for them, complete solutions of their examination papers up to 1975 have also been included. Every care has been taken to make this treatise as self-explanatory as possible. The subject matter has been amply illustrated by incorporating a good number of solved, unsolved and well graded examples of almost every variety. Most of these examples are taken from the recent examination papers of Indian and foreign universities as well as professional examining bodies, to make the students familiar with the type of questions, usually set in their examinations. At the end of each chapter *Highlights* have been added, which summarise the main topics discussed in the chapter for quick revision before the examination. After the highlights, a few exercises have been added for the students to solve them independently. Answers to these problems have been provided, but it is too much to hope that these are entirely free from errors. In short, it is earnestly hoped that the book will earn appreciation of the teachers and students alike.

Although every care has been taken to check mistakes and misprints, yet it is difficult to claim perfection. Any errors, omissions and suggestions for the improvement of this treatise, brought to our notice, will be thankfully acknowledged and incorporated in the next edition.

R.S. KHURMI
J.K. GUPTA

CONTENTS

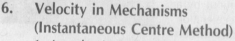

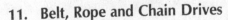

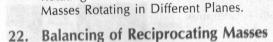

Supported Shaft. 10. Natural Frequency of Free Transverse Vibrations of a Shaft Fixed at Both Ends and Carrying a Uniformly Distributed Load. 11. Natural Frequency of Free Transverse Vibrations for a Shaft Subjected to a Number of Point Loads. 12. Critical or Whirling Speed of a Shaft. 13. Frequency of Free Damped Vibrations (Viscous Damping). 14. Damping Factor or Damping Ratio. 15. Logarithmic Decrement. 16. Frequency of Underdamped Forced Vibrations. 17. Magnification Factor or Dynamic Magnifier. 18. Vibration Isolation and Transmissibility.

1

Introduction

1.1. Definition

The subject **Theory of Machines** may be defined as that branch of Engineering-science, which deals with the study of relative motion between the various parts of a machine, and forces which act on them. The knowledge of this subject is very essential for an engineer in designing the various parts of a machine.

Note: A machine is a device which receives energy in some available form and utilises it to do some particular type of work.

1.2. Sub-divisions of Theory of Machines

The Theory of Machines may be sub-divided into the following four branches :

1. *Kinematics.* It is that branch of Theory of Machines which deals with the relative motion between the various parts of the machines.

2. *Dynamics.* It is that branch of Theory of Machines which deals with the forces and their effects, while acting upon the machine parts in motion.

3. *Kinetics.* It is that branch of Theory of Machines which deals with the inertia forces which arise from the combined effect of the mass and motion of the machine parts.

4. *Statics.* It is that branch of Theory of Machines which deals with the forces and their effects while the machine parts are at rest. The mass of the parts is assumed to be negligible.

1.3. Fundamental Units

The measurement of physical quantities is one of the most important operations in engineering. Every quantity is measured in terms of some arbitrary, but internationally accepted units, called *fundamental units*. All physical quantities, met within this subject, are expressed in terms of the following three fundamental quantities :

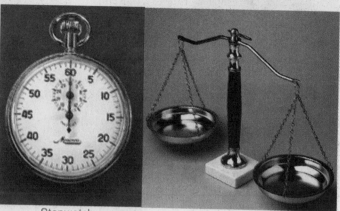

Stopwatch   Simple balance

1. Length (*L* or *l*),
2. Mass (*M* or *m*), and
3. Time (*t*).

1.4. Derived Units

Some units are expressed in terms of fundamental units known as derived units, *e.g.,* the units of area, velocity, acceleration, pressure, etc.

1.5. Systems of Units

There are only four systems of units, which are commonly used and universally recognised. These are known as :

    1. C.G.S. units,   2. F.P.S. units,   3. M.K.S. units, and   4. S.I. units.

1.6. C.G.S. Units

In this system, the fundamental units of length, mass and time are *centimetre, gram* and *second* respectively. The C.G.S. units are known as absolute units or physicist's units.

1.7. F.P.S. Units

In this system, the fundamental units of length, mass and time are *foot, pound* and *second* respectively.

1.8. M.K.S. Units

In this system, the fundamental units of length, mass and time are *metre, kilogram* and *second* respectively. The M.K.S. units are known as gravitational units or engineer's units.

1.9. International System of Units (S.I. Units)

The 11th general conference* of weights and measures have recommended a unified and systematically constituted system of fundamental and derived units for international use. This system is now being used in many countries. In India, the standards of Weights and Measures Act, 1956 (vide which we switched over to M.K.S. units) has been revised to recognise all the S.I. units in industry and commerce.

---

*   It is known as General Conference of Weights and Measures (G.C.W.M.). It is an international organisation, of which most of the advanced and developing countries (including India) are members. The conference has been entrusted with the task of prescribing definitions for various units of weights and measures, which are the very basic of science and technology today.

A man whose mass is 60 kg weighs 588.6 N (60 × 9.81 m/s²) on earth, approximately 96 N (60 × 1.6 m/s²) on moon and zero in space. But mass remains the same everywhere.

In this system of units, the fundamental units are metre (m), kilogram (kg) and second (s) respectively. *But there is a slight variation in their derived units.* The derived units, which will be used in this book are given below :

Density (mass density)	kg/m^3
Force	N (Newton)
Pressure	Pa (Pascal) or N/m^2 (1 Pa = 1 N/m^2)
Work, energy (in joules)	1 J = 1 N-m
Power (in watts)	1 W = 1 J/s
Absolute viscosity	kg/m-s
Kinematic viscosity	m^2/s
Velocity	m/s
Acceleration	m/s^2
Angular acceleration	rad/s^2
Frequency (in hertz)	Hz

The international metre, kilogram and second are discussed below :

1.10. Metre

The international metre may be defined as the shortest distance (at 0°C) between the two parallel lines, engraved upon the polished surface of a platinum-iridium bar, kept at the International Bureau of Weights and Measures at Sevres near Paris.

1.11. Kilogram

The international kilogram may be defined as the mass of the platinum-iridium cylinder, which is also kept at the International Bureau of Weights and Measures at Sevres near Paris.

1.12. Second

The fundamental unit of time for all the three systems, is second, which is 1/24 × 60 × 60 = 1/86 400th of the mean solar day. A solar day may be defined as the interval of time, between the instants, at which the sun crosses a meridian on two consecutive days. This value varies slightly throughout the year. The average of all the solar days, during one year, is called the mean solar day.

1.13. Presentation of Units and their Values

The frequent changes in the present day life are facilitated by an international body known as International Standard Organisation (ISO) which makes recommendations regarding international standard procedures. The implementation of ISO recommendations, in a country, is assisted by its organisation appointed for the purpose. In India, Bureau of Indian Standards (BIS) previously known as Indian Standards Institution (ISI) has been created for this purpose. We have already discussed that the fundamental units in M.K.S. and S.I. units for length, mass and time is metre, kilogram and second respectively. But in actual practice, it is not necessary to express all lengths in metres, all masses in kilograms and all times in seconds. We shall, sometimes, use the convenient units, which are multiples or divisions of our basic units in tens. As a typical example, although the metre is the unit of length, yet a smaller length of one-thousandth of a metre proves to be more convenient unit, especially in the

With rapid development of Information Technology, computers are playing a major role in analysis, synthesis and design of machines.

dimensioning of drawings. Such convenient units are formed by using a prefix in front of the basic units to indicate the multiplier. The full list of these prefixes is given in the following table.

Table 1.1. Prefixes used in basic units

Factor by which the unit is multiplied	Standard form	Prefix	Abbreviation
1 000 000 000 000	10^{12}	tera	T
1 000 000 000	10^9	giga	G
1 000 000	10^6	mega	M
1 000	10^3	kilo	k
100	10^2	hecto*	h
10	10^1	deca*	da
0.1	10^{-1}	deci*	d
0.01	10^{-2}	centi*	c
0.001	10^{-3}	milli	m
0. 000 001	10^{-6}	micro	μ
0. 000 000 001	10^{-9}	nano	n
0. 000 000 000 001	10^{-12}	pico	p

* These prefixes are generally becoming obsolete probably due to possible confusion. Moreover, it is becoming a conventional practice to use only those powers of ten which conform to 10^{3x}, where x is a positive or negative whole number.

1.14. Rules for S.I. Units

The eleventh General Conference of Weights and Measures recommended only the fundamental and derived units of S.I. units. But it did not elaborate the rules for the usage of the units. Later on many scientists and engineers held a number of meetings for the style and usage of S.I. units. Some of the decisions of the meetings are as follows :

1. For numbers having five or more digits, the digits should be placed in groups of three separated by spaces* (instead of commas) counting both to the left and right to the decimal point.

2. In a four digit number,** the space is not required unless the four digit number is used in a column of numbers with five or more digits.

3. A dash is to be used to separate units that are multiplied together. For example, newton metre is written as N-m. It should not be confused with mN, which stands for millinewton.

4. Plurals are never used with symbols. For example, metre or metres are written as m.

5. All symbols are written in small letters except the symbols derived from the proper names. For example, N for newton and W for watt.

6. The units with names of scientists should not start with capital letter when written in full. For example, 90 newton and not 90 Newton.

At the time of writing this book, the authors sought the advice of various international authorities, regarding the use of units and their values. Keeping in view the international reputation of the authors, as well as international popularity of their books, it was decided to present units*** and their values as per recommendations of ISO and BIS. It was decided to use :

4500	not	4 500	or	4,500
75 890 000	not	75890000	or	7,58,90,000
0.012 55	not	0.01255	or	.01255
30×10^6	not	3,00,00,000	or	3×10^7

The above mentioned figures are meant for numerical values only. Now let us discuss about the units. We know that the fundamental units in S.I. system of units for length, mass and time are metre, kilogram and second respectively. While expressing these quantities we find it time consuming to write the units such as metres, kilograms and seconds, in full, every time we use them. As a result of this, we find it quite convenient to use some standard abbreviations.

We shall use :

m	for metre or metres
km	for kilometre or kilometres
kg	for kilogram or kilograms
t	for tonne or tonnes
s	for second or seconds
min	for minute or minutes
N-m	for newton × metres (*e.g.* work done)
kN-m	for kilonewton × metres
rev	for revolution or revolutions
rad	for radian or radians

---

*   In certain countries, comma is still used as the decimal mark.

**   In certain countries, a space is used even in a four digit number.

***   In some of the question papers of the universities and other examining bodies, standard values are not used. The authors have tried to avoid such questions in the text of the book. However, at certain places, the questions with sub-standard values have to be included, keeping in view the merits of the question from the reader's angle.

1.15. Force

It is an important factor in the field of Engineering science, which may be defined as an agent, which produces or tends to produce, destroy or tends to destroy motion.

1.16. Resultant Force

If a number of forces P,Q,R etc. are acting simultaneously on a particle, then a single force, which will produce the same effect as that of all the given forces, is known as a *resultant force*. The forces P,Q,R etc. are called *component forces*. The process of finding out the resultant force of the given component forces, is known as *composition of forces*.

A resultant force may be found out analytically, graphically or by the following three laws:

1. *Parallelogram law of forces*. It states, "If two forces acting simultaneously on a particle be represented in magnitude and direction by the two adjacent sides of a parallelogram taken in order, their resultant may be represented in magnitude and direction by the diagonal of the parallelogram passing through the point."

2. *Triangle law of forces*. It states, "If two forces acting simultaneously on a particle be represented in magnitude and direction by the two sides of a triangle taken in order, their resultant may be represented in magnitude and direction by the third side of the triangle taken in opposite order."

3. *Polygon law of forces*. It states, "If a number of forces acting simultaneously on a particle be represented in magnitude and direction by the sides of a polygon taken in order, their resultant may be represented in magnitude and direction by the closing side of the polygon taken in opposite order."

1.17. Scalars and Vectors

1. Scalar quantities are those quantities, which have magnitude only, *e.g.* mass, time, volume, density etc.

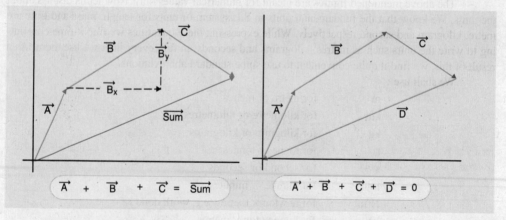

2. Vector quantities are those quantities which have magnitude as well as direction *e.g.* velocity, acceleration, force etc.

3. Since the vector quantities have both magnitude and direction, therefore, while adding or subtracting vector quantities, their directions are also taken into account.

1.18. Representation of Vector Quantities

The vector quantities are represented by vectors. A vector is a straight line of a certain length possessing a starting point and a terminal point at which it carries an arrow head. This vector is cut off along the vector quantity or drawn parallel to the line of action of the vector quantity, so that the length of the vector represents the magnitude to some scale. The arrow head of the vector represents the direction of the vector quantity.

1.19. Addition of Vectors

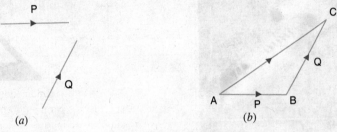

(a)   (b)

Fig. 1.1. Addition of vectors.

Consider two vector quantities P and Q, which are required to be added, as shown in Fig.1.1(a).

Take a point A and draw a line AB parallel and equal in magnitude to the vector P. Through B, draw BC parallel and equal in magnitude to the vector Q. Join AC, which will give the required sum of the two vectors P and Q, as shown in Fig. 1.1 (b).

1.20. Subtraction of Vector Quantities

Consider two vector quantities P and Q whose difference is required to be found out as shown in Fig. 1.2 (a).

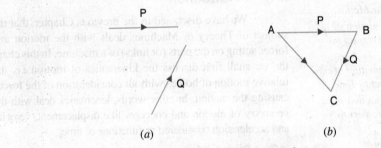

(a)   (b)

Fig. 1.2. Subtraction of vectors.

Take a point A and draw a line AB parallel and equal in magnitude to the vector P. Through B, draw BC parallel and equal in magnitude to the vector Q, *but in opposite direction.* Join AC, which gives the required difference of the vectors P and Q, as shown in Fig. 1.2 (b).

Kinematics of Motion

2.1. Introduction

We have discussed in the previous Chapter, that the subject of Theory of Machines deals with the motion and forces acting on the parts (or links) of a machine. In this chapter, we shall first discuss the kinematics of motion *i.e.* the relative motion of bodies without consideration of the forces causing the motion. In other words, kinematics deal with the geometry of motion and concepts like displacement, velocity and acceleration considered as functions of time.

2.2. Plane Motion

When the motion of a body is confined to only one plane, the motion is said to be *plane motion.* The plane motion may be either rectilinear or curvilinear.

2.3. Rectilinear Motion

It is the simplest type of motion and is along a straight line path. Such a motion is also known as *translatory motion.*

2.4. Curvilinear Motion

It is the motion along a curved path. Such a motion, when confined to one plane, is called *plane curvilinear motion.*

When all the particles of a body travel in concentric circular paths of constant radii (about the axis of rotation perpendicular to the plane of motion) such as a pulley rotating

8

about a fixed shaft or a shaft rotating about its own axis, then the motion is said to be a *plane rotational motion.*

Note: The motion of a body, confined to one plane, may not be either completely rectilinear nor completely rotational. Such a type of motion is called **combined rectilinear and rotational motion.** This motion is discussed in Chapter 6, Art. 6.1.

2.5. Linear Displacement

It may be defined as the distance moved by a body with respect to a certain fixed point. The displacement may be along a straight or a curved path. In a reciprocating steam engine, all the particles on the piston, piston rod and cross-head trace a straight path, whereas all particles on the crank and crank pin trace circular paths, whose centre lies on the axis of the crank shaft. It will be interesting to know, that all the particles on the connecting rod neither trace a straight path nor a circular one; but trace an oval path, whose radius of curvature changes from time to time.

The displacement of a body is a vector quantity, as it has both magnitude and direction. Linear displacement may, therefore, be represented graphically by a straight line.

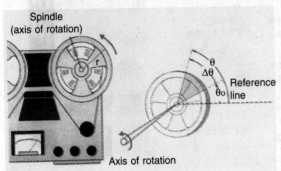

2.6. Linear Velocity

It may be defined as the rate of change of linear displacement of a body with respect to the time. Since velocity is always expressed in a particular direction, therefore it is a vector quantity. Mathematically, linear velocity,

$$v = ds/dt$$

Notes: 1. If the displacement is along a circular path, then the direction of linear velocity at any instant is along the tangent at that point.

2. The speed is the rate of change of linear displacement of a body with respect to the time. Since the speed is irrespective of its direction, therefore, it is a scalar quantity.

2.7. Linear Acceleration

It may be defined as the rate of change of linear velocity of a body with respect to the time. It is also a vector quantity. Mathematically, linear acceleration,

$$a = \frac{dv}{dt} = \frac{d}{dt}\left(\frac{ds}{dt}\right) = \frac{d^2s}{dt^2} \qquad \dots\left(\because \ v = \frac{ds}{dt}\right)$$

Notes: 1. The linear acceleration may also be expressed as follows:

$$a = \frac{dv}{dt} = \frac{ds}{dt} \times \frac{dv}{ds} = v \times \frac{dv}{ds}$$

2. The negative acceleration is also known as *deceleration* or *retardation.*

2.8. Equations of Linear Motion

The following equations of linear motion are important from the subject point of view:

1. $v = u + a.t$ 2. $s = u.t + \dfrac{1}{2}\, a.t^2$

3. $v^2 = u^2 + 2a.s$

4. $s = \dfrac{(u+v)}{2} \times t = v_{av} \times t$

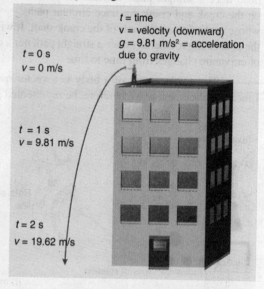

where

u = Initial velocity of the body,

v = Final velocity of the body,

a = Acceleration of the body,

s = Displacement of the body in time t seconds, and

v_{av} = Average velocity of the body during the motion.

Notes: 1. The above equations apply for uniform acceleration. If, however, the acceleration is variable, then it must be expressed as a function of either t, s or v and then integrated.

2. In case of vertical motion, the body is subjected to gravity. Thus g (acceleration due to gravity) should be substituted for 'a' in the above equations.

3. The value of g is taken as $+9.81$ m/s² for downward motion, and -9.81 m/s² for upward motion of a body.

4. When a body falls freely from a height h, then its velocity v, with which it will hit the ground is given by

$$v = \sqrt{2\, g.h}$$

t = time
v = velocity (downward)
g = 9.81 m/s² = acceleration due to gravity

$t = 0$ s
$v = 0$ m/s

$t = 1$ s
$v = 9.81$ m/s

$t = 2$ s
$v = 19.62$ m/s

2.9. Graphical Representation of Displacement with Respect to Time

The displacement of a moving body in a given time may be found by means of a graph. Such a graph is drawn by plotting the displacement as ordinate and the corresponding time as abscissa. We shall discuss the following two cases :

1. When the body moves with uniform velocity. When the body moves with uniform velocity, equal distances are covered in equal intervals of time. By plotting the distances on Y-axis and time on X-axis, a displacement-time curve (*i.e.* s-t curve) is drawn which is a straight line, as shown in Fig. 2.1 (*a*). The motion of the body is governed by the equation $s = u.t$, such that

Velocity at instant $1 = s_1 / t_1$

Velocity at instant $2 = s_2 / t_2$

Since the velocity is uniform, therefore

$$\frac{s_1}{t_1} = \frac{s_2}{t_2} = \frac{s_3}{t_3} = \tan\theta$$

where $\tan\theta$ is called the slope of s-t curve. In other words, the slope of the s-t curve at any instant gives the velocity.

2. *When the body moves with variable velocity.* When the body moves with variable velocity, unequal distances are covered in equal intervals of time or equal distances are covered in unequal intervals of time. Thus the displacement-time graph, for such a case, will be a curve, as shown in Fig. 2.1 (*b*).

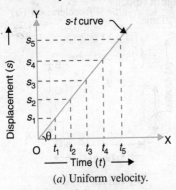

(*a*) Uniform velocity.

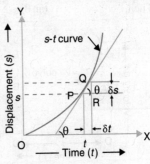

(*b*) Variable velocity.

Fig. 2.1. Graphical representation of displacement with respect to time.

Consider a point *P* on the *s-t* curve and let this point travels to *Q* by a small distance δ*s* in a small interval of time δ*t*. Let the chord joining the points *P* and *Q* makes an angle θ with the horizontal. The average velocity of the moving point during the interval *PQ* is given by

$$\tan \theta = \delta s / \delta t \qquad \ldots \text{(From triangle } PQR \text{)}$$

In the limit, when δ*t* approaches to zero, the point *Q* will tend to approach *P* and the chord *PQ* becomes tangent to the curve at point *P*. Thus the velocity at *P*,

$$v_p = \tan \theta = ds / dt$$

where tan θ is the slope of the tangent at *P*. Thus the slope of the tangent at any instant on the *s-t* curve gives the velocity at that instant.

2.10. Graphical Representation of Velocity with Respect to Time

We shall consider the following two cases :

1. *When the body moves with uniform velocity.* When the body moves with zero acceleration, then the body is said to move with a uniform velocity and the velocity-time curve (*v-t* curve) is represented by a straight line as shown by *AB* in Fig. 2.2 (*a*).

We know that distance covered by a body in time *t* second

= Area under the *v-t* curve *AB*

= Area of rectangle *OABC*

Thus, the distance covered by a body at any interval of time is given by the area under the *v-t* curve.

2. *When the body moves with variable velocity.* When the body moves with

constant acceleration, the body is said to move with variable velocity. In such a case, there is equal variation of velocity in equal intervals of time and the velocity-time curve will be a straight line *AB* inclined at an angle θ, as shown in Fig. 2.2 (*b*). The equations of motion *i.e.* $v = u + a.t$, and $s = u.t + \frac{1}{2} a.t^2$ may be verified from this *v-t* curve.

Let $\qquad u$ = Initial velocity of a moving body, and

$\qquad\qquad v$ = Final velocity of a moving body after time t.

Then, $\qquad\qquad \tan\theta = \dfrac{BC}{AC} = \dfrac{v-u}{t} = \dfrac{\text{Change in velocity}}{\text{Time}} = \text{Acceleration } (a)$

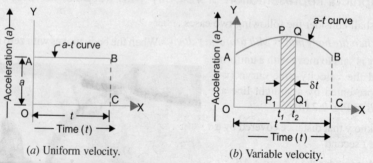

(a) Uniform velocity. $\qquad\qquad\qquad\qquad$ (b) Variable velocity.

Fig. 2.2. Graphical representation of velocity with respect to time.

Thus, the slope of the v-t curve represents the acceleration of a moving body.

Now $\qquad\qquad a = \tan\theta = \dfrac{BC}{AC} = \dfrac{v-u}{t} \qquad$ or $\qquad v = u + a.t$

Since the distance moved by a body is given by the area under the v-t curve, therefore distance moved in time (t),

$$s = \text{Area } OABD = \text{Area } OACD + \text{Area } ABC$$

$$= u.t + \frac{1}{2}(v-u)t = u.t + \frac{1}{2}a.t^2 \qquad\qquad \dots (\because\ v-u = a.t)$$

2.11. Graphical Representation of Acceleration with Respect to Time

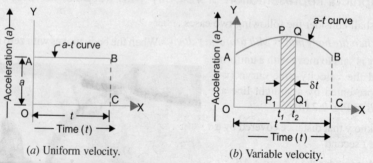

(a) Uniform velocity. $\qquad\qquad\qquad\qquad$ (b) Variable velocity.

Fig. 2.3. Graphical representation of acceleration with respect to time.

We shall consider the following two cases :

1. When the body moves with uniform acceleration. When the body moves with uniform acceleration, the acceleration-time curve (a-t curve) is a straight line, as shown in Fig. 2.3(a). Since the change in velocity is the product of the acceleration and the time, therefore the area under the a-t curve (i.e. OABC) represents the change in velocity.

2. When the body moves with variable acceleration. When the body moves with variable acceleration, the a-t curve may have any shape depending upon the values of acceleration at various instances, as shown in Fig. 2.3(b). Let at any instant of time t, the acceleration of moving body is a.

Mathematically, $\qquad\qquad a = dv/dt \qquad$ or $\qquad dv = a.dt$

Integrating both sides,

$$\int_{v_1}^{v_2} dv = \int_{t_1}^{t_2} a.dt \quad \text{or} \quad v_2 - v_1 = \int_{t_1}^{t_2} a.dt$$

where v_1 and v_2 are the velocities of the moving body at time intervals t_1 and t_2 respectively.

The right hand side of the above expression represents the area (PQQ_1P_1) under the *a-t* curve between the time intervals t_1 and t_2. Thus the area under the *a-t* curve between any two ordinates represents the change in velocity of the moving body. If the initial and final velocities of the body are *u* and *v*, then the above expression may be written as

$$v - u = \int_0^t a.d\,t = \text{Area under } a\text{-}t \text{ curve } AB = \text{Area } OABC$$

Example 2.1. *A car starts from rest and accelerates uniformly to a speed of 72 km. p.h. over a distance of 500 m. Calculate the acceleration and the time taken to attain the speed.*

If a further acceleration raises the speed to 90 km. p.h. in 10 seconds, find this acceleration and the further distance moved. The brakes are now applied to bring the car to rest under uniform retardation in 5 seconds. Find the distance travelled during braking.

Solution. Given : $u = 0$; $v = 72$ km. p.h. $= 20$ m/s ; $s = 500$ m

First of all, let us consider the motion of the car from rest.

Acceleration of the car

Let $\qquad\qquad\qquad a = $ Acceleration of the car.

We know that $\qquad\quad v^2 = u^2 + 2\,a.s$

∴ $\qquad\qquad (20)^2 = 0 + 2a \times 500 = 1000\,a \quad$ or $\quad a = (20)^2 / 1000 = 0.4$ m/s² **Ans.**

Time taken by the car to attain the speed

Let $\qquad\qquad\qquad t = $ Time taken by the car to attain the speed.

We know that $\qquad\quad v = u + a.t$

∴ $\qquad\qquad 20 = 0 + 0.4 \times t \quad$ or $\quad t = 20/0.4 = 50$ s **Ans.**

Now consider the motion of the car from 72 km.p.h. to 90 km.p.h. in 10 seconds.

Given : * $u = 72$ km.p.h. $= 20$ m/s ; $v = 96$ km.p.h. $= 25$ m/s ; $t = 10$ s

Acceleration of the car

Let $\qquad\qquad\qquad a = $ Acceleration of the car.

We know that $\qquad\quad v = u + a.t$

$\qquad\qquad 25 = 20 + a \times 10 \quad$ or $\quad a = (25 - 20)/10 = 0.5$ m/s² **Ans.**

Distance moved by the car

We know that distance moved by the car,

$$s = u.t + \frac{1}{2}a.t^2 = 20 \times 10 + \frac{1}{2} \times 0.5\,(10)^2 = 225\,\text{m} \quad \textbf{Ans.}$$

* It is the final velocity in the first case.

Now consider the motion of the car during the application of brakes for brining it to rest in 5 seconds.

Given : [*]$u = 25$ m/s ; $v = 0$; $t = 5$ s

We know that the distance travelled by the car during braking,

$$s = \frac{u+v}{2} \times t = \frac{25+0}{2} \times 5 = 62.5 \text{ m Ans.}$$

Example 2.2. *The motion of a particle is given by* $a = t^3 - 3t^2 + 5$, *where a is the acceleration in* m/s² *and t is the time in seconds. The velocity of the particle at* $t = 1$ *second is 6.25 m/s, and the displacement is 8.30 metres. Calculate the displacement and the velocity at* $t = 2$ *seconds.*

Solution. Given : $a = t^3 - 3t^2 + 5$

We know that the acceleration, $a = dv/dt$. Therefore the above equation may be written as

$$\frac{dv}{dt} = t^3 - 3t^2 + 5 \quad \text{or} \quad dv = (t^3 - 3t^2 + 5)dt$$

Integrating both sides

$$v = \frac{t^4}{4} - \frac{3t^3}{3} + 5t + C_1 = \frac{t^4}{4} - t^3 + 5t + C_1 \qquad \text{...(i)}$$

where C_1 is the first constant of integration. We know that when $t = 1$ s, $v = 6.25$ m/s. Therefore substituting these values of t and v in equation (i),

$$6.25 = 0.25 - 1 + 5 + C_1 = 4.25 + C_1 \quad \text{or} \quad C_1 = 2$$

Now substituting the value of C_1 in equation (i),

$$v = \frac{t_4}{4} - t^3 + 5t + 2 \qquad \text{...(ii)}$$

Velocity at t = 2 seconds

Substituting the value of $t = 2$ s in the above equation,

$$v = \frac{2^4}{4} - 2^3 + 5 \times 2 + 2 = 8 \text{ m/s Ans.}$$

Displacement at t = 2 seconds

We know that the velocity, $v = ds/dt$, therefore equation (ii) may be written as

$$\frac{ds}{dt} = \frac{t^4}{4} - t^3 + 5t + 2 \quad \text{or} \quad ds = \left(\frac{t^4}{4} - t^3 + 5t + 2\right)dt$$

Integrating both sides,

$$s = \frac{t^5}{20} - \frac{t^4}{4} + \frac{5t^2}{2} + 2t + C_2 \qquad \text{...(iii)}$$

where C_2 is the second constant of integration. We know that when $t = 1$ s, $s = 8.30$ m. Therefore substituting these values of t and s in equation (iii),

$$8.30 = \frac{1}{20} - \frac{1}{4} + \frac{5}{2} + 2 + C_2 = 4.3 + C_2 \quad \text{or} \quad C_2 = 4$$

---

[*] It is the final velocity in the second case.

Substituting the value of C_2 in equation (iii),

$$s = \frac{t^5}{20} - \frac{t^4}{4} + \frac{5t^2}{2} + 2t + 4$$

Substituting the value of $t = 2$ s, in this equation,

$$s = \frac{2^5}{20} - \frac{2^4}{4} + \frac{5 \times 2^2}{2} + 2 \times 2 + 4 = 15.6 \, \text{m} \ \textbf{Ans.}$$

Example 2.3. *The velocity of a train travelling at 100 km/h decreases by 10 per cent in the first 40 s after application of the brakes. Calculate the velocity at the end of a further 80 s assuming that, during the whole period of 120 s, the retardation is proportional to the velocity.*

Solution. Given : Velocity in the beginning (*i.e.* when $t = 0$), $v_0 = 100$ km/h

Since the velocity decreases by 10 per cent in the first 40 seconds after the application of brakes, therefore velocity at the end of 40 s,

$$v_{40} = 100 \times 0.9 = 90 \text{ km/h}$$

Let $\qquad v_{120}$ = Velocity at the end of 120 s (or further 80s).

Since the retardation is proportional to the velocity, therefore,

$$a = -\frac{dv}{dt} = k.v \qquad \text{or} \qquad \frac{dv}{v} = -k.dt$$

where k is a constant of proportionality, whose value may be determined from the given conditions. Integrating the above expression,

$$\log_e v = -k.t + C \qquad\qquad \dots (i)$$

where C is the constant of integration. We know that when $t = 0$, $v = 100$ km/h. Substituting these values in equation (i),

$$\log_e 100 = C \qquad \text{or} \qquad C = 2.3 \log 100 = 2.3 \times 2 = 4.6$$

We also know that when $t = 40$ s, $v = 90$ km/h. Substituting these values in equation (i),

$$\log_e 90 = -k \times 40 + 4.6 \qquad\qquad \dots (\because C = 4.6)$$

$$2.3 \log 90 = -40k + 4.6$$

or

$$k = \frac{4.6 - 2.3\log 90}{40} = \frac{4.6 - 2.3 \times 1.9542}{40} = 0.0026$$

Substituting the values of k and C in equation (i),

$$\log_e v = -0.0026 \times t + 4.6$$

or

$$2.3 \log v = -0.0026 \times t + 4.6 \qquad\qquad \dots (ii)$$

Now substituting the value of t equal to 120 s, in the above equation,

$$2.3 \log v_{120} = -0.0026 \times 120 + 4.6 = 4.288$$

or

$$\log v_{120} = 4.288 / 2.3 = 1.864$$

$\therefore \qquad\qquad v_{120} = 73.1 \text{ km/h} \ \textbf{Ans.} \qquad\qquad \dots \text{(Taking antilog of 1.864)}$

Example 2.4. *The acceleration (a) of a slider block and its displacement (s) are related by the expression, $a = k\sqrt{s}$, where k is a constant. The velocity v is in the direction of the displacement and the velocity and displacement are both zero when time t is zero. Calculate the displacement, velocity and acceleration as functions of time.*

Solution. Given : $a = k\sqrt{s}$

We know that acceleration,

$$a = v \times \frac{dv}{ds} \quad \text{or} \quad k\sqrt{s} = v \times \frac{dv}{ds} \qquad \dots \left[\because \frac{dv}{dt} = \frac{ds}{dt} \times \frac{dv}{ds} = v \times \frac{dv}{ds} \right]$$

$$\therefore \qquad v \times dv = k.s^{1/2}\, ds$$

Integrating both sides,

$$\int_0^v v.dv = k \int s^{1/2} ds \quad \text{or} \quad \frac{v^2}{2} = \frac{k.s^{3/2}}{3/2} + C_1 \qquad \dots (i)$$

where C_1 is the first constant of integration whose value is to be determined from the given conditions of motion. We know that $s = 0$, when $v = 0$. Therefore, substituting the values of s and v in equation (i), we get $C_1 = 0$.

$$\therefore \qquad \frac{v^2}{2} = \frac{2}{3} k.s^{3/2} \quad \text{or} \quad v = \sqrt{\frac{4k}{3}} \times s^{3/4} \qquad \dots (ii)$$

Displacement, velocity and acceleration as functions of time

We know that $\quad \dfrac{ds}{dt} = v = \sqrt{\dfrac{4k}{3}} \times s^{3/4} \qquad \dots \text{[From equation (ii)]}$

$$\therefore \qquad \frac{ds}{s^{3/4}} = \sqrt{\frac{4k}{3}}\, dt \quad \text{or} \quad s^{-3/4}\, ds = \sqrt{\frac{4k}{3}}\, dt$$

Integrating both sides,

$$\int_0^s s^{-3/4}\, ds = \sqrt{\frac{4k}{3}} \int_0^t dt$$

$$\frac{s^{1/4}}{1/4} = \sqrt{\frac{4k}{3}} \times t + C_2 \qquad \dots (iii)$$

where C_2 is the second constant of integration. We know that displacement, $s = 0$ when $t = 0$. Therefore, substituting the values of s and t in equation (iii), we get $C_2 = 0$.

$$\therefore \qquad \frac{s^{1/4}}{1/4} = \sqrt{\frac{4k}{3}} \times t \quad \text{or} \quad s = \frac{k^2.t^4}{144} \quad \textbf{Ans.}$$

We know that velocity,

$$v = \frac{ds}{dt} = \frac{k^2}{144} \times 4t^3 = \frac{k^2.t^3}{36} \quad \textbf{Ans.} \qquad \dots \left(\text{Differentiating } \frac{k^2.t^4}{144} \right)$$

and acceleration, $\qquad a = \dfrac{dv}{dt} = \dfrac{k^2}{36} \times 3\, t^2 = \dfrac{k^2.t^2}{12} \quad \textbf{Ans.} \qquad \dots \left(\text{Differentiating } \dfrac{k^2.t^3}{36} \right)$

Example 2.5. *The cutting stroke of a planing machine is 500 mm and it is completed in 1 second. The planing table accelerates uniformly during the first 125 mm of the stroke, the speed remains constant during the next 250 mm of the stroke and retards uniformly during the last 125 mm of the stroke. Find the maximum cutting speed.*

Solution. Given : $s = 500$ mm ; $t = 1$ s ; $s_1 = 125$ mm ; $s_2 = 250$ mm ; $s_3 = 125$ mm

Fig. 2.4 shows the acceleration-time and velocity-time graph for the planing table of a planing machine.

Let

v = Maximum cutting speed in mm/s.

Planing Machine.

Average velocity of the table during acceleration and retardation,

$$v_{av} = (0+v)/2 = v/2$$

Time of uniform acceleration $t_1 = \dfrac{s_1}{v_{av}} = \dfrac{125}{v/2} = \dfrac{250}{v}$ s

Time of constant speed, $t_2 = \dfrac{s_2}{v} = \dfrac{250}{v}$ s

and time of uniform retardation, $t_3 = \dfrac{s_3}{v_{av}} = \dfrac{125}{v/2} = \dfrac{250}{v}$ s

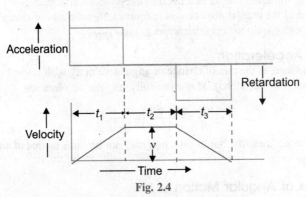

Fig. 2.4

Since the time taken to complete the stroke is 1 s, therefore

$$t_1 + t_2 + t_3 = t$$

$$\frac{250}{v} + \frac{250}{v} + \frac{250}{v} = 1 \text{ or } v = 750 \text{ mm/s Ans.}$$

2.12. Angular Displacement

It may be defined as the angle described by a particle from one point to another, with respect to the time. For example, let a line *OB* has its inclination θ radians to the fixed line *OA*, as shown in

Fig. 2.5. If this line moves from *OB* to *OC*, through an angle $\delta\theta$ during a short interval of time δt, then $\delta\theta$ is known as the *angular displacement* of the line *OB*.

Since the angular displacement has both magnitude and direction, therefore it is also a *vector quantity*.

2.13. Representation of Angular Displacement by a Vector

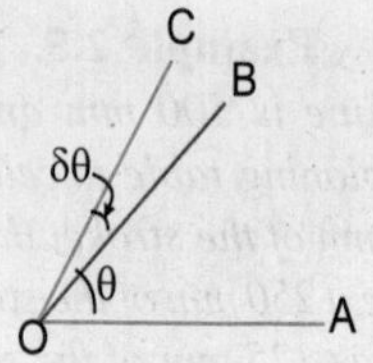

Fig. 2.5. Angular displacement.

In order to completely represent an angular displacement, by a vector, it must fix the following three conditions :

1. *Direction of the axis of rotation*. It is fixed by drawing a line perpendicular to the plane of rotation, in which the angular displacement takes place. In other words, it is fixed along the axis of rotation.

2. *Magnitude of angular displacement*. It is fixed by the length of the vector drawn along the axis of rotation, to some suitable scale.

3. *Sense of the angular displacement.* It is fixed by a right hand screw rule. This rule states that if a screw rotates in a fixed nut in a clockwise direction, *i.e.* if the angular displacement is clockwise and an observer is looking along the axis of rotation, then the arrow head will point away from the observer. Similarly, if the angular displacement is anti-clockwise, then the arrow head will point towards the observer.

2.14. Angular Velocity

It may be defined as the rate of change of angular displacement with respect to time. It is usually expressed by a Greek letter ω (omega). Mathematically, angular velocity,

$$\omega = d\theta / dt$$

Since it has magnitude and direction, therefore, it is a vector quantity. It may be represented by a vector following the same rule as described in the previous article.

Note : If the direction of the angular displacement is constant, then the rate of change of magnitude of the angular displacement with respect to time is termed as *angular speed.*

2.15. Angular Acceleration

It may be defined as the rate of change of angular velocity with respect to time. It is usually expressed by a Greek letter α (alpha). Mathematically, angular acceleration,

$$\alpha = \frac{d\omega}{dt} = \frac{d}{dt}\left(\frac{d\theta}{dt}\right) = \frac{d^2\theta}{dt^2} \qquad \qquad \ldots \left(\because \omega = \frac{d\theta}{dt}\right)$$

It is also a vector quantity, but its direction may not be same as that of angular displacement and angular velocity.

2.16. Equations of Angular Motion

The following equations of angular motion corresponding to linear motion are important from the subject point of view :

1. $\omega = \omega_0 + \alpha . t$

2. $\theta = \omega_0 . t + \dfrac{1}{2}\alpha . t^2$

3. $\omega^2 = \left(\omega_0\right)^2 + 2\alpha . \theta$

4. $\theta = \dfrac{\left(\omega_0 + \omega\right)t}{2}$

where

ω_0 = Initial angular velocity in rad/s,

ω = Final angular velocity in rad/s,

t = Time in seconds,

θ = Angular displacement in time t seconds, and

α = Angular acceleration in rad $/ s^2$.

Note : If a body is rotating at the rate of N r.p.m. (revolutions per minute), then its angular velocity,

$$\omega = 2\pi N / 60 \text{ rad/s}$$

2.17. Relation between Linear Motion and Angular Motion

Following are the relations between the linear motion and the angular motion :

Particulars	Linear motion	Angular motion
Initial velocity	u	ω_0
Final velocity	v	ω
Constant acceleration	a	α
Total distance traversed	s	θ
Formula for final velocity	$v = u + a.t$	$\omega = \omega_0 + \alpha.t$
Formula for distance traversed	$s = u.t + \frac{1}{2} a.t^2$	$\theta = \omega_0.t + \frac{1}{2}\alpha.t^2$
Formula for final velocity	$v^2 = u^2 + 2\,a.s$	$\omega = (\omega_0)^2 + 2\,\alpha.\theta$

2.18. Relation between Linear and Angular Quantities of Motion

Consider a body moving along a circular path from A to B as shown in Fig. 2.6.

Let

r = Radius of the circular path,

θ = Angular displacement in radians,

s = Linear displacement,

v = Linear velocity,

ω = Angular velocity,

a = Linear acceleration, and

α = Angular acceleration.

From the geometry of the figure, we know that

$$s = r . \theta$$

We also know that the linear velocity,

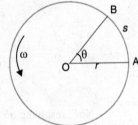

Fig. 2.6. Motion of a body along a circular path.

$$v = \frac{ds}{dt} = \frac{d(r.\theta)}{dt} = r \times \frac{d\theta}{dt} = r.\omega \qquad ...(i)$$

and linear acceleration, $\qquad a = \dfrac{dv}{dt} = \dfrac{d(r.\omega)}{dt} = r \times \dfrac{d\omega}{dt} = r.\alpha \qquad ...(ii)$

Example 2.6. *A wheel accelerates uniformly from rest to 2000 r.p.m. in 20 seconds. What is its angular acceleration? How many revolutions does the wheel make in attaining the speed of 2000 r.p.m.?*

Solution. Given : $N_0 = 0$ or $\omega = 0$; $N = 2000$ r.p.m. or $\omega = 2\pi \times 2000/60 = 209.5$ rad/s ; $t = 20$s

Angular acceleration

Let $\qquad \alpha$ = Angular acceleration in rad/s^2.

We know that

$$\omega = \omega_0 + \alpha.t \qquad \text{or} \qquad 209.5 = 0 + \alpha \times 20$$

$\therefore \qquad \alpha = 209.5 / 20 = 10.475 \text{ rad/s}^2 \textbf{ Ans.}$

Number of revolutions made by the wheel

We know that the angular distance moved by the wheel during 2000 r.p.m. (*i.e.* when $\omega = 209.5$ rad/s),

$$\theta = \frac{(\omega_0 + \omega)t}{2} = \frac{(0 + 209.5)20}{2} = 2095 \text{ rad}$$

Since the angular distance moved by the wheel during one revolution is 2π radians, therefore number of revolutions made by the wheel,

$$n = \theta /2\pi = 2095/2\pi = 333.4 \text{ Ans.}$$

2.19. Acceleration of a Particle along a Circular Path

Consider A and B, the two positions of a particle displaced through an angle $\delta\theta$ in time δt as shown in Fig. 2.7 (*a*).

Let r = Radius of curvature of the circular path,

v = Velocity of the particle at A, and

$v + \delta v$ = Velocity of the particle at B.

The change of velocity, as the particle moves from A to B may be obtained by drawing the vector triangle *oab*, as shown in Fig. 2.7 (*b*). In this triangle, *oa* represents the velocity v and *ob* represents the velocity $v + \delta v$. The change of velocity in time δt is represented by *ab*.

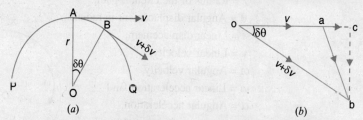

Fig. 2.7. Acceleration of a particle along a circular path.

Now, resolving *ab* into two components *i.e.* parallel and perpendicular to *oa*. Let *ac* and *cb* be the components parallel and perpendicular to *oa* respectively.

∴ $ac = oc - oa = ob \cos \delta\theta - oa = (v + \delta v) \cos \delta\theta - v$

and $cb = ob \sin \delta\theta = (v + \delta v) \sin \delta\theta$

Since the change of velocity of a particle (represented by vector *ab*) has two mutually perpendicular components, therefore the acceleration of a particle moving along a circular path has the following two components of the acceleration which are perpendicular to each other.

1. *Tangential component of the acceleration*. The acceleration of a particle at any instant moving along a circular path in a direction tangential to that instant, is known as tangential component of acceleration or tangential acceleration.

∴ Tangential component of the acceleration of particle at A or tangential acceleration at A,

$$a_t = \frac{ac}{\delta t} = \frac{(v + \delta v)\cos \delta\theta - v}{\delta t}$$

In the limit, when δt approaches to zero, then

$$a_t = dv / dt = \alpha.r \qquad \qquad ... (i)$$

2. *Normal component of the acceleration*. The acceleration of a particle at any instant moving along a circular path in a direction normal to the tangent at that instant and directed towards the centre of the circular path (*i.e.* in the direction from A to O) is known as normal component of the

acceleration or normal acceleration. It is also called *radial* or *centripetal* acceleration.

∴ Normal component of the acceleration of the particle at *A* or normal (or radial or centripetal) acceleration at *A*,

$$a_n = \frac{cb}{\delta t} = \frac{(v + \delta v)\sin \delta\theta}{\delta t}$$

In the limit, when δ*t* approaches to zero, then

$$a_n = v \times \frac{d\theta}{dt} = v.\omega = v \times \frac{v}{r} = \frac{v^2}{r} = \omega^2 .r \qquad \ldots (ii)$$

$$\ldots [\because d\theta/dt = \omega, \text{ and } \omega = v/r]$$

Since the tangential acceleration (a_t) and the normal acceleration (a_n) of the particle at any instant *A* are perpendicular to each other, as shown in Fig. 2.8, therefore total acceleration of the particle (*a*) is equal to the resultant acceleration of a_t and a_n.

∴ Total acceleration or resultant acceleration,

$$a = \sqrt{(a_t)^2 + (a_n)^2}$$

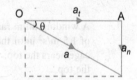

Fig. 2.8. Total acceleration of a particle.

and its angle of inclination with the tangential acceleration is given by

$$\tan \theta = a_n / a_t \text{ or } \theta = \tan^{-1}(a_n / a_t)$$

The total acceleration or resultant acceleration may also be obtained by the vector sum of a_t and a_n.

Notes : 1. From equations (*i*) and (*ii*) we see that the tangential acceleration (a_t) is equal to the rate of change of the magnitude of the velocity whereas the normal or radial or centripetal acceleration (a_n) depends upon its instantaneous velocity and the radius of curvature of its path.

2. When a particle moves along a straight path, then the radius of curvature is infinitely great. This means that v^2/r is zero. In other words, there will be no normal or radial or centripetal acceleration. Therefore, the particle has only tangential acceleration (in the same direction as its velocity and displacement) whose value is given by

$$a_t = dv/dt = \alpha.r$$

3. When a particle moves with a uniform velocity, then *dv/dt* will be zero. In other words, there will be no tangential acceleration; but the particle will have only normal or radial or centripetal acceleration, whose value is given by

$$a_n = v^2/r = v.\omega = \omega^2 r$$

Example 2.7. *A horizontal bar 1.5 metres long and of small cross-section rotates about vertical axis through one end. It accelerates uniformly from 1200 r.p.m. to 1500 r.p.m. in an interval of 5 seconds. What is the linear velocity at the beginning and end of the interval ? What are the normal and tangential components of the acceleration of the mid-point of the bar after 5 seconds after the acceleration begins ?*

Solution. Given : *r* = 1.5 m ; N_0 = 1200 r.p.m. or ω_0 = 2 π × 1200/60 = 125.7 rad/s ; *N* = 1500 r.p.m. or ω = 2 π × 1500/60 = 157 rad/s ; *t* = 5 s

Linear velocity at the beginning

We know that linear velocity at the beginning,

$$v_0 = r . \omega_0 = 1.5 \times 125.7 = 188.6 \text{ m/s Ans.}$$

Linear velocity at the end of 5 seconds

We also know that linear velocity after 5 seconds,

$$v_5 = r . \omega = 1.5 \times 157 = 235.5 \text{ m/s Ans.}$$

Tangential acceleration after 5 seconds

Let $\qquad\qquad$ α = Constant angular acceleration.

We know that $\qquad\qquad$ $\omega = \omega_0 + \alpha.t$

$$157 = 125.7 + \alpha \times 5 \qquad \text{or} \qquad \alpha = (157 - 125.7)/5 = 6.26 \text{ rad/s}^2$$

Radius corresponding to the middle point,

$$r = 1.5/2 = 0.75 \text{ m}$$

$\therefore$ Tangential acceleration $\quad = \alpha.\ r = 6.26 \times 0.75 = 4.7 \text{ m/s}^2$ **Ans.**

Radial acceleration after 5 seconds

Radial acceleration $= \omega^2.\ r = (157)^2\ 0.75 = 18\ 487 \text{ m/s}^2$ **Ans.**

EXERCISES

1. A winding drum raises a cage through a height of 120 m. The cage has, at first, an acceleration of 1.5 m/s^2 until the velocity of 9 m/s is reached, after which the velocity is constant until the cage nears the top, when the final retardation is 6 m/s^2. Find the time taken for the cage to reach the top. **[Ans. 17.1s]**

2. The displacement of a point is given by $s = 2t^3 + t^2 + 6$, where s is in metres and t in seconds. Determine the displacement of the point when the velocity changes from 8.4 m/s to 18 m/s. Find also the acceleration at the instant when the velocity of the particle is 30 m/s. **[Ans. 6.95 m ; 27 m/s^2]**

3. A rotating cam operates a follower which moves in a straight line. The stroke of the follower is 20 mm and takes place in 0.01 second from rest to rest. The motion is made up of uniform acceleration for 1/4 of the time, uniform velocity for $\frac{1}{2}$ of the time followed by uniform retardation. Find the maximum velocity reached and the value of acceleration and retardation. **[Ans. 2.67 m/s ; 1068 m/s^2 ; 1068 m/s^2]**

4. A cage descends a mine shaft with an acceleration of 0.5 m/s^2. After the cage has travelled 25 metres, a stone is dropped from the top of the shaft. Determine : 1. the time taken by the stone to hit the cage, and 2. distance travelled by the cage before impact. **[Ans. 2.92 s ; 41.73 m]**

5. The angular displacement of a body is a function of time and is given by equation :

    $$\theta = 10 + 3\ t + 6\ t^2, \text{ where } t \text{ is in seconds.}$$

    Determine the angular velocity, displacement and acceleration when $t = 5$ seconds. State whether or not it is a case of uniform angular acceleration. **[Ans. 63 rad/s ; 175 rad ; 12 rad/s^2]**

6. A flywheel is making 180 r.p.m. and after 20 seconds it is running at 140 r.p.m. How many revolutions will it make, and what time will elapse before it stops, if the retardation is uniform ? **[Ans. 135 rev. ; 90 s]**

7. A locomotive is running at a constant speed of 100 km/h. The diameter of driving wheels is 1.8 m. The stroke of the piston of the steam engine cylinder of the locomotive is 600 mm. Find the centripetal acceleration of the crank pin relative to the engine frame. **[Ans. 288 m/s^2]**

DO YOU KNOW ?

1. Distinguish clearly between speed and velocity. Give examples.

2. What do you understand by the term 'acceleration' ? Define positive acceleration and negative acceleration.

3. Define 'angular velocity' and 'angular acceleration'. Do they have any relation between them ?

4. How would you find out the linear velocity of a rotating body ?

5. Why the centripetal acceleration is zero, when a particle moves along a straight path ?

6. A particle moving with a uniform velocity has no tangential acceleration. Explain clearly.

OBJECTIVE TYPE QUESTIONS

1. The unit of linear acceleration is
     (*a*) kg-m   (*b*) m/s   (*c*) m/s^2 (*d*) rad/s^2
2. The angular velocity (in rad/s) of a body rotating at *N* r.p.m. is
     (*a*) $\pi N/60$ (*b*) $2\,\pi N/60$ (*c*) $\pi N/120$ (*d*) $\pi N/180$
3. The linear velocity of a body rotating at ω rad/s along a circular path of radius *r* is given by
     (*a*) $\omega.r$ (*b*) ω/r (*c*) $\omega^2.r$ (*d*) ω^2/r
4. When a particle moves along a straight path, then the particle has
     (*a*) tangential acceleration only   (*b*) centripetal acceleration only
     (*c*) both tangential and centripetal acceleration
5. When a particle moves with a uniform velocity along a circular path, then the particle has
     (*a*) tangential acceleration only   (*b*) centripetal acceleration only
     (*c*) both tangential and centripetal acceleration

ANSWERS

1. (*c*)   2. (*b*)   3. (*a*)   4. (*a*)   5. (*b*)

3

Kinetics of Motion

3.1. Introduction

In the previous chapter we have discussed the kinematics of motion, *i.e.* the motion without considering the forces causing the motion. Here we shall discuss the kinetics of motion, *i.e.* the motion which takes into consideration the forces or other factors, *e.g.* mass or weight of the bodies. The force and motion is governed by the three laws of motion.

3.2. Newton's Laws of Motion

Newton has formulated three laws of motion, which are the basic postulates or assumptions on which the whole system of kinetics is based. Like other scientific laws, these are also justified as the results, so obtained, agree with the actual observations. These three laws of motion are as follows:

1. *Newton's First Law of Motion.* It states, *"Every body continues in its state of rest or of uniform motion in a straight line, unless acted upon by some external force."* This is also known as *Law of Inertia.*

The inertia is that property of a matter, by virtue of which a body cannot move of itself, nor change the motion imparted to it.

2. *Newton's Second Law of Motion* . It states, *"The rate of change of momentum is directly proportional to the impressed force and takes place in the same direction in which the force acts."*

3. *Newton's Third Law of Motion* . It states, *"To every action, there is always an equal and opposite reaction."*

3.3. Mass and Weight

Sometimes much confusion and misunder-standing is created, while using the various systems of units in the measurements of force and mass. This happens because of the lack of clear understanding of the difference between the mass and the weight. The following definitions of mass and weight should be clearly understood :

The above picture shows space shuttle. All space vehicles move based on Newton's three laws.

1. *Mass* . It is the amount of matter contained in a given body, and does not vary with the change in its position on the earth's surface. The mass of a body is measured by direct comparison with a standard mass by using a lever balance.

2. *Weight.* It is the amount of pull, which the earth exerts upon a given body. Since the pull varies with distance of the body from the centre of the earth, therefore the weight of the body will vary with its position on the earth's surface (say latitude and elevation). It is thus obvious, that the weight is a force.

The earth's pull in metric units at sea level and 45° latitude has been adopted as one force unit and named as one kilogram of force. Thus, it is a definite amount of force. But, unfor-tunately, it has the same name as the unit of mass. The weight of a body is measured by the use of a spring balance which indicates the varying ten-sion in the spring as the body is moved from place to place.

Note: The confusion in the units of mass and weight is eliminated, to a great extent, in S.I. units. In this system, the mass is taken in kg and force in newtons. The relation between the mass (m) and the weight (W) of a body is

$$W = m.g \quad \text{or} \quad m = W/g$$

where W is in newtons, m is in kg and g is acceleration due to gravity.

3.4. Momentum

It is the total motion possessed by a body. Mathematically,

Momentum = Mass × Velocity

Let m = Mass of the body,

u = Initial velocity of the body,

v = Final velocity of the body,

a = Constant acceleration, and

t = Time required (in seconds) to change the velocity from u to v.

Now, initial momentum = $m.u$

and final momentum = $m.v$

∴ Change of momentum = $m.v - m.u$

and rate of change of momentum $= \dfrac{m.v - m.u}{t} = \dfrac{m(v - u)}{t} = m.a$ ...$\left(\because \dfrac{v - u}{t} = a \right)$

3.5. Force

It is an important factor in the field of Engineering-science, which may be defined as an agent, which produces or tends to produce, destroy or tends to destroy motion.

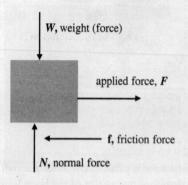

W, weight (force)

applied force, F

f, friction force

N, normal force

According to Newton's Second Law of Motion, the applied force or impressed force is directly proportional to the rate of change of momentum. We have discussed in Art. 3.4, that the rate of change of momentum

$$= m.a$$

where m = Mass of the body, and

a = Acceleration of the body.

∴ Force , $F \propto m.a$ or $F = k.m.a$

where k is a constant of proportionality.

For the sake of convenience, the unit of force adopted is such that it produces a unit acceleration to a body of unit mass.

∴ $F = m.a$ = Mass × Acceleration

In S.I. system of units, the unit of force is called newton (briefly written as N). *A newton may be defined as the force while acting upon a mass of one kg produces an acceleration of 1 m/s² in the direction of which it acts*. Thus

$$1 \text{ N} = 1 \text{ kg} \times 1 \text{ m/s}^2 = 1 \text{ kg-m/s}^2$$

Note: A force equal in magnitude but opposite in direction and collinear with the impressed force producing the acceleration, is known as *inertia force*. Mathematically,

Inertia force = $- m.a$

3.6. Absolute and Gravitational Units of Force

We have already discussed, that when a body of mass 1 kg is moving with an acceleration of 1 m/s², the force acting on the body is one newton (briefly written as N). Therefore, when the same body is moving with an acceleration of 9.81 m/s², the force acting on the body is 9.81 newtons. But we denote 1 kg mass, attracted towards the earth with an acceleration of 9.81 m/s² as 1 kilogram-force (briefly written as kgf) or 1 kilogram-weight (briefly written as kg-wt). It is thus obvious that

$$1 \text{ kgf} = 1 \text{ kg} \times 9.81 \text{ m/s}^2 = 9.81 \text{ kg-m/s}^2 = 9.81 \text{ N} \quad ...(\because 1 \text{ N} = 1 \text{ kg-m/s}^2)$$

The above unit of force *i.e.* kilogram-force (kgf) is called *gravitational* or *engineer's unit of force*, whereas newton is the *absolute* or *scientific* or *S.I. unit of force*. It is thus obvious, that the gravitational units are '*g*' times the unit of force in the absolute or S.I. units.

It will be interesting to know that *the mass of a body in absolute units is numerically equal to the weight of the same body in gravitational units*.

For example, consider a body whose mass, $m = 100$ kg.

∴ The force, with which it will be attracted towards the centre of the earth,

$$F = m.a = m.g = 100 \times 9.81 = 981 \text{ N}$$

Now, as per definition, we know that the weight of a body is the force, by which it is attracted towards the centre of the earth. Therefore, weight of the body,

$$W = 981 \text{ N} = 981 / 9.81 = 100 \text{ kgf} \qquad \ldots (\because 1 \text{ kgf} = 9.81 \text{ N})$$

In brief, the weight of a body of mass m kg at a place where gravitational acceleration is '*g*' m/s^2 is $m.g$ newtons.

3.7. Moment of a Force

It is the turning effect produced by a force, on the body, on which it acts. The moment of a force is equal to the product of the force and the perpendicular distance of the point about which the moment is required, and the line of action of the force. Mathematically,

Moment of a force $= F \times l$

where
F = Force acting on the body, and

l = Perpendicular distance of the point and the line of action of the force, as shown in Fig. 3.1.

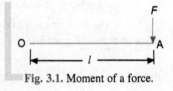
Fig. 3.1. Moment of a force.

3.8. Couple

The two equal and opposite parallel forces, whose lines of action are different, form a couple, as shown in Fig. 3.2.

The perpendicular distance (x) between the lines of action of two equal and opposite parallel forces (F) is known as *arm of the couple*. The magnitude of the couple (*i.e.* moment of a couple) is the product of one of the forces and the arm of the couple. Mathematically,

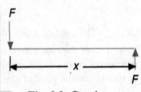
Fig. 3.2. Couple.

Moment of a couple $= F \times x$

A little consideration will show, that a couple does not produce any translatory motion (*i.e.* motion in a straight line). But, a couple produces a motion of rotation of the body, on which it acts.

3.9. Centripetal and Centrifugal Force

Consider a particle of mass m moving with a linear velocity v in a circular path of radius r.

We have seen in Art. 2.19 that the centripetal acceleration,

$$a_c = v^2/r = \omega^2.r$$

and
Force = Mass × Acceleration

∴ Centripetal force = Mass × Centripetal acceleration

or
$$F_c = m.v^2/r = m.\omega^2.r$$

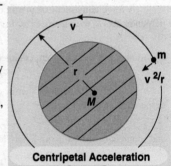
Centripetal Acceleration

This force acts radially inwards and is essential for circular motion.

We have discussed above that the centripetal force acts radially inwards. According to Newton's Third Law of Motion, action and reaction are equal and opposite. Therefore, the particle must exert a force radially outwards of equal magnitude. This force is known as *centrifugal force* whose magnitude is given by

$$F_c = m.v^2/r = m.\omega^2 r$$

3.10. Mass Moment of Inertia

It has been established since long that a rigid body is composed of small particles. If the mass of every particle of a body is multiplied by the square of its perpendicular distance from a fixed line, then the sum of these quantities(for the whole body) is known as *mass moment of inertia* of the body. It is denoted by I.

Consider a body of total mass m. Let it is composed of small particles of masses m_1, m_2, m_3, m_4 etc. If k_1, k_2, k_3, k_4 are the distances of these masses from a fixed line, as shown in Fig. 3.3, then the mass moment of inertia of the whole body is given by

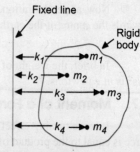

Fig. 3.3. Mass moment of inertia.

$$I = m_1 (k_1)^2 + m_2(k_2)^2 + m_3 (k_3)^2 + m_4 (k_4)^2 + ...$$

If the total mass of body may be assumed to concentrate at one point (known as centre of mass or centre of gravity), at a distance k from the given axis, such that

$$m.k^2 = m_1(k_1)^2 + m_2(k_2)^2 + m_3(k_3)^2 + m_4 (k_4)^2 + ...$$

then
$$I = m.k^2$$

The distance k is called the *radius of gyration*. It may be defined *as the distance, from a given reference, where the whole mass of body is assumed to be concentrated to give the same value of I*.

The unit of mass moment of inertia in S.I. units is kg-m².

Notes : 1. If the moment of inertia of a body about an axis through its centre of gravity is known, then the moment of inertia about any other parallel axis may be obtained by using a parallel axis theorem *i.e.* moment of inertia about a parallel axis,

$$I_p = I_G + m.h^2$$

where
I_G = Moment of inertia of a body about an axis through its centre of gravity, and

h = Distance between two parallel axes.

2. The following are the values of I for simple cases :

(*a*) The moment of inertia of a thin disc of radius r, about an axis through its centre of gravity and perpendicular to the plane of the disc is

$$I = m.r^2/2$$

and moment of inertia about a diameter,

$$I = m.r^2/4$$

(*b*) The moment of inertia of a thin rod of length l, about an axis through its centre of gravity and perpendicular to its length,

$$I_G = m.l^2/12$$

and moment of inertia about a parallel axis through one end of a rod,

$$I_p = m.l^2/3$$

3. The moment of inertia of a solid cylinder of radius r and length l, about the longitudinal axis or polar axis

$$= m.r^2/2$$

and moment of inertia through its centre perpendicular to longitudinal axis

$$= \left(\frac{r^2}{4} + \frac{l^2}{12} \right)$$

3.11. Angular Momentum or Moment of Momentum

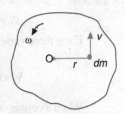

Consider a body of total mass m rotating with an angular velocity of ω rad/s, about the fixed axis O as shown in Fig. 3.4. Since the body is composed of numerous small particles, therefore let us take one of these small particles having a mass dm and at a distance r from the axis of rotation. Let v is its linear velocity acting tangentially at any instant. We know that momentum is the product of mass and velocity, therefore momentum of mass dm

Fig. 3.4. Angular momentum.

$$= dm \times v = dm \times \omega \times r \qquad \qquad ... (\because v = \omega.r)$$

and moment of momentum of mass dm about O

$$= dm \times \omega \times r \times r = dm \times r^2 \times \omega = I_m \times \omega$$

where

$$I_m = \text{Mass moment of inertia of mass } dm \text{ about } O = dm \times r^2$$

∴ Moment of momentum or angular momentum of the whole body about O

$$= \int I_m.\omega = I.\omega$$

where

$$\int I_m = I$$

$$= \text{Mass moment of inertia of the whole body about } O.$$

Thus we see that the angular momentum or the moment of momentum is the product of mass moment of inertia (I) and the angular velocity (ω) of the body.

3.12. Torque

It may be defined as the product of force and the perpendicular distance of its line of action from the given point or axis. A little consideration will show that the torque is equivalent to a couple acting upon a body.

The Newton's Second Law of Motion, when applied to rotating bodies, states that the *torque is directly proportional to the rate of change of angular momentum* . Mathematically, Torque,

$$T \propto \frac{d\,(I.\omega)}{dt}$$

Since I is constant, therefore

$$T = I \times \frac{d\omega}{dt} = I.\alpha \qquad ... \left(\because \frac{d\omega}{dt} = \alpha \right)$$

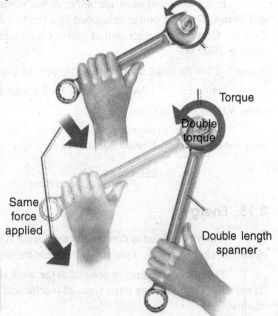

Torque

Double torque

Same force applied

Double length spanner

The unit of torque (T) in S.I. units is N-m when I is in kg-m^2 and α in rad/s^2.

3.13. Work

Whenever a force acts on a body and the body undergoes a displacement in the direction of the force, then work is said to be done. For example, if a force F acting on a body causes a displacement x of the body in the direction of the force, then

$$\text{Work done} = \text{Force} \times \text{Displacement} = F \times x$$

If the force varies linearly from zero to a maximum value of F, then

$$\text{Work done} = \frac{0 + F}{2} \times x = \frac{1}{2} \times F \times x$$

When a couple or torque (T) acting on a body causes the angular displacement (θ) about an axis perpendicular to the plane of the couple, then

$$\text{Work done} = \text{Torque} \times \text{Angular displacement} = T.\theta$$

The unit of work depends upon the unit of force and displacement.

In S.I. system of units, the practical unit of work is N-m. It is the work done by a force of 1 newton, when it displaces a body through 1 metre. The work of 1 N-m is known as joule (briefly written as J) such that 1 N-m = 1 J.

Note: While writing the unit of work, it is general practice to put the unit of force first followed by the unit of displacement (*e.g.* N-m).

3.14. Power

It may be defined as the rate of doing work or work done per unit time. Mathematically,

$$\text{Power} = \frac{\text{Work done}}{\text{Time taken}}$$

In S.I. system of units, the unit of power is watt (briefly written as W) which is equal to 1 J/s or 1 N-m/s. Thus, the power developed by a force of F (in newtons) moving with a velocity v m/s is $F.v$ watt. Generally a bigger unit of power called kilowatt (briefly written as kW) is used which is equal to 1000 W.

Notes: 1. If T is the torque transmitted in N-m or J and ω is the angular speed in rad/s, then

$$\text{Power, } P = T.\omega = T \times 2\pi N/60 \text{ watts} \qquad \ldots (\because \omega = 2\pi N/60)$$

where N is the speed in r.p.m.

2. The ratio of power output to power input is known as efficiency of a machine. It is always less than unity and is represented as percentage. It is denoted by a Greek letter eta (η). Mathematically,

$$\text{Efficiency, } \eta = \frac{\text{Power output}}{\text{Power input}}$$

3.15. Energy

It may be defined as the capacity to do work. The energy exists in many forms *e.g.* mechanical, electrical, chemical, heat, light etc. But we are mainly concerned with mechanical energy.

The mechanical energy is equal to the work done on a body in altering either its position or its velocity. The following three types of mechanical energies are important from the subject point of view.

1. *Potential energy.* It is the energy possessed by a body for doing work, by virtue of its position. For example, a body raised to some height above the ground level possesses potential energy because it can do some work by falling on earth's surface.

Let W = Weight of the body,

m = Mass of the body, and

h = Distance through which the body falls.

Then potential energy,

$$P.E. = W.h = m.g.h \qquad \qquad ...(\because W = m.g)$$

It may be noted that

(a) When W is in newtons and h in metres, then potential energy will be in N-m.

(b) When m is in kg and h in metres, then the potential energy will also be in N-m as discussed below :

We know that potential energy,

$$P.E. = m.g.h = kg \times \frac{m}{s^2} \times m = N\text{-}m \qquad \left(\because 1\,N = \frac{1kg\text{-}m}{s^2} \right)$$

2. *Strain energy.* It is the potential energy stored by an elastic body when deformed. A compressed spring possesses this type of energy, because it can do some work in recovering its original shape. Thus if a compressed spring of stiffness s newton per unit deformation (*i.e.* extension or compression) is deformed through a distance x by a load W, then

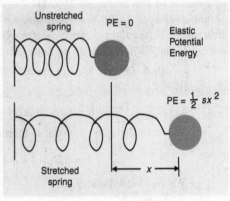

$$\text{Strain energy} = \text{Work done} = \frac{1}{2}\,W.x$$

$$= \frac{1}{2}\,s.x^2 \qquad ...(\because W = s \times x)$$

In case of a torsional spring of stiffness q N-m per unit angular deformation when twisted through an angle θ radians, then

$$\text{Strain energy} = \text{Work done} = \frac{1}{2}\,q.\theta^2$$

3. *Kinetic energy.* It is the energy possessed by a body, for doing work, by virtue of its mass and velocity of motion. If a body of mass m attains a velocity v from rest in time t, under the influence of a force F and moves a distance s, then

$$\text{Work done} = F.s = m.a.s \qquad \qquad ...(\because F = m.a)$$

∴ Kinetic energy of the body or the kinetic energy of translation,

$$K.E. = m.a.s = m \times a \times \frac{\overset{*}{v^2}}{2a} = \frac{1}{2}m.v^2$$

---

* We know that, $v^2 - u^2 = 2\,a.s$

Since $u = 0$ because the body starts from rest, therefore,

$v^2 = 2\,a.s$ or $s = v^2/2a$

It may be noted that when m is in kg and v in m/s, then kinetic energy will be in N-m as discussed below:

We know that kinetic energy,

$$\text{K.E.} = \frac{1}{2}m.v^2 = \text{kg} \times \frac{m^2}{s^2} = \frac{\text{kg - m}}{s^2} \times m = \text{N-m} \qquad ...\left(\because 1N = \frac{1\text{kg-m}}{s^2}\right)$$

Notes : 1. When a body of mass moment of inertia I (about a given axis) is rotated about that axis, with an angular velocity ω, then it possesses some kinetic energy. In this case,

$$\text{Kinetic energy of rotation} = \frac{1}{2}I.\omega^2$$

2. When a body has both linear and angular motions e.g. in the locomotive driving wheels and wheels of a moving car, then the total kinetic energy of the body is equal to the sum of kinetic energies of translation and rotation.

$$\therefore \qquad \text{Total kinetic energy} = \frac{1}{2}m.v^2 + \frac{1}{2}I.\omega^2$$

Example 3.1. *The flywheel of a steam engine has a radius of gyration of 1 m and mass 2500 kg. The starting torque of the steam engine is 1500 N-m and may be assumed constant. Determine :1. Angular acceleration of the flywheel, and2. Kinetic energy of the flywheel after 10 seconds from the start.*

Solution. Given : $k = 1$ m ; $m = 2500$ kg ; $T = 1500$ N-m

Flywheel

1. Angular acceleration of the flywheel

Let $\qquad$ α = Angular acceleration of the flywheel.

We know that mass moment of inertia of the flywheel,

$$I = m.k^2 = 2500 \times 1^2 = 2500 \text{ kg-m}^2$$

We also know that torque (T),

$$1500 = I.\alpha = 2500 \times \alpha \quad \text{or} \quad \alpha = 1500/2500 = 0.6 \text{ rad/s}^2 \text{ Ans.}$$

2. Kinetic energy of the flywheel after 10 seconds from start

First of all, let us find the angular speed of the flywheel (ω_2) after $t = 10$ seconds from the start (i.e. $\omega_1 = 0$).

We know that $\quad \omega_2 = \omega_1 + \alpha.t = 0 + 0.6 \times 10 = 6$ rad/s

$\therefore$ Kinetic energy of the flywheel,

$$E = \frac{1}{2}I(\omega_2)^2 = \frac{1}{2} \times 2500 \times 6^2 = 45\,000\,\text{J} = 45 \text{ kJ Ans.}$$

Example 3.2. *A winding drum raises a cage of mass 500 kg through a height of 100 metres. The mass of the winding drum is 250 kg and has an effective radius of 0.5 m and radius of gyration is 0.35 m. The mass of the rope is 3 kg/m.*

The cage has, at first, an acceleration of 1.5 m/s² until a velocity of 10 m/s is reached, after which the velocity is constant until the cage nears the top and the final retardation is 6 m/s². Find 1. The time taken for the cage to reach the top, 2. The torque which must be applied to the drum at starting; and 3. The power at the end of acceleration period.

Solution. Given : $m_C = 500$ kg ; $s = 100$ m ; $m_D = 250$ kg ; $r = 0.5$ m ; $k = 0.35$ m, $m = 3$ kg/m

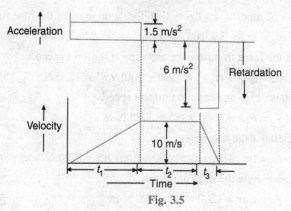

Fig. 3.5

Fig. 3.5 shows the acceleration-time and velocity-time graph for the cage.

1. *Time taken for the cage to reach the top*

        Let t = Time taken for the cage to reach the top = $t_1 + t_2 + t_3$

where t_1 = Time taken for the cage from initial velocity of $u_1 = 0$ to final

                       velocity of $v_1 = 10$ m/s with an acceleration of $a_1 = 1.5$ m/s^2,

                t_2 = Time taken for the cage during constant velocity of $v_2 = 10$ m/s until the

                       cage nears the top, and

                t_3 = Time taken for the cage from initial velocity of $u_3 = 10$ m/s to final velocity

                       of $v_3 = 0$ with a retardation of $a_3 = 6$ m/s^2.

      We know that $v_1 = u_1 + a_1.t_1$

$$10 = 0 + 1.5\, t_1 \quad \text{or} \quad t_1 = 10/1.5 = 6.67 \text{ s}$$

and distance moved by the cage during time t_1,

$$s_1 = \frac{v_1 + u_1}{2} \times t_1 = \frac{10 + 0}{2} \times 6.67 = 33.35 \text{ m}$$

      Similarly, $v_3 = u_3 + a_3.t_3$

$$0 = 10 - 6 \times t_3 \quad \text{or} \quad t_3 = 10/6 = 1.67 \text{ s}$$

and $s_3 = \dfrac{v_3 + u_3}{2} \times t_3 = \dfrac{0 + 10}{2} \times 1.67 = 8.35 \text{ m}$

      Now, distance travelled during constant velocity of $v_2 = 10$ m/s,

$$s_2 = s - s_1 - s_3 = 100 - 33.35 - 8.35 = 58.3 \text{ m}$$

      We know that $s_2 = v_2.t_2 \quad \text{or} \quad t_2 = s_2/v_2 = 58.3/10 = 5.83 \text{ s}$

      $\therefore$ Time taken for the cage to reach the top,

$$t = t_1 + t_2 + t_3 = 6.67 + 5.83 + 1.67 = 14.17 \text{ s } \textbf{Ans.}$$

2. *Torque which must be applied to the drum at starting*

        Let T = Torque which must be applied to the drum at starting = $T_1 + T_2 + T_3$,

where T_1 = Torque to raise the cage and rope at uniform speed,

                T_2 = Torque to accelerate the cage and rope, and

                T_3 = Torque to accelerate the drum.

Since the mass of rope, $m = 3$ kg/m, therefore total mass of the rope for 100 metres,

$$m_R = m.s = 3 \times 100 = 300 \text{ kg}$$

We know that the force to raise cage and rope at uniform speed,

$$F_1 = (m_C + m_R) \, g = (500 + 300) \, 9.81 = 7850 \text{ N}$$

∴ Torque to raise cage and rope at uniform speed,

$$T_1 = F_1.r = 7850 \times 0.5 = 3925 \text{ N-m}$$

Force to accelerate cage and rope,

$$F_2 = (m_C + m_R) \, a_1 = (500 + 300) \, 1.5 = 1200 \text{ N}$$

∴ Torque to accelerate the cage and rope,

$$T_2 = F_2.r = 1200 \times 0.5 = 600 \text{ N-m}$$

We know that mass moment of inertia of the drum,

$$I = m_D.k^2 = 250 \, (0.35)^2 = 30.6 \text{ kg-m}^2$$

and angular acceleration of the drum,

$$\alpha = \frac{a_1}{r} = \frac{1.5}{0.5} = 3 \text{ rad/s}^2$$

∴ Torque to accelerate the drum,

$$T_3 = I.\alpha = 30.6 \times 3 = 91.8 \text{ N-m}$$

and total torque which must be applied to the drum at starting,

$$T = T_1 + T_2 + T_3 = 3925 + 600 + 91.8 = 4616.8 \text{ N-m } \textbf{Ans.}$$

3. Power at the end of acceleration period

When the acceleration period is just finishing, the drum torque will be reduced because there will be $s_1 = 33.35$ m of rope less for lifting. Since the mass of rope is 3 kg/m, therefore mass of 33.35 m rope,

$$m_1 = 3 \times 33.35 = 100.05 \text{ kg}$$

∴ Reduction of torque,

$$T_4 = (m_1.g + m_1.a_1) \, r = (100.05 \times 9.81 + 100.05 \times 1.5) \, 0.5$$
$$= 565.8 \text{ N-m}$$

and angular velocity of drum,

$$\omega = v \, / \, 2\pi r = 10 \, / \, 2\pi \times 0.5 = 3.18 \text{ rad/s}$$

We know that power $= T_4.\omega = 565.8 \times 3.18 = 1799$ W $= 1.799$ kW **Ans.**

Example 3.3. *A riveting machine is driven by a 4 kW motor. The moment of inertia of the rotating parts of the machine is equivalent to 140 kg-m^2 at the shaft on which the flywheel is mounted. At the commencement of operation, the flywheel is making 240 r.p.m. If closing a rivet occupies 1 second and consumes 10 kN-m of energy, find the reduction of speed of the flywheel. What is the maximum rate at which the rivets can be closed ?*

Solution : Given : $P = 4$ kW $= 4000$ W ; $I = 140$ kg-m^2 ; $N_1 = 240$ r.p.m. or $\omega_1 = 2\pi \times 240/60 = 25.14$ rad/s

Reduction of speed of the flywheel

Let ω_2 = Angular speed of the flywheel immediately after closing a rivet.

Since the power of motor is 4000 W, therefore energy supplied by motor in 1 second,

$$E_1 = 4000 \text{ N-m} \qquad \qquad ... (\because 1 \text{ W} = 1 \text{ N-m/s})$$

We know that energy consumed in closing a rivet in 1 second,

$$E_2 = 10 \text{ kN-m} = 10\ 000 \text{ N-m}$$

∴ Loss of kinetic energy of the flywheel during the operation,

$$E = E_2 - E_1 = 10\ 000 - 4000 = 6000 \text{ N-m}$$

We know that kinetic energy of the flywheel at the commencement of operation

$$= \frac{1}{2} I (\omega_1)^2 = \frac{1}{2} \times 140 \ (25.14)^2 = 44\ 240 \text{ N-m}$$

∴ Kinetic energy of the flywheel at the end of operation

$$= 44\ 240 - 6000 = 38\ 240 \text{ N-m} \qquad \qquad ... (i)$$

We also know that kinetic energy of the flywheel at the end of operation

$$= \frac{1}{2} I (\omega_2)^2 = \frac{1}{2} \times 140 \ (\omega_2)^2 = 70 \ (\omega_2)^2 \qquad \qquad ... (ii)$$

Equating equations (*i*) and (*ii*),

$$70 \ (\omega_2)^2 = 38\ 240 \quad \text{or} \quad (\omega_2)^2 = 38\ 240/70 = 546.3 \text{ and } \omega = 23.4 \text{ rad/s}$$

∴ Reduction of speed

$$= \omega_1 - \omega_2 = 25.14 - 23.4 = 1.74 \text{ rad/s}$$

$$= 1.74 \times 60/2\pi = 16.6 \text{ r.p.m. } \textbf{Ans.} \qquad ... (\because \omega = 2\pi N/60)$$

Maximum rate at which the rivets can be closed

Maximum rate at which the rivets can be closed per minute

$$= \frac{\text{Energy supplied by motor per min.}}{\text{Energy consumed to close a rivet}} = \frac{4000 \times 60}{10000} = 24 \ \textbf{Ans.}$$

Example 3.4. *A wagon of mass 14 tonnes is hauled up an incline of 1 in 20 by a rope which is parallel to the incline and is being wound round a drum of 1 m diameter. The drum, in turn, is driven through a 40 to 1 reduction gear by an electric motor. The frictional resistance to the movement of the wagon is 1.2 kN, and the efficiency of the gear drive is 85 per cent. The bearing friction at the drum and motor shafts may be neglected. The rotating parts of the drum have a mass of 1.25 tonnes with a radius of gyration of 450 mm and the rotating parts on the armature shaft have a mass of 110 kg with a radius of gyration of 125 mm.*

At a certain instant the wagon is moving up the slope with a velocity of 1.8 m/s and an acceleration of 0.1 m/s². Find the torque on the motor shaft and the power being developed.

Solution. Given : $m = 14 \text{ t} = 14\ 000 \text{ kg}$; Slope = 1 in 20 ; $d = 1\text{m}$ or $r = 0.5 \text{ m}$; $F = 1.2 \text{ kN} = 1200 \text{ N}$; $\eta = 85\% = 0.85$; $m_1 = 1.25 \text{ t} = 1250 \text{ kg}$; $k_1 = 450 \text{ mm} = 0.45 \text{ m}$; $m_2 = 110 \text{ kg}$; $k_2 = 125 \text{ mm} = 0.125 \text{ m}$; $v = 1.8 \text{ m/s}$; $a = 0.1 \text{ m/s}^2$

Torque on the motor shaft

We know that tension in the rope,

$$P_1 = \text{Forces opposing the motion as shown in}$$

Fig. 3.6.

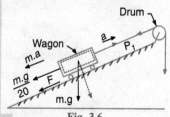

Fig. 3.6

= Component of the weight down the slope

+ *Inertia force + Frictional resistance

$$= m.g \times \frac{1}{20} + m.a + F$$

$$= \frac{14\,000 \times 9.81}{20} + 14\,000 \times 0.1 + 1200 = 9467\,\text{N}$$

∴ Torque on the drum shaft to accelerate load,

$$T_1 = P_1.r = 9467 \times 0.5 = 4733.5\,\text{N-m}$$

We know that mass moment of inertia of the drum,

$$I_1 = m_1\,(k_1)^2 = 1250\,(0.45)^2 = 253\,\text{kg-m}^2$$

and angular acceleration of the drum,

$$\alpha = a/r = 0.1/0.5 = 0.2\,\text{rad/s}$$

∴ Torque on the drum to accelerate drum shaft,

$$T_2 = I_1.\alpha_1 = 253 \times 0.2 = 50.6\,\text{N-m}$$

Since the drum is driven through a 40 to 1 reduction gear and the efficiency of the gear drive is 85%, therefore

Torque on the armature to accelerate drum and load,

$$T_3 = (T_1 + T_2)\frac{1}{40} \times \frac{1}{0.85} = (4733.5 + 50.6)\,\frac{1}{40} \times \frac{1}{0.85} = 140.7\,\text{N-m}$$

We know that mass moment of inertia of the armature,

$$I_2 = m_2\,(k_2)^2 = 110\,(0.125)^2 = 1.72\,\text{kg-m}^2$$

and angular acceleration of the armature,

$$\alpha_2 = \frac{a}{r} \times 40 = \frac{0.1}{0.5} \times 40 = 8\,\text{rad/s}^2$$

... (∵ Armature rotates 40 times that of drum)

∴ Torque on the armature to accelerate armature shaft,

$$T_4 = I_2.\alpha_2 = 1.72 \times 8 = 13.76\,\text{N-m}$$

and torque on the motor shaft

$$T = T_3 + T_4 = 140.7 + 13.76 = 154.46\,\text{N-m} \quad \textbf{Ans.}$$

Power developed by the motor

We know that angular speed of the motor,

$$\omega = \frac{v}{r} \times 40 = \frac{1.8}{0.5} \times 40 = 144\,\text{rad/s}$$

∴ Power developed by the motor

$$= T.\omega = 154.46 \times 144 = 22\,240\,\text{W} = 22.24\,\text{kW} \quad \textbf{Ans.}$$

---

* Inertia force is equal and opposite to the accelerating force.

Example 3.5. *A road roller has a total mass of 12 tonnes. The front roller has a mass of 2 tonnes, a radius of gyration of 0.4 m and a diameter of 1.2 m. The rear axle, together with its wheels, has a mass of 2.5 tonnes, a radius of gyration of 0.6 m and a diameter of 1.5 m. Calculate : 1. Kinetic energy of rotation of the wheels and axles at a speed of 9 km/h, 2. Total kinetic energy of road roller, and 3. Braking force required to bring the roller to rest from 9 km/h in 6 m on the level.*

Solution. Given : $m = 12$ t $= 12\,000$ kg ; $m_1 = 2$ t $= 2000$ kg ; $k_1 = 0.4$ m ; $d_1 = 1.2$ m or $r_1 = 0.6$ m ; $m_2 = 2.5$ t $= 2500$ kg ; $k_2 = 0.6$ m ; $d_2 = 1.5$ m or $r_2 = 0.75$ m ; $v = 9$ km/h $= 2.5$ m/s; $s = 6$ m

1. Kinetic energy of rotation of the wheels and axles

We know that mass moment of inertia of the front roller,

$$I_1 = m_1(k_1)^2 = 2000\,(0.4)^2 = 320 \text{ kg-m}^2$$

and mass moment of inertia of the rear axle together with its wheels,

$$I_2 = m_2\,(k_2)^2 = 2500\,(0.6)^2 = 900 \text{ kg -m}^2$$

Angular speed of the front roller,

$$\omega_1 = v/r_1 = 2.5/0.6 = 4.16 \text{ rad/s}$$

and angular speed of rear wheels,

$$\omega_2 = v/r_2 = 2.5/0.75 = 3.3 \text{ rad/s}$$

We know that kinetic energy of rotation of the front roller,

$$E_1 = \frac{1}{2}I_1\,(\omega_1)^2 = \frac{1}{2} \times 320(4.16)^2 = 2770 \text{ N-m}$$

and kinetic energy of rotation of the rear axle together with its wheels,

$$E_2 = \frac{1}{2}I_2\,(\omega_2)^2 = \frac{1}{2} \times 900(3.3)^2 = 4900 \text{ N-m}$$

∴ Total kinetic energy of rotation of the wheels,

$$E = E_1 + E_2 = 2770 + 4900 = 7670\,\text{N-m} \quad \textbf{Ans.}$$

2. Total kinetic energy of road roller

We know that the kinetic energy of motion (*i.e.* kinetic energy of translation) of the road roller,

$$E_3 = \frac{1}{2}m.v^2 = \frac{1}{2} \times 12\,000\,(2.5)^2 = 37\,500\,\text{N-m}$$

This energy includes the kinetic energy of translation of the wheels also, because the total mass (m) has been considered.

∴ Total kinetic energy of road roller,

$$E_4 = \text{Kinetic energy of translation} + \text{Kinetic energy of rotation}$$

$$= E_3 + E = 37\,500 + 7670 = 45\,170\,\text{N-m} \quad \textbf{Ans.}$$

3. Braking force required to bring the roller to rest

Let F = Braking force required to bring the roller to rest, in newtons.

We know that the distance travelled by the road roller,

$$s = 6 \text{ m} \qquad \qquad \text{... (Given)}$$

∴ Work done by the braking force

$$= F \times s = 6\,F\,\text{N-m}$$

This work done must be equal to the total kinetic energy of road roller to bring the roller to rest, *i.e.*

$$6\,F = 45\,170 \quad \text{or} \quad F = 45\,170/6 = 7528.3 \text{ N} \ \text{Ans.}$$

Example 3.6. *A steam engine drop-valve is closed by a spring after the operation of a trip gear. The stiffness of the spring is such that a force of 4 N is required per mm of compression. The valve is lifted against the spring, and when fully open the compression is 75 mm. When closed the compression is 30 mm. The mass of the valve is 5 kg and the resistance may be taken as constant and equal to 70 N. Find the time taken to close the valve after the operation of the trip.*

Solution. Given : $s = 4$ N/mm = 4000 N/m ; $x_1 = 75$ mm = 0.075 m ; $x_2 = 30$ mm = 0.03 m; $m = 5$ kg ; $R = 70$ N

Let x = Displacement of the valve (in metres) from its highest position in time t seconds.

When the valve is closed, then the value of x

$$= x_1 - x_2 = 0.075 - 0.03 = 0.045 \text{ m}$$

Since the stiffness of the spring is 4000 N/m ; therefore in any position, the push of the spring

$$Q = 4000\,(0.075 - x)\,\text{N}$$

If P is the downward force on the valve, then

$$P = Q + m.g - R = 4000\,(0.075 - x) + 5 \times 9.81 - 70 = 279 - 4000\,x$$

Also   Force, P = Mass × Acceleration

$$279 - 4000\,x = 5 \times \frac{d^2 x}{dt^2}$$

or

$$\frac{d^2 x}{dt^2} = \frac{279 - 4000x}{5} = 56 - 800x = -\,800(x - 0.07)$$

Let $y = x - 0.07$

∴

$$\frac{d^2 y}{dt^2} = \frac{d^2 x}{dt^2} = -\,800y \quad \text{or} \quad \frac{d^2 y}{dt^2} + 800\,y = 0$$

The solution of this differential equation is

$$y = a \cos \sqrt{800}\ t + b \sin \sqrt{800}\ t$$

$$x - 0.07 = a \cos \sqrt{800}\ t + b \sin \sqrt{800}\ t \qquad \qquad \text{... (i)}$$

where a and b are constants to be determined.

Now when $t = 0$, $x = 0$, therefore from equation (i), $a = -0.07$

Differentiating equation (i),

$$\frac{dx}{dt} = -\sqrt{800}\ a \sin \sqrt{800}\,t + \sqrt{800}\ b \cos \sqrt{800}\,t \qquad \qquad \text{... (ii)}$$

Now when $t = 0$, $\dfrac{dx}{dt} = 0$, therefore from equation (*ii*), $b = 0$

Substituting the values of a and b in equation (*i*),

$$x - 0.07 = -0.07 \cos \sqrt{800}\ t \quad \text{or} \quad x = 0.07\ (1 - \cos \sqrt{800}\ t)$$

When $x = 0.045$ m, then

$$0.045 = 0.07\ (1 - \cos \sqrt{800}\ t)$$

or $\qquad 1 - \cos \sqrt{800}\ t = 0.045/0.07 = 0.642 \quad \text{or} \quad \cos \sqrt{800}\ t = 1 - 0.642 = 0.358$

$$\sqrt{800}\ t = \cos^{-1}(0.358) = 69° = 69 \times \frac{\pi}{180} = 1.2 \text{ rad}$$

∴ $\qquad\qquad t = 1.2/\sqrt{800} = 1.2/28.3 = 0.0424 \text{ s} \quad \textbf{Ans.}$

3.16. Principle of Conservation of Energy

It states *"The energy can neither be created nor destroyed, though it can be transformed from one form into any of the forms, in which the energy can exist."*

Note : The loss of energy in any one form is always accompanied by an equivalent increase in another form. When work is done on a rigid body, the work is converted into kinetic or potential energy or is used in overcoming friction. If the body is elastic, some of the work will also be stored as strain energy. Thus we say that the total energy possessed by a system of moving bodies is constant at every instant, provided that no energy is rejected to or received from an external source to the system.

3.17. Impulse and Impulsive Force

The impulse is the product of force and time. Mathematically,

$$\text{Impulse} = F \times t$$

where $\qquad\qquad F = \text{Force, and } t = \text{Time.}$

Now consider a body of mass m. Let a force F changes its velocity from an initial velocity v_1 to a final velocity v_2.

We know that the force is equal to the rate of change of linear momentum, therefore

$$F = \frac{m(v_2 - v_1)}{t} \quad \text{or} \quad F \times t = m(v_2 - v_1)$$

i.e. $\qquad\qquad \text{Impulse} = \text{Change of linear momentum}$

If a force acts for a very short time, it is then known as *impulsive force* or blow. The impulsive force occurs in collisions, in explosions, in the striking of a nail or a pile by a hammer.

Note: When the two rotating gears with angular velocities ω_1 and ω_2 mesh each other, then an impulsive torque acts on the two gears, until they are both rotating at speeds corresponding to their velocity ratio. The impulsive torque,

$$T.t = I\ (\omega_2 - \omega_1)$$

3.18. Principle of Conservation of Momentum

It states *"The total momentum of a system of masses (i.e. moving bodies) in any one direction remains constant, unless acted upon by an external force in that direction."* This principle is applied to problems on impact, *i.e.* collision of two bodies. In other words, if two bodies of masses m_1 and m_2 with linear velocities v_1 and v_2 are moving in the same straight line, and they collide and begin to move together with a common velocity v, then

Momentum before impact = Momentum after impact

i.e.
$$m_1 v_1 \pm m_2 v_2 = (m_1 + m_2)v$$

Notes : 1. The *positive* sign is used when the two bodies move in the same direction after collision. The *negative* sign is used when they move in the opposite direction after collision.

2. Consider two rotating bodies of mass moment of inertia I_1 and I_2 are initially apart from each other and are made to engage as in the case of a clutch. If they reach a common angular velocity ω, after slipping has ceased, then

$$I_1 . \omega_1 \pm I_2 . \omega_2 = (I_1 + I_2)\,\omega$$

The $\pm$ sign depends upon the direction of rotation.

3.19. Energy Lost by Friction Clutch During Engagement

Consider two collinear shafts A and B connected by a *friction clutch (plate or disc clutch) as shown in Fig. 3.7.

Let I_A and I_B = Mass moment of inertias of the rotors attached to shafts A and B respectively.

ω_A and ω_B = Angular speeds of shafts A and B respectively before engagement of clutch, and

ω = Common angular speed of shafts A and B after engagement of clutch.

By the principle of conservation of momentum,

$$I_A . \omega_A + I_B . \omega_B = (I_A + I_B)\,\omega$$

$\therefore$
$$\omega = \frac{I_A . \omega_A + I_B . \omega_B}{I_A + I_B} \qquad \qquad \ldots (i)$$

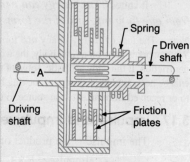

Fig. 3.7. Friction clutch.

Total kinetic energy of the system before engagement,

$$E_1 = \frac{1}{2} I_A (\omega_A)^2 + \frac{1}{2} I_B (\omega_B)^2 = \frac{I_A (\omega_A)^2 + I_B (\omega_B)^2}{2}$$

Kinetic energy of the system after engagement,

$$E_2 = \frac{1}{2} (I_A + I_B)\,\omega^2 = \frac{1}{2}(I_A + I_B)\left(\frac{I_A . \omega_A + I_B . \omega_B}{I_A + I_B}\right)^2$$

$$= \frac{(I_A . \omega_A + I_B . \omega_B)^2}{2(I_A + I_B)}$$

$\therefore$ Loss of kinetic energy during engagement,

$$E = E_1 - E_2 = \frac{I_A (\omega_A)^2 + I_B (\omega_B)^2}{2} - \frac{(I_A . \omega_A + I_B . \omega_B)^2}{2(I_A + I_B)}$$

---

* Please refer Chapter 10 (Art. 10.32) on Friction.

$$= \frac{I_A.I_B(\omega_A - \omega_B)^2}{2(I_A + I_B)} \qquad \qquad ...(ii)$$

Notes: 1. If the rotor attached to shaft B is at rest, then $\omega_B = 0$. Therefore, common angular speed after engagement,

$$\omega = \frac{I_A.\omega_A}{I_A + I_B} \qquad \qquad ...\text{[Substituting } \omega_B = 0 \text{ in equation } (i)] ... (iii)$$

and loss of kinetic energy, $\quad E = \dfrac{I_A.I_B(\omega_A)^2}{2(I_A + I_B)} \qquad \qquad ...\text{[Substituting } \omega_B = 0 \text{ in equation } (ii)] ... (iv)$

2. If I_B is very small as compared to I_A and the rotor B is at rest, then

$$\omega = \frac{I_A.\omega_A}{I_A + I_B} = \omega_A \qquad \qquad ...\text{(Neglecting } I_B)$$

and

$$E = \frac{1}{2} I_B.\omega.\omega_A = \frac{1}{2} I_B.\omega^2 \qquad \qquad ...\text{[From equations } (iii) \text{ and } (iv)]$$

$$= \text{Energy given to rotor } B$$

Example 3.7. *A haulage rope winds on a drum of radius 500 mm, the free end being attached to a truck. The truck has a mass of 500 kg and is initially at rest. The drum is equivalent to a mass of 1250 kg with radius of gyration 450 mm. The rim speed of the drum is 0.75 m/s before the rope tightens. By considering the change in linear momentum of the truck and in the angular momentum of the drum, find the speed of the truck when the motion becomes steady. Find also the energy lost to the system.*

Solution. Given : $r = 500$ mm $= 0.5$ m ; $m_1 = 500$ kg ; $m_2 = 1250$ kg ; $k = 450$ mm $= 0.45$ m ; $u = 0.75$ m/s

We know that mass moment of inertia of drum,

$$I_2 = m_2.k^2 = 1250 (0.45)^2 = 253 \text{ kg-m}^2$$

Speed of the truck

Let $\qquad \qquad v = $ Speed of the truck in m/s, and

$\qquad \qquad F = $ Impulse in rope in N-s.

We know that the impulse is equal to the change of linear momentum of the truck. Therefore

$$F = m_1.v = 500 \ v \text{ N-s}$$

and $\qquad$ moment of impulse = Change in angular momentum of drum

i.e.

$$F \times r = I_2 (\omega_2 - \omega_1) = I_2 \left(\frac{u - v}{r} \right) \qquad ... \left(\because \ \omega_2 - \omega_1 = \frac{u}{r} - \frac{v}{r} = \frac{u - v}{r} \right)$$

$$500 v \times 0.5 = 253 \left(\frac{0.75 - v}{0.5} \right) \quad \text{or} \quad 250 \ v = 380 - 506 \ v$$

$\therefore \qquad \qquad 250 \ v + 506 \ v = 380 \quad \text{or} \quad v = 380/756 = 0.502 \text{ m/s} \quad \textbf{Ans.}$

Energy lost to the system

We know that energy lost to the system

$$= \text{Loss in K.E. of drum} - \text{Gain in K.E. of truck}$$

$$= \frac{1}{2} \times I_2 \left[(\omega_2)^2 - (\omega_1)^2 \right] - \frac{1}{2} \times m_1.v^2$$

$$= \frac{1}{2} \times I_2 \left[\frac{u^2 - v^2}{r^2} \right] - \frac{1}{2} \times m_1.v^2$$

$$= \frac{1}{2} \times 253 \left[\frac{(0.75)^2 - (0.502)^2}{(0.5)^2} \right] - \frac{1}{2} \times 500 (0.502)^2 \text{ N-m}$$

$$= 94 \text{ N-m} \quad \textbf{Ans.}$$

Example 3.8. *The two buffers at one end of a truck each require a force of 0.7 MN/m of compression and engage with similar buffers on a truck which it overtakes on a straight horizontal track. The truck has a mass of 10 tonnes and its initial speed is 1.8 m/s, while the second truck has mass of 15 tonnes with initial speed 0.6 m/s, in the same direction.*

Find : 1. the common velocity when moving together during impact, 2. the kinetic energy lost to the system, 3. the compression of each buffer to store the kinetic energy lost, and 4. the velocity of each truck on separation if only half of the energy offered in the springs is returned.

Solution. Given : $s = 0.7$ MN/m $= 0.7 \times 10^6$ N/m ; $m = 10$ t $= 10 \times 10^3$ kg ; $v_1 = 1.8$ m/s; $m_2 = 15$ t $= 15 \times 10^3$ kg ; $v_2 = 0.6$ m/s

1. *Common velocity when moving together during impact*

Let $\qquad v = $ Common velocity.

We know that momentum before impact = Momentum after impact

i.e. $\qquad m_1 . v_1 + m_2 . v_2 = (m_1 + m_2) v$

$$10 \times 10^3 \times 1.8 + 15 \times 10^3 \times 0.6 = (10 \times 10^3 + 15 + 10^3) v$$

$$27 \times 10^3 = 25 \times 10^3 v \quad \text{or} \quad v = 27 \times 10^3 / 25 \times 10^3 = 1.08 \text{ m/s} \quad \textbf{Ans.}$$

2. *Kinetic energy lost to the system*

Since the kinetic energy lost to the system is the kinetic energy before impact *minus* the kinetic energy after impact, therefore

Kinetic energy lost to the system

$$= \left(\frac{1}{2} m_1 v_1^2 + \frac{1}{2} m_2 v_2^2 \right) - \frac{1}{2} (m_1 + m_2) v^2$$

$$= \left[\frac{1}{2} \times 10 \times 10^3 (1.8)^2 + \frac{1}{2} \times 15 \times 10^3 (0.6)^2 \right]$$

$$- \frac{1}{2} \left(10 \times 10^3 + 15 \times 10^3 \right) (1.08)^2$$

$$= 4.35 \times 10^3 \text{ N-m} = 4.35 \text{ kN-m} \quad \textbf{Ans.}$$

3. *Compression of each buffer spring to store kinetic energy lost*

Let $\qquad x = $ Compression of each buffer spring in metre, and

$\qquad s = $ Force required by each buffer spring or stiffness of each spring

$\qquad = 0.7$ MN/m $= 0.7 \times 10^6$ N/m $\qquad\qquad$ ... (Given)

Since the strain energy stored in the springs (four in number) is equal to kinetic energy lost in impact, therefore

$$4 \times \frac{1}{2} s . x^2 = 4.35 \times 10^3$$

$$4 \times \frac{1}{2} \times 0.7 \times 10^6 x^2 = 4.35 \times 10^3$$

or $\qquad 1.4 \times 10^6 x^2 = 4.35 \times 10^3$

∴ $\qquad x^2 = 4.35 \times 10^3/1.4 \times 10^6 = 3.11 \times 10^{-3}$

or $\qquad x = 0.056 \text{ m} = 56 \text{ mm}$ **Ans.**

4. Velocity of each truck on separation

Let $\qquad v_3$ = Velocity of separation for 10 tonnes truck, and

$\qquad v_4$ = Velocity of separation for 15 tonnes truck.

The final kinetic energy after separation is equal to the kinetic energy at the instant of common velocity *plus* strain energy stored in the springs. Since it is given that only half of the energy stored in the springs is returned, therefore

Final kinetic energy after separation

$$= \text{Kinetic energy at common velocity} + \frac{1}{2} \text{ Energy stored in springs}$$

or $\quad \dfrac{1}{2} m_1 (v_3)^2 + \dfrac{1}{2} m_2 (v_4)^2 = \dfrac{1}{2} (m_1 + m_2) v^2 + \dfrac{1}{2} \left(4 \times \dfrac{1}{2} s.x^2 \right)$

$$\frac{1}{2} \times 10 \times 10^3 \, (v_3)^2 + \frac{1}{2} \times 15 \times 10^3 \, (v_4)^2 = \frac{1}{2} (10 \times 10^3 + 15 \times 10^3) \, (1.08)^2 + \frac{1}{2} (4.35 \times 10^3)$$

$$\dots \left(\because 4 \times \frac{1}{2} s.x^2 = 4.35 \times 10^3 \right)$$

$$10(v_3)^2 + 15(v_4)^2 = 33.51 \qquad \dots (i)$$

We know that initial momentum and final momentum must be equal, *i.e.*

$$m_1.v_3 + m_2.v_4 = (m_1 + m_2) \, v$$

$$10 \times 10^3 \times v_3 + 15 \times 10^3 \times v_4 = (10 \times 10^3 + 15 \times 10^3) \, 1.08$$

$$10v_3 + 15 \, v_4 = 27 \qquad \dots (ii)$$

From equations (*i*) and (*ii*), $\quad v_3 = 0.6 \text{ m/s, and } v_4 = 1.4 \text{ m/s}$ **Ans.**

Example 3.9. *A mass of 300 kg is allowed to fall vertically through 1 metre on to the top of a pile of mass 500 kg. Assume that the falling mass and pile remain in contact after impact and that the pile is moved 150 mm at each blow. Find, allowing for the action of gravity after impact 1. The energy lost in the blow, and 2. The average resistance against the pile.*

Solution. Given : $m_1 = 300 \text{ kg}$; $s = 1 \text{ m}$; $m_2 = 500 \text{ kg}$; $x = 150 \text{ mm} = 0.15 \text{ m}$

1. Energy lost in the blow

First of all, let us find the velocity of mass m_1 with which it hits the pile.

Let $\qquad v_1$ = Velocity with which mass m_1 hits the pile.

We know that $v_1^2 - u^2 = 2 \, g.s$

$$v_1^2 - 0 = 2 \times 9.81 \times 1 = 19.62 \qquad \text{or} \qquad v_1 = 4.43 \text{ m/s} \qquad \dots (\because u = 0)$$

Again, let v_2 = Velocity of the pile before impact, and

v = Common velocity after impact,

We known that momentum before impact

= Momentum after impact

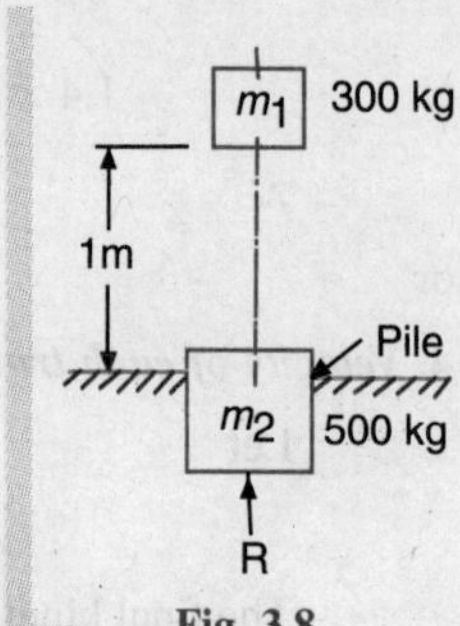

or $m_1 . v_1 + m_2 . v_2 = (m_1 + m_2) v$

$300 \times 4.43 + 500 \times 0 = (300 + 500) v$

$1329 = 800 v$

∴ $v = 1329/800 = 1.66$ m/s

Now, kinetic energy before impact

= Potential energy = $m_1 . g . s$

= $300 \times 9.81 \times 1 = 2943$ N-m

and kinetic energy after impact

$$= \frac{1}{2}(m_1 + m_2) v^2 = \frac{1}{2}(300 + 500)(1.66)^2 = 1102 \text{ N-m}$$

∴ Energy lost in the blow

= 2943 – 1102 = 1841 N-m **Ans.**

2. Average resistance against the pile

Let R = Average resistance against the pile in N.

Since the net work done by R, m_1 and m_2 is equal to the kinetic energy after impact, therefore

$(R - m_1 . g - m_2 . g) x$ = Kinetic energy after impact

$(R - 300 \times 9.81 - 500 \times 9.81) 0.15 = 1102$

∴ $R - 7848 = 1102/0.15 = 7347$

or $R = 7347 + 7848 = 15\ 195$ N = 15.195 kN **Ans.**

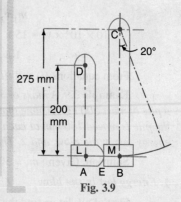

Fig. 3.8

Example 3.10. *A hammer B suspended from pin C, and an anvil A suspended from pin D, are just touching each other at E, when both hang freely as shown in Fig. 3.9. The mass of B is 0.7 kg and its centre of gravity is 250 mm below C and its radius of gyration about C is 270 mm. The mass of A is 2.4 kg and its centre of gravity is 175 mm below D and its radius of gyration about D is 185 mm. The hammer B is rotated 20° to the position shown dotted and released. Assume that the points of contact move horizontally at the instant of impact and that their local relative linear velocity of recoil is 0.8 times their relative linear velocity of impact. Find the angular velocities of hammer and of the anvil immediately after impact.*

Fig. 3.9

Solution. Given : $m_1 = 0.7$ kg ; $k_1 = 270$ mm = 0.27 m ; $m_2 = 2.4$ kg ; $k_2 = 185$ mm = 0.185 m

Let ω = Angular velocity of hammer B just before impact, and

h = Distance from release to impact

h_1 = Distance of c.g. of mass B below C = 250 mm = 0.25 m ...(Given)

We know that K.E. of hammer *B*

$$= \text{Loss of P.E. from release to impact}$$

$$\frac{1}{2} I_1 \omega^2 = m_1 . g . h \quad \text{or} \quad \frac{1}{2} m_1 (k_1)^2 \omega^2 = m_1 . g . h$$

$$\frac{1}{2} \times 0.7 \, (0.27)^2 \, \omega^2 = 0.7 \times 9.81 \times 0.25 \, (1 - \cos 20°)$$

$$0.0255 \, \omega^2 = 0.1032$$

$$\therefore \qquad \omega^2 = 0.1032 / 0.0255 = 4.05 \quad \text{or} \quad \omega = 2.01 \text{ rad/s}$$

Let ω_A and ω_B be the angular velocities of the anvil *A* and hammer *B*, in the same direction, immediately after impact.

$\therefore$ Relative linear velocity

$$= \omega_A \times DL - \omega_A \times CM = \omega_A \times 0.2 - \omega_B \times 0.275$$

... (*DL* and *CM* are taken in metres)

$$= 0.2 \, \omega_A - 0.275 \, \omega_B \qquad \qquad \text{... (i)}$$

But, relative linear velocity

$$= 0.8 \times \text{Relative linear velocity of impact} \qquad \text{... (Given)}$$

$$= 0.8 \omega \times CM = 0.8 \times 2.01 \times 0.275 = 0.44 \qquad \text{... (ii)}$$

Equating (*i*) and (*ii*),

$$0.2 \, \omega_A - 0.275 \, \omega_B = 0.44 \quad \text{or} \quad \omega_B = 0.727 \, \omega_A - 1.6 \qquad \text{... (iii)}$$

Since the linear impulse at *E* is equal and opposite on *A* and *B*, then by moments about *D* for *A* and about *C* for *B*, it follows that the ratio

$$\frac{\text{Decrease in angular momentum of } B}{\text{Increase in angular momentum of } A} = \frac{CM}{DL} = \frac{0.275}{0.2}$$

i.e.

$$\frac{I_B \, (\omega - \omega_B)}{I_A . \omega_A} = \frac{0.275}{0.2} = 1.375$$

$$\frac{m_1 (k_1)^2 (\omega - \omega_B)}{m_2 (k_2)^2 \, \omega_A} = 1.375 \quad \text{or} \quad \frac{0.7 \, (0.27)^2 \, (2.01 - \omega_B)}{2.4 \, (0.185)^2 \, \omega_A} = 1.375$$

$$\therefore \qquad 2.01 - \omega_B = 2.21 \, \omega_A \quad \text{or} \quad \omega_B = 2.01 - 2.21 \, \omega_A \qquad \text{... (iv)}$$

From equations (*iii*) and (*iv*), we get

$$0.727 \, \omega_A - 1.6 = 2.01 - 2.21 \, \omega_A$$

$$0.727 \, \omega_A + 2.21 \, \omega_A = 2.01 + 1.6 \quad \text{or} \quad \omega_A = 1.23 \text{ rad/s} \quad \textbf{Ans.}$$

Substituting $\omega_A = 1.23$ rad/s in equation (*iv*),

$$\omega_B = 2.01 - 2.21 \times 1.23 = -0.71 \text{ rad/s}$$

$$= 0.71 \text{ rad/s, in reverse direction} \quad \textbf{Ans.}$$

Example 3.11. *The pendulum of an Izod impact testing machine has a mass of 30 kg. The centre of gravity of the pendulum is 1 m from the axis of suspension and the striking knife is 150 mm below the centre of gravity. The radius of gyration about the point of suspension is 1.1 m, and about the centre of gravity is 350 mm. In making a test, the pendulum is released from an angle of 60° to the vertical. Determine : 1. striking velocity of the pendulum, 2. impulse on the pendulum and sudden change of axis reaction when a specimen giving an impact value of 54 N-m is broken, 3. angle of swing of the pendulum after impact, and 4. average force exerted at the pivot and at the knife edge if the duration of impact is assumed to be 0.005 second.*

Solution. Given : $m = 30$ kg ; $AG = a = 1$ m ; $GB = b = 150$ mm $= 0.15$ m ; $k_1 = 1.1$ m; $k_2 = 350$ mm $= 0.35$ m ; $\theta = 60°$; $t = 0.005$ s

We know that mass moment of inertia of the pendulum about the point of suspension A,

$$I_A = m\,(k_1)^2 = 30\,(1.1)^2 = 36.3 \text{ kg-m}^2$$

and mass moment of inertia of the pendulum about centre of gravity G,

$$I_G = m\,(k_2)^2 = 30\,(0.35)^2$$
$$= 3.675 \text{ kg-m}^2$$

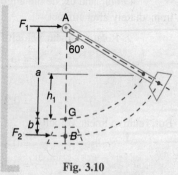

Fig. 3.10

1. *Striking velocity of the pendulum*

Let v = Striking velocity of the pendulum, and

ω = Angular velocity of the pendulum.

Since the potential energy of the pendulum is converted into angular kinetic energy of the pendulum, therefore,

$$m.g.h_1 = \frac{1}{2} I_A.\omega^2$$

$$30 \times 9.81\,(1 - 1\cos 60°) = \frac{1}{2} \times 36.3\,\omega^2 \qquad \dots (\because\ h_1 = a - a\cos 60°)$$

or
$$147.15 = 18.15\,\omega^2$$

∴
$$\omega^2 = 147.15/18.15 = 8.1 \quad \text{or} \quad \omega = 2.85 \text{ rad/s}$$

and
$$v = \omega \times AB = \omega\,(a + b) = 2.85\,(1 + 0.15) = 3.28 \text{ m/s} \quad \textbf{Ans.}$$

2. *Impulse on the pendulum*

Let F_1 = Impulse at the pivot A,

F_2 = Impulse at the knife edge B,

ω = Angular velocity of the pendulum just before the breakage of the specimen, and

ω_1 = Angular velocity of the pendulum just after the breakage of the specimen.

Since the loss in angular kinetic energy of the pendulum is equal to the energy used for breaking the specimen (which is 54 N-m), therefore

$$\frac{1}{2} I_A\,(\omega^2 - \omega_1^2) = 54 \quad \text{or} \quad \frac{1}{2} \times 36.3\,(2.85^2 - \omega_1^2) = 54$$

$$\therefore \qquad \omega_1^2 = (2.85)^2 - \frac{54 \times 2}{36.3} = 5.125 \text{ or } \omega_1 = 2.26 \text{ rad/s}$$

Let v_G and v_G' be the linear velocities of G just before and just after the breakage of specimen.

$$v_G = \omega \times OG = 2.85 \times 1 = 2.85 \, \text{m/s}$$

and

$$v_G' = \omega_1 \times OG = 2.26 \times 1 = 2.26 \, \text{m/s}$$

We know that Impulse = Change of linear momentum

$$F_1 + F_2 = m \, (v_G - v_G') = 30 \, (2.85 - 2.26) = 17.7 \text{ N} \qquad \ldots (i)$$

Taking moments about G, we get

Impulsive torque = Change of angular momentum

$$F_2 \times b - F_1 \times a = I_G \, (\omega - \omega_1)$$

$$F_2 \times 0.15 - F_1 \times 1 = 3.675 \, (2.85 - 2.26) = 2.17 \qquad \ldots (ii)$$

From equations (i) and (ii),

$$F_2 = 17.3 \text{ N ; and } F_1 = 0.4 \text{ N \quad Ans.}$$

3. Angle of swing of the pendulum after impact

Let $\qquad \theta$ = Angle of swing of the pendulum after impact.

Since work done in raising the pendulum is equal to angular kinetic energy of the pendulum, therefore

$$m.g.h_1 = \frac{1}{2} I_A \, (\omega_1)^2$$

$$30 \times 9.81 \, (1 - 1 \cos \theta) = \frac{1}{2} \times 36.3 \, (2.26)^2 = 92.7$$

$$1 - 1 \cos \theta = 92.7/30 \times 9.81 = 0.315 \quad \text{or} \quad \cos \theta = 1 - 0.315 = 0.685$$

$$\therefore \qquad \theta = 46.76° \quad \text{Ans.}$$

4. Average force exerted at the pivot and at the knife edge

We know that average force exerted at the pivot

$$= \frac{F_1}{t} = \frac{0.4}{0.005} = 80 \text{ N \quad Ans.}$$

and average force exerted at the knife edge

$$= \frac{F_2}{t} = \frac{17.3}{0.005} = 3460 \text{ N \quad Ans.}$$

Example 3.12. *A motor drives a machine through a friction clutch which transmits a torque of 150 N-m, while slip occurs during engagement. The rotor, for the motor, has a mass of 60 kg, with radius of gyration 140 mm and the inertia of the machine is equivalent to a mass of 20 kg at the driving shaft with radius of gyration 80 mm. If the motor is running at 750 r.p.m. and the machine is at rest, find the speed after the engagement of the clutch and the time taken. What will be the kinetic energy lost during the operation ?*

Solution. Given : $T = 150$ N-m ; $m_1 = 60$ kg ; $k_1 = 140$ mm $= 0.14$ m ; $m_2 = 20$ kg ; $k_2 = 80$ mm $= 0.08$ m ; $N_1 = 750$ r.p.m. or $\omega_1 = 2\pi \times 750/60 = 78.55$ rad/s ; $N_2 = 0$ or $\omega_2 = 0$

We know that mass moment of inertia of the rotor on motor,

$$I_1 = m_1 (k_1)^2 = 60 (0.14)^2 = 1.176 \text{ kg-m}^2$$

and mass moment of inertia of the parts attached to machine,

$$I_2 = m_2 (k_2)^2 = 20 (0.08)^2 = 0.128 \text{ kg-m}^2$$

Speed after the engagement of the clutch and the time taken

Let ω = Speed after the engagement of the clutch in rad/s,

t = Time taken in seconds, and

α = Angular acceleration during the operation in rad/s^2.

We know that the impulsive torque = change of angular momentum

$$\therefore \quad T.t = I_1 (\omega_1 - \omega) \quad \text{or} \quad t = \frac{I_1 (\omega_1 - \omega)}{T} = \frac{1.176 (78.55 - \omega)}{150} \text{ s} \quad \dots (i)$$

Also $\quad T.t = I_2 (\omega - \omega_2) \quad \text{or} \quad t = \frac{I_2 (\omega - \omega_2)}{T} = \frac{0.128 \times \omega}{150} \text{ s} \quad \dots (ii)$

Equating equations (*i*) and (*ii*), $\qquad \dots (\because \omega_2 = 0)$

$$\frac{1.176 (78.55 - \omega)}{150} = \frac{0.128 \, \omega}{150} \quad \text{or} \quad 92.4 - 1.176 \, \omega = 0.128 \, \omega$$

$$1.304 \, \omega = 92.4 \quad \text{or} \quad \omega = 92.4/1.304 = 70.6 \text{ rad/s Ans.}$$

Substituting the value of ω in equation (*ii*),

$$t = \frac{0.128 \times 70.6}{150} = 0.06 \text{ s Ans.}$$

Kinetic energy lost during the operation

We know that the kinetic energy lost during the operation,

$$E = \frac{I_1.I_2 (\omega_1 - \omega_2)^2}{2 (I_1 + I_2)} = \frac{I_1.I_2.\omega_1^2}{2 (I_1 + I_2)} \qquad \dots (\because \omega_2 = 0)$$

$$= \frac{1.176 \times 0.128 (78.55)^2}{2 (1.176 + 0.128)} = \frac{928.8}{2.61} = 356 \text{ N-m Ans.}$$

3.20. Torque Required to Accelerate a Geared System

Consider that the two shafts A and B are geared together as shown in Fig. 3.11. Let the shaft B rotates G times the speed of shaft A. Therefore, gear ratio,

$$G = \frac{N_B}{N_A}$$

where N_A and N_B are speeds of shafts A and B (in r.p.m.) respectively.

Since the shaft B turns G times the speed of shaft A, therefore the rate of change of angular speed of shaft B with

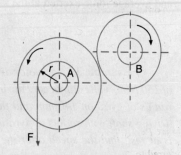

Fig. 3.11. Torque to accelerate a geared system.

respect to time (*i.e.* angular acceleration of shaft *B*, α_B) must be equal to *G* times the rate of change of angular speed of shaft *A* with respect to time (*i.e.* angular acceleration of shaft *A*, α_A).

∴ $$\alpha_B = G.\alpha_A \qquad \qquad ...(i)$$

Let I_A and I_B = Mass moment of inertia of the masses attached to shafts *A* and *B* respectively.

∴ Torque required on shaft *A* to accelerate itself only,

$$T_A = I_A.\alpha_A$$

and torque required on shaft *B* to accelerate itself only,

$$T_B = I_B.\alpha_B = G.I_B.\alpha_A \qquad \text{... [From equation } (i)\text{] ... } (ii)$$

In order to provide a torque T_B on the shaft *B*, the torque applied to shaft *A* must be $G \times T_B$. Therefore, torque applied to shaft *A* in order to accelerate shaft *B*,

$$T_{AB} = G.T_B = G^2.I_B.\alpha_A \qquad \text{... [From equation } (ii)\text{] ... } (iii)$$

∴ Total torque which must be applied to shaft *A* in order to accelerate the geared system,

$$T = T_A + T_{AB} = I_A.\alpha_A + G^2.I_B.\alpha_A$$
$$= (I_A + G^2.I_B)\,\alpha_A = I.\alpha_A \qquad \qquad ... (iv)$$

where $I = I_A + G^2. I_B$ and may be regarded as equivalent mass moment of inertia of geared system referred to shaft *A*.

Let the torque *T* required to accelerate the geared system, as shown in Fig. 3.11, is applied by means of a force *F* which acts tangentially to a drum or pulley of radius *r*.

∴ $$T = F \times r = I.\alpha_A \qquad \qquad ... (v)$$

We know that the tangential acceleration of the drum,

$$a = \alpha_A.r \quad \text{or} \quad \alpha_A = a/r$$

∴ $$F \times r = I \times \frac{a}{r} = \left(I_A + G^2.I_B\right)\frac{a}{r} \qquad ...(\because I = I_A + G^2.I_B)$$

or $$F = \frac{a}{r^2}\left(I_A + G^2.I_B\right) = a.m_e \qquad \qquad ... (vi)$$

where $m_e = \dfrac{1}{r^2}\left(I_A + G^2.I_B\right)$ and may be regarded as equivalent mass of the system referred to the line of action of the accelerating force *F*.

Notes : 1. If η is the efficiency of the gearing between the two shafts *A* and *B*, then the torque applied to shaft *A* in order to accelerate shaft *B*,

$$T_{AB} = \frac{G^2.I_B.\alpha_A}{\eta}$$

and the total torque applied to shaft *A* in order to accelerate the geared system,

$$T = T_A + T_{AB} = I_A.\alpha_A + \frac{G^2.I_B.\alpha_A}{\eta} = \left(I_A + \frac{G^2.I_B}{\eta}\right)\alpha_A = I.\alpha_A$$

where $I = I_A + \dfrac{G^2.I_B}{\eta}$, and may be regarded as the equivalent mass moment of inertia of the geared system referred to shaft *A*.

2. If the number of shafts (say *A* to *X*) are geared together in series, then the equivalent mass moment of inertia referred to shaft *A* is given by,

$$I = I_A + \sum \frac{G_x^2 \, I_x}{\eta_x}$$

where

G_x = Ratio of speed of shaft X to the speed of shaft A,

I_x = Mass moment of inertia of mass attached to shaft X, and

η_x = Overall efficiency of the gearing from shaft A to shaft X.

3. If each pair of gear wheels is assumed to have the same efficiency η and there are m gear pairs through which the power is transmitted from shaft A to shaft X, then the overall efficiency from shaft A to X is given by,

$$\eta_x = \eta^m$$

4. The total kinetic energy of the geared system,

$$\text{K.E.} = \frac{1}{2} I (\omega_A)^2$$

where

I = Equivalent mass moment of inertia of the geared system referred to shaft A, and

ω_A = Angular speed of shaft A.

Example 3.13. *A mass M of 75 kg is hung from a rope wrapped round a drum of effective radius of 0.3 metre, which is keyed to shaft A. The shaft A is geared to shaft B which runs at 6 times the speed of shaft A. The total mass moment of inertia of the masses attached to shaft A is 100 kg-m² and that of shaft B is 5 kg-m².*

Find the acceleration of mass M if 1. it is allowed to fall freely, and 2. when the efficiency of the gearing system is 90%. The configuration of the system is shown in Fig. 3.12.

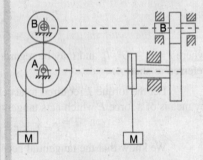

Fig. 3.12

Solution. Given : $M = 75$ kg ; $r = 0.3$ m ; $N_B = 6 \, N_A$ or $G = N_B / N_A = 6$; $I_A = 100$ kg-m² ; $I_B = 5$ kg-m²; $\eta = 90\% = 0.9$

Let a = Acceleration of the mass M, in m/s².

1. When it is allowed to fall freely

We know that equivalent mass of the geared system referred to the circumference of the drum (or the line of action of the accelerating mass M),

$$m_e = \frac{1}{r^2} \left(I_A + G^2 . I_B \right) = \frac{1}{(0.3)^2} \left(100 + 6^2 \times 5 \right) = 3111 \text{ kg}$$

and total equivalent mass to be accelerated,

$$M_e = m_e + M = 3111 + 75 = 3186 \text{ kg}$$

∴ Force required to accelerate this equivalent mass (M_e)

$$= M_e . a = 3186 \, a \text{ N} \qquad \qquad \text{... (i)}$$

and the accelerating force provided by the pull of gravity on the mass M suspended from the rope

$$= M.g = 75 \times 9.81 = 736 \text{ N} \qquad \qquad \text{... (ii)}$$

From equations (i) and (ii),

$$3186 \, a = 736 \quad \text{or} \quad a = 736/3186 = 0.231 \text{ m/s}^2 \text{ Ans.}$$

2. When the efficiency of the gearing system is 90%

We know that the equivalent mass of the geared system referred to the circumference of the drum,

$$m_e = \frac{1}{r^2}\left(I_A + \frac{G^2.I_B}{\eta}\right) = \frac{1}{(0.3)^2}\left[100 + \frac{6^2 \times 5}{0.9}\right] = 3333 \text{ kg}$$

and total equivalent mass to be accelerated,

$$M_e = m_e + M = 3333 + 75 = 3408 \text{ kg}$$

∴ Force required to accelerate this equivalent mass (M_e)

$$= M_e.a = 3408\ a \text{ N} \qquad\qquad ...(iii)$$

and accelerating force provided by the pull of gravity on the mass M suspended from the rope

$$= M.g = 75 \times 9.81 = 736 \text{ N} \qquad\qquad ...(iv)$$

Now equating equations (iii) and (iv),

$$3408\ a = 736 \quad\text{or}\quad a = 736/3408 = 0.216 \text{ m/s}^2 \text{ Ans.}$$

Example. 3.14. *The motor shaft A exerts a constant torque of 100 N-m and is geared to shaft B as shown in Fig. 3.13. The moments of inertia of the parts attached to the motor shaft A is 2 kg-m² and that of the parts attached to other shaft B is 32 kg-m².*

Find the gear ratio which gives the maximum angular acceleration of shaft B and the corresponding angular acceleration of each shaft.

Solution. Given : $T = 100$ N-m ; $I_A = 2$ kg-m² ; $I_B = 32$ kg-m²

Parallel shaft gear motor.

Gear ratio which gives the maximum acceleration

Let G = Gear ratio which gives the maximum acceleration.

α_A = Angular acceleration of shaft A, and

α_B = Angular acceleration of shaft B.

We know that $\alpha_A = G.\alpha_B \qquad ...(i)$

∴ Torque required on motor shaft A to accelerate rotating parts on it,

$$T_A = I_A.\ \alpha_A = I_A.G.\ \alpha_B$$

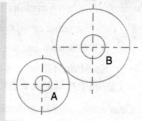

Fig. 3.13

... [From equation (i)]

and torque required on motor shaft A to accelerate rotating parts on shaft B,

$$T_{AB} = \frac{I_B.\alpha_B}{G}$$

Assuming that there is no resisting torque and the torque exerted on the motor shaft A is utilised to overcome the inertia of the geared system.

$$\therefore\quad T = T_A + T_{AB} = I_A.G.\alpha_B + \frac{I_B.\alpha_B}{G} = \alpha_B\left(\frac{I_A.G^2 + I_B}{G}\right)$$

or

$$\alpha_B = \frac{G.T}{I_A.G^2 + I_B} \qquad\qquad ...(ii)$$

For maximum angular acceleration of B, differentiate with respect to G and equate to zero, *i.e.*

$$\frac{d\alpha_B}{dG} = 0 \quad \text{or} \quad \frac{d\left(\dfrac{G.T}{I_A.G^2 + I_B}\right)}{dG} = 0$$

$$\frac{(I_A.G^2 + I_B)\,T - G.T\,(I_A \times 2G)}{(I_A.G^2 + I_B)^2} = 0 \quad \text{or} \quad I_A.G^2 + I_B - 2G^2.I_A = 0$$

$$\therefore \qquad I_B = G^2.I_A \qquad \text{or} \qquad G = \sqrt{\frac{I_B}{I_A}} = \sqrt{\frac{32}{2}} = 4 \text{ Ans.}$$

Angular acceleration of each shaft

Substituting the value of G in equation (*ii*),

$$\alpha_B = \frac{4 \times 100}{2 \times 4^2 + 32} = 6.25 \text{ rad/s}^2 \text{ Ans.}$$

and

$$\alpha_A = G.\alpha_B = 4 \times 6.25 = 25 \text{ rad/s}^2 \text{ Ans.}$$

Example 3.15. *A motor vehicle of total mass 1500 kg has road wheels of 600 mm effective diameter. The effective moment of inertia of the four road wheels and of the rear axle together is 8 kg-m² while that of the engine and flywheels is 1 kg-m². The transmission efficiency is 85% and a tractive resistance at a speed of 24 km/h is 300 N. The total available engine torque is 200 N-m. Determine :*

1. Gear ratio, engine to back axle, to provide maximum acceleration on an upgrade whose sine is 0.25, when travelling at 24 km/h,

2. The value of this maximum acceleration, and

3. The speed and power of the engine under these conditions.

Solution. Given : $m = 1500$ kg ; $d = 600$ mm $= 0.6$ m or $r = 0.3$ m ; $I_A = 8$ kg-m² ; $I_B = 1$ kg-m²; $\eta = 85\% = 0.85$; $v = 24$ km/h ; $F = 300$ N ; $T_B = 200$ N-m ; $\sin \theta = 0.25$

1. Gear ratio, engine to back axle, to provide maximum acceleration

Let G = Gear ratio, engine to back axle, to provide maximum acceleration.

$\therefore$ Torque at road wheels,

$$T_W = \eta \times G \times T_B = 0.85 \times G \times 200 = 170\,G \text{ N-m}$$

and available tangential force at road wheels,

$$P = \frac{T_W}{r} = \frac{170\,G}{0.3} = 567\,G \text{ N}$$

Let the vehicle travels up the gradient a distance of s metre while its speed changes from u to v m/s.

We know that work done by the tangential force P

= Change of linear K.E. of vehicle + Change of angular K.E. of road wheels and axle + Change of angular K.E. of engine and flywheel + Work done in raising vehicle + Work done in overcoming tractive resistance or $\qquad P \times s = \frac{1}{2} m (v^2 - u^2) + \frac{1}{2} I_A (\omega_2^2 - \omega_1^2) + \frac{1}{2} I_B . G^2 . \eta (\omega_2^2 - \omega_1^2) + m.g.s. \sin\theta + F.s$

or $\qquad s(P - m.g.\sin\theta - F) = \frac{v^2 - u^2}{2}\left(m + \frac{I_A}{r^2} + \frac{I_B . G^2 . \eta}{r^2}\right)$

$$\text{... (Substituting } \omega_1 = u/r, \text{ and } \omega_2 = v/r)$$

$$s(567\ G - 1500 \times 9.81 \times 0.25 - 300) = \frac{v^2 - u^2}{2}\left(1500 + \frac{8}{0.3^2} + \frac{1 \times G^2 \times 0.85}{0.3^2}\right)$$

$$s(567G - 3980) = \frac{v^2 - u^2}{2}(1590 + 9.44\ G^2) \qquad\qquad \text{... (i)}$$

We know that linear acceleration,

$$a = \frac{v^2 - u^2}{2s} = \frac{567G - 3980}{1590 + 9.44\ G^2} \qquad \text{... [From equation (i)] ... (ii)}$$

For maximum acceleration, differentiate equation (ii) with respect to G and equate to zero,

i.e.

$$\frac{da}{dG} = 0$$

$$\frac{(1590 + 9.44\ G^2)\ 567 - (567G - 3980)(9.44 \times 2G)}{(1590 + 9.44\ G^2)^2} = 0$$

or $\quad 901\ 530 + 5352\ G^2 - 10\ 705\ G^2 + 75\ 142\ G = 0$

$\qquad G^2 - 14\ G - 168.4 = 0$

$\therefore \qquad\qquad G = \frac{14 \pm \sqrt{(14)^2 + 4 \times 168.4}}{2} = \frac{14 \pm 29.5}{2} = 21.75 \text{ or } 22 \textbf{ Ans.}$

$$\text{... (Taking + ve sign)}$$

2. *Value of maximum acceleration*

Substituting the value of G = 22 in equation (ii), maximum acceleration,

$$a_{max} = \frac{567 \times 22 - 3980}{1590 + 9.44\ (22)^2} = 1.38 \text{ m/s } \textbf{ Ans.}$$

3. *Speed and power of the engine*

Let $\qquad\qquad \omega$ = Speed of the engine in rad/s.

We know that the speed of the road wheels,

$$v = 24 \text{ km/h} = 6.67 \text{ m/s} \qquad\qquad \text{... (Given)}$$

$\therefore$ Angular speed of the road wheels

$$= \frac{v}{r} = \frac{6.67}{0.3} = 22.23 \text{ rad/s}$$

Since the speed of the engine is G times the speed of the road wheels, therefore

$$\omega = G \times 22.23 = 22 \times 22.23 = 489 \, \text{rad/s} \quad \textbf{Ans.}$$

We know that power of the engine

$$= T_{B}.\omega = 200 \times 489 = 97\,800 \, \text{W} = 97.8 \, \text{kW} \quad \textbf{Ans.}$$

Example 3.16. *A super charged road racing automobile has an engine capable of giving an output torque of 1 kN-m, this torque being reasonably constant over a speed range from 100 km/h to 275 km/h in top gear. The road wheels are of 0.9 m effective diameter, and the back axle ratio is 3.3 to 1. When travelling at a steady speed of 170 km/h in top gear on a level road, the power absorbed is 50 kW. The vehicle has a mass of 1000 kg, the four road wheels each has mass of 40 kg and a radius of gyration of 0.25 m. The moment of inertia of the engine and all parts forward of the differential is 1 kg-m².*

Assuming that the resistance caused by windage and road drag varies as the square of the speed, determine the time taken for the speed to rise from 100 km/h to 275 km/h in top gear at full throttle on an upgrade of 1 in 30.

Solution. Given : $T_E = 1$ kN-m $= 1000$ N-m ; $v_1 = 100$ km/h $= 27.8$ m/s ; $v_2 = 275$ km/h $= 76.4$ m/s ; $d = 0.9$ m or $r = 0.45$ m ; $G = 3.3$; $v = 170$ km/h $= 47.2$ m/s ; $P = 50$ kW $= 50 \times 10^3$ W ; $M = 1000$ kg ; $m = 40$ kg ; $k = 0.25$ m ; $I_B = 1$ kg-m²

We know that moment of inertia of four road wheels,

$$I_A = 4 \times m.k^2 = 4 \times 40 \, (0.25)^2 = 10 \, \text{kg -m}^2$$

Let $\quad\quad\quad\quad F$ = Resistance caused by windage and road drag in newtons.

∴ Power absorbed by the automobile at a steady speed (P),

$$50 \times 10^3 = F.v = F \times 47.2 \quad \text{or} \quad F = 50 \times 10^3/47.2 = 1060 \, \text{N}$$

Since the resistance caused by windage and road drag (F) varies as the square of the speed (v), therefore

$$F = k.v^2 \quad \text{or} \quad k = F/v^2 = 1060/(47.2)^2 = 0.476$$

∴ $\quad\quad\quad\quad F = 0.476 \, v^2 \, \text{N}$

We know that the torque at road wheels,

$$T_W = G \times T_E = 3.3 \times 1000 = 3300 \, \text{N-m}$$

and available tangential force at road wheels,

$$F_T = \frac{T_W}{r} = \frac{3300}{0.45} = 7333 \, \text{N}$$

Since the gradient is 1 in 30, therefore proceeding in the same way as discussed in the previous example, we get the linear acceleration,

$$a = \frac{dv}{dt} = \frac{F_T - F - \dfrac{M.g}{30}}{M + \dfrac{I_A}{r^2} + \dfrac{I_B.G^2}{r^2}} = \frac{7333 - 0.476 v^2 - \dfrac{1000 \times 9.81}{30}}{1000 + \dfrac{10}{(0.45)^2} + \dfrac{1 \times 3.3^2}{(0.45)^2}}$$

$$= 6.65 - 0.43 \times 10^{-3} v^2 - 0.3$$

∴ $$dt = \frac{dv}{6.65 - 0.43 \times 10^{-3} v^2 - 0.3} = \frac{dv}{6.35 - 0.43 \times 10^{-3} v^2}$$

Integrating the above expression,

$$\int dt = \int \frac{dv}{6.35 - 0.43 \times 10^{-3} v^2}$$

$$= \frac{10^3}{0.43} \int \frac{dv}{14\ 768 - v^2} = 2325 \int \frac{dv}{(121.5)^2 - v^2}$$

∴
$$t = \frac{2325}{2 \times 121.5} \log_e \frac{121.5 + v}{121.5 - v} + C_1 \qquad \ldots (i)$$

$$\ldots \left[\because \int \frac{dv}{a^2 - v^2} = \frac{1}{2a} \log_e \frac{a + v}{a - v} \right]$$

where C_1 is the constant of integration. We know that when $t = 0$, $v_1 = 27.8$ m/s.

∴
$$0 = \frac{2325}{2 \times 121.5} \log_e \frac{121.5 + 27.8}{121.5 - 27.8} + C_1 \qquad \ldots \text{(Substituting } v = v_1)$$

$$= 9.6 \ \log_e \frac{149.3}{93.7} + C_1 = 9.6 \log_e 1.6 + C_1$$

∴
$$C_1 = -9.6 \log_e 1.6 = -9.6 \times 0.47 = -4.5$$

Now the expression (*i*) may be written as

$$t = \frac{2325}{2 \times 121.5} \log_e \frac{121.5 + v}{121.5 - v} - 4.5$$

When $v_2 = 76.4$ m/s, the time taken for the speed to rise

$$= \frac{2325}{2 \times 121.5} \log_e \frac{121.5 + 76.4}{121.5 - 76.4} - 4.5 = 9.6 \log_e \frac{197.9}{45.1} - 4.5$$

$$= 9.6 \log_e 4.38 - 4.5 = 9.6 \times 1.48 - 4.5 = 9.7 \text{s} \ \textbf{Ans.}$$

Example 3.17. *An electric motor drives a machine through a speed reducing gear of ratio 9:1. The motor armature, with its shaft and gear wheel, has moment of inertia 0.6 kg-m². The rotating part of the driven machine has moment of inertia 45 kg-m². The driven machine has resisting torque of 100 N-m and the efficiency of reduction gear is 95%. Find*

1. The power which the motor must develop to drive the machine at a uniform speed of 160 r.p.m.,

2. The time required for the speed of the machine to increase from zero to 60 r.p.m., when the torque developed on the motor armature in starting from rest is 30 N-m, and

3. If the gear ratio were altered so as to give the machine the greatest possible angular acceleration in starting from rest, what would then be the gear ratio ? The starting torque of the motor is 30 N-m as before.

Solution. Given : $G = 9$; $I_A = 0.6$ kg-m²; $I_B = 45$ kg-m²; $T_B = 100$ N-m; $\eta = 95\% = 0.95$; $N = 160$ r.p.m. ; $N_1 = 0$; $N_2 = 60$ r.p.m. ; $T_A = 30$ N-m

A motor driving a machine is shown in Fig. 3.14.

1. *Power which the motor must develop*

We know that the power which the motor must develop,

$$P = \frac{2\pi \, N.T_B}{60 \times \eta} = \frac{2\pi \times 160 \times 100}{60 \times 0.95} \text{ W}$$

$$= 1764 \text{ W} = 1.764 \text{ kW} \textbf{ Ans.}$$

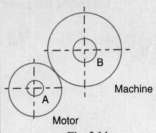

Machine

Motor

Fig. 3.14

2. *Time required for the speed of the machine to increase from zero to 60 r.p.m.*

Let t = Time required for the speed of the machine to increase from zero to 60 r.p.m.

α_A = Angular acceleration of motor, and

α_B = Angular acceleration of machine.

Since the speed of motor A is G times the speed of machine B, therefore

$$\alpha_A = G.\alpha_B = 9 \, \alpha_B$$

We know that torque developed on motor armature,

$$T_A = 30 \text{ N-m} \qquad \text{... (Given)}$$

Due to the torque (T_A) and efficiency of gearing (η), the torque transmitted to machine B,

$$T_{B1} = G.T_A.\eta = 9 \times 30 \times 0.95 = 256.5 \text{ N-m}$$

We know that resisting torque on machine B,

$$T_B = 100 \text{ N-m} \qquad \text{... (Given)}$$

$\therefore$ Net torque on machine B

$$= T_{B1} - T_B = 256.5 - 100 = 156.5 \text{ N-m} \qquad \text{... (i)}$$

We know that total torque to be applied to machine B in order to accelerate the geared system

= Torque required on B to accelerate B only + Torque required on B to accelerate A

$$= I_B.\alpha_B + G.T_A.\eta = I_B.\alpha_B + G.I_A.\alpha_A.\eta \qquad ...(\because T_A = I_A.\alpha_A)$$

$$= I_B.\alpha_B + G^2. I_A .\alpha_B.\eta \qquad ...(\because \alpha_A = G.\alpha_B)$$

$$= 45 \, \alpha_B + 9^2 \times 0.6 \times \alpha_B \times 0.95 = 45 \, \alpha_B + 46.2 \, \alpha_B$$

$$= 91.2 \, \alpha_B \qquad \text{... (ii)}$$

Equating equations (i) and (ii),

$$\alpha_B = 156.5/91.2 = 1.7 \text{ rad/s}^2$$

We are given that initial angular speed, $\omega_1 = 0$, and final angular speed,

$$\omega_2 = \frac{2\pi \, N_2}{60} = \frac{2\pi \times 60}{60} = 6.28 \text{ rad/s} \qquad ...(\because N_2 = 60 \text{ r.p.m.})$$

We know that $\omega_2 = \omega_1 + \alpha_B.t$

$$6.28 = 0 + 1.7 \, t = 1.7 \, t \qquad \text{or} \qquad t = 6.28/1.7 = 3.7 \text{ s } \textbf{Ans.}$$

3. *Gear ratio for maximum angular acceleration of the machine*

Let G_1 = Gear ratio for maximum angular acceleration of the machine.

We know that net torque on machine B

$$= T_{B1} - T_B = G_1.T_A.\eta - T_B = G_1 \times 30 \times 0.95 - 100$$
$$= 27.5\,G_1 - 100 \qquad \qquad ...(iii)$$

We also know that total torque required to be applied to machine B in order to accelerate the geared system

$$= I_B.\alpha_B + (G_1)^2\,\alpha_B.I_A.\eta$$
$$= 45 \times \alpha_B + (G_1)^2\,\alpha_B \times 0.6 \times 0.95 = \alpha_B\,[45 + 0.57\,(G_1)^2] \qquad ...(iv)$$

From equations (iii) and (iv),

$$\alpha_B = \frac{27.5\,G_1 - 100}{45 + 0.57\,(G_1)^2}$$

For maximum angular acceleration, differentiate the above expression and equate to zero, i.e.

$$\frac{d\,\alpha_B}{d\,G_1} = 0$$

or

$$\frac{[45 + 0.57\,(G_1)^2]\,(27.5) - (27.5\,G_1 - 100)\,(2 \times 0.57\,G_1)}{[45 + 0.57\,(G_1)^2]} = 0$$

$$1237.5 + 15.675\,(G_1)^2 - 31.35\,(G_1)^2 + 114\,G_1 = 0$$
$$15.675\,(G_1)^2 - 114\,G_1 - 1237.5 = 0$$
$$(G_1)^2 - 7.27\,G_1 - 78.95 = 0$$

$$\therefore \qquad G_1 = \frac{7.27 \pm \sqrt{(7.27)^2 + 4 \times 78.95}}{2} = \frac{7.27 \pm 19.2}{2} = 13.235 \text{ Ans.}$$

... (Taking + ve sign)

Example 3.18. *A hoisting gear, with a 1.5 m diameter drum, operates two cages by ropes passing from the drum over two guide pulleys of 1 m diameter. One cage (loaded) rises while the other (empty) descends. The drum is driven by a motor through double reduction gearing. The particulars of the various parts are as follows :*

S.No.	Part	Maximum Speed (r.p.m.)	Mass (kg)	Radius of gyration (mm)	Frictional resistance
1.	Motor	900	200	90	– .
2.	Intermediate gear	275	375	225	150 N-m
3.	Drum and shaft	50	2250	600	1125 N-m
4.	Guide pulley (each)	–	200	450	150 N-m
5.	Rising rope and cage	–	1150	–	500 N
6.	Falling rope and cage	–	650	–	500 N

Determine the total motor torque necessary to produce a cage an acceleration of 0.9 m/s².

Solution. Given : $d = 1.5$ m or $r = 0.750$ m ; $d_1 = 1$ m ; $N_M = 900$ r.p.m ; $N_1 = 275$ r.p.m. ; $N_D = 50$ r.p.m ; $m_M = 200$ kg; $k_M = 90$ mm $= 0.09$ m ; $m_I = 375$ kg ; $k_I = 225$ mm $= 0.225$ m ; $M_D = 2250$ kg ; $k_D = 600$ mm $= 0.6$ m ; $m_P = 200$ kg ; $k_P = 450$ mm $= 0.45$ m ; $m_1 = 1150$ kg ; $m_2 = 650$ kg ; $F_I = 150$ N-m ; $F_D = 1125$ N-m ; $F_P = 150$ N-m ; $F_1 = 500$ N ; $F_2 = 350$ N ; $a = 0.9$ m/s²

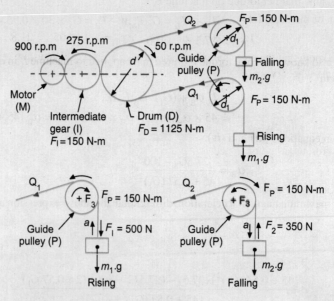

Fig. 3.15

We know that speed of guide pulley (P),

$$N_P = N_D \times \frac{d}{d_1} = 50 \times \frac{1.5}{1} = 75 \text{ r.p.m.}$$

Gear ratio for the intermediate gear and motor,

$$G_1 = N_1 / N_M = 275 / 900 = 0.306$$

Gear ratio for the drum and motor,

$$G_2 = N_D / N_M = 50 / 900 = 0.055$$

Gear ratio for the guide pulley and motor,

$$G_3 = N_P / N_M = 75 / 900 = 0.083$$

Mass moment of inertia of the motor,

$$I_M = m_M \, (k_M)^2 = 200 \, (0.09)^2 = 1.62 \text{ kg-m}^2$$

Mass moment of inertia of the intermediate gear,

$$I_I = m_I \, (k_I)^2 = 375 \, (0.225)^2 = 18.98 \text{ kg-m}^2$$

Mass moment of inertia of the drum and shaft,

$$I_D = m_D \, (k_D)^2 = 2250 \, (0.6)^2 = 810 \text{ kg-m}^2$$

Mass moment of inertia of the guide pulley,

$$I_P = m_P \, (k_P)^2 = 200 \, (0.45)^2 = 40.5 \text{ kg-m}^2$$

and angular acceleration of the drum,

$$\alpha_D = a / r = 0.9 / 0.75 = 1.2 \text{ rad/s}^2$$

Since the speed of the drum (N_D) is 0.055 times the speed of motor (N_M), therefore angular acceleration of the drum (α_D),

$$1.2 = 0.055 \, \alpha_M \quad \text{or} \quad \alpha_M = 1.2 \,/\, 0.055 = 21.8 \text{ rad/s}^2$$

We know that the equivalent mass moment of inertia of the system (*i.e.* motor, intermediate gear shaft and wheel, drum and two guide pulleys) referred to motor M,

$$I = I_M + (G_1)^2 \, I_I + (G_2)^2 \, I_D + 2 \, (G_3)^2 \, I_P$$
$$= 1.62 + (0.306)^2 \, 18.98 + (0.055)^2 \, 810 + 2 \, (0.083)^2 \, 40.5$$
$$= 1.62 + 1.78 + 2.45 + 0.56 = 6.41 \text{ kg-m}^2$$

∴ Torque at motor to accelerate the system,

$$T_1 = I.\alpha_M = 6.41 \times 21.8 = 139.7 \text{ N-m}$$

and torque at motor to overcome friction at intermediate gear, drum and two guide pulleys,

$$T_2 = G_1.F_I + G_2.F_D + 2 \, G_3.F_P$$
$$= 0.306 \times 150 + 0.055 \times 1125 + 2 \times 0.83 \times 150 \text{ N-m}$$
$$= 45.9 + 61.8 + 25 = 132.7 \text{ N-m}$$

Now for the rising rope and cage as shown in Fig. 3.15, tension in the rope between the pulley and drum,

Q_1 = Weight of rising rope and cage + Force to accelerate rising rope and cage (inertia force) + Frictional resistance

$$= m_1.g + m_1.a + F_1 = 1150 \times 9.81 + 1150 \times 0.9 + 500$$
$$= 12\,816 \text{ N}$$

Similarly for the falling rope and cage, as shown in Fig. 3.15, tension in the rope between the pulley and drum,

Q_2 = Weight of falling rope and cage − Force to accelerate falling rope and cage (inertia force) − Frictional resistance

$$= m_2.g - m_2.a - F_2 = 650 \times 9.81 - 650 \times 0.9 - 350 = 5441 \text{ N}$$

∴ Torque at drum, $T_D = (Q_1 - Q_2) \, r = (12\,816 - 5441) \, 0.75 = 5531 \text{ N-m}$

and torque at motor to raise and lower cages and ropes and to overcome frictional resistance,

$$T_3 = G_2 \times T_D = 0.055 \times 5531 = 304 \text{ N-m}$$

∴ Total motor torque required,

$$T = T_1 + T_2 + T_3 = 139.7 + 132.7 + 304 = 576.4 \text{ N-m Ans.}$$

3.21. Collision of Two Bodies

Consider the impact between two bodies which move with different velocities along the same straight line. It is assumed that the point of the impact lies on the line joining the centers of gravity of the two bodies. The behaviour of these colliding bodies during the complete period of impact will depend upon the properties of the materials of which they are made. The material of the two bodies may be *perfectly elastic or perfectly inelastic.

In either case, the first effect of impact is approximately the same. The parts of each body adjacent to the point of impact is deformed and the deformation will continue until the centre of gravity of the two bodies are moving with the same velocity. Assuming that there are no external forces acting on the system, the total momentum must remain constant.

---

* The bodies, which rebound after impact are called **elastic bodies** and the bodies which does not rebound at all after its impact are called **inelastic bodies**.

3.22. Collision of Inelastic Bodies

When two *inelastic bodies A and B, as shown in Fig. 3.16 (a), moving with different velocities, collide with each other as shown in Fig. 3.16 (b), the two bodies will remain together after impact and will move together with a common velocity.

Let m_1 = Mass of first body A.

m_2 = Mass of second body B.

u_1 and u_2 = Velocities of bodies A and B respectively before impact, and

v = Common velocity of bodies A and B after impact.

(a) Before impact.   (b) After impact.

Fig. 3.16. Collision of inelastic bodies.

A little consideration will show that the impact will take place only, if u_1 is greater than u_2. Now according to principle of conservation of momentum,

Momentum before impact = Momentum after impact

$$m_1.u_1 + m_2.u_2 = (m_1 + m_2)\, v$$

∴ $$v = \frac{m_1.u_1 + m_2.u_2}{m_1 + m_2} \qquad \qquad \text{... (i)}$$

The loss of kinetic energy during impact may be obtained by finding out the kinetic energy of the two bodies before and after impact. The difference between the two kinetic energies of the system gives the loss of kinetic energy during impact.

We know that the kinetic energy of the first body, before impact

$$= \frac{1}{2}\, m_1\, (u_1)^2$$

and kinetic energy of the second body, before impact

$$= \frac{1}{2}\, m_2\, (u_2)^2$$

∴ Total kinetic energy of the system before impact,

$$E_1 = \frac{1}{2}\, m_1\, (u_1)^2 + \frac{1}{2}\, m_2\, (u_2)^2$$

When the two bodies move with the same velocity v after impact, then

Kinetic energy of the system after impact,

$$E_2 = \frac{1}{2}\, (m_1 + m_2)\, v^2$$

∴ Loss of kinetic energy during impact,

$$E_L = E_1 - E_2 = \frac{1}{2}\, m_1.u_1^2 + \frac{1}{2}\, m_2.u_2^2 - \frac{1}{2}\, (m_1 + m_2)\, v^2$$

---

* The impact between two lead spheres or two clay spheres is approximately an inelastic impact.

$$= \frac{1}{2} m_1.u_1^2 + \frac{1}{2} m_2.u_2^2 - \frac{1}{2}(m_1 + m_2)\left(\frac{m_1.u_1 + m_2.u_2}{m_1 + m_2}\right)^2$$

... [From equation (*i*)]

$$= \frac{1}{2} m_1.u_1^2 + \frac{1}{2} m_2.u_2^2 - \frac{(m_1.u_1 + m_2.u_2)^2}{2(m_1 + m_2)}$$

$$= \frac{1}{2(m_1 + m_2)} + \left[(m_1 + m_2)(m_1 \cdot u_1^2 + m_2 \cdot u_2^2) - (m_1 \cdot u_1 + m_2 \cdot u_2)^2\right]$$

... [Multiplying the numerator and denominator by $(m_1 + m_2)$]

$$= \frac{1}{2(m_1 + m_2)}\left[m_1^2 \cdot u_1^2 + m_1.m_2.u_2^2 + m_1 \cdot m_2.u_1^2 + m_2^2.u_2^2\right.$$

$$\left. - m_1^2.u_1^2 - m_2^2.u_2^2 - 2m_1 m_2 u_1 u_2\right]$$

$$= \frac{1}{2(m_1 + m_2)}\left[m_1.m_2.u_2^2 + m_1.m_2.u_1^2 - 2m_1 m_2 u_1 u_2\right]$$

$$= \frac{m_1.m_2}{2(m_1 + m_2)}\left[u_1^2 + u_2^2 - 2u_1.u_2\right] = \frac{m_1.m_2}{2(m_1 + m_2)}(u_1 - u_2)^2$$

This *loss of kinetic energy is used for doing the work in deforming the two bodies and is absorbed in overcoming internal friction of the material. Since there will be no strain energy stored up in the material due to elastic deformation, therefore the bodies cannot regain its original shape. Hence the two bodies will adhere together and will move with reduced kinetic energy after impact. The reduction of kinetic energy appears as heat energy because of the work done in overcoming the internal friction during deformation.

3.23. Collision of Elastic Bodies

When two elastic bodies, as shown in Fig. 3.17 (*a*), collide with each other, they suffer a change of form. When the bodies first touch, the pressure between them is zero. For a short time thereafter, the bodies continue to approach each other and the pressure exerted by one body over the other body increases. Thus the two bodies are compressed and deformed at the surface of contact due to their mutual pressures.

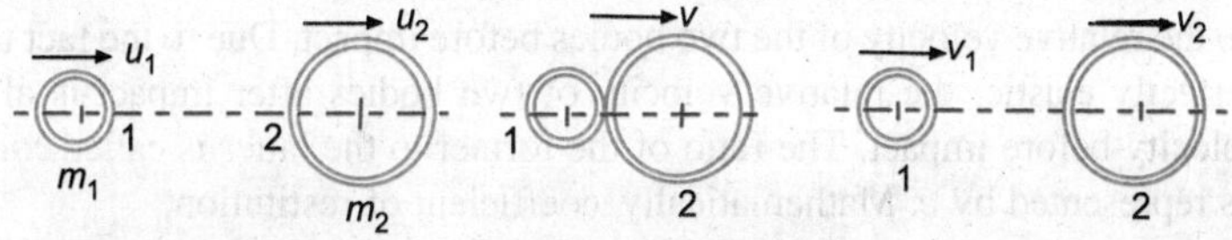

(*a*) Before impact.   (*b*) After compression.   (*c*) After impact.

Fig. 3.17. Collision of elastic bodies.

If one of the bodies is fixed then the other will momentarily come to rest and then rebound. However, if both the bodies are free to move, then each body will momentarily come to rest relative to the other. At this instant, the pressure between the two bodies becomes maximum and the deformation is also a maximum. At this stage the two bodies move with a **common velocity, as shown in Fig. 3.17 (*b*).

---

*   According to principle of conservation of energy, the energy cannot be lost.

**   This common velocity (*v*) may be calculated as discussed in the previous article.

The work done in deforming the two bodies is stored up as strain energy. Since no energy is absorbed in overcoming internal friction, therefore there will be no conversion of kinetic energy into heat energy. Thus immediately after the instant at which the two bodies move with same velocity, the bodies begin to regain their original shape.This process of regaining the original shape is called *restitution.*

The strain energy thus stored is reconverted into kinetic energy and the two bodies ultimately separates as shown in Fig. 3.17 (c). In this case, the change of momentum of each body during the second phase of impact (*i.e.* when the bodies are separating) is exactly equal to the change of momentum during the first phase of impact (*i.e.* when the bodies are approaching or colliding).

Let m_1 = Mass of the first body,

u_1 = Velocity of the first body before impact,

v_1 = Velocity of the first body after impact,

m_2, u_2 and v_2 = Corresponding values for the second body, and

v = Common velocity of the two bodies at the instant when compression has just ended.

∴ Change of momentum of first body during the second phase of impact

$$= m_1 (v_1 - v)$$

and change of momentum of the same body during first phase of impact

$$= m_1 (v - u_1)$$

∴ $m_1 (v_1 - v) = m_1 (v - u_1)$ or $v_1 = 2 v - u_1$ ... (*i*)

Similarly, for the second body, change of momentum of the second body during second phase of impact

$$= m_2 (v_2 - v)$$

and change of momentum of the second body during first phase of impact

$$= m_2 (v - u_2)$$

∴ $m_2 (v_2 - v) = m_2 (v - u_2)$ or $v_2 = 2v - u_2$ ... (*ii*)

Subtracting equation (*ii*) from equation (*i*), we get

$$v_1 - v_2 = (u_2 - u_1) = - (u_1 - u_2) \qquad ... (iii)$$

Therefore, we see that the relative velocity of the two bodies after impact is equal and opposite to the relative velocity of the two bodies before impact. Due to the fact that physical bodies are not perfectly elastic, the relative velocity of two bodies after impact is always less than the relative velocity before impact. The ratio of the former to the latter is called *coefficient of restitution* and is represented by e. Mathematically, coefficient of restitution,

$$e = \frac{\text{Relative velocity after impact}}{\text{Relative velocity before impact}} = \frac{v_1 - v_2}{-(u_1 - u_2)}$$

$$= \frac{v_1 - v_2}{u_2 - u_1} \quad \text{or} \quad \frac{v_2 - v_1}{u_1 - u_2}$$

The value of e = 0, for the perfectly inelastic bodies and e = 1 for perfectly elastic bodies. In case the bodies are neither perfectly inelastic nor perfectly elastic, then the value of e lies between 0 and 1.

The final velocities of the colliding bodies after impact may be calculated as discussed below:

Since the change of velocity of each body during the second phase of impact is e times the change of velocity during first phase of impact, therefore for the first body,

$$v_1 - v = e\,(v - u_1) \quad \text{or} \quad v_1 = v\,(1 + e) - e.u_1 \qquad \text{...(iv)}$$

Similarly for the second body,

$$v_2 - v = e\,(v - u_2) \quad \text{or} \quad v_2 = v\,(1 + e) - e.u_2 \qquad \text{...(v)}$$

When $e = 1$, the above equations (*iv*) and (*v*) reduced to equations (*i*) and (*ii*).

Notes : 1. The time taken by the bodies in compression, after the instant of collision, is called the *time of compression* or *compression period*.

2. The period or time from the end of the compression stage to the instant when the bodies separate (*i.e.* the time for which the restitution takes place) is called *time of restitution* or *restitution period*.

3. The sum of compression period and the restitution period is called *period of collision* or *period of impact*.

4. The velocities of the two bodies at the end of restitution period will be different from their common velocity at the end of the compression period.

3.24. Loss of Kinetic Energy During Elastic Impact

Consider two bodies 1 and 2 having an elastic impact as shown in Fig. 3.17.

Let $\qquad m_1$ = Mass of the first body,

$\qquad\qquad u_1$ = Velocity of the first body before impact,

$\qquad\qquad v_1$ = Velocity of the first body after impact,

$\quad m_2,\ u_2$ and v_2 = Corresponding values for the second body,

$\qquad\qquad e$ = Coefficient of restitution, and

$\qquad\qquad E_L$ = Loss of kinetic energy during impact.

We know that the kinetic energy of the first body, before impact

$$= \frac{1}{2}\, m_1\, . u_1^2$$

Similarly, kinetic energy of the second body, before impact

$$= \frac{1}{2}\, m_2\, . u_2^2$$

∴ Total kinetic energy of the two bodies, before impact,

$$E_1 = \frac{1}{2}\, m_1\, . u_1^2 + \frac{1}{2}\, m_2\, . u_2^2 \qquad \text{...(i)}$$

Similarly, total kinetic energy of the two bodies, after impact

$$E_2 = \frac{1}{2}\, m_1\, . v_1^2 + \frac{1}{2}\, m_2\, . v_2^2 \qquad \text{...(ii)}$$

∴ Loss of kinetic energy during impact,

$$E_L = E_1 - E_2 = \left(\frac{1}{2}\, m_1\, . u_1^2 + \frac{1}{2}\, m_2\, . u_2^2 \right) - \left(\frac{1}{2}\, m_1\, . v_1^2 + \frac{1}{2}\, m_2\, . v_2^2 \right)$$

$$= \frac{1}{2}\left[\left(m_1 \cdot u_1^2 + m_2 \cdot u_2^2\right) - \left(m_1 \cdot v_1^2 + m_2 \cdot v_2^2\right)\right]$$

Multiplying the numerator and denominator by $(m_1 + m_2)$,

$$E_L = \frac{1}{2(m_1 + m_2)}\left[(m_1 + m_2)\left(m_1 \cdot u_1^2 + m_2 \cdot u_2^2\right) - (m_1 + m_2)\left(m_1 \cdot v_1^2 + m_2 \cdot v_2^2\right)\right]$$

$$= \frac{1}{2(m_1 + m_2)}\left[\left(m_1^2 \cdot u_1^2 + m_1 \cdot m_2 \cdot u_2^2 + m_1 \cdot m_2 \cdot u_1^2 + m_2^2 \cdot u_2^2\right)\right.$$
$$\left. - \left(m_1^2 \cdot v_1^2 + m_1 \cdot m_2 \cdot v_2^2 + m_1 \cdot m_2 \cdot v_1^2 + m_2^2 \cdot v_2^2\right)\right]$$

$$= \frac{1}{2(m_1 + m_2)}\left[\left\{m_1^2 \cdot u_1^2 + m_2^2 \cdot u_2^2 + m_1 \cdot m_2 (u_1^2 + u_2^2)\right\}\right.$$
$$\left. - \left\{m_1^2 \cdot v_1^2 + m_2^2 \cdot v_2^2 + m_1 \cdot m_2 (v_1^2 + v_2^2)\right\}\right]$$

$$= \frac{1}{2(m_1 + m_2)}\left[\left\{(m_1.u_1 + m_2.u_2)^2 - (2m_1 m_2 u_1 u_2) + m_1.m_2 (u_1 - u_2)^2 + (2 m_1 m_2 u_1 u_2)\right\}\right.$$
$$\left. - \left\{(m_1.v_1 + m_2.v_2)^2 - (2 m_1 m_2 v_1 v_2) + m_1.m_2 (v_1 - v_2)^2 + (2 m_1 m_2 v_1 v_2)\right\}\right]$$

$$= \frac{1}{2(m_1 + m_2)}\left[\left\{(m_1.u_1 + m_2.u_2)^2 + m_1.m_2 (u_1 - u_2)^2\right\}\right.$$
$$\left. - \left\{(m_1.v_1 + m_2.v_2)^2 + m_1.m_2 (v_1 - v_2)^2\right\}\right]$$

We know that in an elastic impact,

Total momentum before impact = Total momentum after impact

i.e. $$m_1.u_1 + m_2.u_2 = m_1.v_1 + m_2.v_2$$

or $$(m_1.u_1 + m_2.u_2)^2 = (m_1.v_1 + m_2.v_2)^2 \qquad \text{... (Squaring both sides)}$$

∴ Loss of kinetic energy due to impact,

$$E_L = \frac{1}{2(m_1 + m_2)}\left[m_1.m_2 (u_1 - u_2)^2 - m_1.m_2 (v_1 - v_2)^2\right]$$

Substituting $v_1 - v_2 = e(u_1 - u_2)$ in the above equation,

$$E_L = \frac{1}{2(m_1 + m_2)}\left[m_1.m_2 (u_1 - u_2)^2 - m_1.m_2.e^2 (u_1 - u_2)^2\right]$$

$$= \frac{m_1.m_2}{2(m_1 + m_2)} (u_1 - u_2)^2 (1 - e^2)$$

Notes : 1. The loss of kinetic energy may be found out by calculating the kinetic energy of the system before impact, and then by subtracting from it the kinetic energy of the system after impact.

2. For perfectly inelastic bodies, $e = 0$, therefore

$$E_L = \frac{m_1.m_2}{2(m_1+m_2)}(u_1-u_2)^2 \qquad\qquad \text{. . . (same as before)}$$

3. For perfectly elastic bodies, $e = 1$, therefore $E_L = 0$.

4. If weights (instead of masses) of the two bodies are given, then the same may be used in all the relations.

Example 3.19. *A sphere of mass 50 kg moving at 3 m/s overtakes and collides with another sphere of mass 25 kg moving at 1.5 m/s in the same direction. Find the velocities of the two masses after impact and loss of kinetic energy during impact in the following cases :*

1. When the impact is inelastic, 2. When the impact is elastic, and 3. When coefficient of restitution is 0.6.

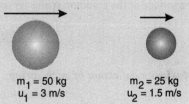

$m_1 = 50$ kg
$u_1 = 3$ m/s

$m_2 = 25$ kg
$u_2 = 1.5$ m/s

Solution. Given : $m_1 = 50$ kg ; $u_1 = 3$ m/s ; $m_2 = 25$ kg ; $u_2 = 1.5$ m/s

1. *When the impact is inelastic*

In case of inelastic impact, the two spheres adhere after impact and move with a common velocity. We know that common velocity after impact,

$$v = \frac{m_1.u_1+m_2.u_2}{m_1+m_2} = \frac{50 \times 3 + 25 \times 1.5}{50+25} = 2.5\,\text{m/s Ans.}$$

and loss of kinetic energy during impact,

$$E_L = \frac{m_1.m_2}{2(m_1+m_2)}(u_1-u_2)^2 = \frac{50 \times 25}{2(50+25)}(3-1.5)^2 \text{ N-m}$$

$$= 18.75 \text{ N-m Ans.}$$

2. *When the impact is elastic*

Let v_1 = Velocity of the first sphere immediately after impact, and

v_2 = Velocity of the second sphere immediately after impact.

We know that when the impact is elastic, the common velocity of the two spheres is the same *i.e.* common velocity, $v = 2.5$ m/s.

$\therefore$ $v_1 = 2v - u_1 = 2 \times 2.5 - 3 = 2$ m/s **Ans.**

and $v_2 = 2v - u_2 = 2 \times 2.5 - 1.5 = 3.5$ m/s **Ans.**

We know that during elastic impact, there is no loss of kinetic energy, *i.e.* $E_L = 0$ **Ans.**

3. *When the coefficient of restitution, e = 0.6*

We know that $v_1 = (1 + e)\,v - e.u_1 = (1 + 0.6)\,2.5 - 0.6 \times 3 = 2.2$ m/s **Ans.**

and $v_2 = (1 + e)\,v - e.u_2 = (1 + 0.6)\,2.5 - 0.6 \times 1.5 = 3.1$ m/s **Ans.**

Loss of kinetic energy during impact,

$$E_L = \frac{m_1.m_2}{2(m_1+m_2)}(u_1-u_2)^2\,(1-e^2)$$

$$= \frac{50 \times 25}{2(50+25)}(3-1.5)^2\,(1-0.6^2) = 12\,\text{N-m Ans.}$$

Example 3.20. *A loaded railway wagon has a mass of 15 tonnes and moves along a level track at 20 km/h. It over takes and collides with an empty wagon of mass 5 tonnes, which is moving along the same track at 12 km/h. If the each wagon is fitted with two buffer springs of stiffness 1000 kN/m, find the maximum deflection of each spring during impact and the speeds of the wagons immediately after impact ends.*

If the coefficient of restitution for the buffer springs is 0.5, how would the final speeds be affected and what amount of energy will be dissipated during impact ?

Solution. Given : $m_1 = 15$ t $= 15\,000$ kg ; $u_1 = 20$ km/h $= 5.55$ m/s ; $m_2 = 5$ t $= 5000$ kg ; $u_2 = 12$ km/h $= 3.33$ m/s ; $s = 1000$ kN/m $= 1 \times 10^6$ N/m ; $e = 0.5$

During impact when both the wagons are moving at the same speed (v) after impact, the magnitude of the common speed (v) is given by

$$v = \frac{m_1.u_1 + m_2.u_2}{m_1 + m_2} = \frac{15\,000 \times 5.55 + 5000 \times 3.33}{15\,000 + 5000} = 5 \text{ m/s } \textbf{ Ans.}$$

Maximum deflection of each spring

Let $x =$ Maximum deflection of each buffer spring during impact, and

$s =$ Stiffness of the spring $= 1000$ kN/m $= 1 \times 10^6$ N/m   ... (Given)

∴ Strain energy stored in one spring

$$= \frac{1}{2} s.x^2 = \frac{1}{2} \times 1 \times 10^6 \times x^2 = 500 \times 10^3 \, x^2 \text{ N-m}$$

Since the four buffer springs (two in each wagon) are strained, therefore total strain energy stored in the springs

$$= 4 \times 500 \times 10^3 \, x^2 = 2 \times 10^6 \, x^2 \text{ N-m} \qquad \qquad ...(i)$$

Difference in kinetic energies before impact and during impact

$$= \frac{m_1.m_2}{2(m_1 + m_2)} (u_1 - u_2)^2 = \frac{15\,000 \times 5000}{2(15\,000 + 5000)} (5.55 - 3.33)^2 \text{ N-m}$$

$$= 9240 \text{ N-m} \qquad \qquad ...(ii)$$

The difference between the kinetic energy before impact and kinetic energy during impact is absorbed by the buffer springs. Thus neglecting all losses, it must be equal to strain energy stored in the springs.

Equating equations (i) and (ii),

$$2 \times 10^6 \, x^2 = 9240$$

or $x^2 = 9240 \,/\, 2 \times 10^6 = 0.00\,462$

∴ $x = 0.068$ m $= 68$ mm **Ans.**

Speeds of the wagons immediately after impact ends

Immediately after impact ends, let v_1 and v_2 be the speeds of the loaded wagon and empty wagon respectively.

We know that $v_1 = 2v - u_1 = 2 \times 5 - 5.55 = 4.45$ m/s **Ans.**

and $v_2 = 2v - u_2 = 2 \times 5 - 3.33 = 6.67$ m/s **Ans.**

When the coefficient of restitution, $e = 0.5$ is taken into account, then

$$v_1 = (1 + e)v - e.u_1 = (1 + 0.5)\,5 - 0.5 \times 5.55 = 4.725 \text{ m/s } \textbf{Ans.}$$

and $\qquad v_2 = (1 + e)v - e.u_2 = (1 + 0.5)5 - 0.5 \times 3.33 = 5.635$ m/s **Ans.**

Amount of energy dissipated during impact

We know that amount of energy dissipated during impact,

$$E_L = \frac{m_1.m_2}{2\,(m_1 + m_2)}\,(u_1 - u_2)^2\,(1 - e^2) = 9240\,(1 - 0.5^2)\,\text{N-m}$$

$$= 9240 \times 0.75 = 6930 \text{ N-m } \textbf{Ans.}$$

Example 3.21. *Fig. 3.18 shows a flywheel A connected through a torsionally flexible spring to one element C of a dog clutch. The other element D of the clutch is free to slide on the shaft but it must revolve with the shaft to which the flywheel B is keyed.*

The moment of inertia of A and B are 22.5 kg-m² 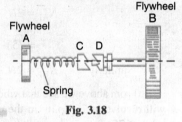 *and 67.5 kg-m² and the torsional stiffness of the spring is 225 N-m per radian. When the flywheel A is revolving at 150 r.p.m. and the flywheel B is at rest, the dog clutch is suddenly engaged. Neglecting all losses, find : 1. strain energy stored in the spring, 2. the maximum twist of the spring, and 3. the speed of flywheel when the spring regains its initial unstrained condition.*

Fig. 3.18

Solution. Given : $I_A = 22.5$ kg-m² ; $I_B = 67.5$ kg-m² ; $q = 225$ N-m/rad ; $N_A = 150$ r.p.m. or $\omega_A = 2\pi \times 150/60 = 15.71$ rad/s

Immediately after the clutch is engaged, the element C of the clutch comes to rest momentarily. But the rotating flywheel A starts to wind up the spring, thus causing equal and opposite torques to act on flywheels A and B. The magnitude of the torque increases continuously until the speeds of flywheels A and B are equal. During this interval, the strain energy is stored in the spring. Beyond this, the spring starts to unwind and the strain energy stored in the spring is reconverted into kinetic energy of the flywheels.

Since there is no external torque acting on the system, therefore the angular momentum will remain constant. Let ω be the angular speed of both the flywheels at the instant their speeds are equal.

$$\therefore \qquad (I_A + I_B)\,\omega = I_A \cdot \omega_A \qquad \text{or} \qquad \omega = \frac{I_A \cdot \omega_A}{I_A + I_B} = \frac{22.5 \times 15.71}{22.5 + 67.5} = 3.93 \text{ rad/s}$$

Kinetic energy of the system at this instant (*i.e.* when speeds are equal),

$$E_2 = \frac{1}{2}\,(I_A + I_B)\,\omega^2 = \frac{1}{2}\,(22.5 + 67.5)\,(3.93)^2 = 695 \text{ N-m}$$

and the initial kinetic energy of the flywheel A,

$$E_1 = \frac{1}{2}\,I_A\,(\omega_A)^2 = \frac{1}{2} \times 22.5\,(15.71)^2 = 2776 \text{ N-m}$$

1. Strain energy stored in the spring

We know that strain energy stored in the spring

$$= E_1 - E_2 = 2776 - 695 = 2081 \text{ N-m } \textbf{Ans.}$$

2. Maximum twist of the spring

Let $\qquad \theta =$ Maximum twist of the spring in radians, and

$\qquad q =$ Torsional stiffness of spring $= 225$ N-m/rad $\qquad\qquad$ ...(Given)

We know that the strain energy,

$$2081 = \frac{1}{2} q.\theta^2 = \frac{1}{2} \times 225\,\theta^2 = 112.5\,\theta^2$$

$$\therefore \qquad \theta^2 = 2081/112.5 = 18.5$$

or $\qquad \theta = 4.3 \text{ rad} = 4.3 \times 180/\pi = 246.3° \textbf{ Ans.}$

3. *Speed of each flywheel when the spring regains its initial unstrained condition*

Let N_{A1} and N_{B1} be the speeds of the flywheels A and B respectively, when the spring regains its initial unstrained condition. We know that

$$N_{A1} = 2N - N_A = 2\left(\frac{60\,\omega}{2\pi}\right) - N_A = 2\left(\frac{60 \times 3.93}{2\pi}\right) - 150$$

$$= 75 - 150 = -75 \text{ r.p.m.}$$

Similarly $\qquad N_{B1} = 2N - N_B = 75 - 0 = 75 \text{ r.p.m.} \qquad \qquad ...(\because N_B = 0)$

From above we see that when the spring regains its initial unstrained condition, the flywheel A will revolve at 75 r.p.m. in the opposite direction to its initial motion and the flywheel B will revolve at 75 r.p.m. in same direction as the initial motion of flywheel A. **Ans.**

EXERCISES

1. A flywheel fitted on the crank shaft of a steam engine has a mass of 1 tonne and a radius of gyration 0.4 m. If the starting torque of the engine is 650 J which may be assumed constant, find 1. Angular acceleration of the flywheel, and 2. Kinetic energy of the flywheel after 10 seconds from the start.
   [Ans. 4.06 rad/s² ; 131.87 kN-m]

2. A load of mass 230 kg is lifted by means of a rope which is wound several times round a drum and which then supports a balance mass of 140 kg. As the load rises, the balance mass falls. The drum has a diameter of 1.2 m and a radius of gyration of 530 mm and its mass is 70 kg. The frictional resistance to the movement of the load is 110 N, and that to the movement of the balance mass 90 N. The frictional torque on the drum shaft is 80 N-m.

   Find the torque required on the drum, and also the power required, at the instant when the load has an upward velocity of 2.5 m/s and an upward acceleration of 1.2 m/s².
   [Ans. 916.2 N-m ; 4.32 kW]

3. A riveting machine is driven by a 3.5 kW motor. The moment of inertia of the rotating parts of the machine is equivalent to 67.5 kg-m² at the shaft on which the flywheel is mounted. At the commencement of an operation, the flywheel is making 240 r.p.m. If closing a rivet occupies 1 second and corresponds to an expenditure of 9 kN-m of energy, find the reduction of speed of the flywheel. What is the maximum rate at which rivets can be closed ? [Ans. 33.2 r.p.m. ; 24 per min]

4. The drum of a goods hoist has a mass of 900 kg. It has an effective diameter of 1.5 m and a radius of gyration of 0.6 m. The loaded cage has a mass of 550 kg and its frictional resistance in the vertical line of travel is 270 N. A maximum acceleration of 0.9 m/s² is required. Determine : 1. The necessary driving torque on the drum, 2. The tension in the rope during acceleration, and 3. The power developed at a steady speed of 3.6 m/s. [Ans. 4.64 kN-m ; 6.16 kN ; 22.3 kW]

5. A valve operating in a vertical direction is opened by a cam and closed by a spring and when fully open the valve is in its lowest position. The mass of the valve is 4 kg and its travel is 12.5 mm and the constant frictional resistance to the motion of the valve is 10 N. The stiffness of the spring is 9.6 N/mm and the initial compression when the valve is closed is 35 mm. Determine 1. the time taken to close the valve from its fully open position, and 2. the velocity of the valve at the moment of impact. [Ans. 0.0161 s ; 1.4755 m/s]

6. A railway truck of mass 20 tonnes, moving at 6.5 km/h is brought to rest by a buffer stop. The buffer exerts a force of 22.5 kN initially and this force increases uniformly by 60 kN for each 1 m compression of the buffer. Neglecting any loss of energy at impact, find the maximum compression of the buffer and the time required for the truck to be brought to rest. **[Ans. 0.73 m ; 0.707 s]**

7. A cage of mass 2500 kg is raised and lowered by a winding drum of 1.5 m diameter. A brake drum is attached to the winding drum and the combined mass of the drums is 1000 kg and their radius of gyration is 1.2 m. The maximum speed of descent is 6 m/s and when descending at this speed, the brake must be capable of stopping the load in 6 m. Find 1. the tension of the rope during stopping at the above rate, 2. the friction torque necessary at the brake, neglecting the inertia of the rope, and 3. In a descent of 30 m, the load starts from rest and falls freely until its speed is 6 m/s. The brake is then applied and the speed is kept constant at 6 m/s until the load is 10 m from the bottom. The brake is then tightened so as to give uniform retardation, and the load is brought to rest at the bottom. Find the total time of descent. **[Ans. 32 kN ; 29.78 kN-m ; 7.27 s]**

8. A mass of 275 kg is allowed to fall vertically through 0.9 m on to the top of a pile of mass 450 kg. Assuming that the falling mass and the pile remain in contact after impact and that the pile is moved 150 mm at each blow, find allowing for the action of gravity after impact, 1. The energy lost in the blow, and 2. The average resistance against the pile. **[Ans. 13.3 kN ; 1.5 kN-m]**

9. Fig. 3.19 shows a hammer of mass 6 kg and pivoted at *A*. It falls against a wedge of mass 1 kg which is driven forward 6 mm, by the impact into a heavy rigid block. The resistance to the wedge varies uniformly with the distance through which it moves, varying zero to *R* newtons.

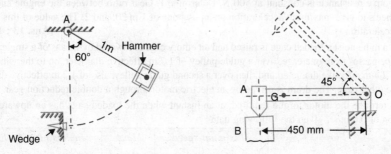

Fig. 3.19   **Fig. 3.20**

Neglecting the small amount by which the hammer rises after passing through the vertical through *A* and assuming that the hammer does not rebound, find the value of *R*. **[Ans. 8.38 kN]**

10. Fig. 3.20 shows a tilt hammer, hinged at *O*, with its head *A* resting on top of the pile *B*. The hammer, including the arm *OA*, has a mass of 25 kg. Its centre of gravity *G* is 400 mm horizontally from *O* and its radius of gyration about an axis through *G* parallel to the axis of the pin *O* is 75 mm. The pile has a mass of 135 kg. The hammer is raised through 45° to the position shown in dotted lines, and released. On striking the pile, there is no rebound. Find the angular velocity of the hammer immediately before impact and the linear velocity of the pile immediately after impact. Neglect any impulsive resistance offered by the earth into which the pile is being driven.

[Ans. 5.8 rad/s, 0.343 m/s]

11. The tail board of a lorry is 1.5 m long and 0.75 m high. It is hinged along the bottom edge to the floor of the lorry. Chains are attached to the top corners of the board and to the sides of the lorry so that when the board is in a horizontal position the chains are parallel and inclined at 45° to the horizontal. A tension spring is inserted in each chain so as to reduce the shock and these are adjusted to prevent the board from dropping below the horizontal. Each spring exerts a force of 60 N/mm of extension.

Find the greatest force in each spring and the resultant force at the hinges when the board falls freely from the vertical position. Assume that the tail board is a uniform body of mass 30 kg.

[Ans. 3636 N ; 9327 N]

12. A motor drives a machine through a friction clutch which transmits 150 N-m while slip occurs during engagement. For the motor, the rotor has a mass of 60 kg with radius of gyration 140 mm and the inertia of the machine is equivalent to a mass of 20 kg with radius of gyration 80 mm. If the motor is running at 750 r.p.m. and the machine is at rest, find the speed after engaging the clutch and the time taken. **[Ans. 70.87 rad/s ; 0.06 s]**

13. A shaft carrying a rotor of moment of inertia 10 kg-m^2 revolves at a speed of 600 r.p.m. and is engaged by means of a friction clutch to another shaft on the same axis having a moment of inertia of 15 kg-m^2. If the second shaft is initially at rest, find 1. the final speed of rotation of the two shafts together after slipping has ceased, 2. the time of slip if the torque is constant at 250 N-m during slipping, and 3. the kinetic energy lost during the operation.
[Ans. 25.136 rad/s ; 1.5 s ; 11.85 kN-m]

14. A self-propelled truck of total mass 25 tonnes and wheel diameter 750 mm runs on a track for which the resistance is 180 N per tonne. The engine develops 60 kW at its maximum speed of 2400 r.p.m. and drives the axle through a gear box. Determine : 1. the time to reach full speed from rest on the level if the gear reduction ratio is 10 to 1. Assume the engine torque to be constant and a gearing efficiency of 94 per cent, and 2. the gear ratio required to give an acceleration of 0.15 m/s^2 on an up gradient of 1 in 70 assuming a gearing efficiency of 90 per cent. **[Ans. 157 s ; 20.5]**

15. A motor vehicle of mass 1000 kg has road wheels of 600 mm rolling diameter. The total moment of inertia of all four road wheels together with the half shafts is 10 kg-m^2, while that of the engine and clutch is 1 kg-m^2. The engine torque is 150 N-m, the transmission efficiency is 90 per cent and the tractive resistance is constant at 500 N. Determine 1. Gear ratio between the engine and the road wheels to give maximum acceleration on an upgrade of 1 in 20, and 2. The value of this maximum acceleration. **[Ans. 13 ; 1.74 m/s^2]**

16. In a mine hoist a loaded cage is raised and an empty cage is lowered by means of a single rope. This rope passes from one cage, over a guide pulley of 1.2 m effective diameter, on to the winding drum of 2.4 m effective diameter, and then over a second guide pulley, also of 1.2 m effective diameter, to the other cage. The drum is driven by an electric motor through a double reduction gear.

Determine the motor torque required, at an instant when the loaded cage has an upward acceleration of 0.6 m/s^2, given the following data :

S.No.	Part	Maximum speed (r.p.m.)	Mass (kg)	Radius of gyration (mm)	Frictional resistance
1	Motor and pinion	N	500	150	–
2	Intermediate gear shaft and attached wheel	$\dfrac{N}{5}$	600	225	45 N-m
3	Drum and attached gear	$\dfrac{N}{20}$	3000	900	1500 N-m
4	Guide pulley, each	–	125	450	30 N-m
5	Rising rope and cage	–	10 000	–	2500 N
6	Falling rope and cage	–	5000	–	1500 N

[Ans. 4003.46 N-m]

DO YOU KNOW ?

1. State Newton's three laws of motion.
2. What do you understand by mass moment of inertia ? Explain clearly.
3. What is energy ? Explain the various forms of mechanical energies.
4. State the law of conservation of momentum.
5. Show that for a relatively small rotor being started from rest with a large rotor, the energy lost in the clutch is approximately equal to that given to the rotor.

6. Prove the relation for the torque required in order to accelerate a geared system.
7. Discuss the phenomenon of collision of elastic bodies.
8. Define the term 'coefficient of restitution'.

OBJECTIVE TYPE QUESTIONS

1. The force which acts along the radius of a circle and directed ...... the centre of the circle is known as centripetal force.

    (a) away from $\qquad$ (b) towards

2. The unit of mass moment of inertia in S.I. units is

    (a) m^4 $\qquad$ (b) $kgf\text{-}m\text{-}s^2$ $\qquad$ (c) $kg\text{-}m^2$ $\qquad$ (d) N-m

3. Joule is a unit of

    (a) force $\qquad$ (b) work $\qquad$ (c) power $\qquad$ (d) none of these

4. The energy possessed by a body, for doing work by virtue of its position, is called

    (a) potential energy $\qquad\qquad\qquad$ (b) kinetic energy

    (c) electrical energy $\qquad\qquad\qquad$ (d) chemical energy

5. When a body of mass moment of inertia I (about a given axis) is rotated about that axis with an angular velocity, then the kinetic energy of rotation is

    (a) $0.5\, I.\omega$ $\qquad$ (b) $I.\omega$ $\qquad$ (c) $0.5\, I.\omega^2$ $\qquad$ (d) $I.\omega^2$

6. The wheels of a moving car possess

    (a) potential energy only

    (b) kinetic energy of translation only

    (c) kinetic energy of rotation only

    (d) kinetic energy of translation and rotation both.

7. The bodies which rebound after impact are called

    (a) inelastic bodies $\qquad\qquad\qquad$ (b) elastic bodies

8. The coefficient of restitution for inelastic bodies is

    (a) zero $\qquad\qquad\qquad\qquad\qquad$ (b) between zero and one

    (c) one $\qquad\qquad\qquad\qquad\qquad$ (d) more than one

9. Which of the following statement is correct ?

    (a) The kinetic energy of a body during impact remains constant.

    (b) The kinetic energy of a body before impact is equal to the kinetic energy of a body after impact.

    (c) The kinetic energy of a body before impact is less than the kinetic energy of a body after impact.

    (d) The kinetic energy of a body before impact is more than the kinetic energy of a body after impact.

10. A body of mass m moving with a constant velocity v strikes another body of same mass m moving with same velocity but in opposite direction. The common velocity of both the bodies after collision is

    (a) v $\qquad$ (b) $2\,v$ $\qquad$ (c) $4\,v$ $\qquad$ (d) $8\,v$

ANSWERS

1. (b)	**2.** (c)	**3.** (b)	**4.** (a)	**5.** (c)
6. (d)	**7.** (b)	**8.** (a)	**9.** (d)	**10.** (b)

Simple Harmonic Motion

4.1. Introduction

Consider a particle moving round the circumference of a circle in an anticlockwise direction, with a constant angular velocity, as shown in Fig. 4.1. Let P be the position of the particle at any instant and N be the projection of P on the diameter XX' of the circle.

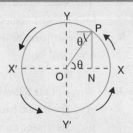

Fig. 4.1. Simple harmonic motion.

It will be noticed that when the point P moves round the circumference of the circle from X to Y, N moves from X to O, when P moves from Y to X', N moves from O to X'. Similarly when P moves from X' to Y', N moves from X' to O and finally when P moves from Y' to X, N moves from O to X. Hence, as P completes one revolution, the point N completes one vibration about the

A clock pendulum executes Simple Harmonic Motion.

72

point O. This to and fro motion of N is known as *simple harmonic motion* (briefly written as S.H.M.).

4.2. Velocity and Acceleration of a Particle Moving with Simple Harmonic Motion

Consider a particle, moving round the circumference of a circle of radius r, with a uniform angular velocity ω rad/s, as shown in Fig. 4.2. Let P be any position of the particle after t seconds and θ be the angle turned by the particle in t seconds. We know that

$$\theta = \omega.t$$

If N is the projection of P on the diameter XX', then displacement of N from its mean position O is

$$x = r.\cos\theta = r.\cos\omega.t \qquad ... (i)$$

The velocity of N is the component of the velocity of P parallel to XX', *i.e.*

Movements of a ship up and down in a vertical plane about transverse axis (called Pitching) and about longitude (called rolling) are in Simple Harmonic Motion.

$$v_N = v\sin\theta = \omega.r\sin\theta = \omega\sqrt{r^2 - x^2} \qquad ... (ii)$$

$$...\left[\because v = \omega r, \text{ and } r\sin\theta = NP = \sqrt{r^2 - x^2}\right]$$

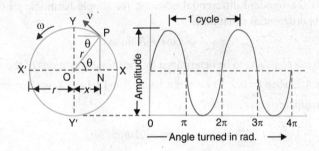

Fig. 4.2. Velocity and acceleration of a particle.

A little consideration will show that velocity is maximum, when $x = 0$, *i.e.* when N passes through O *i.e.*, its mean position.

$$\therefore \qquad v_{max} = \omega.r$$

We also know that the acceleration of P is the centripetal acceleration whose magnitude is $\omega^2.r$. The acceleration of N is the component of the acceleration of P parallel to XX' and is directed towards the centre O, *i.e.*,

$$a_N = \omega^2.r\cos\theta = \omega^2.x \qquad ... (\because x = r\cos\theta) ...(iii)$$

The acceleration is maximum when $x = r$ *i.e.* when P is at X or X'.

$$\therefore \qquad a_{max} = \omega^2.r$$

It will also be noticed from equation (*iii*) that when $x = 0$, the acceleration is zero *i.e.* N passes through O. In other words, the acceleration is zero at the mean position. Thus we see from equation (*iii*) that the acceleration of N is proportional to its displacement from its mean position O, and it is always directed towards the centre O; so that the motion of N is simple harmonic.

In general, a body is said to move or vibrate with simple harmonic motion, if it satisfies the following two conditions :

1. *Its acceleration is always directed towards the centre, known as point of reference or mean position ;*

2. *Its acceleration is proportional to the distance from that point.*

4.3. Differential Equation of Simple Harmonic Motion

We have discussed in the previous article that the displacement of N from its mean position O is

$$x = r.\cos\theta = r.\cos\omega t \qquad \qquad ...(i)$$

Differentiating equation (i), we have velocity of N,

$$\frac{dx}{dt} = v_N = -r.\omega\sin\omega t \qquad \qquad ...(ii)$$

Again differentiating equation (ii), we have acceleration of N,

$$* \quad \frac{d^2x}{dt^2} = a_N = -r.\omega.\omega\cos\omega t = -\omega^2.r\cos\omega t = -\omega^2.x \qquad \qquad ...(iii)$$

$$... (\because r\cos\omega t = x)$$

or $\qquad\qquad \dfrac{d^2x}{dt^2} + \omega^2 x = 0$

This is the standard differential equation for simple harmonic motion of a particle. The solution of this differential equation is

$$x = A\cos\omega t + B\sin\omega t \qquad \qquad ...(iv)$$

where A and B are constants to be determined by the initial conditions of the motion.

In Fig. 4.2, when $t = 0$, $x = r$ *i.e.* when points P and N lie at X, we have from equation (iv), $A = r$

Differentiating equation (iv),

$$\frac{dx}{dt} = -A.\omega.\sin\omega t + B.\omega\cos\omega t$$

When $t = 0$, $\dfrac{dx}{dt} = 0$, therefore, from the above equation, $B = 0$. Now the equation (iv) becomes

$$x = r\cos\omega t \qquad \qquad ...\text{[Same as equation (i)]}$$

The equations (ii) and (iii) may be written as

$$\frac{dx}{dt} = v_N = -\omega.r\sin\omega t = \omega.r\cos(\omega t + \pi/2)$$

and $\qquad\qquad \dfrac{d^2x}{dt^2} = a_N = -\omega^2.r\cos\omega t = \omega^2.r\cos(\omega t + \pi)$

These equations show that the velocity leads the displacement by 90° and acceleration leads the displacement by 180°.

---

* The negative sign shows that the direction of acceleration is opposite to the direction in which x increases, *i.e.* the acceleration is always directed towards the point O.

4.4. Terms Used in Simple Harmonic Motion

The following terms, commonly used in simple harmonic motion, are important from the subject point of view.

1. *Amplitude*. It is the maximum displacement of a body from its mean position. In Fig. 4.2, *OX* or *OX'* is the amplitude of the particle *P*. The amplitude is always equal to the radius of the circle.

2. *Periodic time*. It is the time taken for one complete revolution of the particle.

$\therefore$ Periodic time, $t_p = 2\,\pi/\omega$ seconds

We know that the acceleration,

$$a = \omega^2 . x \quad \text{or} \quad \omega^2 = \frac{a}{x} \quad \text{or} \quad \omega = \sqrt{\frac{a}{x}}$$

$\therefore$

$$t_p = \frac{2\pi}{\omega} = 2\pi\sqrt{\frac{x}{a}} = 2\pi\sqrt{\frac{\text{Displacement}}{\text{Acceleration}}} \text{ seconds}$$

It is thus obvious, that the periodic time is independent of amplitude.

3. *Frequency*. It is the number of cycles per second and is the reciprocal of time period, t_p.

$\therefore$ Frequency, $n = \dfrac{\omega}{2\pi} = \dfrac{1}{t_p} = \dfrac{1}{2\pi}\sqrt{\dfrac{a}{x}}$ Hz

Notes : 1. In S.I. units, the unit of frequency is hertz (briefly written as Hz) which is equal to one cycle per second.

2. When the particle moves with angular simple harmonic motion, then the periodic time,

$$t_p = 2\pi\sqrt{\frac{\text{Angular displacement}}{\text{Angular acceleration}}} = 2\pi\sqrt{\frac{\theta}{\alpha}} \text{ s}$$

and   frequency, $n = \dfrac{1}{2\pi}\sqrt{\dfrac{\alpha}{\theta}}$ Hz

Example 4.1. *The piston of a steam engine moves with simple harmonic motion. The crank rotates at 120 r.p.m. with a stroke of 2 metres. Find the velocity and acceleration of the piston, when it is at a distance of 0.75 metre from the centre.*

Solution. Given : $N = 120$ r.p.m.   or $\omega = 2\pi \times 120/60 = 4\pi$ rad/s ; $2r = 2$ m   or $r = 1$ m; $x = 0.75$ m

Velocity of the piston

We know that velocity of the piston,

$$v = \omega\sqrt{r^2 - x^2} = 4\pi\sqrt{1 - (0.75)^2} = 8.31 \text{ m/s Ans.}$$

Acceleration of the piston

We also know that acceleration of the piston,

$$a = \omega^2 . x = (4\pi)^2\, 0.75 = 118.46 \text{ m/s}^2 \text{ Ans.}$$

Example 4.2. *A point moves with simple harmonic motion. When this point is 0.75 metre from the mid path, its velocity is 11 m/s and when 2 metres from the centre of its path its velocity is 3 m/s. Find its angular velocity, periodic time and its maximum acceleration.*

Solution. Given : When $x = 0.75$ m, $v = 11$ m/s ; when $x = 2$ m, $v = 3$ m/s

Angular velocity

Let ω = Angular velocity of the particle, and

r = Amplitude of the particle.

We know that velocity of the point when it is 0.75 m from the mid path (v),

$$11 = \omega \sqrt{r^2 - x^2} = \omega \sqrt{r^2 - (0.75)^2} \qquad \ldots (i)$$

Similarly, velocity of the point when it is 2 m from the centre (v),

$$3 = \omega \sqrt{r^2 - 2^2} \qquad \ldots (ii)$$

Dividing equation (*i*) by equation (*ii*),

$$\frac{11}{3} = \frac{\omega \sqrt{r^2 - (0.75)^2}}{\omega \sqrt{r^2 - 2^2}} = \frac{\sqrt{r^2 - (0.75)^2}}{\sqrt{r^2 - 2^2}}$$

Squaring both sides,

$$\frac{121}{9} = \frac{r^2 - 0.5625}{r^2 - 4}$$

$$121 \, r^2 - 484 = 9r^2 - 5.06 \quad \text{or} \quad 112 \, r^2 = 478.94$$

∴ $r^2 = 478.94 / 112 = 4.276 \quad \text{or} \quad r = 2.07$ m

Substituting the value of r in equation (*i*),

$$11 = \omega \sqrt{(2.07)^2 - (0.75)^2} = 1.93 \, \omega$$

∴ $\omega = 11/1.93 = 5.7$ rad/s **Ans.**

Periodic time

We know that periodic time,

$$t_p = 2\pi / \omega = 2\pi / 5.7 = 1.1 \text{ s } \textbf{Ans.}$$

Maximum acceleration

We know that maximum acceleration,

$$a_{max} = \omega^2 . r = (5.7)^2 \, 2.07 = 67.25 \text{ m/s}^2 \textbf{ Ans.}$$

4.5. Simple Pendulum

A simple pendulum, in its simplest form, consists of heavy bob suspended at the end of a light inextensible and flexible string. The other end of the string is fixed at O, as shown in Fig. 4.3.

Let L = Length of the string,

m = Mass of the bob in kg,

W = Weight of the bob in newtons

= $m.g$, and

θ = Angle through which the string

is displaced.

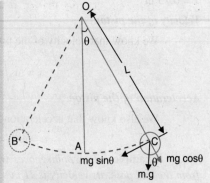

Fig 4.3. Simple pendulum.

When the bob is at A, the pendulum is in equilibrium position. If the bob is brought to B or C and released, it will start oscillating between the two positions B and C, with A as the mean position. It has been observed that if the angle θ is very small (less than $4°$), the bob will have simple harmonic motion. Now, the couple tending to restore the bob to the equilibrium position or restoring torque,

$$T = m.g \sin \theta \times L$$

Since angle θ is very small, therefore $\sin \theta = \theta$ radians.

$$\therefore \qquad T = m.g.L.\theta$$

We know that the mass moment of inertia of the bob about an axis through the point of suspension,

$$I = \text{mass} \times (\text{length})^2 = m.L^2$$

$\therefore$ Angular acceleration of the string,

$$\alpha = \frac{T}{I} = \frac{m.g.L.\theta}{m.L^2} = \frac{g.\theta}{L} \quad \text{or} \quad \frac{\theta}{\alpha} = \frac{L}{g}$$

i.e. $\qquad \dfrac{\text{Angular displacement}}{\text{Angular acceleration}} = \dfrac{L}{g}$

We know that the periodic time,

$$t_p = 2\pi \sqrt{\frac{\text{Displacement}}{\text{Acceleration}}} = 2\pi \sqrt{\frac{L}{g}} \qquad \qquad ... (i)$$

and frequency of oscillation,

$$n = \frac{1}{t_p} = \frac{1}{2\pi} \sqrt{\frac{g}{L}} \qquad \qquad ... (ii)$$

From above we see that the periodic time and the frequency of oscillation of a simple pendulum depends only upon its length and acceleration due to gravity. The mass of the bob has no effect on it.

Notes : 1. The motion of the bob from one extremity to the other (*i.e.* from B to C or C to B) is known as **beat** or **swing**. Thus one beat = $\frac{1}{2}$ oscillation.

$\therefore$ Periodic time for one beat = $\pi \sqrt{L/g}$

2. A pendulum, which executes one beat per second (*i.e.* one complete oscillation in two seconds) is known as a **second's pendulum**.

4.6. Laws of Simple Pendulum

The following laws of a simple pendulum are important from the subject point of view :

1. *Law of isochronism.* It states, "The time period (t_p) of a simple pendulum does not depend upon its amplitude of vibration and remains the same, provided the angular amplitude (θ) does not exceed $4°$."

2. *Law of mass.* It states, "The time period (t_p) of a simple pendulum does not depend upon the mass of the body suspended at the free end of the string."

3. *Law of length.* It states, "The time period (t_p) of a simple pendulum is directly proportional to $\sqrt{L}$, where L is the length of the string."

4. *Law of gravity.* It states, "The time period (t_p) of a simple pendulum is inversely proportional to $\sqrt{g}$, where g is the acceleration due to gravity."

Note: The above laws of a simple pendulum are true from the equation of the periodic time *i.e.*

$$t_p = 2\pi\sqrt{L/g}$$

4.7. Closely-coiled Helical Spring

Consider a closely-coiled helical spring, whose upper end is fixed, as shown in Fig. 4.4. Let a body be attached to the lower end. Let *AA* be the equilibrium position of the spring, after the mass is attached. If the spring is stretched up to *BB* and then released, the mass will move up and down with simple harmonic motion.

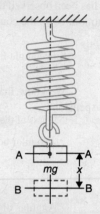

Let
m = Mass of the body in kg,
W = Weight of the body in newtons = $m.g$,
x = Displacement of the load below equilibrium position in metres,
s = Stiffnes of the spring in N/m *i.e.* restoring force per unit displacement from the equilibrium position,
a = Acceleration of the body in m/s².

Fig. 4.4. Closely-coiled helical spring.

We know that the deflection of the spring,

$$\delta = \frac{m.g}{s} \qquad \qquad ...(i)$$

Then disturbing force = $m.a$

and   restoring force = $s.x$ ...(ii)

Equating equations (i) and (ii),

$$m.a = s.x^* \quad \text{or} \quad \frac{x}{a} = \frac{m}{s}$$

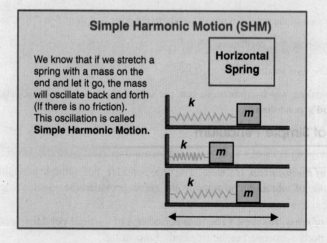

Simple Harmonic Motion (SHM)

We know that if we stretch a spring with a mass on the end and let it go, the mass will oscillate back and forth (If there is no friction). This oscillation is called **Simple Harmonic Motion.**

Horizontal Spring

---

* The differential equation for the motion of the spring is

$$m\frac{d^2x}{dt^2} = -s.x \quad \text{or} \quad \frac{d^2x}{dt^2} = -\frac{s.x}{m} \qquad ...\left(\text{Here } \omega^2 = \frac{s}{m}\right)$$

The – ve sign indicates that the restoring force $s.x$ is opposite to the direction of disturbing force.

We know that periodic time,

$$t_p = 2\pi \sqrt{\frac{\text{Displacement}}{\text{Acceleration}}} = 2\pi \sqrt{\frac{x}{a}}$$

$$= 2\pi \sqrt{\frac{m}{s}} = 2\pi \sqrt{\frac{\delta}{g}} \qquad \qquad ...\left(\because \delta = \frac{mg}{s}\right)$$

and frequency, $n = \dfrac{1}{t_p} = \dfrac{1}{2\pi}\sqrt{\dfrac{s}{m}} = \dfrac{1}{2\pi}\sqrt{\dfrac{g}{\delta}}$

Note: If the mass of the spring (m_1) is also taken into consideration, then the periodic time,

$$t_p = 2\pi \sqrt{\frac{m + m_1/3}{s}} \text{ seconds,}$$

and frequency, $n = \dfrac{1}{2\pi}\sqrt{\dfrac{s}{m + m_1/3}}$ Hz

Example 4.3. *A helical spring, of negligible mass, and which is found to extend 0.25 mm under a mass of 1.5 kg, is made to support a mass of 60 kg. The spring and the mass system is displaced vertically through 12.5 mm and released. Determine the frequency of natural vibration of the system. Find also the velocity of the mass, when it is 5 mm below its rest position.*

Solution. Given : $m = 60$ kg ; $r = 12.5$ mm $= 0.0125$ m ; $x = 5$ mm $= 0.005$ m

Since a mass of 1.5 kg extends the spring by 0.25 mm, therefore a mass of 60 kg will extend the spring by an amount,

$$\delta = \frac{0.25}{1.5} \times 60 = 10 \text{ mm} = 0.01 \text{ m}$$

Frequency of the system

We know that frequency of the system,

$$n = \frac{1}{2\pi}\sqrt{\frac{g}{\delta}} = \frac{1}{2\pi}\sqrt{\frac{9.81}{0.01}} = 4.98 \text{ Hz } \textbf{Ans.}$$

Velocity of the mass

Let $v = $ Linear velocity of the mass.

We know that angular velocity,

$$\omega^* = \sqrt{\frac{g}{\delta}} = \sqrt{\frac{9.81}{0.01}} = 31.32 \text{ rad/s}$$

and $v = \omega\sqrt{r^2 - x^2} = 31.32\sqrt{(0.0125)^2 - (0.005)^2}$

$$= 0.36 \text{ m/s } \textbf{Ans.}$$

4.8. Compound Pendulum

When a rigid body is suspended vertically, and it oscillates with a small amplitude under the action of the force of gravity, the body is known as *compound pendulum*, as shown in Fig. 4.5.

Let $m = $ Mass of the pendulum in kg,

$W = $ Weight of the pendulum in newtons $= m.g,$

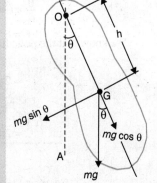

Fig. 4.5. Compound pendulum.

---

* We know that periodic time,

$t_p = 2\pi / \omega$ or $\omega = 2\pi / t_p = 2\pi \times n = 2\pi \times 4.98 = 31.3$ rad/s $\qquad ...(\because n = 1/t_p)$

k_G = Radius of gyration about an axis through the centre of gravity G and perpendicular to the plane of motion, and

h = Distance of point of suspension O from the centre of gravity G of the body.

If the pendulum is given a small angular displacement θ, then the couple tending to restore the pendulum to the equilibrium position OA,

$$T = mg \sin\theta \times h = mgh \sin\theta$$

Since θ is very small, therefore substituting $\sin\theta = \theta$ radians, we get

$$T = mgh\,\theta$$

Now, the mass moment of inertia about the axis of suspension O,

$$I = I_G + m.h^2 = m\left(k_G^2 + h^2\right) \qquad \ldots \text{(By parallel axis theorem)}$$

$\therefore$ Angular acceleration of the pendulum,

$$\alpha = \frac{T}{I} = \frac{mgh\,\theta}{m(k_G^2 + h^2)} = \frac{gh\,\theta}{k_G^2 + h^2} = \text{constant} \times \theta$$

We see that the angular acceleration is directly proportional to angular displacement, therefore the pendulum executes simple harmonic motion.

$$\therefore \qquad \frac{\theta}{\alpha} = \frac{k_G^2 + h^2}{g.h}$$

We know that the periodic time,

$$t_p = 2\pi \sqrt{\frac{\text{Displacement}}{\text{Acceleration}}} = 2\pi \sqrt{\frac{\theta}{\alpha}}$$

$$= 2\pi \sqrt{\frac{k_G^2 + h^2}{g.h}} \qquad \ldots (i)$$

and frequency of oscillation, $n = \dfrac{1}{t_p} = \dfrac{1}{2\pi} \sqrt{\dfrac{g.h}{k_G^2 + h^2}}$ $\qquad \ldots (ii)$

Notes : 1. Comparing this equation with equation (*ii*) of simple pendulum, we see that the equivalent length of a simple pendulum, which gives the same frequency as compound pendulum, is

$$L = \frac{k_G^2 + h^2}{h} = \frac{k_G^2}{h} + h$$

2. Since the equivalent length of simple pendulum (*L*) depends upon the distance between the point of suspension and the centre of gravity (*G*), therefore *L* can be changed by changing the position of point of suspension. This will, obviously, change the periodic time of a compound pendulum. The periodic time will be minimum if *L* is minimum. For *L* to be minimum, the differentiation of *L* with respect to *h* must be equal to zero, *i.e.*

$$\frac{dL}{dh} = 0 \quad \text{or} \quad \frac{d}{dh}\left(\frac{k_G^2}{h} + h\right) = 0$$

∴ $$\frac{-k_G^2}{h^2} + 1 = 0 \quad \text{or} \quad k_G = h$$

Thus the periodic time of a compound pendulum is minimum when the distance between the point of suspension and the centre of gravity is equal to the radius of gyration of the body about its centre of gravity.

∴ Minimum periodic time of a compound pendulum,

$$t_{p(min)} = 2\pi \sqrt{\frac{2k_G}{g}} \qquad \dots \text{[Substituting } h = k_G \text{ in equation (i)]}$$

4.9. Centre of Percussion

The centre of oscillation is sometimes termed as *centre of percussion*. It is defined as that point at which a blow may be struck on a suspended body so that the reaction at the support is zero.

Consider the case of a compound pendulum suspended at *O* as shown in Fig. 4.6. Suppose the pendulum is at rest in the vertical position, and a blow is struck at a distance *L* from the centre of suspension. Let the magnitude of blow is *F* newtons. A little consideration will show that this blow will have the following two effects on the body :

1. A force (*F*) acting at *C* will produce a linear motion with an acceleration *a*, such that

$$F = m.a \qquad \dots (i)$$

where *m* is the mass of the body.

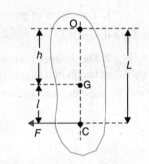

Fig. 4.6. Centre of percusssion.

2. A couple with moment equal to (*F* × *l*) which will tend to produce a motion of rotation in the clockwise direction about the centre of gravity *G*. Let this turning moment (*F* × *l*) produce an angular acceleration (α), such that

$$F \times l = I_G \times \alpha \qquad \dots (ii)$$

where I_G is the moment of inertia of the body about an axis passing through *G* and parallel to the axis of rotation.

From equation (*i*) $\qquad a = F/m \qquad \dots (iii)$

and from equation (*ii*), $\qquad \alpha = \dfrac{F.l}{I_G}$

Now corresponding linear acceleration of O,

$$a_0 = \alpha . h = \frac{F.l.h}{I_G} = \frac{F.l.h}{m.k_G^2} \qquad \ldots (iv)$$

$$(\because I_G = m.k_G^2)$$

where k_G is the radius of gyration of the body about the centre of gravity G.

Since there is no reaction at the support when the body is struck at the centre of percussion, therefore a should be equal to a_0.

Equating equations (*iii*) and (*iv*),

$$\frac{F}{m} = \frac{F.l.h}{m.k_G^2}$$

or

$$k_G^2 = l.h, \text{ and } l = \frac{k_G^2}{h} \qquad \ldots (v)$$

We know that the equivalent length of a simple pendulum,

$$L = \frac{k_G^2 + h^2}{h} = \frac{k_G^2}{h} + h = l + h \qquad \ldots (vi)$$

From equations (*v*) and (*vi*), it follows that

1. The centre of percussion is below the centre of gravity and at a distance k_G^2 / h.

2. The distance between the centre of suspension and the centre of percussion is equal to the equivalent length of a simple pendulum.

Note: We know that mass moment of inertia of the body about O,

$$I_O = I_G + m.h^2 \text{ or } m.k_O^2 = m.k_G^2 + m.h^2$$

$\therefore$

$$k_O^2 = k_G^2 + h^2 = l.h + h^2 = h(l + h) = OG \times OC \qquad \ldots (\because k_G^2 = l.h)$$

It is thus obvious that the centre of suspension (O) and the centre of percussion (C) are inter-changeable. In other words, the periodic time and frequency of oscillation will be same, whether the body is suspended at the point of suspension or at the centre of percussion.

A pendulum clock designed by Galileo. Galileo was the first to deisgn a clock based on the relationship between gravitational force (g), length of the pendulum (l) and time of oscillation (t).

Example 4.4. *A uniform thin rod, as shown in Fig. 4.7, has a mass of 1 kg and carries a concentrated mass of 2.5 kg at B. The rod is hinged at A and is maintained in the horizontal position by a spring of stiffness 1.8 kN/m at C.*

Find the frequency of oscillation, neglecting the effect of the mass of the spring.

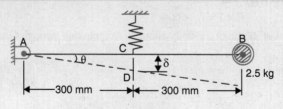

Fig. 4.7

Solution. Given : $m = 1$ kg ; $m_1 = 2.5$ kg ; $s = 1.8$ kN/m $= 1.8 \times 10^3$ N/m

We know that total length of rod,

$$l = 300 + 300 = 600 \text{ mm} = 0.6 \text{ m}$$

∴ Mass moment of inertia of the system about A,

I_A = Mass moment of inertia of 1 kg about A + Mass moment of interia of 2.5 kg about A

$$= \frac{m.l^2}{3} + m_1.l^2 = \frac{1(0.6)^2}{3} + 2.5 \, (0.6)^2 = 1.02 \text{ kg-m}^2$$

If the rod is given a small angular displacement θ and then released, the extension of the spring,

$$\delta = 0.3 \sin \theta = 0.3\theta \text{ m}$$

$$\dots \, (\because \theta \text{ is very small, therefore substituting } \sin \theta = \theta \,)$$

∴ Restoring force $= s.\delta = 1.8 \times 10^3 \times 0.3 \, \theta = 540 \, \theta$ N

and restoring torque about A $= 540 \, \theta \times 0.3 = 162 \, \theta$ N-m ... (*i*)

We know that disturbing torque about A

$$= I_A \times \alpha = 1.02\alpha \text{ N-m} \qquad \dots (ii)$$

Equating equations (*i*) and (*ii*),

$$1.02 \, \alpha = 162 \, \theta \quad \text{or} \quad \alpha / \theta = 162 / 1.02 = 159$$

We know that frequency of oscillation,

$$n = \frac{1}{2\pi} \sqrt{\frac{\alpha}{\theta}} = \frac{1}{2\pi} \sqrt{159} = 2.01 \text{ Hz Ans.}$$

Example 4.5. *A small flywheel of mass 85 kg is suspended in a vertical plane as a compound pendulum. The distance of centre of gravity from the knife edge support is 100 mm and the flywheel makes 100 oscillations in 145 seconds. Find the moment of inertia of the flywheel through the centre of gravity.*

Solution. Given : $m = 85$ kg ; $h = 100$ mm $= 0.1$ m

Since the flywheel makes 100 oscillations in 145 seconds, therefore frequency of oscillation,

$$n = 100/145 = 0.69 \text{ Hz}$$

Let L = Equivalent length of simple pendulum, and

k_G = Radius of gyration through C.G.

We know that frequency of oscillation (n),

$$0.69 = \frac{1}{2\pi} \sqrt{\frac{g}{L}} = \frac{1}{2\pi} \sqrt{\frac{9.81}{L}} = \frac{0.5}{\sqrt{L}}$$

∴ $$\sqrt{L} = 0.5/0.69 = 0.7246 \quad \text{or} \quad L = 0.525 \text{ m}$$

We also know that equivalent length of simple pendulum (L),

$$0.525 = \frac{k_G^2}{h} + h = \frac{k_G^2}{0.1} + 0.1 = \frac{k_G^2 + (0.1)^2}{0.1}$$

$$k_G^2 = 0.525 \times 0.1 - (0.1)^2 = 0.0425 \text{ m}^2$$

and moment of inertia of the flywheel through the centre of gravity,

$$I = m.k_G^2 = 85 \times 0.0425 = 3.6 \text{ kg-m}^2 \text{ Ans.}$$

Example 4.6. *The connecting rod of an oil engine has a mass of 60 kg, the distance between the bearing centres is 1 metre. The diameter of the big end bearing is 120 mm and of the small end bearing is 75 mm. When suspended vertically with a knife-edge through the small end, it makes 100 oscillations in 190 seconds and with knife-edge through the big end it makes 100 oscillations in 165 seconds. Find the moment of inertia of the rod in kg-m² and the distance of C.G. from the small end centre.*

Solution. Given : $m = 60$ kg ; $h_1 + h_2 = 1$ m ; $d_2{}^* = 102$ mm; $d_1{}^* = 75$ mm

Moment of inertia of the rod

First of all, let us find the radius of gyration of the connecting rod about the centre of gravity (*i.e.* k_G).

Let h_1 and h_2 = Distance of centre of gravity from the small and big end centres respectively,

L_1 and L_2 = Equivalent length of simple pendulum when the axis of oscillation coincides with the small and big end centres respectively.

Connecting rod

When the axis of oscillation coincides with the small end centre, then frequency of oscillation,

$$n_1 = 100/190 = 0.526 \text{ Hz}$$

When the axis of oscillation coincides with the big end centre, the frequency of oscillation,

$$n_2 = 100/165 = 0.606 \text{ Hz}$$

We know that for a simple pendulum,

$$n_1 = \frac{1}{2\pi}\sqrt{\frac{g}{L_1}} \text{ Hz}$$

$\therefore$
$$L_1 = \frac{g}{(2\pi n_1)^2} = \frac{9.81}{(2\pi \times 0.526)^2} = 0.9 \text{ m}$$

Similarly
$$L_2 = \frac{g}{(2\pi n_2)^2} = \frac{9.81}{(2\pi \times 0.606)^2} = 0.67 \text{ m}$$

We know that
$$L_1 = \frac{k_G^2 + (h_1)^2}{h_1} \text{ or } k_G^2 = L_1.h_1 - (h_1)^2 \qquad \dots(i)$$

Similarly
$$k_G^2 = L_2.h_2 - (h_2)^2 \qquad \dots(ii)$$

From equations (*i*) and (*ii*), we have

$$L_1.h_1 - (h_1)^2 = L_2.h_2 - (h_2)^2$$

---

* Superfluous data.

$$0.9 \times h_1 - (h_1)^2 = 0.67 (1 - h_1) - (1 - h_1)^2 \qquad \ldots (\because h_1 + h_2 = 1 \text{ m})$$

$$= 0.67 - 0.67 \, h_1 - 1 - (h_1)^2 + 2h_1$$

$$0.9 \, h_1 + 0.67 \, h_1 - 2 \, h_1 = -0.33 \quad \text{or} \quad -0.43 \, h_1 = -0.33$$

$$\therefore \qquad h_1 = 0.33/0.43 = 0.767 \text{ m}$$

Substituting the value of h_1 in equation (*i*), we have

$$k_G^2 = 0.9 \times 0.767 - (0.767)^2 = 0.69 - 0.59 = 0.1 \, \text{m}^2$$

We know that mass moment of inertia of the rod,

$$I = m.k_G^2 = 60 \times 0.1 = 6 \text{ kg-m}^2 \text{ Ans.}$$

Distance of C.G. from the small end centre

We have calculated above that the distance of C.G. from the small end centre,

$$h_1 = 0.767 \text{ m Ans.}$$

Example 4.7. *A uniform slender rod 1.2 m long is fitted with a transverse pair of knife-edges, so that it can swing in a vertical plane as a compound pendulum. The position of the knife edges is variable. Find the time of swing of the rod, if **1.** the knife edges are 50 mm from one end of the rod, and **2.** the knife edges are so placed that the time of swing is minimum.*

*In case (**1**) find also the maximum angular velocity and the maximum angular acceleration of the rod if it swings through 3° on either side of the vertical.*

Solution. Given : $l = 1.2$ m ; $\theta = 3° = 3 \times \pi /180 = 0.052$ rad

1. *Time of swing of the rod when knife edges are 50 mm*

Since the distance between knife edges from one end of the rod is 50 mm = 0.05 m, therefore distance between the knife edge and C.G. of the rod,

$$h = \frac{1.2}{2} - 0.05 = 0.55 \, \text{m}$$

We know that radius of gyration of the rod about C.G.,

$$k^*_G = \frac{l}{\sqrt{12}} = \frac{1.2}{\sqrt{12}} = 0.35 \text{ m}$$

$\therefore$ Time of swing of the rod,

$$t_p = 2\pi \sqrt{\frac{k_G^2 + h^2}{g.h}} = 2\pi \sqrt{\frac{(0.35)^2 + (0.55)^2}{9.81 \times 0.55}}$$

$$= 1.76 \text{ s Ans.}$$

2. *Minimum time of swing*

We know that minimum time of swing,

$$t_{p(min)} = 2\pi \sqrt{\frac{2k_G}{g}} = 2\pi \sqrt{\frac{2 \times 0.35}{9.81}} = 1.68 \text{ s Ans.}$$

---

* We know that mass moment of inertia of the rod about an axis through C.G.

$$I = m. \, l^2/12$$

Also $\qquad I = m.k^2 \quad$ or $\qquad k^2 = I/m = m.l^2/12 \times m = l^2/12 \quad$ or $\quad k = l/\sqrt{12}$

Maximum angular velocity

In case (1), the angular velocity,

$$\omega = 2\pi / t_p = 2\pi /1.76 = 3.57 \text{ rad/s}$$

We know that maximum angular velocity,

$$\omega_{max} = \omega.\theta = 3.57 \times 0.052 = 0.1856 \text{ rad/s Ans.}$$

Maximum angular acceleration

We know that maximum angular acceleration,

$$\alpha_{max} = \omega^2.\theta = (3.57)^2 \times 0.052 = 0.663 \text{ rad/s}^2 \text{ Ans.}$$

Example 4.8. *The pendulum of an Izod impact testing machine has a mass of 30 kg. Its centre of gravity is 1.05 m from the axis of suspension and the striking knife is 150 mm below the centre of gravity. The time for 20 small free oscillations is 43.5 seconds. In making a test the pendulum is released from an angle of 60° to the vertical. Determine :*

1. the position of the centre of percussion relative to the striking knife and the striking velocity of the pendulum, and 2. the impulse on the pendulum and the sudden change of axis reaction when a specimen giving an impact value of 55 N-m is broken.

Solution. Given : $m = 30 \text{ kg}$; $OG = h = 1.05 \text{ m}$; $AG = 0.15 \text{ m}$

Since the time for 20 small free oscillations is 43.5 s, therefore frequency of oscillation,

$$n = \frac{20}{43.5} = 0.46 \text{ Hz}$$

1. The position of centre of percussion relative to the striking knife and the striking velocity of the pendulum

Let L = Equivalent length of simple pendulum,

          k_G = Radius of gyration of the pendulum about the centre of gravity, and

          k_O = Radius of gyration of the pendulum about O.

We know that the frequency of oscillation,

$$n = \frac{1}{2\pi} \sqrt{\frac{g}{L}}$$

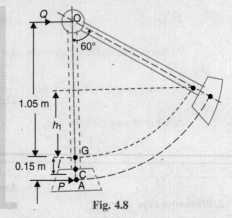

or $L = \dfrac{g}{(2\pi n)^2} = \dfrac{9.81}{(2\pi \times 0.46)^2}$

          $= 1.174 \text{ m}$

∴ Distance of centre of percussion (C) from the centre of gravity (G),

$$CG = OC - OG = L - OG$$

$$= 1.174 - 1.05 = 0.124 \text{ m}$$

Fig. 4.8

and distance of centre of percussion (C) from knife edge A,

$$AC = AG - CG = 0.15 - 0.124 = 0.026 \text{ m Ans.}$$

We know that $k_O^2 = (h + l) \, h = L.h = 1.174 \times 1.05 = 1.233 \text{ m}^2$

A little consideration will show that the potential energy of the pendulum is converted into kinetic energy of the pendulum before it strikes the test piece. Let v and ω be the linear and angular velocity of the pendulum before it strikes the test piece.

$$\therefore \qquad m.g.h_1 = \frac{1}{2} m.v^2 = \frac{1}{2} m.k_O^2.\omega^2 \qquad\qquad \dots (\because v = k_O.\omega)$$

$$30 \times 9.81 \times 1.05 \,(1 - \cos 60°) = \frac{1}{2} \times 30 \times 1.233\,\omega^2 \quad \text{or} \quad 154.5 = 18.5\,\omega^2$$

$$\therefore \qquad \omega^2 = 154.5/18.5 = 8.35 \quad \text{or} \quad \omega = 2.9 \text{ rad/s}$$

∴ Velocity of striking = $\omega \times OA = 2.9\,(1.05 + 0.15) = 3.48$ m/s **Ans.**

2. *Impulse on the pendulum and sudden change of axis reaction*

It is given that the impact value of the specimen (*i.e.* the energy used for breaking the specimen) is 55 N-m. Let ω_1 be the angular velocity of the pendulum immediately after impact. We know that

$$\text{Loss of kinetic energy} = \frac{1}{2}\,I\,(\omega^2 - \omega_1^2) = \frac{1}{2}\,m.k_O^2\,(\omega^2 - \omega_1^2) = 55 \text{ N-m}$$

$$\therefore \quad \frac{1}{2} \times 30 \times 1.233\,(2.9^2 - \omega_1^2) = 55$$

$$18.5\,(8.41 - \omega_1^2) = 55 \quad \text{or} \quad \omega_1^2 = 8.41 - 55/18.5 = 5.44$$

$$\therefore \qquad \omega_1 = 2.33 \text{ rad/s}$$

Let *P* and *Q* be the impulses at the knife edge *A* and at the pivot *O* respectively as shown in Fig. 4.8.

$$\therefore \qquad P + Q = \text{Change of linear momentum}$$
$$= m.h\,(\omega - \omega_1) = 30 \times 1.05\,(2.9 - 2.33) = 17.95 \qquad \dots (i)$$

Taking moments about *G*,

$$0.15\,P - 1.05\,Q = \text{Change of angular momentum}$$
$$= m.k_G^2\,(\omega - \omega_1) = m\,(k_O^2 - h^2)\,(\omega - \omega_1)$$
$$= 30\,(1.233 - 1.05^2)\,(2.9 - 2.33) = 2.27 \qquad \dots (ii)$$

From equations (*i*) and (*ii*),

$$P = 17.6 \text{ N-s; and } Q = 0.35 \text{ N-s } \textbf{Ans.}$$

∴ Change in axis reaction when pendulum is vertical

$$= \text{Change in centrifugal force}$$

$$= m\,(\omega^2 - \omega_1^2)\,h = 30\,(2.9^2 - 2.33^2)\,1.05 = 94 \text{ N } \textbf{Ans.}$$

4.10. Bifilar Suspension

The moment of inertia of a body may be determined experimentally by an apparatus called *bifilar suspension*. The body whose moment of inertia is to be determined (say *AB*) is suspended by two long parallel flexible strings as shown in Fig. 4.9. When the body is twisted through a small angle θ about a vertical axis through the centre of gravity *G*, it will vibrate with simple harmonic motion in a horizontal plane.

Let
     m = Mass of the body,

     W = Weight of the body in newtons = $m.g$,

     k_G = Radius of gyration about an axis through the centre of gravity,

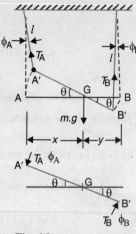

I = Mass moment of inertia of the body about a vertical axis through $G = m.k_G^2$,

l = Length of each string,

x = Distance of A from G (i.e. AG),

y = Distance of B from G (i.e. BG),

θ = Small angular displacement of the body from the equilibrium position in the horizontal plane,

ϕ_A and ϕ_B = Corresponding angular displacements of the strings, and

α = Angular acceleration towards the equilibrium position.

Fig. 4.9. Bifilar suspension.

When the body is stationary, the tension in the strings are given by

$$T_A = \frac{m.g.y}{x+y}, \quad \text{and} \quad T_B = \frac{m.g.x}{x+y} \quad \text{...(Taking moments about } B \text{ and } A \text{ respectively,)}$$

When the body is displaced from its equilibrium position in a horizontal plane through a small angle θ, then the angular displacements of the strings are given by

$$AA' = \phi_A.l = x.\theta \; ; \text{ and } BB' = \phi_B.l = y.\theta$$

∴

$$\phi_A = \frac{x.\theta}{l}; \text{ and } \phi_B = \frac{y.\theta}{l}$$

Component of tension T_A in the horizontal plane, acting normal to $A'B'$ at A' as shown in Fig. 4.9

$$= T_A.\phi_A = \frac{m.g.y}{x+y} \times \frac{x.\theta}{l} = \frac{m.g.x.y.\theta}{l\,(x+y)}$$

Component of tension T_B in the horizontal plane, acting normal to $A'B'$ at B' as shown in Fig. 4.9

$$= T_B.\phi_B = \frac{m.g.x}{x+y} \times \frac{y.\theta}{l} = \frac{m.g.x.y.\theta}{l\,(x+y)}$$

These components of tensions T_A and T_B are equal and opposite in direction, which gives rise to a couple. The couple or torque applied to each string to restore the body to its initial equilibrium position, i.e. restoring torque

$$= T_A.\phi_A.x + T_B.\phi_B.y$$

$$= \frac{m.g.x.y.\theta}{l\,(x+y)}(x+y) = \frac{m.g.x.y.\theta}{l} \qquad \text{... (i)}$$

and accelerating (or disturbing) torque

$$= I.\alpha = m.k_G^2.\alpha \qquad \text{... (ii)}$$

Equating equations (i) and (ii),

$$\frac{m.g.x.y.\theta}{l} = m.k_G^2.\alpha \quad \text{or} \quad \frac{\theta}{\alpha} = \frac{k_G^2 l}{g.x.y}$$

i.e. $\quad \dfrac{\text{Angular displacement}}{\text{Angular acceleration}} = \dfrac{k_G^2 . l}{g.x.y}$

We know that periodic time,

$$t_p = 2\pi \sqrt{\dfrac{\text{Angular displacement}}{\text{Angular acceleration}}} = 2\pi \sqrt{\dfrac{k_G^2 . l}{g.x.y}}$$

$$= 2\pi k_G \sqrt{\dfrac{l}{g.x.y}}$$

and $\qquad$ frequency, $\quad n = \dfrac{1}{t_p} = \dfrac{1}{2\pi k_G} \sqrt{\dfrac{g.x.y}{l}}$

Note : The bifilar suspension is usually used for finding the moment of inertia of a connecting rod of an engine. In this case, the wires are attached at equal distances from the centre of gravity of the connecting rod (*i.e. x = y*) so that the tension in each wire is same.

Example 4.9. *A small connecting rod of mass 1.5 kg is suspended in a horizontal plane by two wires 1.25 m long. The wires are attached to the rod at points 120 mm on either side of the centre of gravity. If the rod makes 20 oscillations in 40 seconds, find the radius of gyration and the mass moment of inertia of the rod about a vertical axis through the centre of gravity.*

Solution. Given : $m = 1.5$ kg ; $l = 1.25$ m ; $x = y = 120$ mm $= 0.12$ m

Since the rod makes 20 oscillations in 40 s, therefore frequency of oscillation,

$$n = 20/40 = 0.5 \text{ Hz}$$

Radius of gyration of the connecting rod

Let $\qquad k_G$ = Radius of gyration of the connecting rod.

We know that frequency of oscillation (n);

$$0.5 = \dfrac{1}{2\pi k_G} \sqrt{\dfrac{g.x.y}{l}} = \dfrac{1}{2\pi k_G} \sqrt{\dfrac{9.81 \times 0.12 \times 0.12}{1.25}} = \dfrac{0.0535}{k}$$

$\therefore \qquad k_G = 0.0535/0.5 = 0.107$ m $= 107$ mm **Ans.**

Mass moment of inertia of the connecting rod

We know that mass moment of inertia,

$$I = m \, (k_G)^2 = 1.5 \, (0.107)^2 = 0.017 \text{ kg-m}^2 \text{ **Ans.**}$$

4.11. Trifilar Suspension (Torsional Pendulum)

It is also used to find the moment of inertia of a body experimentally. The body (say a disc or flywheel) whose moment of inertia is to be determined is suspended by three long flexible wires *A, B* and *C*, as shown in Fig. 4.10. When the body is twisted about its axis through a small angle θ and then released, it will oscillate with simple harmonic motion.

Let $\qquad m$ = Mass of the body in kg,

$\qquad W$ = Weight of the body in newtons $= m.g$,

$\qquad k_G$ = Radius of gyration about an axis through c.g.,

$\qquad I$ = Mass moment of inertia of the disc about an axis through O and perpendicular to it $= m.k^2$,

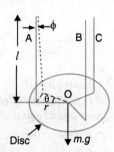

Fig. 4.10. Trifilar suspension.

l = Length of each wire,

r = Distance of each wire from the axis of the disc,

θ = Small angular displacement of the disc,

ϕ = Corresponding angular displacement of the wires, and

α = Angular acceleration towards the equilibrium position.

Then, for small displacements,

$$r.\theta = l.\phi \quad \text{or} \quad \phi = r.\theta/l$$

Since the three wires are attached symmetrically with respect to the axis, therefore the tension in each wire will be one-third of the weight of the body.

∴ Tension in each wire $= m.g/3$

Component of the tension in each wire perpendicular to r

$$= \frac{m.g.\sin\phi}{3} = \frac{m.g.\phi}{3} = \frac{m.g.r.\theta}{3l} \quad \dots (\because \phi \text{ is a small angle, and } \phi = r.\theta/l)$$

∴ Torque applied to each wire to restore the body to its initial equilibrium position *i.e.* restoring torque

$$= \frac{m.g.r.\theta}{3l} \times r = \frac{m.g.r^2.\theta}{3l}$$

Total restoring torque applied to three wires,

$$T = 3 \times \frac{m.g.r^2.\theta}{3l} = \frac{m.g.r^2.\theta}{l} \qquad \dots (i)$$

We know that disturbing torque

$$= I.\alpha = m.k_G^2.\alpha \qquad \dots (ii)$$

Equating equations (*i*) and (*ii*),

$$\frac{m.g.r^2.\theta}{l} = m.k_G^2.\alpha \quad \text{or} \quad \frac{\theta}{\alpha} = \frac{l.k_G^2}{g.r^2}$$

i.e. $\dfrac{\text{Angular displacement}}{\text{Angular acceleration}} = \dfrac{l.k_G^2}{g.r^2}$

We know that periodic time,

$$t_p = 2\pi \sqrt{\frac{\text{Angular displacement}}{\text{Angular acceleration}}} = 2\pi \sqrt{\frac{l.k_G^2}{g.r^2}} = \frac{2\pi k_G}{r}\sqrt{\frac{l}{g}}$$

and frequency, $n = \dfrac{1}{t_p} = \dfrac{r}{2\pi k_G}\sqrt{\dfrac{g}{l}}$

Example 4.10. *In order to find the radius of gyration of a car, it is suspended with its axis vertical from three parallel wires 2.5 metres long. The wires are attached to the rim at points spaced 120° apart and at equal distances 250 mm from the axis.*

It is found that the wheel makes 50 torsional oscillations of small amplitude about its axis in 170 seconds. Find the radius of gyration of the wheel.

Solution. Given : $l = 2.5$ m ; $r = 250$ mm $= 0.25$ m ;

Since the wheel makes 50 torsional oscillations in 170 seconds, therefore frequency of oscillation,

$$n = 50/170 = 5/17 \text{ Hz}$$

Let k_G = Radius of gyration of the wheel

We know that frequency of oscillation (n),

$$\frac{5}{17} = \frac{r}{2\pi\,k_G}\sqrt{\frac{g}{l}} = \frac{0.25}{2\pi\,k_G}\sqrt{\frac{9.81}{2.5}} = \frac{0.079}{k_G}$$

$\therefore \qquad k_G = 0.079 \times 17/5 = 0.268 \text{ m} = 268 \text{ mm Ans.}$

Example 4.11. *A connecting rod of mass 5.5 kg is placed on a horizontal platform whose mass is 1.5 kg. It is suspended by three equal wires, each 1.25 m long, from a rigid support. The wires are equally spaced round the circumference of a circle of 125 mm radius. When the c.g. of the connecting rod coincides with the axis of the circle, the platform makes 10 angular oscillations in 30 seconds. Determine the mass moment of inertia about an axis through its c.g.*

Solution. Given : $m_1 = 5.5$ kg ; $m_2 = 1.5$ kg ; $l = 1.25$ m ; $r = 125$ mm $= 0.125$ m

Since the platform makes 10 angular oscillations in 30 s, therefore frequency of oscillation,

$$n = 10/30 = 1/3 \text{ Hz}$$

Let $\qquad k_G$ = Radius of gyration about an axis through the c.g.

We know that frequency of oscillation (n),

$$\frac{1}{3} = \frac{r}{2\pi k_G}\sqrt{\frac{g}{l}} = \frac{0.125}{2\pi\,k_G}\sqrt{\frac{9.81}{1.25}} = \frac{0.056}{k_G}$$

$\therefore \qquad k_G = 0.056 \times 3 = 0.168 \text{ m}$

and mass moment of inertia about an axis through its c.g.,

$$I = m.k_G^2 = (m_1 + m_2)\,k_G^2 = (5.5 + 1.5)\,(0.168)^2 \text{ kg-m}^2$$

$$= 0.198 \text{ kg-m}^2 \text{ Ans.}$$

EXERCISES

1. A particle, moving with simple harmonic motion, performs 10 complete oscillations per minute and its speed, when at a distance of 80 mm from the centre of oscillation is 3/5 of the maximum speed. Find the amplitude, the maximum acceleration and the speed of the particle, when it is 60 mm from the centre of the oscillation. **[Ans. 100 mm ; 109.6 mm/s² ; 83.76 mm/s]**

2. A piston, moving with a simple harmonic motion, has a velocity of 8 m/s, when it is 1 metre from the centre position and a velocity of 4 m/s, when it is 2 metres from the centre. Find : 1. Amplitude, 2. Periodic time, 3. Maximum velocity, and 4. Maximum acceleration.

    [Ans. 2.236 m ; 1.571 s ; 8.94 m/s ; 35.77 m/s²]

3. The plunger of a reciprocating pump is driven by a crank of radius 250 mm rotating at 12.5 rad/s. Assuming simple harmonic motion, determine the maximum velocity and maximum acceleration of the plunger. **[Ans. 3.125 m/s ; 39.1 m/s²]**

4. A part of a machine of mass 4.54 kg has a reciprocating motion which is simple harmonic in character. It makes 200 complete oscillations in 1 minute. Find : 1. the accelerating force upon it and its velocity when it is 75 mm, from midstroke ; 2. the maximum accelerating force, and 3. the maximum velocity if its total stroke is 225 mm *i.e.* if the amplitude of vibration is 112.5 mm.

    [Ans. 149.5 N ; 1.76 m/s ; 224 N ; 2.36 m/s]

5. A helical spring of negligible mass is required to support a mass of 50 kg. The stiffness of the spring is 60 kN/m. The spring and the mass system is displaced vertically by 20 mm below the equilibrium position and then released. Find : 1. the frequency of natural vibration of the system ; 2. the velocity and acceleration of the mass when it is 10 mm below the rest position.

    [Ans. 5.5 Hz ; 0.6 m/s ; 11.95 m/s²]

6. A spring of stiffness 2 kN/m is suspended vertically and two equal masses of 4 kg each are attached to the lower end. One of these masses is suddenly removed and the system oscillates. Determine : 1. the amplitude of vibration, 2. the frequency of vibration, 3. the velocity and acceleration of the mass when

passing through half amplitude position, and 4. kinetic energy of the vibration in joules.

[**Ans. 0.019 62 m ; 3.56 Hz ; 0.38 m/s , 4.9 m/s^2 ; 0.385 J**]

7. A vertical helical spring having a stiffness of 1540 N/m is clamped at its upper end and carries a mass of 20 kg attached to the lower end. The mass is displaced vertically through a distance of 120 mm and released. Find : 1. Frequency of oscillation ; 2. Maximum velocity reached ; 3. Maximum acceleration; and 4. Maximum value of the inertia force on the mass.

[**Ans. 1.396 Hz ; 1.053 m/s ; 9.24 m/s^2 ; 184.8 N**]

8. A small flywheel having mass 90 kg is suspended in a vertical plane as a compound pendulum. The distance of centre of gravity from the knife edge support is 250 mm and the flywheel makes 50 oscillations in 64 seconds. Find the moment of inertia of the flywheel about an axis through the centre of gravity. [**Ans. 3.6 kg-m^2**]

9. The connecting rod of a petrol engine has a mass 12 kg. In order to find its moment of inertia it is suspended from a horizontal edge, which passes through small end and coincides with the small end centre. It is made to swing in a vertical plane, such that it makes 100 oscillations in 96 seconds. If the point of suspension of the connecting rod is 170 mm from its c.g., find : 1. radius of gyration about an axis through its c.g., 2. moment of inertia about an axis through its c.g., and 3. length of the equivalent simple pendulum. [**Ans. 101 mm ; 0.1224 kg-m^2 ; 0.23 m**]

10. A connecting rod of mass 40 kg is suspended vertically as a compound pendulum. The distance between the bearing centres is 800 mm. The time for 60 oscillations is found to be 92.5 seconds when the axis of oscillation coincides with the small end centre and 88.4 seconds when it coincides with the big end centre. Find the distance of the centre of gravity from the small end centre, and the moment of inertia of the rod about an axis through the centre of gravity. [**Ans. 0.442 m ; 2.6 kg-m^2**]

11. The following data were obtained from an experiment to find the moment of inertia of a pulley by bifilar suspension :

Mass of the pulley = 12 kg ; Length of strings = 3 m ; Distance of strings on either side of centre of gravity = 150 mm ; Time for 20 oscillations about the vertical axis through c.g. = 46.8 seconds
Calculate the moment of inertia of the pulley about the axis of rotation.

[**Ans. 0.1226 kg-m^2**]

12. In order to find the moment of inertia of a flywheel, it is suspended in the horizontal plane by three wires of length 1.8 m equally spaced around a circle of 185 mm diameter. The time for 25 oscillations in a horizontal plane about a vertical axis through the centre of flywheel is 54 s. Find the radius of gyration and the moment of inertia of the flywheel if it has a mass of 50 kg.

[**Ans. 74.2 mm; 0.275 kg-m^2**]

DO YOU KNOW ?

1. Explain the meaning of S.H.M. and give an example of S.H.M.
2. Define the terms amplitude, periodic time, and frequency as applied to S.H.M.
3. Show that when a particle moves with simple harmonic motion, its time for a complete oscillation is independent of the amplitude of its motion.
4. Derive an expression for the period of oscillation of a mass when attached to a helical spring.
5. What is a simple pendulum ? Under what conditions its motion is regarded as simple harmonic?
6. Prove the formula for the frequency of oscillation of a compound pendulum. What is the length of a simple pendulum which gives the same frequency as compound pendulum ?
7. Show that the minimum periodic time of a compound pendulum is

$$t_{p(min)} = 2\pi \sqrt{\frac{2k_G}{g}}$$

where k_G is the radius of gyration about the centre of gravity.

8. What do you understand by centre of percussion ? Prove that it lies below the centre of gravity of the body and at a distance k_G^2/h, where k_G is the radius of gyration about c.g. and h is the distance between the centre of suspension and centre of gravity.

9. Describe the method of finding the moment of inertia of a connecting rod by means of bifilar suspension. Derive the relations for the periodic time and frequency of oscillation.

10. What is a torsional pendulum ? Show that periodic time of a torsional pendulum is

$$t_p = \frac{2\pi k_G}{r} \sqrt{\frac{l}{g}}$$

where k_G = Radius of gyration,

                 l = Length of each wire, and

                 r = Distance of each wire from the axis of the disc.

OBJECTIVE TYPE QUESTIONS

1. The periodic time (t_p) is given by
   (a) $\omega / 2\pi$ (b) $2\pi / \omega$ (c) $2\pi \times \omega$ (d) π / ω

2. The velocity of a particle moving with simple harmonic motion is . . . . at the mean position.
   (a) zero   (b) minimum   (c) maximum

3. The velocity of a particle (v) moving with simple harmonic motion, at any instant is given by
   (a) $\omega \sqrt{r^2 - x^2}$ (b) $\omega \sqrt{x^2 - r^2}$ (c) $\omega^2 \sqrt{r^2 - x^2}$ (d) $\omega^2 \sqrt{x^2 - r^2}$

4. The maximum acceleration of a particle moving with simple harmonic motion is
   (a) ω (b) $\omega . r$ (c) $\omega^2 . r$ (d) ω^2 / r

5. The frequency of oscillation for the simple pendulum is
   (a) $\frac{1}{2\pi} \sqrt{\frac{L}{g}}$ (b) $\frac{1}{2\pi} \sqrt{\frac{g}{L}}$ (c) $2\pi \sqrt{\frac{L}{g}}$ (d) $2\pi \sqrt{\frac{g}{L}}$

6. When a rigid body is suspended vertically and it oscillates with a small amplitude under the action of the force of gravity, the body is known as
   (a) simple pendulum   (b) torsional pendulum
   (c) compound pendulum   (d) second's pendulum

7. The frequency of oscillation of a compound pendulum is
   (a) $\frac{1}{2\pi} \sqrt{\frac{g.h}{k_G^2 + h^2}}$ (b) $\frac{1}{2\pi} \sqrt{\frac{k_G^2 + h^2}{g.h}}$ (c) $2\pi \sqrt{\frac{g.h}{k_G^2 + h^2}}$ (d) $2\pi \sqrt{\frac{k_G^2 + h^2}{g.h}}$

   where k_G = Radius of gyration about the centroidal axis, and

                 h = Distance between the point of suspension and centre of gravity of the body.

8. The equivalent length of a simple pendulum which gives the same frequency as the compound pendulum is
   (a) $\frac{h}{k_G^2 + h^2}$ (b) $\frac{k_G^2 + h^2}{h}$ (c) $\frac{h^2}{k_G^2 + h^2}$ (d) $\frac{k_G^2 + h^2}{h^2}$

9. The centre of percussion is below the centre of gravity of the body and is at a distance equal to
   (a) h / k_G (b) $h . k_G$ (c) h^2 / k_G (d) k_G^2 / h

10. The frequency of oscillation of a torsional pendulum is
    (a) $\frac{2\pi k_G}{r} \sqrt{\frac{g}{l}}$ (b) $\frac{r}{2\pi k_G} \sqrt{\frac{g}{l}}$ (c) $\frac{2\pi k_G}{r} \sqrt{\frac{l}{g}}$ (d) $\frac{r}{2\pi k_G} \sqrt{\frac{l}{g}}$

ANSWERS

1. (b)	2. (c)	3. (a)	4. (c)	5. (b)
6. (c)	7. (a)	8. (b)	9. (d)	10. (b)

BEAM ENGINE

5

Simple Mechanisms

5.1. Introduction

We have already discussed that a machine is a device which receives energy and transforms it into some useful work. A machine consists of a number of parts or bodies. In this chapter, we shall study the mechanisms of the various parts or bodies from which the machine is assembled. This is done by making one of the parts as fixed, and the relative motion of other parts is determined with respect to the fixed part.

5.2. Kinematic Link or Element

Each part of a machine, which moves relative to some other part, is known as a *kinematic link* (or simply link) or *element*. A link may consist of several parts, which are rigidly fastened together, so that they do not move relative to one another. For example, in a reciprocating steam engine, as shown in Fig. 5.1, piston, piston rod and crosshead constitute one link ; connecting rod with big and small end bearings constitute a second link ; crank, crank shaft and flywheel a third link and the cylinder, engine frame and main bearings a fourth link.

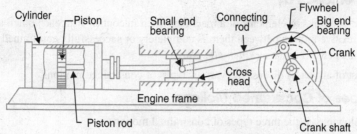

Fig. 5.1. Reciprocating steam engine.

A link or element need not to be a rigid body, but it must be a *resistant body*. A body is said to be a resistant body if it is capable of transmitting the required forces with negligible deformation. Thus a link should have the following two characteristics:

1. It should have relative motion, and

2. It must be a resistant body.

5.3. Types of Links

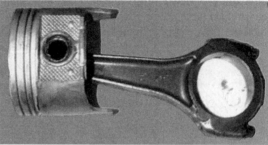

Piston and piston rod of an IC engine.

In order to transmit motion, the driver and the follower may be connected by the following three types of links :

1. *Rigid link*. A rigid link is one which does not undergo any deformation while transmitting motion. Strictly speaking, rigid links do not exist. However, as the deformation of a connecting rod, crank etc. of a reciprocating steam engine is not appreciable, they can be considered as rigid links.

2. *Flexible link*. A flexible link is one which is partly deformed in a manner not to affect the transmission of motion. For example, belts, ropes, chains and wires are flexible links and transmit tensile forces only.

3. *Fluid link*. A fluid link is one which is formed by having a fluid in a receptacle and the motion is transmitted through the fluid by pressure or compression only, as in the case of hydraulic presses, jacks and brakes.

5.4. Structure

It is an assemblage of a number of resistant bodies (known as members) having no relative motion between them and meant for carrying loads having straining action. A railway bridge, a roof truss, machine frames etc., are the examples of a structure.

5.5. Difference Between a Machine and a Structure

The following differences between a machine and a structure are important from the subject point of view :

1. The parts of a machine move relative to one another, whereas the members of a structure do not move relative to one another.

2. A machine transforms the available energy into some useful work, whereas in a structure no energy is transformed into useful work.

3. The links of a machine may transmit both power and motion, while the members of a structure transmit forces only.

5.6. Kinematic Pair

The two links or elements of a machine, when in contact with each other, are said to form a pair. If the relative motion between them is completely or successfully constrained (*i.e.* in a definite direction), the pair is known as *kinematic pair*.

First of all, let us discuss the various types of constrained motions.

5.7. Types of Constrained Motions

Following are the three types of constrained motions :

1. *Completely constrained motion.* When the motion between a pair is limited to a definite direction irrespective of the direction of force applied, then the motion is said to be a completely constrained motion. For example, the piston and cylinder (in a steam engine) form a pair and the motion of the piston is limited to a definite direction (*i.e.* it will only reciprocate) relative to the cylinder irrespective of the direction of motion of the crank, as shown in Fig. 5.1.

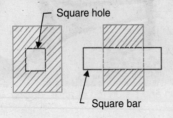

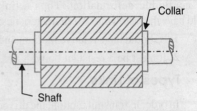

Fig. 5.2. Square bar in a square hole. **Fig. 5.3.** Shaft with collars in a circular hole.

The motion of a square bar in a square hole, as shown in Fig. 5.2, and the motion of a shaft with collars at each end in a circular hole, as shown in Fig. 5.3, are also examples of completely constrained motion.

2. *Incompletely constrained motion.* When the motion between a pair can take place in more than one direction, then the motion is called an incompletely constrained motion. The change in the direction of impressed force may alter the direction of relative motion between the pair. A circular bar or shaft in a circular hole, as shown in Fig. 5.4, is an example of an incompletely constrained motion as it may either rotate or slide in a hole. These both motions have no relationship with the other.

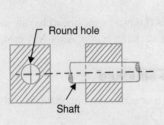

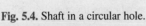

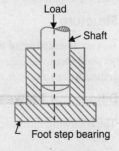

Fig. 5.4. Shaft in a circular hole. **Fig. 5.5.** Shaft in a foot step bearing.

3. *Successfully constrained motion.* When the motion between the elements, forming a pair, is such that the constrained motion is not completed by itself, but by some other means, then the motion is said to be successfully constrained motion. Consider a shaft in a foot-step bearing as shown in Fig. 5.5. The shaft may rotate in a bearing or it may move upwards. This is a case of incompletely constrained motion. But if the load is placed on the shaft to prevent axial upward movement of the shaft, then the motion of the pair is said to be successfully constrained motion. The motion of an I.C. engine valve (these are kept on their seat by a spring) and the piston reciprocating inside an engine cylinder are also the examples of successfully constrained motion.

5.8. Classification of Kinematic Pairs

The kinematic pairs may be classified according to the following considerations :

1. *According to the type of relative motion between the elements.* The kinematic pairs according to type of relative motion between the elements may be classified as discussed below:

(a) Sliding pair. When the two elements of a pair are connected in such a way that one can only slide relative to the other, the pair is known as a sliding pair. The piston and cylinder, cross-head and guides of a reciprocating steam engine, ram and its guides in shaper, tail stock on the lathe bed etc. are the examples of a sliding pair. A little consideration will show, that a sliding pair has a completely constrained motion.

(b) Turning pair. When the two elements of a pair are connected in such a way that one can only turn or revolve about a fixed axis of another link, the pair is known as turning pair. A shaft with collars at both ends fitted into a circular hole, the crankshaft in a journal bearing in an engine, lathe spindle supported in head stock, cycle wheels turning over their axles etc. are the examples of a turning pair. A turning pair also has a completely constrained motion.

(c) Rolling pair. When the two elements of a pair are connected in such a way that one rolls over another fixed link, the pair is known as rolling pair. Ball and roller bearings are examples of rolling pair.

(d) Screw pair. When the two elements of a pair are connected in such a way that one element can turn about the other by screw threads, the pair is known as screw pair. The lead screw of a lathe with nut, and bolt with a nut are examples of a screw pair.

(e) Spherical pair. When the two elements of a pair are connected in such a way that one element (with spherical shape) turns or swivels about the other fixed element, the pair formed is called a spherical pair. The ball and socket joint, attachment of a car mirror, pen stand etc., are the examples of a spherical pair.

2. *According to the type of contact between the elements.* The kinematic pairs according to the type of contact between the elements may be classified as discussed below :

(a) Lower pair. When the two elements of a pair have a surface contact when relative motion takes place and the surface of one element slides over the surface of the other, the pair formed is known as lower pair. It will be seen that sliding pairs, turning pairs and screw pairs form lower pairs.

(b) Higher pair. When the two elements of a pair have a line or point contact when relative motion takes place and the motion between the two elements is partly turning and partly sliding,then the pair is known as higher pair. A pair of friction discs, toothed gearing, belt and rope drives, ball and roller bearings and cam and follower are the examples of higher pairs.

3. *According to the type of closure.* The kinematic pairs according to the type of closure between the elements may be classified as discussed below :

(a) Self closed pair. When the two elements of a pair are connected together mechanically in such a way that only required kind of relative motion occurs, it is then known as self closed pair. The lower pairs are self closed pair.

(b) Force - closed pair. When the two elements of a pair are not connected mechanically but are kept in contact by the action of external forces, the pair is said to be a force-closed pair. The cam and follower is an example of force closed pair, as it is kept in contact by the forces exerted by spring and gravity.

5.9. Kinematic Chain

When the kinematic pairs are coupled in such a way that the last link is joined to the first link to transmit definite motion (*i.e.* completely or successfully constrained motion), it is called a *kinematic chain*. In other words, a kinematic chain may be defined as a combination of kinematic pairs, joined in such a way that each link forms a part of two pairs and the relative motion between the links or elements is completely or successfully constrained. For example, the crankshaft of an engine forms a kinematic pair with the bearings which are fixed in a pair, the connecting rod with the crank forms a second kinematic pair,

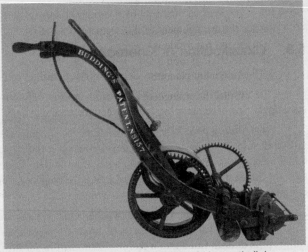

Lawn-mover is a combination of kinematic links.

the piston with the connecting rod forms a third pair and the piston with the cylinder forms a fourth pair. The total combination of these links is a kinematic chain.

If each link is assumed to form two pairs with two adjacent links, then the relation between the number of pairs (p) forming a kinematic chain and the number of links (l) may be expressed in the form of an equation :

$$l = 2p - 4 \qquad \ldots (i)$$

Since in a kinematic chain each link forms a part of two pairs, therefore there will be as many links as the number of pairs.

Another relation between the number of links (l) and the number of joints (j) which constitute a kinematic chain is given by the expression :

$$j = \frac{3}{2}l - 2 \qquad \ldots (ii)$$

The equations (*i*) and (*ii*) are applicable only to kinematic chains, in which lower pairs are used. These equations may also be applied to kinematic chains, in which higher pairs are used. In that case each higher pair may be taken as equivalent to two lower pairs with an additional element or link.

Let us apply the above equations to the following cases to determine whether each of them is a kinematic chain or not.

1. Consider the arrangement of three links *AB*, *BC* and *CA* with pin joints at *A*, *B* and *C* as shown in Fig. 5.6. In this case,

	Number of links,	$l = 3$
	Number of pairs,	$p = 3$
and	number of joints,	$j = 3$
	From equation (*i*),	$l = 2p - 4$
or		$3 = 2 \times 3 - 4 = 2$
i.e.	L.H.S. > R.H.S.	

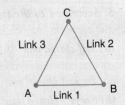

Fig. 5.6. Arrangement of three links.

Now from equation (*ii*),

$$j = \frac{3}{2}l - 2 \quad \text{or} \quad 3 = \frac{3}{2} \times 3 - 2 = 2.5$$

i.e.   L.H.S. > R.H.S.

Since the arrangement of three links, as shown in Fig. 5.6, does not satisfy the equations (*i*) and (*ii*) and the left hand side is greater than the right hand side, therefore it is not a kinematic chain and hence no relative motion is possible. Such type of chain is called *locked chain* and forms a rigid frame or structure which is used in bridges and trusses.

2. Consider the arrangement of four links *AB*, *BC*, *CD* and *DA* as shown in Fig. 5.7. In this case

$$l = 4, p = 4, \text{ and } j = 4$$

From equation (*i*), $l = 2p - 4$

$$4 = 2 \times 4 - 4 = 4$$

i.e.   L.H.S. = R.H.S.

From equation (*ii*), $j = \dfrac{3}{2}l - 2$

$$4 = \dfrac{3}{2} \times 4 - 2 = 4$$

i.e.   L.H.S. = R.H.S.

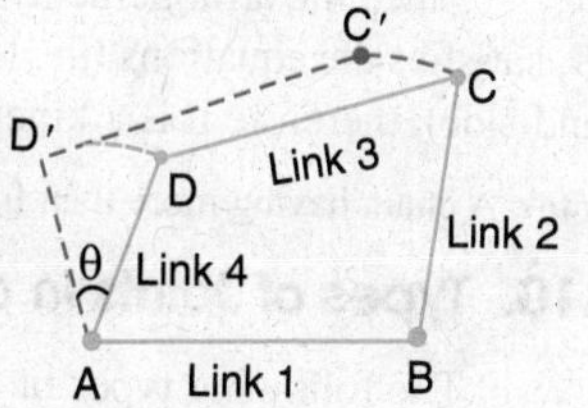

Fig. 5.7. Arrangement of four links.

Since the arrangement of four links, as shown in Fig. 5.7, satisfy the equations (*i*) and (*ii*), therefore it is a *kinematic chain of one degree of freedom*.

A chain in which a single link such as *AD* in Fig. 5.7 is sufficient to define the position of all other links, it is then called a kinematic chain of one degree of freedom.

A little consideration will show that in Fig. 5.7, if a definite displacement (say θ) is given to the link *AD*, keeping the link *AB* fixed, then the resulting displacements of the remaining two links *BC* and *CD* are also perfectly definite. Thus we see that in a four bar chain, the relative motion is completely constrained. Hence it may be called as a *constrained kinematic chain*, and it is the basis of all machines.

3. Consider an arrangement of five links, as shown in Fig. 5.8. In this case,

$$l = 5, p = 5, \text{ and } j = 5$$

From equation (*i*),

$$l = 2p - 4 \quad \text{or} \quad 5 = 2 \times 5 - 4 = 6$$

i.e.   L.H.S. < R.H.S.

From equation (*ii*),

$$j = \dfrac{3}{2}l - 2 \quad \text{or} \quad 5 = \dfrac{3}{2} \times 5 - 2 = 5.5$$

i.e.   L.H.S. < R.H.S.

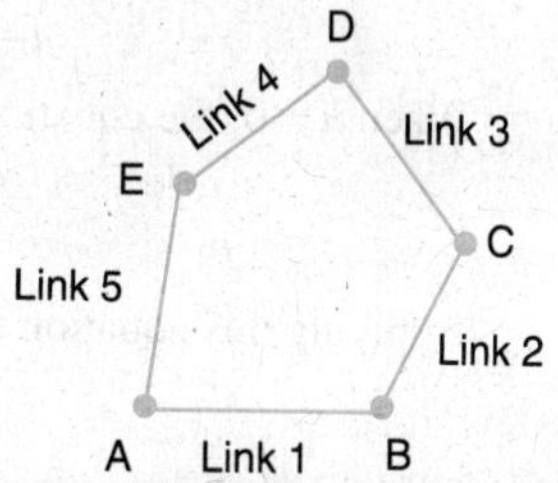

Fig. 5.8. Arrangement of five links.

Since the arrangement of five links, as shown in Fig. 5.8 does not satisfy the equations and left hand side is less than right hand side, therefore it is not a kinematic chain. Such a type of chain is called *unconstrained chain* i.e. the relative motion is not completely constrained. This type of chain is of little practical importance.

4. Consider an arrangement of six links, as shown in Fig. 5.9. This chain is formed by adding two more links in such a way that these two links form a pair with the existing links as well as form themselves a pair. In this case

$$l = 6, p = 5, \text{ and } j = 7$$

From equation (*i*),

$$l = 2p - 4 \quad \text{or} \quad 6 = 2 \times 5 - 4 = 6$$

i.e.   L.H.S. = R.H.S.

From equation (*ii*),

$$j = \frac{3}{2}l - 2 \quad \text{or} \quad 7 = \frac{3}{2} \times 6 - 2 = 7$$

i.e.   L.H.S. = R.H.S.

Since the arrangement of six links, as shown in Fig. 5.9, satisfies the equations (*i.e.* left hand side is equal to right hand side), therefore it is a kinematic chain.

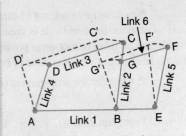

Fig. 5.9. Arrangement of six links.

Note : A chain having more than four links is known as **compound kinematic chain.**

5.10. Types of Joints in a Chain

The following types of joints are usually found in a chain :

1. Binary joint. When two links are joined at the same connection, the joint is known as binary joint. For example, a chain as shown in Fig. 5.10, has four links and four binary joins at *A*, *B*, *C* and *D*.

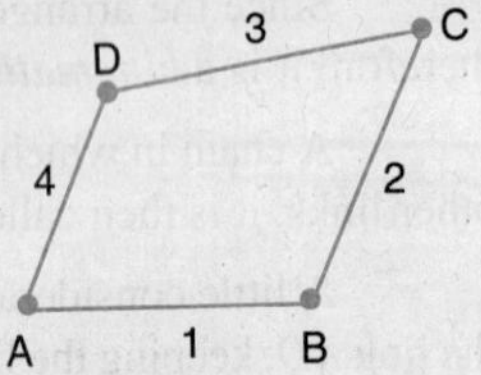

In order to determine the nature of chain, *i.e.* whether the chain is a locked chain (or structure) or kinematic chain or unconstrained chain, the following relation between the number of links and the number of binary joints, as given by A.W. Klein, may be used :

$$j + \frac{h}{2} = \frac{3}{2}l - 2 \qquad \dots (i)$$

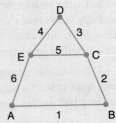

Fig. 5.10. Kinematic chain with all binary joints.

where

j = Number of binary joints,

h = Number of higher pairs, and

l = Number of links.

When $h = 0$, the equation (*i*), may be written as

$$j = \frac{3}{2}l - 2 \qquad \dots (ii)$$

Applying this equation to a chain, as shown in Fig. 5.10, where $l = 4$ and $j = 4$, we have

$$4 = \frac{3}{2} \times 4 - 2 = 4$$

Since the left hand side is equal to the right hand side, therefore the chain is a kinematic chain or constrained chain.

2. Ternary joint. When three links are joined at the same connection, the joint is known as ternary joint. It is equivalent to two binary joints as one of the three links joined carry the pin for the other two links. For example, a chain, as shown in Fig. 5.11, has six links. It has three binary joints at *A*, *B* and *D* and two ternary joints at *C* and *E*. Since one ternary joint is equivalent to two binary joints, therefore equivalent binary joints in a chain, as shown in Fig. 5.11, are $3 + 2 \times 2 = 7$

Fig. 5.11. Kinematic chain having binary and ternary joints.

Let us now determine whether this chain is a kinematic chain or not. We know that $l = 6$ and $j = 7$, therefore from equation (*ii*),

$$j = \frac{3}{2} l - 2$$

or
$$7 = \frac{3}{2} \times 6 - 2 = 7$$

Since left hand side is equal to right hand side, therefore the chain, as shown in Fig. 5.11, is a kinematic chain or constrained chain.

3. *Quaternary joint.* When four links are joined at the same connection, the joint is called a quaternary joint. It is equivalent to three binary joints. In general, when *l* number of links are joined at the same connection, the joint is equivalent to (*l* – 1) binary joints.

For example consider a chain having eleven links, as shown in Fig. 5.12 (*a*). It has one binary joint at *D*, four ternary joints at *A, B, E* and *F*, and two quaternary joints at *C* and *G*. Since one quaternary joint is equivalent to three binary joints and one ternary joint is equal to two binary joints, therefore total number of binary joints in a chain, as shown in Fig. 5.12 (*a*), are

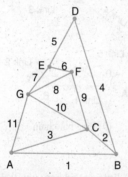 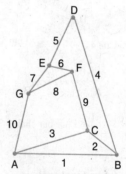

| (*a*) Looked chain having binary, ternary and quaternary joints. | (*b*) Kinematic chain having binary and ternary joints. |

Fig. 5.12

$$1 + 4 \times 2 + 2 \times 3 = 15$$

Let us now determine whether the chain, as shown in Fig. 5.12 (*a*), is a kinematic chain or not. We know that *l* = 11 and *j* = 15. We know that,

$$j = \frac{3}{2} l - 2, \quad \text{or} \quad 15 = \frac{3}{2} \times 11 - 2 = 14.5, \text{ i.e., L.H.S.} > \text{R.H.S.}$$

Since the left hand side is greater than right hand side, therefore the chain, as shown in Fig. 5.12 (*a*) , is not a kinematic chain. We have discussed in Art 5.9 , that such a type of chain is called locked chain and forms a rigid frame or structure.

If the link *CG* is removed, as shown in Fig. 5.12 (*b*), it has ten links and has one binary joint at *D* and six ternary joints at *A, B, C, E, F* and *G*.

Therefore total number of binary joints are 1 + 2 × 6 = 13. We know that

$$j = \frac{3}{2} l - 2, \quad \text{or} \quad 13 = \frac{3}{2} \times 10 - 2 = 13, \text{ i.e. L.H.S.} = \text{R.H.S.}$$

Since left hand side is equal to right hand side, therefore the chain, as shown in Fig. 5.12 (*b*), is a kinematic chain or constrained chain.

5.11. Mechanism

When one of the links of a kinematic chain is fixed, the chain is known as *mechanism*. It may be used for transmitting or transforming motion *e.g.* engine indicators, typewriter etc.

A mechanism with four links is known as *simple mechanism*, and the mechanism with more than four links is known as *compound mechanism*. When a mechanism is required to transmit power or to do some particular type of work, it then becomes a *machine*. In such cases, the various links or elements have to be designed to withstand the forces (both static and kinetic) safely.

A little consideration will show that a mechanism may be regarded as a machine in which each part is reduced to the simplest form to transmit the required motion.

5.12. Number of Degrees of Freedom for Plane Mechanisms

In the design or analysis of a mechanism, one of the most important concern is the number of degrees of freedom (also called movability) of the mechanism. It is defined as the number of input parameters (usually pair variables) which must be independently controlled in order to bring the mechanism into a useful engineering purpose. It is possible to determine the number of degrees of freedom of a mechanism directly from the number of links and the number and types of joints which it includes.

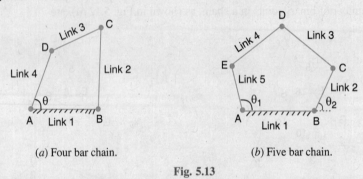

(a) Four bar chain.   (b) Five bar chain.

Fig. 5.13

Consider a four bar chain, as shown in Fig. 5.13 (a). A little consideration will show that only one variable such as θ is needed to define the relative positions of all the links. In other words, we say that the number of degrees of freedom of a four bar chain is one. Now, let us consider a five bar chain, as shown in Fig. 5.13 (b). In this case two variables such as θ_1 and θ_2 are needed to define completely the relative positions of all the links. Thus, we say that the number of degrees of freedom is * two.

In order to develop the relationship in general, consider two links *AB* and *CD* in a plane motion as shown in Fig. 5.14 (a).

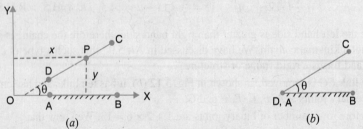

Fig. 5.14. Links in a plane motion.

The link *AB* with co-ordinate system *OXY* is taken as the reference link (or fixed link). The position of point *P* on the moving link *CD* can be completely specified by the three variables, *i.e.* the

---

* The differential of an automobile requires that the angular velocity of two elements be fixed in order to know the velocity of the remaining elements. The differential mechanism is thus said to have two degrees of freedom. Many computing mechanisms have two or more degrees of freedom.

co-ordinates of the point P denoted by x and y and the inclination θ of the link CD with X-axis or link AB. In other words, we can say that each link of a mechanism has three degrees of freedom before it is connected to any other link. But when the link CD is connected to the link AB by a turning pair at A, as shown in Fig. 5.14 (*b*), the position of link CD is now determined by a single variable θ and thus has one degree of freedom.

From above, we see that when a link is connected to a fixed link by a turning pair (*i.e.* lower pair), two degrees of freedom are destroyed. This may be clearly understood from Fig. 5.15, in which the resulting four bar mechanism has one degree of freedom (*i.e.* $n = 1$).

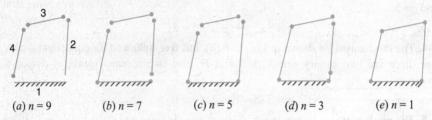

| (*a*) $n = 9$ | (*b*) $n = 7$ | (*c*) $n = 5$ | (*d*) $n = 3$ | (*e*) $n = 1$ |

Fig. 5.15. Four bar mechanism.

Now let us consider a plane mechanism with l number of links. Since in a mechanism, one of the links is to be fixed, therefore the number of movable links will be $(l - 1)$ and thus the total number of degrees of freedom will be $3\,(l - 1)$ before they are connected to any other link. In general, a mechanism with l number of links connected by j number of binary joints or lower pairs (*i.e.* single degree of freedom pairs) and h number of higher pairs (*i.e.* two degree of freedom pairs), then the number of degrees of freedom of a mechanism is given by

$$n = 3\,(l - 1) - 2\,j - h \qquad\qquad \ldots (i)$$

This equation is called Kutzbach criterion for the movability of a mechanism having plane motion.

If there are no two degree of freedom pairs (*i.e.* higher pairs), then $h = 0$. Substituting $h = 0$ in equation (*i*), we have

$$n = 3\,(l - 1) - 2\,j \qquad\qquad \ldots (ii)$$

5.13. Application of Kutzbach Criterion to Plane Mechanisms

We have discussed in the previous article that Kutzbach criterion for determining the number of degrees of freedom or movability (n) of a plane mechanism is

$$n = 3\,(l - 1) - 2\,j - h$$

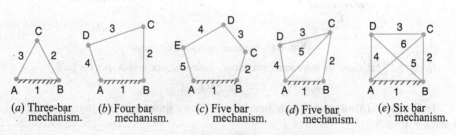

| (*a*) Three-bar mechanism. | (*b*) Four bar mechanism. | (*c*) Five bar mechanism. | (*d*) Five bar mechanism. | (*e*) Six bar mechanism. |

Fig. 5.16. Plane mechanisms.

The number of degrees of freedom or movability (n) for some simple mechanisms having no higher pair (*i.e.* $h = 0$), as shown in Fig. 5.16, are determined as follows :

1. The mechanism, as shown in Fig. 5.16 (*a*), has three links and three binary joints, *i.e.* $l = 3$ and $j = 3$.

$$\therefore \qquad n = 3 (3 - 1) - 2 \times 3 = 0$$

2. The mechanism, as shown in Fig. 5.16 (*b*), has four links and four binary joints, *i.e.* $l = 4$ and $j = 4$.

$$\therefore \qquad n = 3 (4 - 1) - 2 \times 4 = 1$$

3. The mechanism, as shown in Fig. 5.16 (*c*), has five links and five binary joints, *i.e.* $l = 5$, and $j = 5$.

$$\therefore \qquad n = 3 (5 - 1) - 2 \times 5 = 2$$

4. The mechanism, as shown in Fig. 5.16 (*d*), has five links and six equivalent binary joints (because there are two binary joints at *B* and *D*, and two ternary joints at *A* and *C*), *i.e.* $l = 5$ and $j = 6$.

$$\therefore \qquad n = 3 (5 - 1) - 2 \times 6 = 0$$

5. The mechanism, as shown in Fig. 5.16 (*e*), has six links and eight equivalent binary joints (because there are four ternary joints at *A, B, C* and *D*), *i.e.* $l = 6$ and $j = 8$.

$$\therefore \qquad n = 3 (6 - 1) - 2 \times 8 = -1$$

It may be noted that

(a) When $n = 0$, then the mechanism forms a structure and no relative motion between the links is possible, as shown in Fig. 5.16 (*a*) and (*d*).

(b) When $n = 1$, then the mechanism can be driven by a single input motion, as shown in Fig. 5.16 (*b*).

(c) When $n = 2$, then two separate input motions are necessary to produce constrained motion for the mechanism, as shown in Fig. 5.16 (*c*).

(d) When $n = -1$ or less, then there are redundant constraints in the chain and it forms a statically indeterminate structure, as shown in Fig. 5.16 (*e*).

The application of Kutzbach's criterion applied to mechanisms with a higher pair or two degree of freedom joints is shown in Fig. 5.17.

(*a*) (*b*)

Fig. 5.17. Mechanism with a higher pair.

In Fig. 5.17 (*a*), there are three links, two binary joints and one higher pair, *i.e.* $l = 3, j = 2$ and $h = 1$.

$$\therefore \qquad n = 3 (3 - 1) - 2 \times 2 - 1 = 1$$

In Fig. 5.17 (*b*), there are four links, three binary joints and one higher pair, *i.e.* $l = 4$, $j = 3$ and $h = 1$

$$\therefore \qquad n = 3 (4 - 1) - 2 \times 3 - 1 = 2$$

Here it has been assumed that the slipping is possible between the links (*i.e.* between the wheel and the fixed link). However if the friction at the contact is high enough to prevent slipping, the joint will be counted as one degree of freedom pair, because only one relative motion will be possible between the links.

5.14. Grubler's Criterion for Plane Mechanisms

The Grubler's criterion applies to mechanisms with only single degree of freedom joints where the overall movability of the mechanism is unity. Substituting $n = 1$ and $h = 0$ in Kutzbach equation, we have

$$1 = 3\,(l-1) - 2j \qquad \text{or} \qquad 3l - 2j - 4 = 0$$

This equation is known as the Grubler's criterion for plane mechanisms with constrained motion.

A little consideration will show that a plane mechanism with a movability of 1 and only single degree of freedom joints can not have odd number of links. The simplest possible machanisms of this type are a four bar mechanism and a slider-crank mechanism in which $l = 4$ and $j = 4$.

5.15. Inversion of Mechanism

We have already discussed that when one of links is fixed in a kinematic chain, it is called a mechanism. So we can obtain as many mechanisms as the number of links in a kinematic chain by fixing, in turn, different links in a kinematic chain. This method of obtaining different mechanisms by fixing different links in a kinematic chain, is known as *inversion of the mechanism*.

It may be noted that the relative motions between the various links is not changed in any manner through the process of inversion, but their absolute motions (those measured with respect to the fixed link) may be changed drastically.

Note: The part of a mechanism which initially moves with respect to the frame or fixed link is called *driver* and that part of the mechanism to which motion is transmitted is called *follower*. Most of the mechanisms are reversible, so that same link can play the role of a driver and follower at different times. For example, in a reciprocating steam engine, the piston is the driver and flywheel is a follower while in a reciprocating air compressor, the flywheel is a driver.

5.16. Types of Kinematic Chains

The most important kinematic chains are those which consist of four lower pairs, each pair being a sliding pair or a turning pair. The following three types of kinematic chains with four lower pairs are important from the subject point of view :

1. Four bar chain or quadric cyclic chain,

2. Single slider crank chain, and

3. Double slider crank chain.

These kinematic chains are discussed, in detail, in the following articles.

5.17. Four Bar Chain or Quadric Cycle Chain

We have already discussed that the kinematic chain is a combination of four or more kinematic pairs, such that the relative motion between the links or elements is completely constrained. The simplest and the basic kinematic chain is a four bar chain or quadric cycle chain, as shown in Fig. 5.18. It consists of four links, each of them forms a turning pair at A, B, C and D. The four links may be of different lengths. According to **Grashof 's law** for a four bar mechanism, the sum of the shortest and longest link lengths should not be greater than the sum of the remaining two link lengths if there is to be continuous relative motion between the two links.

A very important consideration in designing a mechanism is to ensure that the input crank makes a complete revolution relative to the

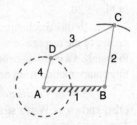

Fig. 5.18. Four bar chain.

other links. The mechanism in which no link makes a complete revolution will not be useful. In a four bar chain, one of the links, in particular the shortest link, will make a complete revolution relative to the other three links, if it satisfies the Grashof's law. Such a link is known as *crank* or *driver*. In Fig. 5.18, *AD* (link 4) is a crank. The link *BC* (link 2) which makes a partial rotation or oscillates is known as *lever* or *rocker* or *follower* and the link *CD* (link 3) which connects the crank and lever is called *connecting rod* or *coupler*. The fixed link *AB* (link 1) is known as *frame* of the mechanism.

When the crank (link 4) is the driver, the mechanism is transforming rotary motion into oscillating motion.

5.18. Inversions of Four Bar Chain

Though there are many inversions of the four bar chain, yet the following are important from the subject point of view :

1. Beam engine (crank and lever mechanism).
A part of the mechanism of a beam engine (also known as crank and lever mechanism) which consists of four links, is shown in Fig. 5.19. In this mechanism, when the crank rotates about the fixed centre *A*, the lever oscillates about a fixed centre *D*. The end *E* of the lever *CDE* is connected to a piston rod which reciprocates due to the rotation of the crank. In other words, the purpose of this mechanism is to convert rotary motion into reciprocating motion.

Beam Engine

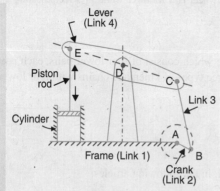

Fig. 5.19. Beam engine.

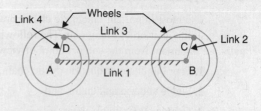

Fig. 5.20. Coupling rod of a locomotive.

2. Coupling rod of a locomotive (Double crank mechanism). The mechanism of a coupling rod of a locomotive (also known as double crank mechanism) which consists of four links, is shown in Fig. 5.20.

In this mechanism, the links *AD* and *BC* (having equal length) act as cranks and are connected to the respective wheels. The link *CD* acts as a coupling rod and the link *AB* is fixed in order to maintain a constant centre to centre distance between them. This mechanism is meant for transmitting rotary motion from one wheel to the other wheel.

3. Watt's indicator mechanism (Double lever mechanism). A *Watt's indicator mechanism (also known as Watt's straight line mechanism or double lever mechanism) which consists of four

---
*   Refer Chapter 9, Art. 9.6

links, is shown in Fig. 5.21. The four links are : fixed link at *A*, link *AC*, link *CE* and link *BFD*. It may be noted that *BF* and *FD* form one link because these two parts have no relative motion between them. The links *CE* and *BFD* act as levers. The displacement of the link *BFD* is directly proportional to the pressure of gas or steam which acts on the indicator plunger. On any small displacement of the mechanism, the tracing point *E* at the end of the link *CE* traces out approximately a straight line.

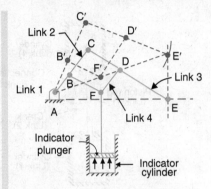

Fig. 5.21. Watt's indicator mechanism.

The initial position of the mechanism is shown in Fig. 5.21 by full lines whereas the dotted lines show the position of the mechanism when the gas or steam pressure acts on the indicator plunger.

5.19. Single Slider Crank Chain

A single slider crank chain is a modification of the basic four bar chain. It consist of one sliding pair and three turning pairs. It is,usually, found in reciprocating steam engine mechanism. This type of mechanism converts rotary motion into reciprocating motion and vice versa.

In a single slider crank chain, as shown in Fig. 5.22, the links 1 and 2, links 2 and 3, and links 3 and 4 form three turning pairs while the links 4 and 1 form a sliding pair.

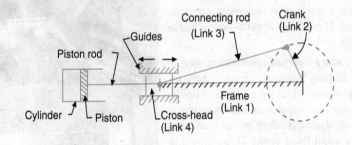

Fig. 5.22. Single slider crank chain.

The link 1 corresponds to the frame of the engine, which is fixed. The link 2 corresponds to the crank ; link 3 corresponds to the connecting rod and link 4 corresponds to cross-head. As the crank rotates, the cross-head reciprocates in the guides and thus the piston reciprocates in the cylinder.

5.20. Inversions of Single Slider Crank Chain

We have seen in the previous article that a single slider crank chain is a four-link mechanism. We know that by fixing, in turn, different links in a kinematic chain, an inversion is obtained and we can obtain as many mechanisms as the links in a kinematic chain. It is thus obvious, that four inversions of a single slider crank chain are possible. These inversions are found in the following mechanisms.

1. Pendulum pump or Bull engine. In this mechanism, the inversion is obtained by fixing the cylinder or link 4 (*i.e.* sliding pair), as shown in Fig. 5.23. In this case, when the crank (link 2) rotates, the connecting rod (link 3) oscillates about a pin pivoted to the fixed link 4 at *A* and the piston attached to the piston rod (link 1) reciprocates. The duplex pump which is used to supply feed water to boilers have two pistons attached to link 1, as shown in Fig. 5.23.

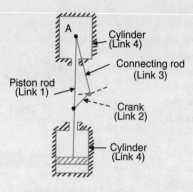

Fig. 5.23. Pendulum pump.

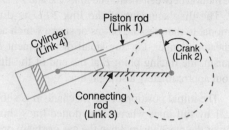

Fig. 5.24. Oscillating cylinder engine.

2. *Oscillating cylinder engine*. The arrangement of oscillating cylinder engine mechanism, as shown in Fig. 5.24, is used to convert reciprocating motion into rotary motion. In this mechanism, the link 3 forming the turning pair is fixed. The link 3 corresponds to the connecting rod of a reciprocating steam engine mechanism. When the crank (link 2) rotates, the piston attached to piston rod (link 1) reciprocates and the cylinder (link 4) oscillates about a pin pivoted to the fixed link at *A*.

3. *Rotary internal combustion engine or Gnome engine*. Sometimes back, rotary internal combustion engines were used in aviation. But now-a-days gas turbines are used in its place. It consists of seven cylinders in one plane and all revolves about fixed centre *D*, as shown in Fig. 5.25, while the crank (link 2) is fixed. In this mechanism, when the connecting rod (link 4) rotates, the piston (link 3) reciprocates inside the cylinders forming link 1.

Rotary engine

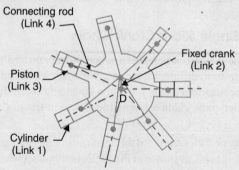

Fig. 5.25. Rotary internal combustion engine.

4. *Crank and slotted lever quick return motion mechanism*. This mechanism is mostly used in shaping machines, slotting machines and in rotary internal combustion engines.

In this mechanism, the link *AC* (*i.e.* link 3) forming the turning pair is fixed, as shown in Fig. 5.26. The link 3 corresponds to the connecting rod of a reciprocating steam engine. The driving crank *CB* revolves with uniform angular speed about the fixed centre *C*. A sliding block attached to the crank pin at *B* slides along the slotted bar *AP* and thus causes *AP* to oscillate about the pivoted point *A*. A short link *PR* transmits the motion from *AP* to the ram which carries the tool and reciprocates along the line of stroke R_1R_2. The line of stroke of the ram (*i.e.* R_1R_2) is perpendicular to *AC* produced.

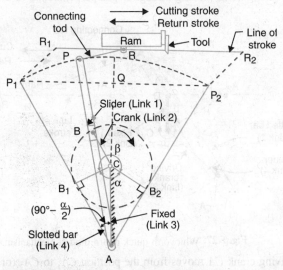

Fig. 5.26. Crank and slotted lever quick return motion mechanism.

In the extreme positions, AP_1 and AP_2 are tangential to the circle and the cutting tool is at the end of the stroke. The forward or cutting stroke occurs when the crank rotates from the position CB_1 to CB_2 (or through an angle β) in the clockwise direction. The return stroke occurs when the crank rotates from the position CB_2 to CB_1 (or through angle α) in the clockwise direction. Since the crank has uniform angular speed, therefore,

$$\frac{\text{Time of cutting stroke}}{\text{Time of return stroke}} = \frac{\beta}{\alpha} = \frac{\beta}{360° - \beta} \text{ or } \frac{360° - \alpha}{\alpha}$$

The Shaping Machine

Since the tool travels a distance of $R_1 R_2$ during cutting and return stroke, therefore travel of the tool or length of stroke

$$= R_1R_2 = P_1P_2 = 2P_1Q = 2AP_1 \sin \angle P_1 AQ$$

$$= 2AP_1 \sin\left(90° - \frac{\alpha}{2}\right) = 2AP \cos \frac{\alpha}{2} \qquad \dots (\because AP_1 = AP)$$

$$= 2AP \times \frac{CB_1}{AC} \qquad \dots \left(\because \cos \frac{\alpha}{2} = \frac{CB_1}{AC}\right)$$

$$= 2AP \times \frac{CB}{AC} \qquad \dots (\because CB_1 = CB)$$

Note: From Fig. 5.26, we see that the angle β made by the forward or cutting stroke is greater than the angle α described by the return stroke. Since the crank rotates with uniform angular speed, therefore the return stroke is completed within shorter time. Thus it is called quick return motion mechanism.

5. *Whitworth quick return motion mechanism.* This mechanism is mostly used in shaping and slotting machines. In this mechanism, the link *CD* (link 2) forming the turning pair is fixed, as shown in Fig. 5.27. The link 2 corresponds to a crank in a reciprocating steam engine. The driving crank *CA* (link 3) rotates at a uniform angular speed. The slider (link 4) attached to the crank pin at *A* slides along the slotted bar *PA* (link 1) which oscillates at a pivoted point *D*. The connecting rod *PR* carries the ram at *R* to which a cutting tool is fixed. The motion of the tool is constrained along the line *RD* produced, *i.e.* along a line passing through *D* and perpendicular to *CD*.

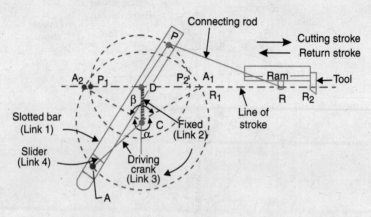

Fig. 5.27. Whitworth quick return motion mechanism.

When the driving crank *CA* moves from the position *CA₁* to *CA₂* (or the link *DP* from the position *DP₁* to *DP₂*) through an angle α in the clockwise direction, the tool moves from the left hand end of its stroke to the right hand end through a distance 2 *PD*.

Now when the driving crank moves from the position *CA₂* to *CA₁* (or the link *DP* from *DP₂* to *DP₁*) through an angle β in the clockwise direction, the tool moves back from right hand end of its stroke to the left hand end.

A little consideration will show that the time taken during the left to right movement of the ram (*i.e.* during forward or cutting stroke) will be equal to the time taken by the driving crank to move from *CA₁* to *CA₂*. Similarly, the time taken during the right to left movement of the ram (or during the idle or return stroke) will be equal to the time taken by the driving crank to move from *CA₂* to *CA₁*.

Since the crank link *CA* rotates at uniform angular velocity therefore time taken during the cutting stroke (or forward stroke) is more than the time taken during the return stroke. In other words, the mean speed of the ram during cutting stroke is less than the mean speed during the return stroke. The ratio between the time taken during the cutting and return strokes is given by

$$\frac{\text{Time of cutting stroke}}{\text{Time of return stroke}} = \frac{\alpha}{\beta} = \frac{\alpha}{360° - \alpha} \quad \text{or} \quad \frac{360° - \beta}{\beta}$$

Note. In order to find the length of effective stroke $R_1 R_2$, mark $P_1 R_1 = P_2 R_2 = PR$. The length of effective stroke is also equal to 2 *PD*.

Example 5.1. *A crank and slotted lever mechanism used in a shaper has a centre distance of 300 mm between the centre of oscillation of the slotted lever and the centre of rotation of the crank. The radius of the crank is 120 mm. Find the ratio of the time of cutting to the time of return stroke.*

Solution. Given : $AC = 300$ mm ; $CB_1 = 120$ mm

The extreme positions of the crank are shown in Fig. 5.28. We know that

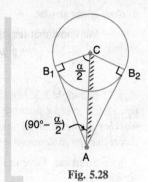

$$\sin \angle CAB_1 = \sin(90° - \alpha/2)$$

$$= \frac{CB_1}{AC} = \frac{120}{300} = 0.4$$

∴ $\angle CAB_1 = 90° - \alpha/2$

$$= \sin^{-1} 0.4 = 23.6°$$

or $\alpha/2 = 90° - 23.6° = 66.4°$

and $\alpha = 2 \times 66.4 = 132.8°$

We know that

Fig. 5.28

$$\frac{\text{Time of cutting stroke}}{\text{Time of return stroke}} = \frac{360° - \alpha}{\alpha} = \frac{360° - 132.8°}{132.8°} = 1.72 \text{ Ans.}$$

Example 5.2. *In a crank and slotted lever quick return motion mechanism, the distance between the fixed centres is 240 mm and the length of the driving crank is 120 mm. Find the inclination of the slotted bar with the vertical in the extreme position and the time ratio of cutting stroke to the return stroke.*

If the length of the slotted bar is 450 mm, find the length of the stroke if the line of stroke passes through the extreme positions of the free end of the lever.

Solution. Given : $AC = 240$ mm ; $CB_1 = 120$ mm ; $AP_1 = 450$ mm

Inclination of the slotted bar with the vertical

Let $\angle CAB_1$ = Inclination of the slotted bar with the vertical.

The extreme positions of the crank are shown in Fig. 5.29. We know that

$$\sin \angle CAB_1 = \sin\left(90° - \frac{\alpha}{2}\right)$$

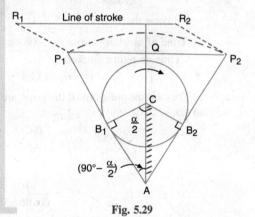

$$= \frac{B_1C}{AC} = \frac{120}{240} = 0.5$$

∴ $\angle CAB_1 = 90° - \frac{\alpha}{2}$

$$= \sin^{-1} 0.5 = 30° \text{ Ans.}$$

Time ratio of cutting stroke to the return stroke

Fig. 5.29

We know that

$$90° - \alpha/2 = 30°$$

∴ $\alpha/2 = 90° - 30° = 60°$

or $\alpha = 2 \times 60° = 120°$

∴ $$\frac{\text{Time of cutting stroke}}{\text{Time of return stroke}} = \frac{360° - \alpha}{\alpha} = \frac{360° - 120°}{120°} = 2 \text{ Ans.}$$

Length of the stroke

We know that length of the stroke,

$$R_1 R_2 = P_1 P_2 = 2 P_1 Q = 2 A P_1 \sin (90° - \alpha / 2)$$
$$= 2 \times 450 \sin (90° - 60°) = 900 \times 0.5 = 450 \text{ mm } \textbf{Ans.}$$

Example 5.3. *Fig. 5.30 shows the lay out of a quick return mechanism of the oscillating link type, for a special purpose machine. The driving crank BC is 30 mm long and time ratio of the working stroke to the return stroke is to be 1.7. If the length of the working stroke of R is 120 mm, determine the dimensions of AC and AP.*

Solution. Given : $BC = 30$ mm ; $R_1 R_2 = 120$ mm ; Time ratio of working stroke to the return stroke = 1.7

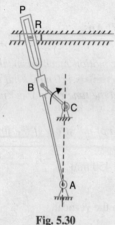

Fig. 5.30

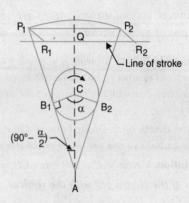

Fig. 5.31

We know that

$$\frac{\text{Time of working stroke}}{\text{Time of return stroke}} = \frac{360 - \alpha}{\alpha} \quad \text{or} \quad 1.7 = \frac{360 - \alpha}{\alpha}$$

$$\therefore \qquad\qquad \alpha = 133.3° \quad \text{or} \quad \alpha / 2 = 66.65°$$

The extreme positions of the crank are shown in Fig. 5.31. From right angled triangle $AB_1 C$, we find that

$$\sin (90° - \alpha/2) = \frac{B_1 C}{AC} \quad \text{or} \quad AC = \frac{B_1 C}{\sin (90° - \alpha / 2)} = \frac{BC}{\cos \alpha / 2}$$

$$\dots (\because B_1 C = BC)$$

$$\therefore \qquad\qquad AC = \frac{30}{\cos 66.65°} = \frac{30}{0.3963} = 75.7 \text{ mm } \textbf{Ans.}$$

We know that length of stroke,

$$R_1 R_2 = P_1 P_2 = 2 P_1 Q = 2 A P_1 \sin (90° - \alpha / 2) = 2 A P_1 \cos \alpha / 2$$

$$120 = 2 AP \cos 66.65° = 0.7926 AP \qquad\qquad \dots (\because AP_1 = AP)$$

$$\therefore \qquad\qquad AP = 120 / 0.7926 = 151.4 \text{ mm } \textbf{Ans.}$$

Example 5.4. *In a Whitworth quick return motion mechanism, as shown in Fig. 5.32, the distance between the fixed centers is 50 mm and the length of the driving crank is 75 mm. The length of the slotted lever is 150 mm and the length of the connecting rod is 135 mm. Find the ratio of the time of cutting stroke to the time of return stroke and also the effective stroke.*

Solution. Given : $CD = 50$ mm ; $CA = 75$ mm ; $PA = 150$ mm ; $PR = 135$ mm

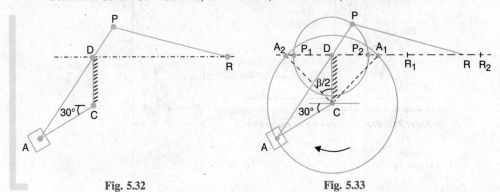

| Fig. 5.32 | Fig. 5.33 |

The extreme positions of the driving crank are shown in Fig. 5.33. From the geometry of the figure,

$$\cos \beta / 2 = \frac{CD}{CA_2} = \frac{50}{75} = 0.667 \qquad\qquad ... (\because CA_2 = CA)$$

$$\therefore \qquad\qquad \beta / 2 = 48.2° \quad \text{or} \quad \beta = 96.4°$$

Ratio of the time of cutting stroke to the time of return stroke

We know that

$$\frac{\text{Time of cutting stroke}}{\text{Time of return stroke}} = \frac{360 - \beta}{\beta} = \frac{360 - 96.4}{96.4} = 2.735 \text{ Ans.}$$

Length of effective stroke

In order to find the length of effective stroke (*i.e.* $R_1 R_2$), draw the space diagram of the mechanism to some suitable scale, as shown in Fig. 5.33. Mark $P_1 R_1 = P_2 R_2 = PR$. Therefore by measurement we find that,

Length of effective stroke = $R_1 R_2 = 87.5$ mm **Ans.**

5.21. Double Slider Crank Chain

A kinematic chain which consists of two turning pairs and two sliding pairs is known as *double slider crank chain*, as shown in Fig. 5.34. We see that the link 2 and link 1 form one turning pair and link 2 and link 3 form the second turning pair. The link 3 and link 4 form one sliding pair and link 1 and link 4 form the second sliding pair.

5.22. Inversions of Double Slider Crank Chain

The following three inversions of a double slider crank chain are important from the subject point of view :

1. *Elliptical trammels*. It is an instrument used for drawing ellipses. This inversion is obtained by fixing the slotted plate (link 4), as shown in Fig. 5.34. The fixed plate or link 4 has two straight grooves cut in it, at right angles to each other. The link 1 and link 3, are known as sliders and form sliding pairs with link 4. The link AB (link 2) is a bar which forms turning pair with links 1 and 3.

When the links 1 and 3 slide along their respective grooves, any point on the link 2 such as P traces out an ellipse on the surface of link 4, as shown in Fig. 5.34 (*a*). A little consideration will show that AP and BP are the semi-major axis and semi-minor axis of the ellipse respectively. This can be proved as follows :

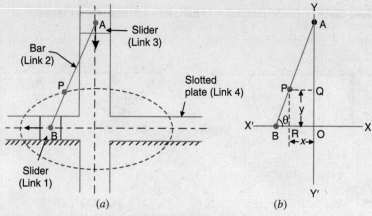

Fig. 5.34. Elliptical trammels.

Let us take OX and OY as horizontal and vertical axes and let the link BA is inclined at an angle θ with the horizontal, as shown in Fig. 5.34 (*b*). Now the co-ordinates of the point P on the link BA will be

$$x = PQ = AP \cos \theta; \text{ and } y = PR = BP \sin \theta$$

or

$$\frac{x}{AP} = \cos \theta; \text{ and } \frac{y}{BP} = \sin \theta$$

Squaring and adding,

$$\frac{x^2}{(AP)^2} + \frac{y^2}{(BP)^2} = \cos^2 \theta + \sin^2 \theta = 1$$

This is the equation of an ellipse. Hence the path traced by point P is an ellipse whose semi-major axis is AP and semi-minor axis is BP.

Note : If P is the mid-point of link BA, then $AP = BP$. The above equation can be written as

$$\frac{x^2}{(AP)^2} + \frac{y^2}{(AP)^2} = 1 \qquad \text{or} \qquad x^2 + y^2 = (AP)^2$$

This is the equation of a circle whose radius is AP. Hence if P is the mid-point of link BA, it will trace a circle.

2. Scotch yoke mechanism. This mechanism is used for converting rotary motion into a reciprocating motion. The inversion is obtained by fixing either the link 1 or link 3. In Fig. 5.35, link 1 is fixed. In this mechanism, when the link 2 (which corresponds to crank) rotates about B as centre, the link 4 (which corresponds to a frame) reciprocates. The fixed link 1 guides the frame.

3. Oldham's coupling. An oldham's coupling is used for connecting two parallel shafts whose axes are at a small distance apart. The shafts are coupled in such a way that if one shaft rotates, the other shaft also rotates at the same speed. This inversion is obtained by fixing the link 2, as shown in Fig. 5.36 (*a*). The shafts to be connected have two flanges (link 1 and link 3) rigidly fastened at their ends by forging.

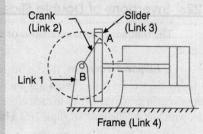

Fig. 5.35. Scotch yoke mechanism.

The link 1 and link 3 form turning pairs with link 2. These flanges have diametrical slots cut in their inner faces, as shown in Fig. 5.36 (*b*). The intermediate piece (link 4) which is a circular disc, have two tongues (*i.e.* diametrical projections) T_1 and T_2 on each face at right angles to each other, as shown in Fig. 5.36 (*c*). The tongues on the link 4 closely fit into the slots in the two flanges (link 1 and link 3). The link 4 can slide or reciprocate in the slots in the flanges.

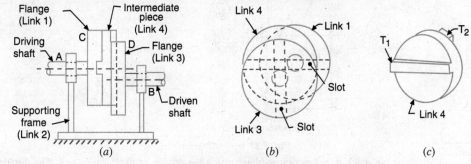

Fig. 5.36. Oldham's coupling.

When the driving shaft *A* is rotated, the flange *C* (link 1) causes the intermediate piece (link 4) to rotate at the same angle through which the flange has rotated, and it further rotates the flange *D* (link 3) at the same angle and thus the shaft *B* rotates. Hence links 1, 3 and 4 have the same angular velocity at every instant. A little consideration will show, that there is a sliding motion between the link 4 and each of the other links 1 and 3.

If the distance between the axes of the shafts is constant, the centre of intermediate piece will describe a circle of diameter equal to the distance between the axes of the two shafts. Therefore, the maximum sliding speed of each tongue along its slot is equal to the peripheral velocity of the centre of the disc along its circular path.

Let ω = Angular velocity of each shaft in rad/s, and

d = Distance between the axes of the shafts in metres.

∴ Maximum sliding speed of each tongue (in m/s),

$$v = \omega.d$$

EXERCISES

1. In a crank and slotted lever quick return mechanism, the distance between the fixed centres is 150 mm and the driving crank is 75 mm long. Determine the ratio of the time taken on the cutting and return strokes. **[Ans. 2]**

2. In a crank and slotted lever quick return motion mechanism, the distance between the fixed centres *O* and *C* is 200 mm. The driving crank *CP* is 75 mm long. The pin *Q* on the slotted lever, 360 mm from the fulcrum *O*, is connected by a link *QR* 100 mm long, to a pin *R* on the ram. The line of stroke of *R* is perpendicular to *OC* and intersects *OC* produced at a point 150 mm from *C*. Determine the ratio of times taken on the cutting and return strokes. **[Ans. 1.647]**

3. In a crank and slotted lever quick return mechanism, as shown in Fig. 5.37, the driving crank length is 75 mm. The distance between the fixed centres is 200 mm and the length of the slotted lever is 500 mm. Find the ratio of the times taken on the cutting and idle strokes. Determine the effective stroke also. **[Ans. 1.67 ; 380 mm]**

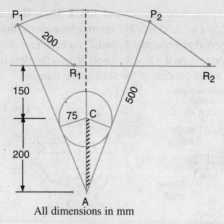

All dimensions in mm

Fig. 5.37

4. The Whitworth quick return motion mechanism has the driving crank 150 mm long. The distance between fixed centres is 100 mm. The line of stroke of the ram passes through the centre of rotation of the slotted lever whose free end is connected to the ram by a connecting link. Find the ratio of time of cutting to time of return. **[Ans. 2.735]**

5. A Whitworth quick return motion mechanism, as shown in Fig. 5.38, has the following particulars :

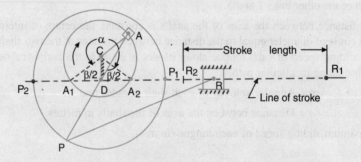

Fig. 5.38

Length of stroke = 150 mm ; Driving crank length = 40 mm; $\dfrac{\text{Time of cutting stroke}}{\text{Time of return stroke}} = 2$

Find the lengths of CD and PD. Also determine the angles α and β.

[**Hint :** Length of stroke = $R_1 R_2 = P_1 P_2 = 2PD$] **[Ans. 20 mm, 75 mm; 240°, 120°]**

DO YOU KNOW ?

1. Explain the term kinematic link. Give the classification of kinematic link.
2. What is a machine ? Giving example, differentiate between a machine and a structure.
3. Write notes on complete and incomplete constraints in lower and higher pairs, illustrating your answer with neat sketches.
4. Explain different kinds of kinematic pairs giving example for each one of them.
5. Explain the terms : 1. Lower pair, 2. Higher pair, 3. Kinematic chain, and 4. Inversion.
6. In what way a mechanism differ from a machine ?
7. What is the significance of degrees of freedom of a kinematic chain when it functions as a mechanism? Give examples.

8. Determine the mobility (degrees of freedom) of the mechanism shown in Fig. 5.39 (*a*) and (*b*) using Kutzbach mobility criterion and classify them.

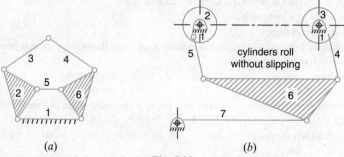

cylinders roll without slipping

(*a*)   (*b*)

Fig. 5.39

9. Explain Grubler's criterion for determining degree of freedom for mechanisms. Using Grubler's criterion for plane mechanism, prove that the minimum number of binary links in a constrained mechanism with simple hinges is four.

10. Sketch and explain the various inversions of a slider crank chain.

11. Sketch and describe the four bar chain mechanism. Why it is considered to be the basic chain?

12. Show that slider crank mechanism is a modification of the basic four bar mechanism.

13. Sketch slider crank chain and its various inversions, stating actual machines in which these are used in practice.

14. Sketch and describe the working of two different types of quick return mechanisms. Give examples of their applications. Derive an expression for the ratio of times taken in forward and return stroke for one of these mechanisms.

15. Sketch and explain any two inversions of a double slider crank chain.

16. Identify the kinematic chains to which the following mechanisms belong :
   1. Steam engine mechanism ; 2. Beam engine ; 3. Whitworth quick return motion mechanism; 4. Elliptical trammels.

OBJECTIVE TYPE QUESTIONS

1. In a reciprocating steam engine, which of the following forms a kinematic link ?
   - (*a*) cylinder and piston
   - (*b*) piston rod and connecting rod
   - (*c*) crank shaft and flywheel
   - (*d*) flywheel and engine frame

2. The motion of a piston in the cylinder of a steam engine is an example of
   - (*a*) completely constrained motion
   - (*b*) incompletely constrained motion
   - (*c*) successfully constrained motion
   - (*d*) none of these

3. The motion transmitted between the teeth of gears in mesh is
   - (*a*) sliding
   - (*b*) rolling
   - (*c*) may be rolling or sliding depending upon the shape of teeth
   - (*d*) partly sliding and partly rolling

4. The cam and follower without a spring forms a
   - (*a*) lower pair
   - (*b*) higher pair
   - (*c*) self closed pair
   - (*d*) force closed pair

5. A ball and a socket joint forms a
   - (*a*) turning pair
   - (*b*) rolling pair
   - (*c*) sliding pair
   - (*d*) spherical pair

6. The lead screw of a lathe with nut forms a
   - (*a*) sliding pair
   - (*b*) rolling pair
   - (*c*) screw pair
   - (*d*) turning pair

7. When the elements of the pair are kept in contact by the action of external forces, the pair is said to be a
   - (*a*) lower pair
   - (*b*) higher pair
   - (*c*) self closed pair
   - (*d*) force closed pair

8. Which of the following is a turning pair ?
   (a) Piston and cylinder of a reciprocating steam engine
   (b) Shaft with collars at both ends fitted in a circular hole
   (c) Lead screw of a lathe with nut
   (d) Ball and socket joint

9. A combination of kinematic pairs, joined in such a way that the relative motion between the links is completely constrained, is called a
   (a) structure   (b) mechanism
   (c) kinematic chain   (d) inversion

10. The relation between the number of pairs (p) forming a kinematic chain and the number of links (l) is
    (a) $l = 2p - 2$ (b) $l = 2p - 3$ (c) $l = 2p - 4$ (d) $l = 2p - 5$

11. The relation between the number of links (l) and the number of binary joints (j) for a kinematic chain having constrained motion is given by $j = \dfrac{3}{2} l - 2.$ If the left hand side of this equation is greater than right hand side, then the chain is
    (a) locked chain   (b) completely constrained chain
    (c) successfully constrained chain (d) incompletely constrained chain

12. In a kinematic chain, a quaternary joint is equivalent to
    (a) one binary joint   (b) two binary joints   (c) three binary joints   (d) four binary joints

13. If n links are connected at the same joint, the joint is equivalent to
    (a) $(n-1)$ binary joints   (b) $(n-2)$ binary joints   (c) $(2n-1)$ binary joints   (d) none of these

14. In a 4 – bar linkage, if the lengths of shortest, longest and the other two links are denoted by s, l, p and q, then it would result in Grashof's linkage provided that
    (a) $l + p < s + q$ (b) $l + s < p + q$ (c) $l + p = s + q$ (d) none of these

15. A kinematic chain is known as a mechanism when
    (a) none of the links is fixed   (b) one of the links is fixed
    (c) two of the links are fixed   (d) all of the links are fixed

16. The Grubler's criterion for determining the degrees of freedom (n) of a mechanism having plane motion is
    (a) $n = (l-1) - j$ (b) $n = 2(l-1) - 2j$ (c) $n = 3(l-1) - 2j$ (d) $n = 4(l-1) - 3j$
    where l = Number of links, and j = Number of binary joints.

17. The mechanism forms a structure, when the number of degrees of freedom (n) is equal to
    (a) 0   (b) 1   (c) 2   (d) – 1

18. In a four bar chain or quadric cycle chain
    (a) each of the four pairs is a turning pair   (b) one is a turning pair and three are sliding pairs
    (c) three are turning pairs and one is sliding pair (d) each of the four pairs is a sliding pair.

19. Which of the following is an inversion of single slider crank chain ?
    (a) Beam engine   (b) Watt's indicator mechanism
    (c) Elliptical trammels   (d) Whitworth quick return motion mechanism

20. Which of the following is an inversion of double slider crank chain ?
    (a) Coupling rod of a locomotive   (b) Pendulum pump
    (c) Elliptical trammels   (d) Oscillating cylinder engine

ANSWERS

1. (c)	2. (a)	3. (d)	4. (c)	5. (d)
6. (c)	7. (d)	8. (b)	9. (c)	10. (c)
11. (a)	12. (c)	13. (a)	14. (b)	15. (b)
16. (c)	17. (a)	18. (a)	19. (d)	20. (c)

Velocity in Mechanisms

(Instantaneous Centre Method)

6.1. Introduction

Sometimes, a body has simultaneously a motion of rotation as well as translation, such as wheel of a car, a sphere rolling (but not slipping) on the ground. Such a motion will have the combined effect of rotation and translation.

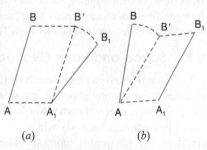

Fig. 6.1. Motion of a link.

Consider a rigid link AB, which moves from its initial position AB to $A_1 B_1$ as shown in Fig. 6.1 (*a*). A little consideration will show that the link neither has wholly a motion of translation nor wholly rotational, but a combination of the two motions. In Fig. 6.1 (*a*), the link has first the motion of translation from AB to A_1B' and then the motion of rotation about A_1, till it occupies the final position $A_1 B_1$. In Fig. 6.1 (*b*), the link AB has first the motion of rotation from AB to $A B'$ about A and then the motion of translation from $A B'$ to

$A_1 B_1$. Such a motion of link AB to $A_1 B_1$ is an example of combined motion of rotation and translation, it being immaterial whether the motion of rotation takes first, or the motion of translation.

In actual practice, the motion of link AB is so gradual that it is difficult to see the two separate motions. But we see the two separate motions, though the point B moves faster than the point A. Thus, this combined motion of rotation and

Mechanisms on a steam automobile engine.

translation of the link AB may be assumed to be a motion of pure rotation about some centre I, known as the *instantaneous centre of rotation (also called centro or virtual centre)*. The position of instantaneous centre may be located as discussed below:

Since the points A and B of the link has moved to A_1 and B_1 respectively under the motion of rotation (as assumed above), therefore the position of the centre of rotation must lie on the intersection of the right bisectors of chords $A A_1$ and $B B_1$. Let these bisectors intersect at I as shown in Fig. 6.2, which is the instantaneous centre of rotation or virtual centre of the link AB.

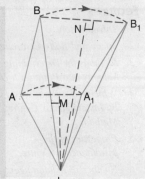

From above, we see that the position of the link AB goes on changing, therefore the centre about which the motion is assumed to take place (*i.e.* the instantaneous centre of rotation) also goes on changing. Thus the instantaneous centre of a moving body may be defined as *that centre which goes on changing from one instant to another*. The locus of all such instantaneous centres is known as *centrode*. A line drawn through an instantaneous centre and perpendicular to the plane

Fig. 6.2. Instantaneous centre of rotation.

of motion is called *instantaneous axis*. The locus of this axis is known as *axode*.

6.2. Space and Body Centrodes

A rigid body in plane motion relative to a second rigid body, supposed fixed in space, may be assumed to be rotating about an instantaneous centre at that particular moment. In other words, the instantaneous centre is a point in the body which may be considered fixed at any particular moment. The locus of the instantaneous centre in space during a definite motion of the body is called the *space centrode* and the locus of the instantaneous centre relative to the body itself is called the *body centrode*. These two centrodes have the instantaneous centre as a common point at any instant and during the motion of the body, the body centrode rolls without slipping over the space centrode.

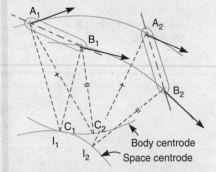

Fig. 6.3. Space and body centrode.

Let I_1 and I_2 be the instantaneous centres for the two different positions $A_1 B_1$ and $A_2 B_2$ of the link $A_1 B_1$ after executing a plane motion as shown in Fig. 6.3. Similarly, if the number of positions of the link $A_1 B_1$ are considered and a curve is drawn passing through these instantaneous centres (I_1, I_2....), then the curve so obtained is called the space centrode.

Now consider a point C_1 to be attached to the body or link $A_1 B_1$ and moves with it in such a way that C_1 coincides with I_1 when the body is in position $A_1 B_1$. Let C_2 be the position of the point C_1 when the link $A_1 B_1$ occupies the position $A_2 B_2$. A little consideration will show that the point C_2 will coincide with I_2 (when the link is in position $A_2 B_2$) only if triangles $A_1 B_1 C_1$ and $A_2 B_2 C_2$ are identical.

$$\therefore \qquad A_1 C_2 = A_2 I_2 \qquad \text{and} \qquad B_1 C_2 = B_2 I_2$$

In the similar way, the number of positions of the point C_1 can be obtained for different positions of the link $A_1 B_1$. The curve drawn through these points (C_1, C_2....) is called the body centrode.

6.3. Methods for Determining the Velocity of a Point on a Link

Though there are many methods for determining the velocity of any point on a link in a mechanism whose direction of motion (*i.e.* path) and velocity of some other point on the same link is known in magnitude and direction, yet the following two methods are important from the subject point of view.

1. Instantaneous centre method, and **2.** Relative velocity method.

The instantaneous centre method is convenient and easy to apply in simple mechanisms, whereas the relative velocity method may be used to any configuration diagram. We shall discuss the relative velocity method in the next chapter.

6.4. Velocity of a Point on a Link by Instantaneous Centre Method

The instantaneous centre method of analysing the motion in a mechanism is based upon the concept (as discussed in Art. 6.1) that any displacement of a body (or a rigid link) having motion in one plane, can be considered as a pure rotational motion of a rigid link as a whole about some centre, known as instantaneous centre or virtual centre of rotation.

Consider two points A and B on a rigid link. Let v_A and v_B be the velocities of points A and B, whose directions are given by angles α and β as shown in Fig. 6.4. If v_A is known in

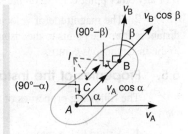

Fig. 6.4. Velocity of a point on a link.

magnitude and direction and v_B in direction only, then the magnitude of v_B may be determined by the instantaneous centre method as discussed below :

Draw AI and BI perpendiculars to the directions v_A and v_B respectively. Let these lines intersect at I, which is known as instantaneous centre or virtual centre of the link. The complete rigid link is to rotate or turn about the centre I.

Since A and B are the points on a rigid link, therefore there cannot be any relative motion between them along the line AB.

Robots use various mechanisms to perform jobs.

Now resolving the velocities along AB,
$$v_A \cos \alpha = v_B \cos \beta$$
or
$$\frac{v_A}{v_B} = \frac{\cos \beta}{\cos \alpha} = \frac{\sin(90° - \beta)}{\sin(90° - \alpha)} \qquad \qquad ...(i)$$

Applying Lami's theorem to triangle ABI,
$$\frac{AI}{\sin(90° - \beta)} = \frac{BI}{\sin(90° - \alpha)}$$
or
$$\frac{AI}{BI} = \frac{\sin(90° - \beta)}{\sin(90° - \alpha)} \qquad \qquad ...(ii)$$

From equation (i) and (ii),
$$\frac{v_A}{v_B} = \frac{AI}{BI} \qquad \text{or} \qquad \frac{v_A}{AI} = \frac{v_B}{BI} = \omega \qquad \qquad ...(iii)$$

where ω = Angular velocity of the rigid link.

If C is any other point on the link, then
$$\frac{v_A}{AI} = \frac{v_B}{BI} = \frac{v_C}{CI} \qquad \qquad ...(iv)$$

From the above equation, we see that

1. If v_A is known in magnitude and direction and v_B in direction only, then velocity of point B or any other point C lying on the same link may be determined in magnitude and direction.

2. The magnitude of velocities of the points on a rigid link is inversely proportional to the distances from the points to the instantaneous centre and is perpendicular to the line joining the point to the instantaneous centre.

6.5. Properties of the Instantaneous Centre

The following properties of the instantaneous centre are important from the subject point of view :

1. A rigid link rotates instantaneously relative to another link at the instantaneous centre for the configuration of the mechanism considered.

2. The two rigid links have no linear velocity relative to each other at the instantaneous centre. At this point (*i.e.* instantaneous centre), the two rigid links have the same linear velocity relative to the third rigid link. In other words, the velocity of the instantaneous centre relative to any third rigid link will be same whether the instantaneous centre is regarded as a point on the first rigid link or on the second rigid link.

6.6. Number of Instantaneous Centres in a Mechanism

The number of instantaneous centres in a constrained kinematic chain is equal to the number of possible combinations of two links. The number of pairs of links or the number of instantaneous centres is the number of combinations of n links taken two at a time. Mathematically, number of instantaneous centres,

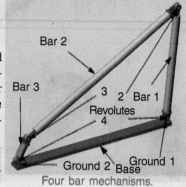

Four bar mechanisms.

$$N = \frac{n(n-1)}{2}, \text{ where } n = \text{Number of links.}$$

6.7. Types of Instantaneous Centres

The instantaneous centres for a mechanism are of the following three types :

1. Fixed instantaneous centres, **2.** Permanent instantaneous centres, and **3.** Neither fixed nor permanent instantaneous centres.

The first two types *i.e.* fixed and permanent instantaneous centres are together known as *primary instantaneous centres* and the third type is known as *secondary instantaneous centres*.

Consider a four bar mechanism *ABCD* as shown in Fig. 6.5. The number of instantaneous centres (*N*) in a four bar mechanism is given by

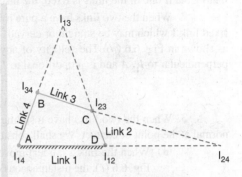

Fig. 6.5. Types of instantaneous centres.

$$N = \frac{n(n-1)}{2} = \frac{4(4-1)}{2} = 6 \qquad \dots (\because n = 4)$$

The instantaneous centres I_{12} and I_{14} are called the *fixed instantaneous centres* as they remain in the same place for all configurations of the mechanism. The instantaneous centres I_{23} and I_{34} are the *permanent instantaneous centres* as they move when the mechanism moves, but the joints are of permanent nature. The instantaneous centres I_{13} and I_{24} are *neither fixed nor permanent instantaneous centres* as they vary with the configuration of the mechanism.

Note: The instantaneous centre of two links such as link 1 and link 2 is usually denoted by I_{12} and so on. It is read as *I* one two and not *I* twelve.

6.8. Location of Instantaneous Centres ·

The following rules may be used in locating the instantaneous centres in a mechanism :

1. When the two links are connected by a pin joint (or pivot joint), the instantaneous centre

Arm moves to a track to retrive information stored there

Track selector mechanism

The read/write head is guided by information stored on the disk itself

The hard disk is coated with a magnetic materials

Computer disk drive mechanisms.

Note : This picture is given as additional information.

lies on the centre of the pin as shown in Fig. 6.6 (*a*). Such a instantaneous centre is of permanent nature, but if one of the links is fixed, the instantaneous centre will be of fixed type.

2. When the two links have a pure rolling contact (*i.e.* link 2 rolls without slipping upon the fixed link 1 which may be straight or curved), the instantaneous centre lies on their point of contact, as shown in Fig. 6.6 (*b*). The velocity of any point *A* on the link 2 relative to fixed link 1 will be perpendicular to $I_{12} A$ and is proportional to $I_{12} A$. In other words

$$\frac{v_A}{v_B} = \frac{I_{12} A}{I_{12} B}$$

3. When the two links have a sliding contact, the instantaneous centre lies on the common normal at the point of contact. We shall consider the following three cases :

    (*a*) When the link 2 (slider) moves on fixed link 1 having straight surface as shown in Fig. 6.6 (*c*), the instantaneous centre lies at infinity and each point on the slider have the same velocity.

    (*b*) When the link 2 (slider) moves on fixed link 1 having curved surface as shown in Fig. 6.6 (*d*),the instantaneous centre lies on the centre of curvature of the curvilinear path in the configuration at that instant.

    (*c*) When the link 2 (slider) moves on fixed link 1 having constant radius of curvature as shown in Fig. 6.6 (*e*), the instantaneous centre lies at the centre of curvature *i.e.* the centre of the circle, for all configuration of the links.

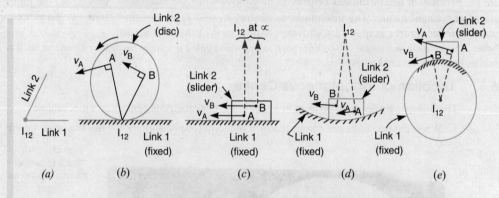

Fig. 6.6. Location of instantaneous centres.

6.9. Aronhold Kennedy (or Three Centres in Line) Theorem

The Aronhold Kennedy's theorem states that *if three bodies move relatively to each other, they have three instantaneous centres and lie on a straight line.*

Consider three kinematic links *A*, *B* and *C* having relative plane motion. The number of instantaneous centres (*N*) is given by

$$N = \frac{n(n-1)}{2} = \frac{3(3-1)}{2} = 3$$

where   *n* = Number of links = 3

The two instantaneous centres at the pin joints of *B* with *A*, and *C* with *A* (*i.e.* I_{ab} and I_{ac}) are the permanent instantaneous centres. According to Aronhold Kennedy's theorem, the third instantaneous centre I_{bc} must lie on the line joining I_{ab} and I_{ac}. In order to prove this,

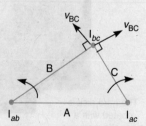

Fig. 6.7. Aronhold Kennedy's theorem.

let us consider that the instantaneous centre I_{bc} lies outside the line joining I_{ab} and I_{ac} as shown in Fig. 6.7. The point I_{bc} belongs to both the links B and C. Let us consider the point I_{bc} on the link B. Its velocity v_{BC} must be perpendicular to the line joining I_{ab} and I_{bc}. Now consider the point I_{bc} on the link C. Its velocity v_{BC} must be perpendicular to the line joining I_{ac} and I_{bc}.

We have already discussed in Art. 6.5, that the velocity of the instantaneous centre is same whether it is regarded as a point on the first link or as a point on the second link. Therefore, the velocity of the point I_{bc} cannot be perpendicular to both lines $I_{ab} I_{bc}$ and $I_{ac} I_{bc}$ unless the point I_{bc} lies on the line joining the points I_{ab} and I_{ac}. Thus the three instantaneous centres (I_{ab}, I_{ac} and I_{bc}) must lie on the same straight line. The exact location of I_{bc} on line $I_{ab} I_{ac}$ depends upon the directions and magnitudes of the angular velocities of B and C relative to A.

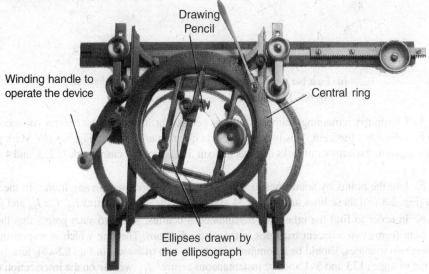

The above picture shows ellipsograph which is used to draw ellipses.

Note : This picture is given as additional information.

6.10. Method of Locating Instantaneous Centres in a Mechanism

Consider a pin jointed four bar mechanism as shown in Fig. 6.8 (*a*). The following procedure is adopted for locating instantaneous centres.

1. First of all, determine the number of instantaneous centres (N) by using the relation

$$N = \frac{n(n-1)}{2}, \quad \text{where } n = \text{Number of links.}$$

In the present case, $\quad N = \dfrac{4(4-1)}{2} = 6 \qquad \qquad ...(\because n = 4)$

2. Make a list of all the instantaneous centres in a mechanism. Since for a four bar mechanism, there are six instantaneous centres, therefore these centres are listed as shown in the following table (known as book-keeping table).

Links	1	2	3	4
Instantaneous centres (6 in number)	12 13 14	23 24	34	–

3. Locate the fixed and permanent instantaneous centres by inspection. In Fig. 6.8 (*a*), I_{12} and I_{14} are fixed instantaneous centres and I_{23} and I_{34} are permanent instantaneous centres.

Note. The four bar mechanism has four turning pairs, therefore there are four primary (*i.e.* fixed and permanent) instantaneous centres and are located at the centres of the pin joints.

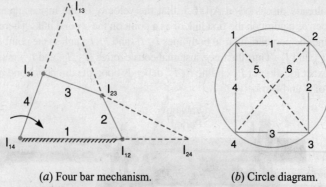

(*a*) Four bar mechanism. (*b*) Circle diagram.

Fig. 6.8. Method of locating instantaneous centres.

4. Locate the remaining neither fixed nor permanent instantaneous centres (or secondary centres) by Kennedy's theorem. This is done by circle diagram as shown in Fig. 6.8 (*b*). Mark points on a circle equal to the number of links in a mechanism. In the present case, mark 1, 2, 3, and 4 on the circle.

5. Join the points by solid lines to show that these centres are already found. In the circle diagram [Fig. 6.8 (*b*)] these lines are 12, 23, 34 and 14 to indicate the centres I_{12}, I_{23}, I_{34} and I_{14}.

6. In order to find the other two instantaneous centres, join two such points that the line joining them forms two adjacent triangles in the circle diagram. The line which is responsible for completing two triangles, should be a common side to the two triangles. In Fig. 6.8 (*b*), join 1 and 3 to form the triangles 123 and 341 and the instantaneous centre[*] I_{13} will lie on the intersection of I_{12} I_{23} and I_{14} I_{34}, produced if necessary, on the mechanism. Thus the instantaneous centre I_{13} is located. Join 1 and 3 by a dotted line on the circle diagram and mark number 5 on it. Similarly the instantaneous centre I_{24} will lie on the intersection of I_{12} I_{14} and I_{23} I_{34}, produced if necessary, on the mechanism. Thus I_{24} is located. Join 2 and 4 by a dotted line on the circle diagram and mark 6 on it. Hence all the six instantaneous centres are located.

Note: Since some of the neither fixed nor permanent instantaneous centres are not required in solving problems, therefore they may be omitted.

Example 6.1. *In a pin jointed four bar mechanism, as shown in Fig. 6.9, AB = 300 mm, BC = CD = 360 mm, and AD = 600 mm. The angle BAD = 60°. The crank AB rotates uniformly at 100 r.p.m. Locate all the instantaneous centres and find the angular velocity of the link BC.*

Solution. Given : N_{AB} = 100 r.p.m or

ω_{AB} = 2 π × 100/60 = 10.47 rad/s

Since the length of crank *AB* = 300 mm = 0.3 m, therefore velocity of point *B* on link *AB*,

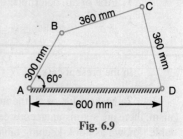

Fig. 6.9

---

[*] We may also say as follows: Considering links 1, 2 and 3, the instantaneous centres will be I_{12}, I_{23} and I_{13}. The centres I_{12} and I_{23} have already been located. Similarly considering links 1, 3 and 4, the instantaneous centres will be I_{13}, I_{34} and I_{14}, from which I_{14} and I_{34} have already been located. Thus we see that the centre I_{13} lies on the intersection of the lines joining the points I_{12} I_{23} and I_{14} I_{34}.

$$v_B = \omega_{AB} \times AB = 10.47 \times 0.3 = 3.141 \text{ m/s}$$

Location of instantaneous centres

The instantaneous centres are located as discussed below:

1. Since the mechanism consists of four links (*i.e.* $n = 4$), therefore number of instantaneous centres,

$$N = \frac{n(n-1)}{2} = \frac{4(4-1)}{2} = 6$$

2. For a four bar mechanism, the book keeping table may be drawn as discussed in Art. 6.10.

3. Locate the fixed and permanent instantaneous centres by inspection. These centres are I_{12}, I_{23}, I_{34} and I_{14}, as shown in Fig. 6.10.

4. Locate the remaining neither fixed nor permanent instantaneous centres by Aronhold Kennedy's theorem. This is done by circle diagram as shown in Fig. 6.11. Mark four points (equal to the number of links in a mechanism) 1, 2, 3, and 4 on the circle.

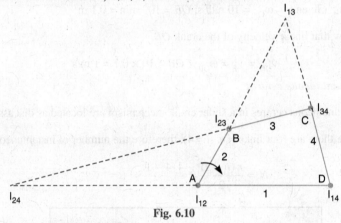

Fig. 6.10

5. Join points 1 to 2, 2 to 3, 3 to 4 and 4 to 1 to indicate the instantaneous centres already located *i.e.* I_{12}, I_{23}, I_{34} and I_{14}.

6. Join 1 to 3 to form two triangles 1 2 3 and 3 4 1. The side 13, common to both triangles, is responsible for completing the two triangles. Therefore the instantaneous centre I_{13} lies on the intersection of the lines joining the points I_{12} I_{23} and I_{34} I_{14} as shown in Fig. 6.10. Thus centre I_{13} is located. Mark number 5 (because four instantaneous centres have already been located) on the dotted line 1 3.

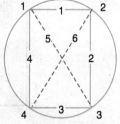

7. Now join 2 to 4 to complete two triangles 2 3 4 and 1 2 4. The side 2 4, common to both triangles, is responsible for completing the two triangles. Therefore centre I_{24} lies on the intersection of the lines joining the points I_{23} I_{34} and I_{12} I_{14} as shown in Fig. 6.10. Thus centre I_{24} is located. Mark number 6 on the dotted line 2 4. Thus all the six instantaneous centres are located.

Fig. 6.11

Angular velocity of the link BC

Let ω_{BC} = Angular velocity of the link *BC*.

Since *B* is also a point on link *BC*, therefore velocity of point *B* on link *BC*,

$$v_B = \omega_{BC} \times I_{13} B$$

By measurement, we find that $I_{13} B = 500$ mm $= 0.5$ m

$$\therefore \qquad \omega_{BC} = \frac{v_B}{I_{13} B} = \frac{3.141}{0.5} = 6.282 \text{ rad/s} \textbf{ Ans.}$$

Example 6.2. *Locate all the instantaneous centres of the slider crank mechanism as shown in Fig. 6.12. The lengths of crank OB and connecting rod AB are 100 mm and 400 mm respectively. If the crank rotates clockwise with an angular velocity of 10 rad/s, find: 1. Velocity of the slider A, and 2. Angular velocity of the connecting rod AB.*

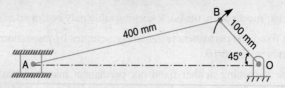

Fig. 6.12

Solution. Given : $\omega_{OB} = 10$ rad/ s; $OB = 100$ mm $= 0.1$ m

We know that linear velocity of the crank *OB*,

$$v_{OB} = v_B = \omega_{OB} \times OB = 10 \times 0.1 = 1 \text{ m/s}$$

Location of instantaneous centres

The instantaneous centres in a slider crank mechanism are located as discussed below:

1. Since there are four links (*i.e. n* = 4), therefore the number of instantaneous centres,

$$N = \frac{n(n-1)}{2} = \frac{4(4-1)}{2} = 6$$

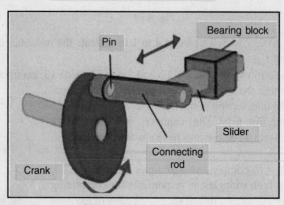

Slider crank mechanism.

2. For a four link mechanism, the book keeping table may be drawn as discussed in Art. 6.10.

3. Locate the fixed and permanent instantaneous centres by inspection. These centres are I_{12}, I_{23} and I_{34} as shown in Fig. 6.13. Since the slider (link 4) moves on a straight surface (link 1), therefore the instantaneous centre I_{14} will be at infinity.

Note: Since the slider crank mechanism has three turning pairs and one sliding pair, therefore there will be three primary (*i.e.* fixed and permanent) instantaneous centres.

4. Locate the other two remaining neither fixed nor permanent instantaneous centres, by Aronhold Kennedy's theorem. This is done by circle diagram as shown in Fig. 6.14. Mark four points 1, 2, 3 and 4 (equal to the number of links in a mechanism) on the circle to indicate I_{12}, I_{23}, I_{34} and I_{14}.

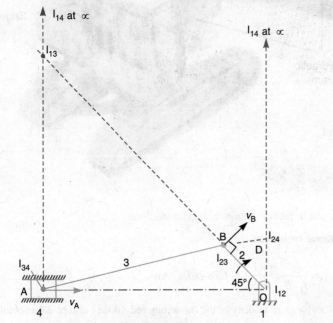

Fig. 6.13

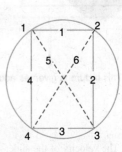

Fig. 6.14

5. Join 1 to 3 to form two triangles 1 2 3 and 3 4 1 in the circle diagram. The side 1 3, common to both triangles, is responsible for completing the two triangles. Therefore the centre I_{13} will lie on the intersection of $I_{12} I_{23}$ and $I_{14} I_{34}$, produced if necessary. Thus centre I_{13} is located. Join 1 to 3 by a dotted line and mark number 5 on it.

6. Join 2 to 4 by a dotted line to form two triangles 2 3 4 and 1 2 4. The side 2 4, common to both triangles, is responsible for completing the two triangles. Therefore the centre I_{24} lies on the intersection of $I_{23} I_{34}$ and $I_{12} I_{14}$. Join 2 to 4 by a dotted line on the circle diagram and mark number 6 on it. Thus all the six instantaneous centres are located.

By measurement, we find that

$$I_{13} A = 460 \text{ mm} = 0.46 \text{ m ; and } I_{13} B = 560 \text{ mm} = 0.56 \text{ m}$$

1. *Velocity of the slider A*

Let $\quad\quad\quad\quad v_A$ = Velocity of the slider A.

We know that $\quad \dfrac{v_A}{I_{13} A} = \dfrac{v_B}{I_{13} B}$

or $\quad\quad\quad\quad v_A = v_B \times \dfrac{I_{13} A}{I_{13} B} = 1 \times \dfrac{0.46}{0.56} = 0.82 \text{ m/s}$ **Ans.**

2. *Angular velocity of the connecting rod AB*

Let $\quad\quad\quad\quad \omega_{AB}$ = Angular velocity of the connecting rod AB.

We know that $\quad \dfrac{v_A}{I_{13} A} = \dfrac{v_B}{I_{13} B} = \omega_{AB}$

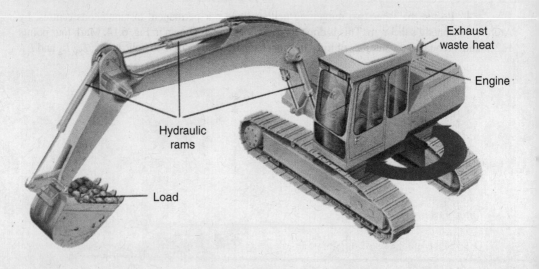

The above picture shows a digging machine.

Note : This picture is given as additional information.

$$\therefore \quad \omega_{AB} = \frac{v_B}{I_{13}\,B} = \frac{1}{0.56} = 1.78 \text{ rad/s} \quad \textbf{Ans.}$$

Note: The velocity of the slider A and angular velocity of the connecting rod AB may also be determined as follows :

From similar triangles $I_{13}\,I_{23}\,I_{34}$ and $I_{12}\,I_{23}\,I_{24}$,

$$\frac{I_{12}\,I_{23}}{I_{13}\,I_{23}} = \frac{I_{23}\,I_{24}}{I_{23}\,I_{34}} \qquad \qquad \dots(i)$$

and

$$\frac{I_{13}\,I_{34}}{I_{34}\,I_{23}} = \frac{I_{12}\,I_{24}}{I_{23}\,I_{24}} \qquad \qquad \dots(ii)$$

We know that $\qquad \omega_{AB} = \dfrac{v_B}{I_{13}\,B} = \dfrac{\omega_{OB} \times OB}{I_{13}\,B} \qquad \dots(\because v_B = \omega_{OB} \times OB)$

$$= \omega_{OB} \times \frac{I_{12}\,I_{23}}{I_{13}\,I_{23}} = \omega_{OB} \times \frac{I_{23}\,I_{24}}{I_{23}\,I_{34}} \qquad \dots\text{[From equation } (i)] \dots(iii)$$

Also $\qquad v_A = \omega_{AB} \times I_{13}\,A = \omega_{OB} \times \dfrac{I_{23}\,I_{24}}{I_{23}\,I_{34}} \times I_{13}\,I_{34}. \qquad \dots\text{[From equation } (iii)]$

$$= \omega_{OB} \times I_{12}\,I_{24} = \omega_{OB} \times OD \qquad \dots\text{[From equation } (ii)]$$

Example 6.3. *A mechanism, as shown in Fig. 6.15, has the following dimensions:*

OA = 200 mm; AB = 1.5 m; BC = 600 mm; CD = 500 mm and BE = 400 mm. Locate all the instantaneous centres.

If crank OA rotates uniformly at 120 r.p.m. clockwise, find 1. the velocity of B, C and D, 2. the angular velocity of the links AB, BC and CD.

Solution. Given : N_{OA} = 120 r.p.m. or $\omega_{OA} = 2\pi \times 120/60 = 12.57$ rad/s

Since the length of crank OA = 200 mm = 0.2 m, therefore linear velocity of crank OA,

$$v_{OA} = v_A = \omega_{OA} \times OA = 12.57 \times 0.2 = 2.514 \text{ m/s}$$

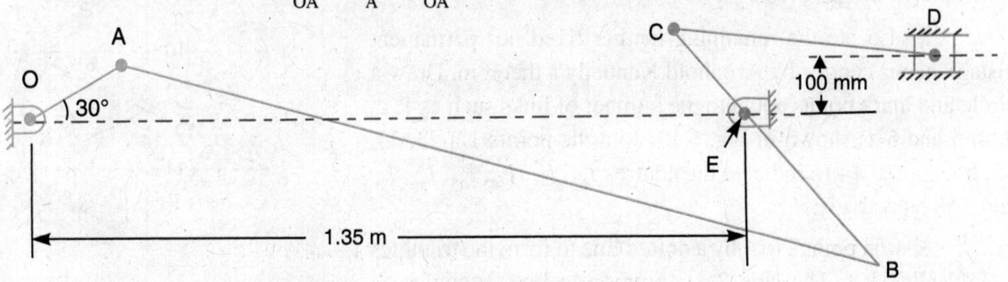

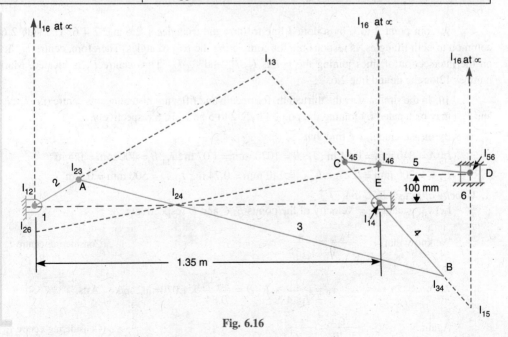

Fig. 6.15

Location of instantaneous centres

The instantaneous centres are located as discussed below:

1. Since the mechanism consists of six links (*i.e.* n = 6), therefore the number of instantaneous centres,

$$N = \frac{n(n-1)}{2} = \frac{6(6-1)}{2} = 15$$

2. Make a list of all the instantaneous centres in a mechanism. Since the mechanism has 15 instantaneous centres, therefore these centres are listed in the following book keeping table.

Links	1	2	3	4	5	6
Instantaneous centres (15 in number)	12 13 14 15 16	23 24 25 26	34 35 36	45 46	56	

Fig. 6.16

3. Locate the fixed and permanent instantaneous centres by inspection. These centres are I_{12} I_{23}, I_{34}, I_{45}, I_{56}, I_{16} and I_{14} as shown in Fig. 6.16.

4. Locate the remaining neither fixed nor permanent instantaneous centres by Aronhold Kennedy's theorem. Draw a circle and mark points equal to the number of links such as 1, 2, 3, 4, 5 and 6 as shown in Fig. 6.17. Join the points 12, 23, 34, 45, 56, 61 and 14 to indicate the centres I_{12}, I_{23}, I_{34}, I_{45}, I_{56}, I_{16} and I_{14} respectively.

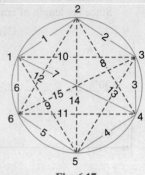

Fig. 6.17

5. Join point 2 to 4 by a dotted line to form the triangles 1 2 4 and 2 3 4. The side 2 4, common to both triangles, is responsible for completing the two triangles. Therefore the instantaneous centre I_{24} lies on the intersection of I_{12} I_{14} and I_{23} I_{34} produced if necessary. Thus centre I_{24} is located. Mark number 8 on the dotted line 24 (because seven centres have already been located).

6. Now join point 1 to 5 by a dotted line to form the triangles 1 4 5 and 1 5 6. The side 1 5, common to both triangles, is responsible for completing the two triangles. Therefore the instantaneous centre I_{15} lies on the intersection of I_{14} I_{45} and I_{56} I_{16} produced if necessary. Thus centre I_{15} is located. Mark number 9 on the dotted line 1 5.

7. Join point 1 to 3 by a dotted line to form the triangles 1 2 3 and 1 3 4. The side 1 3, common to both triangles, is responsible for completing the two triangles. Therefore the instantaneous centre I_{13} lies on the intersection I_{12} I_{23} and I_{34} I_{14} produced if necessary. Thus centre I_{13} is located. Mark number 10 on the dotted line 1 3.

8. Join point 4 to 6 by a dotted line to form the triangles 4 5 6 and 1 4 6. The side 4 6, common to both triangles, is responsible for completing the two triangles. Therefore, centre I_{46} lies on the intersection of I_{45} I_{56} and I_{14} I_{16}. Thus centre I_{46} is located. Mark number 11 on the dotted line 4 6.

9. Join point 2 to 6 by a dotted line to form the triangles 1 2 6 and 2 4 6. The side 2 6, common to both triangles, is responsible for completing the two triangles. Therefore, centre I_{26} lies on the intersection of lines joining the points I_{12} I_{16} and I_{24} I_{46}. Thus centre I_{26} is located. Mark number 12 on the dotted line 2 6.

10. In the similar way the thirteenth, fourteenth and fifteenth instantaneous centre (*i.e.* I_{35}, I_{25} and I_{36}) may be located by joining the point 3 to 5, 2 to 5 and 3 to 6 respectively.

By measurement, we find that

$I_{13} A = 840$ mm $= 0.84$ m ; $I_{13} B = 1070$ mm $= 1.07$ m ; $I_{14} B = 400$ mm $= 0.4$ m ;

$I_{14} C = 200$ mm $= 0.2$ m ; $I_{15} C = 740$ mm $= 0.74$ m ; $I_{15} D = 500$ mm $= 0.5$ m

1. *Velocity of points B, C and D*

Let v_B, v_C and v_D = Velocity of the points B, C and D respectively.

We know that $\dfrac{v_A}{I_{13} A} = \dfrac{v_B}{I_{13} B}$ ...(Considering centre I_{13})

$\therefore$ $v_B = \dfrac{v_A}{I_{13} A} \times I_{13} B = \dfrac{2.514}{0.84} \times 1.07 = 3.2$ m/s **Ans.**

Again, $\dfrac{v_B}{I_{14} B} = \dfrac{v_C}{I_{14} C}$ ...(Considering centre I_{14})

$$\therefore \qquad v_C = \frac{v_B}{I_{14}\, B} \times I_{14}\, C = \frac{3.2}{0.4} \times 0.2 = 1.6\,\text{m/s} \quad \textbf{Ans.}$$

Similarly, $\qquad \dfrac{v_C}{I_{15}\, C} = \dfrac{v_D}{I_{15}\, D}$ \hfill ...(Considering centre I_{15})

$$\therefore \qquad v_D = \frac{v_C}{I_{15}\, C} \times I_5\, D = \frac{1.6}{0.74} \times 0.5 = 1.08 \text{ m/s} \quad \textbf{Ans.}$$

2. Angular velocity of the links AB, BC and CD

Let $\quad \omega_{AB}$, ω_{BC} and ω_{CD} = Angular velocity of the links *AB*, *BC* and *CD* respectively.

We know that $\qquad \omega_{AB} = \dfrac{v_A}{I_{13}\, A} = \dfrac{2.514}{0.84} = 2.99 \text{ rad/s} \quad \textbf{Ans.}$

$$\omega_{BC} = \frac{v_B}{I_{14}\, B} = \frac{3.2}{0.4} = 8 \text{ rad/s} \quad \textbf{Ans.}$$

and $\qquad \omega_{CD} = \dfrac{v_C}{I_{15}\, C} = \dfrac{1.6}{0.74} = 2.16 \text{ rad/s} \quad \textbf{Ans.}$

Example 6.4. *The mechanism of a wrapping machine, as shown in Fig. 6.18, has the following dimensions :*

O_1A = 100 mm; AC = 700 mm; BC = 200 mm; O_3C = 200 mm; O_2E = 400 mm; O_2D = 200 mm and BD = 150 mm.

The crank O_1A rotates at a uniform speed of 100 rad/s. Find the velocity of the point E of the bell crank lever by instantaneous centre method.

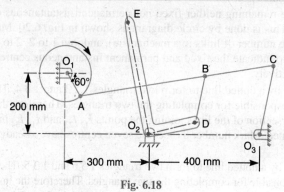

Fig. 6.18

Solution. Given : ω_{O1A} = 100 rad/s ; O_1A = 100 mm = 0.1 m

We know that the linear velocity of crank O_1A,

$$v_{O1A} = v_A = \omega_{O1A} \times O_1A = 100 \times 0.1 = 10 \text{ m/s}$$

Now let us locate the required instantaneous centres as discussed below :

1. Since the mechanism consists of six links (*i.e.* n = 6), therefore number of instantaneous centres,

$$N = \frac{n(n-1)}{2} = \frac{6(6-1)}{2} = 15$$

2. Since the mechanism has 15 instantaneous centres, therefore these centres may be listed in the book keeping table, as discussed in Example 6.3.

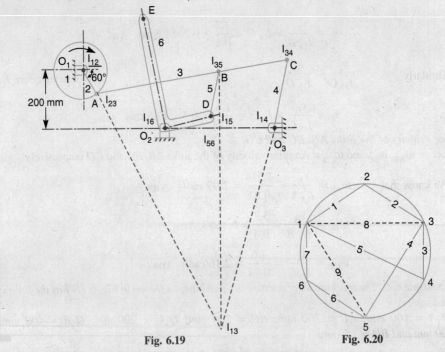

Fig. 6.19   **Fig. 6.20**

3. Locate the fixed and the permanent instantaneous centres by inspection. These centres are I_{12}, I_{23}, I_{34}, I_{35}, I_{14}, I_{56} and I_{16} as shown in Fig. 6.19.

4. Locate the remaining neither fixed nor permanent instantaneous centres by Aronhold Kennedy's theorem. This is done by circle diagram as shown in Fig. 6.20. Mark six points on the circle (*i.e.* equal to the number of links in a mechanism), and join 1 to 2, 2 to 3, 3 to 4, 3 to 5, 4 to 1, 5 to 6, and 6 to 1, to indicate the fixed and permanent instantaneous centres *i.e.* I_{12}, I_{23}, I_{34}, I_{35}, I_{14}, I_{56}, and I_{16} respectively.

5. Join 1 to 3 by a dotted line to form two triangles 1 2 3 and 1 3 4. The side 1 3, common to both triangles, is responsible for completing the two triangles. Therefore the instantaneous centre I_{13} lies on the intersection of the lines joining the points I_{12} I_{23} and I_{14} I_{34} produced if necessary. Thus centre I_{13} is located. Mark number 8 (because seven centres have already been located) on the dotted line 1 3.

6. Join 1 to 5 by a dotted line to form two triangles 1 5 6 and 1 3 5. The side 1 5, common to both triangles, is responsible for completing the two triangles. Therefore the instantaneous centre I_{15} lies on the intersection of the lines joining the points I_{16} I_{56} and I_{13} I_{35} produced if necessary. Thus centre I_{15} is located. Mark number 9 on the dotted line 1 5.

Note: For the given example, we do not require other instantaneous centres.

By measurement, we find that

$$I_{13} A = 910 \text{ mm} = 0.91 \text{ m} ; I_{13} B = 820 \text{ mm} = 0.82 \text{ m} ; I_{15} B = 130 \text{ mm} = 0.13 \text{ m} ;$$

$$I_{15} D = 50 \text{ mm} = 0.05 \text{ m} ; I_{16} D = 200 \text{ mm} = 0.2 \text{ m} ; I_{16} E = 400 \text{ mm} = 0.4 \text{ m}$$

Velocity of point E on the bell crank lever

Let v_E = Velocity of point E on the bell crank lever,

             v_B = Velocity of point B, and

             v_D = Velocity of point D.

We know that $\dfrac{v_A}{I_{13} A} = \dfrac{v_B}{I_{13} B}$ ...(Considering centre I_{13})

$$\therefore \qquad v_B = \frac{v_A}{I_{13}A} \times I_{13}B = \frac{10}{0.91} \times 0.82 = 9.01 \text{ m/s} \quad \textbf{Ans.}$$

and
$$\frac{v_B}{I_{15}B} = \frac{v_D}{I_{15}D} \qquad \qquad \text{...(Considering centre } I_{15})$$

$$\therefore \qquad v_D = \frac{v_B}{I_{15}B} \times I_{15}D = \frac{9.01}{0.13} \times 0.05 = 3.46 \text{ m/s} \quad \textbf{Ans.}$$

Similarly,
$$\frac{v_D}{I_{16}D} = \frac{v_E}{I_{16}E} \qquad \qquad \text{...(Considering centre } I_{16})$$

$$\therefore \qquad v_E = \frac{v_D}{I_{16}D} \times I_{16}E = \frac{3.46}{0.2} \times 0.4 = 6.92 \text{ m/s} \quad \textbf{Ans.}$$

Example 6.5. *Fig. 6.21 shows a sewing needle bar mechanism O_1ABO_2CD wherein the different dimensions are as follows:*

Crank $O_1A = 16$ mm; $\angle \beta = 45°$; Vertical distance between O_1 and $O_2 = 40$ mm; Horizontal distance between O_1 and $O_2 = 13$ mm; $O_2B = 23$ mm; $AB = 35$ mm; $\angle O_2BC = 90°$; $BC = 16$ mm; $CD = 40$ mm. D lies vertically below O_1.

Find the velocity of needle at D for the given configuration. The crank O_1A rotates at 400 r.p.m.

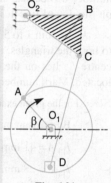

Fig. 6.21

Solution. Given : $N_{O1A} = 400$ r.p.m or $\omega_{O1A} = 2\pi \times 400/60 = 41.9$ rad/s ; $O_1A = 16$ mm $= 0.016$ m

We know that linear velocity of the crank O_1A,

$$v_{O1A} = v_A = \omega_{O1A} \times O_1A = 41.9 \times 0.016 = 0.67 \text{ m/s}$$

Now let us locate the required instantaneous centres as discussed below :

1. Since the mechanism consists of six links (*i.e.* $n = 6$), therefore number of instantaneous centres,

$$N = \frac{n(n-1)}{2} = \frac{6(6-1)}{2} = 15$$

2. Since the mechanism has 15 instantaneous centres, therefore these centres may be listed in the book keeping table, as discussed in Example 6.3.

3. Locate the fixed and permanent instantaneous centres by inspection. These centres are $I_{12}, I_{23}, I_{34}, I_{45}, I_{56}, I_{16}$ and I_{14}, as shown in Fig. 6.22.

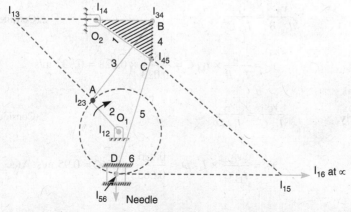

Fig. 6.22

4. Locate the remaining neither fixed nor permanent instantaneous centres by Aronhold Kennedy's theorem. This is done by circle diagram as shown in Fig. 6.23. Mark six points on the circle (*i.e.* equal to the number of links in a mechanism) and join 1 to 2, 2 to 3, 3 to 4, 4 to 5, 5 to 6, 6 to 1 and 1 to 4 to indicate the fixed and permanent instantaneous centres *i.e.* I_{12}, I_{23}, I_{34}, I_{45}, I_{56}, I_{16} and I_{14} respectively.

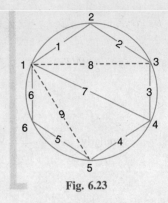

Fig. 6.23

5. Join 1 to 3 by a dotted line to form two triangles 1 2 3 and 1 3 4. The side 1 3, common to both the triangles, is responsible for completing the two triangles. Therefore the instantaneous centre I_{13} lies on the intersection of I_{12} I_{23} and I_{14} I_{34} produced if necessary. Thus centre I_{13} is located. Mark number 8 (because seven centres have already been located) on the dotted line 1 3.

6. Join 1 to 5 by a dotted line to form two triangles 1 5 6 and 1 4 5. The side 1 5, common to both the triangles, is responsible for completing the two triangles. Therefore the instantaneous centre I_{15} lies on the intersection of I_{16} I_{56} and I_{14} I_{45} produced if necessary. Thus centre I_{15} is located. Mark number 9 on the dotted line 1 5.

Note: For the given example, we do not require other instantaneous centres.

By measurement, we find that

I_{13} A = 41 mm = 0.041 m ; I_{13} B = 50 mm = 0.05 m ; I_{14} B = 23 mm = 0.023 m ;

I_{14} C = 28 mm = 0.028 m ; I_{15} C = 65 mm = 0.065 m ; I_{15} D = 62 mm = 0.062 m

Let v_B = Velocity of point B,

  v_C = Velocity of point C, and

  v_D = Velocity of the needle at D.

We know that $\dfrac{v_A}{I_{13}\,A} = \dfrac{v_B}{I_{13}\,B}$ ...(Considering centre I_{13})

∴ $v_B = \dfrac{v_A}{I_{13}\,A} \times I_{13}\,B = \dfrac{0.67}{0.041} \times 0.05 = 0.817$ m/s

and $\dfrac{v_B}{I_{14}\,B} = \dfrac{v_C}{I_{14}\,C}$ ...(Considering centre I_{14})

∴ $v_C = \dfrac{v_B}{I_{14}\,B} \times I_{14}\,C = \dfrac{0.817}{0.023} \times 0.028 = 0.995$ m/s

Similarly, $\dfrac{v_C}{I_{15}\,C} = \dfrac{v_D}{I_{15}\,D}$ ...(Considering centre I_{15})

∴ $v_D = \dfrac{v_C}{I_{15}\,C} \times I_{15}\,D = \dfrac{0.995}{0.065} \times 0.062 = 0.95$ m/s **Ans.**

Example 6.6. *Fig. 6.24 shows a Whitworth quick return motion mechanism. The various dimensions in the mechanism are as follows :*

OQ = 100 mm ; OA = 200 mm ; QC = 150 mm ; and CD = 500 mm.

The crank OA makes an angle of 60° with the vertical and rotates at 120 r.p.m. in the clockwise direction.

Locate all the instantaneous centres and find the velocity of ram D.

Solution : Given. N_{OA} = 120 r.p.m. or ω_{OA} = $2 \pi \times 120 / 60$ = 12.57 rad/s

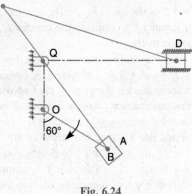

Fig. 6.24

Location of instantaneous centres

The instantaneous centres are located as discussed below :

1. Since the mechanism consists of six links (*i.e. n* = 6), therefore the number of instantaneous centres,

$$N = \frac{n(n-1)}{2} = \frac{6(6-1)}{2} = 15$$

2. Make a list of all the instantaneous centres in a mechanism as discussed in Example 6.3.

3. Locate the fixed and permanent instantaneous centres by inspection. These centres are I_{12}, I_{23}, I_{34}, I_{45}, I_{56}, I_{16} and I_{14} as shown in Fig. 6.25.

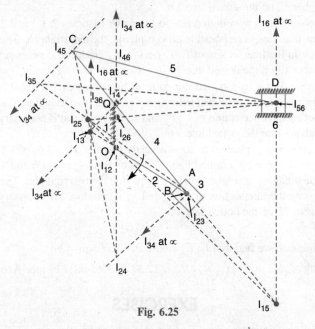

Fig. 6.25

4. Locate the remaining neither fixed nor permanent instantaneous centres by Aronhold Kennedy's theorem. Draw a circle and mark points equal to the number of links such as 1, 2, 3, 4, 5, and 6 as shown in Fig. 6.26. Join the points 1 2, 2 3, 3 4, 4 5, 5 6, 6 1 and 1 4 to indicate the centres I_{12}, I_{23}, I_{34}, I_{45}, I_{56}, I_{16} and I_{14} respectively.

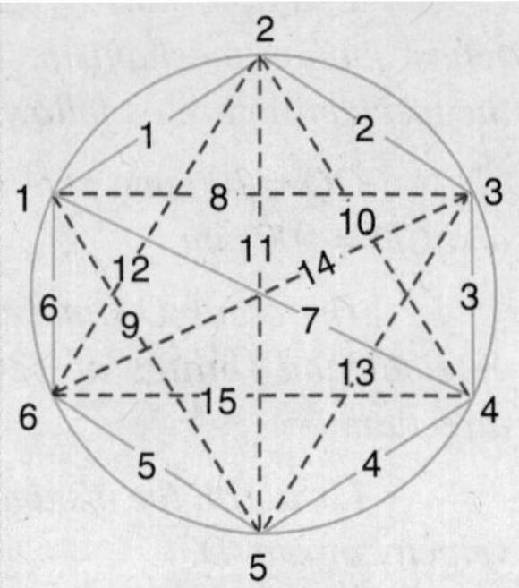

Fig. 6.26

5. Join point 1 to 3 by a dotted line to form two triangles 1 2 3 and 1 3 4. The side 1 3, common to both the triangles, is responsible for completing the two triangles. Therefore the instantaneous centre I_{13} lies on the intersection of I_{12} I_{23}, and I_{14} I_{34} produced if necessary. Thus centre I_{13} is located. Mark number 8 on the dotted line 1 3 (because seven centres have already been located).

6. Join point 1 to 5 by a dotted line to form two triangles 1 4 5 and 1 5 6. The side 1 5, common to both the triangles, is responsible for completing the two triangles. Therefore the instantaneous centre I_{15} lies on the intersection of I_{14} I_{45} and I_{56} I_{16} produced if necessary. Thus centre I_{15} is located. Mark number 9 on the dotted line 1 5.

7. Join point 2 to 4 by a dotted line to form two triangles 1 2 4 and 2 3 4. The side 2 4, common to both the triangles, is responsible for completing the two triangles. Therefore the instantaneous centre I_{24} lies on the intersection of I_{12} I_{14} and I_{23} I_{34} produced if necessary. Thus centre I_{24} is located. Mark number 10 on the dotted line 2 4.

8. Join point 2 to 5 by a dotted line to form two triangles 1 2 5 and 2 4 5. The side 2 5, common to both the triangles, is responsible for completing the two triangles. Therefore the instantaneous centre I_{25} lies on the intersection of I_{12} I_{15} and I_{24} I_{45} produced if necessary. Thus centre I_{25} is located. Mark number 11 on the dotted line 2 5.

9. Join point 2 to 6 by a dotted line to form two triangles 1 2 6 and 2 5 6. The side 2 6 common to both the triangles, is responsible for completing the two triangles. Therefore the instantaneous centre I_{26} lies on the intersection of I_{12} I_{16} and I_{25} I_{56} produced if necessary. Thus centre I_{26} is located. Mark number 12 on the dotted line 2 6.

10. Join point 3 to 5 by a dotted line to form two triangles 2 3 5 and 3 4 5. The side 3 5, common to both the triangles, is responsible for completing the two triangles. Therefore the instantaneous centre I_{35} lies on the intersection of I_{23} I_{25} and I_{34} I_{45} produced if necessary. Thus centre $I_{35}$is located. Mark number 13 on the dotted line 3 5.

11. Join point 3 to 6 by a dotted line to form two triangles 1 3 6 and 3 5 6. The side 3 6, common to both the triangles, is responsible for completing the two triangles. Therefore the instantaneous centre I_{36} lies on the intersection of I_{13} I_{16} and I_{35} I_{56} produced if necessary. Thus centre I_{36} is located. Mark number 14 on the dotted line 3 6.

Note. The centre I_{36} may also be obtained by considering the two triangles 2 3 6 and 3 4 6.

12. Join point 4 to 6 by a dotted line to form two triangles 1 4 6 and 4 5 6. The side 4 6, common to both the triangles, is responsible for completing the two triangles. Therefore the instantaneous centre I_{46} lies on the intersection of I_{14} I_{16} and I_{45} I_{56} produced if necessary. Thus centre I_{46} is located. Mark number 15 on the dotted line 4 6.

Velocity of ram D

By measurement, we find that I_{12} I_{26} = 65 mm = 0.065 m

∴ Velocity of ram, v_D = $\omega_{OA} \times I_{12} I_{26}$ = 12.57 × 0.065 = 0.817 m/s **Ans.**

EXERCISES

1. Locate all the instantaneous centres for a four bar mechanism as shown in Fig. 6.27.
   The lengths of various links are : AD = 125 mm ; AB = 62.5 mm ; $BC = CD$ = 75 mm.
   If the link AB rotates at a uniform speed of 10 r.p.m. in the clockwise direction, find the angular velocity of the links BC and CD.   [Ans. 0.63 rad/s ; 0.65 rad/s]

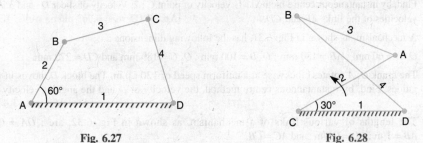

Fig. 6.27   Fig. 6.28

2.   Locate all the instantaneous centres for the crossed four bar mechanism as shown in Fig. 6.28. The dimensions of various links are : *CD* = 65 mm; *CA* = 60 mm ; *DB* = 80 mm ; and *AB* = 55 mm.

Find the angular velocities of the links *AB* and *DB*, if the crank *CA* rotates at 100 r.p.m. in the anticlockwise direction.
[Ans. 50 rad/s ; 27 rad/s]

3.   Locate all the instantaneous centres of the mechanism as shown in Fig. 6.29. The lengths of various links are : *AB* = 150 mm ; *BC* = 300 mm ; *CD* = 225 mm ; and *CE* = 500 mm.

When the crank *AB* rotates in the anticlockwise direction at a uniform speed of 240 r.p.m. ; find 1. Velocity of the slider *E*, and 2. Angular velocity of the links *BC* and *CE*.
[Ans. 1.6 m/s ; 2.4 rad/s ; 6.6 rad/s]

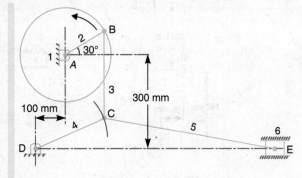

Fig. 6.29

4.   The crank *OA* of a mechanism, as shown in Fig. 6.30, rotates clockwise at 120 r.p.m. The lengths of various links are : *OA* = 100 mm ; *AB* = 500 mm ; *AC* = 100 mm and *CD* = 750 mm.

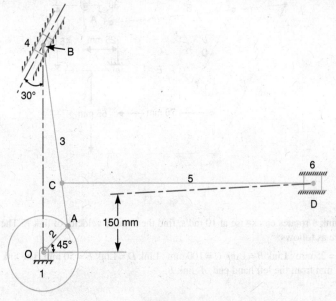

Fig. 6.30

Find, by instantaneous centre method : 1. Velocity of point C ; 2. Velocity of slider D ; and 3. Angular velocities of the links AB and CD. [Ans. 0.115 m/s; 0.065 m/s; 3 rad/s; 1.3 rad/s]

5. A mechanism, as shown in Fig. 6.31, has the following dimensions :

$O_1 A$ = 60 mm ; AB = 180 mm ; $O_2 B$ = 100 mm ; $O_2 C$ = 180 mm and CD = 270 mm.

The crank $O_1 A$ rotates clockwise at a uniform speed of 120 r.p.m. The block D moves in vertical guides. Find, by instantaneous centre method, the velocity of D and the angular velocity of CD. [Ans. 0.08 m/s ; 1.43 rad/s]

6. The lengths of various links of a mechanism, as shown in Fig. 6.32, are : OA = 0.3 m ; AB = 1 m ; CD = 0.8 m ; and AC = CB.

Determine, for the given configuration, the velocity of the slider D if the crank OA rotates at 60 r.p.m. in the clockwise direction. Also find the angular velocity of the link CD. Use instantaneous centre method. [Ans. 480 mm/s ; 2.5 rad/s]

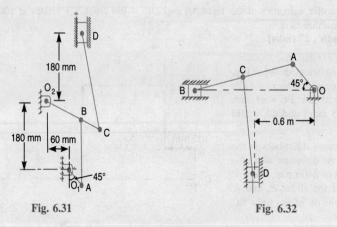

Fig. 6.31   Fig. 6.32

7. In the mechanism shown in Fig. 6.33, find the instantaneous centres of the links B, C and D.

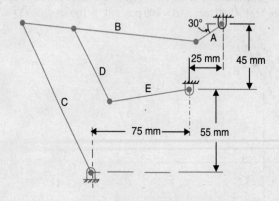

Fig. 6.33

If the link A rotates clockwise at 10 rad/s, find the angular velocity of link E. The lengths of various links are as follows:

Link A = 25 mm ; Link B = Link C = 100 mm ; Link D = Link E = 50 mm. The link D is hinged to link B at 25 mm from the left hand end of link B. [Ans. 1.94 rad/s]

8. The dimensions of various links in a mechanism, as shown in Fig. 6.34, are as follows :

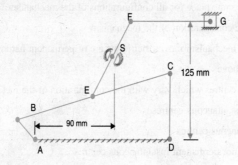

Fig. 6.34

$AB = 25$ mm ; $BC = 175$ mm ; $CD = 60$ mm ; $AD = 150$ mm ; $BE = EC$; and $EF = FG = 100$ mm.

The crank AB rotates at 200 r.p.m. When the angle BAD is 135°, determine by instantaneous centre method : 1. Velocity of G, 2. Angular velocity of EF, and 3. Velocity of sliding of EF in the swivel block S.

[Ans. 120 mm/s ; 6.5 rad/s ; 400 mm/s]

DO YOU KNOW ?

1. What do you understand by the instantaneous centre of rotation (centro) in kinematic of machines? Answer briefly.

2. Explain, with the help of a neat sketch, the space centrode and body centrode.

3. Explain with sketch the instantaneous centre method for determination of velocities of links and mechanisms.

4. Write the relation between the number of instantaneous centres and the number of links in a mechanism.

5. Discuss the three types of instantaneous centres for a mechanism.

6. State and prove the 'Aronhold Kennedy's Theorem' of three instantaneous centres.

OBJECTIVE TYPE QUESTIONS

1. The total number of instantaneous centres for a mechanism consisting of n links are

   (a) $\dfrac{n}{2}$ (b) n

   (c) $\dfrac{n-1}{2}$ (d) $\dfrac{n(n-1)}{2}$

2. According to Aronhold Kennedy's theorem, if three bodies move relatively to each other, their instantaneous centres will lie on a

   (a) straight line   (b) parabolic curve

   (c) ellipse   (d) none of these

3. In a mechanism, the fixed instantaneous centres are those centres which
   (a) remain in the same place for all configurations of the mechanism
   (b) vary with the configuration of the mechanism
   (c) moves as the mechanism moves, but joints are of permanent nature
   (d) none of the above

4. The instantaneous centres which vary with the configuration of the mechanism, are called
   (a) permanent instantaneous centres
   (b) fixed instantaneous centres
   (c) neither fixed nor permanent instantaneous centres
   (d) none of these

5. When a slider moves on a fixed link having curved surface, their instantaneous centre lies
   (a) on their point of contact   (b) at the centre of curvature
   (c) at the centre of circle   (d) at the pin joint

ANSWERS

1. (d)	**2.** (a)	**3.** (a)	**4.** (c)	**5.** (b)

7

Velocity in Mechanisms
(Relative Velocity Method)

7.1. Introduction

We have discussed, in the previous chapter, the instantaneous centre method for finding the velocity of various points in the mechanisms. In this chapter, we shall discuss the relative velocity method for determining the velocity of different points in the mechanism. The study of velocity analysis is very important for determining the acceleration of points in the mechanisms which is discussed in the next chapter.

7.2. Relative Velocity of Two Bodies Moving in Straight Lines

Here we shall discuss the application of vectors for the relative velocity of two bodies moving along parallel lines and inclined lines, as shown in Fig. 7.1 (a) and 7.2 (a) respectively.

Consider two bodies A and B moving along parallel lines in the same direction with absolute velocities v_A and v_B such that $v_A > v_B$, as shown in Fig. 7.1 (a). The relative velocity of A with respect to B,

$$v_{AB} = \text{Vector difference of } v_A \text{ and } v_B = \overline{v_A} - \overline{v_B}$$

$$...(i)$$

From Fig. 7.1 (*b*), the relative velocity of *A* with respect to *B* (*i.e.* v_{AB}) may be written in the vector form as follows :

$$\overline{ba} = \overline{oa} - \overline{ob}$$

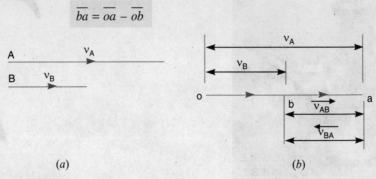

(*a*)   (*b*)

Fig. 7.1. Relative velocity of two bodies moving along parallel lines.

Similarly, the relative velocity of *B* with respect to *A*,

$$v_{BA} = \text{Vector difference of } v_B \text{ and } v_A = \overline{v}_B - \overline{v}_A \qquad ...(ii)$$

or $$\overline{ab} = \overline{ob} - \overline{oa}$$

Now consider the body *B* moving in an inclined direction as shown in Fig. 7.2 (*a*). The relative velocity of *A* with respect to *B* may be obtained by the law of parallelogram of velocities or triangle law of velocities. Take any fixed point *o* and draw vector *oa* to represent v_A in magnitude and direction to some suitable scale. Similarly, draw vector *ob* to represent v_B in magnitude and direction to the same scale. Then vector *ba* represents the relative velocity of *A* with respect to *B* as shown in Fig. 7.2 (*b*). In the similar way as discussed above, the relative velocity of *A* with respect to *B*,

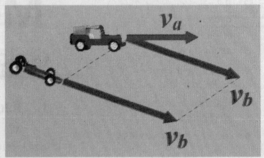

$$v_{AB} = \text{Vector difference of } v_A \text{ and } v_B = \overline{v}_A - \overline{v}_B$$

or $$\overline{ba} = \overline{oa} - \overline{ob}$$

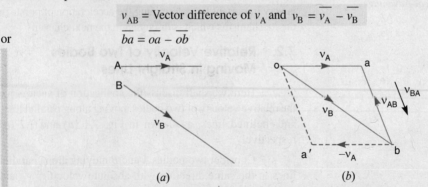

(*a*)   (*b*)

Fig. 7.2. Relative velocity of two bodies moving along inclined lines.

Similarly, the relative velocity of *B* with respect to *A*,

$$v_{BA} = \text{Vector difference of } v_B \text{ and } v_A = \overline{v}_B - \overline{v}_A$$

or $$\overline{ab} = \overline{ob} - \overline{oa}$$

From above, we conclude that the relative velocity of point A with respect to B (v_{AB}) and the relative velocity of point B with respect A (v_{BA}) are equal in magnitude but opposite in direction, *i.e.*

$$v_{AB} = -v_{BA} \quad \text{or} \quad \overline{ba} = -\overline{ab}$$

Note: It may be noted that to find v_{AB}, start from point b towards a and for v_{BA}, start from point a towards b.

7.3. Motion of a Link

Consider two points A and B on a rigid link AB, as shown in Fig. 7.3 (*a*). Let one of the extremities (*B*) of the link move relative to A, in a clockwise direction. Since the distance from A to B remains the same, therefore there can be no relative motion between A and B, along the line AB. It is thus obvious, that the relative motion of B with respect to A must be perpendicular to AB.

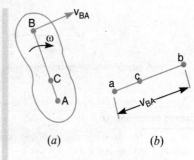

Hence *velocity of any point on a link with respect to another point on the same link is always perpendicular to the line joining these points on the configuration (or space) diagram.*

(*a*)   (*b*)

Fig. 7.3. Motion of a Link.

The relative velocity of B with respect to A (*i.e.* v_{BA}) is represented by the vector ab and is perpendicular to the line AB as shown in Fig. 7.3 (*b*).

Let ω = Angular velocity of the link AB about A.

We know that the velocity of the point B with respect to A,

$$v_{BA} = \overline{ab} = \omega . AB \qquad \qquad ...(i)$$

Similarly, the velocity of any point C on AB with respect to A,

$$v_{CA} = \overline{ac} = \omega . AC \qquad \qquad ...(ii)$$

From equations (*i*) and (*ii*),

$$\frac{v_{CA}}{v_{BA}} = \frac{\overline{ac}}{\overline{ab}} = \frac{\omega . AC}{\omega . AB} = \frac{AC}{AB} \qquad \qquad ...(iii)$$

Thus, we see from equation (*iii*), that the point c on the vector ab divides it in the same ratio as C divides the link AB.

Note: The relative velocity of A with respect to B is represented by ba, although A may be a fixed point. The motion between A and B is only relative. Moreover, it is immaterial whether the link moves about A in a clockwise direction or about B in a clockwise direction.

7.4. Velocity of a Point on a Link by Relative Velocity Method

The relative velocity method is based upon the relative velocity of the various points of the link as discussed in Art. 7.3.

Consider two points A and B on a link as shown in Fig. 7.4 (*a*). Let the absolute velocity of the point A *i.e.* v_A is known in magnitude and direction and the absolute velocity of the point B *i.e.* v_B is known in direction only. Then the velocity of B may be determined by drawing the velocity diagram as shown in Fig. 7.4 (*b*). The velocity diagram is drawn as follows :

1. Take some convenient point o, known as the pole.

2. Through o, draw oa parallel and equal to v_A, to some suitable scale.

3. Through a, draw a line perpendicular to AB of Fig. 7.4 (*a*). This line will represent the velocity of B with respect to A, *i.e.* v_{BA}.

4. Through o, draw a line parallel to v_B intersecting the line of v_{BA} at b.

5. Measure *ob*, which gives the required velocity of point B (v_B), to the scale.

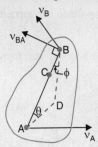

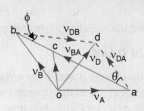

(*a*) Motion of points on a link.   (*b*) Velocity diagram.

Fig. 7.4

Notes : 1. The vector *ab* which represents the velocity of B with respect to A (v_{BA}) is known as **velocity of image** of the link *AB*.

2. The absolute velocity of any point C on *AB* may be determined by dividing vector *ab* at *c* in the same ratio as C divides *AB* in Fig. 7.4 (*a*).

In other words

$$\frac{ac}{ab} = \frac{AC}{AB}$$

Join *oc*. The *vector *oc* represents the absolute velocity of point C (v_C) and the vector *ac* represents the velocity of C with respect to A *i.e.* v_{CA}.

3. The absolute velocity of any other point D outside *AB*, as shown in Fig. 7.4 (*a*), may also be obtained by completing the velocity triangle *abd* and similar to triangle *ABD*, as shown in Fig. 7.4 (*b*).

4. The angular velocity of the link *AB* may be found by dividing the relative velocity of B with respect to A (*i.e.* v_{BA}) to the length of the link *AB*. Mathematically, angular velocity of the link *AB*,

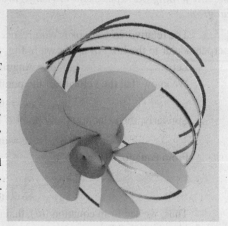

$$\omega_{AB} = \frac{v_{BA}}{AB} = \frac{ab}{AB}$$

7.5. Velocities in Slider Crank Mechanism

In the previous article, we have discussed the relative velocity method for the velocity of any point on a link, whose direction of motion and velocity of some other point on the same link is known. The same method may also be applied for the velocities in a slider crank mechanism.

A slider crank mechanism is shown in Fig. 7.5 (*a*). The slider A is attached to the connecting rod *AB*. Let the radius of crank *OB* be r and let it rotates in a clockwise direction, about the point O with uniform angular velocity ω rad/s. Therefore, the velocity of B *i.e.* v_B is known in magnitude and direction. The slider reciprocates along the line of stroke *AO*.

The velocity of the slider A (*i.e.* v_A) may be determined by relative velocity method as discussed below :

1. From any point *o*, draw vector *ob* parallel to the direction of v_B (or perpendicular to *OB*) such that $ob = v_B = \omega.r$, to some suitable scale, as shown in Fig. 7.5 (*b*).

---

* The absolute velocities of the points are measured from the pole (*i.e.* fixed points) of the velocity diagram.

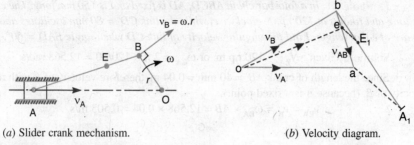

| (*a*) Slider crank mechanism. | (*b*) Velocity diagram. |

Fig. 7.5

2. Since *AB* is a rigid link, therefore the velocity of *A* relative to *B* is perpendicular to *AB*. Now draw vector *ba* perpendicular to *AB* to represent the velocity of *A* with respect to *B i.e.* v_{AB}.

3. From point *o*, draw vector *oa* parallel to the path of motion of the slider *A* (which is along *AO* only). The vectors *ba* and *oa* intersect at *a*. Now *oa* represents the velocity of the slider *A i.e.* v_A, to the scale.

The angular velocity of the connecting rod *AB* (ω_{AB}) may be determined as follows:

$$\omega_{AB} = \frac{v_{BA}}{AB} = \frac{ab}{AB} \qquad \text{(Anticlockwise about A)}$$

The direction of vector *ab* (or *ba*) determines the sense of ω_{AB} which shows that it is anticlockwise.

Note : The absolute velocity of any other point *E* on the connecting rod *AB* may also be found out by dividing vector *ba* such that *be/ba = BE/BA* . This is done by drawing any line bA_1 equal in length of *BA*. Mark $bE_1 = BE$. Join aA_1. From E_1 draw a line E_1e parallel to aA_1. The vector *oe* now represents the velocity of *E* and vector *ae* represents the velocity of *E* with respect to *A*.

7.6. Rubbing Velocity at a Pin Joint

The links in a mechanism are mostly connected by means of pin joints. The rubbing velocity is defined as **the algebraic sum between the angular velocities of the two links which are connected by pin joints, multiplied by the radius of the pin.**

Consider two links *OA* and *OB* connected by a pin joint at *O* as shown in Fig. 7.6.

Let ω_1 = Angular velocity of the link *OA* or the angular velocity of the point *A* with respect to *O*.

ω_2 = Angular velocity of the link *OB* or the angular velocity of the point *B* with respect to *O*, and

r = Radius of the pin.

According to the definition,

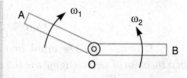

Fig. 7.6. Links connected by pin joints.

Rubbing velocity at the pin joint *O*

= $(\omega_1 - \omega_2) \, r$, if the links move in the same direction

= $(\omega_1 + \omega_2) \, r$, if the links move in the opposite direction

Note : When the pin connects one sliding member and the other turning member, the angular velocity of the sliding member is zero. In such cases,

Rubbing velocity at the pin joint = $\omega.r$

where ω = Angular velocity of the turning member, and

r = Radius of the pin.

Example 7.1. *In a four bar chain ABCD, AD is fixed and is 150 mm long. The crank AB is 40 mm long and rotates at 120 r.p.m. clockwise, while the link CD = 80 mm oscillates about D. BC and AD are of equal length. Find the angular velocity of link CD when angle BAD = 60°.*

Solution. Given : $N_{BA} = 120$ r.p.m. or $\omega_{BA} = 2\pi \times 120/60 = 12.568$ rad/s

Since the length of crank $AB = 40$ mm $= 0.04$ m, therefore velocity of B with respect to A or velocity of B, (because A is a fixed point),

$$v_{BA} = v_B = \omega_{BA} \times AB = 12.568 \times 0.04 = 0.503 \text{ m/s}$$

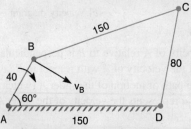

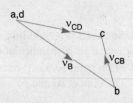

(*a*) Space diagram (All dimensions in mm).   (*b*) Velocity diagram.

Fig. 7.7

First of all, draw the space diagram to some suitable scale, as shown in Fig. 7.7 (*a*). Now the velocity diagram, as shown in Fig. 7.7 (*b*), is drawn as discussed below :

1. Since the link AD is fixed, therefore points *a* and *d* are taken as one point in the velocity diagram. Draw vector *ab* perpendicular to BA, to some suitable scale, to represent the velocity of B with respect to A or simply velocity of B (*i.e.* v_{BA} or v_B) such that

vector $ab = v_{BA} = v_B = 0.503$ m/s

2. Now from point *b*, draw vector *bc* perpendicular to CB to represent the velocity of C with respect to B (*i.e.* v_{CB}) and from point *d*, draw vector *dc* perpendicular to CD to represent the velocity of C with respect to D or simply velocity of C (*i.e.* v_{CD} or v_C). The vectors *bc* and *dc* intersect at *c*.

By measurement, we find that

$$v_{CD} = v_C = \text{vector } dc = 0.385 \text{ m/s}$$

We know that $CD = 80$ mm $= 0.08$ m

∴ Angular velocity of link CD,

$$\omega_{CD} = \frac{v_{CD}}{CD} = \frac{0.385}{0.08} = 4.8 \text{ rad/s (clockwise about D) } \textbf{Ans.}$$

Example 7.2. *The crank and connecting rod of a theoretical steam engine are 0.5 m and 2 m long respectively. The crank makes 180 r.p.m. in the clockwise direction. When it has turned 45° from the inner dead centre position, determine : 1. velocity of piston, 2. angular velocity of connecting rod, 3. velocity of point E on the connecting rod 1.5 m from the gudgeon pin, 4. velocities of rubbing at the pins of the crank shaft, crank and crosshead when the diameters of their pins are 50 mm, 60 mm and 30 mm respectively, 5. position and linear velocity of any point G on the connecting rod which has the least velocity relative to crank shaft.*

Solution. Given : $N_{BO} = 180$ r.p.m. or $\omega_{BO} = 2\pi \times 180/60 = 18.852$ rad/s

Since the crank length $OB = 0.5$ m, therefore linear velocity of B with respect to O or velocity of B (because O is a fixed point),

$$v_{BO} = v_B = \omega_{BO} \times OB = 18.852 \times 0.5 = 9.426 \text{ m/s}$$

. . . (Perpendicular to BO)

1. Velocity of piston

First of all, draw the space diagram, to some suitable scale, as shown in Fig. 7.8 (*a*). Now the velocity diagram, as shown in Fig. 7.8 (*b*), is drawn as discussed below :

1. Draw vector *ob* perpendicular to BO, to some suitable scale, to represent the velocity of B with respect to O or velocity of B such that

$$\text{vector } ob = v_{BO} = v_B = 9.426 \text{ m/s}$$

2. From point *b*, draw vector *bp* perpendicular to BP to represent velocity of P with respect to B (*i.e.* v_{PB}) and from point *o*, draw vector *op* parallel to PO to represent velocity of P with respect to O (*i.e.* v_{PO} or simply v_P). The vectors *bp* and *op* intersect at point *p*.

By measurement, we find that velocity of piston P,

$$v_P = \text{vector } op = 8.15 \text{ m/s } \textbf{Ans.}$$

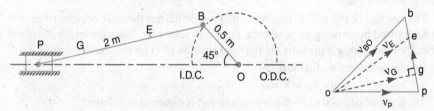

(*a*) Space diagram.   (*b*) Velocity diagram.

Fig. 7.8

2. Angular velocity of connecting rod

From the velocity diagram, we find that the velocity of P with respect to B,

$$v_{PB} = \text{vector } bp = 6.8 \text{ m/s}$$

Since the length of connecting rod PB is 2 m, therefore angular velocity of the connecting rod,

$$\omega_{PB} = \frac{v_{PB}}{PB} = \frac{6.8}{2} = 3.4 \text{ rad/s (Anticlockwise) } \textbf{Ans.}$$

3. Velocity of point E on the connecting rod

The velocity of point E on the connecting rod 1.5 m from the gudgeon pin (*i.e.* $PE = 1.5$ m) is determined by dividing the vector *bp* at *e* in the same ratio as E divides PB in Fig. 7.8 (*a*). This is done in the similar way as discussed in Art 7.6. Join *oe*. The vector *oe* represents the velocity of E. By measurement, we find that velocity of point E,

$$v_E = \text{vector } oe = 8.5 \text{ m/s } \textbf{Ans.}$$

Note : The point *e* on the vector *bp* may also be obtained as follows :

$$\frac{BE}{BP} = \frac{be}{bp} \quad \text{or} \quad be = \frac{BE \times bp}{BP}$$

4. Velocity of rubbing

We know that diameter of crank-shaft pin at O,

$$d_O = 50 \text{ mm} = 0.05 \text{ m}$$

Diameter of crank-pin at B,

$$d_B = 60 \text{ mm} = 0.06 \text{ m}$$

and diameter of cross-head pin,

$$d_C = 30 \text{ mm} = 0.03 \text{ m}$$

We know that velocity of rubbing at the pin of crank-shaft

$$= \frac{d_O}{2} \times \omega_{BO} = \frac{0.05}{2} \times 18.85 = 0.47 \text{ m/s} \quad \textbf{Ans.}$$

Velocity of rubbing at the pin of crank

$$= \frac{d_B}{2} (\omega_{BO} + \omega_{PB}) = \frac{0.06}{2} (18.85 + 3.4) = 0.6675 \text{ m/s} \quad \textbf{Ans.}$$

$$\ldots(\because \omega_{BO} \text{ is clockwise and } \omega_{PB} \text{ is anticlockwise.})$$

and velocity of rubbing at the pin of cross-head

$$= \frac{d_C}{2} \times \omega_{PB} = \frac{0.03}{2} \times 3.4 = 0.051 \text{ m/s} \quad \textbf{Ans.}$$

...($\because$ At the cross-head, the slider does not rotate and only the connecting rod has angular motion.)

5. *Position and linear velocity of point G on the connecting rod which has the least velocity relative to crank-shaft*

The position of point G on the connecting rod which has the least velocity relative to crank-shaft is determined by drawing perpendicular from o to vector bp. Since the length of og will be the least, therefore the point g represents the required position of G on the connecting rod.

By measurement, we find that

vector $bg = 5$ m/s

The position of point G on the connecting rod is obtained as follows:

$$\frac{bg}{bp} = \frac{BG}{BP} \quad \text{or} \quad BG = \frac{bg}{bp} \times BP = \frac{5}{6.8} \times 2 = 1.47 \text{ m} \quad \textbf{Ans.}$$

By measurement, we find that the linear velocity of point G,

$$v_G = \text{vector } og = 8 \text{ m/s} \quad \textbf{Ans.}$$

Example 7.3. *In Fig. 7.9, the angular velocity of the crank OA is 600 r.p.m. Determine the linear velocity of the slider D and the angular velocity of the link BD, when the crank is inclined at an angle of 75° to the vertical. The dimensions of various links are : OA = 28 mm ; AB = 44 mm ; BC = 49 mm ; and BD = 46 mm. The centre distance between the centres of rotation O and C is 65 mm. The path of travel of the slider is 11 mm below the fixed point C. The slider moves along a horizontal path and OC is vertical.*

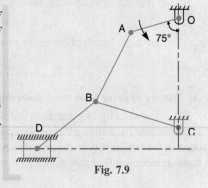

Fig. 7.9

Solution. Given: $N_{AO} = 600$ r.p.m. or

$\omega_{AO} = 2\pi \times 600/60 = 62.84$ rad/s

Since $OA = 28$ mm $= 0.028$ m, therefore velocity of A with respect to O or velocity of A (because O is a fixed point),

$$v_{AO} = v_A = \omega_{AO} \times OA = 62.84 \times 0.028 = 1.76 \text{ m/s}$$

$$\ldots \text{(Perpendicular to } OA)$$

Linear velocity of the slider D

First of all draw the space diagram, to some suitable scale, as shown in Fig. 7.10 (*a*). Now the velocity diagram, as shown in Fig. 7.10 (*b*), is drawn as discussed below :

1. Since the points O and C are fixed, therefore these points are marked as one point, in the velocity diagram. Now from point o, draw vector oa perpendicular to OA, to some suitable scale, to represent the velocity of A with respect to O or simply velocity of A such that

$$\text{vector } oa = v_{AO} = v_A = 1.76 \text{ m/s}$$

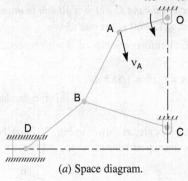

| (*a*) Space diagram. | (*b*) Velocity diagram. |

Fig. 7.10

2. From point a, draw vector ab perpendicular to AB to represent the velocity of B with respect A (*i.e.* v_{BA}) and from point c, draw vector cb perpendicular to CB to represent the velocity of B with respect to C or simply velocity of B (*i.e.* v_{BC} or v_B). The vectors ab and cb intersect at b.

3. From point b, draw vector bd perpendicular to BD to represent the velocity of D with respect to B (*i.e.* v_{DB}) and from point o, draw vector od parallel to the path of motion of the slider D which is horizontal, to represent the velocity of D (*i.e.* v_D). The vectors bd and od intersect at d.

By measurement, we find that velocity of the slider D,

$$v_D = \text{vector } od = 1.6 \text{ m/s } \textbf{Ans.}$$

Angular velocity of the link BD

By measurement from velocity diagram, we find that velocity of D with respect to B,

$$v_{DB} = \text{vector } bd = 1.7 \text{ m/s}$$

Since the length of link $BD = 46 \text{ mm} = 0.046 \text{ m}$, therefore angular velocity of the link BD,

$$\omega_{BD} = \frac{v_{DB}}{BD} = \frac{1.7}{0.046} = 36.96 \text{ rad/s (Clockwise about } B) \textbf{ Ans.}$$

Example 7.4. *The mechanism, as shown in Fig. 7.11, has the dimensions of various links as follows :*

$$AB = DE = 150 \text{ mm} \text{ ; } BC = CD = 450 \text{ mm} \text{ ; } EF = 375 \text{ mm}.$$

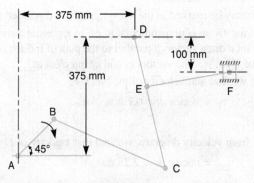

Fig. 7.11

The crank AB makes an angle of 45° with the horizontal and rotates about A in the clockwise direction at a uniform speed of 120 r.p.m. The lever DC oscillates about the fixed point D, which is connected to AB by the coupler BC.

The block F moves in the horizontal guides, being driven by the link EF. Determine: 1. velocity of the block F, 2. angular velocity of DC, and 3. rubbing speed at the pin C which is 50 mm in diameter.

Solution. Given : N_{BA} = 120 r.p.m. or ω_{BA} = $2\pi \times 120/60$ = 4π rad/s

Since the crank length AB = 150 mm = 0.15 m, therefore velocity of B with respect to A or simply velocity of B (because A is a fixed point),

$$v_{BA} = v_B = \omega_{BA} \times AB = 4\pi \times 0.15 = 1.885 \text{ m/s}$$

. . . (Perpendicular to AB)

1. *Velocity of the block F*

First of all draw the space diagram, to some suitable scale, as shown in Fig. 7.12 (*a*). Now the velocity diagram, as shown in Fig. 7.12 (*b*), is drawn as discussed below:

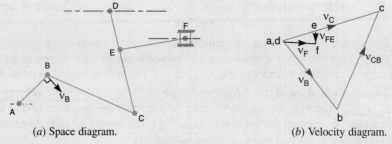

(*a*) Space diagram.   (*b*) Velocity diagram.

Fig. 7.12

1. Since the points A and D are fixed, therefore these points are marked as one point[*] as shown in Fig. 7.12 (*b*). Now from point *a*, draw vector *ab* perpendicular to AB, to some suitable scale, to represent the velocity of B with respect to A or simply velocity of B, such that

vector $ab = v_{BA} = v_B = 1.885$ m/s

2. The point C moves relative to B and D, therefore draw vector *bc* perpendicular to BC to represent the velocity of C with respect to B (*i.e.* v_{CB}), and from point *d*, draw vector *dc* perpendicular to DC to represent the velocity of C with respect to D or simply velocity of C (*i.e.* v_{CD} or v_C). The vectors *bc* and *dc* intersect at *c*.

3. Since the point E lies on DC, therefore divide vector *dc* in *e* in the same ratio as E divides CD in Fig. 7.12 (*a*). In other words

$ce/cd = CE/CD$

The point *e* on *dc* may be marked in the same manner as discussed in Example 7.2.

4. From point *e*, draw vector *ef* perpendicular to EF to represent the velocity of F with respect to E (*i.e.* v_{FE}) and from point *d* draw vector *df* parallel to the path of motion of F, which is horizontal, to represent the velocity of F *i.e.* v_F. The vectors *ef* and *df* intersect at *f*.

By measurement, we find that velocity of the block F,

$$v_F = \text{vector } df = 0.7 \text{ m/s} \text{ Ans.}$$

2. *Angular velocity of DC*

By measurement from velocity diagram, we find that velocity of C with respect to D,

$$v_{CD} = \text{vector } dc = 2.25 \text{ m/s}$$

---

[*] When the fixed elements of the mechanism appear at more than one place, then all these points lie at one place in the velocity diagram.

Since the length of link $DC = 450$ mm $= 0.45$ m, therefore angular velocity of DC,

$$\omega_{DC} = \frac{v_{CD}}{DC} = \frac{2.25}{0.45} = 5 \text{ rad/s} \qquad \text{...(Anticlockwise about } D)$$

3. Rubbing speed at the pin C

We know that diameter of pin at C,

$$d_C = 50 \text{ mm} = 0.05 \text{ m} \quad \text{or} \quad \text{Radius}, \; r_C = 0.025 \text{ m}$$

From velocity diagram, we find that velocity of C with respect to B,

$$v_{CB} = \text{vector } bc = 2.25 \text{ m/s} \qquad \text{...(By measurement)}$$

Length $BC = 450$ mm $= 0.45$ m

$\therefore$ Angular velocity of BC,

$$\omega_{CB} = \frac{v_{CB}}{BC} = \frac{2.25}{0.45} = 5 \text{ rad/s} \qquad \text{...(Anticlockwise about } B)$$

We know that rubbing speed at the pin C

$$= (\omega_{CB} - \omega_{CD}) \, r_C = (5 - 5) \, 0.025 = 0 \text{ Ans.}$$

Example 7.5. *In a mechanism shown in Fig. 7.13, the crank OA is 100 mm long and rotates clockwise about O at 120 r.p.m. The connceting rod AB is 400 mm long.*

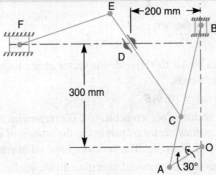

Fig. 7.13.

At a point C on AB, 150 mm from A, the rod CE 350 mm long is attached. This rod CE slides in a slot in a trunnion at D. The end E is connected by a link EF, 300 mm long to the horizontally moving slider F.

For the mechanism in the position shown, find 1. velocity of F, 2. velocity of sliding of CE in the trunnion, and 3. angular velocity of CE.

Solution. Given : $v_{AO} = 120$ r.p.m. or $\omega_{AO} = 2\pi \times 120/60 = 4\pi$ rad/s

Since the length of crank $OA = 100$ mm $= 0.1$ m, therefore velocity of A with respect to O or velocity of A (because O is a fixed point),

$$v_{AO} = v_A = \omega_{AO} \times OA = 4\pi \times 0.1 = 1.26 \text{ m/s}$$
$$\text{...(Perpendicular to } AO)$$

1. Velocity of F

First of all draw the space diagram, to some suitable scale, as shown in Fig. 7.14 (*a*). Now the velocity diagram, as shown in Fig. 7.14 (*b*), is drawn as discussed below :

An aircraft uses many mechanisms in engine, power transmission and steering.

Note : This picture is given as additional information.

1. Draw vector *oa* perpendicular to *AO*, to some suitable scale, to represent the velocity of *A* with respect to *O* or simply velocity of *A* (*i.e.* v_{AO} or v_A), such that

$$\text{vector } oa = v_{AO} = v_A = 1.26 \text{ m/s}$$

2. From point *a*, draw vector *ab* perpendicular to *AB* to represent the velocity of *B* with respect to *A* *i.e.* v_{BA}, and from point *o* draw vector *ob* parallel to the motion of *B* (which moves along *BO* only) to represent the velocity of *B* *i.e.* v_B. The vectors *ab* and *ob* intersect at *b*.

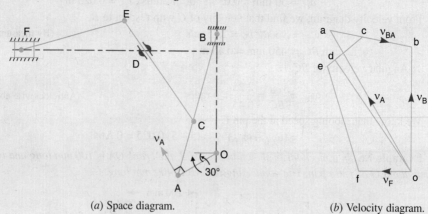

| (*a*) Space diagram. | (*b*) Velocity diagram. |

Fig. 7.14

3. Since the point *C* lies on *AB*, therefore divide vector *ab* at *c* in the same ratio as *C* divides *AB* in the space diagram. In other words,

$$ac/ab = AC/AB$$

4. From point *c*, draw vector *cd* perpendicular to *CD* to represent the velocity of *D* with respect to *C* *i.e.* v_{DC}, and from point *o* draw vector *od* parallel to the motion of *CD*, which moves along *CD* only, to represent the velocity of *D*, *i.e.* v_D. The vectors cd and od intersect at d.

5. Since the point *E* lies on *CD* produced, therefore divide vector *cd* at *e* in the same ratio as *E* divides *CD* in the space diagram. In other words,

$$cd/ce = CD/CE$$

6. From point *e*, draw vector *ef* perpendicular to *EF* to represent the velocity of *F* with respect to *E* *i.e.* v_{FE}, and from point *o* draw vector *of* parallel to the motion of *F*, which is along *FD* to represent the velocity of *F* *i.e.* v_F. The vectors ef and of intersect at f.

By measurement, we find that velocity of *F*,

$$v_F = \text{vector } of = 0.53 \text{ m/s} \textbf{ Ans.}$$

2. *Velocity of sliding of CE in the trunnion*

Since velocity of sliding of *CE* in the trunnion is the velocity of *D*, therefore velocity of sliding of *CE* in the trunnion

$$= \text{vector } od = 1.08 \text{ m/s} \textbf{ Ans.}$$

3. *Angular velocity of CE*

By measurement, we find that linear velocity of *C* with respect to *E*,

$$v_{CE} = \text{vector } ec = 0.44 \text{ m/s}$$

Since the length *CE* = 350 mm = 0.35 m, therefore angular velocity of *CE*,

$$\omega_{CE} = \frac{v_{CE}}{CE} = \frac{0.44}{0.35} = 1.26 \text{ rad/s (Clockwise about } E) \textbf{ Ans.}$$

Example 7.6. *In a mechanism as shown in Fig. 7.15, the various dimensions are : OC = 125 mm ; CP = 500 mm ; PA = 125 mm ; AQ = 250 mm and QE = 125 mm.*

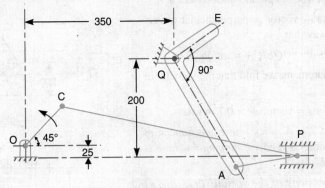

Fig. 7.15. All dimensions in mm.

The slider P translates along an axis which is 25 mm vertically below point O. The crank OC rotates uniformly at 120 r.p.m. in the anti-clockwise direction. The bell crank lever AQE rocks about fixed centre Q.

Draw the velocity diagram and calculate the absolute velocity of point E of the lever.

Solution. Given : N_{CO} = 120 r.p.m. or ω_{CO} = 2 π × 120/60 = 12.57 rad/s ; OC = 125 mm = 0.125 m

We know that linear velocity of C with respect to O or velocity of C, (because O is as fixed point)

$$v_{CO} = v_C = \omega_{CO} \times OC = 12.57 \times 0.125 = 1.57 \text{ m/s}$$

First of all, draw the space diagram, as shown in Fig. 7.16 (*a*), to some suitable scale. Now the velocity diagram, as shown in Fig. 7.16 (*b*) is drawn as discussed below :

1. Since the points O and Q are fixed, therefore these points are taken as one point in the velocity diagram. From point *o*, draw vector *oc* perpendicular to *OC*, to some suitable scale, to represent the velocity of C with respect to O or velocity of C, such that

$$\text{vector } oc = v_{CO} = v_C = 1.57 \text{ m/s}$$

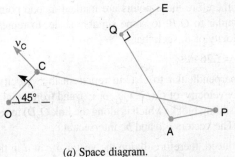

(*a*) Space diagram.

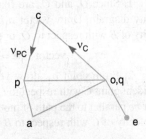

(*b*) Velocity diagram.

Fig. 7.16

2. From point *c*, draw vector *cp* perpendicular to *CP* to represent the velocity of P with respect to C (*i.e.* v_{PC}) and from point *o*, draw vector *op* parallel to the path of motion of slider P (which is horizontal) to represent the velocity of P (*i.e.* v_P). The vectors *cp* and *op* intersect at *p*.

3. From point p, draw vector pa perpendicular to PA to represent the velocity of A with respect to P (*i.e.* v_{AP}) and from point q, draw vector qa perpendicular to QA to represent the velocity of A (*i.e.* v_A). The vectors pa and qa intersect at a.

4. Now draw vector qe perpendicular to vector qa in such a way that

$$QE/QA = qe/qa$$

By measurement, we find that the velocity of point E,

$$v_E = \text{vector } oe = 0.7 \text{ m/s Ans.}$$

Example 7.7. *A quick return mechanism of the crank and slotted lever type shaping machine is shown in Fig. 7.17.*

The dimensions of the various links are as follows :

$O_1O_2 = 800 \text{ mm}$; $O_1B = 300 \text{ mm}$;

$O_2D = 1300 \text{ mm}$; $DR = 400 \text{ mm}$.

The crank O_1B makes an angle of 45° with the vertical and rotates at 40 r.p.m. in the counter clockwise direction. Find : 1. velocity of the ram R, or the velocity of the cutting tool, and 2. angular velocity of link O_2D.

Solution. Given: $N_{BO1} = 40$ r.p.m. or $\omega_{BO1} = 2\pi \times 40/60 = 4.2$ rad/s

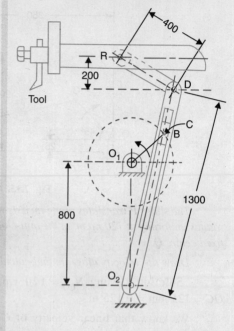

Fig. 7.17. All dimensions in mm.

Since the length of crank $O_1B = 300 \text{ mm} = 0.3\text{m}$, therefore velocity of B with respect to O_1 or simply velocity of B (because O_1 is a fixed point),

$$v_{BO1} = v_B = \omega_{BO1} \times O_1B = 4.2 \times 0.3 = 1.26 \text{ m/s} \qquad \text{. . . (Perpendicular to } O_1B)$$

1. Velocity of the ram R

First of all draw the space diagram, to some suitable scale, as shown in Fig. 7.18 (*a*). Now the velocity diagram, as shown in Fig. 7.18 (*b*), is drawn as discussed below :

1. Since O_1 and O_2 are fixed points, therefore these points are marked as one point in the velocity diagram. Draw vector o_1b perpendicular to O_1B, to some suitable scale, to represent the velocity of B with respect to O_1 or simply velocity of B, such that

$$\text{vector } o_1b = v_{BO1} = v_B = 1.26 \text{ m/s}$$

2. From point o_2, draw vector o_2c perpendicular to O_2C to represent the velocity of the coincident point C with respect to O_2 or simply velocity of C (*i.e.* v_{CO2} or v_C), and from point b, draw vector bc parallel to the path of motion of the sliding block (which is along the link O_2D) to represent the velocity of C with respect to B (*i.e.* v_{CB}). The vectors o_2c and bc intersect at c.

3. Since the point D lies on O_2C produced, therefore divide the vector o_2c at d in the same ratio as D divides O_2C in the space diagram. In other words,

$$cd / o_2d = CD/O_2D$$

4. Now from point d, draw vector dr perpendicular to DR to represent the velocity of R with respect to D (*i.e.* v_{RD}), and from point o_1 draw vector o_1r parallel to the path of motion of R (which is horizontal) to represent the velocity of R (*i.e.* v_R). The vectors dr and o_1r intersect at r.

By measurement, we find that velocity of the ram R,

$$v_R = \text{vector } o_1 r = 1.44 \text{ m/s} \quad \textbf{Ans.}$$

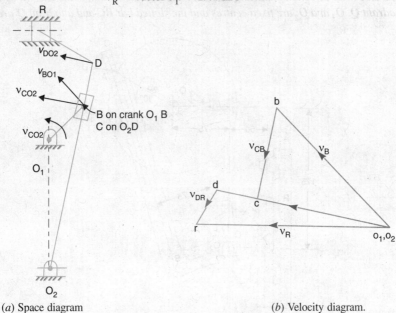

(a) Space diagram   (b) Velocity diagram.

Fig. 7.18

2. Angular velocity of link O_2D

By measurement from velocity diagram, we find that velocity of D with respect to O_2 or velocity of D,

$$v_{DO2} = v_D = \text{vector } o_2 d = 1.32 \text{ m/s}$$

We know that length of link $O_2D = 1300 \text{ mm} = 1.3 \text{ m}$. Therefore angular velocity of the link O_2D,

$$\omega_{DO2} = \frac{v_{DO2}}{O_2D} = \frac{1.32}{1.3} = 1.015 \text{ rad/s} \quad \text{(Anticlockwise about } O_2) \quad \textbf{Ans.}$$

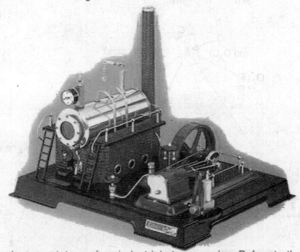

The above picture shows prototype of an industrial steam engine. Before to the invention of electricity, steam engines used to provide the power needed to turn wheels in the factories.

Note : This picture is given as additional information.

Example 7.8. *In the mechanism, as shown in Fig. 7.19, the crank O_1A rotates at a speed of 60 r.p.m. in a clockwise direction imparting vertical reciprocating motion to the rack R, by means of toothed quadrant Q. O_1 and O_2 are fixed centres and the slotted bar BC and quadrant Q are rocking on O_2.*

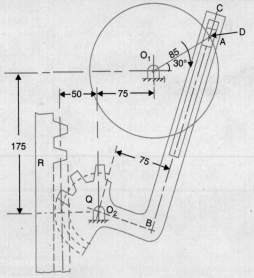

Fig. 7.19. All dimensions are in mm.

Determine : **1.** *the linear speed of the rack when the crank makes an angle of 30° to the horizontal,* **2.** *the ratio of the times of lowering and raising the rack, and* **3.** *the length of the stroke of the rack.*

Solution. Given : $N_{AO1} = 60$ r.p.m. or $\omega_{AO1} = 2\pi \times 60/60 = 6.28$ rad/s

Since crank length $O_1A = 85$ mm, therefore velocity of A with respect to O_1 or velocity of A, (because O_1 is a fixed point),

$$v_{AO1} = v_A = \omega_{AO1} \times O_1A = 6.28 \times 85 = 534 \text{ mm/s}$$

... (Perpendicular to O_1A)

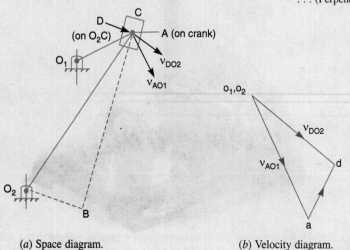

(a) Space diagram. (b) Velocity diagram.

Fig. 7.20

1. *Linear speed of the rack*

First of all draw the space diagram, to some suitable scale, as shown in Fig. 7.20 (*a*). Now the velocity diagram, as shown in Fig. 7.20 (*b*), is drawn as discussed below :

1. Since O_1 and O_2 are fixed points, therefore they are marked as one point in the velocity diagram. From point o_1, draw vector o_1a perpendicular to O_1A, to some suitable scale, to represent the velocity of A with respect to O_1 or simply velocity of A, such that

$$\text{vector } o_1a = v_{AO1} = v_A = 534 \text{ mm/s}$$

2. From point a, draw vector ad parallel to the path of motion of D (which is along the slot in the link BC) to represent the velocity D with respect to A (*i.e.* v_{DA}), and from point o_2 draw vector o_2d perpendicular to the line joining the points O_2 and D (because O_2 and D lie on the same link) to represent the velocity of D (*i.e.* v_{DO_2} or v_D). The vectors ad and o_2d intersect at d.

Note : The point A represents the point on the crank as well as on the sliding block whereas the point D represents the coincident point on the lever O_2C.

By measurement, we find that

$$v_{DO2} = v_D = \text{vector } o_2d = 410 \text{ mm/s, and } O_2D = 264 \text{ mm}$$

We know that angular velocity of the quadrant Q,

$$\omega_Q = \frac{v_{DO2}}{O_2D} = \frac{410}{264} = 1.55 \text{ rad/s (Clockwise about } O_2)$$

Radius of the quadrant Q,

$$r_Q = 50 \text{ mm}$$

Since the rack and the quadrant have a rolling contact, therefore the linear velocity at the points of contact will be same as that of quadrant.

∴ Linear speed of the rack,

$$v_R = \omega_Q.r_Q = 1.55 \times 50 \ = 77.5 \text{ mm/s} \quad \textbf{Ans.}$$

2. *Ratio of the times of lowering and raising the rack*

The two extreme positions of the rack (or AB) are when the tangent to the circle with centre O_1 is also a tangent to the circle with centre O_2, as shown in Fig. 7.21. The rack will be raising when the crank moves from A_1 to A_2 through an angle α and it will be lowering when the crank moves from A_2 to A_1 through an angle β. Since the times of lowering and raising the rack is directly proportional to their respective angles, therefore

$$\frac{\text{Time of lowering}}{\text{Time of raising}} = \frac{\beta}{\alpha} = \frac{240°}{120°} = 2 \quad \textbf{Ans.}$$

$$\dots \text{(By measurement)}$$

3. *Length of stroke of the rack*

By measurement, we find that angle $B_1O_2B_2 = 60° = 60 \times \pi / 180 = 1.047$ rad

We know that length of stroke of the rack

= Radius of the quadrant × Angular rotation of the quadrant in radians

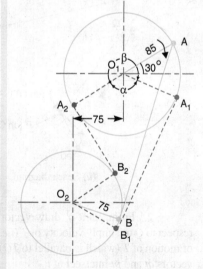

Fig. 7.21. All dimensions in mm.

= $r_Q \times \angle B_1O_2B_2$ in radians = $50 \times 1.047 = 52.35$ mm   **Ans.**

Example 7.9. *Fig. 7.22 shows the structure of Whitworth quick return mechanism used in reciprocating machine tools. The various dimensions of the tool are as follows :*

OQ = 100 mm ; OP = 200 mm, RQ = 150 mm and RS = 500 mm.

The crank OP makes an angle of 60° with the vertical. Determine the velocity of the slider S (cutting tool) when the crank rotates at 120 r.p.m. clockwise.

Find also the angular velocity of the link RS and the velocity of the sliding block T on the slotted lever QT.

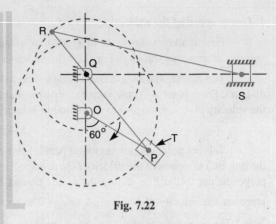

Fig. 7.22

Solution. Given : N_{PO} = 120 r.p.m. or ω_{PO} = 2 π × 120/60 = 12.57 rad/s

Since the crank OP = 200 mm = 0.2 m, therefore velocity of P with respect to O or velocity of P (because O is a fixed point),

$$v_{PO} = v_P = \omega_{PO} \times OP = 12.57 \times 0.2 = 2.514 \text{ m/s}$$

... (Perpendicular to PO)

Velocity of slider S (cutting tool)

First of all draw the space diagram, to some suitable scale, as shown in Fig. 7.23 (a). Now the velocity diagram, as shown in Fig. 7.23 (b) is drawn as discussed below :

1. Since O and Q are fixed points, therefore they are taken as one point in the velocity diagram. From point o, draw vector op perpendicular to OP, to some suitable scale, to represent the velocity of P with respect to O or simply velocity of P, such that

vector $op = v_{PO} = v_P = 2.514$ m/s

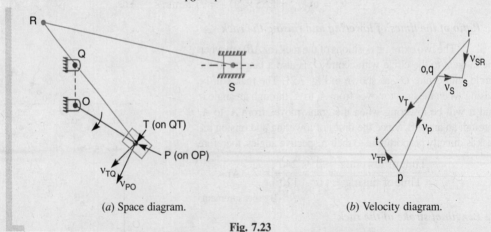

(a) Space diagram.　　　　　　　　　(b) Velocity diagram.

Fig. 7.23

2. From point q, draw vector qt perpendicular to QT to represent the velocity of T with respect to Q or simply velocity of T (i.e. v_{TQ} or v_T) and from point p draw vector pt parallel to the path of motion of T (which is parallel to TQ) to represent the velocity of T with respect to P (i.e. v_{TP}). The vectors qt and pt intersect at t.

Note : The point T is a coincident point with P on the link QT.

3. Since the point R lies on the link TQ produced, therefore divide the vector tq at r in the same ratio as R divides TQ, in the space diagram. In other words,

$$qr/qt = QR/QT$$

The vector qr represents the velocity of R with respect to Q or velocity of R (*i.e.* v_{RQ} or v_R).

4. From point r, draw vector rs perpendicular to RS to represent the velocity of S with respect to R and from point o draw vector or parallel to the path of motion of S (which is parallel to QS) to represent the velocity of S (*i.e* v_S). The vectors rs and os intersect at s.

By measurement, we find that velocity of the slider S (cutting tool),

$$v_S = \text{vector } os = 0.8 \text{ m/s } \textbf{Ans.}$$

Angular velocity of link RS

From the velocity diagram, we find that the linear velocity of the link RS,

$$v_{SR} = \text{vector } rs = 0.96 \text{ m/s}$$

Since the length of link $RS = 500$ mm $= 0.5$ m, therefore angular velocity of link RS,

$$\omega_{RS} = \frac{v_{SR}}{RS} = \frac{0.96}{0.5} = 1.92 \text{ rad/s (Clockwise about } R) \textbf{ Ans.}$$

Velocity of the sliding block T on the slotted lever QT

Since the block T moves on the slotted lever with respect to P, therefore velocity of the sliding block T on the slotted lever QT,

$$v_{TP} = \text{vector } pt = 0.85 \text{ m/s } \quad \textbf{Ans.} \qquad \text{. . . (By measurement)}$$

7.7. Forces Acting in a Mechanism

Consider a mechanism of a four bar chain, as shown in Fig. 7.24. Let force F_A newton is acting at the joint A in the direction of the velocity of A (v_A m/s) which is perpendicular to the link DA. Suppose a force F_B newton is transmitted to the joint B in the direction of the velocity of B (*i.e.* v_B m/s) which is perpendicular to the link CB. If we neglect the effect of friction and the change of kinetic energy of the link (*i.e.*, assuming the efficiency of transmission as 100%), then by the principle of conservation of energy,

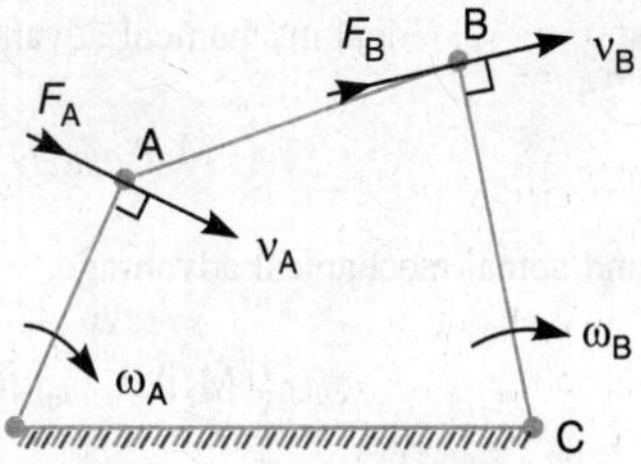

Input work per unit time

Fig. 7.24. Four bar mechanism.

$$= \text{Output work per unit time}$$
$$\therefore \text{ Work supplied to the joint } A$$
$$= \text{Work transmitted by the joint } B$$

or $$F_A.v_A = F_B.v_B \text{ or } F_B = \frac{F_A.v_A}{v_B} \qquad \text{. . . (i)}$$

If we consider the effect of friction and assuming the efficiency of transmission as η, then

$$\eta = \frac{\text{Output}}{\text{Input}} = \frac{F_B.v_B}{F_A.v_A}. \text{ or } F_B = \frac{\eta.F_A.v_A}{v_B} \qquad \text{. . . (ii)}$$

Notes : 1. If the turning couples due to the forces F_A and F_B about D and C are denoted by T_A (known as driving torque) and T_B (known as resisting torque) respectively, then the equations (*i*) and (*ii*) may be written as

$$T_A.\omega_A = T_B.\omega_B, \text{ and } \eta = \frac{T_B.\omega_B}{T_A.\omega_A} \qquad \text{. . . (iii)}$$

where ω_A and ω_B are the angular velocities of the links DA and CB respectively.

2. If the forces F_A and F_B do not act in the direction of the velocities of the points A and B respectively, then the component of the force in the direction of the velocity should be used in the above equations.

7.8. Mechanical Advantage

It is defined as the ratio of the load to the effort. In a four bar mechanism, as shown in Fig. 7.24, the link DA is called the driving link and the link CB as the driven link. The force F_A acting at A is the effort and the force F_B at B will be the load or the resistance to overcome. We know from the principle of conservation of energy, neglecting effect of friction,

$$F_A \times v_A = F_B \times v_B \text{ or } \frac{F_B}{F_A} = \frac{v_A}{v_B}$$

∴ Ideal mechanical advantage,

$$\text{M.A.}_{(ideal)} = \frac{F_B}{F_A} = \frac{v_A}{v_B}$$

If we consider the effect of friction, less resistance will be overcome with the given effort. Therefore the actual mechanical advantage will be less.

Let η = Efficiency of the mechanism.

∴ Actual mechanical advantage,

$$\text{M.A.}_{(actual)} = \eta \times \frac{F_B}{F_A} = \eta \times \frac{v_A}{v_B}$$

Note : The mechanical advantage may also be defined as the ratio of output torque to the input torque.

Let T_A = Driving torque,

T_B = Resisting torque,

ω_A and ω_B = Angular velocity of the driving and driven links respectively.

∴ Ideal mechanical advantage,

$$\text{M.A.}_{(ideal)} = \frac{T_B}{T_A} = \frac{\omega_A}{\omega_B} \qquad \dots \text{(Neglecting effect of friction)}$$

and actual mechanical advantage,

$$\text{M.A.}_{(actual)} = \eta \times \frac{T_B}{T_A} = \eta \times \frac{\omega_A}{\omega_B} \qquad \dots \text{(Considering the effect of friction)}$$

Example 7.10. *A four bar mechanism has the following dimensions :*

DA = 300 mm ; CB = AB = 360 mm ; DC = 600 mm. The link DC is fixed and the angle ADC is 60°. The driving link DA rotates uniformly at a speed of 100 r.p.m. clockwise and the constant driving torque has the magnitude of 50 N-m. Determine the velocity of the point B and angular velocity of the driven link CB. Also find the actual mechanical advantage and the resisting torque if the efficiency of the mechanism is 70 per cent.

Solution. Given : N_{AD} = 100 r.p.m. or ω_{AD} = 2 π × 100/60 = 10.47 rad/s ; T_A = 50 N-m

Since the length of driving link, DA = 300 mm = 0.3 m, therefore velocity of A with respect to D or velocity of A (because D is a fixed point),

$$v_{AD} = v_A = \omega_{AD} \times DA = 10.47 \times 0.3 = 3.14 \text{ m/s}$$

$$\dots \text{(Perpendicular to } DA)$$

Velocity of point B

First of all draw the space diagram, to some suitable scale, as shown in Fig. 7.25 (a). Now the velocity diagram, as shown in Fig. 7.25 (b), is drawn as discussed below :

1. Since the link *DC* is fixed, therefore points *d* and *c* are taken as one point in the velocity diagram. Draw vector *da* perpendicular to *DA*, to some suitable scale, to represent the velocity of *A* with respect to *D* or simply velocity of *A* (*i.e.* v_{AD} or v_A) such that

$$\text{vector } da = v_{AD} = v_A = 3.14 \text{ m/s}$$

2. Now from point *a*, draw vector *ab* perpendicular to *AB* to represent the velocity of *B* with respect to *A* (*i.e.* v_{BA}), and from point *c* draw vector *cb* perpendicular to *CB* to represent the velocity of *B* with respect to *C* or simply velocity of *B* (*i.e.* v_{BC} or v_B). The vectors *ab* and *cb* intersect at *b*.

By measurement, we find that velocity of point *B*,

$$v_B = v_{BC} = \text{vector } cb = 2.25 \text{ m/s } \textbf{Ans.}$$

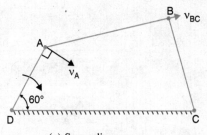 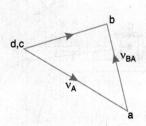

(*a*) Space diagram. (*b*) Velocity diagram.

Fig. 7.25

Angular velocity of the driven link CB

Since *CB* = 360 mm = 0.36 m, therefore angular velocity of the driven link *CB*,

$$\omega_{BC} = \frac{v_{BC}}{BC} = \frac{2.25}{0.36} = 6.25 \text{ rad/s (Clockwise about } C) \textbf{ Ans.}$$

Actual mechanical advantage

We know that the efficiency of the mechanism,

$$\eta = 70\% = 0.7 \qquad \qquad \ldots \text{(Given)}$$

∴ Actual mechanical advantage,

$$\text{M.A.}_{(actual)} = \eta \times \frac{\omega_A}{\omega_B} = 0.7 \times \frac{10.47}{6.25} = 1.17 \textbf{ Ans.}$$

$$\ldots (\because \omega_A = \omega_{AD}; \text{ and } \omega_B = \omega_{BC})$$

Resisting torque

Let $\qquad\qquad T_B$ = Resisting torque.

We know that efficiency of the mechanism (η),

$$0.7 = \frac{T_B \cdot \omega_B}{T_A \cdot \omega_A} = \frac{T_B \times 6.25}{50 \times 10.47} = 0.012 T_B$$

∴ $\qquad\qquad\qquad T_B = 58.3$ N–m **Ans.**

Example 7.11. *The dimensions of the various links of a pneumatic riveter, as shown in Fig. 7.26, are as follows :*

$\qquad OA = 175 \text{ mm} ; AB = 180 \text{ mm} ; AD = 500 \text{ mm} ;$ *and BC = 325 mm.*

Find the velocity ratio between C and ram D when OB is vertical. What will be the efficiency of the machine if a load of 2.5 kN on the piston C causes a thrust of 4 kN at the ram D ?

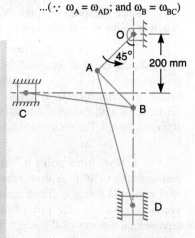

Fig. 7.26

Solution. Given : $W_C = 2.5$ kN $= 2500$ N ; $W_D = 4$ kN $= 4000$ N

Let $N =$ Speed of crank OA.

∴ Angular velocity of crank OA,

$$\omega_{AO} = 2\pi N/60 \text{ rad/s}$$

Since the length of crank $OA = 175$ mm $= 0.175$ m, therefore velocity of A with respect to O or velocity of A (because O is a fixed point),

$$v_{AO} = v_A = \frac{2\pi N}{60} \times 0.175 = 0.0183\, N \text{ m/s} \qquad \dots \text{(Perpendicular to } OA)$$

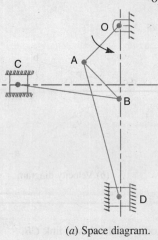

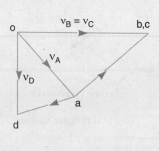

(a) Space diagram.   (b) Velocity diagram.

Fig. 7.27

Velocity ratio between C and the ram D

First of all draw the space diagram, to some suitable scale, as shown in Fig. 7.27 (a), Now the velocity diagram, as shown in Fig. 7.27 (b), is drawn as discussed below :

1. Draw vector oa perpendicular to OA to represent the velocity of A (*i.e.* v_A) such that

vector $oa = v_A = 0.0183\, N$ m/s

Since the speed of crank (N) is not given, therefore let we take vector $oa = 20$ mm.

2. From point a, draw a vector ab perpendicular to AB to represent the velocity of B with respect to A (*i.e.* v_{BA}), and from point o draw vector ob perpendicular to OB to represent the velocity of B with respect to A or simply velocity of B (*i.e.* v_{BO} or v_B). The vectors ab and ob intersect at b.

3. Now from point b, draw vector bc perpendicular to BC to represent the velocity of C with respect to B (*i.e.* v_{CB}) and from point o draw vector oc parallel to the path of motion of C to represent the velocity of C (*i.e.* v_C). The vectors bc and oc intersect at c. We see from Fig. 7.27 (b) that

the points *b* and *c* coincide. Therefore velocity of *B* with respect to *C* is zero and velocity of *B* is equal to velocity of *C*, *i.e.*

$$v_{BC} = 0 \qquad \qquad \dots (\because \ b \text{ and } c \text{ coincide})$$

and

$$v_B = v_C \qquad \qquad \dots (\because \text{ vector } ob = \text{ vector } oc)$$

4. From point *a*, draw vector *ad* perpendicular to *AD* to represent velocity of *D* with respect to *A i.e.* v_{DA}, and from point *o* draw vector *ob* parallel to the path of motion of *D* to represent the velocity of *D i.e.* v_D. The vectors *ad* and *od* intersect at *d*.

By measurement from velocity diagram, we find that velocity of *C*,

$$v_C = \text{vector } oc = 35 \text{ mm}$$

and velocity of *D*, $v_D = \text{vector } od = 21 \text{ mm}$

∴ Velocity ratio between *C* and the ram *D*

$$= v_C / v_D = 35/21 = 1.66 \ \textbf{Ans.}$$

Efficiency of the machine

Let η = Efficiency of the machine,

We know that work done on the piston *C* or input,

$$= W_C \times v_C = 2500 \ v_C$$

and work done by the ram *D* or output,

$$= W_D \times v_D = 4000 \ v_D$$

∴ $$\eta = \frac{\text{Output}}{\text{Input}} = \frac{4000 \ v_D}{2500 \ v_C} = \frac{4000}{2500} \times \frac{1}{1.66} \qquad \dots \left(\because \frac{v_C}{v_D} = 1.66 \right)$$

$$= 0.96 \text{ or } 96\% \ \textbf{Ans.}$$

Example 7.12. *In the toggle mechanism, as shown in Fig. 7.28, the slider D is constrained to move on a horizontal path. The crank OA is rotating in the counter-clockwise direction at a speed of 180 r.p.m.*

The dimensions of various links are as follows :

OA = 180 mm ; CB = 240 mm ; AB = 360 mm ; and BD = 540 mm.

For the given configuration, find : 1. Velocity of slider D, 2. Angular velocity of links AB, CB and BD; 3. Velocities of rubbing on the pins of diameter 30 mm at A and D, and 4. Torque applied to the crank OA, for a force of 2 kN at D.

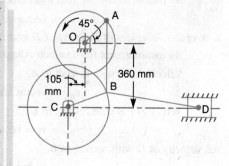

Fig. 7.28

Solution. Given : $N_{AO} = 180$ r.p.m. or $\omega_{AO} = 2 \pi \times 180/60 = 18.85$ rad/s

Since the crank length *OA* = 180 mm = 0.18 m, therefore velocity of *A* with respect to *O* or velocity of *A* (because *O* is a fixed point),

$$v_{AO} = v_A = \omega_{AO} \times OA = 18.85 \times 0.18 = 3.4 \text{ m/s}$$

. . . (Perpendicular to *OA*)

1. Velocity of slider D

First of all draw the space diagram, to some suitable scale, as shown in Fig. 7.29 (*a*). Now the velocity diagram, as shown in Fig. 7.29 (*b*), is drawn as discussed below :

1. Draw vector *oa* perpendicular to *OA*, to some suitable scale, to represent the velocity of *A* with respect to *O* or velocity of *A* (*i.e.* v_{AO} or v_A,) such that

$$\text{vector } oa = v_{AO} = v_A = 3.4 \text{ m/s}$$

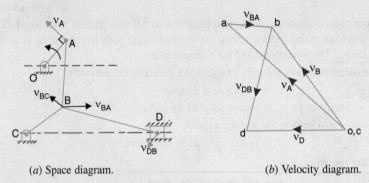

| (*a*) Space diagram. | (*b*) Velocity diagram. |

Fig. 7.29

2. Since point *B* moves with respect to *A* and also with respect to *C*, therefore draw vector *ab* perpendicular to *AB* to represent the velocity of *B* with respect to *A i.e.* v_{BA}, and draw vector *cb* perpendicular to *CB* to represent the velocity of *B* with respect to *C*, *i.e.* v_{BC}. The vectors *ab* and *cb* intersect at *b*.

3. From point *b*, draw vector *bd* perpendicular to *BD* to represent the velocity of *D* with respect to *B i.e.* v_{DB}, and from point *c* draw vector *cd* parallel to the path of motion of the slider *D* (which is along *CD*) to represent the velocity of *D*, *i.e.* v_D. The vectors *bd* and *cd* intersect at *d*.

By measurement, we find that velocity of the slider *D*,

$$v_D = \text{vector } cd = 2.05 \text{ m/s} \textbf{ Ans.}$$

2. *Angular velocities of links AB, CB and BD*

By measurement from velocity diagram, we find that

Velocity of *B* with respect to *A*,

$$v_{BA} = \text{vector } ab = 0.9 \text{ m/s}$$

Velocity of *B* with respect to *C*,

$$v_{BC} = v_B = \text{vector } cb = 2.8 \text{ m/s}$$

and velocity of *D* with respect to *B*,

$$v_{DB} = \text{vector } bd = 2.4 \text{ m/s}$$

We know that $AB = 360 \text{ mm} = 0.36 \text{ m}$; $CB = 240 \text{ mm} = 0.24 \text{ m}$ and $BD = 540 \text{ mm} = 0.54 \text{ m}$.

∴ Angular velocity of the link *AB*,

$$\omega_{AB} = \frac{v_{BA}}{AB} = \frac{0.9}{0.36} = 2.5 \text{ rad/s} \text{ (Anticlockwise about } A\text{) } \textbf{Ans.}$$

Similarly angular velocity of the link *CB*,

$$\omega_{CB} = \frac{v_{BC}}{CB} = \frac{2.8}{0.24} = 11.67 \text{ rad/s} \text{ (Anticlockwise about } C\text{) } \textbf{Ans.}$$

and angular velocity of the link *BD*,

$$\omega_{BD} = \frac{v_{DB}}{BD} = \frac{2.4}{0.54} = 4.44 \text{ rad/s} \text{ (Clockwise about } B\text{) } \textbf{Ans.}$$

3. *Velocities of rubbing on the pins A and D*

      Given : Diameter of pins at A and D,

$$D_A = D_D = 30 \text{ mm} = 0.03 \text{ m}$$

$\therefore$ Radius, $r_A = r_D = 0.015$ m

We know that relative angular velocity at A

$$= \omega_{BC} - \omega_{BA} + \omega_{DB} = 11.67 - 2.5 + 4.44 = 13.61 \text{ rad/s}$$

and relative angular velocity at D

$$= \omega_{DB} = 4.44 \text{ rad/s}$$

$\therefore$ Velocity of rubbing on the pin A

$$= 13.61 \times 0.015 = 0.204 \text{ m/s} = 204 \text{ mm/s} \textbf{ Ans.}$$

and velocity of rubbing on the pin D

$$= 4.44 \times 0.015 = 0.067 \text{ m/s} = 67 \text{ mm/s} \textbf{ Ans.}$$

4. *Torque applied to the crank OA*

      Let T_A = Torque applied to the crank OA, in N-m

$\therefore$ Power input or work supplied at A

$$= T_A \times \omega_{AO} = T_A \times 18.85 = 18.85 \ T_A \text{ N-m}$$

We know that force at D,

$$F_D = 2 \text{ kN} = 2000 \text{ N} \hspace{3cm} \dots \text{(Given)}$$

$\therefore$ Power output or work done by D,

$$= F_D \times v_D = 2000 \times 2.05 = 4100 \text{ N-m}$$

Assuming 100 per cent efficiency, power input is equal to power output.

$\therefore$ $18.85 \ T_A = 4100$ or $T_A = 217.5$ N-m **Ans.**

Example 7.13. *The dimensions of the mechanism, as shown in Fig. 7.30, are as follows :*
AB = 0.45 m; BD = 1.5 m : BC = CE = 0.9 m.

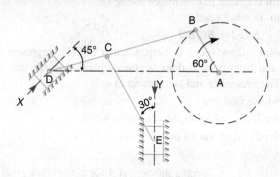

Fig. 7.30

      The crank AB turns uniformly at 180 r.p.m. in the clockwise direction and the blocks at D and E are working in frictionless guides.

      Draw the velocity diagram for the mechanism and find the velocities of the sliders D and E in their guides. Also determine the turning moment at A if a force of 500 N acts on D in the direction of arrow X and a force of 750 N acts on E in the direction of arrow Y.

      Solution. Given : $N_{BA} = 180$ r.p.m. or $\omega_{BA} = 2\,\pi \times 180/60 = 18.85$ rad/s

Since $AB = 0.45$ m, therefore velocity of B with respect to A or velocity of B (because A is a fixed point),

$$v_{BA} = v_B = \omega_{BA} \times AB = 18.85 \times 0.45 = 8.5 \text{ m/s}$$

. . . (Perpendicular to AB)

Velocities of the sliders D and E

First of all draw the space diagram, to some suitable scale, as shown in Fig. 7.31 (*a*). Now the velocity diagram, as shown in Fig. 7.31 (*b*), is drawn as discussed below :

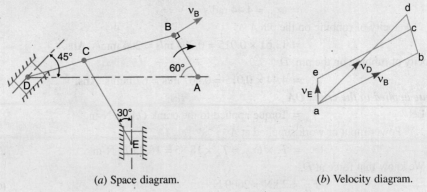

(*a*) Space diagram.   (*b*) Velocity diagram.

Fig. 7.31

1. Draw vector ab perpendicular to AB, to some suitable scale, to represent the velocity of B with respect to A or simply velocity of B (*i.e.* v_{BA} or v_B), such that

vector $ab = v_{BA} = v_B = 8.5$ m/s

2. From point b, draw vector bd perpendicular to BD to represent the velocity of D with respect to B (*i.e.* v_{DB}) and from point a draw vector ad parallel to the motion of D to represent the velocity of D (v_D). The vectors bd and ad intersect at d.

3. Since the point C lies on BD, therefore divide vector bd at c in the same ratio as C divides BD in the space diagram. In other words,

$$bc/bd = BC/BD$$

4. Now from point c, draw vector ce perpendicular to CE to represent the velocity of E with respect to C (*i.e.* v_{EC}) and from point a draw vector ae parallel to the path of E to represent the velocity of E (*i.e.* v_E). The vectors ce and ae intersect at e.

By measurement, we find that

Velocity of slider D, v_D = vector $ad = 9.5$ m/s **Ans.**

Velocity of slider E, v_E = vector $ae = 1.7$ m/s **Ans.**

Turning moment at A

Let T_A = Turning moment at A (or at the crank-shaft).

We know that force at D, $F_D = 500$ N   . . . (Given)

and   Force at E, $F_E = 750$ N   . . . (Given)

∴ Power input $= F_D \times v_D - F_E \times v_E$

. . . (– ve sign indicates that F_E opposes the motion)

$$= 500 \times 9.5 - 750 \times 1.7 = 3475 \text{ N-m/s}$$

Power output $= T_A \cdot \omega_{BA} = T_A \times 18.85 \ T_A$ N-m/s

Neglecting losses, power input is equal to power output.

∴ $3475 = 18.85 \ T_A$ or $T_A = 184.3$ N-m **Ans.**

EXERCISES

1. In a slider crank mechanism, the length of crank *OB* and connecting rod *AB* are 125 mm and 500 mm respectively. The centre of gravity *G* of the connecting rod is 275 mm from the slider *A*. The crank speed is 600 r.p.m. clockwise. When the crank has turned 45° from the inner dead centre position, determine: 1. velocity of the slider *A*, 2. velocity of the point *G*, and 3. angular velocity of the connecting rod *AB*. **[Ans. 6.45 m/s ; 6.75 m/s ; 10.8 rad/s]**

2. In the mechanism, as shown in Fig. 7.32, *OA* and *OB* are two equal cranks at right angles rotating about *O* at a speed of 40 r.p.m. anticlockwise. The dimensions of the various links are as follows :

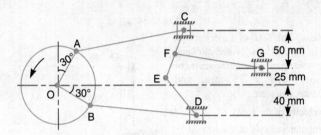

Fig. 7.32

OA = *OB* = 50 mm ; *AC* = *BD* = 175 mm ; *DE* = *CE* = 75 mm ; *FG* = 115 mm and *EF* = *FC*.

Draw velocity diagram for the given configuration of the mechanism and find velocity of the slider *G*.
[Ans. 68 mm/s]

3. The dimensions of various links in a mechanism, as shown in Fig. 7.33, are as follows :

AB = 60 mm ; *BC* = 400 mm ; *CD* = 150 mm ; *DE* = 115 mm ; and *EF* = 225 mm.

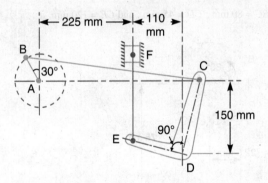

Fig. 7.33

Find the velocity of the slider *F* when the crank *AB* rotates uniformly in clockwise direction at a speed of 60 r.p.m. **[Ans. 250 mm/s]**

4. In a link work, as shown in Fig. 7.34, the crank *AB* rotates about *A* at a uniform speed of 150 r.p.m. The lever *DC* oscillates about the fixed point *D*, being connected to *AB* by the connecting link *BC*. The block *F* moves, in horizontal guides being driven by the link *EF*, when the crank *AB* is at 30°. The dimensions of the various links are :

AB = 150 mm ; *BC* = 450 mm ; *CE* = 300 mm ; *DE* = 150 mm ; and *EF* = 350 mm.

Find, for the given configuration, 1. velocity of slider *F*, 2. angular velocity of *DC*, and 3. rubbing speed at pin *C* which is 50 mm in diameter. **[Ans. 500 mm/s ; 3.5 rad/s ; 2.4 m/s]**

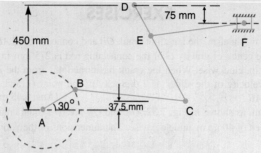

Fig. 7.34

5. The oscillating link *OAB* of a mechanism, as shown in Fig. 7.35, is pivoted at *O* and is moving at 90 r.p.m. anticlockwise. If *OA* = 150 mm ; *AB* = 75 mm, and *AC* = 250 mm, calculate

1. the velocity of the block *C*;

2. the angular velocity of the link *AC*; and

3. the rubbing velocities of the pins at *O*, *A* and *C*, assuming that these pins are of equal diameters of 20 mm.
   [Ans. 1.2 m/s; 1.6 rad/s² clockwise; 21 200 mm/s, 782 mm/s, 160 mm/s]

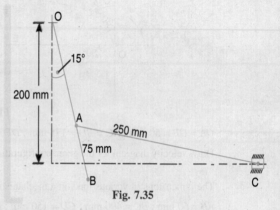

Fig. 7.35

6. The dimensions of the various links of a mechanism, as shown in Fig. 7.36, are as follows :

AB = 30 mm ; *BC* = 80 mm ; *CD* = 45 mm ; and *CE* = 120 mm.

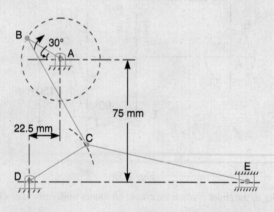

Fig. 7.36

The crank *AB* rotates uniformly in the clockwise direction at 120 r.p.m. Draw the velocity diagram for the given configuration of the mechanism and determine the velocity of the slider *E* and angular velocities of the links *BC*, *CD* and *CE*.

Also draw a diagram showing the extreme top and bottom positions of the crank *DC* and the corresponding configurations of the mechanism.

Find the length of each of the strokes.

[Ans. 120 mm/s ; 2.8 rad/s ; 5.8 rad/s ; 2 rad/s ; 10 mm ; 23 mm]

7. Fig. 7.37 shows a mechanism in which the crank *OA*, 100 mm long rotates clockwise about *O* at 130 r.p.m. The connecting rod *AB* is 400 mm long. The rod *CE*, 350 mm long, is attached to *AB* at *C*, 150 mm from *A*. This rod slides in a slot in a trunnion at *D*. The end *E* is connected by a link *EF*, 300 mm long, to the horizontally moving slider *F*.

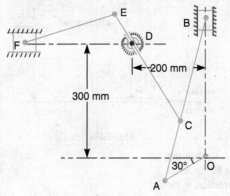

Fig. 7.37

Determine, for the given configuration : 1. velocity of *F*, 2. velocity of sliding of *CE* in the trunnion, and 3. angular velocity of *CE*. **[Ans. 0.54 m/s ; 1.2 m/s ; 1.4 rad/s]**

8. Fig. 7.38 shows the mechanism of a quick return motion of the crank and slotted lever type shaping machine. The dimensions of the various links are as follows :

OA = 200 mm ; *AB* = 100 mm ; *OC* = 400 mm ; and *CR* = 150 mm.

The driving crank *AB* makes 120° with the vertical and rotates at 60 r.p.m. in the clockwise direction. Find : 1. velocity of ram *R*, and 2. angular velocity of the slotted link *OC*.

[Ans. 0.8 m/s ; 1.83 rad/s]

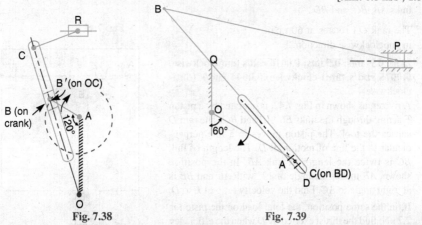

Fig. 7.38   **Fig. 7.39**

9. In a Whitworth quick return motion mechanism, as shown in Fig. 7.39, the dimensions of various links are as follows :

OQ = 100 mm ; *OA* = 200 mm ; *BQ* = 150 mm and *BP* = 500 mm.

If the crank *OA* turns at 120 r.p.m. in clockwise direction and makes an angle of 120° with *OQ*, Find : 1. velocity of the block *P*, and 2. angular velocity of the slotted link *BQ*.

[Ans. 0.63 m/s ; 6.3 rad/s]

10. A toggle press mechanism, as shown in Fig. 7.40, has the dimensions of various links as follows : *OP* = 50 mm ; *RQ* = *RS* = 200 mm ; *PR* = 300 mm.

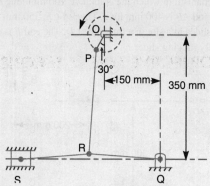

Fig. 7.40

Find the velocity of S when the crank OP rotates at 60 r.p.m. in the anticlockwise direction. If the torque on P is 115 N-m, what pressure will be exerted at S when the overall efficiency is 60 per-cent.

[Ans. 400 m/s ; 3.9 kN]

11. Fig. 7.41 shows a toggle mecha-nism in which link D is constained to move in horizontal direction. For the given configuration, find out : 1. velocities of points b and D; and 2. angular velocities of links AB, BC, and BD.

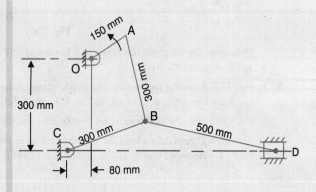

Fig. 7.41

The rank OA rotates at 60 r.p.m. in anticlockwise direction.

[Ans. 0.9 m/s; 0.5 m/s; 0.0016 rad/s (anticlockwise) 0.0075 rad/s (anti-clockwise),0.0044 rad/s (anti-clockwise)]

12. A riveter, as shown in Fig. 7.42, is operated by a piston F acting through the links EB, AB and BC. The ram D carries the tool. The piston moves in a line perpen-dicular to the line of motion of D. The length of link BC is twice the length of link AB. In the position shown, AB makes an angle of 12° with AC and BE is at right angle to AC. Find the velocity ratio of E to D.

If, in the same position, the total load on the piston is 2.2 kN, find the thrust exerted by D when the efficiency of the mechanism is 72 per cent,

[Ans. 3.2 ; 5 kN]

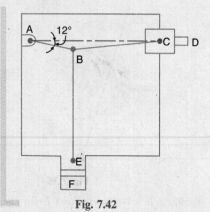

Fig. 7.42

DO YOU KNOW ?

1. Describe the method to find the velocity of a point on a link whose direction (or path) is known and the velocity of some other point on the same link in magnitude and direction is given.

2. Explain how the velocities of a slider and the connecting rod are obtained in a slider crank mechanism.

3. Define rubbing velocity at a pin joint. What will be the rubbing velocity at pin joint when the two links move in the same and opposite directions ?

4. What is the difference between ideal mechanical advantage and actual mechanical advantage ?

OBJECTIVE TYPE QUESTIONS

1. The direction of linear velocity of any point on a link with respect to another point on the same link is

 (a) parallel to the link joining the points   (b) perpendicular to the link joining the points

 (c) at 45° to the link joining the points   (d) none of these

2. The magnitude of linear velocity of a point B on a link AB relative to point A is

 (a) $\omega.AB$

 (c) $\omega^2.AB$

 (b) $\omega(AB)^2$

 (d) $(\omega.AB)^2$

 where ω = Angular velocity of the link AB.

3. The two links OA and OB are connected by a pin joint at O. If the link OA turns with angular velocity ω_1 rad/s in the clockwise direction and the link OB turns with angular velocity ω_2 rad/s in the anti-clockwise direction, then the rubbing velocity at the pin joint O is

 (a) $\omega_1.\omega_2.r$

 (c) $(\omega_1+\omega_2)r$

 (b) $(\omega_1-\omega_2)r$

 (d) $(\omega_1-\omega_2)2r$

 where r = Radius of the pin at O.

4. In the above question, if both the links OA and OB turn in clockwise direction, then the rubbing velocity at the pin joint O is

 (a) $\omega_1.\omega_2.r$

 (c) $(\omega_1+\omega_2)r$

 (b) $(\omega_1-\omega_2)r$

 (d) $(\omega_1-\omega_2)2r$

5. In a four bar mechanism, as shown in Fig. 7.43, if a force F_A is acting at point A in the direction of its velocity v_A and a force F_B is transmitted to the joint B in the direction of its velocity v_B, then the ideal mechanical advantage is equal to

 (a) $F_B.v_A$

 (b) $F_A.v_B$

 (c) $\dfrac{F_B}{v_B}$

 (d) $\dfrac{F_B}{F_A}$

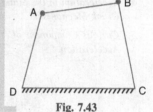

Fig. 7.43

ANSWERS

     1. (b)   **2.** (a)   **3.** (c)   **4.** (b)   **5.** (d)

Warping Machine

8

Acceleration in Mechanisms

8.1. Introduction

We have discussed in the previous chapter the velocities of various points in the mechanisms. Now we shall discuss the acceleration of points in the mechanisms. The acceleration analysis plays a very important role in the development of machines and mechanisms.

8.2. Acceleration Diagram for a Link

Consider two points A and B on a rigid link as shown in Fig. 8.1 (a). Let the point B moves with respect to A, with an angular velocity of ω rad/s and let α rad/s^2 be the angular acceleration of the link AB.

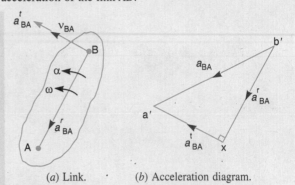

(a) Link.   (b) Acceleration diagram.

Fig. 8.1. Acceleration for a link.

We have already discussed that acceleration of a particle whose velocity changes both in magnitude and direction at any instant has the following two components :

1. The *centripetal or radial component,* which is perpendicular to the velocity of the particle at the given instant.

2. The *tangential component,* which is parallel to the velocity of the particle at the given instant.

Thus for a link *AB*, the velocity of point *B* with respect to *A* (*i.e.* v_{BA}) is perpendicular to the link *AB* as shown in Fig. 8.1 (*a*). Since the point *B* moves with respect to *A* with an angular velocity of ω rad/s, therefore centripetal or radial component of the acceleration of *B* with respect to *A*,

$$a_{BA}^{r} = \omega^2 \times \text{Length of link } AB = \omega^2 \times AB = v_{BA}^2 / AB \qquad \cdots \left(\because \omega = \frac{v_{BA}}{AB} \right)$$

This radial component of acceleration acts perpendicular to the velocity v_{BA}, In other words, it acts *parallel* to the link *AB*.

We know that tangential component of the acceleration of *B* with respect to *A*,

$$a_{BA}^{t} = \alpha \times \text{Length of link } AB = \alpha \times AB$$

This tangential component of acceleration acts parallel to the velocity v_{BA}. In other words, it acts *perpendicular* to the link *AB*.

In order to draw the acceleration diagram for a link *AB*, as shown in Fig. 8.1 (*b*), from any point *b'*, draw vector *b'x parallel to BA* to represent the radial component of acceleration of *B* with respect to *A i.e.* a_{BA}^{r} and from point *x* draw vector *xa'* perpendicular to *BA* to represent the tangential component of acceleration of *B* with respect to *A i.e.* a_{BA}^{t} . *Join b' a'.* The vector *b' a'* (known as *acceleration image* of the link *AB*) represents the total acceleration of *B* with respect to *A* (*i.e.* a_{BA}) and it is the vector sum of radial component (a_{BA}^{r}) and tangential component (a_{BA}^{t}) of acceleration.

8.3. Acceleration of a Point on a Link

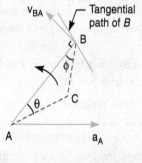

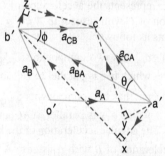

(*a*) Points on a Link.   (*b*) Acceleration diagram.

Fig. 8.2. Acceleration of a point on a link.

Consider two points *A* and *B* on the rigid link, as shown in Fig. 8.2 (*a*). Let the acceleration of the point *A i.e.* a_A is known in magnitude and direction and the direction of path of *B* is given. The acceleration of the point *B* is determined in magnitude and direction by drawing the acceleration diagram as discussed below.

1. From any point *o'*, draw vector *o'a'* parallel to the direction of absolute acceleration at point *A i.e.* a_A , to some suitable scale, as shown in Fig. 8.2 (*b*).

2. We know that the acceleration of B with respect to A *i.e.* a_{BA} has the following two components:

(*i*) Radial component of the acceleration of B with respect to A *i.e.* a_{BA}^r, and

(*ii*) Tangential component of the acceleration B with respect to A *i.e.* a_{BA}^t. These two components are mutually perpendicular.

3. Draw vector $a'x$ parallel to the link AB (because radial component of the acceleration of B with respect to A will pass through AB), such that

$$\text{vector } a'x = a_{BA}^r = v_{BA}^2 / AB$$

where v_{BA} = Velocity of B with respect to A.

Note: The value of v_{BA} may be obtained by drawing the velocity diagram as discussed in the previous chapter.

4. From point x, draw vector xb' perpendicular to AB or vector $a'x$ (because tangential component of B with respect to A *i.e.* a_{BA}^t, is perpendicular to radial component a_{BA}^r) and through o' draw a line parallel to the path of B to represent the absolute acceleration of B *i.e.* a_B. The vectors xb' and $o'b'$ intersect at b'. Now the values of a_B and a_{BA}^t may be measured, to the scale.

A refracting telescope uses mechanisms to change directions.

Note : This picture is given as additional information.

5. By joining the points a' and b' we may determine the total acceleration of B with respect to A *i.e.* a_{BA}. The vector $a'b'$ is known as ***acceleration image*** of the link AB.

6. For any other point C on the link, draw triangle $a'b'c'$ similar to triangle ABC. Now vector $b'c'$ represents the acceleration of C with respect to B *i.e.* a_{CB}, and vector $a'c'$ represents the acceleration of C with respect *to* A *i.e.* a_{CA}. As discussed above, a_{CB} and a_{CA} will each have two components as follows :

(*i*) a_{CB} has two components; a_{CB}^r and a_{CB}^t as shown by triangle $b'zc'$ in Fig. 8.2 (*b*), in which $b'z$ is parallel to BC and zc' is perpendicular to $b'z$ or BC.

(*ii*) a_{CA} has two components ; a_{CA}^r and a_{CA}^t as shown by triangle $a'yc'$ in Fig. 8.2 (*b*), in which $a'y$ is parallel to AC and yc' is perpendicular to $a'y$ or AC.

7. The angular acceleration of the link AB is obtained by dividing the tangential components of the acceleration of B with respect to A (a_{BA}^t) to the length of the link. Mathematically, angular acceleration of the link AB,

$$\alpha_{AB} = a_{BA}^t / AB$$

8.4. Acceleration in the Slider Crank Mechanism

A slider crank mechanism is shown in Fig. 8.3 (*a*). Let the crank OB makes an angle θ with the inner dead centre (*I.D.C*) and rotates in a clockwise direction about the fixed point O with uniform angular velocity ω_{BO} rad/s.

∴ Velocity of B with respect to O or velocity of B (because O is a fixed point),

$$v_{BO} = v_B = \omega_{BO} \times OB, \text{ acting tangentially at } B.$$

We know that centripetal or radial acceleration of B with respect to O or acceleration of B (because O is a fixed point),

$$a_{BO}^r = a_B = \omega_{BO}^2 \times OB = \frac{v_{BO}^2}{OB}$$

Note : A point at the end of a link which moves with constant angular velocity has no tangential component of acceleration.

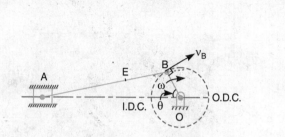

(*a*) Slider crank mechanism. (*b*) Acceleration diagram.

Fig. 8.3. Acceleration in the slider crank mechanism.

The acceleration diagram, as shown in Fig. 8.3 (*b*), may now be drawn as discussed below:

1. Draw vector $o' b'$ parallel to BO and set off equal in magnitude of $a_{BO}^r = a_B$, to some suitable scale.

2. From point b', draw vector $b'x$ parallel to BA. The vector $b'x$ represents the radial component of the acceleration of A with respect to B whose magnitude is given by :

$$a_{AB}^r = v_{AB}^2 / BA$$

Since the point B moves with constant angular velocity, therefore there will be *no tangential* component of the acceleration.

3. From point x, draw vector xa' perpendicular to $b'x$ (or AB). The vector xa' represents the tangential component of the acceleration of A with respect to B *i.e.* a_{AB}^t.

Note: When a point moves along a straight line, it has **no centripetal or radial** component of the acceleration.

4. Since the point A reciprocates along AO, therefore the acceleration must be parallel to velocity. Therefore from o', draw $o' a'$ parallel to AO, intersecting the vector xa' at a'.

Now the acceleration of the piston or the slider A (a_A) and a_{AB}^t may be measured to the scale.

5. The vector $b'a'$, which is the sum of the vectors $b'x$ and xa', represents the total acceleration of A with respect to B *i.e.* a_{AB}. The vector $b' a'$ represents the acceleration of the connecting rod AB.

6. The acceleration of any other point on AB such as E may be obtained by dividing the vector $b' a'$ at e' in the same ratio as E divides AB in Fig. 8.3 (*a*). In other words

$$a'e'/a'b' = AE/AB$$

7. The angular acceleration of the connecting rod AB may be obtained by dividing the tangential component of the acceleration of A with respect to B $\left(a_{AB}^t \right)$ to the length of AB. In other words, angular acceleration of AB,

$$\alpha_{AB} = a_{AB}^t / AB \text{ (Clockwise about } B)$$

Example 8.1. *The crank of a slider crank mechanism rotates clockwise at a constant speed of 300 r.p.m. The crank is 150 mm and the connecting rod is 600 mm long. Determine : 1. linear velocity and acceleration of the midpoint of the connecting rod, and 2. angular velocity and angular acceleration of the connecting rod, at a crank angle of 45° from inner dead centre position.*

Solution. Given : N_{BO} = 300 r.p.m. or ω_{BO} = 2 π × 300/60 = 31.42 rad/s; OB = 150 mm = 0.15 m ; BA = 600 mm = 0.6 m

We know that linear velocity of B with respect to O or velocity of B,

$$v_{BO} = v_B = \omega_{BO} \times OB = 31.42 \times 0.15 = 4.713 \text{ m/s}$$

...(Perpendicular to BO)

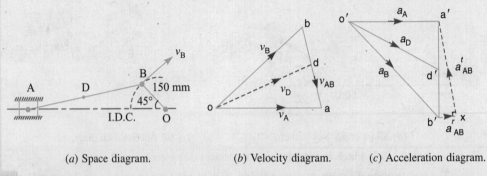

(a) Space diagram.	(b) Velocity diagram.	(c) Acceleration diagram.

Fig. 8.4

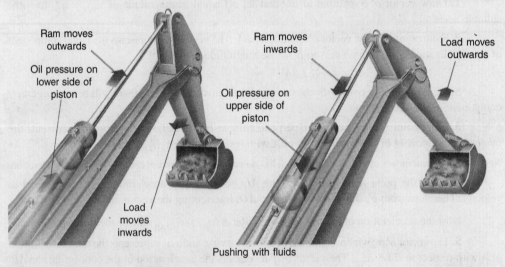

Pushing with fluids

Note : This picture is given as additional information.

1. *Linear velocity of the midpoint of the connecting rod*

First of all draw the space diagram, to some suitable scale; as shown in Fig. 8.4 (a). Now the velocity diagram, as shown in Fig. 8.4 (b), is drawn as discussed below:

1. Draw vector *ob* perpendicular to BO, to some suitable scale, to represent the velocity of B with respect to O or simply velocity of B i.e. v_{BO} or v_B, such that

$$\text{vector } ob = v_{BO} = v_B = 4.713 \text{ m/s}$$

2. From point b, draw vector *ba* perpendicular to BA to represent the velocity of A with respect to B i.e. v_{AB}, and from point o draw vector *oa* parallel to the motion of A (which is along AO) to represent the velocity of A i.e. v_A. The vectors *ba* and *oa* intersect at a.

By measurement, we find that velocity of *A* with respect to *B*,

$$v_{AB} = \text{vector } ba = 3.4 \text{ m/s}$$

and Velocity of *A*, $v_A = \text{vector } oa = 4 \text{ m/s}$

3. In order to find the velocity of the midpoint *D* of the connecting rod *AB*, divide the vector *ba* at *d* in the same ratio as *D* divides *AB*, in the space diagram. In other words,

$$bd / ba = BD/BA$$

Note: Since *D* is the midpoint of *AB*, therefore *d* is also midpoint of vector *ba*.

4. Join *od*. Now the vector *od* represents the velocity of the midpoint *D* of the connecting rod *i.e.* v_D.

By measurement, we find that

$$v_D = \text{vector } od = 4.1 \text{ m/s } \textbf{Ans.}$$

Acceleration of the midpoint of the connecting rod

We know that the radial component of the acceleration of *B* with respect to *O* or the acceleration of *B*,

$$a_{BO}^r = a_B = \frac{v_{BO}^2}{OB} = \frac{(4.713)^2}{0.15} = 148.1 \text{ m/s}^2$$

and the radial component of the acceleraiton of *A* with respect to *B*,

$$a_{AB}^r = \frac{v_{AB}^2}{BA} = \frac{(3.4)^2}{0.6} = 19.3 \text{ m/s}^2$$

Now the acceleration diagram, as shown in Fig. 8.4 (*c*) is drawn as discussed below:

1. Draw vector *o' b'* parallel to *BO*, to some suitable scale, to represent the radial component of the acceleration of *B* with respect to *O* or simply acceleration of *B i.e.* a_{BO}^r or a_B, such that

$$\text{vector } o'b' = a_{BO}^r = a_B = 148.1 \text{ m/s}^2$$

Note: Since the crank *OB* rotates at a constant speed, therefore there will be no tangential component of the acceleration of *B* with respect to *O*.

2. The acceleration of *A* with respect to *B* has the following two components:

(*a*) The radial component of the acceleration of *A* with respect to *B i.e.* a_{AB}^r, and

(*b*) The tangential component of the acceleration of *A* with respect to *B i.e.* a_{AB}^t. These two components are mutually perpendicular.

Therefore from point *b'*, draw vector *b' x* parallel to *AB* to represent $a_{AB}^r = 19.3 \text{ m/s}^2$ and from point *x* draw vector *xa'* perpendicular to vector *b'x* whose magnitude is yet unknown.

3. Now from *o'*, draw vector *o' a'* parallel to the path of motion of *A* (which is along *AO*) to represent the acceleration of *A i.e.* a_A. The vectors *xa'* and *o' a'* intersect at *a'*. Join *a' b'*.

4. In order to find the acceleration of the midpoint *D* of the connecting rod *AB*, divide the vector *a' b'* at *d'* in the same ratio as *D* divides *AB*. In other words

$$b'd' / b'a' = BD / BA$$

Note: Since *D* is the midpoint of *AB*, therefore *d'* is also midpoint of vector *b' a'*.

5. Join *o' d'*. The vector *o' d'* represents the acceleration of midpoint *D* of the connecting rod *i.e.* a_D.

By measurement, we find that

$$a_D = \text{vector } o' d' = 117 \text{ m/s}^2 \textbf{ Ans.}$$

2. Angular velocity of the connecting rod

We know that angular velocity of the connecting rod AB,

$$\omega_{AB} = \frac{v_{AB}}{BA} = \frac{3.4}{0.6} = 5.67 \text{ rad/s}^2 \text{ (Anticlockwise about } B) \text{ Ans.}$$

Angular acceleration of the connecting rod

From the acceleration diagram, we find that

$$a^t_{AB} = 103 \text{ m/s}^2 \qquad \qquad \text{...(By measurement)}$$

We know that angular acceleration of the connecting rod AB,

$$\alpha_{AB} = \frac{a^t_{AB}}{BA} = \frac{103}{0.6} = 171.67 \text{ rad/s}^2 \text{ (Clockwise about } B) \text{ Ans.}$$

Example 8.2. *An engine mechanism is shown in Fig. 8.5. The crank CB = 100 mm and the connecting rod BA = 300 mm with centre of gravity G, 100 mm from B. In the position shown, the crankshaft has a speed of 75 rad/s and an angular acceleration of 1200 rad/s². Find: 1. velocity of G and angular velocity of AB, and 2. acceleration of G and angular acceleration of AB.*

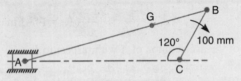

Fig. 8.5

Solution. Given : $\omega_{BC} = 75$ rad/s ; $\alpha_{BC} = 1200$ rad/s², $CB = 100$ mm $= 0.1$ m; $BA = 300$ mm $= 0.3$ m

We know that velocity of B with respect to C or velocity of B,

$$v_{BC} = v_B = \omega_{BC} \times CB = 75 \times 0.1 = 7.5 \text{ m/s} \qquad \text{...(Perpendicular to } BC)$$

Since the angular acceleration of the crankshaft, $\alpha_{BC} = 1200$ rad/s², therefore tangential component of the acceleration of B with respect to C,

$$a^t_{BC} = \alpha_{BC} \times CB = 1200 \times 0.1 = 120 \text{ m/s}^2$$

Note: When the angular acceleration is not given, then there will be no tangential component of the acceleration.

1. Velocity of G and angular velocity of AB

First of all, draw the space diagram, to some suitable scale, as shown in Fig. 8.6 (*a*). Now the velocity diagram, as shown in Fig. 8.6 (*b*), is drawn as discussed below:

1. Draw vector *cb* perpendicular to CB, to some suitable scale, to represent the velocity of B with respect to C or velocity of B (*i.e.* v_{BC} or v_B), such that

$$\text{vector } cb = v_{BC} = v_B = 7.5 \text{ m/s}$$

2. From point *b*, draw vector *ba* perpendicular to BA to represent the velocity of A with respect to B *i.e.* v_{AB}, and from point *c*, draw vector *ca* parallel to the path of motion of A (which is along AC) to represent the velocity of A *i.e.* v_A. The vectors *ba* and *ca* intersect at *a*.

3. Since the point G lies on AB, therefore divide vector *ab* at *g* in the same ratio as G divides AB in the space diagram. In other words,

$$ag / ab = AG / AB$$

The vector *cg* represents the velocity of G.

By measurement, we find that velocity of G,

$$v_G = \text{vector } cg = 6.8 \text{ m/s} \text{ Ans.}$$

From velocity diagram, we find that velocity of A with respect to B,

$$v_{AB} = \text{vector } ba = 4 \text{ m/s}$$

We know that angular velocity of AB,

$$\omega_{AB} = \frac{v_{AB}}{BA} = \frac{4}{0.3} = 13.3 \text{ rad/s (Clockwise)} \text{ **Ans.**}$$

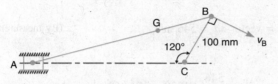
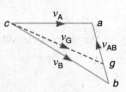

(a) Space diagram.	(b) Velocity diagram.

Fig. 8.6

2. Acceleration of G and angular acceleration of AB

We know that radial component of the acceleration of B with respect to C,

$$*a_{BC}^r = \frac{v_{BC}^2}{CB} = \frac{(7.5)^2}{0.1} = 562.5 \text{ m/s}^2$$

and radial component of the acceleration of A with respect to B,

$$a_{AB}^r = \frac{v_{AB}^2}{BA} = \frac{4^2}{0.3} = 53.3 \text{ m/s}^2$$

Now the acceleration diagram, as shown in Fig. 8.6 (c), is drawn as discussed below:

1. Draw vector $c'\,b''$ parallel to CB, to some suitable scale, to represent the radial component of the acceleration of B with respect to C, i.e. a_{BC}^r, such that

$$\text{vector } c'b'' = a_{BC}^r = 562.5 \text{ m/s}^2$$

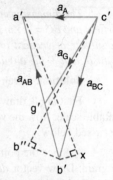

(c) Acceleration diagram.

Fig. 8.6

2. From point b'', draw vector $b''\,b'$ perpendicular to vector $c'\,b''$ or CB to represent the tangential component of the acceleration of B with respect to C i.e. a_{BC}^t, such that

$$\text{vector } b''b' = a_{BC}^t = 120 \text{ m/s}^2 \qquad \qquad \text{... (Given)}$$

3. Join $c'\,b'$. The vector $c'\,b'$ represents the total acceleration of B with respect to C i.e. a_{BC}.

4. From point b', draw vector $b'\,x$ parallel to BA to represent radial component of the acceleration of A with respect to B i.e. a_{AB}^r such that

$$\text{vector } b'x = a_{AB}^r = 53.3 \text{ m/s}^2$$

5. From point x, draw vector xa' perpendicular to vector $b'x$ or BA to represent tangential component of the acceleration of A with respect to B i.e. a_{AB}^t, whose magnitude is not yet known.

6. Now draw vector $c'\,a'$ parallel to the path of motion of A (which is along AC) to represent the acceleration of A i.e. a_A. The vectors xa' and $c'a'$ intersect at a'. Join $b'\,a'$. The vector $b'\,a'$ represents the acceleration of A with respect to B i.e. a_{AB}.

---

* When angular acceleration of the crank is not given, then there is no a_{BC}^t. In that case, $a_{BC}^r = a_{BC} = a_B$, as discussed in the previous example.

7. In order to find the acceleratio of G, divide vector $a'b'$ in g' in the same ratio as G divides BA in Fig. 8.6 (a). Join $c'g'$. The vector $c'g'$ represents the acceleration of G.

By measurement, we find that acceleration of G,

$$a_G = \text{vector } c'g' = 414 \text{ m/s}^2 \text{ Ans.}$$

From acceleration diagram, we find that tangential component of the acceleration of A with respect to B,

$$a^t_{AB} = \text{vector } xa' = 546 \text{ m/s}^2 \qquad \text{...(By measurement)}$$

∴ Angular acceleration of AB,

$$\alpha_{AB} = \frac{a^t_{AB}}{BA} = \frac{546}{0.3} = 1820 \text{ rad/s}^2 \text{ (Clockwise) Ans.}$$

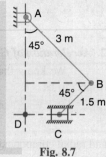

Example 8.3. *In the mechanism shown in Fig. 8.7, the slider C is moving to the right with a velocity of 1 m/s and an acceleration of 2.5 m/s².*

*The dimensions of various links are AB = 3 m inclined at 45° with the vertical and BC = 1.5 m inclined at 45° with the horizontal. Determine: **1.** the magnitude of vertical and horizontal component of the acceleration of the point B, and **2.** the angular acceleration of the links AB and BC.*

Fig. 8.7

Solution. Given : $v_C = 1$ m/s ; $a_C = 2.5$ m/s²; $AB = 3$ m ; $BC = 1.5$ m

First of all, draw the space diagram, as shown in Fig. 8.8 (a), to some suitable scale. Now the velocity diagram, as shown in Fig. 8.8 (b), is drawn as discussed below:

1. Since the points A and D are fixed points, therefore they lie at one place in the velocity diagram. Draw vector dc parallel to DC, to some suitable scale, which represents the velocity of slider C with respect to D or simply velocity of C, such that

$$\text{vector } dc = v_{CD} = v_C = 1 \text{ m/s}$$

2. Since point B has two motions, one with respect to A and the other with respect to C, therefore from point a, draw vector ab perpendicular to AB to represent the velocity of B with respect to A, i.e. v_{BA} and from point c draw vector cb perpendicular to CB to represent the velocity of B with respect to C i.e. v_{BC}. The vectors ab and cb intersect at b.

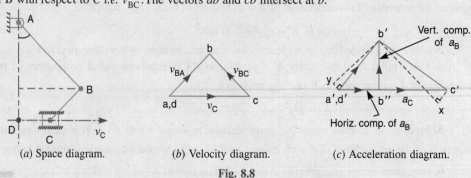

| (a) Space diagram. | (b) Velocity diagram. | (c) Acceleration diagram. |

Fig. 8.8

By measurement, we find that velocity of B with respect to A,

$$v_{BA} = \text{vector } ab = 0.72 \text{ m/s}$$

and velocity of B with respect to C,

$$v_{BC} = \text{vector } cb = 0.72 \text{ m/s}$$

We know that radial component of acceleration of B with respect to C,

$$a_{BC}^r = \frac{v_{BC}^2}{CB} = \frac{(0.72)^2}{1.5} = 0.346 \text{ m/s}^2$$

and radial component of acceleration of B with respect to A,

$$a_{BA}^r = \frac{v_{BA}^2}{AB} = \frac{(0.72)^2}{3} = 0.173 \text{ m/s}^2$$

Now the acceleration diagram, as shown in Fig. 8.8 (*c*), is drawn as discussed below:

1. *Since the points A and D are fixed points, therefore they lie at one place in the acceleration diagram. Draw vector $d'\,c'$ parallel to DC, to some suitable scale, to represent the acceleration of C with respect to D or simply acceleration of C *i.e.* a_{CD} or a_C such that

$$\text{vector } d'c' = a_{CD} = a_C = 2.5 \text{ m/s}^2$$

2. The acceleration of B with respect to C will have two components, *i.e.* one radial component of B with respect to C $\left(a_{BC}^r\right)$ and the other tangential component of B with respect to C $\left(a_{BC}^t\right)$. Therefore from point c', draw vector $c'\,x$ parallel to CB to represent a_{BC}^r such that

$$\text{vector } c'x = a_{BC}^r = 0.346 \text{ m/s}^2$$

3. Now from point x, draw vector xb' perpendicular to vector $c'\,x$ or CB to represent a_{BC}^t whose magnitude is yet unknown.

4. The acceleration of B with respect to A will also have two components, *i.e.* one radial component of B with respect to A (a_{BA}^r) and other tangential component of B with respect to A (a_{BA}^t). Therefore from point a' draw vector $a'\,y$ parallel to AB to represent a_{BA}^r, such that

$$\text{vector } a'\,y = a_{BA}^r = 0.173 \text{ m/s}^2$$

5. From point y, draw vector yb' perpendicular to vector $a'y$ or AB to represent a_{BA}^t. The vector yb' intersect the vector xb' at b'. Join $a'\,b'$ and $c'\,b'$. The vector $a'\,b'$ represents the acceleration of point B (a_B) and the vector $c'\,b'$ represents the acceleration of B with respect to C.

1. *Magnitude of vertical and horizontal component of the acceleration of the point B*

Draw $b'\,b''$ perpendicular to $a'\,c'$. The vector $b'\,b''$ is the vertical component of the acceleration of the point B and $a'\,b''$ is the horizontal component of the acceleration of the point B. By measurement,

$$\text{vector } b'\,b'' = 1.13 \text{ m/s}^2 \text{ and vector } a'\,b'' = 0.9 \text{ m/s}^2 \text{ \textbf{Ans.}}$$

2. *Angular acceleration of AB and BC*

By measurement from acceleration diagram, we find that tangential component of acceleration of the point B with respect to A,

$$a_{BA}^t = \text{vector } yb' = 1.41 \text{ m/s}^2$$

and tangential component of acceleration of the point B with respect to C,

$$a_{BC}^t = \text{vector } xb' = 1.94 \text{ m/s}^2$$

---

* If the mechanism consists of more than one fixed point, then all these points lie at the same place in the velocity and acceleration diagrams.

We know that angular acceleration of AB,

$$\alpha_{AB} = \frac{a_{BA}^t}{AB} = \frac{1.41}{3} = 0.47 \text{ rad/s}^2 \text{ Ans.}$$

and angular acceleration of BC,

$$\alpha_{BC} = \frac{a_{BC}^t}{CB} = \frac{1.94}{1.5} = 1.3 \text{ rad/s}^2 \text{ Ans.}$$

Example 8.4. *PQRS is a four bar chain with link PS fixed. The lengths of the links are PQ = 62.5 mm ; QR = 175 mm ; RS = 112.5 mm ; and PS = 200 mm. The crank PQ rotates at 10 rad/s clockwise. Draw the velocity and acceleration diagram when angle QPS = 60° and Q and R lie on the same side of PS. Find the angular velocity and angular acceleration of links QR and RS.*

Solution. Given : $\omega_{QP} = 10$ rad/s; $PQ = 62.5$ mm $= 0.0625$ m ; $QR = 175$ mm $= 0.175$ m ; $RS = 112.5$ mm $= 0.1125$ m ; $PS = 200$ mm $= 0.2$ m

We know that velocity of Q with respect to P or velocity of Q,

$$v_{QP} = v_Q = \omega_{QP} \times PQ = 10 \times 0.0625 = 0.625 \text{ m/s}$$

...(Perpendicular to PQ)

Angular velocity of links QR and RS

First of all, draw the space diagram of a four bar chain, to some suitable scale, as shown in Fig. 8.9 (*a*). Now the velocity diagram as shown in Fig. 8.9 (*b*), is drawn as discussed below:

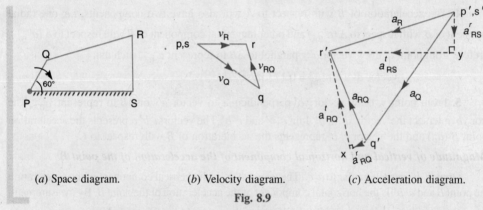

(*a*) Space diagram.   (*b*) Velocity diagram.   (*c*) Acceleration diagram.

Fig. 8.9

1. Since P and S are fixed points, therefore these points lie at one place in velocity diagram. Draw vector pq perpendicular to PQ, to some suitable scale, to represent the velocity of Q with respect to P or velocity of Q *i.e.* v_{QP} or v_Q such that

vector $pq = v_{QP} = v_Q = 0.625$ m/s

2. From point q, draw vector qr perpendicular to QR to represent the velocity of R with respect to Q (*i.e.* v_{RQ}) and from point s, draw vector sr perpendicular to SR to represent the velocity of R with respect to S or velocity of R (*i.e.* v_{RS} or v_R). The vectors qr and sr intersect at r. By measurement, we find that

$$v_{RQ} = \text{vector } qr = 0.333 \text{ m/s, and } v_{RS} = v_R = \text{vector } sr = 0.426 \text{ m/s}$$

We know that angular velocity of link QR,

$$\omega_{QR} = \frac{v_{RQ}}{QR} = \frac{0.333}{0.175} = 1.9 \text{ rad/s (Anticlockwise) } \textbf{Ans.}$$

and angular velocity of link *RS*,

$$\omega_{RS} = \frac{v_{RS}}{SR} = \frac{0.426}{0.1125} = 3.78 \text{ rad/s (Clockwise) } \textbf{Ans.}$$

Angular acceleration of links QR and RS

Since the angular acceleration of the crank *PQ* is not given, therefore there will be no tangential component of the acceleration of *Q* with respect to *P*.

We know that radial component of the acceleration of *Q* with respect to *P* (or the acceleration of *Q*),

$$a_{QP}^r = a_{QP} = a_Q = \frac{v_{QP}^2}{PQ} = \frac{(0.625)^2}{0.0625} = 6.25 \text{ m/s}^2$$

Radial component of the acceleration of *R* with respect to *Q*,

$$a_{RQ}^r = \frac{v_{RQ}^2}{QR} = \frac{(0.333)^2}{0.175} = 0.634 \text{ m/s}^2$$

and radial component of the acceleration of *R* with respect to *S* (or the acceleration of *R*),

$$a_{RS}^r = a_{RS} = a_R = \frac{v_{RS}^2}{SR} = \frac{(0.426)^2}{0.1125} = 1.613 \text{ m/s}^2$$

The acceleration diagram, as shown in Fig. 8.9 (*c*) is drawn as follows :

1. Since *P* and *S* are fixed points, therefore these points lie at one place in the acceleration diagram. Draw vector *p'q'* parallel to *PQ*, to some suitable scale, to represent the radial component of acceleration of *Q* with respect to *P* or acceleration of *Q i.e* a_{QP}^r or a_Q such that

$$\text{vector } p'q' = a_{QP}^r = a_Q = 6.25 \text{ m/s}^2$$

2. From point *q'*, draw vector *q' x* parallel to *QR* to represent the radial component of acceleration of *R* with respect to *Q i.e.* a_{RQ}^r such that

$$\text{vector } q'x = a_{RQ}^r = 0.634 \text{ m/s}^2$$

3. From point *x*, draw vector *xr'* perpendicular to *QR* to represent the tangential component of acceleration of *R* with respect to *Q i.e* a_{RQ}^t whose magnitude is not yet known.

4. Now from point *s'*, draw vector *s'y* parallel to *SR* to represent the radial component of the acceleration of *R* with respect to *S i.e.* a_{RS}^r such that

$$\text{vector } s'y = a_{RS}^r = 1.613 \text{ m/s}^2$$

5. From point *y*, draw vector *yr'* perpendicular to *SR* to represent the tangential component of acceleration of *R* with respect to *S i.e.* a_{RS}^t.

6. The vectors *xr'* and *yr'* intersect at *r'*. Join *p'r* and *q' r'*. By measurement, we find that

$$a_{RQ}^t = \text{vector } xr' = 4.1 \text{ m/s}^2 \text{ and } a_{RS}^t = \text{vector } yr' = 5.3 \text{ m/s}^2$$

We know that angular acceleration of link *QR*,

$$\alpha_{QR} = \frac{a_{RQ}^t}{QR} = \frac{4.1}{0.175} = 23.43 \text{ rad/s}^2 \text{ (Anticlockwise) } \textbf{Ans.}$$

and angular acceleration of link *RS*,

$$\alpha_{RS} = \frac{a_{RS}^t}{SR} = \frac{5.3}{0.1125} = 47.1 \text{ rad/s}^2 \text{ (Anticlockwise) } \textbf{Ans.}$$

Example 8.5. *The dimensions and configuration of the four bar mechanism, shown in Fig. 8.10, are as follows :*

$P_1A = 300$ *mm;* $P_2B = 360$ *mm; AB = 360 mm, and* $P_1P_2 = 600$ *mm.*

The angle $AP_1P_2 = 60°$. *The crank* P_1A *has an angular velocity of 10 rad/s and an angular acceleration of 30 rad/s², both clockwise. Determine the angular velocities and angular accelerations of* P_2B, *and AB and the velocity and acceleration of the joint B.*

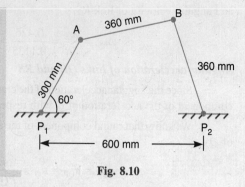

Fig. 8.10

Solution. Given : $\omega_{AP1} = 10$ rad/s ; $\alpha_{AP1} = 30$ rad/s²; $P_1A = 300$ mm = 0.3 m ; $P_2B = AB = 360$ mm = 0.36 m

We know that the velocity of A with respect to P_1 or velocity of A,

$$v_{AP1} = v_A = \omega_{AP1} \times P_1A = 10 \times 0.3 = 3 \text{ m/s}$$

Velocity of B and angular velocitites of P_2B and AB

First of all, draw the space diagram, to some suitable scale, as shown in Fig. 8.11 (*a*). Now the velocity diagram, as shown in Fig. 8.11 (*b*), is drawn as discussed below:

1. Since P_1 and P_2 are fixed points, therefore these points lie at one place in velocity diagram. Draw vector $p_1 a$ perpendicular to P_1A, to some suitable scale, to represent the velocity of A with respect to P_1 or velocity of A *i.e.* v_{AP1} or v_A, such that

$$\text{vector } p_1a = v_{A\,P1} = v_A = 3 \text{ m/s}$$

2. From point *a*, draw vector *ab* perpendicular to *AB* to represent velocity of B with respect to A (*i.e.* v_{BA}) and from point p_2 draw vector p_2b perpendicular to P_2B to represent the velocity of B with respect to P_2 or velocity of B *i.e.* v_{BP2} or v_B. The vectors *ab* and p_2b intersect at *b*.

By measurement, we find that

$$v_{BP2} = v_B = \text{vector } p_2b = 2.2 \text{ m/s} \textbf{ Ans.}$$

and $\qquad\qquad v_{BA} = \text{vector } ab = 2.05 \text{ m/s}$

We know that angular velocity of P_2B,

$$\omega_{P2B} = \frac{v_{BP2}}{P_2B} = \frac{2.2}{0.36} = 6.1 \text{ rad/s (Clockwise) } \textbf{Ans.}$$

and angular velocity of *AB*,

$$\omega_{AB} = \frac{v_{BA}}{AB} = \frac{2.05}{0.36} = 5.7 \text{ rad/s (Anticlockwise) } \textbf{Ans.}$$

Acceleration of B and angular acceleration of P_2B and AB

We know that tangential component of the acceleration of A with respect to P_1,

$$a^t_{AP1} = \alpha_{AP1} \times P_1A = 30 \times 0.3 = 9 \text{ m/s}^2$$

Radial component of the acceleration of A with respect to P_1,

$$a^r_{AP1} = \frac{v^2_{AP1}}{P_1A} = \omega^2_{AP1} \times P_1A = 10^2 \times 0.3 = 30 \text{ m/s}^2$$

Radial component of the acceleration of B with respect to A.

$$a_{BA}^r = \frac{v_{BA}^2}{AB} = \frac{(2.05)^2}{0.36} = 11.67 \text{ m/s}^2$$

and radial component of the acceleration of B with respect to P_2,

$$a_{BP_2}^r = \frac{v_{BP_2}^2}{P_2 B} = \frac{(2.2)^2}{0.36} = 13.44 \text{ m/s}^2$$

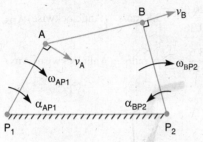

(a) Space diagram.

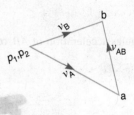

(b) Velocity diagram.

Fig. 8.11

The acceleration diagram, as shown in Fig. 8.11 (*c*), is drawn as follows:

1. Since P_1 and P_2 are fixed points, therefore these points will lie at one place, in the acceleration diagram. Draw vector $p_1' x$ parallel to P_1A, to some suitable scale, to represent the radial component of the acceleration of A with respect to P_1, such that

$$\text{vector } p_1' x = a_{AP_1}^r = 30 \text{ m/s}^2$$

2. From point x, draw vector xa' perpendicular to P_1A to represent the tangential component of the acceleration of A with respect to P_1, such that

$$\text{vector } xa' = a_{AP_1}^t = 9 \text{ m/s}^2$$

3. Join $p_1' a'$. The vector $p_1' a'$ represents the acceleration of A. By measurement, we find that the acceleration of A,

$$a_A = a_{AP_1} = 31.6 \text{ m/s}^2$$

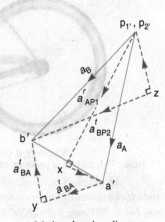

(c) Acceleration diagram

Fig. 8.11

4. From point a', draw vector $a'y$ parallel to AB to represent the radial component of the acceleration of B with respect to A, such that

$$\text{vector } a'y = a_{BA}^r = 11.67 \text{ m/s}^2$$

5. From point y, draw vector yb' perpendicular to AB to represent the tangential component of the acceleration of B with respect to A (*i.e.* a_{BA}^t) whose magnitude is yet unknown.

6. Now from point p_2', draw vector $p_2'z$ parallel to P_2B to represent the radial component of the acceleration B with respect to P_2, such that

$$\text{vector } p_2'z = a_{BP_2}^r = 13.44 \text{ m/s}^2$$

7. From point z, draw vector zb' perpendicular to P_2B to represent the tangential component of the acceleration of B with respect to P_2 i.e. $a^t_{BP_2}$.

8. The vectors yb' and zb' intersect at b'. Now the vector $p_2'b'$ represents the acceleration of B with respect to P_2 or the acceleration of B i.e. a_{BP2} or a_B. By measurement, we find that

$$a_{BP2} = a_B = \text{vector } p_2'\,b' = 29.6 \text{ m/s}^2 \text{ Ans.}$$

Also   vector $yb' = a^t_{BA} = 13.6$ m/s^2, and vector $zb' = a^t_{BP_2} = 26.6$ m/s^2

We know that angular acceleration of P_2B,

$$\alpha_{P2B} = \frac{a^t_{BP_2}}{P_2B} = \frac{26.6}{0.36} = 73.8 \text{ rad/s}^2 \text{ (Anticlockwise)} \textbf{ Ans.}$$

and angular acceleration of AB, $\alpha_{AB} = \dfrac{a^t_{BA}}{AB} = \dfrac{13.6}{0.36} = 37.8$ rad/s^2 (Anticlockwise) **Ans.**

Bicycle is a common example where simple mechanisms are used.
Note : This picture is given as additional information.

Example 8.6. *In the mechanism, as shown in Fig. 8.12, the crank OA rotates at 20 r.p.m. anticlockwise and gives motion to the sliding blocks B and D. The dimensions of the various links are OA = 300 mm; AB = 1200 mm; BC = 450 mm and CD = 450 mm.*

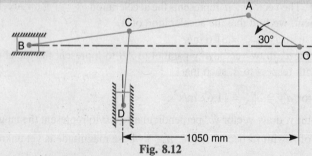

1050 mm

Fig. 8.12

*For the given configuration, determine : **1.** velocities of sliding at B and D, **2.** angular velocity of CD, **3.** linear acceleration of D, and **4.** angular acceleration of CD.*

Solution. Given : $N_{AO} = 20$ r.p.m. or $\omega_{AO} = 2\pi \times 20/60 = 2.1$ rad/s ; $OA = 300$ mm $= 0.3$ m ; $AB = 1200$ mm $= 1.2$ m ; $BC = CD = 450$ mm $= 0.45$ m

We know that linear velocity of A with respect to O or velocity of A,

$$v_{AO} = v_A = \omega_{AO} \times OA = 2.1 \times 0.3 = 0.63 \text{ m/s} \qquad \text{...(Perpendicular to } OA)$$

1. *Velocities of sliding at B and D*

First of all, draw the space diagram, to some suitable scale, as shown in Fig. 8.13 (*a*). Now the velocity diagram, as shown in Fig. 8.13 (*b*), is drawn as discussed below:

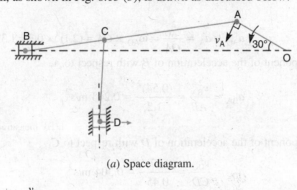

(*a*) Space diagram.

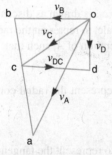

(*b*) Velocity diagram.

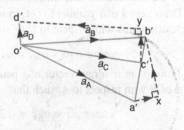

(*c*) Acceleration diagram.

Fig. 8.13

1. Draw vector *oa* perpendicular to *OA*, to some suitable scale, to represent the velocity of A with respect to O (or simply velocity of A), such that

$$\text{vector } oa = v_{AO} = v_A = 0.63 \text{ m/s}$$

2. From point *a*, draw vector *ab* perpendicular to *AB* to represent the velocity of B with respect to A (*i.e.* v_{BA}) and from point *o* draw vector *ob* parallel to path of motion B (which is along *BO*) to represent the velocity of B with respect to O (or simply velocity of B). The vectors *ab* and *ob* intersect at *b*.

3. Divide vector *ab* at *c* in the same ratio as C divides AB in the space diagram. In other words,

$$BC/CA = bc/ca$$

4. Now from point *c*, draw vector *cd* perpendicular to *CD* to represent the velocity of D with respect to C (*i.e.* v_{DC}) and from point *o* draw vector *od* parallel to the path of motion of D (which along the vertical direction) to represent the velocity of D.

By measurement, we find that velocity of sliding at B,

$$v_B = \text{vector } ob = 0.4 \text{ m/s } \textbf{Ans.}$$

and velocity of sliding at D, $\qquad v_D = \text{vector } od = 0.24 \text{ m/s } \textbf{Ans.}$

2. *Angular velocity of CD*

By measurement from velocity diagram, we find that velocity of D with respect to C,

$$v_{DC} = \text{vector } cd = 0.37 \text{ m/s}$$

∴ Angular velocity of CD,

$$\omega_{CD} = \frac{v_{DC}}{CD} = \frac{0.37}{0.45} = 0.82 \text{ rad/s (Anticlockwise). } \textbf{Ans.}$$

3. *Linear acceleration of D*

We know that the radial component of the acceleration of A with respect to O or acceleration of A,

$$a_{AO}^r = a_A = \frac{v_{AO}^2}{OA} = \omega_{AO}^2 \times OA = (2.1)^2 \times 0.3 = 1.323 \text{ m/s}^2$$

Radial component of the acceleration of B with respect to A,

$$a_{BA}^r = \frac{v_{BA}^2}{AB} = \frac{(0.54)^2}{1.2} = 0.243 \text{ m/s}^2$$

...(By measurement, $v_{BA} = 0.54$ m/s)

Radial component of the acceleration of D with respect to C,

$$a_{DC}^r = \frac{v_{DC}^2}{CD} = \frac{(0.37)^2}{0.45} = 0.304 \text{ m/s}^2$$

Now the acceleration diagram, as shown in Fig. 8.13 (c), is drawn as discussed below:

1. Draw vector $o'a'$ parallel to OA, to some suitable scale, to represent the radial component of the acceleration of A with respect to O or simply the acceleration of A, such that

$$\text{vector } o'a' = a_{AO}^r = a_A = 1.323 \text{ m/s}^2$$

2. From point a', draw vector $a'x$ parallel to AB to represent the radial component of the acceleration of B with respect to A, such that

$$\text{vector } a'x = a_{BA}^r = 0.243 \text{ m/s}^2$$

3. From point x, draw vector xb' perpendicular to AB to represent the tangential component of the acceleration of B with respect to A (*i.e.* a_{BA}^t) whose magnitude is not yet known.

4. From point o', draw vector $o'b'$ parallel to the path of motion of B (which is along BO) to represent the acceleration of B (a_B). The vectors xb' *and* $o'b'$ intersect at b'. Join $a'b'$. The vector $a'b'$ represents the acceleration of B with respect to A.

5. Divide vector $a'b'$ at c' in the same ratio as C divides AB in the space diagram. In other words,

$$BC/BA = b'c'/b'a'$$

6. From point c', draw vector $c'y$ parallel to CD to represent the radial component of the acceleration of D with respect to C, such that

$$\text{vector } c'y = a_{DC}^r = 0.304 \text{ m/s}^2$$

7. From point y, draw yd' perpendicular to CD to represent the tangential component of acceleration of D with respect to C (*i.e.* a_{DC}^t) whose magnitude is not yet known.

8. From point o', draw vector $o'd'$ parallel to the path of motion of D (which is along the vertical direction) to represent the acceleration of D (a_D). The vectors yd' *and* $o'd'$ intersect at d'.

By measurement, we find that linear acceleration of D,

$$a_D = \text{vector } o'd' = 0.16 \text{ m/s}^2 \qquad \textbf{Ans.}$$

4. *Angular acceleration of CD*

From the acceleration diagram, we find that the tangential component of the acceleration of D with respect to C,

$$a_{DC}^t = \text{vector } yd' = 1.28 \text{ m/s}^2 \qquad \text{...(By measurement)}$$

∴ Angular acceleration of *CD*,

$$\alpha_{CD} = \frac{a^t_{DC}}{CD} = \frac{1.28}{0.45} = 2.84 \text{ rad/s}^2 \text{ (Clockwise) } \textbf{Ans.}$$

Example 8.7. *Find out the acceleration of the slider D and the angular acceleration of link CD for the engine mechanism shown in Fig. 8.14.*

The crank OA rotates uniformly at 180 r.p.m. in clockwise direction. The various lengths are: OA = 150 mm ; AB = 450 mm; PB = 240 mm ; BC = 210 mm ; CD = 660 mm.

Solution. Given: $N_{AO} = 180$ r.p.m., or $\omega_{AO} = 2\pi \times 180/60 = 18.85$ rad/s ; $OA = 150$ mm $= 0.15$ m ; $AB = 450$ mm $= 0.45$ m ; $PB = 240$ mm $= 0.24$ m ; $CD = 660$ mm $= 0.66$ m

We know that velocity of *A* with respect to *O* or velocity of *A*,

$$v_{AO} = v_A = \omega_{AO} \times OA$$
$$= 18.85 \times 0.15 = 2.83 \text{ m/s}$$

...(Perpendicular to *OA*)

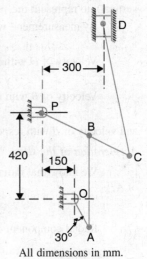

All dimensions in mm.

Fig. 8.14

First of all draw the space diagram, to some suitable scale, as shown in Fig. 8.15 (*a*). Now the velocity diagram, as shown in Fig. 8.15 (*b*), is drawn as discussed below:

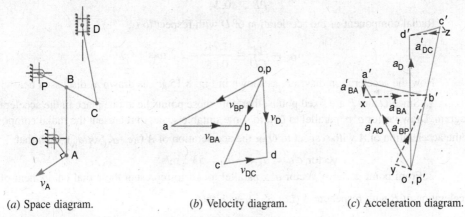

(*a*) Space diagram.   (*b*) Velocity diagram.   (*c*) Acceleration diagram.

Fig. 8.15

1. Since *O* and *P* are fixed points, therefore these points lie at one place in the velocity diagram. Draw vector *oa* perpendicular to *OA*, to some suitable scale, to represent the velocity of *A* with respect to *O* or velocity of *A* (*i.e.* v_{AO} or v_A), such that

vector $oa = v_{AO} = v_A = 2.83$ m/s

2. Since the point *B* moves with respect to *A* and also with respect to *P*, therefore draw vector *ab* perpendicular to *AB* to represent the velocity of *B* with respect to *A i.e.* v_{BA} ,and from point *p* draw vector *pb* perpendicular to *PB* to represent the velocity of *B* with respect to *P* or velocity of *B* (*i.e.* v_{BP} or v_B). The vectors *ab* and *pb* intersect at *b*.

3. Since the point *C* lies on *PB* produced, therefore divide vector *pb* at *c* in the same ratio as *C* divides *PB* in the space diagram. In other words, *pb/pc = PB/PC*.

4. From point c, draw vector cd perpendicular to CD to represent the velocity of D with respect to C and from point o draw vector od parallel to the path of motion of the slider D (which is vertical), to represent the velocity of D, i.e. v_D.

By measurement, we find that velocity of the slider D,

$$v_D = \text{vector } od = 2.36 \text{ m/s}$$

Velocity of D with respect to C,

$$v_{DC} = \text{vector } cd = 1.2 \text{ m/s}$$

Velocity of B with respect to A,

$$v_{BA} = \text{vector } ab = 1.8 \text{ m/s}$$

and velocity of B with respect to P, $v_{BP} = \text{vector } pb = 1.5 \text{ m/s}$

Acceleration of the slider D

We know that radial component of the acceleration of A with respect to O or acceleration of A,

$$a_{AO}^r = a_A = \omega_{AO}^2 \times AO = (18.85)^2 \times 0.15 = 53.3 \text{ m/s}^2$$

Radial component of the acceleration of B with respect to A,

$$a_{BA}^r = \frac{v_{BA}^2}{AB} = \frac{(1.8)^2}{0.45} = 7.2 \text{ m/s}^2$$

Radial component of the acceleration of B with respect to P,

$$a_{BP}^r = \frac{v_{BP}^2}{PB} = \frac{(1.5)^2}{0.24} = 9.4 \text{ m/s}^2$$

Radial component of the acceleration of D with respect to C,

$$a_{DC}^r = \frac{v_{DC}^2}{CD} = \frac{(1.2)^2}{0.66} = 2.2 \text{ m/s}^2$$

Now the acceleration diagram, as shown in Fig. 8.15 (c), is drawn as discussed below:

1. Since O and P are fixed points, therefore these points lie at one place in the acceleration diagram. Draw vector $o'a'$ parallel to OA, to some suitable scale, to represent the radial component of the acceleration of A with respect to O or the acceleration of A (i.e. a_{AO}^r or a_A), such that

$$\text{vector } o'a' = a_{AO}^r = a_A = 53.3 \text{ m/s}^2$$

2. From point a', draw vector $a'x$ parallel to AB to represent the radial component of the acceleration of B with respect to A (i.e. a_{BA}^r), such that

$$\text{vector } a'x = a_{BA}^r = 7.2 \text{ m/s}^2$$

3. From point x, draw vector xb' perpendicular to the vector $a'x$ or AB to represent the tangential component of the acceleration of B with respect to A i.e. a_{BA}^t whose magnitude is yet unknown.

4. Now from point p', draw vector $p'y$ parallel to PB to represent the radial component of the acceleration of B with respect to P (i.e. a_{BP}^r), such that

$$\text{vector } p'y = a_{BP}^r = 9.4 \text{ m/s}^2$$

5. From point y, draw vector yb' perpendicular to vector $b'y$ or PB to represent the tangential component of the acceleration of B, with respect to P i.e. a_{BP}^t. The vectors xb' and yb' intersect at b'. Join $p'b'$. The vector $p'b'$ represents the acceleration of B, i.e. a_B.

6. Since the point C lies on PB produced, therefore divide vector $p'b'$ at c' in the same ratio as C divides PB in the space diagram. In other words, $p'b'/p'c' = PB/PC$

7. From point c', draw vector $c'z$ parallel to CD to represent the radial component of the acceleration of D with respect to C *i.e.* a_{DC}^r, such that

$$\text{vector } c'z = a_{DC}^r = 2.2 \text{ m/s}^2$$

8. From point z, draw vector zd' perpendicular to vector $c'z$ or CD to represent the tangential component of the acceleration of D with respect to C *i.e.* a_{DC}^t, whose magnitude is yet unknown.

9. From point o', draw vector $o'd'$ parallel to the path of motion of D (which is vertical) to represent the acceleration of D, *i.e.* a_D. The vectors zd' and $o'd'$ intersect at d'. Join $c'd'$.

By measurement, we find that acceleration of D,

$$a_D = \text{vector } o'd' = 69.6 \text{ m/s}^2 \text{ **Ans.**}$$

Angular acceleration of CD

From acceleration diagram, we find that tangential component of the acceleration of D with respect to C,

$$a_{DC}^t = \text{vector } zd' = 17.4 \text{ m/s}^2 \qquad \qquad \text{...(By measurement)}$$

We know that angular acceleration of CD,

$$\alpha_{CD} = \frac{a_{DC}^t}{CD} = \frac{17.4}{0.66} = 26.3 \text{ rad/s}^2 \text{ (Anticlockwise) } \text{**Ans.**}$$

Example 8.8. *In the toggle mechanism shown in Fig. 8.16, the slider D is constrained to move on a horizontal path. The crank OA is rotating in the counter-clockwise direction at a speed*

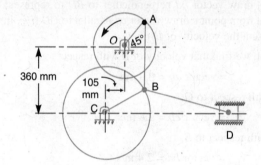

Fig. 8.16

of 180 r.p.m. increasing at the rate of 50 rad/s². The dimensions of the various links are as follows:

OA = 180 mm ; CB = 240 mm ; AB = 360 mm ; and BD = 540 mm.

For the given configuration, find 1. Velocity of slider D and angular velocity of BD, and 2. Acceleration of slider D and angular acceleration of BD.

Solution. Given : $N_{AO} = 180$ r.p.m. or $\omega_{AO} = 2\pi \times 180/60 = 18.85$ rad/s ; $OA = 180$ mm $= 0.18$ m ; $CB = 240$ mm $= 0.24$ m ; $AB = 360$ mm $= 0.36$ m ; $BD = 540$ mm $= 0.54$ m

We know that velocity of A with respect to O or velocity of A,

$$v_{AO} = v_A = \omega_{AO} \times OA = 18.85 \times 0.18 = 3.4 \text{ m/s}$$

...(Perpendicular to OA)

1. *Velocity of slider D and angular velocity of BD*

First of all, draw the space diagram to some suitable scale, as shown in Fig. 8.17 (*a*). Now the velocity diagram, as shown in Fig. 8.17 (*b*), is drawn as discussed below:

1. Since *O* and *C* are fixed points, therefore these points lie at one place in the velocity diagram. Draw vector *oa* perpendicular to *OA*, to some suitable scale, to represent the velocity of *A* with respect to *O* or velocity of *A* i.e. v_{AO} or v_A, such that

$$\text{vector } oa = v_{AO} = v_A = 3.4 \text{ m/s}$$

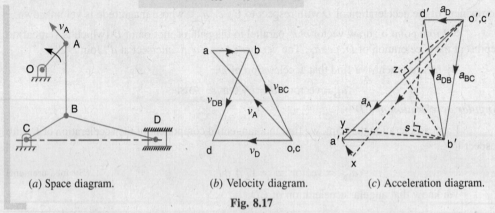

| (*a*) Space diagram. | (*b*) Velocity diagram. | (*c*) Acceleration diagram. |

Fig. 8.17

2. Since *B* moves with respect to *A* and also with respect to *C*, therefore draw vector *ab* perpendicular to *AB* to represent the velocity of *B* with respect to *A* i.e. v_{BA}, and draw vector *cb* perpendicular to *CB* to represent the velocity of *B* with respect to *C* ie. v_{BC}. The vectors *ab* and *cb* intersect at *b*.

3. From point *b*, draw vector *bd* perpendicular to *BD* to represent the velocity of *D* with respect to *B* i.e. v_{DB}, and from point *c* draw vector *cd* parallel to *CD* (*i.e.,* in the direction of motion of the slider *D*) to represent the velocity of *D* i.e. v_D.

By measurement, we find that velocity of *B* with respect to *A*,

$$v_{BA} = \text{vector } ab = 0.9 \text{ m/s}$$

Velocity of *B* with respect to *C*,

$$v_{BC} = \text{vector } cb = 2.8 \text{ m/s}$$

Velocity of *D* with respect to *B*,

$$v_{DB} = \text{vector } bd = 2.4 \text{ m/s}$$

and velocity of slider *D*, $v_D = \text{vector } cd = 2.05 \text{ m/s}$ **Ans.**

Angular velocity of BD

We know that the angular velocity of *BD*,

$$\omega_{BD} = \frac{v_{DB}}{BD} = \frac{2.4}{0.54} = 4.5 \text{ rad/s} \text{ **Ans.**}$$

2. *Acceleration of slider D and angular acceleration of BD*

Since the angular acceleration of *OA* increases at the rate of 50 rad/s², *i.e.* $\alpha_{AO} = 50$ rad/s², therefore

Tangential component of the acceleration of *A* with respect to *O*,

$$a_{AO}^t = \alpha_{AO} \times OA = 50 \times 0.18 = 9 \text{ m/s}^2$$

Radial component of the acceleration of A with respect to O,

$$a^r_{AO} = \frac{v^2_{AO}}{OA} = \frac{(3.4)^2}{0.18} = 63.9 \text{ m/s}^2$$

Radial component of the acceleration of B with respect to A,

$$a^r_{BA} = \frac{v^2_{BA}}{AB} = \frac{(0.9)^2}{0.36} = 2.25 \text{ m/s}^2$$

Radial component of the acceleration of B with respect to C,

$$a^r_{BC} = \frac{v^2_{BC}}{CB} = \frac{(2.8)^2}{0.24} = 32.5 \text{ m/s}^2$$

and radial component of the acceleration of D with respect to B,

$$a^r_{DB} = \frac{v^2_{DB}}{BD} = \frac{(2.4)^2}{0.54} = 10.8 \text{ m/s}^2$$

Now the acceleration diagram, as shown in Fig. 8.17 (c), is drawn as discussed below:

1. Since O and C are fixed points, therefore these points lie at one place in the acceleration diagram. Draw vector $o'x$ parallel to OA, to some suitable scale, to represent the radial component of the acceleration of A with respect to O i.e. a^r_{AO}, such that

$$\text{vector } o'x = a^r_{AO} = 63.9 \text{ m/s}^2$$

2. From point x, draw vector xa' perpendicular to vector $o'x$ or OA to represent the tangential component of the acceleration of A with respect to O i.e. a^t_{AO}, such that

$$\text{vector } xa' = a^t_{AO} = 9 \text{ m/s}^2$$

3. Join $o'a'$. The vector $o'a'$ represents the total acceleration of A with respect to O or acceleration of A i.e. a_{AO} or a_A.

An experimental IC engine with crankshaft and cylinders.

Note : This picture is given as additional information.

4. Now from point a', draw vector $a'y$ parallel to AB to represent the radial component of the acceleration of B with respect to A i.e. a^r_{BA}, such that

$$\text{vector } a'y = a^r_{BA} = 2.25 \text{ m/s}^2$$

5. From point y, draw vector yb' perpendicular to vector $a'y$ or AB to represent the tangential component of the acceleration of B with respect to A i.e. a^t_{BA} whose magnitude is yet unknown.

6. Now from point c', draw vector $c'z$ parallel to CB to represent the radial component of the acceleration of B with respect to C i.e. a^r_{BC}, such that

$$\text{vector } c'z = a^r_{BC} = 32.5 \text{ m/s}^2$$

7. From point z, draw vector zb' perpendicular to vector $c'z$ or CB to represent the tangential component of the acceleration of B with respect to C i.e. a^t_{BC}. The vectors yb' and zb' intersect at b'. Join $c'b'$. The vector $c'b'$ represents the acceleration of B with respect to C i.e. a_{BC}.

8. Now from point b', draw vector $b's$ parallel to BD to represent the radial component of the acceleration of D with respect to B i.e. a^r_{DB}, such that

$$\text{vector } b's = a^r_{DB} = 10.8 \text{ m/s}^2$$

9. From point s, draw vector sd' perpendicular to vector $b's$ or BD to represent the tangential component of the acceleration of D with respect to B i.e. a^t_{DB} whose magnitude is yet unknown.

10. From point c', draw vector $c'd'$ parallel to the path of motion of D (which is along CD) to represent the acceleration of D i.e. a_D. The vectors sd' and $c'd'$ intersect at d'.

By measurement, we find that acceleration of slider D,

$$a_D = \text{vector } c'd' = 13.3 \text{ m/s}^2 \text{ Ans.}$$

Angular acceleration of BD

By measurement, we find that tangential component of the acceleration of D with respect to B,

$$a^t_{DB} = \text{vector } sd' = 38.5 \text{ m/s}^2$$

We know that angular acceleration of BD,

$$\alpha_{BD} = \frac{a^t_{DB}}{BD} = \frac{38.5}{0.54} = 71.3 \text{ rad/s}^2 \text{ (Clockwise) Ans.}$$

Example 8.9. *The mechanism of a warping machine, as shown in Fig. 8.18, has the dimensions as follows:*

$O_1A = 100$ mm; $AC = 700$ mm ; $BC = 200$ mm ; $BD = 150$ mm ; $O_2D = 200$ mm ; $O_2E = 400$ mm ; $O_3C = 200$ mm.

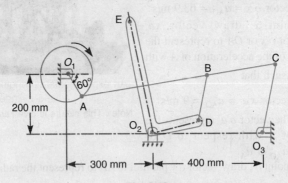

Fig. 8.18

The crank O_1A rotates at a uniform speed of 100 rad/s. For the given configuration, determine: 1. linear velocity of the point E on the bell crank lever, 2. acceleration of the points E and B, and 3. angular acceleration of the bell crank lever.

Solution. Given : $\omega_{AO1} = 100$ rad/s ; $O_1A = 100$ mm $= 0.1$ m

We know that linear velocity of A with respect to O_1, or velocity of A,

$$v_{AO1} = v_A = \omega_{AO1} \times O_1A = 100 \times 0.1 = 10 \text{ m/s} \qquad \text{...(Perpendicular to } O_1A)$$

1. Linear velocity of the point E on bell crank lever

First of all draw the space diagram, as shown in Fig. 8.19 (a), to some suitable scale. Now the velocity diagram, as shown in Fig. 8.19 (b), is drawn as discussed below:

1. Since O_1, O_2 and O_3 are fixed points, therefore these points are marked as one point in the velocity diagram. From point o_1, draw vector o_1a perpendicular to O_1A to some suitable scale, to represent the velocity of A with respect to O_1 or velocity of A, such that

$$\text{vector } o_1a = v_{AO1} = v_A = 10 \text{ m/s}$$

2. From point *a*, draw vector *ac* perpendicular to *AC* to represent the velocity of *C* with respect to *A* (*i.e.* v_{CA}) and from point o_3 draw vector o_3c perpendicular to O_3C to represent the velocity of *C* with respect to O_3 or simply velocity of *C* (*i.e.* v_C). The vectors *ac* and o_3c intersect at point *c*.

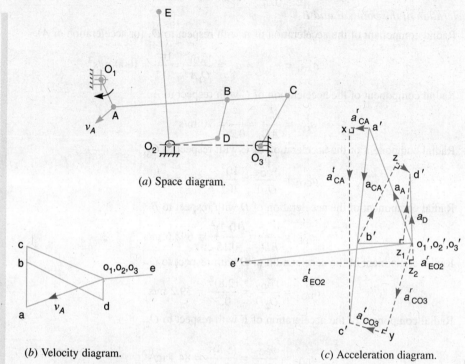

(*a*) Space diagram.

(*b*) Velocity diagram.

(*c*) Acceleration diagram.

Fig. 8.19

3. Since *B* lies on *AC*, therefore divide vector *ac* at *b* in the same ratio as *B* divides *AC* in the space diagram. In other words, *ab/ac = AB/AC*

4. From point *b*, draw vector *bd* perpendicular to *BD* to represent the velocity of *D* with respect to *B* (*i.e.* v_{DB}), and from point o_2 draw vector o_2d perpendicular to O_2D to represent the velocity of *D* with respect to O_2 or simply velocity of *D* (*i.e.* v_D). The vectors *bd* and o_2d intersect at *d*.

5. From point o_2, draw vector o_2e perpendicular to vector o_2d in such a way that

$$o_2e/o_2d = O_2E/O_2D$$

By measurement, we find that velocity of point *C* with respect to *A*,

$$v_{CA} = \text{vector } ac = 7 \text{ m/s}$$

Velocity of point *C* with respect to O_3,

$$v_{CO3} = v_C = \text{vector } o_3c = 10 \text{ m/s}$$

Velocity of point *D* with respect to *B*,

$$v_{DB} = \text{vector } bd = 10.2 \text{ m/s}$$

Warping machine uses many mechanisms.

Velocity of point D with respect to O_2,

$$v_{DO2} = v_D = \text{vector } o_2d = 2.8 \text{ m/s}$$

and velocity of the point E on the bell crank lever,

$$v_E = v_{EO2} = \text{vector } o_2e = 5.8 \text{ m/s} \text{ Ans.}$$

2. Acceleration of the points E and B

Radial component of the acceleration of A with respect to O_1 (or acceleration of A),

$$a^r_{AO1} = a_{AO1} = a_A = \frac{v^2_{AO1}}{O_1A} = \frac{10^2}{0.1} = 1000 \text{ m/s}^2$$

Radial component of the acceleration of C with respect to A,

$$a^r_{CA} = \frac{v^2_{CA}}{AC} = \frac{7^2}{0.7} = 70 \text{ m/s}^2$$

Radial component of the acceleration of C with respect to O_3,

$$a^r_{CO3} = \frac{v^2_{CO3}}{O_3C} = \frac{10^2}{0.2} = 500 \text{ m/s}^2$$

Radial component of the acceleration of D with respect to B,

$$a^r_{DB} = \frac{v^2_{DB}}{BD} = \frac{(10.2)^2}{0.15} = 693.6 \text{ m/s}^2$$

Radial component of the acceleration of D with respect to O_2,

$$a^r_{DO2} = \frac{v^2_{DO2}}{O_2D} = \frac{(2.8)^2}{0.2} = 39.2 \text{ m/s}^2$$

Radial component of the acceleration of E with respect to O_2,

$$a^r_{EO2} = \frac{v^2_{EO2}}{O_2E} = \frac{(5.8)^2}{0.4} = 84.1 \text{ m/s}^2$$

Now the acceleration diagram, as shown in Fig. 8.19 (c), is drawn as discussed below:

1. Since O_1, O_2 and O_3 are fixed points, therefore these points are marked as one point in the acceleration diagram. Draw vector $o_1' a'$ parallel to O_1A, to some suitable scale, to represent the radial component of the acceleration of A with respect to O_1 (or simply acceleration of A), such that

$$\text{vector } o_1' a' = a^r_{AO_1} = a_A = 1000 \text{ m/s}^2$$

2. From point a', draw $a'x$ parallel to AC to represent the radial component of the acceleration of C with respect to A (i.e. a^r_{CA}), such that

$$\text{vector } a'x = a^r_{CA} = 70 \text{ m/s}^2$$

3. From point x, draw vector xc' perpendicular to AC to represent the tangential component of the acceleration of C with respect to A (i.e. a^t_{CA}), the magnitude of which is yet unknown.

4. From point o_3', draw vector $o_3'y$ parallel to O_3C to represent the radial component of the acceleration of C with respect to O_3 (i.e. a^r_{CO3}), such that

$$\text{vector } o_3' y = a^r_{CO3} = 500 \text{ m/s}^2$$

5. From point y, draw vector yc' perpendicular to O_3C to represent the tangential component of the acceleration of C with respect to O_3 (i.e. a^t_{CO3}). The vectors xc' and yc' intersect at c'.

6. Join $a'\,c'$. The vector $a'\,c'$ represents the acceleration of C with respect to A (*i.e.* a_{CA}).

7. Since B lies on AC, therefore divide vector $a'c'$ at b' in the same ratio as B divides AC in the space diagram. In other words, $a'b'/a'c' = AB/AC$. Join $b'\,o_2'$ which represents the acceleration of point B with respect to O_2 or simply acceleration of B. By measurement, we find that

Acceleration of point B = vector $o_2'\,b'$ = 440 m/s² Ans.

8. Now from point b', draw vector $b'\,z$ parallel to BD to represent the radial component of the acceleration of D with respect to B (*i.e.* a_{DB}^r), such that

$$\text{vector } b'z = a_{DB}^r = 693.6 \text{ m/s}^2$$

9. From point z, draw vector zd' perpendicular to BD to represent the tangential component of the acceleration of D with respect to B (*i.e.* a_{DB}^t), whose magnitude is yet unknown.

10. From point o_2', draw vector $o_2'\,z_1$ parallel to O_2D to represent the radial component of the acceleration of D with respect to O_2 (*i.e.* $a_{DO_2}^r$), such that

$$\text{vector } o_2'\,z_1 = a_{DO_2}^r = 39.2 \text{ m/s}^2$$

11. From point z_1, draw vector $z_1 d'$ perpendicular to O_2D to represent the tangential component of the acceleration of D with respect to O_2 (*i.e.* $a_{DO_2}^t$). The vectors zd' and $z_1 d'$ intersect at d'.

12. Join $o_2'\,d'$. The vector $o_2'd'$ represents the acceleration of D with respect to O_2 or simply acceleration of D (*i.e.* a_{DO2} or a_D).

13. From point o_2', draw vector $o_2'\,e'$ perpendicular to $o_2'\,d'$ in such a way that

$$o_2'e'/o_2'd' = O_2E/O_2D$$

Note: The point e' may also be obtained drawing $a_{EO_2}^r$ and $a_{EO_2}^t$ as shown in Fig. 8.19 (c).

By measurement, we find that acceleration of point E,

$$a_E = a_{EO2} = \text{vector } o'_2\,e' = 1200 \text{ m/s}^2 \text{ Ans.}$$

3. *Angular acceleration of the bell crank lever*

By measurement, we find that the tangential component of the acceleration of D with respect to O_2,

$$a_{DO2}^t = \text{vector } z_1\,d' = 610 \text{ m/s}^2$$

$\therefore$ Angular acceleration of the bell crank lever

$$= \frac{a_{DO2}^t}{O_2D} = \frac{610}{0.2} = 3050 \text{ rad/s}^2 \text{ (Anticlockwise)Ans.}$$

Example 8.10. *A pump is driven from an engine crank-shaft by the mechanism as shown in Fig. 8.20. The pump piston shown at F is 250 mm in diameter and the crank speed is 100 r.p.m. The dimensions of various links are as follows:*

OA = 150 mm ; AB = 600 mm ; BC = 350 mm ; CD = 150 mm; and DE = 500 mm.

Determine for the position shown : 1. The velocity of the cross-head E, 2. The rubbing velocity of the pins A and B which are 50 mm diameter. 3. The torque required at the crank shaft to overcome a presure of 0.35 N/mm², and 4. The acceleration of the cross-head E.

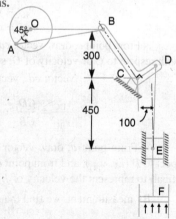

All dimensions in mm.

Fig. 8.20

Solution. Given : $N_{AO} = 100$ r.p.m. or $\omega_{AO} = 2\pi \times 100/60 = 10.47$ rad/s; $OA = 150$ mm $= 0.15$ m ; $AB = 600$ mm $= 0.6$ m ; $BC = 350$ mm $= 0.35$ m ; $CD = 150$ mm $= 0.15$ m ; $DE = 500$ mm $= 0.5$ m

We know that velocity of A with respect to O or velocity of A,

$$v_{AO} = v_A = \omega_{AO} \times OA = 10.47 \times 0.15 = 1.57 \text{ m/s} \qquad \text{...(Perpendicular to } OA)$$

1. *Velocity of the cross-head E*

First of all, draw the space diagram, to some suitable scale, as shown in Fig. 8.21 (*a*). Now the velocity diagram, as shown in Fig. 8.21 (*b*), is drawn as discussed below:

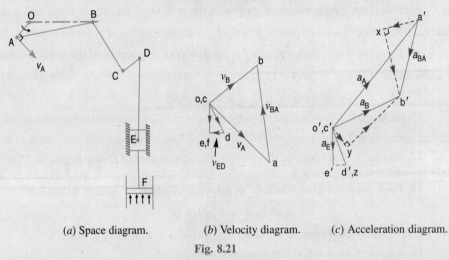

(*a*) Space diagram. (*b*) Velocity diagram. (*c*) Acceleration diagram.

Fig. 8.21

1. Since O and C are fixed points, therefore these points are marked as one point in the velocity diagram. Now draw vector oa perpendicular to OA, to some suitable scale, to represent the velocity of A with respect ot O or the velocity of A, such that

$$\text{vector } oa = v_{AO} = v_A = 1.57 \text{ m/s}$$

2. From point a, draw vector ab perpendicular to AB to represent the velocity of B with respect to A (*i.e.* v_{BA}), and from point c draw vector cb perpendicular to CB to represent the velocity of B with respect to C (*i.e.* v_{BC}). The vectors ab and cb intersect at b.

By measurement, we find that

$$v_{BA} = \text{vector } ab = 1.65 \text{ m/s}$$

and $$v_{BC} = v_B = \text{vector } cb = 0.93 \text{ m/s}$$

3. From point c, draw vector cd perpendicular to CD or vector cb to represent the velocity of D with respect to C or velocity of D, such that

$$\text{vector } cd : \text{vector } cb = CD : CB \qquad \text{or} \qquad v_{DC} : v_{BC} = CD : CB$$

$$\therefore \qquad \frac{v_{DC}}{v_{BC}} = \frac{CD}{CB} \quad \text{or} \quad v_{DC} = v_{BC} \times \frac{CD}{CB} = 0.93 \times \frac{0.15}{0.35} = 0.4 \text{ m/s}$$

4. From point d, draw vector de perpendicular to DE to represent the velocity of E with respect to D (*i.e.* v_{ED}), and from point o draw vector oe parallel to the path of motion of E (which is vertical) to represent the velocity of E or F. The vectors oe and de intersect at e.

By measurement, we find that velocity of E with respect to D,

$$v_{ED} = \text{vector } de = 0.18 \text{ m/s}$$

and velocity of the cross-head E,

$$v_{EO} = v_E = \text{vector } oe = 0.36 \text{ m/s } \textbf{Ans.}$$

2. *Rubbing velocity of the pins at A and B*

We know that angular velocity of A with respect to O,

$$\omega_{AO} = 10.47 \text{ rad/s} \qquad \text{...(Anticlockwise)}$$

Angular velocity of B with respect to A,

$$\omega_{BA} = \frac{v_{BA}}{AB} = \frac{1.65}{0.6} = 2.75 \text{ rad/s} \qquad \text{...(Anticlockwise)}$$

and angular velocity of B with respect to C,

$$\omega_{BC} = \frac{v_{BC}}{CB} = \frac{0.93}{0.35} = 2.66 \text{ rad/s} \qquad \text{...(Clockwise)}$$

We know that diameter of pins at A and B,

$$d_A = d_B = 50 \text{ mm} = 0.05 \text{ m} \qquad \text{...(Given)}$$

or $\qquad$ Radius, $r_A = r_B = 0.025 \text{ m}$

∴ Rubbing velocity of pin at A

$$= (\omega_{AO} - \omega_{BA}) \, r_A = (10.47 - 2.75) \, 0.025 = 0.193 \text{ m/s } \textbf{Ans.}$$

and rubbing velocity of pin at B

$$= (\omega_{BA} + \omega_{BC}) \, r_B = (2.75 + 2.66) \, 0.025 = 0.135 \text{ m/s } \textbf{Ans.}$$

3. *Torque required at the crankshaft*

Given: Pressure to overcome by the crankshaft,

$$p_F = 0.35 \text{ N/mm}^2$$

Diameter of the pump piston

$$D_F = 250 \text{ mm}$$

∴ Force at the pump piston at F,

$$F_F = \text{Pressure} \times \text{Area} = p_F \times \frac{\pi}{4} (D_F)^2 = 0.35 \times \frac{\pi}{4} (250)^2 = 17\ 183 \text{ N}$$

Let $\qquad F_A = $ Force required at the crankshaft at A.

Assuming transmission efficiency as 100 per cent,

Work done at A = Work done at F

$$F_A \times v_A = F_F \times v_F \quad \text{or} \quad F_A = \frac{F_F \times v_F}{v_A} = \frac{17\ 183 \times 0.36}{1.57} = 3940 \text{ N}$$

$$\text{...(}\because v_F = v_E)$$

∴ Torque required at the crankshaft,

$$T_A = F_A \times OA = 3940 \times 0.15 = 591 \text{ N-m } \textbf{Ans.}$$

Acceleration of the crosshead E

We know that the radial component of the acceleration of A with respect to O or the acceleration of A,

$$a_{AO}^r = a_A = \frac{v_{AO}^2}{OA} = \frac{(1.57)^2}{0.15} = 16.43 \text{ m/s}^2$$

Radial component of the acceleration of B with respect to A,

$$a_{BA}^r = \frac{v_{BA}^2}{AB} = \frac{(1.65)^2}{0.6} = 4.54 \, \text{m/s}^2$$

Radial component of the acceleration of B with respect to C.

$$a_{BC}^r = \frac{v_{BC}^2}{CB} = \frac{(0.93)^2}{0.35} = 2.47 \, \text{m/s}^2$$

and radial component of the acceleration of E with respect to D,

$$a_{ED}^r = \frac{v_{ED}^2}{DE} = \frac{(0.18)^2}{0.5} = 0.065 \, \text{m/s}^2$$

Now the acceleration diagram, as shown in Fig. 8.21 (c), is drawn as discussed below:

1. Since O and C are fixed points, therefore these points are marked as one point in the acceleration diagram. Draw vector $o'a'$ parallel to OA, to some suitable scale, to represent the radial component of the acceleration of A with respect to O or the acceleration of A, such that

$$\text{vector } o'a' = a_{AO}^r = a_A = 16.43 \, \text{m/s}^2 = 38 \, \text{mm}$$

2. From point a', draw vector $a'x$ parallel to AB to represent the radial component of the acceleration of B with respect to A (*i.e.* a_{BA}^r), such that

$$\text{vector } a'x = a_{BA}^r = 4.54 \, \text{m/s}^2$$

3. From point x, draw vector xb' perpendicular to AB to represent the tangential component of the acceleration of B with respect to A (*i.e.* a_{BA}^t) whose magnitude is yet unknown.

4. Now from point c', draw vector $c'y$ parallel to CB to represent the radial component of the acceleration of B with respect to C (*i.e.* a_{BC}^r), such that

$$\text{vector } c'y = a_{BC}^r = 2.47 \, \text{m/s}^2$$

5. From point y, draw vector yb' perpendicular to CB to represent the tangential component of the acceleration of B with respect to C (*i.e.* a_{BC}^t). The vectors yb' and xb' intersect at b'. Join $c'b'$ and $a'b'$. The vector $c'b'$ represents the acceleration of B with respect to C (*i.e.* a_{BC}) or the acceleration of B (*i.e.* a_B) and vector $a'b'$ represents the acceleration of B with respect to A (*i.e.* a_{BA}).

By measurement, we find that

$$a_{BC} = a_B = \text{vector } c'b' = 9.2 \, \text{m/s}^2$$

and
$$a_{BA} = \text{vector } a'b' = 9 \, \text{m/s}^2$$

6. From point c', draw vector $c'd'$ perpendicular to CD or vector $c'b'$ to represent the acceleration of D with respect to C or the acceleration of D (*i.e.* a_{DC} or a_D), such that

$$\text{vector } c'd' : \text{vector } c'b' = CD : CB \quad \text{or} \quad a_D : a_{BC} = CD : CB$$

$$\therefore \quad \frac{a_D}{a_{BC}} = \frac{CD}{CB} \quad \text{or} \quad a_D = a_{BC} \times \frac{CD}{CB} = 9.2 \times \frac{0.15}{0.35} = 3.94 \, \text{m/s}^2$$

7. Now from point d', draw vector $d'z$ parallel to DE to represent the radial component of E with respect to D (*i.e.* a_{ED}^r), such that

$$\text{vector } d'z = a_{ED}^r = 0.065 \, \text{m/s}^2$$

Note: Since the magnitude of a'_{ED} is very small, therefore the points d' and z coincide.

8. From point z, draw vector ze' perpendicular to DE to represent the tangential component of the acceleration of E with respect to D (*i.e.* a_{ED}^t) whose magnitude is yet unknown.

9. From point o', draw vector $o'e'$ parallel to the path of motion of E (which is vertical) to represent the acceleration of E. The vectors ze' and $o'e'$ intersect at e'.

By measurement, we find that acceleration of the crosshead E,
$$a_E = \text{vector } o'e' = 3.8 \text{ m/s}^2 \text{ Ans.}$$

Example 8.11. *Fig. 8.22 shows the mechanism of a radial valve gear. The crank OA turns uniformly at 150 r.p.m and is pinned at A to rod AB. The point C in the rod is guided in the circular path with D as centre and DC as radius. The dimensions of various links are:*

OA = 150 mm ; AB = 550 mm ; AC = 450 mm ; DC = 500 mm ; BE = 350 mm.

Determine velocity and acceleration of the ram E for the given position of the mechanism.

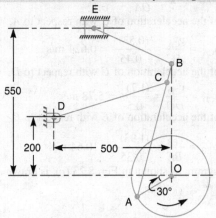

All dimensions in mm.

Fig. 8.22

Solution. Given : $N_{AO} = 150$ r.p.m. or $\omega_{AO} = 2\pi \times 150/60 = 15.71$ rad/s; $OA = 150$ mm $= 0.15$ m; $AB = 550$ mm $= 0.55$ m ; $AC = 450$ mm $= 0.45$ m ; $DC = 500$ mm $= 0.5$ m ; $BE = 350$ mm $= 0.35$ m

We know that linear velocity of A with respect to O or velocity of A,
$$v_{AO} = v_A = \omega_{AO} \times OA = 15.71 \times 0.15 = 2.36 \text{ m/s}$$

...(Perpendicular to OA)

Velocity of the ram E

First of all draw the space diagram, as shown in Fig. 8.23 (*a*), to some suitable scale. Now the velocity diagram, as shown in Fig. 8.23 (*b*), is drawn as discussed below:

1. Since O and D are fixed points, therefore these points are marked as one point in the velocity diagram. Draw vector *oa* perpendicular to OA, to some suitable scale, to represent the velocity of A with respect to O or simply velocity of A, such that

vector $oa = v_{AO} = v_A = 2.36$ m/s

2. From point a, draw vector *ac* perpendicular to AC to represent the velocity of C with respect to A (*i.e.* v_{CA}), and from point d draw vector *dc* perpendicular to DC to represent the velocity of C with respect to D or simply velocity of C (*i.e.* v_{CD} or v_C). The vectors *ac* and *dc* intersect at c.

3. Since the point B lies on AC produced, therefore divide vector *ac* at b in the same ratio as B divides AC in the space diagram. In other words $ac:cb = AC:CB$. Join *ob*. The vector *ob* represents the velocity of B (*i.e.* v_B)

4. From point b, draw vector *be* perpendicular to *be* to represent the velocity of E with respect to B (*i.e.* v_{EB}), and from point o draw vector *oe* parallel to the path of motion of the ram E (which is horizontal) to represent the velocity of the ram E. The vectors *be* and *oe* intersect at e.

By measurement, we find that velocity of C with respect to A,
$$v_{CA} = \text{vector } ac = 0.53 \text{ m/s}$$

Velocity of C with respect to D,
$$v_{CD} = v_C = \text{vector } dc = 1.7 \text{ m/s}$$

Velocity of E with respect to B,
$$v_{EB} = \text{vector } be = 1.93 \text{ m/s}$$
and velocity of the ram E, $v_E = \text{vector } oe = 1.05 \text{ m/s }$ **Ans.**

Acceleration of the ram E

We know that the radial component of the acceleration of A with respect to O or the acceleration of A,

$$a^r_{AO} = a_A = \frac{v^2_{AO}}{OA} = \frac{(2.36)^2}{0.15} = 37.13 \text{ m/s}^2$$

Radial component of the acceleration of C with respect to A,

$$a^r_{CA} = \frac{v^2_{CA}}{AC} = \frac{(0.53)^2}{0.45} = 0.624 \text{ m/s}^2$$

Radial component of the acceleration of C with respect to D,

$$a^r_{CD} = \frac{v^2_{CD}}{DC} = \frac{(1.7)^2}{0.5} = 5.78 \text{ m/s}^2$$

Radial component of the acceleration of E with respect to B,

$$a^r_{EB} = \frac{v^2_{EB}}{BE} = \frac{(1.93)^2}{0.35} = 10.64 \text{ m/s}^2$$

The acceleration diagram, as shown in Fig. 8.23 (c), is drawn as discussed below:

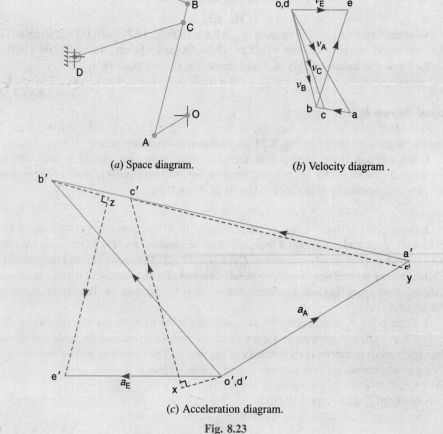

(a) Space diagram. (b) Velocity diagram .

(c) Acceleration diagram.

Fig. 8.23

1. Since O and D are fixed points, therefore these points are marked as one point in the acceleration diagram. Draw vector $o'a'$ parallel to OA, to some suitable scale, to represent the radial component of the acceleration of A with respect to O or simply the acceleration of A, such that

$$\text{vector } o'a' = a_{AO}^r = a_A = 37.13 \text{ m/s}^2$$

2. From point d', draw vector $d'x$ parallel to DC to represent the radial component of the acceleration of C with respect to D, such that

$$\text{vector } d'x = a_{CD}^r = 5.78 \text{ m/s}^2$$

3. From point x, draw vector xc' perpendicular to DC to represent the tangential component of the acceleration of C with respect to D (*i.e.* a_{CD}^t) whose magnitude is yet unknown.

4. Now from point a', draw vector $a'y$ parallel to AC to represent the radial component of the acceleration of C with respect to A, such that

$$\text{vector } a'y = a_{CA}^r = 0.624 \text{ m/s}^2$$

5. From point y, draw vector yc' perpendicular to AC to represent the tangential component of acceleration of C with respect to A (*i.e.* a_{CA}^t). The vectors xc' and yc' intersect at c'.

6. Join $a'c'$. The vector $a'c'$ represents the acceleration of C with respect to A (*i.e.* a_{CA}).

7. Since the point B lies on AC produced, therefore divide vector $a'c'$ at b' in the same ratio as B divides AC in the space diagram. In other words, $a'c' : c'b' = AC : CB$.

8. From point b', draw vector $b'z$ parallel to BE to represent the radial component of the acceleration of E with respect to B, such that

A lathe is a machine for shaping a piece of metal, by rotating it rapidly along its axis while pressing against a fixed cutting or abrading tool.

Note : This picture is given as additional information.

$$\text{vector } b'z = a_{EB}^r = 10.64 \text{ m/s}^2$$

9. From point z, draw vector ze' perpendicular to BE to represent the tangential component of the acceleration of E with respect to B (*i.e.* a_{EB}^t) whose magnitude is yet unknown.

10. From point o', draw vector $o'e'$ parallel to the path of motion of E (which is horizontal) to represent the acceleration of the ram E. The vectors ze' and $o'e'$ intersect at e'.

By measurement, we find that the acceleration of the ram E,

$$a_E = \text{vector } o'e' = 3.1 \text{ m/s}^2 \text{ Ans.}$$

Example 8.12. *The dimensions of the Andreau differential stroke engine mechanism, as shown in Fig. 8.24, are as follows:*

$AB = 80$ mm ; $CD = 40$ mm ; $BE = DE = 150$ mm ; and $EP = 200$ mm.

The links AB and CD are geared together. The speed of the smaller wheel is 1140 r.p.m. Determine the velocity and acceleration of the piston P for the given configuration.

Solution. Given: N_{DC} = 1140 r.p.m. or ω_{DC} = 2 π × 1140/60 = 119.4 rad/s ; AB = 80 mm = 0.08 m ; CD = 40 mm = 0.04 m ; $BE = DE$ = 150 mm = 0.15 m ; EP = 200 mm = 0.2 m

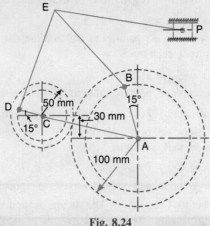

Fig. 8.24

We know that velocity of D with respect to C or velocity of D,

$$v_{DC} = v_D = \omega_{DC} \times CD = 119.4 \times 0.04 = 4.77 \text{ m/s} \qquad \text{...(Perpendicular to } CD\text{)}$$

Since the speeds of the gear wheels are inversely proportional to their diameters, therefore

$$\frac{\text{Angular speed of larger wheel}}{\text{Angular speed of smaller wheel}} = \frac{\omega_{BA}}{\omega_{DC}} = \frac{2CD}{2AB}$$

∴ Angular speed of larger wheel,

$$\omega_{BA} = \omega_{DC} \times \frac{CD}{AB} = 119.4 \times \frac{0.04}{0.08} = 59.7 \text{ rad/s}$$

and velocity of B with respect to A or velocity of B,

$$v_{BA} = v_B = \omega_{BA} \times AB = 59.7 \times 0.08 = 4.77 \text{ m/s}$$

$$\text{...(Perpendicular to } AB\text{)}$$

Velocity of the piston P

First of all draw the space diagram, to some suitable scale, as shown in Fig. 8.25 (*a*). Now the velocity diagram, as shown in Fig. 8.25 (*b*), is drawn as discussed below:

1. Since A and C are fixed points, therefore these points are marked as one point in the velocity diagram. Draw vector cd perpendicular to CD, to some suitable scale, to represent the velocity of D with respect to C or velocity of D (*i.e.* v_{DC} or v_D), such that

$$\text{vector } cd = v_{DC} = v_D = 4.77 \text{ m/s}$$

2. Draw vector ab perpendicular to AB to represent the velocity of B with respect to A or velocity of B (*i.e.* v_{BA} or v_B), such that

$$\text{vector } ab = v_{BA} = v_B = 4.77 \text{ m/s}$$

3. Now from point b, draw vector be perpendicular to BE to represent the velocity of E with respect to B (*i.e.* v_{EB}), and from point d draw vector de perpendicular to DE to represent the velocity of E with respect to D (*i.e.* v_{ED}). The vectors be and de intersect at e.

4. From point e, draw vector ep perpendicular to EP to represent the velocity of P with respect to E (*i.e.* v_{PE}), and from point a draw vector ap parallel to the path of motion of P (which is horizontal) to represent the velocity of P. The vectors ep and ap intersect at p.

By measurement, we find that velocity of E with respect to B,

$$v_{EB} = \text{vector } be = 8.1 \text{ m/s}$$

Velocity of E with respect to D,

$$v_{ED} = \text{vector } de = 0.15 \text{ m/s}$$

Velocity of P with respect to E,

$$v_{PE} = \text{vector } ep = 4.7 \text{ m/s}$$

and velocity of P, $v_P = \text{vector } ap = 0.35$ m/s **Ans.**

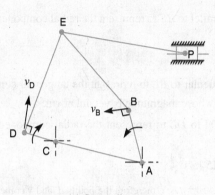

| (a) Space diagram. | (b) Velocity diagram. |

Fig. 8.25

Acceleration of the piston P

We know that the radial component of the acceleration of B with respect A (or the acceleration of B),

$$a_{BA}^r = a_B = \frac{v_{BA}^2}{AB} = \frac{(4.77)^2}{0.08} = 284.4 \text{ m/s}^2$$

Radial component of the acceleration of D with respect to C (or the acceleration of D),

$$a_{DC}^r = a_D = \frac{v_{DC}^2}{CD} = \frac{(4.77)^2}{0.04} = 568.8 \text{ m/s}^2$$

Radial component of the acceleration of E with respect to B,

$$a_{EB}^r = \frac{v_{EB}^2}{BE} = \frac{(8.1)^2}{0.15} = 437.4 \text{ m/s}^2$$

Radial component of the acceleration of E with respect to D,

$$a_{ED}^r = \frac{v_{ED}^2}{DE} = \frac{(0.15)^2}{0.15} = 0.15 \text{ m/s}^2$$

and radial component of the acceleration of P with respect to E,

$$a_{PE}^r = \frac{v_{PE}^2}{EP} = \frac{(4.7)^2}{0.2} = 110.45 \text{ m/s}^2$$

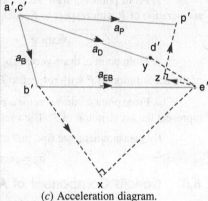

(c) Acceleration diagram.

Fig. 8.25

Now the acceleration diagram, as shown in Fig. 8.25 (c), is drawn as discussed below:

1. Since A and C are fixed points, therefore these points are marked as one point in the acceleration diagram. Draw vector $a'b'$ parallel to AB, to some suitable scale, to represent the radial component of the acceleration of B with respect to A or the acceleration of B, such that

$$\text{vector } a'b' = a_{BA}^r = a_B = 284.4 \text{ m/s}^2$$

2. Draw vector $c'd'$ parallel to CD to represent the radial component of the acceleration of D with respect to C or the acceleration of D, such that

$$\text{vector } c'd' = a_{DC}^r = a_D = 568.8 \text{ m/s}^2$$

3. Now from point b', draw vector $b'x$ parallel to BE to represent the radial component of the acceleration of E with respect to B, such that

$$\text{vector } b'x' = a_{EB}^r = 437.4 \text{ m/s}^2$$

4. From point x, draw vector xe' perpendicular to BE to represent the tangential component of acceleration of E with respect to B (*i.e.* a_{EB}^t) whose magnitude is yet unknown.

5. From point d', draw vector $d'y$ parallel to DE to represent the radial component of the acceleration of E with respect to D, such that

$$\text{vector } d'y = a_{ED}^r = 0.15 \text{ m/s}^2$$

Note: Since the magnitude of a_{ED}^r is very small (*i.e.* 0.15 m/s^2), therefore the points d' and y coincide.

6. From point y, draw vector ye' perpendicular to DE to represent the tangential component of the acceleration of E with respect to D (*i.e.* a_{ED}^t). The vectors xe' and ye' intersect at e'.

7. From point e', draw vector $e'z$ parallel to EP to represent the radial component of the acceleration of P with respect to E, such that

$$\text{vector } e'z = a_{PE}^r = 110.45 \text{ m/s}^2$$

8. From point z, draw vector zp' perpendicular to EP to represent the tangential component of the acceleration of P with respect to E (*i.e.* a_{PE}^t) whose magnitude is yet unknown.

9. From point a', draw vector $a'p'$ parallel to the path of motion of P (which is horizontal) to represent the acceleration of P. The vectors zp' and $a'p'$ intersect at p'.

By measurement, we find that acceleration of the piston P,

$$a_P = \text{vector } a'p' = 655 \text{ m/s}^2 \textbf{ Ans.}$$

8.5. Coriolis Component of Acceleration

When a point on one link is sliding along another rotating link, such as in quick return motion mechanism, then the coriolis component of the acceleration must be calculated.

Consider a link OA and a slider B as shown in Fig. 8.26 (a). The slider B moves along the link OA. The point C is the coincident point on the link OA.

Let ω = Angular velocity of the link OA at time t seconds.

v = Velocity of the slider B along the link OA at time t seconds.

$\omega.r$ = Velocity of the slider B with respect to O (perpendicular to the link OA) at time t seconds, and

$(\omega + \delta\omega)$, $(v + \delta v)$ and $(\omega + \delta\omega)(r + \delta r)$

= Corresponding values at time $(t + \delta t)$ seconds.

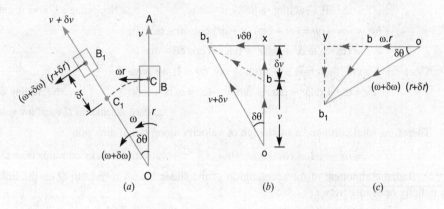

Fig. 8.26. Coriolis component of acceleration.

Let us now find out the acceleration of the slider B with respect to O and with respect to its coincident point C lying on the link OA.

Fig. 8.26 (*b*) shows the velocity diagram when their velocities v and $(v + \delta v)$ are considered. In this diagram, the vector bb_1 represents the change in velocity in time δt sec ; the vector bx represents the component of change of velocity bb_1 along OA (*i.e.* along radial direction) and vector xb_1 represents the component of change of velocity bb_1 in a direction perpendicular to OA (*i.e.* in tangential direction). Therefore

$$bx = ox - ob = (v + \delta v) \cos \delta\theta - v \uparrow$$

Since $\delta\theta$ is very small, therefore substituting $\cos \delta\theta = 1$, we have

$$bx = (v + \delta v - v) \uparrow = \delta v \uparrow$$

...(Acting radially outwards)

and
$$xb_1 = (v + \delta v) \sin \delta\theta$$

Since $\delta\theta$ is very small, therefore substituting $\sin \delta\theta = \delta\theta$, we have

$$xb_1 = (v + \delta v)\, \delta\theta = v.\delta\theta + \delta v.\delta\theta$$

Neglecting $\delta v.\delta\theta$ being very small, therefore

$$xb_1 = v.\overset{\leftarrow}{\delta\theta}$$

...(Perpendicular to OA and towards left)

A drill press has a pointed tool which is used for boring holes in hard materials usually by rotating abrasion or repeated blows.

Note : This picture is given as additional information.

Fig. 8.26 (*c*) shows the velocity diagram when the velocities $\omega.r$ and $(\omega + \delta\omega)(r + \delta r)$ are considered. In this diagram, vector bb_1 represents the change in velocity ; vector yb_1 represents the component of change of velocity bb_1 along OA (*i.e.* along radial direction) and vector by represents the component of change of velocity bb_1 in a direction perpendicular to OA (*i.e.* in a tangential direction). Therefore

$$yb_1 = (\omega + \delta\omega)(r + \delta r) \sin \delta\theta \downarrow$$

$$= (\omega.r + \omega.\delta r + \delta\omega.r + \delta\omega.\delta r) \sin \delta\theta$$

Since $\delta\theta$ is very small, therefore substituting $\sin \delta\theta = \delta\theta$ in the above expression, we have

$$yb_1 = \omega.r.\delta\theta + \omega.\delta r.\delta\theta + \delta\omega.r.\delta\theta + \delta\omega.\delta r.\delta\theta$$

$$= \omega.r.\delta\theta \downarrow, \text{ acting radially inwards} \qquad ...(\text{Neglecting all other quantities})$$

and

$$by = oy - ob = (\omega + \delta\omega)(r + \delta r) \cos \delta\theta - \omega.r$$

$$= (\omega.r + \omega.\delta r + \delta\omega.r + \delta\omega.\delta r) \cos \delta\theta - \omega.r$$

Since $\delta\theta$ is small, therefore substituting $\cos \delta\theta = 1$, we have

$$by = \omega.r + \omega.\delta r + \delta\omega.r + \delta\omega.\delta r - \omega.r = \omega.\delta r + r.\delta\omega \qquad ...(\text{Neglecting } \delta\omega.\delta r)$$

$$...(\text{Perpendicular to } OA \text{ and towards left})$$

Therefore, total component of change of velocity along radial direction

$$= bx - yb_1 = (\delta v - \omega.r.\delta\theta) \uparrow \qquad ...(\text{Acting radially outwards from } O \text{ to } A)$$

$\therefore$ Radial component of the acceleration of the slider B with respect to O on the link OA, acting radially outwards from O to A,

$$a_{BO}^r = \mathrm{Lt}\, \frac{\delta v - \omega.r.\delta\theta}{\delta t} = \frac{dv}{dt} - \omega.r \times \frac{d\theta}{dt} = \frac{dv}{dt} - \omega^2.r \uparrow \qquad ...(i)$$

$$...(\because d\theta/dt = \omega)$$

Also, the total component of change of velocity along tangential direction,

$$= xb_1 + by = v.\overleftarrow{\delta\theta} + (\omega.\delta r + r.\delta\omega)$$

$$...(\text{Perpendicular to } OA \text{ and towards left})$$

$\therefore$ Tangential component of acceleration of the slider B with respect to O on the link OA, acting perpendicular to OA and towards left,

$$a_{BO}^t = \mathrm{Lt}\, \frac{v.\delta\theta + (\omega.\delta r + r.\delta\omega)}{\delta t} = v\frac{d\theta}{dt} + \omega\frac{dr}{dt} + r\frac{d\omega}{dt}$$

$$= v.\omega + \omega.v + r.\alpha = \overleftarrow{(2v.\omega + r.\alpha)} \qquad ...(ii)$$

$$...(\because dr/dt = v, \text{ and } d\omega/dt = \alpha)$$

Now radial component of acceleration of the coincident point C with respect to O, acting in a direction from C to O,

$$a_{CO}^r = \omega^2.r \uparrow \qquad ...(iii)$$

and tangential component of acceleration of the coincident point C with respect to O, acting in a direction perpendicular to CO and towards left,

$$a_{CO}^t = \overleftarrow{\alpha.r} \uparrow \qquad ...(iv)$$

Radial component of the slider B with respect to the coincident point C on the link OA, acting radially outwards,

$$a_{BC}^r = a_{BO}^r - a_{CO}^r = \left(\frac{dv}{dt} - \omega^2.r\right) - \left(-\omega^2.r\right) = \frac{dv}{dt} \uparrow$$

and tangential component of the slider B with respect to the coincident point C on the link OA acting in a direction perpendicular to OA and towards left,

$$a_{BC}^t = a_{BO}^t - a_{CO}^t = (2\omega v + \alpha.r) - \alpha.r = \overleftarrow{2\omega v}$$

This tangential component of acceleration of the slider *B* with respect to the coincident point *C* on the link is known as *coriolis component of acceleration* and is always perpendicualr to the link.

∴ Coriolis component of the acceleration of *B* with respect of *C*,

$$a_{BC}^c = a_{BC}^t = 2\,\omega.v$$

where
$$\omega = \text{Angular velocity of the link } OA, \text{ and}$$
$$v = \text{Velocity of slider } B \text{ with respect to coincident point } C.$$

In the above discussion, the anticlockwise direction for ω and the radially outward direction for *v* are taken as *positive.* It may be noted that the direction of coriolis component of acceleration changes sign, if either ω or *v* is reversed in direction. But the direction of coriolis component of acceleration will not be changed in sign if both ω and *v* are reversed in direction. It is concluded that the direction of coriolis component of acceleration is obtained by rotating *v*, at 90°, about its origin in the same direction as that of ω.

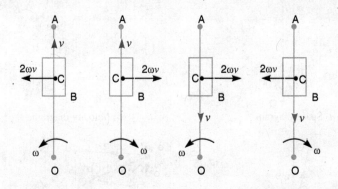

Fig. 8.27. Direction of coriolis component of acceleration.

The direction of coriolis component of acceleration (2 ω.*v*) for all four possible cases, is shown in Fig. 8.27. The directions of ω and *v* are given.

Example 8.13. *A mechanism of a crank and slotted lever quick return motion is shown in Fig. 8.28. If the crank rotates counter clockwise at 120 r.p.m., determine for the configuration shown, the velocity and acceleration of the ram D. Also determine the angular acceleration of the slotted lever.*

Crank, AB = 150 mm ; Slotted arm, OC = 700 mm and link CD = 200 mm.

Solution. Given : $N_{BA} = 120$ r.p.m or $\omega_{BA} = 2\,\pi \times 120/60$ = 12.57 rad/s ; $AB = 150$ mm = 0.15 m; $OC = 700$ mm = 0.7 m; $CD = 200$ mm = 0.2 m

We know that velocity of *B* with respect to *A*,

$$v_{BA} = \omega_{BA} \times AB$$

$$= 12.57 \times 0.15 = 1.9 \text{ m/s}$$

...(Perpendicular to *AB*)

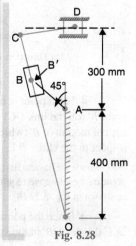

Fig. 8.28

Velocity of the ram D

First of all draw the space diagram, to some suitable scale, as shown in Fig. 8.29 (*a*). Now the velocity diagram, as shown in Fig. 8.29

(*b*), is drawn as discussed below:

1. Since *O* and *A* are fixed points, therefore these points are marked as one point in velocity diagram. Now draw vector *ab* in a direction perpendicular to *AB*, to some suitable scale, to represent the velocity of slider *B* with respect to *A* i.e. v_{BA}, such that

$$\text{vector } ab = v_{BA} = 1.9 \text{ m/s}$$

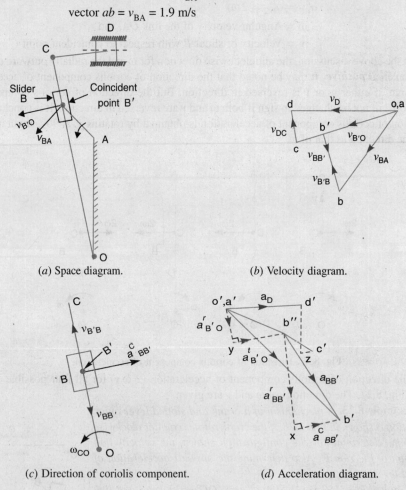

(*a*) Space diagram. (*b*) Velocity diagram.

(*c*) Direction of coriolis component. (*d*) Acceleration diagram.

Fig. 8.29

2. From point *o*, draw vector *ob'* perpendicular to *OB'* to represent the velocity of coincident point *B'* (on the link *OC*) with respect to *O* i.e. $v_{B'O}$ and from point *b* draw vector *bb'* parallel to the path of motion of *B'* (which is along the link *OC*) to represent the velocity of coincident point *B'* with respect to the slider *B* i.e. $v_{BB'}$. The vectors *ob'* and *bb'* intersect at *b'*.

Note: Since we have to find the coriolis component of acceleration of the slider *B* with respect to the coincident point *B'*, therefore we require the velocity of *B* with respect to *B'* i.e. $v_{BB'}$. The vector *b'b* will represent $v_{BB'}$ as shown in Fig. 8.29 (*b*).

3. Since the point *C* lies on *OB'* produced, therefore, divide vector *ob'* at *c* in the same ratio as *C* divides *OB'* in the space diagram. In other words,

$$ob' / oc = OB' / OC$$

The vector *oc* represents the velocity of *C* with respect to *O* i.e. v_{CO}.

4. Now from point c, draw vector cd perpendicular to CD to represent the velocity of D with respect to C i.e. v_{DC}, and from point o draw vector od parallel to the path of motion of D (which is along the horizontal) to represent the velocity of D i.e. v_D. The vectors cd and od intersect at d.

By measurement, we find that velocity of the ram D,
$$v_D = \text{vector } od = 2.15 \text{ m/s } \textbf{Ans.}$$

From velocity diagram, we also find that

Velocity of B with respect to B',
$$v_{BB'} = \text{vector } b'b = 1.05 \text{ m/s}$$

Velocity of D with respect to C,
$$v_{DC} = \text{vector } cd = 0.45 \text{ m/s}$$

Velocity of B' with respect to O
$$v_{B'O} = \text{vector } ob' = 1.55 \text{ m/s}$$

Velocity of C with respect to O,
$$v_{CO} = \text{vector } oc = 2.15 \text{ m/s}$$

∴ Angular velocity of the link OC or OB',
$$\omega_{CO} = \omega_{B'O} = \frac{v_{CO}}{OC} = \frac{2.15}{0.7} = 3.07 \text{ rad/s (Anticlockwise)}$$

Acceleration of the ram D

We know that radial component of the acceleration of B with respect to A,
$$a_{BA}^r = \omega_{BA}^2 \times AB = (12.57)^2 \times 0.15 = 23.7 \text{ m/s}^2$$

Coriolis component of the acceleration of slider B with respect to the coincident point B',
$$a_{BB'}^c = 2\omega.v = 2\omega_{CO}.v_{BB'} = 2 \times 3.07 \times 1.05 = 6.45 \text{ m/s}^2$$
$$\ldots(\because \omega = \omega_{CO} \text{ and } v = v_{BB'})$$

Radial component of the acceleration of D with respect to C,
$$a_{DC}^r = \frac{v_{DC}^2}{CD} = \frac{(0.45)^2}{0.2} = 1.01 \text{ m/s}^2$$

Radial component of the acceleration of the coincident point B' with respect to O,
$$a_{B'O}^r = \frac{v_{B'O}^2}{OB'} = \frac{(1.55)^2}{0.52} = 4.62 \text{ m/s}^2 \qquad \ldots \text{(By measurement } OB' = 0.52 \text{ m)}$$

Now the acceleration diagram, as shown in Fig. 8.29 (*d*), is drawn as discussed below:

1. Since O and A are fixed points, therefore these points are marked as one point in the acceleration diagram. Draw vector $a'b'$ parallel to AB, to some suitable scale, to represent the radial component of the acceleration of B with respect to A i.e. a_{BA}^r or a_B, such that
$$\text{vector } a'b' = a_{BA}^r = a_B = 23.7 \text{ m/s}^2$$

2. The acceleration of the slider B with respect to the coincident point B' has the following two components :

(*i*) Coriolis component of the acceleration of B with respect to B' i.e. $a_{BB'}^c$, and

(*ii*) Radial component of the acceleration of B with respect to B' i.e. $a_{BB'}^r$.

These two components are mutually perpendicular. Therefore from point b' draw vector $b'x$ perpendicular to $B'O$ i.e. in a direction as shown in Fig. 8.29 (*c*) to represent $a_{BB'}^c = 6.45 \text{ m/s}^2$. The direction of $a_{BB'}^c$ is obtained by rotating $v_{BB'}$ (represented by vector $b'b$ in velocity diagram) through $90°$ in the same sense as that of link OC which rotates in the counter clockwise direction. Now from point x, draw vector xb'' perpendicular to vector $b'x$ (or parallel to $B'O$) to represent $a_{BB'}^r$ whose magnitude is yet unknown.

3. The acceleration of the coincident point B' with respect to O has also the following two components:

(i) Radial component of the acceleration of coincident point B' with respect to O i.e. $a_{B'O}^r$, and

(ii) Tangential component of the acceleration of coincident point B' with respect to O, i.e. $a_{B'O}^t$.

These two components are mutually perpendicular. Therefore from point o', draw vector $o'y$ parallel to $B'O$ to represent $a_{B'O}^r = 4.62$ m/s^2 and from point y draw vector yb'' perpendicular to vector $o'y$ to represent $a_{B'O}^t$. The vectors xb'' and yb'' intersect at b''. Join $o'b''$. The vector $o'b''$ represents the acceleration of B' with respect to O, i.e. $a_{B'O}$.

4. Since the point C lies on OB' produced, therefore divide vector $o'b''$ at c' in the same ratio as C divides OB' in the space diagram. In other words,

$$o'b''/o'c' = OB'/OC$$

5. The acceleration of the ram D with respect to C has also the following two components:

(i) Radial component of the acceleration of D with respect to C i.e. a_{DC}^r, and

(ii) Tangential component of the acceleration of D with respect to C, i.e. a_{DC}^t.

The two components are mutually perpendicular. Therefore draw vector $c'z$ parallel to CD to represent $a_{DC}^r = 1.01$ m/s^2 and from z draw zd' perpendicular to vector zc' to represent a_{DC}^t, whose magnitude is yet unknown.

6. From point o', draw vector $o'd'$ in the direction of motion of the ram D which is along the horizontal. The vectors zd' and $o'd'$ intersect at d'. The vector $o'd'$ represents the acceleration of ram D i.e. a_D.

By measurement, we find that acceleration of the ram D,

$$a_D = \text{vector } o'd' = 8.4 \text{ m/s}^2 \text{ Ans.}$$

Angular acceleration of the slotted lever

By measurement from acceleration diagram, we find that tangential component of the coincident point B' with respect to O,

$$a_{B'O}^t = \text{vector } yb'' = 6.4 \text{ m/s}^2$$

We know that angular acceleration of the slotted lever,

$$= \frac{a_{B'O}^t}{OB'} = \frac{6.4}{0.52} = 12.3 \text{ rad/s}^2 \text{ (Anticlockwise) } \textbf{Ans.}$$

Example 8.14. *The driving crank AB of the quick-return mechanism, as shown in Fig. 8.30, revolves at a uniform speed of 200 r.p.m. Find the velocity and acceleration of the tool-box R, in the position shown, when the crank makes an angle of $60°$ with the vertical line of centres PA. What is the acceleration of sliding of the block at B along the slotted lever PQ ?*

Solution. Given : $N_{BA} = 200$ r.p.m. or $\omega_{BA} = 2\pi \times 200/60 = 20.95$ rad/s ; $AB = 75$ mm $= 0.075$ m

We know that velocity of B with respect to A,

$$v_{BA} = \omega_{BA} \times AB = 20.95 \times 0.075 = 1.57 \text{ m/s} \qquad ...(\text{Perpendicular to } AB)$$

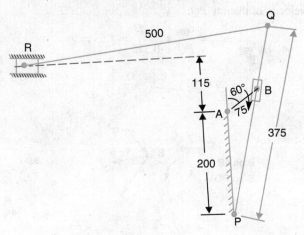

All dimensions in mm.

Fig. 8.30

Velocity of the tool-box R

First of all draw the space diagram, to some suitable scale, as shown in Fig. 8.31 (*a*). Now the velocity diagram, as shown in Fig. 8.31 (*b*), is drawn as discussed below:

1. Since A and P are fixed points, therefore these points are marked as one point in the velocity diagram. Now draw vector ab in a direction perpendicular to AB, to some suitable scale, to represent the velocity of B with respect to A or simply velocity of B (*i.e.* v_{BA} or v_B), such that

$$\text{vector } ab = v_{BA} = v_B = 1.57 \text{ m/s}$$

2. From point p, draw vector pb' perpendicular to PB' to represent the velocity of coincident point B' with respect to P (*i.e.* $v_{B'P}$ or $v_{B'}$) and from point b, draw vector bb' parallel to the path of motion of B' (which is along PQ) to represent the velocity of coincident point B' with respect to the slider B *i.e.* $v_{B'B}$. The vectors pb' and bb' intersect at b'.

Note. The vector $b'b$ will represent the velocity of the slider B with respect to the coincident point B' *i.e.* $v_{BB'}$.

3. Since the point Q lies on PB' produced, therefore divide vector pb' at q in the same ratio as Q divides PB'. In other words,

$$pb'/pq = PB'/PQ$$

The vector pq represents the velocity of Q with respect to P *i.e.* v_{QP}.

4. Now from point q, draw vector qr perpendicular to QR to represent the velocity of R with respect to Q *i.e.* v_{RQ}, and from point a draw vector ar parallel to the path of motion of the tool-box R (which is along the horizontal), to represent the velocity of R *i.e.* v_R. The vectors qr and ar intersect at r.

By measurement, we find that velocity of the tool-box R,

$$v_R = \text{vector } ar = 1.6 \text{ m/s Ans.}$$

We also find that velocity of B' with respect to B,

$$v_{B'B} = \text{vector } bb' = 1.06 \text{ m/s}$$

Velocity of B' with respect to P,

$$v_{B'P} = \text{vector } pb' = 1.13 \text{ m/s}$$

Velocity of R with respect to Q,
$$v_{RQ} = \text{vector } qr = 0.4 \text{ m/s}$$
Velocity of Q with respect to P,
$$v_{QP} = \text{vector } pq = 1.7 \text{ m/s}$$
∴ Angular velocity of the link PQ,

$$\omega_{PQ} = \frac{v_{QP}}{PQ} = \frac{1.7}{0.375} = 4.53 \text{ rad/s} \qquad ...(\because PQ = 0.375 \text{ m})$$

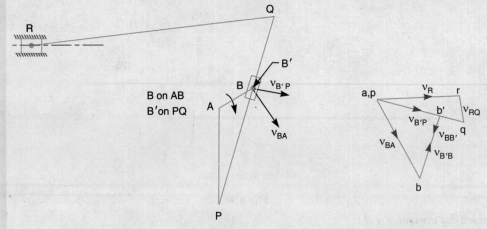

(a) Space diagram.	(b) Velocity diagram.

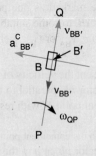 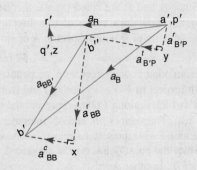

(c) Direction of coriolis component.	(d) Acceleration diagram.

Fig. 8.31

Acceleration of the tool box R

We know that the radial component of the acceleration of B with respect to A,
$$a_{BA}^{r} = \omega_{BA}^{2} \times AB = (20.95)^{2} \times 0.075 = 32.9 \text{ m/s}^{2}$$
Coriolis component of the acceleration of the slider B with respect to coincident point B'.

$$a_{BB'}^{c} = 2\omega.v = 2\omega_{QP} \times v_{BB'} = 2 \times 4.53 \times 1.06 = 9.6 \text{ m/s}^{2}$$

$$...(\because \omega = \omega_{QP}, \text{ and } v = v_{BB'})$$

Radial component of the acceleration of R with respect to Q,

$$a_{RQ}^{r} = \frac{v_{RQ}^{2}}{QR} = \frac{(0.4)^{2}}{0.5} = 0.32 \text{ m/s}^{2}$$

Radial component of the acceleration of B' with respect to P,

$$a_{B'P}^r = \frac{v_{B'P}^2}{PB'} = \frac{(1.13)^2}{0.248} = 5.15 \text{ m/s}^2$$

...(By measurement, $PB' = 248$ mm $= 0.248$ m)

Now the acceleration diagram, as shown in Fig. 8.31 (*d*), is drawn as discussed below:

1. Since A and P are fixed points, therefore these points are marked as one point in the acceleration diagram. Draw vector $a'b'$ parallel to AB, to some suitable scale, to represent the radial component of the acceleration of B with respect to A i.e. a_{BA}^r, or a_B such that

$$\text{vector } a'b' = a_{BA}^r = a_B = 32.9 \text{ m/s}^2$$

2. The acceleration of the slider B with respect to the coincident point B' has the following two components:

(*i*) Coriolis component of the acceleration of B with respect to B' i.e. $a_{BB'}^c$, and

(*ii*) Radial component of the acceleration of B with respect to B' i.e. $a_{BB'}^r$.

These two components are mutually perpendicular. Therefore from point b', draw vector $b'x$ perpendicular to BP [*i.e.* in a direction as shown in Fig. 8.31 (*c*)] to represent $a_{BB'}^c = 9.6$ m/s^2. The direction of $a_{BB'}^c$ is obtained by rotating $v_{BB'}$ (represented by vector $b'b$ in the velocity diagram) through 90° in the same sense as that of link PQ which rotates in the clockwise direction. Now from point x, draw vector xb'' perpendicular to vector $b'x$ (or parallel to $B'P$) to represent $a_{BB'}^r$ whose magnitude is yet unknown.

3. The acceleration of the coincident point B' with respect to P has also the following two components:

(*i*) Radial component of the acceleration of B' with respect to P i.e. $a_{B'P}^r$, and

(*ii*) Tangential component of the acceleration of B' with respect to P i.e. $a_{B'P}^t$.

These two components are mutually perpendicular. Therefore from point p' draw vector $p'y$ parallel to $B'P$ to represent $a_{B'P}^r = 5.15$ m/s^2, and from point y draw vector yb'' perpendicular to vector $p'y$ to represent $a_{B'P}^t$. The vectors xb'' and yb'' intersect at b'', join $p'b''$. The vector $p'b''$ represents the acceleration of B' with respect to P i.e. $a_{B'P}$ and the vector $b''b$ represents the acceleration of B with respect to B' i.e. $a_{BB'}$.

4. Since the point Q lies on PB' produced, therefore divide vector $p'b''$ at q' in the same ratio as Q divides PB in the space diagram. In other words,

$$p'b''/p'q' = PB'/PQ$$

5. The acceleration of the tool-box R with respect to Q has the following two components:

(*i*) Radial component of the acceleration of R with respect to Q i.e. a_{RQ}^r, and

(*ii*) Tangential component of the acceleration of R with respect to Q i.e. a_{RQ}^t.

These two components are mutually perpendicular. Therefore from point q', draw vector $a'z$ parallel to QR to represent $a_{RQ}^r = 0.32$ m/s^2. Since the magnitude of this component is very small, therefore the points q' and z coincide as shown in Fig. 8.31 (*d*). Now from point z (same as q'), draw vector zr' perpendicular to vector $q'z$ (or QR) to represent a_{RQ}^t whose magnitude is yet unknown.

6. From point a' draw vector $a'r'$ parallel to the path of motion of the tool-box R (*i.e.* along the horizontal) which intersects the vector zr' at r'. The vector $a'r'$ represents the acceleration of the tool-box R i.e. a_R.

By measurement, we find that

$$a_R = \text{vector } a'r' = 22 \text{ m/s}^2 \text{ Ans.}$$

Acceleration of sliding of the block B along the slotted lever PQ

By measurement, we find that the acceleration of sliding of the block B along the slotted lever PQ

$$= a_{BB'} = \text{vector } b''x = 18 \text{ m/s}^2 \text{ Ans.}$$

Example 8.15. *In a Whitworth quick return motion, as shown in Fig. 8.32. OA is a crank rotating at 30 r.p.m. in a clockwise direction. The dimensions of various links are : OA = 150 mm; OC = 100 mm; CD = 125 mm; and DR = 500 mm.*

Determine the acceleraion of the sliding block R and the angular acceleration of the slotted lever CA.

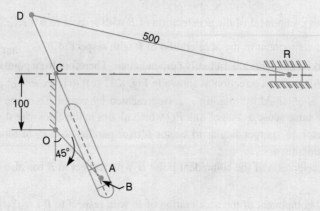

All dimensions in mm.

Fig. 8.32

Solution. Given : N_{AO} = 30 r.p.m. or $\omega_{AO} = 2\pi \times 30/60 = 3.142$ rad/s ; OA = 150 mm = 0.15 m; OC = 100 mm = 0.1 m ; CD = 125 mm = 0.125 m ; DR = 500 mm = 0.5 m

We know that velocity of A with respect to O or velocity of A,

$$v_{AO} = v_A = \omega_{AO} \times OA = 3.142 \times 0.15 = 0.47 \text{ m/s}$$

...(Perpendicular to OA)

First of all draw the space diagram, to some suitable scale, as shown in Fig. 8.33 (*a*). Now the velocity diagram, as shown in Fig. 8.33 (*b*), is drawn as discussed below:

1. Since O and C are fixed points, therefore these are marked at the same place in velocity diagram. Now draw vector oa perpendicular to OA, to some suitable scale, to represent the velocity of A with respect to O or simply velocity of A *i.e.* v_{AO} or v_A, such that

$$\text{vector } oa = v_{AO} = v_A = 0.47 \text{ m/s}$$

2. From point c, draw vector cb perpendicular to BC to represent the velocity of the coincident point B with respect to C *i.e.* v_{BC} or v_B and from point a draw vector ab parallel to the path of motion of B (which is along BC) to represent the velocity of coincident point B with respect to A *i.e.* v_{BA}. The vectors cb and ab intersect at b.

Note: Since we have to find the coriolis component of acceleration of slider A with respect to coincident point B, therefore we require the velocity of A with respect to B *i.e.* v_{AB}. The vector ba will represent v_{AB} as shown in Fig. 8.33 (*b*).

3. Since *D* lies on *BC* produced, therefore divide vector *bc* at *d* in the same ratio as *D* divides *BC* in the space diagram. In other words,

$$bd/bc = BD/BC$$

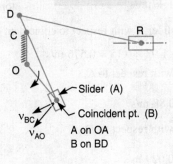

(a) Space diagram.

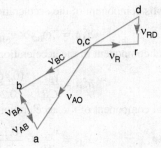

(b) Velocity diagram.

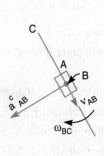

(c) Direction of coriolis component.

(d) Acceleration diagram.

Fig. 8.33

4. Now from point *d*, draw vector *dr* perpendicular to *DR* to represent the velocity of *R* with respect to *D i.e.* v_{RD}, and from point *c* draw vector *cr* parallel to the path of motion of *R* (which is horizontal) to represent the velocity of *R i.e.* v_R.

By measurement, we find that velocity of *B* with respect to *C*,

$$v_{BC} = \text{vector } cb = 0.46 \text{ m/s}$$

Velocity of *A* with respect to *B*,

$$v_{AB} = \text{vector } ba = 0.15 \text{ m/s}$$

and velocity of *R* with respect to *D*,

$$v_{RD} = \text{vector } dr = 0.12 \text{ m/s}$$

We know that angular velocity of the link *BC*,

$$\omega_{BC} = \frac{v_{BC}}{CB} = \frac{0.46}{0.24} = 1.92 \text{ rad/s (Clockwise)}$$

...(By measurement, *CB* = 0.24 m)

Acceleration of the sliding-block R

We know that the radial component of the acceleration of A with respect to O,

$$a_{AO}^r = \frac{v_{AO}^2}{OA} = \frac{(0.47)^2}{0.15} = 1.47 \text{ m/s}^2$$

Coriolis component of the acceleration of slider A with respect to coincident point B,

$$a_{AB}^c = 2\omega_{BC} \times v_{AB} = 2 \times 1.92 \times 0.15 = 0.576 \text{ m/s}^2$$

Radial component of the acceleration of B with respect to C,

$$a_{BC}^r = \frac{v_{BC}^2}{CB} = \frac{(0.46)^2}{0.24} = 0.88 \text{ m/s}^2$$

Radial component of the acceleration of R with respect to D,

$$a_{RD}^r = \frac{v_{RD}^2}{DR} = \frac{(0.12)^2}{0.5} = 0.029 \text{ m/s}^2$$

Now the acceleration diagram, as shown in Fig. 8.33 (*d*), is drawn as discussed below:

1. Since O and C are fixed points, therefore these are marked at the same place in the acceleration diagram. Draw vector $o'a'$ parallel to OA, to some suitable scale, to represent the radial component of the acceleration of A with respect to O i.e. a_{AO}^r or a_A such that

$$\text{vector } o'a' = a_{AO}^r = a_A = 1.47 \text{ m/s}^2$$

2. The acceleration of the slider A with respect to coincident point B has the following two components:

(*i*) Coriolis component of the acceleration of A with respect to B i.e. a_{AB}^c, and

(*ii*) Radial component of the acceleration of A with respect to B i.e. a_{AB}^r.

These two components are mutually perpendicular. Therefore from point a' draw vector $a'x$ perpendicular to BC to represent $a_{AB}^c = 0.576 \text{ m/s}^2$ in a direction as shown in Fig. 8.33 (*c*), and draw vector xb' perpendicular to vector $a'x$ (or parallel to BC) to represent a_{AB}^r whose magnitude is yet unknown.

Note: The direction of a_{AB}^c is obtained by rotating v_{AB} (represented by vector ba in velocity diagram) through $90°$ in the same sense as that of ω_{BC} which rotates in clockwise direction.

3. The acceleration of B with respect to C has the following two components:

(*i*) Radial component of B with respect to C i.e. a_{BC}^r, and

(*ii*) Tangential component of B with respect to C i.e. a_{BC}^t.

These two components are mutually perpendicular. Therefore, draw vector $c'y$ parallel to BC to represent $a_{BC}^r = 0.88 \text{ m/s}^2$ and from point y draw vector yb' perpendicular to $c'y$ to represent a_{BC}^t. The vectors xb' and yb' intersect at b'. Join $b'c'$.

4. Since the point D lies on BC produced, therefore divide vector $b'c'$ at d' in the same ratio as D divides BC in the space diagram. In other words,

$$b'd'/b'c' = BD/BC.$$

5. The acceleration of the sliding block R with respect to D has also the following two components:

(*i*) Radial component of R with respect to D i.e. a_{RD}^r, and

(*ii*) Tangential component of R with respect to D i.e. a_{RD}^t.

These two components are mutually perpendicular. Therefore from point d', draw vector $d'z$ parallel to *DR* to represent $a_{RD}^r = 0.029$ m/s² and from z draw zr' perpendicular to $d'z$ to represent a_{RD}^t whose magnitude is yet unknown.

6. From point c', draw vector $c'r'$ parallel to the path of motion of *R* (which is horizontal). The vector $c'r'$ intersects the vector zr' at r'. The vector $c'r'$ represents the acceleration of the sliding block *R*.

By measurement, we find that acceleration of the sliding block *R*,

$$a_R = \text{vector } c'r' = 0.18 \text{ m/s}^2 \textbf{ Ans.}$$

Angular acceleration of the slotted lever CA

By measurement from acceleration diagram, we find that tangential component of *B* with respect to *C*,

$$a_{BC}^t = \text{vector } yb' = 0.14 \text{ m/s}^2$$

We know that angular acceleration of the slotted lever *CA*,

$$\alpha_{CA} = \alpha_{BC} = \frac{a_{CB}^t}{BC} = \frac{0.14}{0.24} = 0.583 \text{ rad/s}^2 \text{ (Anticlockwise) } \textbf{Ans.}$$

Example 8.16. *The kinematic diagram of one of the cylinders of a rotary engine is shown in Fig. 8.34. The crank OA which is vertical and fixed, is 50 mm long. The length of the connecting rod AB is 125 mm. The line of the stroke OB is inclined at 50° to the vertical.*

The cylinders are rotating at a uniform speed of 300 r.p.m., in a clockwise direction, about the fixed centre O. Determine: 1. acceleration of the piston inside the cylinder, and 2. angular acceleration of the connecting rod.

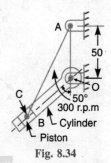

Fig. 8.34

Solution. Given: $AB = 125$ mm $= 0.125$ m ; $N_{CO} = 300$ r.p.m. or $\omega_{CO} = 2\pi \times 300/60 = 31.4$ rad/s

First of all draw the space diagram, as shown in Fig. 8.35 *(a)*, to some suitable scale. By measurement from the space diagram, we find that

$$OC = 85 \text{ mm} = 0.085 \text{ m}$$

∴ Velocity of *C* with respect to *O*,

$$v_{CO} = \omega_{CO} \times OC = 31.4 \times 0.85 = 2.7 \text{ m/s}$$

...(Perpendicular to *CO*)

Now the velocity diagram, as shown in Fig. 8.35 *(b)*, is drawn as discussed below:

1. Since *O* and *A* are fixed points, therefore these are marked at the same place in the velocity diagram. Draw vector *oc* perpendicular to *OC* to represent the velocity of *C* with respect to *O i.e.* v_{CO}, such that

$$\text{vector } oc = v_{CO} = v_C = 2.7 \text{ m/s.}$$

2. From point *c*, draw vector *cb* parallel to the path of motion of the piston *B* (which is along *CO*) to represent the velocity of *B* with respect to *C i.e.* v_{BC}, and from point *a* draw vector *ab* perpendicular to *AB* to represent the velocity of *B* with respect to *A i.e.* v_{BA} or v_B.

By measurement, we find that velocity of piston *B* with respect to coincident point *C*,

$$v_{BC} = \text{vector } cb = 0.85 \text{ m/s}$$

and velocity of piston B with respect to A,

$$v_{BA} = v_B = \text{vector } ab = 2.85 \text{ m/s}.$$

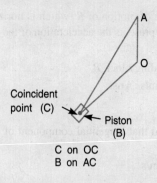

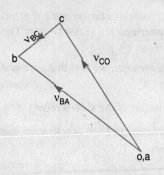

(a) Space diagram.

(b) Velocity diagram.

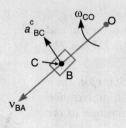

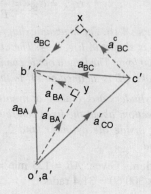

(c) Direction of coriolis component.

(d) Acceleration diagram.

Fig. 8.35

1. Acceleration of the piston inside the cylinder

We know that the radial component of the acceleration of the coincident point C with respect to O,

$$a_{CO}^r = \frac{v_{CO}^2}{OC} = \frac{(2.7)^2}{0.085} = 85.76 \text{ m/s}^2$$

Coriolis component of acceleration of the piston B with respect to the cylinder or coincident point C,

$$a_{BC}^c = 2\,\omega_{CO} \times v_{BC} = 2 \times 31.4 \times 0.85 = 53.4 \text{ m/s}^2$$

Radial component of acceleration of B with respect to A,

$$a_{BA}^r = \frac{v_{BA}^2}{AB} = \frac{(2.85)^2}{0.125} = 65 \text{ m/s}^2$$

The acceleration diagram, as shown in Fig. 8.35 (d), is drawn as discussed below:

1. Since O and A are fixed points, therefore these are marked as one point in the acceleration diagram. Draw vector $o'c'$ parallel to OC, to some suitable scale, to represent the radial component of the acceleration of C with respect to O i.e., a_{CO}^r, such that

$$\text{vector } o'c' = a_{CO}^r = 85.76 \text{ m/s}^2.$$

2. The acceleration of piston B with respect to coincident point C has the following two components:

(i) Coriolis component of the acceleration of B with respect to C i.e. a_{BC}^c, and

(ii) Radial component of the acceleration of B with respect to C i.e. a_{BC}^r.

These two components are mutually perpendicular. Therefore from point c', draw vector $c'x$ perpendicular to CO to represent $a_{BC}^c = 53.4 \text{ m/s}^2$ in a direction as shown in Fig. 8.35 (c). The direction of a_{BC}^c is obtained by rotating v_{BC} (represented by vector cb in velocity diagram) through $90°$ in the same sense as that of ω_{CO} which rotates in the clockwise direction. Now from point x, draw vector xb' perpendicular to vector $c'x$ (or parallel to OC) to represent a_{BC}^r whose magnitude is yet unknown.

3. The acceleration of B with respect to A has also the following two components:

(i) Radial component of the acceleration of B with respect to A i.e. a_{BA}^r, and

(ii) Tangential component of the acceleration of B with respect to A i.e. a_{BA}^t.

These two components are mutually perpendicular. Therefore from point a', draw vector $a'y$ parallel to AB to represent $a_{BA}^r = 65 \text{ m/s}^2$, and from point y draw vector yb' perpendicular to vector $a'y$ to represent a_{BA}^t. The vectors xb' and yb' intersect at b'.

4. Join $c'b'$ and $a'b'$. The vector $c'b'$ represents the acceleration of B with respect to C (i.e. acceleration of the piston inside the cylinder).

By measurement, we find that acceleration of the piston inside the cylinder,

$$a_{BC} = \text{vector } c'b' = 73.2 \text{ m/s}^2 \text{ Ans.}$$

2. *Angular acceleration of the connecting rod*

By measurement from acceleration diagram, we find that the tangential component of the acceleration of B with respect to A,

$$a_{BA}^t = \text{vector } yb' = 37.6 \text{ m/s}^2$$

∴ Angular acceleration of the connecting rod AB,

$$\alpha_{AB} = \frac{a_{BA}^t}{AB} = \frac{37.6}{0.125} = 301 \text{ rad/s}^2 \text{ (Clockwise) Ans.}$$

Example 8.17. *In a swivelling joint mechanism, as shown in Fig. 8.36, the driving crank OA is rotating clockwise at 100 r.p.m. The lengths of various links are : OA = 50 mm ; AB = 350 mm; AD = DB ; DE = EF = 250 mm and CB = 125 mm. The horizontal distance between the fixed points O and C is 300 mm and the vertical distance between F and C is 250 mm.*

For the given configuration, determine: 1. Velocity of the slider block F, 2. Angular velocity of the link DE, 3. Velocity of sliding of the link DE in the swivel block, and 4. Acceleration of sliding of the link DE in the trunnion.

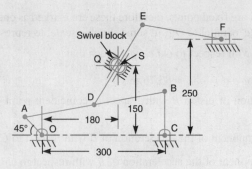

All dimensions in mm.

Fig. 8.36

Solution. Given: $N_{AO} = 100$ r.p.m. or $\omega_{AO} = 2\pi \times 100/60 = 10.47$ rad/s ; $OA = 50$ mm $= 0.05$ m; $AB = 350$ mm $= 0.35$ m ; $CB = 125$ mm $= 0.125$ m ; $DE = EF = 250$ mm $= 0.25$ m

We know that velocity of A with respect to O or velocity of A,

$$v_{AO} = v_A = \omega_{AO} \times OA = 10.47 \times 0.05 = 0.523 \text{ m/s}$$

...(Perpendicular to OA)

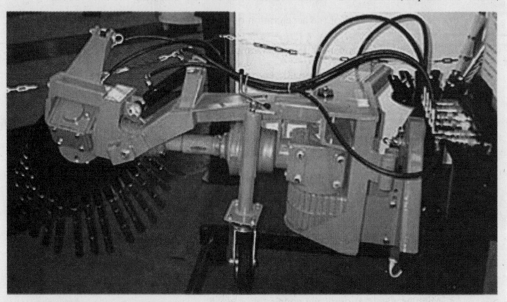

This machine uses swivelling joint.

1. *Velocity of slider block F*

First of all draw the space diagram, to some suitable scale, as shown in Fig. 8.37 (*a*). Now the velocity diagram, as shown in Fig. 8.37 (*b*), is drawn as discussed below:

1. Since O, C and Q are fixed points, therefore these points are marked at one place in the velocity diagram. Draw vector *oa* perpendicular to *OA*, to some suitable scale, to represent the velocity of A with respect to O or simply velocity of A, *i.e.* v_{AO} or v_A, such that

vector $oa = v_{AO} = v_A = 0.523$ m/s

2. From point *a*, draw vector *ab* perpendicular to *AB* to represent the velocity of *B* with respect to *A i.e.* v_{BA}, and from point *c* draw vector *cb* perpendicular to *CB* to represent the velocity of *B* with respect to *C* or simply velocity of *B i.e.* v_{BC} or v_B. The vectors *ab* and *cb* intersect at *b*.

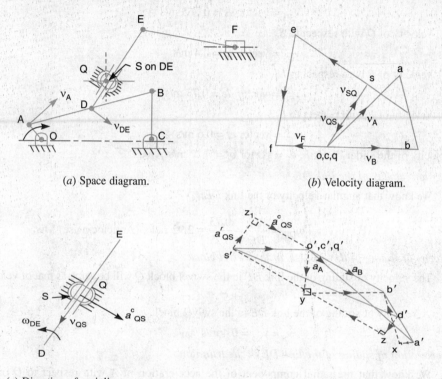

(*a*) Space diagram.

(*b*) Velocity diagram.

(*c*) Direction of coriolis component.

(*d*) Acceleration diagram.

Fig. 8.37

3. Since point *D* lies on *AB*, therefore divide vector *ab* at *d* in the same ratio as *D* divides *AB* in the space diagram. In other words,

$$ad/ab = AD/AB$$

Note: Since point *D* is mid-point of *AB*, therefore *d* is also mid-point of *ab*.

4. Now from point *d*, draw vector *ds* perpendicular to *DS* to represent the velocity of *S* with respect to *D i.e.* v_{SD}, and from point *q* draw vector *qs* parallel to the path of motion of swivel block *Q* (which is along *DE*) to represent the velocity of *S* with respect to *Q i.e.* v_{SQ}. The vectors *ds* and *qs* intersect at *s*.

Note: The vector *sq* will represent the velocity of swivel block *Q* with respect to *S i.e.* v_{QS}.

5. Since point *E* lies on *DS* produced, therefore divide vector *ds* at *e* in the same ratio as *E* divides *DS* in the space diagram. In other words,

$$de/ds = DE/DS$$

6. From point *e*, draw vector *ef* perpendicular to *EF* to represent the velocity of *F* with respect to *E i.e.* v_{FE}, and from point *o* draw vector *of* parallel to the path of motion of *F* (which is along the horizontal direction) to represent the velocity of *F i.e.* v_F. The vectors *ef* and *of* intersect at *f*.

By measurement, we find that velocity of *B* with respect to *A*,

$$v_{BA} = \text{vector } ab = 0.4 \text{ m/s}$$

Velocity of B with respect to C,

$$v_{BC} = v_B = \text{vector } cb = 0.485 \text{ m/s}$$

Velocity of S with respect to D,

$$v_{SD} = \text{vector } ds = 0.265 \text{ m/s}$$

Velocity of Q with respect to S,

$$v_{QS} = \text{vector } sq = 0.4 \text{ m/s}$$

Velocity of E with respect to D,

$$v_{ED} = \text{vector } de = 0.73 \text{ m/s}$$

Velocity of F with respect to E,

$$v_{FE} = \text{vector } ef = 0.6 \text{ m/s}$$

and velocity of the slider block F, $v_F = \text{vector } of = 0.27$ m/s **Ans.**

2. *Angular velocity of the link DE*

We know that angular velocity of the link DE,

$$\omega_{DE} = \frac{v_{ED}}{DE} = \frac{0.73}{0.25} = 2.92 \text{ rad/s (Anticlockwise)} \textbf{ Ans.}$$

3. *Velocity of sliding of the link DE in the swivel block*

The velocity of sliding of the link DE in the swivel block Q will be same as that of velocity of S i.e. v_S.

∴ Velocity of sliding of the link DE in the swivel block,

$$v_S = v_{SQ} = 0.4 \text{ m/s} \textbf{ Ans.}$$

4. *Acceleration of sliding of the link DE in the trunnion*

We know that the radial component of the acceleration of A with respect to O or the acceleration of A,

$$a_{AO}^r = a_A = \frac{v_{AO}^2}{OA} = \frac{(0.523)^2}{0.05} = 5.47 \text{ m/s}^2$$

Radial component of the acceleration of B with respect to A,

$$a_{BA}^r = \frac{v_{BA}^2}{AB} = \frac{(0.4)^2}{0.35} = 0.457 \text{ m/s}^2 .$$

Radial component of the acceleration of B with respect to C,

$$a_{BC}^r = \frac{v_{BC}^2}{CB} = \frac{(0.485)^2}{0.125} = 1.88 \text{ m/s}^2$$

Radial component of the acceleration of S with respect to D,

$$a_{SD}^r = \frac{v_{SD}^2}{DS} = \frac{(0.265)^2}{0.085} = 0.826 \text{ m/s}^2$$

...(By measurement $DS = 85$ mm $= 0.085$ m)

Coriolis component of the acceleration of Q with respect to S,

$$a_{QS}^c = 2\,\omega_{DE} \times v_{QS} = 2 \times 2.92 \times 0.4 = 2.336 \text{ m/s}^2$$

and radial component of the acceleration of F with respect to E,

$$a^r_{FE} = \frac{v^2_{FE}}{EF} = \frac{(0.6)^2}{0.25} = 1.44 \text{ m/s}^2$$

Now the acceleration diagram, as shown in Fig. 8.37 (*d*), is drawn as discussed below:

1. Since O, C and Q are fixed points, therefore these points are marked at one place in the acceleration diagram. Now draw vector $o'a'$ parallel to OA, to some suitable scale, to represent a^r_{AO}, or a_A such that

$$\text{vector } o'a' = a^r_{AO} = a_A = 5.47 \text{ m/s}^2$$

Note : Since OA rotates with uniform speed, therefore there will be no tangential component of the acceleration.

2. The acceleration of B with respect to A has the following two components:

(*i*) Radial component of the acceleration of B with respect to A *i.e.* a^r_{BA}, and

(*ii*) Tangential component of the acceleration of B with respect to A *i.e.* a^t_{BA}.

These two components are mutually perpendicular. Therefore from point a', draw vector $a'x$ parallel to AB to represent $a^r_{BA} = 0.457 \text{ m/s}^2$, and from point x draw vector xb' perpendicular to vector $a'x$ to represent a^t_{BA} whose magnitude is yet unknown.

3. The acceleration of B with respect to C has the following two components:

(*i*) Radial component of the acceleration of B with respect to C *i.e.* a^r_{BC}, and

(*ii*) Tangential component of the acceleration of B with respect to C *i.e.* a^t_{BC}.

These two components are mutually perpendicular. Therefore from point c', draw vector $c'y$ parallel to CB to represent $a^r_{BC} = 1.88 \text{ m/s}^2$ and from point y draw vector yb' perpendicular to vector $c'y$ to represent a^t_{BC}. The vectors xb' and yb' intersect at b'.

4. Join $a'b'$ and $c'b'$. The vector $a'b'$ represents the acceleration of B with respect to A *i.e.* a_{BA} and the vector $c'b'$ represents the acceleration of B with respect to C or simply the acceleration of B *i.e.* a_{BC} or a_B, because C is a fixed point.

5. Since the point D lies on AB, therefore divide vector $a'b'$ at d' in the same ratio as D divides AB in the space diagram. In other words,

$$a'd'/a'b' = AD/AB$$

Note: Since D is the mid-point of AB, therefore d' is also mid-point of vector $a'd'$.

6. The acceleration of S with respect to D has the following two components:

(*i*) Radial component of the acceleration of S with respect to D *i.e.* a^r_{SD}, and

(*ii*) Tangential component of the acceleration of S with respect to D *i.e.* a^t_{SD}.

These two components are mutually perpendicular. Therefore from point d', draw vector $d'z$ parallel to DS to represent $a^r_{SD} = 0.826 \text{ m/s}^2$, and from point z draw vector zs' perpendicular to vector $d'z$ to represent a^t_{SD} whose magnitude is yet unknown.

7. The acceleration of Q (swivel block) with respect to S (point on link DE *i.e.* coincident point) has the following two components:

(*i*) Coriolis component of acceleration of Q with respect to S *i.e.* a_{QS}^c, and

(*ii*) Radial component of acceleration of Q with respect to S, *i.e.* a_{QS}^r.

These two components are mutually perpendicular. Therefore from point q', draw vector $q'z_1$, perpendicular to DS to represent $a_{QS}^c = 2.336$ m/s^2 in a direction as shown in Fig. 8.37 (*c*). The direction of a_{QS}^c is obtained by rotating v_{QS} (represented by vector sq in velocity diagram) through 90° in the same sense as that of ω_{DE} which rotates in the anticlockwise direction. Now from z_1, draw vector z_1s' perpendicular to vector $q'z_1$ (or parallel to DS) to represent a_{QS}^r. The vectors zs' and z_1s' intersect at s'.

8. Join $s'q'$ and $d's'$. The vector $s'q'$ represents the acceleration of Q with respect to S *i.e.* a_{QS} and vector $d's'$ represents the acceleration of S with respect to D *i.e.* a_{SD}.

By measurement, we find that the acceleration of sliding of the link DE in the trunnion,

$$= a_{QS}^r = \text{vector } z_1s' = 1.55 \text{ m/s}^2 \text{ Ans.}$$

EXERCISES

1. The engine mechanism shown in Fig. 8.38 has crank $OB = 50$ mm and length of connecting rod $AB = 225$ mm. The centre of gravity of the rod is at G which is 75 mm from B. The engine speed is 200 r.p.m.

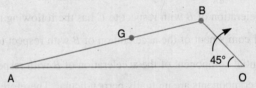

Fig. 8.38

For the position shown, in which OB is turned 45° from OA, Find 1. the velocity of G and the angular velocity of AB, and 2. the acceleration of G and angular acceleration of AB.

[Ans. 6.3 m/s ; 22.6 rad/s ; 750 m/s^2 ; 6.5 rad/s^2]

2. In a pin jointed four bar mechanism $ABCD$, the lengths of various links are as follows:

$AB = 25$ mm ; $BC = 87.5$ mm ; $CD = 50$ mm and $AD = 80$ mm.

The link AD is fixed and the angle $BAD = 135°$. If the velocity of B is 1.8 m/s in the clockwise direction, find 1. velocity and acceleration of the mid point of BC, and 2. angular velocity and angular acceleration of link CB and CD.

[Ans. 1.67 m/s, 110 m/s^2 ; 8.9 rad/s, 870 rad/s^2 ; 32.4 rad/s, 1040 rad/s^2]

3. In a four bar chain $ABCD$, link AD is fixed and the crank AB rotates at 10 radians per second clockwise. Lengths of the links are $AB = 60$ mm ; $BC = CD = 70$ mm ; $DA = 120$ mm. When angle $DAB = 60°$ and both B and C lie on the same side of AD, find 1. angular velocities (magnitude and direction) of BC and CD ; and 2. angular acceleration of BC and CD.

[Ans. 6.43 rad/s (anticlockwise), 6.43 rad/s (clockwise) ; 10 rad/s^2 105 rad/s^2]

4. In a mechanism as shown in Fig. 8.39, the link AB rotates with a uniform angular velocity of 30 rad/s. The lengths of various links are :

$AB = 100$ mm ; $BC = 300$ mm ; $BD = 150$ mm ; $DE = 250$ mm ; $EF = 200$ mm ; $DG = 165$ mm.

Determine the velocity and acceleration of G for the given configuration.

[Ans. 0.6 m/s ; 66 m/s^2]

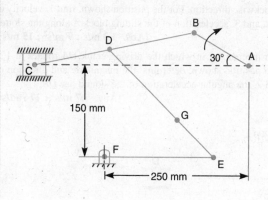

Fig. 8.39

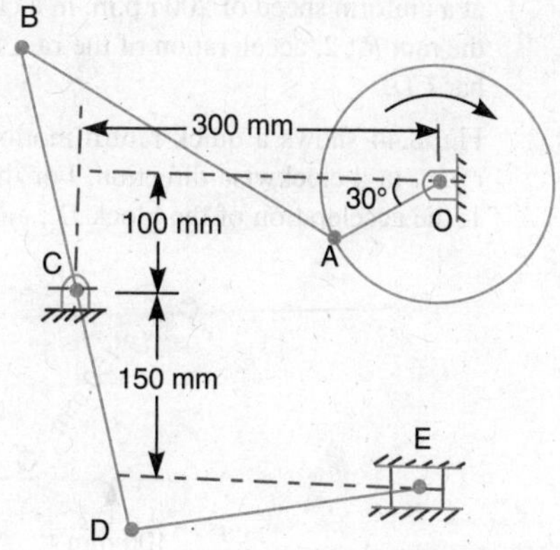

Fig. 8.40

5. In a mechanism as shown in Fig. 8.40, the crank *OA* is 100 mm long and rotates in a clockwise direction at a speed of 100 r.p.m. The straight rod *BCD* rocks on a fixed point at *C*. The links *BC* and *CD* are each 200 mm long and the link *AB* is 300 mm long. The slider *E*, which is driven by the rod *DE* is 250 mm long. Find the velocity and acceleration of *E*.

[**Ans. 1.26 m/s; 10.5 m/s²**]

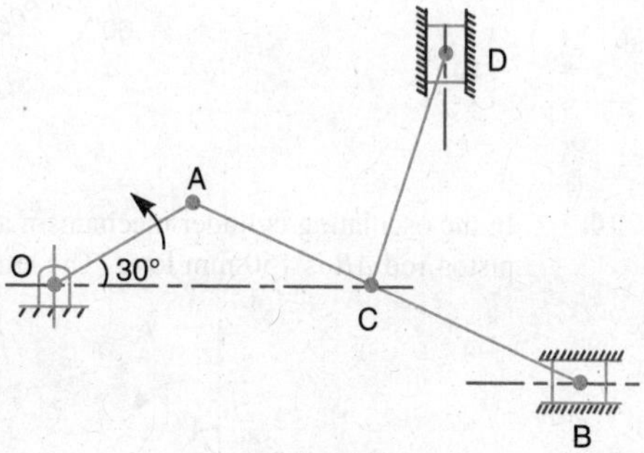

6. The dimensions of the various links of a mechanism, as shown in Fig. 8.41, are as follows:

OA = 80 mm ; *AC* = *CB* = *CD* = 120 mm

Fig. 8.41

If the crank *OA* rotates at 150 r.p.m. in the anti-clockwise direction, find, for the given configuration: 1. velocity and acceleration of *B* and *D* ; 2. rubbing velocity on the pin at *C*, if its diameter is 20 mm ; and 3. angular acceleration of the links *AB* and *CD*.

[**Ans. 1.1 m/s ; 0.37 m/s ; 20.2 m/s², 16.3 m/s² ; 0.15 m/s ; 34.6 rad/s²; 172.5 rad/s²**]

7. In the toggle mechanism, as shown in Fig. 8.42, *D* is constrained to move on a horizontal path. The dimensions of various links are : *AB* = 200 mm; *BC* = 300 mm ; *OC* = 150 mm; and *BD* = 450 mm.

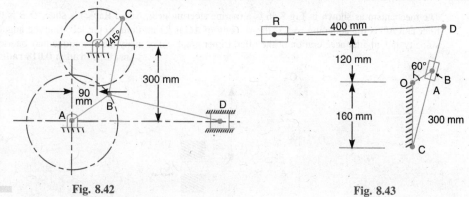

Fig. 8.42

Fig. 8.43

The crank *OC* is rotating in a counter clockwise direction at a speed of 180 r.p.m., increasing at the rate of 50 rad/s². Find, for the given configuration 1. velocity and acceleration of *D*, and 2. angular velocity and angular acceleration of *BD*.

8.   In a quick return mechanism, as shown in Fig. 8.43, the driving crank *OA* is 60 mm long and rotates at a uniform speed of 200 r.p.m. in a clockwise direction. For the position shown, find 1. velocity of the ram *R* ; 2. acceleration of the ram *R*, and 3. acceleration of the sliding block *A* along the slotted bar *CD*.   [**Ans. 1.3 m/s ; 9 m/s^2 ; 15 m/s^2**]

9.   Fig. 8.44 shows a quick return motion mechanism in which the driving crank *OA* rotates at 120 r.p.m. in a clockwise direction. For the position shown, determine the magnitude and direction of 1, the acceleration of the block *D* ; and 2. the angular acceleration of the slotted bar *QB*.   [**Ans. 7.7 m/s^2 ; 17 rad/s^2**]

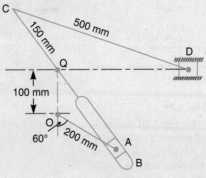

Fig. 8.44

10.   In the oscillating cylinder mechanism as shown in Fig. 8.45, the crank *OA* is 50 mm long while the piston rod *AB* is 150 mm long. The crank *OA* rotates uniformly about *O* at 300 r.p.m.

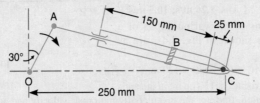

Fig. 8.45

Determine, for the position shown : 1. velocity of the piston *B* relative to the cylinder walls, 2. angular velocity of the piston rod *AB*, 3. sliding acceleration of the piston *B* relative to the cylinder walls, and 4. angular acceleration of the piston rod *AB*.

[**Ans. 1.5 m/s ; 2.2 rad/s (anticlockwise) ; 16.75 m/s^2 ; 234 rad/s^2**]

11.   The mechanism as shown in Fig 8.46 is a marine steering gear, called Rapson's slide. O_2B is the tiller and *AC* is the actuating rod. If the velocity of *AC* is 25 mm/min to the left, find the angular velocity and angular acceleration of the tiller. Either graphical or analytical technique may be used.   [**Ans. 0.125 rad/s; 0.018 rad/s^2**]

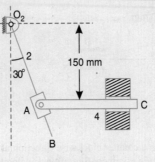

Fig. 8.46

DO YOU KNOW ?

1. Explain how the acceleration of a point on a link (whose direction is known) is obtained when the acceleration of some other point on the same link is given in magnitude and direction.

2. Draw the acceleration diagram of a slider crank mechanism.

3. Explain how the coriolis component of acceleration arises when a point is rotating about some other fixed point and at the same time its distance from the fixed point varies.

4. Derive an expression for the magnitude and direction of coriolis component of acceleration.

5. Sketch a quick return motion of the crank and slotted lever type and explain the procedure of drawing the velocity and acceleration diagram, for any given configuration of the mechanism.

OBJECTIVE TYPE QUESTIONS

1. The component of the acceleration, parallel to the velocity of the particle, at the given instant is called

    (*a*) radial component   (*b*) tangential component

    (*c*) coriolis component   (*d*) none of these

2. A point B on a rigid link AB moves with respect to A with angular velocity ω rad/s. The radial component of the acceleration of B with respect to A,

    (*a*) $v_{BA} \times AB$ (*b*) $v^2_{BA} \times AB$ (*c*) $\dfrac{v_{BA}}{AB}$ (*d*) $\dfrac{v^2_{BA}}{AB}$

    where v_{BA} = Linear velocity of B with respect to $A = \omega \times AB$

3. A point B on a rigid link AB moves with respect to A with angular velocity ω rad/s. The angular acceleration of the link AB is

    (*a*) $\dfrac{a^r_{BA}}{AB}$ (*b*) $\dfrac{a^t_{BA}}{AB}$ (*c*) $v_{BA} \times AB$ (*d*) $\dfrac{v^2_{BA}}{AB}$

4. A point B on a rigid link AB moves with respect to A with angular velocity ω rad/s. The total acceleration of B with respect to A will be equal to

    (*a*) vector sum of radial component and coriolis component

    (*b*) vector sum of tangential component and coriolis component

    (*c*) vector sum of radial component and tangential component

    (*d*) vector difference of radial component and tangential component

5. The coriolis component of acceleration is taken into account for

    (*a*) slider crank mechanism   (*b*) four bar chain mechanism

    (*c*) quick return motion mechanism   (*d*) none of these

ANSWERS

1. (*b*)   2. (*d*)   3. (*b*)   4. (*c*)   5. (*c*)

Pantograph

9

Mechanisms with Lower Pairs

9.1. Introduction

We have already discussed, that when the two elements of a pair have a surface contact and a relative motion takes place, the surface of one element slides over the surface of the other, the pair formed is known as *lower pair*. In this chapter we shall discuss such mechanisms with lower pairs.

9.2. Pantograph

A pantograph is an instrument used to reproduce to an enlarged or a reduced scale and as exactly as possible the path described by a given point.

It consists of a jointed parallelogram ABCD as shown in Fig. 9.1.
It is made up of bars connected by turning pairs. The bars BA and BC are extended to O and E respectively, such that

$$OA/OB = AD/BE$$

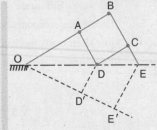
Fig. 9.1. Pantograph.

232

Thus, for all relative positions of the bars, the triangles *OAD* and *OBE* are similar and the points *O*, *D* and *E* are in one straight line. It may be proved that point *E* traces out the same path as described by point *D*.

From similar triangles *OAD* and *OBE*, we find that

$$OD/OE = AD/BE$$

Let point *O* be fixed and the points *D* and *E* move to some new positions *D'* and *E'*. Then

$$OD/OE = OD'/OE'$$

A little consideration will show that the straight line *DD'* is parallel to the straight line *EE'*.

Pantograph.

Hence, if *O* is fixed to the frame of a machine by means of a turning pair and *D* is attached to a point in the machine which has rectilinear motion relative to the frame, then *E* will also trace out a straight line path. Similarly, if *E* is constrained to move in a straight line, then *D* will trace out a straight line parallel to the former.

A pantograph is mostly used for the reproduction of plane areas and figures such as maps, plans etc., on enlarged or reduced scales. It is, sometimes, used as an indicator rig in order to reproduce to a small scale the displacement of the crosshead and therefore of the piston of a reciprocating steam engine. It is also used to guide cutting tools. A modified form of pantograph is used to collect power at the top of an electric locomotive.

9.3. Straight Line Mechanisms

One of the most common forms of the constraint mechanisms is that it permits only relative motion of an oscillatory nature along a straight line. The mechanisms used for this purpose are called *straight line mechanisms*. These mechanisms are of the following two types:

1. in which only turning pairs are used, and

2. in which one sliding pair is used.

These two types of mechanisms may produce exact straight line motion or approximate straight line motion, as discussed in the following articles.

9.4. Exact Straight Line Motion Mechanisms Made up of Turning Pairs

The principle adopted for a mathematically correct or exact straight line motion is described in Fig.9.2. Let *O* be a point on the circumference of a circle of diameter *OP*. Let *OA* be any chord and *B* is a point on *OA* produced, such that

$$OA \times OB = \text{constant}$$

Then the locus of a point *B* will be a straight line perpendicular to the diameter *OP*. This may be proved as follows:

Draw *BQ* perpendicular to *OP* produced. Join *AP*. The triangles *OAP* and *OBQ* are similar.

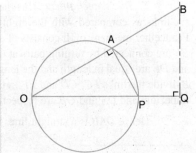

Fig. 9.2. Exact straight line motion mechanism.

$$\therefore \qquad \frac{OA}{OP} = \frac{OQ}{OB}$$

or $\qquad OP \times OQ = OA \times OB$

or $\qquad OQ = \dfrac{OA \times OB}{OP}$

But OP is constant as it is the diameter of a circle, therefore, if $OA \times OB$ is constant, then OQ will be constant. Hence the point B moves along the straight path BQ which is perpendicular to OP.

Following are the two well known types of exact straight line motion mechanisms made up of turning pairs.

1. Peaucellier mechanism. It consists of a fixed link OO_1 and the other straight links O_1A, OC, OD, AD, DB, BC and CA are connected by turning pairs at their intersections, as shown in Fig. 9.3. The pin at A is constrained to move along the circumference of a circle with the fixed diameter OP, by means of the link O_1A. In Fig. 9.3,

$$AC = CB = BD = DA \; ; \; OC = OD \; ; \text{ and } OO_1 = O_1A$$

It may be proved that the product $OA \times OB$ remains constant, when the link O_1A rotates. Join CD to bisect AB at R. Now from right angled triangles ORC and BRC, we have

$$OC^2 = OR^2 + RC^2 \qquad \dots(i)$$

and $\qquad BC^2 = RB^2 + RC^2 \qquad \dots(ii)$

Subtracting equation (ii) from (i), we have

$$OC^2 - BC^2 = OR^2 - RB^2$$

$$= (OR + RB)(OR - RB)$$

$$= OB \times OA$$

Since OC and BC are of constant length, therefore the product $OB \times OA$ remains constant. Hence the point B traces a straight path perpendicular to the diameter OP.

2. Hart's mechanism. This mechanism requires only six links as compared with the eight links required by the Peaucellier mechanism. It consists of a fixed link OO_1 and other straight links O_1A, FC, CD, DE and EF are connected by turning pairs at their points of intersection, as shown in Fig. 9.4. The links FC and DE are equal in length and the lengths of the links CD and EF are also equal. The points O, A and B divide the links FC, CD and EF in the same ratio. A little consideration will show that $BOCE$ is a trapezium and OA and OB are respectively parallel to $*FD$ and CE.

Hence OAB is a straight line. It may be proved now that the product $OA \times OB$ is constant.

A modified form of pantograph is used to collect electricity at the top of electric trains and buses.

Fig. 9.3. Peaucellier mechanism.

---

* In ΔFCE, O and B divide FC and EF in the same ratio, *i.e.*

$$CO/CF = EB/EF$$

$\therefore OB$ is parallel to CE. Similarly, in triangle FCD, OA is parallel to FD.

From similar triangles *CFE* and *OFB*,

$$\frac{CE}{FC} = \frac{OB}{OF} \qquad \text{or} \qquad OB = \frac{CE \times OF}{FC} \qquad \qquad ...(i)$$

and from similar triangles *FCD* and *OCA*

$$\frac{FD}{FC} = \frac{OA}{OC} \qquad \text{or} \qquad OA = \frac{FD \times OC}{FC} \qquad \qquad ...(ii)$$

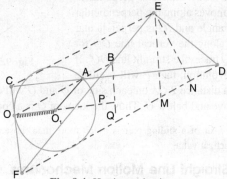

Fig. 9.4. Hart's mechanism.

Multiplying equations (*i*) and (*ii*), we have

$$OA \times OB = \frac{FD \times OC}{FC} \times \frac{CE \times OF}{FC} = FD \times CE \times \frac{OC \times OF}{FC^2}$$

Since the lengths of *OC*, *OF* and *FC* are fixed, therefore

$$OA \times OB = FD \times CE \times \text{constant} \qquad \qquad ...(iii)$$

$$...\left(\text{substituting } \frac{OC \times OF}{FC^2} = \text{constant} \right)$$

Now from point *E*, draw *EM* parallel to *CF* and *EN* perpendicular to *FD*. Therefore

$$FD \times CE = FD \times FM \qquad \qquad ...(\because CE = FM\,)$$
$$= (FN + ND)\,(FN - MN) = FN^2 - ND^2 \qquad \qquad ...(\because MN = ND)$$
$$= (FE^2 - NE^2) - (ED^2 - NE^2)$$

...(From right angled triangles *FEN* and *EDN*)

$$= FE^2 - ED^2 = \text{constant} \qquad \qquad ...(iv)$$

...(∵ Length *FE* and *ED* are fixed)

From equations (*iii*) and (*iv*),

$$OA \times OB = \text{constant}$$

It therefore follows that if the mechanism is pivoted about *O* as a fixed point and the point *A* is constrained to move on a circle with centre O_1, then the point *B* will trace a straight line perpendicular to the diameter *OP* produced.

Note: This mechanism has a great practical disadvantage that even when the path of *B* is short, a large amount of space is taken up by the mechanism.

9.5. Exact Straight Line Motion Consisting of One Sliding Pair-Scott Russell's Mechanism

It consists of a fixed member and moving member *P* of a sliding pair as shown in Fig. 9.5.

The straight link *PAQ* is connected by turning pairs to the link *OA* and the link *P*. The link *OA* rotates about *O*. A little consideration will show that the mechanism *OAP* is same as that of the reciprocating engine mechanism in which *OA* is the crank and *PA* is the connecting rod. In this mechanism, the straight line motion is not generated but it is merely copied.

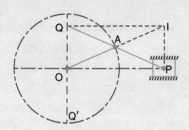

In Fig. 9.5, *A* is the middle point of *PQ* and *OA = AP = AQ*. The instantaneous centre for the link *PAQ* lies at *I* in *OA* produced and is such that *IP* is perpendicular to *OP*. Join *IQ*. Then *Q* moves along the perpendicular to *IQ*. Since *OPIQ* is a rectangle and *IQ* is perpendicular to *OQ*, therefore *Q* moves along the vertical line *OQ* for all positions of *QP*. Hence *Q* traces the straight line *OQ'*. If *OA* makes one complete revolution, then *P* will oscillate

Fig. 9.5. Scott Russell's mechanism.

along the line *OP* through a distance 2 *OA* on each side of *O* and *Q* will oscillate along *OQ'* through the same distance 2 *OA* above and below *O*. Thus, the locus of *Q* is a copy of the locus of *P*.

Note: Since the friction and wear of a sliding pair is much more than those of turning pair, therefore this mechanism is not of much practical value.

9.6. Approximate Straight Line Motion Mechanisms

The approximate straight line motion mechanisms are the modifications of the four-bar chain mechanisms. Following mechanisms to give approximate straight line motion, are important from the subject point of view :

1. *Watt's mechanism.* It is a crossed four bar chain mechanism and was used by Watt for his early steam engines to guide the piston rod in a cylinder to have an approximate straight line motion.

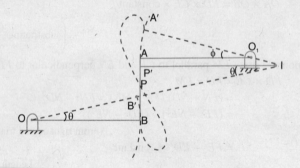

Fig. 9.6. Watt's mechanism.

In Fig. 9.6, *OBAO₁* is a crossed four bar chain in which *O* and *O₁* are fixed. In the mean position of the mechanism, links *OB* and *O₁A* are parallel and the coupling rod *AB* is perpendicular to *O₁A* and *OB*. The tracing point *P* traces out an approximate straight line over certain positions of its movement, if *PB/PA = O₁A/OB*. This may be proved as follows :

A little consideration will show that in the initial mean position of the mechanism, the instantaneous centre of the link *BA* lies at infinity. Therefore the motion of the point *P* is along the vertical line *BA* . Let *OB′ A′O₁* be the new position of the mechanism after the links *OB* and *O₁A* are displaced through an angle θ and ϕ respectively. The instantaneous centre now lies at *I*. Since the angles θ and ϕ are very small, therefore

$$\text{arc } B\,B' = \text{arc } A\,A' \qquad \text{or} \qquad OB \times \theta = O_1A \times \phi \qquad \qquad ...(i)$$

∴ $\qquad OB / O_1A = \phi / \theta$

Also $\qquad A'P' = IP' \times \phi$, and $B'P' = IP' \times \theta$

∴ $\qquad A'P' / B'P' = \phi / \theta$ $\qquad\qquad\qquad\qquad\qquad$ ...(ii)

From equations (*i*) and (*ii*),

$$\frac{OB}{O_1A} = \frac{A'P'}{B'P'} = \frac{AP}{BP} \qquad \text{or} \qquad \frac{O_1A}{OB} = \frac{PB}{PA}$$

Thus, the point P divides the link AB into two parts whose lengths are inversely proportional to the lengths of the adjacent links.

2. *Modified Scott-Russel mechanism.* This mechanism, as shown in Fig. 9.7, is similar to Scott-Russel mechanism (discussed in Art. 9.5), but in this case AP is not equal to AQ and the points P and Q are constrained to move in the horizontal and vertical directions. A little consideration will show that it forms an elliptical trammel, so that any point A on PQ traces an ellipse with semi-major axis AQ and semi-minor axis AP.

If the point A moves in a circle, then for point Q to move along an approximate straight line, the length OA must be equal $(AP)^2 / AQ$. This is limited to only small displacement of P.

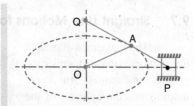

Fig. 9.7. Modified Scott-Russel mechanism.

3. *Grasshopper mechanism.* This mechanism is a modification of modified Scott-Russel's mechanism with the difference that the point P does not slide along a straight line, but moves in a circular arc with centre O.

It is a four bar mechanism and all the pairs are turning pairs as shown in Fig. 9.8. In this mechanism, the centres O and O_1 are fixed. The link OA oscillates about O through an angle AOA_1 which causes the pin P to move along a circular arc with O_1 as centre and O_1P as radius. For small angular displacements of OP on each side of the horizontal, the point Q on the extension of the link PA traces out an approximately straight path QQ', if the lengths are such that $OA = (AP)^2 / AQ$.

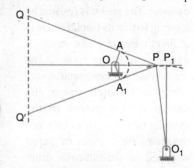

Note: The Grasshopper mechanism was used in early days as an engine mechanism which gave long stroke with a very short crank.

Fig. 9.8. Grasshopper mechanism.

4. *Tchebicheff's mechanism.* It is a four bar mechanism in which the crossed links OA and O_1B are of equal length, as shown in Fig. 9.9. The point P, which is the mid-point of AB traces out an approximately straight line parallel to OO_1. The proportions of the links are, usually, such that point P is exactly above O or O_1 in the extreme positions of the mechanism *i.e.* when BA lies along OA or when BA lies along BO_1. It may be noted that the point P will lie on a straight line parallel to OO_1, in the two extreme positions and in the mid position, if the lengths of the links are in proportions $AB : OO_1 : OA = 1 : 2 : 2.5$.

5. *Roberts mechanism.* It is also a four bar chain mechanism, which, in its mean position, has the form of a trapezium. The links OA and O_1B are of equal length and OO_1 is fixed. A bar PQ is rigidly attached to the link AB at its middle point P.

A little consideration will show that if the mechanism is displaced as shown by the dotted lines in Fig. 9.10, the point Q will trace out an approximately straight line.

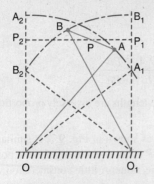

Fig. 9.9. Tchebicheff's mechanism.

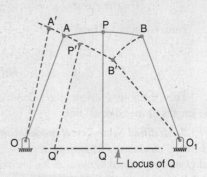

Fig. 9.10. Roberts mechanism

9.7. Straight Line Motions for Engine Indicators

The application of straight line motions is mostly found in the engine indicators. In these instruments, the cylinder of the indicator is in direct communication with the steam or gas inside the cylinder of an engine. The indicator piston rises and falls in response to pressure variation within the engine cylinder. The piston is resisted by a spring so that its displacement is a direct measure of the steam or gas pressure acting upon it. The displacement is communicated to the pencil which traces the variation of pressure in the cylinder (also known as indicator diagram) on a sheet of paper wrapped on the indicator drum which oscillates with angular motion about its axis, according to the motion of the engine piston. The variation in pressure is recorded to an enlarged scale. Following are the various engine indicators which work on the straight line motion mechanism.

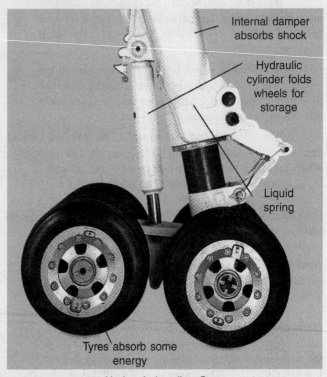

Internal damper absorbs shock

Hydraulic cylinder folds wheels for storage

Liquid spring

Tyres absorb some energy

Airplane's Landing Gear.

Note : This picture is given as additional information.

1. Simplex indicator. It closely resembles to the pantograph copying mechanism, as shown in Fig. 9.11. It consists of a fixed pivot O attached to the body of the indicator. The links AB, BC, CD

and *DA* form a parallelogram and are pin jointed. The link *BC* is extended to point *P* such that *O, D* and *P* lie in one straight line. The point *D* is attached to the piston rod of the indicator and moves along the line of stroke of the piston (*i.e.* in the vertical direction). A little consideration will show that the displacement of *D* is reproduced on an enlarged scale, on the paper wrapped on the indicator drum, by the pencil fixed at point *P* which describes the path similar to that of *D*. In other words, when the piston moves vertically by a distance DD_1, the path traced by *P* is also a vertical straight line PP_1, as shown in Fig. 9.11.

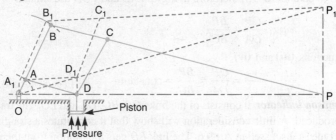

Fig. 9.11. Simplex indicator.

The magnification may be obtained by the following relation :

$$\frac{OP}{OD} = \frac{OB}{OA} = \frac{BP}{BC} = \frac{PP_1}{DD_1}$$

From the practical point of view, the following are the serious objections to this mechanism:

(*a*) Since the accuracy of straight line motion of *P* depends upon the accuracy of motion of *D*, therefore any deviation of *D* from a straight path involves a proportionate deviation of *P* from a straight path.

(*b*) Since the mechanism has five pin joints at *O, A, B, C* and *D*, therefore slackness due to wear in any one of pin joints destroys the accuracy of the motion of *P*.

2. Cross-by indicator. It is a modified form of the pantograph copying mechanism, as shown in Fig. 9.12.

In order to obtain a vertical straight line for *P*, it must satisfy the following two conditions:

1. The point *P* must lie on the line joining the points *O* and *A*, and

2. The velocity ratio between points *P* and *A* must be a constant.

This can be proved by the instantaneous centre method as discussed below :

The instantaneous centre I_1 of the link *AC* is obtained by drawing a horizontal line from *A* to meet the line *ED* produced at I_1. Similarly, the

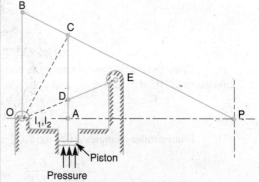

Fig. 9.12. Cross-by indicator.

instantaneous centre I_2 of the link *BP* is obtained by drawing a horizontal line from *P* to meet the line *BO* at I_2. We see from Fig. 9.12, that the points I_1 and I_2 lie on the fixed pivot *O*. Let v_A, v_B, v_C and v_P be the velocities of the points *A, B, C* and *P* respectively.

We know that $$\frac{v_C}{v_A} = \frac{I_1 C}{I_1 A} = \frac{I_2 C}{I_2 A} \qquad ...(i)$$

and
$$\frac{v_P}{v_C} = \frac{I_2 P}{I_2 C} \qquad \qquad ...(ii)$$

Multiplying equations (i) and (ii), we get

$$\frac{v_C}{v_A} \times \frac{v_P}{v_C} = \frac{I_2 C}{I_2 A} \times \frac{I_2 P}{I_2 C} \quad \text{or} \quad \frac{v_P}{v_A} = \frac{I_2 P}{I_2 A} = \frac{OP}{OA} \qquad ...(iii)$$

$$...(\because O \text{ and } I_2 \text{ are same points.})$$

Since AC is parallel to OB, therefore triangles PAC and POB are similar.

$$\therefore \qquad \qquad \frac{OP}{OA} = \frac{BP}{BC} \qquad \qquad ...(iv)$$

From equations (iii) and (iv),

$$\frac{v_P}{v_A} = \frac{OP}{OA} = \frac{BP}{BC} = \text{constant} \qquad ...(\because \text{ Lengths } BP \text{ and } BC \text{ are constant.})$$

3. *Thompson indicator.* It consists of the links OB, BD, DE and EO. The tracing point P lies on the link BD produced. A little consideration will show that it constitutes a straight line motion of the Grasshopper type as discussed in Art.9.6. The link BD gets the motion from the piston rod of the indicator at C which is connected by the link AC at A to the end of the indicator piston rod. The condition of velocity ratio to be constant between P and A may be proved by the instantaneous centre method, as discussed below :

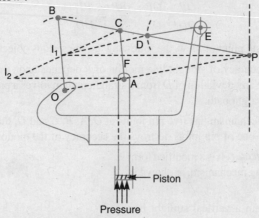

Fig. 9.13. Thompson indicator.

Draw the instantaneous centres I_1 and I_2 of the links BD and AC respectively. The line $I_1 P$ cuts the links AC at F. Let v_A, v_C and v_P be the velocities of the points A, C and P respectively.

$$\therefore \qquad \qquad \frac{v_C}{v_A} = \frac{I_2 C}{I_2 A} \qquad \qquad ...(i)$$

From similar triangles $I_1 CF$ and $I_2 CA$

$$\frac{I_2 C}{I_2 A} = \frac{I_1 C}{I_1 F} \quad \text{or} \quad \frac{v_C}{v_A} = \frac{I_2 C}{I_2 A} = \frac{I_1 C}{I_1 F} \qquad ...(ii)$$

$$...[\text{From equation } (i)]$$

Also
$$\frac{v_P}{v_C} = \frac{I_1 P}{I_1 C} \qquad \qquad ...(iii)$$

Multiplying equations (ii) and (iii), we get

$$\frac{v_C}{v_A} \times \frac{v_P}{v_C} = \frac{I_1 C}{I_1 F} \times \frac{I_1 P}{I_1 C} \quad \text{or} \quad \frac{v_P}{v_A} = \frac{I_1 P}{I_1 F} \qquad ...(iv)$$

Now if the links *AC* and *OB* are parallel, the triangles *PCF* and *PBI*₁ are similar.

$$\therefore \qquad \frac{I_1 P}{I_1 F} = \frac{BP}{BC} \qquad\qquad\qquad ...(v)$$

From equations (*iv*) and (*v*),

$$\frac{v_P}{v_A} = \frac{I_1 P}{I_1 F} = \frac{BP}{BC} = \text{constant} \qquad ...(\because \text{Lengths } BP \text{ and } BC \text{ are constant})$$

Note: The links *AC* and *OB* can not be exactly parallel, nor the line *I*₁*P* be exactly perpendicular to the line of stroke of the piston for all positions of the mechanism. Hence the ratio *BP/BC* cannot be quite constant. Since the variations are negligible for all practical purposes, therefore the above relation gives fairly good results.

4. *Dobbie Mc Innes indicator.* It is similar to Thompson indicator with the difference that the motion is given to the link *DE* (instead of *BD* in Thompson indicator) by the link *AC* connected to the indicator piston as shown in Fig. 9.14. Let v_A, v_C, v_D and v_P be the velocities of the points *A*, *C*, *D* and *P* respectively. The condition of velocity ratio (*i.e.* v_P / v_A) to be constant between points *P* and *A* may be determined by instantaneous centre method as discussed in Thompson indicator.

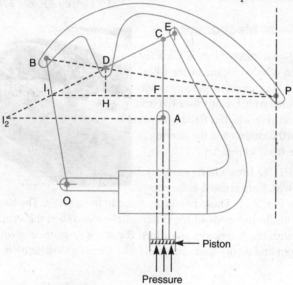

Fig. 9.14. Dobbie McInnes indicator.

Draw the instantaneous centres *I*₁ and *I*₂ of the links *BD* and *AC* respectively. The line *I*₁*P* cuts the link *AC* at *F*. Draw *DH* perpendicular to *I*₁*P*. We know that

$$\therefore \qquad \frac{v_C}{v_A} = \frac{I_2 C}{I_2 A} \qquad\qquad\qquad ...(i)$$

From similar triangles *I*₁*CF* and *I*₂*CA*,

$$\frac{I_2 C}{I_2 A} = \frac{I_1 C}{I_1 F} \quad \text{or} \quad \frac{v_C}{v_A} = \frac{I_2 C}{I_2 A} = \frac{I_1 C}{I_1 F} \qquad ...\text{[From equation (}i\text{)]} \quad ...(ii)$$

Again from similar triangles *I*₁*CF* and *I*₁*DH*,

$$\frac{I_1 C}{I_1 F} = \frac{I_1 D}{I_1 H} \quad \text{or} \quad \frac{v_C}{v_A} = \frac{I_1 D}{I_1 H} \qquad ...\text{[From equation (}ii\text{)]} \quad ...(iii)$$

Since the link *ED* turns about the centre *E*, therefore

$$\frac{v_D}{v_C} = \frac{ED}{EC} \qquad\qquad\qquad ...(iv)$$

Also, $$\frac{v_P}{v_D} = \frac{I_1 P}{I_1 D}$$ ...(v)

Multiplying equations (iii), (iv) and (v), we get

$$\frac{v_C}{v_A} \times \frac{v_D}{v_C} \times \frac{v_P}{v_D} = \frac{I_1 D}{I_1 H} \times \frac{ED}{EC} \times \frac{I_1 P}{I_1 D} \quad \text{or} \quad \frac{v_P}{v_A} = \frac{I_1 P}{I_1 H} \times \frac{ED}{EC}$$ ...(vi)

From similar triangles $I_1 BP$ and PDH,

$$\frac{I_1 P}{I_1 H} = \frac{PB}{BD}$$

$\therefore$
$$\frac{v_P}{v_A} = \frac{PB}{BD} \times \frac{ED}{EC} = \text{constant}$$ ...[From equation (vi)]

...[∵ Lengths PB, BD, ED and EC are constant.]

9.8. Steering Gear Mechanism

The steering gear mechanism is used for changing the direction of two or more of the wheel axles with reference to the chassis, so as to move the automobile in any desired path. Usually the two back wheels have a common axis, which is fixed in direction with reference to the chassis and the steering is done by means of the front wheels.

In automobiles, the front wheels are placed over the front axles, which are pivoted at the points A and B, as shown in Fig. 9.15. These points are fixed to the chassis. The back wheels are placed over the back axle, at the two ends of the differential tube. When the vehicle takes a turn, the front wheels along with the respective axles turn about the respective pivoted points. The back wheels remain straight and do not turn. Therefore, the steering is done by means of front wheels only.

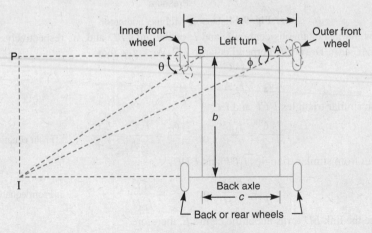

Fig. 9.15. Steering gear mechanism.

In order to avoid skidding (*i.e.* slipping of the wheels sideways), the two front wheels must turn about the same instantaneous centre *I* which lies on the axis of the back wheels. If the instantaneous centre of the two front wheels do not coincide with the instantaneous centre of the back wheels, the skidding on the front or back wheels will definitely take place, which will cause more wear and tear of the tyres.

Thus, the condition for correct steering is that all the four wheels must turn about the same instantaneous centre. The axis of the inner wheel makes a larger turning angle θ than the angle φ subtended by the axis of outer wheel.

Let a = Wheel track,

b = Wheel base, and

c = Distance between the pivots *A* and *B* of the front axle.

Now from triangle *IBP*,

$$\cot\theta = \frac{BP}{IP}$$

and from triangle *IAP*,

$$\cot\phi = \frac{AP}{IP} = \frac{AB + BP}{IP} = \frac{AB}{IP} + \frac{BP}{IP} = \frac{c}{b} + \cot\theta \qquad \qquad ...(\because IP = b)$$

$$\therefore \cot\phi - \cot\theta = c\,/\,b$$

This is the fundamental equation for correct steering. If this condition is satisfied, there will be no skidding of the wheels, when the vehicle takes a turn.

9.9. Davis Steering Gear

The Davis steering gear is shown in Fig. 9.16. It is an exact steering gear mechanism. The slotted links *AM* and *BH* are attached to the front wheel axle, which turn on pivots *A* and *B* respectively. The rod *CD* is constrained to move in the direction of its length, by the sliding members at *P* and *Q*. These constraints are connected to the slotted link *AM* and *BH* by a sliding and a turning pair at each end. The steering is affected by moving *CD* to the right or left of its normal position. *C'D'* shows the position of *CD* for turning to the left.

Let a = Vertical distance between *AB* and *CD*,

b = Wheel base,

d = Horizontal distance between *AC* and *BD*,

c = Distance between the pivots *A* and *B* of the front axle.

x = Distance moved by *AC* to *AC'* = *CC'* = *DD'*, and

α = Angle of inclination of the links *AC* and *BD*, to the vertical.

From triangle *AA'C'*,

$$\tan(\alpha + \phi) = \frac{A'C'}{AA'} = \frac{d + x}{a} \qquad\qquad ...(i)$$

From triangle $AA'C$,

$$\tan \alpha = \frac{A'C}{AA'} = \frac{d}{a} \qquad ...(ii)$$

From triangle $BB'D'$,

$$\tan (\alpha - \theta) = \frac{B'D'}{BB'} = \frac{d - x}{a} \qquad ...(iii)$$

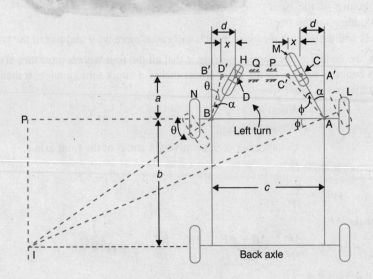

Fig. 9.16. Davis steering gear.

We know that

$$\tan (\alpha + \phi) = \frac{\tan \alpha + \tan \phi}{1 - \tan \alpha . \tan \phi}$$

or

$$\frac{d + x}{a} = \frac{d / a + \tan \phi}{1 - d / a \times \tan \phi} = \frac{d + a \tan \phi}{a - d \tan \phi}$$

...[From equations (i) and (ii)]

$$(d + x) (a - d \tan \phi) = a (d + a \tan \phi)$$

$$a . d - d^2 \tan \phi + a . x - d.x \tan \phi = a.d + a^2 \tan \phi$$

$$\tan \phi (a^2 + d^2 + d.x) = ax \quad \text{or} \quad \tan \phi = \frac{a.x}{a^2 + d^2 + d.x} \qquad ...(iv)$$

Similarly, from $\tan (\alpha - \theta) = \dfrac{d - x}{a}$, we get

$$\tan \theta = \frac{ax}{a^2 + d^2 - d.x} \qquad ...(v)$$

We know that for correct steering,

$$\cot \phi - \cot \theta = \frac{c}{b} \quad \text{or} \quad \frac{1}{\tan \phi} - \frac{1}{\tan \theta} = \frac{c}{b}$$

$$\frac{a^2 + d^2 + d.x}{a.x} - \frac{a^2 + d^2 - d.x}{a.x} = \frac{c}{b}$$

...[From equations (iv) and (v)]

or
$$\frac{2d \cdot x}{a \cdot x} = \frac{c}{b} \quad \text{or} \quad \frac{2d}{a} = \frac{c}{b}$$

$$\therefore \quad 2 \tan \alpha = \frac{c}{b} \quad \text{or} \quad \tan \alpha = \frac{c}{2b} \qquad \qquad ...(\because d / a = \tan \alpha)$$

Note: Though the gear is theoretically correct, but due to the presence of more sliding members, the wear will be increased which produces slackness between the sliding surfaces, thus eliminating the original accuracy. Hence Davis steering gear is not in common use.

Example 9.1. *In a Davis steering gear, the distance between the pivots of the front axle is 1.2 metres and the wheel base is 2.7 metres. Find the inclination of the track arm to the longitudinal axis of the car, when it is moving along a straight path.*

Solution. Given : $c = 1.2$ m ; $b = 2.7$ m

Let $\alpha = $ Inclination of the track arm to the longitudinal axis.

We know that $\tan \alpha = \dfrac{c}{2b} = \dfrac{1.2}{2 \times 2.7} = 0.222 \qquad$ or $\qquad \alpha = 12.5°$ **Ans.**

9.10. Ackerman Steering Gear

The Ackerman steering gear mechanism is much simpler than Davis gear. The difference between the Ackerman and Davis steering gears are :

1. The whole mechanism of the Ackerman steering gear is on back of the front wheels; whereas in Davis steering gear, it is in front of the wheels.

2. The Ackerman steering gear consists of turning pairs, whereas Davis steering gear consists of sliding members.

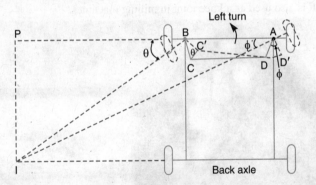

Fig. 9.17. Ackerman steering gear.

In Ackerman steering gear, the mechanism *ABCD* is a four bar crank chain, as shown in Fig. 9.17. The shorter links *BC* and *AD* are of equal length and are connected by hinge joints with front wheel axles. The longer links *AB* and *CD* are of unequal length. The following are the only three positions for correct steering.

1. When the vehicle moves along a straight path, the longer links *AB* and *CD* are parallel and the shorter links *BC* and *AD* are equally inclined to the longitudinal axis of the vehicle, as shown by firm lines in Fig. 9.17.

2. When the vehicle is steering to the left, the position of the gear is shown by dotted lines in Fig. 9.17. In this position, the lines of the front wheel axle intersect on the back wheel axle at *I*, for correct steering.

3. When the vehicle is steering to the right, the similar position may be obtained.

In order to satisfy the fundamental equation for correct steering, as discussed in Art. 9.8, the links AD and DC are suitably proportioned. The value of θ and ϕ may be obtained either graphically or by calculations.

9.11. Universal or Hooke's Joint

A *Hooke's joint is used to connect two shafts, which are intersecting at a small angle, as shown in Fig. 9.18. The end of each shaft is forked to U-type and each fork provides two bearings

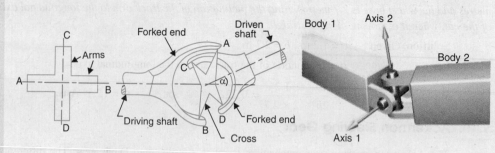

Fig. 9.18. Universal or Hooke's joint.

for the arms of a cross. The arms of the cross are perpendicular to each other. The motion is transmitted from the driving shaft to driven shaft through a cross. The inclination of the two shafts may be constant, but in actual practice it varies, when the motion is transmitted. The main application of the Universal or Hooke's joint is found in the transmission from the **gear box to the differential or back axle of the automobiles. It is also used for transmission of power to different spindles of multiple drilling machine. It is also used as a knee joint in milling machines.

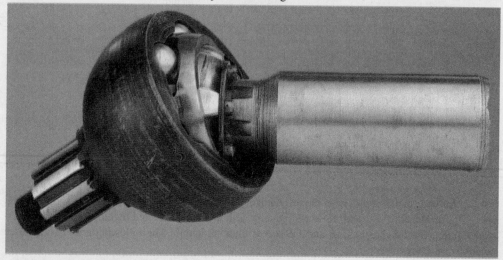

Universal Joint.

---

* This joint was first suggested by Da Vinci and was named after English physicist and mathematician Robert Hooke who first applied it to connect two offset misaligned shafts.

** In case of automobiles, we use two Hooke's joints one at each end of the propeller shaft, connecting the gear box on one end and the differential on the other end.

9.12. Ratio of the Shafts Velocities

The top and front views connecting the two shafts by a universal joint are shown in Fig. 9.19. Let the initial position of the cross be such that both arms lie in the plane of the paper in front view, while the arm *AB* attached to the driving shaft lies in the plane containing the axes of the two shafts. Let the driving shaft rotates through an angle θ, so that the arm *AB* moves in a circle to a new position $A_1 B_1$ as shown in front view. A little consideration will show that the arm *CD* will also move in a circle of the same size. This circle when projected in the plane of paper appears to be an ellipse. Therefore the arm *CD* takes new position $C_1 D_1$ on the ellipse, at an angle θ. But the true angle must be on the circular path. To find the true angle, project the point C_1 horizontally to intersect the circle at C_2. Therefore the angle COC_2 (equal to ϕ) is the true angle turned by the driven shaft. Thus when the driving shaft turns through an angle θ, the driven shaft turns through an angle ϕ. It may be noted that it is not necessary that ϕ may be greater than θ or less than θ. At a particular point, it may be equal to θ.

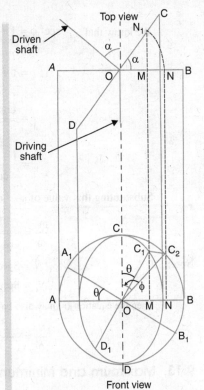

Fig. 9.19. Ratio of shafts velocities.

In triangle OC_1M, $\angle OC_1M = \theta$

$\therefore \qquad \tan \theta = \dfrac{OM}{MC_1}$ ...(*i*)

and in triangle OC_2N, $\angle OC_2N = \phi$

$\therefore \qquad \tan \phi = \dfrac{ON}{NC_2} = \dfrac{ON}{MC_1}$ ...($\because NC_2 = MC_1$) ...(*ii*)

Dividing equation (*i*) by (*ii*),

$$\frac{\tan \theta}{\tan \phi} = \frac{OM}{MC_1} \times \frac{MC_1}{ON} = \frac{OM}{ON}$$

But $\qquad OM = ON_1 \cos \alpha = ON \cos \alpha$

...(where α = Angle of inclination of the driving and driven shafts)

$\therefore \qquad \dfrac{\tan \theta}{\tan \phi} = \dfrac{ON \cos \alpha}{ON} = \cos \alpha$

or $\qquad \tan \theta = \tan \phi . \cos \alpha$ ...(*iii*)

Let $\qquad \omega$ = Angular velocity of the driving shaft = $d\theta / dt$

$\qquad \omega_1$ = Angular velocity of the driven shaft = $d\phi / dt$

Differentiating both sides of equation (*iii*),

$$\sec^2 \theta \times d\theta / dt = \cos \alpha . \sec^2 \phi \times d\phi / dt$$

$$\sec^2 \theta \times \omega = \cos \alpha . \sec^2 \phi \times \omega_1$$

$\therefore \qquad \dfrac{\omega_1}{\omega} = \dfrac{\sec^2 \theta}{\cos \alpha . \sec^2 \phi} = \dfrac{1}{\cos^2 \theta . \cos \alpha . \sec^2 \phi}$ ...(*iv*)

We know that $\sec^2\phi = 1 + \tan^2\phi = 1 + \dfrac{\tan^2\theta}{\cos^2\alpha}$ ...[From equation (*iii*)]

$$= 1 + \frac{\sin^2\theta}{\cos^2\theta.\cos^2\alpha} = \frac{\cos^2\theta.\cos^2\alpha + \sin^2\theta}{\cos^2\theta.\cos^2\alpha}$$

$$= \frac{\cos^2\theta(1 - \sin^2\alpha) + \sin^2\theta}{\cos^2\theta.\cos^2\alpha} = \frac{\cos^2\theta - \cos^2\theta.\sin^2\alpha + \sin^2\theta}{\cos^2\theta.\cos^2\alpha}$$

$$= \frac{1 - \cos^2\theta.\sin^2\alpha}{\cos^2\theta.\cos^2\alpha} \qquad ...(\because \cos^2\theta + \sin^2\theta = 1)$$

Substituting this value of $\sec^2\phi$ in equation (*iv*), we have veloity ratio,

$$\frac{\omega_1}{\omega} = \frac{1}{\cos^2\theta.\cos\alpha} \times \frac{\cos^2\theta.\cos^2\alpha}{1 - \cos^2\theta.\sin^2\alpha} = \frac{\cos\alpha}{1 - \cos^2\theta.\sin^2\alpha} \qquad ...(v)$$

Note: If N = Speed of the driving shaft in r.p.m., and

         N_1 = Speed of the driven shaft in r.p.m.

Then the equation (*v*) may also be written as

$$\frac{N_1}{N} = \frac{\cos\alpha}{1 - \cos^2\theta.\sin^2\alpha}.$$

9.13. Maximum and Minimum Speeds of Driven Shaft

We have discussed in the previous article that velocity ratio,

$$\frac{\omega_1}{\omega} = \frac{\cos\alpha}{1 - \cos^2\theta.\sin^2\alpha} \quad \text{or} \quad \omega_1 = \frac{\omega.\cos\alpha}{1 - \cos^2\theta.\sin^2\alpha} \qquad ...(i)$$

The value of ω_1 will be maximum for a given value of α, if the denominator of equation (*i*) is minimum. This will happen, when

$$\cos^2\theta = 1, \quad i.e. \text{ when } \theta = 0°, 180°, 360° \text{ etc.}$$

∴ Maximum speed of the driven shaft,

$$\omega_{1(max)} = \frac{\omega\cos\alpha}{1 - \sin^2\alpha} = \frac{\omega\cos\alpha}{\cos^2\alpha} = \frac{\omega}{\cos\alpha} \qquad ...(ii)$$

or $N_{1(max)} = \dfrac{N}{\cos\alpha}$ ...(where N and N_1 are in r.p.m.)

Similarly, the value of ω_1 is minimum, if the denominator of equation (*i*) is maximum. This will happen, when $(\cos^2\theta . \sin^2\alpha)$ is maximum, or

$$\cos^2\theta = 0, i.e. \text{ when } \theta = 90°, 270° \text{ etc.}$$

∴ Minimum speed of the driven shaft,

$$\omega_{1\,(min)} = \omega \cos\alpha$$

or $N_{1\,(min)} = N \cos\alpha$ ...(where N and N_1 are in r.p.m.)

Fig. 9.20, shows the polar diagram depicting the salient features of the driven shaft speed.

From above, we see that

1. For one complete revolution of the driven shaft, there are two points *i.e.* at $0°$ and $180°$ as shown by points 1 and 2 in Fig. 9.20, where the speed of the driven shaft is maximum and there are two points *i.e.* at $90°$ and $270°$ as shown by point 3 and 4 where the speed of the driven shaft is minimum.

2. Since there are two maximum and two minimum speeds of the driven shaft, therefore there are four points when the speeds of the driven and driver shaft are same. This is shown by points, 5,6,7 and 8 in Fig. 9.20 (See Art 9.14).

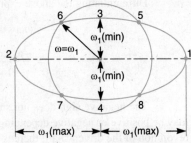

Fig. 9.20. Polar diagram-salient features of driven shaft speed.

3. Since the angular velocity of the driving shaft is usually constant, therefore it is represented by a circle of radius ω. The driven shaft has a variation in angular velocity, the maximum value being $\omega/\cos \alpha$ and minimum value is $\omega \cos \alpha$. Thus it is represented by an ellipse of semi-major axis $\omega/\cos \alpha$ and semi-minor axis $\omega \cos \alpha$, as shown in Fig. 9.20.

Note: Due to the variation in speed of the driven shaft, there will be some vibrations in it, the frequency of which may be decreased by having a heavy mass (a sort of flywheel) on the driven shaft. This heavy mass of flywheel does not perform the actual function of flywheel.

9.14. Condition for Equal Speeds of the Driving and Driven Shafts

We have already discussed that the ratio of the speeds of the driven and driving shafts is

$$\frac{\omega_1}{\omega} = \frac{\cos \alpha}{1 - \cos^2 \theta . \sin^2 \alpha} \qquad \text{or} \qquad \omega = \frac{\omega_1 (1 - \cos^2 \theta . \sin^2 \alpha)}{\cos \alpha}$$

For equal speeds, $\omega = \omega_1$, therefore

$$\cos \alpha = 1 - \cos^2 \theta . \sin^2 \alpha \qquad \text{or} \qquad \cos^2 \theta . \sin^2 \alpha = 1 - \cos \alpha$$

and

$$\cos^2 \theta = \frac{1 - \cos \alpha}{\sin^2 \alpha} \qquad \qquad ...(i)$$

We know that $\sin^2 \theta = 1 - \cos^2 \theta = 1 - \dfrac{1 - \cos\alpha}{\sin^2 \alpha} = 1 - \dfrac{1 - \cos\alpha}{1 - \cos^2 \alpha}$

$$= 1 - \frac{1 - \cos\alpha}{(1 + \cos\alpha)(1 - \cos\alpha)} = 1 - \frac{1}{1 + \cos\alpha} = \frac{\cos\alpha}{1 + \cos\alpha} \qquad ...(ii)$$

Dividing equation (*ii*) by equation (*i*),

$$\frac{\sin^2 \theta}{\cos^2 \theta} = \frac{\cos\alpha}{1 + \cos\alpha} \times \frac{\sin^2 \alpha}{1 - \cos\alpha}$$

or

$$\tan^2 \theta = \frac{\cos\alpha \sin^2 \alpha}{1 - \cos^2 \alpha} = \frac{\cos\alpha . \sin^2 \alpha}{\sin^2 \alpha} = \cos\alpha$$

$$\therefore \qquad \tan \theta = \pm \sqrt{\cos\alpha}$$

There are two values of θ corresponding to positive sign and two values corresponding to negative sign. Hence, there are four values of θ, at which the speeds of the driving and driven shafts are same. This is shown by points 5, 6, 7 and 8 in Fig. 9.20.

9.15. Angular Acceleration of the Driven Shaft

We know that $\quad \omega_1 = \dfrac{\omega\cos\alpha}{1 - \cos^2 \theta . \sin^2 \alpha} = \omega . \cos\alpha (1 - \cos^2 \theta . \sin^2 \alpha)^{-1}$

Differentiating the above expression, we have the angular acceleration of the driven shaft,

$$\frac{d\omega_1}{dt} = \omega\cos\alpha\left[-1(1 - \cos^2\theta\sin^2\alpha)^{-2} \times (2\cos\theta\sin\theta\sin^2\alpha)\right]\frac{d\theta}{dt}$$

$$= \frac{-\omega^2\cos\alpha \times \sin 2\theta.\sin^2\alpha}{(1 - \cos^2\theta\sin^2\alpha)^2} \qquad \dots(i)$$

$$\dots(2\cos\theta\sin\theta = \sin 2\theta, \text{ and } d\theta/dt = \omega)$$

The negative sign does not show that there is always retardation. The angular acceleration may be positive or negative depending upon the value of sin 2 θ. It means that during one complete revolution of the driven shaft, there is an angular acceleration corresponding to increase in speed of ω_1 and retardation due to decrease in speed of ω_1.

For angular acceleration to be maximum, differentiate $d\omega_1 / dt$ with respect to θ and equate to zero. The result is * approximated as

$$\cos 2\theta = \frac{\sin^2\alpha(2 - \cos^2 2\theta)}{2 - \sin^2\alpha}$$

Note: If the value of α is less than 30°, then cos 2 θ may approximately be written as

$$\cos 2\theta = \frac{2\sin^2\alpha}{2 - \sin^2\alpha}$$

9.16. Maximum Fluctuation of Speed

We know that the maximum speed of the driven shaft,

$$\omega_{1\ (max)} = \omega/\cos\alpha$$

and minimum speed of the driven shaft,

$$\omega_{1\ (min)} = \omega\cos\alpha$$

∴ Maximum fluctuation of speed of the driven shaft,

$$q = \omega_{1(max)} - \omega_{1(min)} = \frac{\omega}{\cos\alpha} - \omega\cos\alpha$$

$$= \omega\left(\frac{1}{\cos\alpha} - \cos\alpha\right) = \omega\left(\frac{1 - \cos^2\alpha}{\cos\alpha}\right) = \frac{\omega\sin^2\alpha}{\cos\alpha}$$

$$= \omega\tan\alpha.\sin\alpha$$

Since α is a small angle, therefore substituting cos α = 1, and sin α = α radians.

∴ Maximum fluctuation of speed

$$= \omega.\alpha^2$$

Hence, *the maximum fluctuation of speed of the driven shaft approximately varies as the square of the angle between the two shafts.*

Note: If the speed of the driving shaft is given in r.p.m. (*i.e.* N r.p.m.), then in the above relations ω may be replaced by N.

9.17. Double Hooke's Joint

We have seen in the previous articles, that the velocity of the driven shaft is not constant, but varies from maximum to minimum values. In order to have a constant velocity ratio of the driving and driven shafts, an intermediate shaft with a Hooke's joint at each end as shown in Fig. 9.21, is used. This type of joint is known as *double Hooke's joint.*

---

* Since the differentiation of $d\omega_1/dt$ is very cumbersome, therefore only the result is given.

Let the driving, intermediate and driven shafts, in the same time, rotate through angles θ, ϕ and γ from the position as discussed previously in Art. 9.12.

Now for shafts *A* and *B*, $\tan \theta = \tan \phi . \cos \alpha$ ...(*i*)

and   for shafts *B* and *C*, $\tan \gamma = \tan \phi . \cos \alpha$ ...(*ii*)

From equations (*i*) and (*ii*), we see that $\theta = \gamma$ or $\omega_A = \omega_C$.

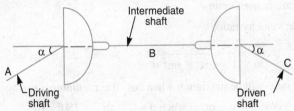

Fig. 9.21. Double Hooke's joint.

This shows that the speed of the driving and driven shaft is constant. In other words, this joint gives a velocity ratio equal to unity, if

1. The axes of the driving and driven shafts are in the same plane, and

2. The driving and driven shafts make equal angles with the intermediate shaft.

Example. 9.2. *Two shafts with an included angle of 160° are connected by a Hooke's joint. The driving shaft runs at a uniform speed of 1500 r.p.m. The driven shaft carries a flywheel of mass 12 kg and 100 mm radius of gyration. Find the maximum angular acceleration of the driven shaft and the maximum torque required.*

Solution. Given : $\alpha = 180° - 160° = 20°$; $N = 1500$ r.p.m.; $m = 12$ kg ; $k = 100$ mm $= 0.1$ m

We know that angular speed of the driving shaft,

$$\omega = 2\pi \times 1500 / 60 = 157 \text{ rad/s}$$

and mass moment of inertia of the driven shaft,

$$I = m.k^2 = 12 (0.1)^2 = 0.12 \text{ kg - m}^2$$

Maximum angular acceleration of the driven shaft

Let $d\omega_1 / dt$ = Maximum angular acceleration of the driven shaft, and

           θ = Angle through which the driving shaft turns.

We know that, for maximum angular acceleration of the driven shaft,

$$\cos 2\theta = \frac{2\sin^2 \alpha}{2 - \sin^2 \alpha} = \frac{2\sin^2 20°}{2 - \sin^2 20°} = 0.124$$

$\therefore$ $2\theta = 82.9°$ or $\theta = 41.45°$

and

$$\frac{d\omega_1}{dt} = \frac{\omega^2 \cos\alpha . \sin 2\theta . \sin^2 \alpha}{(1 - \cos^2 \theta . \sin^2 \alpha)^2}$$

$$= \frac{(157)^2 \cos 20° \times \sin 82.9° \times \sin^2 20°}{(1 - \cos^2 41.45° \times \sin^2 20°)^2} = 3090 \text{ rad/s}^2 \text{ Ans.}$$

Maximum torque required

We know that maximum torque required

$$= I \times d\omega_1 / dt = 0.12 \times 3090 = 371 \text{ N-m} \quad \text{Ans.}$$

Example. 9.3. *The angle between the axes of two shafts connected by Hooke's joint is 18°. Determine the angle turned through by the driving shaft when the velocity ratio is maximum and unity.*

Solution. Given : $\alpha = 18°$

Let θ = Angle turned through by the driving shaft.

When the velocity ratio is maximum

We know that velocity ratio,

$$\frac{\omega_1}{\omega} = \frac{\cos\alpha}{1 - \cos^2\theta.\sin^2\alpha}$$

The velocity ratio will be maximum when $\cos^2\theta$ is minimum, *i.e.* when

$$\cos^2\theta = 1 \quad \text{or} \quad \text{when } \theta = 0° \quad \text{or} \quad 180° \text{ **Ans.**}$$

When the velocity ratio is unity

The velocity ratio (ω / ω_1) will be unity, when

$$1 - \cos^2\theta . \sin^2\alpha = \cos\alpha \quad \text{or} \quad \cos^2\theta = \frac{1 - \cos\alpha}{\sin^2\alpha}$$

$$\therefore \quad \cos\theta = \pm\sqrt{\frac{1 - \cos\alpha}{\sin^2\alpha}} = \pm\sqrt{\frac{1 - \cos\alpha}{1 - \cos^2\alpha}} = \pm\sqrt{\frac{1}{1 + \cos\alpha}}$$

$$= \pm\sqrt{\frac{1}{1 + \cos 18°}} = \pm\sqrt{\frac{1}{1 + 0.9510}} = \pm 0.7159$$

$$\therefore \quad \theta = 44.3° \quad \text{or} \quad 135.7° \text{ **Ans.**}$$

Example. 9.4. *Two shafts are connected by a Hooke's joint. The driving shaft revolves uniformly at 500 r.p.m. If the total permissible variation in speed of the driven shaft is not to exceed ± 6% of the mean speed, find the greatest permissible angle between the centre lines of the shafts.*

Solution. Given : $N = 500$ r.p.m. or $\omega = 2\pi \times 500 / 60 = 52.4$ rad/s

Let α = Greatest permissible angle between the centre lines of the shafts.

Since the variation in speed of the driven shaft is ± 6% of the mean speed (*i.e.* speed of the driving speed), therefore total fluctuation of speed of the driven shaft,

$$q = 12 \% \text{ of mean speed } (\omega) = 0.12\ \omega$$

We know that maximum or total fluctuation of speed of the driven shaft (q),

$$0.12\ \omega = \omega\left(\frac{1 - \cos^2\alpha}{\cos\alpha}\right) \quad \text{or} \quad \cos^2\alpha + 0.12\cos\alpha - 1 = 0$$

and

$$\cos\alpha = \frac{-0.12 \pm\sqrt{(0.12)^2 + 4}}{2} = \frac{-0.12 \pm 2.0036}{2} = 0.9418$$

...(Taking + sign)

$$\alpha = 19.64° \text{ **Ans.**}$$

Example. 9.5. *Two shafts are connected by a universal joint. The driving shaft rotates at a uniform speed of 1200 r.p.m. Determine the greatest permissible angle between the shaft axes so that the total fluctuation of speed does not exceed 100 r.p.m. Also calculate the maximum and minimum speeds of the driven shaft.*

Solution. Given : $N = 1200$ r.p.m.; $q = 100$ r.p.m.

Greatest permissible angle between the shaft axes

Let α = Greatest permissible angle between the shaft axes.

We know that total fluctuation of speed (q),

$$100 = N\left(\frac{1 - \cos^2 \alpha}{\cos \alpha}\right) = 1200\left(\frac{1 - \cos^2 \alpha}{\cos \alpha}\right)$$

$\therefore$ $\quad \dfrac{1 - \cos^2 \alpha}{\cos \alpha} = \dfrac{100}{1200} = 0.083$

$\cos^2 \alpha + 0.083 \cos \alpha - 1 = 0$

and $\qquad \cos \alpha = \dfrac{-0.083 \pm \sqrt{(0.083)^2 + 4}}{2} = 0.9593 \qquad$ ...(Taking + sign)

$\therefore$ $\qquad \alpha = 16.4°$ **Ans.**

Maximum and minimum speed of the driven shaft

We know that maximum speed of the driven shaft,

$$N_{1\,(max)} = N\,/\cos\alpha = 1200 \,/\, 0.9593 = 1251 \text{ r.p.m. } \textbf{Ans.}$$

and minimum speed of the driven shaft,

$$N_{1\,(min)} = N \cos\alpha = 1200 \times 0.9593 = 1151 \text{ r.p.m. } \textbf{Ans.}$$

Example. 9.6. *The driving shaft of a Hooke's joint runs at a uniform speed of 240 r.p.m. and the angle α between the shafts is 20°. The driven shaft with attached masses has a mass of 55 kg at a radius of gyration of 150 mm.*

1. If a steady torque of 200 N-m resists rotation of the driven shaft, find the torque required at the driving shaft, when $\theta = 45°$.

2. At what value of 'α' will the total fluctuation of speed of the driven shaft be limited to 24 r.p.m ?

Solution. Given : $N = 240$ r.p.m or $\omega = 2\pi \times 240/60 = 25.14$ rad/s ; $\alpha = 20°$; $m = 55$ kg ; $k = 150$ mm $= 0.15$ m ; $T_1 = 200$ N-m ; $\theta = 45°$; $q = 24$ r.p.m.

1. *Torque required at the driving shaft*

Let T' = Torque required at the driving shaft.

We know that mass moment inertia of the driven shaft,

$$I = m.k^2 = 55\,(0.15)^2 = 1.24 \text{ kg-m}^2$$

and angular acceleration of the driven shaft,

$$\frac{d\omega_1}{dt} = \frac{-\omega^2 \cos\alpha.\sin 2\theta.\sin^2\alpha}{(1 - \cos^2\theta\sin^2\alpha)^2} = \frac{-(25.14)^2 \cos 20° \times \sin 90° \times \sin^2 20°}{(1 - \cos^2 45°\sin^2 20°)^2}$$

$$= -78.4 \text{ rad} / s^2$$

$\therefore$ Torque required to accelerate the driven shaft,

$$T_2 = I \times \frac{d\omega_1}{dt} = 1.24 \times -78.4 = -97.2\,\text{N} - \text{m}$$

and total torque required on the driven shaft,

$$T = T_1 + T_2 = 200 - 97.2 = 102.8 \text{ N–m}$$

Since the torques on the driving and driven shafts are inversely proportional to their angular speeds, therefore

$$T'. \omega = T . \omega_1$$

or

$$T' = \frac{T . \omega_1}{\omega} = \frac{T \cos \alpha}{1 - \cos^2 \theta . \sin^2 \alpha} \qquad \cdots \left(\because \frac{\omega_1}{\omega} = \frac{\cos \alpha}{1 - \cos^2 \theta . \sin \alpha} \right)$$

$$= \frac{102.8 \cos 20°}{1 - \cos^2 45° \sin^2 20°} = 102.6 \text{ N-m \textbf{Ans.}}$$

2. Value of α for the total fluctuation of speed to be 24 r.p.m.

We know that the total fluctuation of speed of the driven shaft (q),

$$24 = N \left(\frac{1 - \cos^2 \alpha}{\cos \alpha} \right) = 240 \left(\frac{1 - \cos^2 \alpha}{\cos \alpha} \right)$$

or

$$\frac{1 - \cos^2 \alpha}{\cos \alpha} = \frac{24}{240} = 0.1$$

$$\cos^2 \alpha + 0.1 \cos \alpha - 1 = 0$$

$$\cos \alpha = \frac{-0.1 \pm \sqrt{(0.1)^2 + 4}}{2} = 0.95 \qquad \cdots \text{(Taking + sign)}$$

∴ $$\alpha = 18.2° \text{ \textbf{Ans.}}$$

Example 9.7. *A double universal joint is used to connect two shafts in the same plane. The intermediate shaft is inclined at an angle of 20° to the driving shaft as well as the driven shaft. Find the maximum and minimum speed of the intermediate shaft and the driven shaft if the driving shaft has a constant speed of 500 r.p.m.*

Solution. Given $\alpha = 20°$; $N_A = 500$ r.p.m.

Maximum and minimum speed of the intermediate shaft

Let A, B and C are the driving shaft, intermediate shaft and driven shaft respectively. We know that for the driving shaft (A) and intermediate shaft (B),

Maximum speed of the intermediate shaft,

$$N_{B(max)} = \frac{N_A}{\cos \alpha} = \frac{500}{\cos 20°} = 532.1 \text{ r.p.m \textbf{Ans.}}$$

and minimum speed of the intermediate shaft,

$$N_{B \, (min)} = N_A \cos \alpha = 500 \times \cos 20° = 469.85 \text{ r.p.m. \textbf{Ans.}}$$

Maximum and minimum speed of the driven shaft

We know that for the intermediate shaft (B) and driven shaft (C),

Maximum speed of the driven shaft,

$$N_{C(max)} = \frac{N_{B(max)}}{\cos \alpha} = \frac{N_A}{\cos^2 \alpha} = \frac{500}{\cos^2 20°} = 566.25 \text{ r.p.m. \textbf{Ans.}}$$

and minimum speed of the driven shaft,

$$N_{C\,(min)} = N_{B\,(min)} \times \cos \alpha = N_A \cdot \cos^2 \alpha$$
$$= 500 \times \cos^2 20° = 441.5 \text{ r.p.m. } \textbf{Ans.}$$

EXERCISES

1. Fig. 9.22 shows the link *GAB* which oscillates on a fixed centre at *A* and the link *FD* on a fixed centre at *F*. The link *AB* is equal to *AC* and *DB*, *BE*, *EC* and *CD* are equal in length.

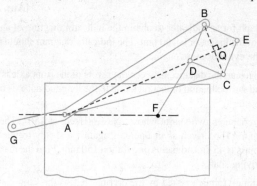

Fig. 9.22

(*a*) Find the length of *AF* and the position of centre *F* so that the point *E* may move in a straight line.

(*b*) If the point *E* is required to move in a circle passing through centre *A*, what will be the path of point *D* ? [**Ans.** *AF = FD*]

(**Hint.** The mechanism is similar to Peaucellier's mechanism)

2. Fig. 9.23 shows a part of the mechanism of a circuit breaker. *A* and *D* are fixed centres and the lengths of the links are : *AB* = 110 mm, *BC* = 105 mm, and *CD* = 150 mm.

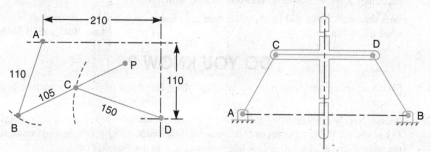

All dimensions in mm.

Fig. 9.23 **Fig. 9.24**

Find the position of a point *P* on *BC* produced that will trace out an approximately straight vertical path 250 mm long.

3. The mechanism, as shown in Fig. 9.24, is a four bar kinematic chain of which the centres *A* and *B* are fixed. The lengths are : *AB* = 600 mm, *AC* = *BD* = *CD* = 300 mm. Find the point *G* on the centre line of the cross arm of which the locus is an approximately straight line even for considerable displacements from the position shown in the figure. [**Ans. 400 mm.**]

(**Hint** : It is a Robert's approximate straight line mechanism. Produce *AC* and *BD* to intersect at point *E*. Draw a vertical line from *E* to cut the centre line of cross arm at *G*. The distance of *G* from *CD* is the required distance).

4. The distance between the fixed centres O and O_1 of a Watt's straight line motion, as shown in Fig. 9.6, is 250 mm. The lengths of the three moving links OB, BA and AO_1 are 150 mm, 75 mm and 100 mm respectively. Find the position of a point P on BA which gives the best straight line motion. ·

5. A Watt's parallel motion has two bars OA and $O'B$ pivoted at O and O' respectively and joined by the link AB in the form of a crossed four bar mechanism. When the mechanism is in its mean position, the bars OA and $O'B$ are perpendicular to the link AB. If $OA = 75$ mm, $O'B = 25$ mm and $AB = 100$ mm, find the position of the tracing point P and also find how far P is from the straight line given by the mean position of AB, when

    1. OA and OB are in one straight line, and   2. $O'B$ and AB are in one straight line.

    [Ans. 37.5 mm, 6.5 mm,12 mm]

6. Design a pantograph for an indicator to obtain the indicator diagram of an engine. The distance from the tracing point of the indicator is 100 mm. The indicator diagram should represent four times the gas pressure inside the cylinder of an engine.

7. In a Davis steering gear, the distance between the pivots of the front axle is 1 metre and the wheel base is 2.5 metres. Find the inclination of the track arm to the longitudinal axis of the car, when it is moving along a straight path. **[Ans. 11.17°]**

8. A Hooke's joint connects two shafts whose axes intersect at 150°. The driving shaft rotates uniformly at 120 r.p.m. The driven shaft operates against a steady torque of 150 N-m and carries a flywheel whose mass is 45 kg and radius of gyration 150 mm. Find the maximum torque which will be exerted by the driving shaft. **[Ans. 187 N-m]**

    (**Hint :** The maximum torque exerted by the driving shaft is the sum of steady torque and the maximum accelerating torque of the driven shaft).

9. Two shafts are connected by a Hooke's joint. The driving shaft revolves uniformly at 500 r.p.m. If the total permissible variation in speed of a driven shaft is not to exceed 6% of the mean speed, find the greatest permissible angle between the centre lines of the shafts. Also determine the maximum and minimum speed of the driven shaft. **[Ans. 19.6° ; 530 r.p.m. ; 470 r.p.m.]**

10. Two inclined shafts are connected by means of a universal joint. The speed of the driving shaft is 1000 r.p.m. If the total fluctuation of speed of the driven shaft is not to exceed 12.5% of this, what is the maximum possible inclination between the two shafts?

    With this angle, what will be the maximum acceleration to which the driven shaft is subjected and when this will occur ? **[Ans. 20.4° ; 1570 rad/s² ; 41.28°]**

DO YOU KNOW ?

1. Sketch a pantograph, explain its working and show that it can be used to reproduce to an enlarged scale a given figure.

2. A circle has OR as its diameter and a point Q lies on its circumference. Another point P lies on the line OQ produced. If OQ turns about O as centre and the product $OQ \times OP$ remains constant, show that the point P moves along a straight line perpendicular to the diameter OR.

3. What are straight line mechanisms ? Describe one type of exact straight line motion mechanism with the help of a sketch.

4. Describe the Watt's parallel mechanism for straight line motion and derive the condition under which the straight line is traced.

5. Sketch an intermittent motion mechanism and explain its practical applications.

6. Give a neat sketch of the straight line motion 'Hart mechanism.' Prove that it produces an exact straight line motion.

7. (a) Sketch and describe the Peaucellier straight line mechanism indicating clearly the conditions under which the point P on the corners of the rhombus of the mechanism, generates a straight line.

    (b) Prove geometrically that the above mechanism is capable of producing straight line.

8. Draw the sketch of a mechanism in which a point traces an exact straight line. The mechanism must be made of only revolute pairs. Prove that the point traces an exact straight line motion.
(**Hint.** Peaucellier straight line mechanism)

9. Sketch the Dobbie-McInnes indicator mechanism and show that the displacement of the pencil which traces the indicator diagram is proportional to the displacement of the indicator piston.

10. What is the condition for correct steering ? Sketch and show the two main types of steering gears and discuss their relative advantages.

11. Explain why two Hooke's joints are used to transmit motion from the engine to the differential of an automobile.

12. Derive an expression for the ratio of shafts velocities for Hooke's joint and draw the polar diagram depicting the salient features of driven shaft speed.

OBJECTIVE TYPE QUESTIONS

1. In a pantograph, all the pairs are
   - (a) turning pairs
   - (b) sliding pairs
   - (c) spherical pairs
   - (d) self-closed pairs

2. Which of the following mechanism is made up of turning pairs ?
   - (a) Scott Russel's mechanism
   - (b) Peaucellier's mechanism
   - (c) Hart's mechanism
   - (d) none of these

3. Which of the following mechanism is used to enlarge or reduce the size of a drawing ?
   - (a) Grasshopper mechanism
   - (b) Watt mechanism
   - (c) Pantograph
   - (d) none of these

4. The Ackerman steering gear mechanism is preferred to the Davis steering gear mechanism, because
   - (a) whole of the mechanism in the Ackerman steering gear is on the back of the front wheels.
   - (b) the Ackerman steering gear consists of turning pairs
   - (c) the Ackerman steering gear is most economical
   - (d) both (a) and (b)

5. The driving and driven shafts connected by a Hooke's joint will have equal speeds, if
   - (a) $\cos \theta = \sin \alpha$
   - (b) $\sin \theta = \pm \sqrt{\tan \alpha}$
   - (c) $\tan \theta = \pm \sqrt{\cos \alpha}$
   - (d) $\cot \theta = \cos \alpha$

   where θ = Angle through which the driving shaft turns, and
   α = Angle of inclination of the driving and driven shafts.

ANSWERS

1. (a)	**2.** (b), (c)	**3.** (c)	**4.** (d)	**5.** (c)

10

Friction

10.1. Introduction

It has been established since long, that the surfaces of the bodies are never perfectly smooth. When, even a very smooth surface is viewed under a microscope, it is found to have roughness and irregularities, which may not be detected by an ordinary touch. If a block of one substance is placed over the level surface of the same or of different material, a certain degree of interlocking of the minutely projecting particles takes place. This does not involve any force, so long as the block does not move or tends to move. But whenever one block moves or tends to move tangentially with respect to the surface, on which it rests, the interlocking property of the projecting particles opposes the motion. This opposing force, which acts in the opposite direction of the movement of the upper block, is called the *force of friction* or simply *friction*. It thus follows, that at every joint in a machine, force of friction arises due to the relative motion between two parts and hence some energy is wasted in overcoming the friction. Though the friction is considered undesirable, yet it plays an important role both in nature and in engineering *e.g.* walking on a road, motion of locomotive on rails, transmission of power by belts, gears etc. The friction between the wheels and the road is essential for the car to move forward.

10.2. Types of Friction

In general, the friction is of the following two types :

1. *Static friction.* It is the friction, experienced by a body, when at rest.

2. *Dynamic friction.* It is the friction, experienced by a body, when in motion. The dynamic friction is also called *kinetic friction* and is less than the static friction. It is of the following three types :

- (*a*) *Sliding friction.* It is the friction, experienced by a body, when it *slides* over another body.
- (*b*) *Rolling friction.* It is the friction, experienced between the surfaces which has *balls* or *rollers* interposed between them.
- (*c*) *Pivot friction.* It is the friction, experienced by a body, due to the *motion of rotation* as in case of foot step bearings.

The friction may further be classified as :

1. Friction between unlubricated surfaces, and

2. Friction between lubricated surfaces.

These are discussed in the following articles.

10.3. Friction Between Unlubricated Surfaces

The friction experienced between two dry and unlubricated surfaces in contact is known as *dry* or *solid friction*. It is due to the surface roughness. The dry or solid friction includes the sliding friction and rolling friction as discussed above.

10.4. Friction Between Lubricated Surfaces

When lubricant (*i.e.* oil or grease) is applied between two surfaces in contact, then the friction may be classified into the following two types depending upon the thickness of layer of a lubricant.

1. *Boundary friction (or greasy friction or non-viscous friction).* It is the friction, experienced between the rubbing surfaces, when the surfaces have a very thin layer of lubricant. The thickness of this very thin layer is of the molecular dimension. In this type of friction, a thin layer of lubricant forms a bond between the two rubbing surfaces. The lubricant is absorbed on the surfaces and forms a thin film. This thin film of the lubricant results in less friction between them. The boundary friction follows the laws of solid friction.

2. *Fluid friction (or film friction or viscous friction).* It is the friction, experienced between the rubbing surfaces, when the surfaces have a thick layer of the lubricant. In this case, the actual surfaces do not come in contact and thus do not rub against each other. It is thus obvious that fluid friction is not due to the surfaces in contact but it is due to the *viscosity* and *oiliness* of the lubricant.

Note : The *viscosity* is a measure of the resistance offered to the sliding one layer of the lubricant over an adjacent layer. The absolute viscosity of a lubricant may be defined as the force required to cause a plate of unit area to slide with unit velocity relative to a parallel plate, when the two plates are separated by a layer of lubricant of unit thickness.

The *oiliness* property of a lubricant may be clearly understood by considering two lubricants of equal viscosities and at equal temperatures. When these lubricants are smeared on two different surfaces, it is found that the force of friction with one lubricant is different than that of the other. This difference is due to the property of the lubricant known as oiliness. The lubricant which gives lower force of friction is said to have greater oiliness.

10.5. Limiting Friction

Consider that a body *A* of weight *W* is lying on a rough horizontal body *B* as shown in Fig. 10.1 (*a*). In this position, the body *A* is in equilibrium under the action of its own weight *W*, and the normal reaction R_N (equal to W) of B on A. Now if a small horizontal force P_1 is applied to the body A acting through its centre of gravity as shown in Fig. 10.1 (*b*), it does not move because of the frictional force which prevents the motion. This shows that the applied force P_1 is exactly balanced by the force of friction F_1 acting in the opposite direction.

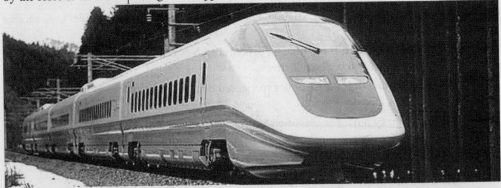

If we now increase the applied force to P_2 as shown in Fig. 10.1 (*c*), it is still found to be in equilibrium. This means that the force of friction has also increased to a value $F_2 = P_2$. Thus every time the effort is increased the force of friction also increases, so as to become exactly equal to the applied force. There is, however, a limit beyond which the force of friction cannot increase as shown in Fig. 10.1 (*d*). After this, any increase in the applied effort will not lead to any further increase in the force of friction, as shown in Fig. 10.1 (*e*), thus the body A begins to move in the direction of the applied force. This maximum value of frictional force, which comes into play, when a body just begins to slide over the surface of the other body, is known as *limiting force of friction* or simply *limiting friction*. It may be noted that when the applied force is less than the limiting friction, the body remains at rest, and the friction into play is called **static friction** which may have any value between zero and limiting friction.

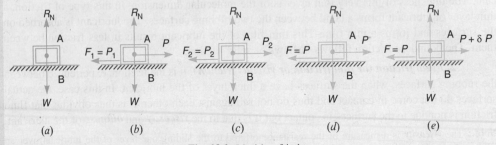

Fig. 10.1. Limiting friction.

10.6. Laws of Static Friction

Following are the laws of static friction :

1. The force of friction always acts in a direction, opposite to that in which the body tends to move.
2. The magnitude of the force of friction is exactly equal to the force, which tends the body to move.
3. The magnitude of the limiting friction (F) bears a constant ratio to the normal reaction (R_N) between the two surfaces. Mathematically

$$F/R_N = \text{constant}$$

4. The force of friction is independent of the area of contact, between the two surfaces.

5. The force of friction depends upon the roughness of the surfaces.

10.7. Laws of Kinetic or Dynamic Friction

Following are the laws of kinetic or dynamic friction :

1. The force of friction always acts in a direction, opposite to that in which the body is moving.

2. The magnitude of the kinetic friction bears a constant ratio to the normal reaction between the two surfaces. But this ratio is slightly less than that in case of limiting friction.

3. For moderate speeds, the force of friction remains constant. But it decreases slightly with the increase of speed.

10.8. Laws of Solid Friction

Following are the laws of solid friction :
1. The force of friction is directly proportional to the normal load between the surfaces.
2. The force of friction is independent of the area of the contact surface for a given normal load.
3. The force of friction depends upon the material of which the contact surfaces are made.
4. The force of friction is independent of the velocity of sliding of one body relative to the other body.

10.9. Laws of Fluid Friction

Following are the laws of fluid friction :

1. The force of friction is almost independent of the load.

2. The force of friction reduces with the increase of the temperature of the lubricant.

3. The force of friction is independent of the substances of the bearing surfaces.

4. The force of friction is different for different lubricants.

10.10. Coefficient of Friction

It is defined as the ratio of the limiting friction (F) to the normal reaction (R_N) between the two bodies. It is generally denoted by μ. Mathematically, coefficient of friction,

$$\mu = F/R_N$$

10.11. Limiting Angle of Friction

Consider that a body A of weight (W) is resting on a horizontal plane B, as shown in Fig. 10.2. If a horizontal force P is applied to the body, no relative motion will take place until the applied force P is equal to the force of friction F, acting opposite to the direction of motion. The magnitude of this force of friction is $F = \mu.W = \mu.R_N$, where R_N is the normal reaction. In the limiting case, when the motion just begins, the body will be in equilibrium under the action of the following three forces :

1. Weight of the body (W),

2. Applied horizontal force (P), and

3. Reaction (R) between the body A and the plane B.

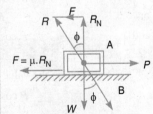

Fig. 10.2. Limiting angle of friction.

The reaction R must, therefore, be equal and opposite to the resultant of W and P and will be inclined at an angle ϕ to the normal reaction R_N. This angle ϕ is known as the *limiting angle of friction*. It may be defined as the angle which the resultant reaction R makes with the normal reaction R_N.

From Fig. 10.2, $\tan \phi = F/R_N = \mu\, R_N / R_N = \mu$

10.12. Angle of Repose

Consider that a body A of weight (W) is resting on an inclined plane B, as shown in Fig. 10.3. If the angle of inclination α of the plane to the horizontal is such that the body begins to move down the plane, then the angle α is called the *angle of repose*.

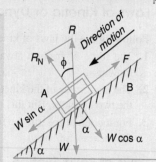

Fig. 10.3. Angle of repose.

A little consideration will show that the body will begin to move down the plane when the angle of inclination of the plane is equal to the angle of friction (*i.e.* $\alpha = \phi$). This may be proved as follows :

The weight of the body (W) can be resolved into the following two components :

1. $W \sin \alpha$, parallel to the plane B. This component tends to slide the body down the plane.

2. $W \cos \alpha$, perpendicular to the plane B. This component is balanced by the normal reaction (R_N) of the body A and the plane B.

The body will only begin to move down the plane, when

Friction is essential to provide grip between tyres and road. This is a positive aspect of 'friction'.

$$W \sin \alpha = F = \mu.R_N = \mu.W \cos \alpha \qquad ...(\because R_N = W \cos \alpha)$$

∴ $$\tan \alpha = \mu = \tan \phi \quad \text{or} \quad \alpha = \phi \qquad ...(\because \mu = \tan \phi)$$

10.13. Minimum Force Required to Slide a Body on a Rough Horizontal Plane

Consider that a body A of weight (W) is resting on a horizontal plane B as shown in Fig. 10.4. Let an effort P is applied at an angle θ to the horizontal such that the body A just moves. The various forces acting on the body are shown in Fig. 10.4. Resolving the force P into two components, *i.e.* $P \sin \theta$ acting upwards and $P \cos \theta$ acting horizontally. Now for the equilibrium of the body A,

$$R_N + P \sin \theta = W$$

or $$R_N = W - P \sin \theta \qquad ...(i)$$

and $$P \cos \theta = F = \mu.R_N \qquad ...(ii)$$

Fig. 10.4. Minimum force required to slide a body.

$$...(\because F = \mu.R_N)$$

Substituting the value of R_N from equation (i), we have

$$P \cos \theta = \mu\,(W - P \sin \theta) = \tan \phi\,(W - P \sin \theta) \qquad ...(\because \mu = \tan \phi)$$

$$= \frac{\sin \phi}{\cos \phi}\,(W - P \sin \theta)$$

$$P \cos \theta .\cos \phi = W \sin \phi - P \sin \theta .\sin \phi$$

$$P \cos \theta .\cos \phi + P \sin \theta .\sin \phi = W \sin \phi$$

$$P \cos (\theta - \phi) = W \sin \phi \qquad \qquad ...[\because \cos \theta . \cos \phi + \sin \theta .\sin \phi = \cos (\theta - \phi)]$$

$$P = \frac{W \sin \phi}{\cos (\theta - \phi)} \qquad \qquad ...(iii)$$

For P to be minimum, $\cos (\theta - \phi)$ should be maximum, *i.e.*

$$\cos (\theta - \phi) = 1 \quad \text{or} \quad \theta - \phi = 0° \quad \text{or} \quad \theta = \phi$$

In other words, the effort P will be minimum, if its inclination with the horizontal is equal to the angle of friction.

$$\therefore \qquad \qquad P_{min} = W \sin \theta \qquad \qquad ...[\text{From equation } (iii)]$$

Example 10.1. *A body, resting on a rough horizontal plane required a pull of 180 N inclined at 30° to the plane just to move it. It was found that a push of 220 N inclined at 30° to the plane just moved the body. Determine the weight of the body and the coefficient of friction.*

Solution. Given : $\theta = 30°$

Let $\qquad \qquad \qquad W$ = Weight of the body in newtons,

$\qquad \qquad \qquad \qquad R_N$ = Normal reaction,

$\qquad \qquad \qquad \qquad \mu$ = Coefficient of friction, and

$\qquad \qquad \qquad \qquad F$ = Force of friction.

First of all, let us consider a pull of 180 N. The force of friction (F) acts towards left as shown in Fig. 10.5 (*a*).

Resolving the forces horizontally,

$$F = 180 \cos 30° = 180 \times 0.866 = 156 \text{ N}$$

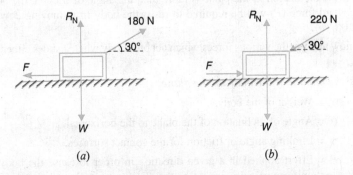

Fig. 10.5

Now resolving the forces vertically,

$$R_N = W - 180 \sin 30° = W - 180 \times 0.5 = (W - 90) \text{ N}$$

We know that $\qquad F = \mu .R_N \quad \text{or} \quad 156 = \mu (W - 90) \qquad \qquad ...(i)$

Now let us consider a push of 220 N. The force of friction (F) acts towards right as shown in Fig. 10.5 (*b*).

Resolving the forces horizontally,

$$F = 220 \cos 30° = 220 \times 0.866 = 190.5 \text{ N}$$

Now resolving the forces vertically,

$$R_N = W + 220 \sin 30° = W + 220 \times 0.5 = (W + 110) \text{ N}$$

We know that $\qquad F = \mu.R_N \quad$ or $\quad 190.5 = \mu (W + 110) \qquad$ ...(ii)

From equations (i) and (ii),

$$W = 1000 \text{ N, and } \mu = 0.1714 \text{ Ans.}$$

10.14. Friction of a Body Lying on a Rough Inclined Plane

Consider that a body of weight (W) is lying on a plane inclined at an angle α with the horizontal, as shown in Fig. 10.6 (a) and (b).

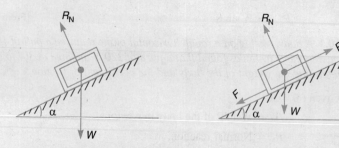

(a) Angle of inclination less than angle of friction.

(b) Angle of inclination more than angle of friction.

Fig. 10.6. Body lying on a rough inclined plane.

A little consideration will show that if the inclination of the plane, with the horizontal, is less than the angle of friction, the body will be in equilibrium as shown in Fig. 10.6 (a). If, in this condition, the body is required to be moved upwards and downwards, a corresponding force is required for the same. But, if the inclination of the plane is more than the angle of friction, the body will move down and an upward force (P) will be required to resist the body from moving down the plane as shown in Fig. 10.6 (b).

Let us now analyse the various forces which act on a body when it slides either up or down an inclined plane.

1. *Considering the motion of the body up the plane*

Let $\qquad W$ = Weight of the body,

$\qquad \alpha$ = Angle of inclination of the plane to the horizontal,

$\qquad \phi$ = Limiting angle of friction for the contact surfaces,

$\qquad P$ = Effort applied in a given direction in order to cause the body to slide with uniform velocity parallel to the plane, considering friction,

$\qquad P_0$ = Effort required to move the body up the plane neglecting friction,

$\qquad \theta$ = Angle which the line of action of P makes with the weight of the body W,

$\qquad \mu$ = Coefficient of friction between the surfaces of the plane and the body,

$\qquad R_N$ = Normal reaction, and

$\qquad R$ = Resultant reaction.

When the friction is neglected, the body is in equilibrium under the action of the three forces, i.e. P_0, W and R_N, as shown in Fig. 10.7 (a). The triangle of forces is shown in Fig. 10.7 (b). Now applying sine rule for these three concurrent forces,

$$\frac{P_0}{\sin \alpha} = \frac{W}{\sin (\theta - \alpha)} \quad \text{or} \quad {}^* P_0 = \frac{W \sin \alpha}{\sin (\theta - \alpha)}$$

...(i)

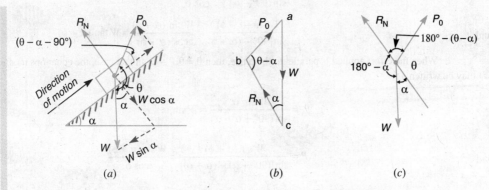

Fig. 10.7. Motion of the body up the plane, neglecting friction.

When friction is taken into account, a frictional force $F = \mu.R_N$ acts in the direction opposite to the motion of the body, as shown in Fig. 10.8 (a). The resultant reaction R between the plane and the body is inclined at an angle ϕ with the normal reaction R_N. The triangle of forces is shown in Fig. 10.8 (b). Now applying sine rule,

$$\frac{P}{\sin (\alpha + \phi)} = \frac{W}{\sin [\theta - (\alpha + \phi)]}$$

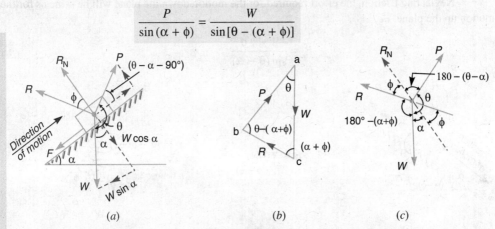

Fig. 10.8. Motion of the body up the plane, considering friction.

---

1. The effort P_0 (or P) may also be obtained by applying Lami's theorem to the three forces, as shown in Fig. 10.7 (c) and 10.8 (c). From Fig. 10.7 (c),

$$\frac{P_0}{\sin (180° - \alpha)} = \frac{W}{\sin [180° - (\theta - \alpha)]}$$

or

$$\frac{P_0}{\sin \alpha} = \frac{W}{\sin (\theta - \alpha)}$$

...[same as before]

2. The effort P_0 (or P) may also be obtained by resolving the forces along the plane and perpendicular to the plane and then applying $\Sigma H = 0$ and $\Sigma V = 0$.

$$\therefore \qquad P = \frac{W \sin(\alpha + \phi)}{\sin[\theta - (\alpha + \phi)]} \qquad \qquad ...(ii)$$

Notes : 1. When the effort applied is horizontal, then $\theta = 90°$. In that case, the equations (*i*) and (*ii*) may be written as

$$P_0 = \frac{W \sin \alpha}{\sin(90° - \alpha)} = \frac{W \sin \alpha}{\cos \alpha} = W \tan \alpha$$

and

$$P = \frac{W \sin(\alpha + \phi)}{\sin[90° - (\alpha + \phi)]} = \frac{W \sin(\alpha + \phi)}{\cos(\alpha + \phi)} = W \tan(\alpha + \phi)$$

2. When the effort applied is parallel to the plane, then $\theta = 90° + \alpha$. In that case, the equations (*i*) and (*ii*) may be written as

$$P_0 = \frac{W \sin \alpha}{\sin(90° + \alpha - \alpha)} = W \sin \alpha$$

and

$$P = \frac{W \sin(\alpha + \phi)}{\sin[(90° + \alpha) - (\alpha + \phi)]} = \frac{W \sin(\alpha + \phi)}{\cos \phi}$$

$$= \frac{W(\sin \alpha \cos \phi + \cos \alpha \sin \phi)}{\cos \phi} = W(\sin \alpha + \cos \alpha . \tan \phi)$$

$$= W(\sin \alpha + \mu \cos \alpha) \qquad \qquad ...(\because \mu = \tan \phi)$$

2. Considering the motion of the body down the plane

Neglecting friction, the effort required for the motion down the plane will be same as for the motion up the plane, *i.e.*

$$P_0 = \frac{W \sin \alpha}{\sin(\theta - \alpha)} \qquad \qquad ...(iii)$$

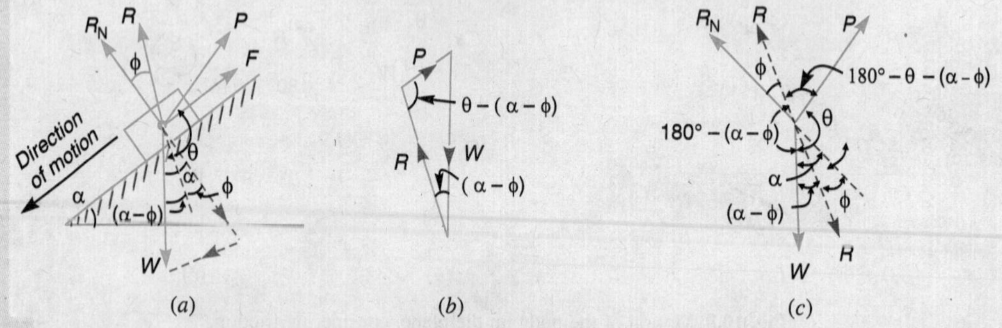

Fig. 10.9. Motion of the body down the plane, considering friction.

When the friction is taken into account, the force of friction $F = \mu . R_N$ will act up the plane and the resultant reaction R will make an angle ϕ with R_N towards its right as shown in Fig. 10.9 (*a*). The triangle of forces is shown in Fig. 10.9 (*b*). Now from sine rule,

$$\frac{P}{\sin(\alpha - \phi)} = \frac{W}{\sin[\theta - (\alpha - \phi)]}$$

or

$$P = \frac{W \sin(\alpha - \phi)}{\sin[\theta - (\alpha - \phi)]} \qquad \qquad ...(iv)$$

Notes : 1. The value of P may also be obtained either by applying Lami's theorem to Fig. 10.9 (c), or by resolving the forces along the plane and perpendicular to the plane and then using $\Sigma H = 0$ and $\Sigma V = 0$ (See Art. 10.18 and 10.19).

2. When P is applied horizontally, then $\theta = 90°$. In that case, equation (iv) may be written as

$$P = \frac{W \sin(\alpha - \phi)}{\sin[90° - (\alpha - \phi)]} = \frac{W \sin(\alpha - \phi)}{\cos(\alpha - \phi)} = W \tan(\alpha - \phi))$$

3. When P is applied parallel to the plane, then $\theta = 90° + \alpha$. In that case, equation (iv) may be written as

$$P = \frac{W \sin(\alpha - \phi)}{\sin[90° + \alpha) - (\alpha - \phi)]} = \frac{W \sin(\alpha - \phi)}{\cos \phi}$$

$$= \frac{W(\sin \alpha \cos \phi - \cos \alpha \sin \phi)}{\cos \phi} = W(\sin \alpha - \tan \phi \cos \alpha)$$

$$= W(\sin \alpha - \mu \cos \alpha) \qquad \qquad ...(\because \tan \phi = \mu)$$

10.15. Efficiency of Inclined Plane

The ratio of the effort required neglecting friction (i.e. P_0) to the effort required considering friction (i.e. P) is known as efficiency of the inclined plane. Mathematically, efficiency of the inclined plane,

$$\eta = P_0 / P$$

Let us consider the following two cases :

1. *For the motion of the body up the plane*

Efficiency, $\quad \eta = \dfrac{P_0}{P} = \dfrac{W \sin \alpha}{\sin(\theta - \alpha)} \times \dfrac{\sin[\theta - (\alpha + \phi)]}{W \sin(\alpha + \phi)}$

$$= \frac{\sin \alpha}{\sin \theta \cos \alpha - \cos \theta \sin \alpha} \times \frac{\sin \theta \cos(\alpha + \phi) - \cos \theta \sin(\alpha + \phi)}{\sin(\alpha + \phi)}$$

Multiplying the numerator and denominator by $\sin(\alpha + \phi) \sin \theta$, we get

$$\eta = \frac{\cot(\alpha + \phi) - \cot \theta}{\cot \alpha - \cot \theta}$$

Notes : 1. When effort is applied horizontally, then $\theta = 90°$.

$$\therefore \qquad \eta = \frac{\tan \alpha}{\tan(\alpha + \phi)}$$

2. When effort is applied parallel to the plane, then $\theta = 90° + \alpha$.

$$\therefore \qquad \eta = \frac{\cot(\alpha + \phi) - \cot(90° + \alpha)}{\cot \alpha - \cot(90° + \alpha)} = \frac{\cot(\alpha + \phi) + \tan \alpha}{\cot \alpha + \tan \alpha} = \frac{\sin \alpha \cos \phi}{\sin(\alpha + \phi)}$$

2. *For the motion of the body down the plane*

Since the value of P will be less than P_0, for the motion of the body down the plane, therefore in this case,

$$\eta = \frac{P}{P_0} = \frac{W \sin(\alpha - \phi)}{\sin[\theta - (\alpha - \phi)]} \times \frac{\sin(\theta - \alpha)}{W \sin \alpha}$$

$$= \frac{\sin(\alpha - \phi)}{\sin \theta \cos(\alpha - \phi) - \cos \theta \sin(\alpha - \phi)} \times \frac{\sin \theta \cos \alpha - \cos \theta \sin \alpha}{\sin \alpha}$$

Multiplying the numerator and denominator by $\sin(\alpha - \phi) \sin\theta$, we get

$$\eta = \frac{\cot\alpha - \cot\theta}{\cot(\alpha - \phi) - \cot\theta}$$

Notes : 1. When effort is applied horizontally, then $\theta = 90°$.

$$\therefore \qquad \eta = \frac{\cot\alpha}{\cot(\alpha - \phi)} = \frac{\tan(\alpha - \phi)}{\tan\alpha}$$

2. When effort is applied parallel to the plane, then $\theta = 90° + \alpha$.

$$\therefore \qquad \eta = \frac{\cot\alpha - \cot(90° + \alpha)}{\cot(\alpha - \phi) - \cot(90° + \alpha)} = \frac{\cot\alpha + \tan\alpha}{\cot(\alpha - \phi) + \tan\alpha} = \frac{\sin(\alpha - \phi)}{\sin\alpha\cos\phi}$$

Example 10.2. *An effort of 1500 N is required to just move a certain body up an inclined plane of angle 12°, force acting parallel to the plane. If the angle of inclination is increased to 15°, then the effort required is 1720 N. Find the weight of the body and the coefficient of friction.*

Solution. Given : $P_1 = 1500$ N ; $\alpha_1 = 12°$; $\alpha_2 = 15°$; $P_2 = 1720$ N

Let $\qquad\qquad W =$ Weight of the body in newtons, and

$\qquad\qquad \mu =$ Coefficient of friction.

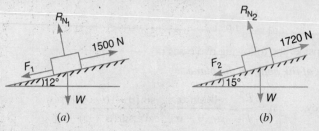

Fig. 10.10

First of all, let us consider a body lying on a plane inclined at an angle of 12° with the horizontal and subjected to an effort of 1500 N parallel to the plane as shown in Fig. 10.10 (*a*).

Let $\qquad\qquad R_{N_1} =$ Normal reaction, and

$\qquad\qquad F_1 =$ Force of friction.

We know that for the motion of the body up the inclined plane, the effort applied parallel to the plane (P_1),

$$1500 = W(\sin\alpha_1 + \mu\cos\alpha_1) = W(\sin 12° + \mu\cos 12°) \qquad\qquad ...(i)$$

Now let us consider the body lying on a plane inclined at an angle of 15° with the horizontal and subjected to an effort of 1720 N parallel to the plane as shown in Fig. 10.10 (*b*).

Let $\qquad\qquad R_{N_2} =$ Normal reaction, and

$\qquad\qquad F_2 =$ Force of friction.

We know that for the motion of the body up the inclined plane, the effort applied parallel to the plane (P_2),

$$1720 = W(\sin\alpha_2 + \mu\cos\alpha_2) = W(\sin 15° + \mu\cos 15°) \qquad\qquad ...(ii)$$

Coefficient of friction

Dividing equation (*ii*) by equation (*i*),

$$\frac{1720}{1500} = \frac{W(\sin 15° + \mu\cos 15°)}{W(\sin 12° + \mu\cos 12°)}$$

$$1720 \sin 12° + 1720 \, \mu \cos 12° = 1500 \sin 15° + 1500 \, \mu \cos 15°$$

$$\mu \,(1720 \cos 12° - 1500 \cos 15°) = 1500 \sin 15° - 1720 \sin 12°$$

$$\therefore \quad \mu = \frac{1500 \sin 15° - 1720 \sin 12°}{1720 \cos 12° - 1500 \cos 15°} = \frac{1500 \times 0.2588 - 1720 \times 0.2079}{1720 \times 0.9781 - 1500 \times 0.9659}$$

$$= \frac{388.2 - 357.6}{1682.3 - 1448.5} = \frac{30.6}{233.8} = 0.131 \, \textbf{Ans.}$$

Weight of the body

Substituting the value of μ in equation (*i*),

$$1500 = W \,(\sin 12° + 0.131 \cos 12°)$$

$$= W \,(0.2079 + 0.131 \times 0.9781) = 0.336 \, W$$

$$\therefore \qquad W = 1500/0.336 = 4464 \text{ N } \textbf{Ans.}$$

Jet engine used in Jet aircraft.

Note : This picture is given as additional information.

10.16. Screw Friction

The screws, bolts, studs, nuts etc. are widely used in various machines and structures for temporary fastenings. These fastenings have screw threads, which are made by cutting a continuous helical groove on a cylindrical surface. If the threads are cut on the outer surface of a solid rod, these are known as *external threads*. But if the threads are cut on the internal surface of a hollow rod, these are known as *internal threads*. The screw threads are mainly of two types *i.e.* V-threads and square threads. The V-threads are stronger and offer more frictional resistance to motion than square threads. Moreover, the V-threads have an advantage of preventing the nut from slackening. In general, the V-threads are used for the purpose of tightening pieces together *e.g.* bolts and nuts etc. But the square threads are used in screw jacks, vice screws etc. The following terms are important for the study of screw :

1. *Helix*. It is the curve traced by a particle, while describing a circular path at a uniform speed and advancing in the axial direction at a uniform rate. In other words, it is the curve traced by a particle while moving along a screw thread.

2. *Pitch*. It is the distance from a point of a screw to a corresponding point on the next thread, measured parallel to the axis of the screw.

3. *Lead*. It is the distance, a screw thread advances axially in one turn.

4. *Depth of thread*. It is the distance between the top and bottom surfaces of a thread (also known as **crest** and **root** of a thread).

5. *Single-threaded screw*. If the lead of a screw is equal to its pitch, it is known as single threaded screw.

6. *Multi-threaded screw.* If more than one thread is cut in one lead distance of a screw, it is known as multi-threaded screw *e.g.* in a double threaded screw, two threads are cut in one lead length. In such cases, all the threads run independently along the length of the rod. Mathematically,

Lead = Pitch × Number of threads

7. *Helix angle*. It is the slope or inclination of the thread with the horizontal. Mathematically,

$$\tan \alpha = \frac{\text{Lead of screw}}{\text{Circumference of screw}}$$

$$= p/\pi d \qquad \text{...(In single-threaded screw)}$$

$$= n.p/\pi d \qquad \text{...(In multi-threaded screw)}$$

where

α = Helix angle,

p = Pitch of the screw,

d = Mean diameter of the screw, and

n = Number of threads in one lead.

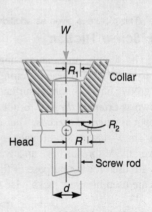

Screw Jack.

10.17. Screw Jack

The screw jack is a device, for lifting heavy loads, by applying a comparatively smaller effort at its handle. The principle, on which a screw jack works is similar to that of an inclined plane.

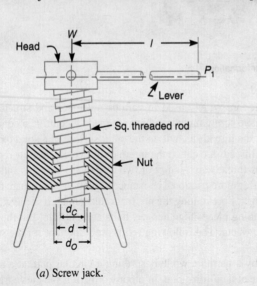

(a) Screw jack.

(b) Thrust collar.

Fig. 10.11

Fig. 10.11 (*a*) shows a common form of a screw jack, which consists of a square threaded rod (also called screw rod or simply screw) which fits into the inner threads of the nut. The load, to be raised or lowered, is placed on the head of the square threaded rod which is rotated by the application of an effort at the end of the lever for lifting or lowering the load.

10.18. Torque Required to Lift the Load by a Screw Jack

If one complete turn of a screw thread by imagined to be unwound, from the body of the screw and developed, it will form an inclined plane as shown in Fig. 10.12 (*a*).

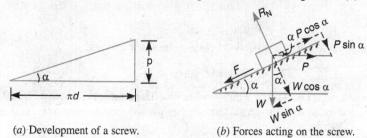

| (*a*) Development of a screw. | (*b*) Forces acting on the screw. |

Fig. 10.12

Let p = Pitch of the screw,

d = Mean diameter of the screw,

α = Helix angle,

P = Effort applied at the circumference of the screw to lift the load,

W = Load to be lifted, and

μ = Coefficient of friction, between the screw and nut = $\tan \phi$, where ϕ is the friction angle.

From the geometry of the Fig. 10.12 (*a*), we find that

$$\tan \alpha = p/\pi d$$

Since the principle on which a screw jack works is similar to that of an inclined plane, therefore the force applied on the lever of a screw jack may be considered to be horizontal as shown in Fig. 10.12 (*b*).

Since the load is being lifted, therefore the force of friction ($F = \mu.R_N$) will act downwards. All the forces acting on the screw are shown in Fig. 10.12 (*b*).

Resolving the forces along the plane,

$$P \cos \alpha = W \sin \alpha + F = W \sin \alpha + \mu.R_N \qquad ...(i)$$

and resolving the forces perpendicular to the plane,

$$R_N = P \sin \alpha + W \cos \alpha \qquad ...(ii)$$

Substituting this value of R_N in equation (*i*),

$$P \cos \alpha = W \sin \alpha + \mu (P \sin \alpha + W \cos \alpha)$$

$$= W \sin \alpha + \mu P \sin \alpha + \mu W \cos \alpha$$

or $$P \cos \alpha - \mu P \sin \alpha = W \sin \alpha + \mu W \cos \alpha$$

or $$P (\cos \alpha - \mu \sin \alpha) = W (\sin \alpha + \mu \cos \alpha)$$

$$\therefore \qquad P = W \times \frac{\sin \alpha + \mu \cos \alpha}{\cos \alpha - \mu \sin \alpha}$$

Substituting the value of $\mu = \tan \phi$ in the above equation, we get

$$P = W \times \frac{\sin \alpha + \tan \phi \cos \alpha}{\cos \alpha - \tan \phi \sin \alpha}$$

Multiplying the numeractor and denominator by $\cos \phi$,

$$P = W \times \frac{\sin \alpha \cos \phi + \sin \phi \cos \alpha}{\cos \alpha \cos \phi - \sin \alpha \sin \phi} = W \times \frac{\sin (\alpha + \phi)}{\cos (\alpha + \phi)}$$

$$= W \tan (\alpha + \phi)$$

∴ Torque required to overcome friction between the screw and nut,

$$T_1 = P \times \frac{d}{2} = W \tan (\alpha + \phi) \frac{d}{2}$$

When the axial load is taken up by a thrust collar or a flat surface, as shown in Fig. 10.11 (b), so that the load does not rotate with the screw, then the torque required to overcome friction at the collar,

$$T_2 = \mu_1 . W \left(\frac{R_1 + R_2}{2} \right) = \mu_1 . W.R$$

where $\qquad R_1$ and R_2 = Outside and inside radii of the collar,

$\qquad R$ = Mean radius of the collar, and

$\qquad \mu_1$ = Coefficient of friction for the collar.

∴ Total torque required to overcome friction (*i.e.* to rotate the screw),

$$T = T_1 + T_2 = P \times \frac{d}{2} + \mu_1 . W.R$$

If an effort P_1 is applied at the end of a lever of arm length l, then the total torque required to overcome friction must be equal to the torque applied at the end of the lever, *i.e.*

$$T = P \times \frac{d}{2} = P_1 . l$$

Notes : 1. When the *nominal diameter (d_0) and the **core diameter (d_c) of the screw thread is given, then the mean diameter of the screw,

$$d = \frac{d_0 + d_c}{2} = d_0 - \frac{p}{2} = d_c + \frac{p}{2}$$

2. Since the mechanical advantage is the ratio of load lifted (W) to the effort applied (P_1) at the end of the lever, therefore mechanical advantage,

$$M.A. = \frac{W}{P_1} = \frac{W \times 2l}{P.d} \qquad\qquad \dots\left(\because P_1 = \frac{P.d}{2l} \right)$$

$$= \frac{W \times 2l}{W \tan (\alpha + \phi) d} = \frac{2l}{d . \tan (\alpha + \phi)}$$

Example 10.3. *An electric motor driven power screw moves a nut in a horizontal plane against a force of 75 kN at a speed of 300 mm/min. The screw has a single square thread of 6 mm pitch on a major diameter of 40 mm. The coefficient of friction at the screw threads is 0.1. Estimate power of the motor.*

---

* The **nominal diameter** of a screw thread is also known as **outside diameter** or **major diameter.**

** The **core diameter** of a screw thread is also known as inner diameter or **root diameter** or **minor diameter.**

Solution. Given : $W = 75$ kN $= 75 \times 10^3$ N ; $v = 300$ mm/min ; $p = 6$ mm ; $d_0 = 40$ mm ; $\mu = \tan\phi = 0.1$

We know that mean diameter of the screw,

$$d = d_0 - p/2 = 40 - 6/2 = 37 \text{ mm} = 0.037 \text{ m}$$

and

$$\tan\alpha = \frac{p}{\pi d} = \frac{6}{\pi \times 37} = 0.0516$$

∴ Force required at the circumference of the screw,

$$P = W\tan(\alpha + \phi) = W\left[\frac{\tan\alpha + \tan\phi}{1 - \tan\alpha.\tan\phi}\right]$$

$$= 75 \times 10^3\left[\frac{0.0516 + 0.1}{1 - 0.0516 \times 0.1}\right] = 11.43 \times 10^3 \text{ N}$$

and torque required to overcome friction,

$$T = P \times d/2 = 11.43 \times 10^3 \times 0.037/2 = 211.45 \text{ N-m}$$

We know that speed of the screw,

$$N = \frac{\text{Speed of the nut}}{\text{Pitch of the screw}} = \frac{300}{6} = 50 \text{ r.p.m.}$$

and angular speed, $\omega = 2\pi \times 50/60 = 5.24$ rad/s

∴ Power of the motor $= T.\omega = 211.45 \times 5.24 = 1108$ W $= 1.108$ **kW Ans.**

Example 10.4. *A turnbuckle, with right and left hand single start threads, is used to couple two wagons. Its thread pitch is 12 mm and mean diameter 40 mm. The coefficient of friction between the nut and screw is 0.16.*

1. Determine the work done in drawing the wagons together a distance of 240 mm, against a steady load of 2500 N.

2. If the load increases from 2500 N to 6000 N over the distance of 240 mm, what is the work to be done?

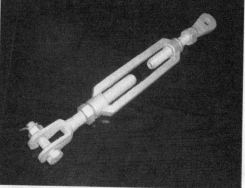

Turnbuckle.

Solution. Given : $p = 12$ mm ; $d = 40$ mm ; $\mu = \tan\phi = 0.16$; $W = 2500$ N

1. *Work done in drawing the wagons together against a steady load of 2500 N*

We know that $\qquad \tan\alpha = \dfrac{p}{\pi d} = \dfrac{12}{\pi \times 40} = 0.0955$

∴ Effort required at the circumference of the screw,

$$P = W\tan(\alpha + \phi) = W\left[\frac{\tan\alpha + \tan\phi}{1 - \tan\alpha.\tan\phi}\right]$$

$$= 2500 \left[\frac{0.0955 + 0.16}{1 - 0.0955 \times 0.16} \right] = 648.7 \text{ N}$$

and torque required to overcome friction between the screw and nut,

$$T = P \times d/2 = 648.7 \times 40/2 = 12\,947 \text{ N-mm} = 12.974 \text{ N-m}$$

A little consideration will show that for one complete revolution of the screwed rod, the wagons are drawn together through a distance equal to $2\,p$, i.e. $2 \times 12 = 24$ mm. Therefore in order to draw the wagons together through a distance of 240 mm, the number of turns required are given by

$$N = 240/24 = 10$$

∴ Work done $= T \times 2\,\pi\,N = 12.974 \times 2\,\pi \times 10 = 815.3$ N-m **Ans.**

2. *Work done in drawing the wagons together when load increases from 2500 N to 6000 N*

For an increase in load from 2500 N to 6000 N,

$$\text{Work done} = \frac{815.3(6000 - 2500)}{2500} = 1141.4 \text{ N-m Ans.}$$

Example 10.5. *A 150 mm diameter valve, against which a steam pressure of 2 MN/m^2 is acting, is closed by means of a square threaded screw 50 mm in external diameter with 6 mm pitch. If the coefficient of friction is 0.12 ; find the torque required to turn the handle.*

Solution. Given : $D = 150$ mm $= 0.15$ m ; $Ps = 2$ MN/m$^2 = 2 \times 10^6$ N/m^2 ; $d_0 = 50$ mm ; $p = 6$ mm ; $\mu = \tan\phi = 0.12$

We know that load on the valve,

$$W = \text{Pressure} \times \text{Area} = p_S \times \frac{\pi}{4} D^2 = 2 \times 10^6 \times \frac{\pi}{4}(0.15)^2 \text{ N}$$

$$= 35\,400 \text{ N}$$

Mean diameter of the screw,

$$d = d_0 - p/2 = 50 - 6/2 = 47 \text{ mm} = 0.047 \text{ m}$$

∴

$$\tan\alpha = \frac{p}{\pi d} = \frac{6}{\pi \times 47} = 0.0406$$

We know that force required to turn the handle,

$$P = W \tan(\alpha + \phi) = W \left[\frac{\tan\alpha + \tan\phi}{1 - \tan\alpha.\tan\phi} \right]$$

$$= 35\,400 \left[\frac{0.0406 + 0.12}{1 - 0.0406 \times 0.12} \right] = 5713 \text{ N}$$

∴ Torque required to turn the handle,

$$T = P \times d/2 = 5713 \times 0.047/2 = 134.2 \text{ N-m Ans.}$$

Example 10.6. *A square threaded bolt of root diameter 22.5 mm and pitch 5 mm is tightened by screwing a nut whose mean diameter of bearing surface is 50 mm. If coefficient of friction for nut and bolt is 0.1 and for nut and bearing surface 0.16, find the force required at the end of a spanner 500 mm long when the load on the bolt is 10 kN.*

Solution. Given : $d_c = 22.5$ mm ; $p = 5$ mm ; $D = 50$ mm or $R = 25$ mm ; $\mu = \tan\phi = 0.1$; $\mu_1 = 0.16$; $l = 500$ mm ; $W = 10$ kN $= 10 \times 10^3$ N

Let $P_1 = $ Force required at the end of a spanner in newtons.

We know that mean diameter of the screw,

$$d = d_c + p/2 = 22.5 + 5/2 = 25 \text{ mm}$$

$$\therefore \qquad \tan \alpha = \frac{p}{\pi d} = \frac{5}{\pi \times 25} = 0.0636$$

Force requred at the circumference of the screw,

$$P = W \tan(\alpha + \phi) = W \left[\frac{\tan \alpha + \tan \phi}{1 - \tan \alpha . \tan \phi} \right]$$

$$= 10 \times 10^3 \left[\frac{0.0636 + 0.1}{1 - 0.06363 \times 0.1} \right] = 1646 \text{ N}$$

We know that total torque required,

$$T = P \times \frac{d}{2} + \mu_1 . W . R = 1646 \times \frac{25}{2} + 0.16 \times 10 \times 10^3 \times 25$$

$$= 60\,575 \text{ N - mm} \qquad \qquad ...(i)$$

We also know that torque required at the end of a spanner,

$$T = P_1 \times l = P_1 \times 500 = 500 \, P_1 \text{ N-mm} \qquad \qquad ...(ii)$$

Equating equations (*i*) and (*ii*),

$$P_1 = 60\,575 / 500 = 121.15 \text{ N} \quad \textbf{Ans.}$$

Example 10.7. *A vertical screw with single start square threads 50 mm mean diameter and 12.5 mm pitch is raised against a load of 10 kN by means of a hand wheel, the boss of which is threaded to act as a nut. The axial load is taken up by a thrust collar which supports the wheel boss and has a mean diameter of 60 mm. If the coefficient of friction is 0.15 for the screw and 0.18 for the collar and the tangential force applied by each hand to the wheel is 100 N ; find suitable diameter of the hand wheel.*

Solution. Given : $d = 50$ mm ; $p = 12.5$ mm ; $W = 10$ kN $= 10 \times 10^3$ N ; $D = 60$ mm or $R = 30$ mm ; $\mu = \tan \phi = 0.15$; $\mu_1 = 0.18$; $P_1 = 100$ N

We know that $\quad \tan \alpha = \dfrac{p}{\pi d} = \dfrac{12.5}{\pi \times 50} = 0.08$

and the tangential force required at the circumference of the screw,

$$P = W \tan(\alpha + \phi) = W \left[\frac{\tan \alpha + \tan \phi}{1 - \tan \alpha . \tan \phi} \right]$$

$$= 10 \times 10^3 \left[\frac{0.08 + 0.15}{1 - 0.08 \times 0.15} \right] = 2328 \text{ N}$$

Also we know that the total torque required to turn the hand wheel,

$$T = P \times \frac{d}{2} + \mu_1 . W . R = 2328 \times \frac{50}{2} + 0.18 \times 10 \times 10^3 \times 30$$

$$= 112\,200 \text{ N-mm} \qquad \qquad ...(i)$$

Let $\qquad D_1 = $ Diameter of the hand wheel in mm.

We know that the torque applied to the hand wheel,

$$T = 2 P_1 \times \frac{D_1}{2} = 2 \times 100 \times \frac{D_1}{2} = 100 \, D_1 \text{ N-mm} \qquad \qquad ...(ii)$$

Equating equations (i) and (ii),

$$D_1 = 112\ 200/100 = 1122 \text{ mm} = 1.122 \text{ m } \textbf{Ans.}$$

Example 10.8. *The cutter of a broaching machine is pulled by square threaded screw of 55 mm external diameter and 10 mm pitch. The operating nut takes the axial load of 400 N on a flat surface of 60 mm internal diameter and 90 mm external diameter. If the coefficient of firction is 0.15 for all contact surfaces on the nut, determine the power required to rotate the operating nut, when the cutting speed is 6 m/min.*

Solution. Given : $d_0 = 55$ mm ; $p = 10$ mm $= 0.01$ m ; $W = 400$ N ; $D_2 = 60$ mm   or $R_2 = 30$ mm ; $D_1 = 90$ mm or $R_1 = 45$ mm ; $\mu = \tan \phi = \mu_1 = 0.15$; cutting speed $= 6$ m/min

We know that mean diameter of the screw,

$$d = d_0 - p/2 = 55 - 10/2 = 50 \text{ mm}$$

$$\therefore \qquad \tan \alpha = \frac{p}{\pi d} = \frac{10}{\pi \times 50} = 0.0637$$

and force required at the circumference of the screw,

$$P = W \tan (\alpha + \phi) = W \left[\frac{\tan \alpha + \tan \phi}{1 - \tan \alpha . \tan \phi} \right]$$

$$= 400 \left[\frac{0.0637 + 0.15}{1 - 0.0637 \times 0.15} \right] = 86.4 \text{ N}$$

We know that mean radius of the flat surface,

$$R = \frac{R_1 + R_2}{2} = \frac{45 + 30}{2} = 37.5 \text{ mm}$$

∴ Total torque required,

$$T = P \times \frac{d}{2} + \mu_1 . W . R = 86.4 \times \frac{50}{2} + 0.15 \times 400 \times 37.5 \text{ N-mm}$$

$$= 4410 \text{ N-mm} = 4.41 \text{ N-m} \qquad \qquad ...(\because \mu_1 = \mu)$$

Since the cutting speed is 6 m/min, therefore speed of the screw,

$$N = \frac{\text{Cutting speed}}{\text{Pitch}} = \frac{6}{0.01} = 600 \text{ r.p.m.}$$

and   angular speed, $\omega = 2 \pi \times 600/60 = 62.84$ rad/s

We know that power required to operate the nut

$$= T . \omega = 4.41 \times 62.84 = 277 \text{ W} = 0.277 \text{ kW } \textbf{Ans.}$$

10.19. Torque Required to Lower the Load by a Screw Jack

We have discussed in Art. 10.18, that the principle on which the screw jack works is similar to that of an inclined plane. If one complete turn of a screw thread be imagined to be unwound from the body of the screw and developed, it will form an inclined plane as shown in Fig. 10.13 (a).

Let p = Pitch of the screw,

d = Mean diameter of the screw,

α = Helix angle,

P = Effort applied at the circumference of the screw to lower the load,

W = Weight to be lowered, and

μ = Coefficient of friction between the screw and nut = tan ϕ, where ϕ is the friction angle.

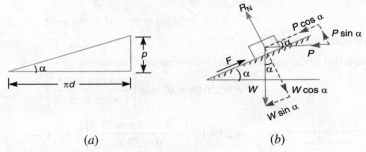

(a) (b)

Fig. 10.13

From the geometry of the figure, we find that

$$\tan \alpha = p/\pi d$$

Since the load is being lowered, therefore the force of friction ($F = \mu.R_N$) will act upwards. All the forces acting on the screw are shown in Fig. 10.13 (b).

Resolving the forces along the plane,

$$P \cos \alpha = F - W \sin \alpha = \mu.R_N - W \sin \alpha \qquad ...(i)$$

and resolving the forces perpendicular to the plane,

$$R_N = W \cos \alpha - P \sin \alpha \qquad ...(ii)$$

Substituting this value of R_N in equation (i),

$$P \cos \alpha = \mu (W \cos \alpha - P \sin \alpha) - W \sin \alpha$$
$$= \mu.W \cos \alpha - \mu.P \sin \alpha - W \sin \alpha$$

or $\quad P \cos \alpha + \mu.P \sin \alpha = \mu.W \cos \alpha - W \sin \alpha$

or $\quad P (\cos \alpha + \mu \sin \alpha) = W (\mu \cos \alpha - \sin \alpha)$

∴ $$P = W \times \frac{(\mu \cos \alpha - \sin \alpha)}{(\cos \alpha + \mu \sin \alpha)}$$

Substituting the value of μ = tan ϕ in the above equation, we get

$$P = W \times \frac{(\tan \phi \cos \alpha - \sin \alpha)}{(\cos \alpha + \tan \phi \sin \alpha)}$$

Multiplying the numerator and denominator by cos ϕ,

$$P = W \times \frac{(\sin \phi \cos \alpha - \sin \alpha \cos \phi)}{(\cos \alpha \cos \phi + \sin \phi \sin \alpha)} = W \times \frac{\sin (\phi - \alpha)}{\cos (\phi - \alpha)}$$

$$= W \tan (\phi - \alpha)$$

∴ Torque required to overcome friction between the screw and nut,

$$T = P \times \frac{d}{2} = W \tan (\phi - \alpha) \frac{d}{2}$$

Note : When $\alpha > \phi$, then $P = \tan (\alpha - \phi)$.

Example 10.9. *The mean diameter of a square threaded screw jack is 50 mm. The pitch of the thread is 10 mm. The coefficient of friction is 0.15. What force must be applied at the end of a 0.7 m long lever, which is perpendicular to the longitudinal axis of the screw to raise a load of 20 kN and to lower it?*

Solution. Given : $d = 50$ mm $= 0.05$ m ; $p = 10$ mm ; $\mu = \tan \phi = 0.15$; $l = 0.7$ m ; $W = 20$ kN $= 20 \times 10^3$ N

We know that $\tan \alpha = \dfrac{p}{\pi d} = \dfrac{10}{\pi \times 50} = 0.0637$

Let $P_1 =$ Force required at the end of the lever.

Force required to raise the load

We know that force required at the circumference of the screw,

$$P = W \tan (\alpha + \phi) = W \left[\frac{\tan \alpha + \tan \phi}{1 - \tan \alpha . \tan \phi} \right]$$

$$= 20 \times 10^3 \left[\frac{0.0637 + 0.15}{1 - 0.0637 \times 0.15} \right] = 4314 \text{ N}$$

Now the force required at the end of the lever may be found out by the relation,

$$P_1 \times l = P \times d/2$$

$$\therefore \qquad P_1 = \frac{P \times d}{2\,l} = \frac{4314 \times 0.05}{2 \times 0.7} = 154 \text{ N } \textbf{Ans.}$$

Force required to lower the load

We know that the force required at the circumference of the screw,

$$P = W \tan (\phi - \alpha) = W \left[\frac{\tan \phi - \tan \alpha}{1 + \tan \phi . \tan \alpha} \right]$$

$$= 20 \times 10^3 \left[\frac{0.15 - 0.0637}{1 + 0.15 \times 0.0637} \right] = 1710 \text{ N}$$

Now the force required at the end of the lever may be found out by the relation,

$$P_1 \times l = P \times \frac{d}{2} \quad \text{or} \quad P_1 = \frac{P \times d}{2l} = \frac{1710 \times 0.05}{2 \times 0.7} = 61 \text{ N } \textbf{Ans.}$$

10.20. Efficiency of a Screw Jack

The efficiency of a screw jack may be defined as **the ratio between the ideal effort** (*i.e.* the effort required to move the load, neglecting friction) to **the actual effort** (*i.e.* the effort required to move the load taking friction into account).

We know that the effort required to lift the load (W) when friction is taken into account,

$$P = W \tan (\alpha + \phi) \qquad \qquad ...(i)$$

where $\alpha =$ Helix angle,

$\phi =$ Angle of friction, and

$\mu =$ Coefficient of friction, between the screw and nut $= \tan \phi$.

If there would have been no friction between the screw and the nut, then ϕ will be equal to zero. The value of effort P_0 necessary to raise the load, will then be given by the equation,

$$P_0 = W \tan \alpha \qquad \qquad (\textit{i.e. } \text{Putting } \phi = 0 \text{ in equation } (i)]$$

$$\therefore \text{ Efficiency, } \eta = \frac{\text{Ideal effort}}{\text{Actual effort}} = \frac{P_0}{P} = \frac{W \tan \alpha}{W \tan (\alpha + \phi)} = \frac{\tan \alpha}{\tan (\alpha + \phi)}$$

which shows that the efficiency of a screw jack, is independent of the load raised.

In the above expression for efficiency, only the screw friction is considered. However, if the screw friction and the collar friction is taken into account, then

$$\therefore \quad \eta = \frac{\text{Torque required to move the load, neglecting friction}}{\text{Torque required to move the load, including screw and collar friction}}$$

$$= \frac{T_0}{T} = \frac{P_0 \times d/2}{P \times d/2 + \mu_1 . W . R}$$

Note: The efficiency of the screw jack may also be defined as **the ratio of mechanical advantage to the velocity ratio.**

We know that mechanical advantage,

$$M.A. = \frac{W}{P_1} = \frac{W \times 2l}{P \times d} = \frac{W \times 2l}{W \tan(\alpha + \phi)d} = \frac{2l}{\tan(\alpha + \phi)d} \qquad ...(\text{Refer Art 10.17})$$

and velocity ratio,

$$V.R. = \frac{\text{Distance moved by the effort } (P_1), \text{ in one revolution}}{\text{Distance moved by the load } (W), \text{ in one revolution}}$$

$$= \frac{2\pi l}{p} = \frac{2\pi l}{\tan \alpha \times \pi d} = \frac{2l}{\tan \alpha \times d} \qquad ...(\because \tan \alpha = p/\pi d)$$

$$\therefore \text{ Efficiency, } \quad \eta = \frac{M.A.}{V.R.} = \frac{2l}{\tan(\alpha + \phi)d} \times \frac{\tan \alpha \times d}{2l} = \frac{\tan \times \alpha}{\tan(\alpha + \phi)}$$

10.21. Maximum Efficiency of a Screw Jack

We have seen in Art. 10.20 that the efficiency of a screw jack,

$$\eta = \frac{\tan \alpha}{\tan(\alpha + \theta)} = \frac{\dfrac{\sin \alpha}{\cos \alpha}}{\dfrac{\sin(\alpha + \phi)}{\cos(\alpha + \phi)}} = \frac{\sin \alpha \times \cos(\alpha + \phi)}{\cos \alpha \times \sin(\alpha + \phi)} \qquad ...(i)$$

$$= \frac{2 \sin \alpha \times \cos(\alpha + \phi)}{2 \cos \alpha \times \sin(\alpha + \phi)}$$

$$...(\text{Multiplying the numerator and denominator by 2})$$

$$= \frac{\sin(2\alpha + \phi) - \sin \phi}{\sin(2\alpha + \phi) + \sin \phi} \qquad ...(ii)$$

$$...\begin{bmatrix} \because & 2 \sin A \cos B = \sin(A + B) + \sin(A - B) \\ & 2 \cos A \sin B = \sin(A + B) - \sin(A - B) \end{bmatrix}$$

The efficiency given by equation (ii) is maximum when $\sin(2\alpha + \phi)$ is maximum, *i.e.* when

$$\sin(2\alpha + \phi) = 1 \quad \text{or} \quad \text{when } 2\alpha + \phi = 90°$$

$$\therefore \quad 2\alpha = 90° - \phi \quad \text{or} \quad \alpha = 45° - \phi/2$$

Substituting the value of 2α in equation (ii), we have maximum efficiency,

$$\eta_{max} = \frac{\sin(90° - \phi + \phi) - \sin \phi}{\sin(90° - \phi + \phi) + \sin \phi} = \frac{\sin 90° - \sin \phi}{\sin 90° + \sin \phi} = \frac{1 - \sin \phi}{1 + \sin \phi}$$

Example 10.10. *The pitch of 50 mm mean diameter threaded screw of a screw jack is 12.5 mm. The coefficient of friction between the screw and the nut is 0.13. Determine the torque required on the screw to raise a load of 25 kN, assuming the load to rotate with the screw. Determine the ratio of the torque required to raise the load to the torque required to lower the load and also the efficiency of the machine.*

Solution. Given : $d = 50$ mm ; $p = 12.5$ mm ; $\mu = \tan \phi = 0.13$; $W = 25$ kN $= 25 \times 10^3$ N

We know that, $\quad \tan \alpha = \dfrac{p}{\pi d} = \dfrac{12.5}{\pi \times 50} = 0.08$

and force required on the screw to raise the load,

$$P = W \tan(\alpha + \phi) = W \left[\dfrac{\tan \alpha \times \tan \phi}{1 - \tan \alpha . \tan \phi .} \right]$$

$$= 25 \times 10^3 \left[\dfrac{0.08 + 0.13}{1 - 0.08 \times 0.13} \right] = 5305 \text{ N}$$

Torque required on the screw

We know that the torque required on the screw to raise the load,

$$T_1 = P \times d/2 = 5305 \times 50/2 = 132\,625 \text{ N-mm } \textbf{Ans.}$$

Ratio of the torques required to raise and lower the load

We know that the force required on the screw to lower the load,

$$P = W \tan(\phi - \alpha) = W \left[\dfrac{\tan \phi - \tan \alpha}{1 + \tan \phi . \tan \alpha} \right]$$

$$= 25 \times 10^3 \left[\dfrac{0.13 - 0.08}{1 + 0.13 \times 0.08} \right] = 1237 \text{ N}$$

and torque required to lower the load

$$T_2 = P \times d/2 = 1237 \times 50/2 = 30\,905 \text{ N-mm}$$

∴ Ratio of the torques required,

$$= T_1/T_2 = 132\,625/30\,925 = 4.3 \quad \textbf{Ans.}$$

Efficiency of the machine

We know that the efficiency,

$$\eta = \dfrac{\tan \alpha}{\tan(\alpha + \phi)} = \dfrac{\tan \alpha (1 - \tan \alpha . \tan \phi)}{\tan \alpha + \tan \phi} = \dfrac{0.08(1 - 0.08 \times 0.13)}{0.08 + 0.13}$$

$$= 0.377 = 37.7\% \quad \textbf{Ans.}$$

Example 10.11. *The mean diameter of the screw jack having pitch of 10 mm is 50 mm. A load of 20 kN is lifted through a distance of 170 mm. Find the work done in lifting the load and efficiency of the screw jack when*

1. the load rotates with the screw, and

2. the load rests on the loose head which does not rotate with the screw.

The external and internal diameter of the bearing surface of the loose head are 60 mm and 10 mm respectively. The coefficient of friction for the screw as well as the bearing surface may be taken as 0.08.

Solution. Given : $p = 10$ mm ; $d = 50$ mm ; $W = 20$ kN $= 20 \times 10^3$ N ; $D_2 = 60$ mm or $R_2 = 30$ mm ; $D_1 = 10$ mm or $R_1 = 5$ mm ; $\mu = \tan \phi = \mu_1 = 0.08$

We know that $\quad \tan \alpha = \dfrac{p}{\pi d} = \dfrac{10}{\pi \times 50} = 0.0637$

∴ Force required at the circumference of the screw to lift the load,

$$P = W \tan(\alpha + \phi) = W \left[\frac{\tan \alpha + \tan \phi}{1 - \tan \alpha . \tan \phi} \right]$$

$$= 20 \times 10^3 \left[\frac{0.0637 + 0.08}{1 - 0.0637 \times 0.08} \right] = 2890 \text{ N}$$

and torque required to overcome friction at the screw,

$$T = P \times d/2 = 2890 \times 50/2 = 72\,250 \text{ N-mm} = 72.25 \text{ N-m}$$

Since the load is lifted through a vertical distance of 170 mm and the distance moved by the screw in one rotation is 10 mm (equal to pitch), therefore number of rotations made by the screw,

$$N = 170/10 = 17$$

1. When the load rotates with the screw

We know that work done in lifting the load

$$= T \times 2\pi N = 72.25 \times 2\pi \times 17 = 7718 \text{ N-m} \text{ **Ans.**}$$

and efficiency of the screw jack,

$$\eta = \frac{\tan \alpha}{\tan(\alpha + \phi)} = \frac{\tan \alpha (1 - \tan \alpha . \tan \phi)}{\tan \alpha + \tan \phi}$$

$$= \frac{0.0637 (1 - 0.0637 \times 0.08)}{0.0637 + 0.08} = 0.441 \text{ or } 44.1\% \text{ **Ans.**}$$

2. When the load does not rotate with the screw

We know that mean radius of the bearing surface,

$$R = \frac{R_1 + R_2}{2} = \frac{30 + 5}{2} = 17.5 \text{ mm}$$

and torque required to overcome friction at the screw and the collar,

$$T = P \times d/2 + \mu_1 . W . R$$

$$= 2890 \times 50/2 + 0.08 \times 20 \times 10^3 \times 17.5 = 100\,250 \text{ N-mm}$$

$$= 100.25 \text{ N-m}$$

∴ Work done by the torque in lifting the load

$$= T \times 2\pi N = 100.25 \times 2\pi \times 17 = 10\,710 \text{ N-m} \text{ **Ans.**}$$

We know that the torque required to lift the load, neglecting friction,

$$T_0 = P_0 \times d/2 = W \tan \alpha \times d/2 \qquad \ldots(\because P_0 = W \tan \alpha)$$

$$= 20 \times 10^3 \times 0.0637 \times 50/2 = 31\,850 \text{ N-mm} = 31.85 \text{ N-m}$$

∴ Efficiency of the screw jack,

$$\eta = T_0/T = 31.85/100.25 = 0.318 \text{ or } 31.8\% \text{ **Ans.**}$$

10.22. Over Hauling and Self Locking Screws

We have seen in Art. 10.20 that the effort required at the circumference of the screw to lower the load is

$$P = W \tan(\phi - \alpha)$$

and the torque required to lower the load

$$T = P \times \frac{d}{2} = W \tan{(\phi - \alpha)} \frac{d}{2}$$

In the above expression, if $\phi < \alpha$, then torque required to lower the load will be **negative.** In other words, the load will start moving downward without the application of any torque. Such a condition is known as **over hauling of screws.** If however, $\phi > \alpha$, the torque required to lower the load will **positive**, indicating that an effort is applied to lower the load. Such a screw is known as **self locking screw.** In other words, a screw will be self locking if the friction angle is greater than helix angle or coefficient of friction is greater than tangent of helix angle *i.e.* μ or $\tan{\phi} > \tan{\alpha}$.

10.23. Efficiency of Self Locking Screws

We know that efficiency of the screw,

$$\eta = \frac{\tan{\alpha}}{\tan{(\alpha + \phi)}}$$

and for self locking screws, $\phi \geq \alpha$ or $\alpha \leq \phi$.

∴ Efficiency of self locking screws,

$$\eta \leq \frac{\tan{\phi}}{\tan{(\phi + \phi)}} \leq \frac{\tan{\phi}}{\tan{2\phi}} \leq \frac{\tan{\phi}(1 - \tan^2{\phi})}{2\tan{\phi}}$$

$$\leq \frac{1}{2} - \frac{\tan^2{\phi}}{2} \qquad \qquad ...\left(\because \tan{2\phi} = \frac{2\tan{\phi}}{1 - \tan^2{\phi}}\right)$$

From this expression we see that efficiency of self locking screws is less than $\dfrac{1}{2}$ or 50%. If the efficiency is more than 50%, then the screw is said to be overhauling,

Note : It can also be proved as follows :

Let $\qquad\qquad\qquad\qquad W =$ Load to be lifted, and

$\qquad\qquad\qquad\qquad\qquad h =$ Distance through which the load is lifted.

∴ $\qquad\qquad\qquad$ Output $= W.h$

and $\qquad\qquad\qquad$ Input $= \dfrac{\text{Output}}{\eta} = \dfrac{W.h}{\eta}$

∴ Work lost in over coming friction.

$$= \text{Input} - \text{Output} = \frac{W.h}{\eta} - W.h = W.h\left(\frac{1}{\eta} - 1\right)$$

For self locking,, $\quad W.h\left(\dfrac{1}{\eta} - 1\right) \leq W.h$

∴ $\qquad\qquad\qquad \dfrac{1}{\eta} - 1 \leq 1$ or $\eta \leq \dfrac{1}{2}$ or 50%

Example 10.12. *A load of 10 kN is raised by means of a screw jack, having a square threaded screw of 12 mm pitch and of mean diameter 50 mm. If a force of 100 N is applied at the end of a lever to raise the load, what should be the length of the lever used? Take coefficient of friction = 0.15. What is the mechanical advantage obtained? State whether the screw is self locking.*

Solution. Given : $W = 10$ kN $= 10 \times 10^3$ N ; $p = 12$ mm ; $d = 50$ mm ; $P_1 = 100$ N ; $\mu = \tan{\phi} = 0.15$

Length of the lever

Let $\qquad\qquad\qquad\qquad l =$ Length of the lever.

We know that $\tan \alpha = \dfrac{p}{\pi d} = \dfrac{12}{\pi \times 50} = 0.0764$

∴ Effort required at the circumference of the screw to raise the load,

$$P = W \tan(\alpha + \phi) = W \left[\frac{\tan \alpha + \tan \phi}{1 - \tan \alpha . \tan \phi} \right]$$

$$= 10 \times 10^3 \left[\frac{0.0764 + 0.15}{1 - 0.0764 \times 0.15} \right] = 2290 \text{ N}$$

and torque required to overcome friction,

$$T = P \times d/2 = 2290 \times 50/2 = 57\,250 \text{ N-mm} \qquad \ldots(i)$$

We know that torque applied at the end of the lever,

$$T = P_1 \times l = 100 \times l \text{ N-mm} \qquad \ldots(ii)$$

Equating equations (*i*) and (*ii*)

$$l = 57\,250/100 = 572.5 \text{ mm } \textbf{Ans.}$$

Mechanical advantage

We know that mechanical advantage,

$$M.A. = \frac{W}{P_1} = \frac{10 \times 10^3}{100} = 100 \text{ Ans.}$$

Self locking of the screw

We know that efficiency of the screw jack,

$$\eta = \frac{\tan \alpha}{\tan(\alpha + \phi)} = \frac{\tan \alpha (1 - \tan \alpha . \tan \phi)}{\tan \alpha + \tan \phi}$$

$$= \frac{0.0764(1 - 0.0764 \times 0.15)}{0.0764 + 0.15} = \frac{0.0755}{0.2264} = 0.3335 \text{ or } 33.35\%$$

Since the efficiency of the screw jack is less than 50%, therefore the screw is a self locking screw. **Ans.**

10.24. Friction of a V-thread

We have seen in Art. 10.18 that the normal reaction in case of a square threaded screw is

$$R_N = W \cos \alpha, \text{ where } \alpha = \text{Helix angle.}$$

But in case of V-thread (or acme or trapezoidal threads), the normal reaction between the screw and nut is increased because the axial component of this normal reaction must be equal to the axial load W, as shown in Fig. 10.14.

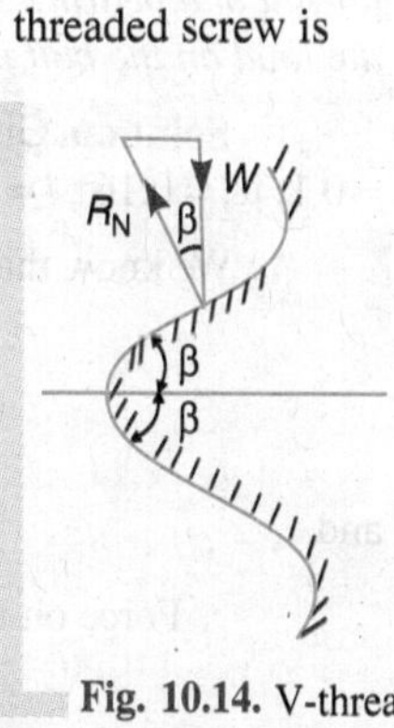

Let 2β = Angle of the V-thread, and

β = Semi-angle of the V-thread.

$$\therefore \qquad R_N = \frac{W}{\cos \beta}$$

and frictional force, $F = \mu . R_N = \mu \times \dfrac{W}{\cos \beta} = \mu_1 . W$

Fig. 10.14. V-thread.

where $\dfrac{\mu}{\cos \beta} = \mu_1$, known as virtual coefficient of friction.

Notes : 1. When coefficient of friction, $\mu_1 = \dfrac{\mu}{\cos\beta}$ is considered, then the V-thread is equivalent to a square thread.

2. All the equations of square threaded screw also hold good for V-threads. In case of V-threads, μ_1 (*i.e.* $\tan \phi_1$) may be substituted in place of μ (*i.e.* $\tan \phi$). Thus for V-threads,

$$P = W \tan (\alpha \pm \phi_1)$$

where ϕ_1 = Virtual friction angle, such that $\tan \phi_1 = \mu_1$.

Example 10.13. *Two co-axial rods are connected by a turn buckle which consists of a box nut, the one screw being right handed and the other left handed on a pitch diameter of 22 mm, the pitch of thread being 3 mm. The included angle of the thread is 60°. Assuming that the rods do not turn, calculate the torque required on the nut to produce a pull of 40 kN, given that the coefficient of friction is 0.15.*

Solution. Given : $d = 22$ mm ; $p = 3$ mm ; $2\beta = 60°$ or $\beta = 30°$, $W = 40$ kN $= 40 \times 10^3$ N ; $\mu = 0.15$

We know that $\tan \alpha = \dfrac{p}{\pi d} = \dfrac{3}{\pi \times 22} = 0.0434$

and virtual coefficient of friction

$$\mu_1 = \tan \phi_1 = \frac{\mu}{\cos \beta} = \frac{0.15}{\cos 30°} = 0.173$$

We know that the force required at the circumference of the screw,

$$P = W \tan (\alpha + \phi_1) = W \left[\frac{\tan \alpha + \tan \phi_1}{1 - \tan \alpha . \tan \phi_1} \right]$$

$$= 40 \times 10^3 \left[\frac{0.0434 + 0.173}{1 - 0.0434 \times 0.173} \right] = 8720 \text{ N}$$

and   torque on one rod, $T = P \times d/2 = 8720 \times 22/2 = 95\,920$ N-mm $= 95.92$ N-m

Since the turn buckle has right and left hand threads and the torque on each rod is $T = 95.92$ N-m, therefore the torque required on the nut,

$$T_1 = 2T = 2 \times 95.92 = 191.84 \text{ N-m } \textbf{Ans.}$$

Example 10.14. *The mean diameter of a Whitworth bolt having V-threads is 25 mm. The pitch of the thread is 5 mm and the angle of V is 55°. The bolt is tightened by screwing a nut whose mean radius of the bearing surface is 25 mm. If the coefficient of friction for nut and bolt is 0.1 and for nut and bearing surfaces 0.16 ; find the force required at the end of a spanner 0.5 m long when the load on the bolt is 10 kN.*

Solution. Given : $d = 25$ mm ; $p = 5$ mm ; $2\beta = 55°$ or $\beta = 27.5°$; $R = 25$ mm ; $\mu = \tan \phi$ $= 0.1$; $\mu_2 = 0.16$; $l = 0.5$ m ; $W = 10$ kN $= 10 \times 10^3$ N

We know that virtual coefficient of friction,

$$\mu_1 = \tan \phi_1 = \frac{\mu}{\cos \beta} = \frac{0.1}{\cos 27.5°} = \frac{0.1}{0.887} = 0.113$$

and $\tan \alpha = \dfrac{p}{\pi d} = \dfrac{5}{\pi \times 25} = 0.064$

∴ Force on the screw,

$$P = W \tan (\alpha + \phi_1) = W \left[\frac{\tan \alpha + \tan \phi_1}{1 - \tan \alpha . \tan \phi_1} \right]$$

$$= 10 \times 10^3 \left[\frac{0.064 + 0.113}{1 - 0.064 \times 0.113} \right] = 1783 \text{ N}$$

We know that total torque transmitted,

$$T = P \times \frac{d}{2} + \mu_2 . W . R = 1783 \times \frac{25}{2} + 0.16 \times 10 \times 10^3 \times 25 \text{ N-mm}$$

$$= 62\ 300 \text{ N-mm} = 62.3 \text{ N-m} \qquad \qquad ...(i)$$

Let P_1 = Force required at the end of a spanner.

∴ Torque required at the end of a spanner,

$$T = P_1 \times l = P_1 \times 0.5 = 0.5\ P_1 \text{ N-m} \qquad \qquad ...(ii)$$

Equating equations (*i*) and (*ii*),

$$P_1 = 62.3/0.5 = 124.6 \text{ N} \quad \textbf{Ans.}$$

10.25. Friction in Journal Bearing-Friction Circle

A journal bearing forms a turning pair as shown in Fig. 10.15 (*a*). The fixed outer element of a turning pair is called a *bearing* and that portion of the inner element (*i.e.* shaft) which fits in the bearing is called a *journal*. The journal is slightly less in diameter than the bearing, in order to permit the free movement of the journal in a bearing.

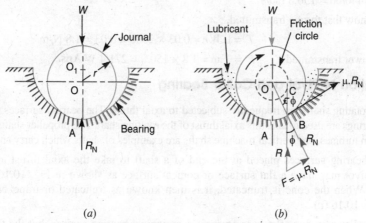

(*a*)   (*b*)

Fig. 10.15. Friction in journal bearing.

When the bearing is not lubricated (or the journal is stationary), then there is a line contact between the two elements as shown in Fig. 10.15 (*a*). The load W on the journal and normal reaction R_N (equal to W) of the bearing acts through the centre. The reaction R_N acts vertically upwards at point A. This point A is known as *seat* or *point of pressure*.

Now consider a shaft rotating inside a bearing in clockwise direction as shown in Fig. 10.15 (*b*). The lubricant between the journal and bearing forms a thin layer which gives rise to a greasy friction. Therefore, the reaction R does not act vertically upward, but acts at another point of pressure B. This is due to the fact that when shaft rotates, a frictional force $F = \mu R_N$ acts at the circumference of the shaft which has a tendency to rotate the shaft in opposite direction of motion and this shifts the point A to point B.

In order that the rotation may be maintained, there must be a couple rotating the shaft.

Let ϕ = Angle between R (resultant of F and R_N) and R_N,

                        μ = Coefficient of friction between the journal and bearing,

                      T = Frictional torque in N-m, and

                      r = Radius of the shaft in metres.

For uniform motion, the resultant force acting on the shaft must be zero and the resultant turning moment on the shaft must be zero. In other words,

$$R = W, \text{ and } T = W \times OC = W \times OB \sin \phi = W.r \sin \phi$$

Since ϕ is very small, therefore substituting $\sin \phi = \tan \phi$

$$\therefore \qquad T = W.r \tan \phi = \mu.W.r \qquad \qquad ...(\because \mu = \tan \phi)$$

If the shaft rotates with angular velocity ω rad/s, then power wasted in friction,

$$P = T.\omega = T \times 2\pi N/60 \text{ watts}$$

where $\qquad\qquad\qquad N = $ Speed of the shaft in r.p.m.

Notes : 1. If a circle is drawn with centre O and radius $OC = r \sin \phi$, then this circle is called the *friction circle* of a bearing.

2. The force R exerted by one element of a turning pair on the other element acts along a tangent to the friction circle.

Example 10.15. *A 60 mm diameter shaft running in a bearing carries a load of 2000 N. If the coefficient of friction between the shaft and bearing is 0.03, find the power transmitted when it runs at 1440 r.p.m.*

Solution. Given : $d = 60$ mm or $r = 30$ mm $= 0.03$ m ; $W = 2000$ N ; $\mu = 0.03$; $N = 1440$ r.p.m. or $\omega = 2\pi \times 1440/60 = 150.8$ rad/s

We know that torque transmitted,

$$T = \mu.W.r = 0.03 \times 2000 \times 0.03 = 1.8 \text{ N-m}$$

$\therefore$ Power transmitted, $\qquad P = T.\omega = 1.8 \times 150.8 = 271.4$ W **Ans.**

10.26. Friction of Pivot and Collar Bearing

The rotating shafts are frequently subjected to axial thrust. The bearing surfaces such as pivot and collar bearings are used to take this axial thrust of the rotating shaft. The propeller shafts of ships, the shafts of steam turbines, and vertical machine shafts are examples of shafts which carry an axial thrust.

The bearing surfaces placed at the end of a shaft to take the axial thrust are known as *pivots*. The pivot may have a flat surface or conical surface as shown in Fig. 10.16 (*a*) and (*b*) respectively. When the cone is truncated, it is then known as truncated or trapezoidal pivot as shown in Fig. 10.16 (*c*).

The collar may have flat bearing surface or conical bearing surface, but the flat surface is most commonly used. There may be a single collar, as shown in Fig. 10.16 (*d*) or several collars along the length of a shaft, as shown in Fig. 10.16 (*e*) in order to reduce the intensity of pressure.

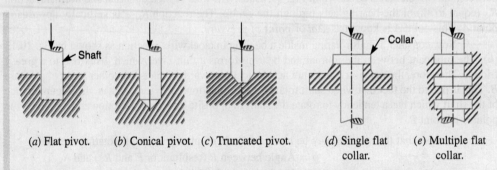

(*a*) Flat pivot.　(*b*) Conical pivot.　(*c*) Truncated pivot.　(*d*) Single flat collar.　(*e*) Multiple flat collar.

Fig. 10.16. Pivot and collar bearings.

In modern practice, ball and roller thrust bearings are used when power is being transmitted and when thrusts are large as in case of propeller shafts of ships.

A little consideration will show that in a new bearing, the contact between the shaft and bearing may be good over the whole surface. In other words, we can say that the pressure over the rubbing surfaces is uniformly distributed. But when the bearing becomes old, all parts of the rubbing surface will not move with the same velocity, because the velocity of rubbing surface increases with the distance from the axis of the bearing. This means that wear may be different at different radii and this causes to alter the distribution of pressure. Hence, in the study of friction of bearings, it is assumed that

Collar bearing.

1. The pressure is uniformly distributed throughout the bearing surface, and

2. The wear is uniform throughout the bearing surface.

10.27. Flat Pivot Bearing

When a vertical shaft rotates in a flat pivot bearing (known as **foot step bearing**), as shown in Fig. 10.17, the sliding friction will be along the surface of contact between the shaft and the bearing.

Let W = Load transmitted over the bearing surface,

        R = Radius of bearing surface,

        p = Intensity of pressure per unit area of bearing surface between rubbing surfaces, and

        μ = Coefficient of friction.

We will consider the following two cases :

1. When there is a uniform pressure ; and

2. When there is a uniform wear.

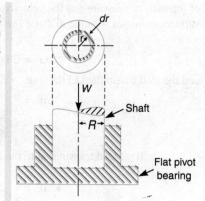

Fig. 10.17. Flat pivot or footstep bearing.

1. *Considering uniform pressure*

When the pressure is uniformly distributed over the bearing area, then

$$p = \frac{W}{\pi R^2}$$

Consider a ring of radius r and thickness dr of the bearing area.

$\therefore$ Area of bearing surface, $A = 2\pi r . dr$

Load transmitted to the ring,

$$\delta W = p \times A = p \times 2\pi r . dr \qquad \qquad ...(i)$$

Frictional resistance to sliding on the ring acting tangentially at radius r,

$$F_r = \mu . \delta W = \mu p \times 2\pi r . dr = 2\pi \mu . p . r . dr$$

$\therefore$ Frictional torque on the ring,

$$T_r = F_r \times r = 2\pi \mu p \, r . dr \times r = 2\pi \mu p \, r^2 \, dr \qquad \qquad ...(ii)$$

Integrating this equation within the limits from 0 to R for the total frictional torque on the pivot bearing.

$\therefore$ Total frictional torque, $T = \int\limits_{0}^{R} 2\pi\mu\, p\, r^2 \; dr = 2\pi\mu\, p \int\limits_{0}^{R} r^2 \; dr$

$$= 2\pi\mu\, p \left[\frac{r^3}{3}\right]_0^R = 2\pi\mu\, p \times \frac{R^3}{3} = \frac{2}{3} \times \pi\mu.p.R^3$$

$$= \frac{2}{3} \times \pi\mu \times \frac{W}{\pi R^2} \times R^3 = \frac{2}{3} \times \mu.W.R \qquad \dots\left(\because\; p = \frac{W}{\pi R^2}\right)$$

When the shaft rotates at ω rad/s, then power lost in friction,

$$P = T.\omega = T \times 2\pi\, N/60 \qquad \dots(\because\; \omega = 2\pi N/60)$$

where N = Speed of shaft in r.p.m.

2. Considering uniform wear

We have already discussed that the rate of wear depends upon the intensity of pressure (p) and the velocity of rubbing surfaces (v). It is assumed that the rate of wear is proportional to the product of intensity of pressure and the velocity of rubbing surfaces (*i.e.* *p.v.*). Since the velocity of rubbing surfaces increases with the distance (*i.e.* radius r) from the axis of the bearing, therefore for uniform wear

$$p.r = C \;\text{(a constant)} \quad \text{or} \quad p = C/r$$

and the load transmitted to the ring,

$$\delta W = p \times 2\pi r.dr \qquad \dots\text{[From equation (i)]}$$

$$= \frac{C}{r} \times 2\pi r.dr = 2\pi C.dr$$

$\therefore$ Total load transmitted to the bearing

$$W = \int\limits_{0}^{R} 2\pi\, C.dr = 2\pi\, C\,[r]_0^R = 2\pi C.R \quad \text{or} \quad C = \frac{W}{2\pi R}$$

We know that frictional torque acting on the ring,

$$T_r = 2\pi\mu\, p\, r^2 \; dr = 2\pi\mu \times \frac{C}{r} \times r^2 \; dr \qquad \dots\left(\because\; p = \frac{C}{r}\right)$$

$$= 2\pi\,\mu.C.r\; dr \qquad \dots(iii)$$

$\therefore$ Total frictional torque on the bearing,

$$T = \int\limits_{0}^{R} 2\pi\,\mu.C.r.dr = 2\pi\mu.C\left[\frac{r^2}{2}\right]_0^R$$

$$= 2\pi\mu.C \times \frac{R^2}{2} = \pi\mu.C.R^2$$

$$= \pi\mu \times \frac{W}{2\pi R} \times R^2 = \frac{1}{2} \times \mu.W.R \qquad \dots\left(\because\; C = \frac{W}{2\pi R}\right)$$

Example 10.16. *A vertical shaft 150 mm in diameter rotating at 100 r.p.m. rests on a flat end footstep bearing. The shaft carries a vertical load of 20 kN. Assuming uniform pressure distribution and coefficient of friction equal to 0.05, estimate power lost in friction.*

Solution. Given : D = 150 mm or R = 75 mm = 0.075 m ; N = 100 r.p.m or $\omega = 2\,\pi \times 100/60$ = 10.47 rad/s ; W = 20 kN = 20×10^3 N ; μ = 0.05

We know that for uniform pressure distribution, the total frictional torque,

$$T = \frac{2}{3} \times \mu.W.R = \frac{2}{3} \times 0.05 \times 20 \times 10^3 \times 0.075 = 50 \text{ N-m}$$

∴ Power lost in friction,

$$P = T.\omega = 50 \times 10.47 = 523.5 \text{ W } \textbf{Ans.}$$

10.28. Conical Pivot Bearing

The conical pivot bearing supporting a shaft carrying a load W is shown in Fig. 10.18.

Let p_n = Intensity of pressure normal to the cone,

      α = Semi angle of the cone,

      μ = Coefficient of friction between the shaft and the bearing, and

      R = Radius of the shaft.

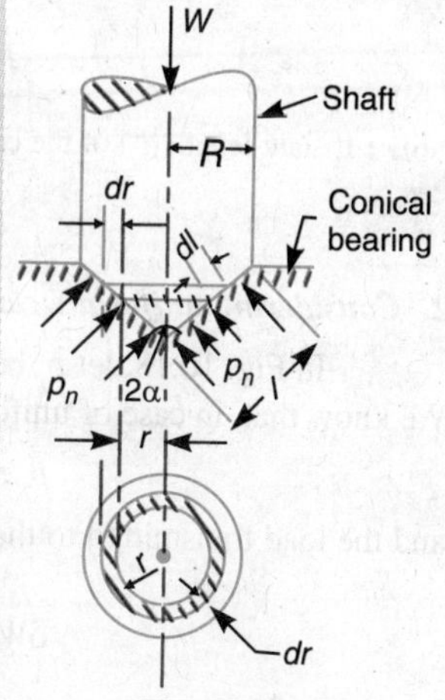

Consider a small ring of radius r and thickness dr. Let dl is the length of ring along the cone, such that

$$dl = dr \operatorname{cosec} \alpha$$

∴ Area of the ring,

$$A = 2\pi r.dl = 2\pi r.dr \operatorname{cosec} \alpha$$
$$...(\because dl = dr \operatorname{cosec} \alpha)$$

Fig. 10.18
Conical pivot bearing.

1. *Considering uniform pressure*

We know that normal load acting on the ring,

$$\delta W_n = \text{Normal pressure} \times \text{Area}$$
$$= p_n \times 2\pi r.dr \operatorname{cosec} \alpha$$

and vertical load acting on the ring,

$$^*\delta W = \text{Vertical component of } \delta W_n = \delta W_n.\sin \alpha$$
$$= p_n \times 2\pi r.dr \operatorname{cosec} \alpha. \sin \alpha = p_n \times 2\pi r.dr$$

∴ Total vertical load transmitted to the bearing,

$$W = \int_0^R p_n \times 2\pi r.dr = 2\pi p_n \left[\frac{r^2}{2} \right]_0^R = 2\pi p_n \times \frac{R^2}{2} = \pi R^2.p_n$$

or

$$p_n = W / \pi R^2$$

We know that frictional force on the ring acting tangentially at radius r,

$$F_r = \mu.\delta W_n = \mu.p_n.2\pi r.dr \operatorname{cosec} \alpha = 2\pi \mu.p_n.\operatorname{cosec} \alpha.r.dr$$

and frictional torque acting on the ring,

$$T_r = F_r \times r = 2\pi \mu.p_n.\operatorname{cosec} \alpha.r.dr \times r = 2\pi \mu.p_n \operatorname{cosec} \alpha.r^2.dr$$

---

* The vertical load acting on the ring is also given by

$$\delta W = \text{Vertical component of } p_n \times \text{Area of the ring}$$
$$= p_n \sin \alpha \times 2\pi r.dr.\operatorname{cosec} \alpha = p_n \times 2\pi r.dr$$

Integrating the expression within the limits from 0 to R for the total frictional torque on the conical pivot bearing.

∴ Total frictional torque,

$$T = \int_0^R 2\pi\mu.p_n \cosec \alpha.r^2\, dr = 2\pi\mu.p_n.\cosec\alpha \left[\frac{r^3}{3}\right]_0^R$$

$$= 2\pi\mu.p_n.\cosec\alpha \times \frac{R^3}{3} = \frac{2\pi R^3}{3} \times \mu.p_n.\cosec\alpha \qquad ...(i)$$

Substituting the value of p_n in equation (i),

$$T = \frac{2\pi R^3}{3} \times \mu \times \frac{W}{\pi R^2} \times \cosec\alpha = \frac{2}{3} \times \mu.W.R.\cosec\alpha$$

Note : If slant length (l) of the cone is known, then

$$T = \frac{2}{3} \times \mu.W.l \qquad\qquad ...(\because\ l = R\cosec\alpha)$$

2. Considering uniform wear

In Fig. 10.18, let p_r be the normal intensity of pressure at a distance r from the central axis. We know that, in case of uniform wear, the intensity of pressure varies inversely with the distance.

∴ $$p_r.r = C \text{ (a constant)} \quad \text{or} \quad p_r = C/r$$

and the load transmitted to the ring,

$$\delta W = p_r \times 2\pi r.dr = \frac{C}{r} \times 2\pi r.dr = 2\pi C.dr$$

∴ Total load transmitted to the bearing,

$$W = \int_0^R 2\pi C.dr = 2\pi C\ [r]_0^R = 2\pi C.R \quad \text{or} \quad C = \frac{W}{2\pi R}$$

We know that frictional torque acting on the ring,

$$T_r = 2\pi\mu.p_r.\cosec\alpha.r^2.dr = 2\pi\mu \times \frac{C}{r} \times \cosec\alpha.r^2.dr$$

$$= 2\pi\mu.C.\cosec\alpha.r.dr$$

∴ Total frictional torque acting on the bearing,

$$T = \int_0^R 2\pi\mu.C.\cosec\alpha.r.dr = 2\pi\mu.C.\cosec\alpha\left[\frac{r^2}{2}\right]_0^R$$

$$= 2\pi\mu.C.\cosec\alpha \times \frac{R^2}{2} = \pi\mu.C.\cosec\alpha.R^2$$

Substituting the value of C, we have

$$T = \pi\mu \times \frac{W}{2\pi R} \times \cosec\alpha.R^2 = \frac{1}{2} \times \mu.W.R\cosec\alpha = \frac{1}{2} \times \mu.W.l$$

10.29. Trapezoidal or Truncated Conical Pivot Bearing

If the pivot bearing is not conical, but a frustrum of a cone with r_1 and r_2, the external and internal radius respectively as shown in Fig. 10.19, then.

Area of the bearing surface,

$$A = \pi[(r_1)^2 - (r_2)^2]$$

∴ Intensity of uniform pressure,

$$p_n = \frac{W}{A} = \frac{W}{\pi[(r_1)^2 - (r_2)^2]} \qquad ...(i)$$

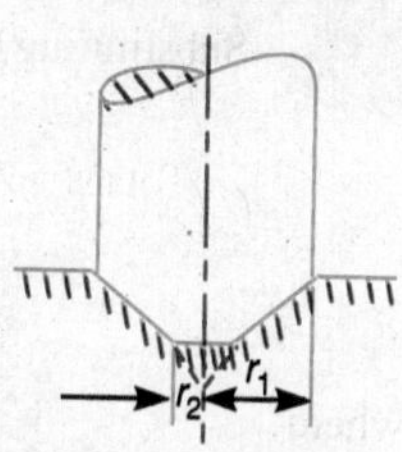

Fig. 10.19. Trapezoidal pivot bearing.

1. Considering uniform pressure

The total torque acting on the bearing is obtained by integrating the value of T_r (as discussed in Art. 10.28) within the limits r_1 and r_2.

∴ Total torque acting on the bearing,

$$T = \int_{r_2}^{r_1} 2\pi\mu.p_n \ \mathrm{cosec}\ \alpha.r^2.dr = 2\pi\mu.p_n.\mathrm{cosec}\ \alpha \left[\frac{r^3}{3}\right]_{r_2}^{r_1}$$

$$= 2\pi\mu.p_n.\mathrm{cosec}\ \alpha \left[\frac{(r_1)^3 - (r_2)^3}{3}\right]$$

Substituting the value of p_n from equation (*i*),

$$T = 2\pi\mu \times \frac{W}{\pi[(r_1)^2 - (r_2)^2]} \times \mathrm{cosec}\ \alpha \left[\frac{(r_1)^3 - (r_2)^3}{3}\right]$$

$$= \frac{2}{3} \times \mu.W.\mathrm{cosec}\ \alpha \left[\frac{(r_1)^3 - (r_2)^3}{(r_1)^2 - (r_2)^2}\right]$$

2. Considering uniform wear

We have discussed in Art. 10.28 that the load transmitted to the ring,

$$\delta W = 2\pi C.dr$$

∴ Total load transmitted to the ring,

$$W = \int_{r_2}^{r_1} 2\pi\ C.dr = 2\pi C[r]_{r_2}^{r_1} = 2\pi C(r_1 - r_2)$$

or

$$C = \frac{W}{2\pi(r_1 - r_2)} \qquad\qquad ...(ii)$$

We know that the torque acting on the ring, considering uniform wear, is

$$T_r = 2\pi\ \mu.C\ \mathrm{cosec}\ \alpha.r.dr$$

∴ Total torque acting on the bearing,

$$T = \int_{r_2}^{r_1} 2\pi\ \mu.C\ \mathrm{cosec}\ \alpha.r.dr = 2\pi\ \mu.C.\mathrm{cosec}\ \alpha \left[\frac{r^2}{2}\right]_{r_2}^{r_1}$$

$$= \pi\ \mu.C.\mathrm{cosec}\ \alpha \left[(r_1)^2 - (r_2)^2\right]$$

Substituting the value of C from equation (ii), we get

$$T = \pi\mu \times \frac{W}{2\pi(r_1 - r_2)} \times \text{cosec}\,\alpha\,[(r_1)^2 - (r_2)^2]$$

$$= \frac{1}{2} \times \mu.W\,(r_1 + r_2)\,\text{cosec}\,\alpha = \mu.W.R\,\text{cosec}\,\alpha$$

where R = Mean radius of the bearing = $\dfrac{r_1 + r_2}{2}$

Example 10.17. *A conical pivot supports a load of 20 kN, the cone angle is 120° and the intensity of normal pressure is not to exceed 0.3 N/mm². The external diameter is twice the internal diameter. Find the outer and inner radii of the bearing surface. If the shaft rotates at 200 r.p.m. and the coefficient of friction is 0.1, find the power absorbed in friction. Assume uniform pressure.*

Solution. Given : W = 20 kN = 20×10^3 N ; 2α = 120° or α = 60° ; p_n = 0.3 N/mm² ; N = 200 r.p.m. or $\omega = 2\pi \times 200/60 = 20.95$ rad/s ; $\mu = 0.1$

Outer and inner radii of the bearing surface

Let r_1 and r_2 = Outer and inner radii of the bearing surface, in mm.

Since the external diameter is twice the internal diameter, therefore

$$r_1 = 2\,r_2$$

We know that intensity of normal pressure (p_n),

$$0.3 = \frac{W}{\pi[(r_1)^2 - (r_2)^2]} = \frac{20 \times 10^3}{\pi[(2r_2)^2 - (r_2)^2]} = \frac{2.12 \times 10^3}{(r_2)^2}$$

∴ $(r_2)^2 = 2.12 \times 10^3 / 0.3 = 7.07 \times 10^3$ or $r_2 = 84$ mm **Ans.**

and $r_1 = 2\,r_2 = 2 \times 84 = 168$ mm **Ans.**

Power absorbed in friction

We know that total frictional torque (assuming uniform pressure),

$$T = \frac{2}{3} \times \mu.W.\text{cosec}\,\alpha\left[\frac{(r_1)^3 - (r_2)^3}{(r_1)^2 - (r_2)^2}\right]$$

$$= \frac{2}{3} \times 0.1 \times 20 \times 10^3 \times \text{cosec}\,60° = \left[\frac{(168)^3 - (84)^3}{(168)^2 - (84)^2}\right]\text{N-mm}$$

$$= 30\,1760 \text{ N-mm} = 301.76 \text{ N-m}$$

∴ Power absorbed in friction,

$$P = T.\omega = 301.76 \times 20.95 = 6322 \text{ W} = 6.322 \text{ kW} \textbf{ Ans.}$$

Example 10.18. *A conical pivot bearing supports a vertical shaft of 200 mm diameter. It is subjected to a load of 30 kN. The angle of the cone is 120° and the coefficient of friction is 0.025. Find the power lost in friction when the speed is 140 r.p.m., assuming 1. uniform pressure ; and 2. uniform wear.*

Solution. Given : D = 200 mm or R = 100 mm = 0.1 m ; W = 30 kN = 30×10^3 N ; 2α = 120° or α = 60° ; $\mu = 0.025$; N = 140 r.p.m. or $\omega = 2\pi \times 140/160 = 14.66$ rad/s

1. *Power lost in friction assuming uniform pressure*

We know that total frictional torque,

$$T = \frac{2}{3} \times \mu.W.R.\,\text{cosec}\,\alpha$$

$$= \frac{2}{3} \times 0.025 \times 30 \times 10^3 \times 0.1 \times \text{cosec } 60° = 57.7 \text{ N-m}$$

∴ Power lost in friction,

$$P = T.\omega = 57.7 \times 14.66 = 846 \text{ W } \textbf{Ans.}$$

2. *Power lost in friction assuming uniform wear*

We know that total frictional torque,

$$T = \frac{1}{2} \times \mu.W.R. \text{ cosec } \alpha$$

$$= \frac{1}{2} \times 0.025 \times 30 \times 10^3 \times 0.1 \times \text{cosec } 60° = 43.3 \text{ N-m}$$

∴ Power lost in friction, $P = T.\omega = 43.3 \times 14.66 = 634.8 \text{ W } \textbf{Ans.}$

10.30. Flat Collar Bearing

We have already discussed that collar bearings are used to take the axial thrust of the rotating shafts. There may be a single collar or multiple collar bearings as shown in Fig. 10.20 (*a*) and (*b*) respectively. The collar bearings are also known as *thrust bearings*. The friction in the collar bearings may be found as discussed below :

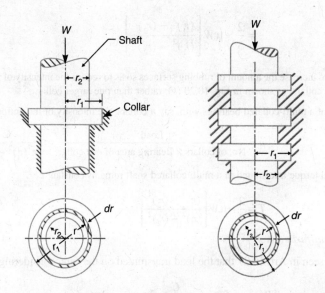

(*a*) Single collar bearing   (*b*) Multiple collar bearing.

Fig. 10.20. Flat collar bearings.

Consider a single flat collar bearing supporting a shaft as shown in Fig. 10.20 (*a*).

Let r_1 = External radius of the collar, and

              r_2 = Internal radius of the collar.

∴ Area of the bearing surface,

$$A = \pi [(r_1)^2 - (r_2)^2]$$

1. *Considering uniform pressure*

When the pressure is uniformly distributed over the bearing surface, then the intensity of pressure,

$$p = \frac{W}{A} = \frac{W}{\pi[(r_1)^2 - (r_2)^2]} \qquad \text{...}(i)$$

We have seen in Art. 10.27, that the frictional torque on the ring of radius r and thickness dr,

$$T_r = 2\pi\mu.p.r^2.dr$$

Integrating this equation within the limits from r_2 to r_1 for the total frictional torque on the collar.

∴ Total frictional torque,

$$T = \int_{r_2}^{r_1} 2\pi\mu.p.r^2.dr = 2\pi\mu.p\left[\frac{r^3}{3}\right]_{r_2}^{r_1} = 2\pi\mu.p\left[\frac{(r_1)^3 - (r_2)^3}{3}\right]$$

Substituting the value of p from equation (i),

$$T = 2\pi\mu \times \frac{W}{\pi[(r_1)^2 - (r_2)^2]}\left[\frac{(r_1)^3 - (r_2)^3}{3}\right]$$

$$= \frac{2}{3} \times \mu.W\left[\frac{(r_1)^3 - (r_2)^3}{(r_1)^2 - (r_2)^2}\right]$$

Notes: 1. In order to increase the amount of rubbing surfaces so as to reduce the intensity of pressure, it is better to use two or more collars, as shown in Fig. 10.20 (*b*), rather than one larger collar.

2. In case of a multi-collared bearings with, say n collars, the intensity of the uniform pressure,

$$p = \frac{\text{Load}}{\text{No. of collars} \times \text{Bearing area of one collar}} = \frac{W}{n\pi[(r_1)^2 - (r_2)^2]}$$

3. The total torque transmitted in a multi collared shaft remains constant *i.e.*

$$T = \frac{2}{3} \times \mu.W\left[\frac{(r_1)^3 - (r_2)^3}{(r_1)^2 - (r_2)^2}\right]$$

2. *Considering uniform wear*

We have seen in Art. 10.27 that the load transmitted on the ring, considering uniform wear is,

$$\delta W = p_r.2\pi r.dr = \frac{C}{r} \times 2\pi r.dr = 2\pi C.dr$$

∴ Total load transmitted to the collar,

$$W = \int_{r_2}^{r_1} 2\pi C.dr = 2\pi C[r]_{r_2}^{r_1} = 2\pi C(r_1 - r_2)$$

or

$$C = \frac{W}{2\pi(r_1 - r_2)} \qquad \text{...}(ii)$$

We also know that frictional torque on the ring,

$$T_r = \mu.\delta W.r = \mu \times 2\pi C.dr.r = 2\pi \mu.C.r.dr$$

∴ Total frictional torque on the bearing,

$$T = \int_{r_2}^{r_1} 2\pi\mu\, C.r.dr = 2\pi\mu.C \left[\frac{r^2}{2}\right]_{r_2}^{r_1} = 2\pi\mu.C \left[\frac{(r_1)^2 - (r_2)^2}{2}\right]$$

$$= \pi\mu.C[(r_1)^2 - (r_2)^2]$$

Substituting the value of *C* from equation (*ii*),

$$T = \pi\mu \times \frac{W}{2\pi(r_1 - r_2)}\,[(r_1)^2 - (r_2)^2] = \frac{1}{2} \times \mu.W\,(r_1 + r_2)$$

Example 10.19. *A thrust shaft of a ship has 6 collars of 600 mm external diameter and 300 mm internal diameter. The total thrust from the propeller is 100 kN. If the coefficient of friction is 0.12 and speed of the engine 90 r.p.m., find the power absorbed in friction at the thrust block, assuming l. uniform pressure ; and 2. uniform wear.*

Solution. Given : $n = 6$; $d_1 = 600$ mm or $r_1 = 300$ mm ; $d_2 = 300$ mm or $r_2 = 150$ mm ; $W = 100$ kN $= 100 \times 10^3$ N ; $\mu = 0.12$; $N = 90$ r.p.m. or $\omega = 2\pi \times 90/60 = 9.426$ rad/s

Ship propeller.

1. *Power absorbed in friction, assuming uniform pressure*

We know that total frictional torque transmitted,

$$T = \frac{2}{3} \times \mu.W \left[\frac{(r_1)^3 - (r_2)^3}{(r_1)^2 - (r_2)^2}\right]$$

$$= \frac{2}{3} \times 0.12 \times 100 \times 10^3 \left[\frac{(300)^3 - (150)^3}{(300)^2 - (150)^2}\right] = 2800 \times 10^3 \text{ N-mm}$$

$$= 2800 \text{ N-m}$$

∴ Power absorbed in friction,

$$P = T.\omega = 2800 \times 9.426 = 26\,400 \text{ W} = 26.4 \text{ kW } \textbf{Ans.}$$

2. *Power absorbed in friction assuming uniform wear*

We know that total frictional torque transmitted,

$$T = \frac{1}{2} \times \mu.W\,(r_1 + r_2) = \frac{1}{2} \times 0.12 \times 100 \times 10^3\,(300 + 150) \text{ N-mm}$$

$$= 2700 \times 10^3 \text{ N-mm} = 2700 \text{ N-m}$$

∴ Power absorbed in friction,

$$P = T.\omega = 2700 \times 9.426 = 25\,450 \text{ W} = 25.45 \text{ kW } \textbf{Ans.}$$

Example 10.20. *A shaft has a number of a collars integral with it. The external diameter of the collars is 400 mm and the shaft diemater is 250 mm. If the intensity of pressure is 0.35 N/mm² (uniform) and the coefficient of friction is 0.05, estimate : 1. power absorbed when the shaft runs at 105 r.p.m. carrying a load of 150 kN ; and 2. number of collars required.*

Solution. Given : $d_1 = 400$ mm or $r_1 = 200$ mm ; $d_2 = 250$ mm or $r_2 = 125$ mm ; $p = 0.35$ N/mm² ; $\mu = 0.05$; $N = 105$ r.p.m or $\omega = 2\pi \times 105/60 = 11$ rad/s ; $W = 150$ kN $= 150 \times 10^3$ N

1. *Power absorbed*

We know that for uniform pressure, total frictional torque transmitted,

$$T = \frac{2}{3} \times \mu.W \left[\frac{(r_1)^3 - (r_2)^3}{(r_1)^2 - (r_2)^2} \right] = \frac{2}{3} \times 0.05 \times 150 \times 10^3 \left[\frac{(200)^3 - (125)^3}{(200)^2 - (125)^2} \right] \text{N-mm}$$

$$= 5000 \times 248 = 1240 \times 10^3 \text{ N-mm} = 1240 \text{ N-m}$$

∴ Power absorbed,

$$P = T.\omega = 1240 \times 11 = 13640 \text{ W} = 13.64 \text{ kW } \textbf{Ans.}$$

2. *Number of collars required*

Let n = Number of collars required.

We know that the intensity of uniform pressure (p),

$$0.35 = \frac{W}{n.\pi[(r_1)^2 - (r_2)^2]} = \frac{150 \times 10^3}{n.\pi[(200)^2 - (125)^2]} = \frac{1.96}{n}$$

∴ $n = 1.96/0.35 = 5.6$ say 6 **Ans.**

Example 10.21. *The thrust of a propeller shaft in a marine engine is taken up by a number of collars integral with the shaft which is 300 mm in diameter. The thrust on the shaft is 200 kN and the speed is 75 r.p.m. Taking μ constant and equal to 0.05 and assuming intensity of pressure as uniform and equal to 0.3 N/mm², find the external diameter of the collars and the number of collars required, if the power lost in friction is not to exceed 16 kW.*

Solution. Given : $d_2 = 300$ mm or $r_2 = 150$ mm $= 0.15$ m ; $W = 200$ kN $= 200 \times 10^3$ N ; $N = 75$ r.p.m. or $\omega = 2\pi \times 75/60 = 7.86$ rad/s ; $\mu = 0.05$; $p = 0.3$ N/mm² ; $P = 16$ kW $= 16 \times 10^3$ W

Let T = Total frictional torque transmitted in N-m.

We know that power lost in friction (P),

$$16 \times 10^3 = T.\omega = T \times 7.86 \text{ or } T = 16 \times 10^3/7.86 = 2036 \text{ N-m}$$

External diameter of the collar

Let d_1 = External diameter of the collar in metres = $2\, r_1$.

We know that for uniform pressure, total frictional torque transmitted (T),

$$2036 = \frac{2}{3} \times \mu.W \left[\frac{(r_1)^3 - (r_2)^3}{(r_1)^2 - (r_2)^2} \right] = \frac{2}{3} \times \mu \times W \left[\frac{(r_1)^2 + (r_2)^2 + r_1.r_2}{r_1 + r_2} \right]^*$$

$$= \frac{2}{3} \times 0.05 \times 200 \times 10^3 \left[\frac{(r_1)^2 + (0.15)^2 + r_1 \times 0.15}{r_1 + 0.15} \right]$$

$$2036 \times 3(r_1 + 0.15) = 20 \times 10^3 [(r_1)^2 + 0.15\, r_1 + 0.0225]$$

$$* \quad \frac{(r_1)^3 - (r_2)^3}{(r_1)^2 - (r_2)^3} = \frac{(r_1 - r_2)[(r_1)^2 + (r_2)^2 + r_1.r_2]}{(r_1 + r_2)(r_1 - r_2)} = \frac{(r_1)^2 + (r_2)^2 + r_1.r_2}{r_1 + r_2}$$

Dividing throughout by 20×10^3,

$$0.305 \, (r_1 + 0.15) = (r_1)^2 + 0.15 \, r_1 + 0.0225$$

$$(r_1)^2 - 0.155 \, r_1 - 0.0233 = 0$$

Solving this as a quadratic equation,

$$r_1 = \frac{0.155 \pm \sqrt{(0.155)^2 + 4 \times 0.0233}}{2} = \frac{0.155 \pm 0.342}{2}$$

$$= 0.2485 \text{ m} = 248.5 \text{ mm} \qquad\qquad ...(\text{Taking} + \text{ve sign})$$

$$\therefore \qquad d_1 = 2 \, r_1 = 2 \times 248.5 = 497 \text{ mm } \textbf{Ans.}$$

Number of collars

Let $\qquad\qquad n = $ Number of collars.

We know that intensity of pressure (p),

$$0.3 = \frac{W}{n\pi[(r_1)^2 - (r_2)^2]} = \frac{200 \times 10^3}{n\pi[(248.5)^2 - (150)^2]} = \frac{1.62}{n}$$

$$\therefore \qquad\qquad n = 1.62/0.3 = 5.4 \text{ or } \text{ 6 } \textbf{Ans.}$$

10.31. Friction Clutches

A friction clutch has its principal application in the transmission of power of shafts and machines which must be started and stopped frequently. Its application is also found in cases in which power is to be delivered to machines partially or fully loaded. The force of friction is used to start the driven shaft from rest and gradually brings it up to the proper speed without excessive slipping of the friction surfaces. In automobiles, friction clutch is used to connect the engine to the driven shaft. In operating such a clutch, care should be taken so that the friction surfaces engage easily and gradually brings the driven shaft up to proper speed. The proper alignment of the bearing must be maintained and it should be located as close to the clutch as possible. It may be noted that

1. The contact surfaces should develop a frictional force that may pick up and hold the load with reasonably low pressure between the contact surfaces.

2. The heat of friction should be rapidly dissipated and tendency to grab should be at a minimum.

3. The surfaces should be backed by a material stiff enough to ensure a reasonably uniform distribution of pressure.

The friction clutches of the following types are important from the subject point of view :

1. Disc or plate clutches (single disc or multiple disc clutch),

2. Cone clutches, and

3. Centrifugal clutches.

We shall now discuss, these clutches, in detail, in the following pages. It may be noted that the disc and cone clutches are based on the same theory as the pivot and collar bearings.

10.32. Single Disc or Plate Clutch

A single disc or plate clutch, as shown in Fig. 10.21, consists of a clutch plate whose both sides are faced with a friction material (usually of Ferrodo). It is mounted on the hub which is free to move axially along the splines of the driven shaft. The pressure plate is mounted inside the clutch body which is bolted to the flywheel. Both the pressure plate and the flywheel rotate with the engine crankshaft or the driving shaft. The pressure plate pushes the clutch plate towards the flywheel by a set of strong springs which are arranged radially inside the body. The three levers (also known as release levers or fingers) are carried on pivots suspended from the case of the body. These are arranged in such a manner so that the pressure plate moves away from the flywheel by the inward movement of a thrust bearing. The bearing is mounted upon a forked shaft and moves forward when the clutch pedal is pressed.

Single disc clutch

When the clutch pedal is pressed down, its linkage forces the thrust release bearing to move in towards the flywheel and pressing the longer ends of the levers inward. The levers are forced to turn on their suspended pivot and the pressure plate moves away from the flywheel by the knife edges, thereby compressing the clutch springs. This action removes the pressure from the clutch plate and thus moves back from the flywheel and the driven shaft becomes stationary. On the other hand, when the foot is taken off from the clutch pedal, the thrust bearing moves back by the levers. This allows the springs to extend and thus the pressure plate pushes the clutch plate back towards the flywheel.

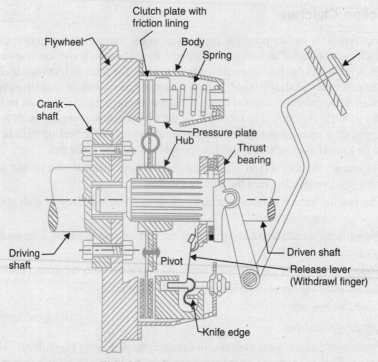

Fig. 10.21. Single disc or plate clutch.

The axial pressure exerted by the spring provides a frictional force in the circumferential direction when the relative motion between the driving and driven members tends to take place. If the torque due to this frictional force exceeds the torque to be transmitted, then no slipping takes place and the power is transmitted from the driving shaft to the driven shaft.

Now consider two friction surfaces, maintained in contact by an axial thrust W, as shown in Fig. 10.22 (a).

Let T = Torque transmitted by the clutch,

p = Intensity of axial pressure with which the contact surfaces are held together,

r_1 and r_2 = External and internal radii of friction faces, and

μ = Coefficient of friction.

Consider an elementary ring of radius r and thickness dr as shown in Fig. 10.22 (*b*).

We know that area of contact surface or friction surface,

$$= 2\,\pi\,r.dr$$

∴ Normal or axial force on the ring,

$$\delta W = \text{Pressure} \times \text{Area} = p \times 2\,\pi\,r.dr$$

and the frictional force on the ring acting tangentially at radius r,

$$F_r = \mu.\delta W = \mu.p \times 2\,\pi\,r.dr$$

∴ Frictional torque acting on the ring,

$$T_r = F_r \times r = \mu.p \times 2\,\pi\,r.dr \times r = 2\,\pi \times \mu\,.p.r^2\,dr$$

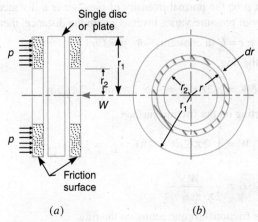

Single disc or plate

p

r_1

r_2

W

p

Friction surface

dr

r_2 r

r_1

(*a*)   (*b*)

Fig. 10.22. Forces on a single disc or plate clutch.

We shall now consider the following two cases :

1. When there is a uniform pressure, and

2. When there is a uniform wear.

1. *Considering uniform pressure*

When the pressure is uniformly distributed over the entire area of the friction face, then the intensity of pressure,

$$p = \frac{W}{\pi[(r_1)^2 - (r_2)^2]} \qquad \qquad ...(i)$$

where W = Axial thrust with which the contact or friction surfaces are held together.

We have discussed above that the frictional torque on the elementary ring of radius r and thickness dr is

$$T_r = 2\,\pi\,\mu.p.r^2\,dr$$

Integrating this equation within the limits from r_2 to r_1 for the total frictional torque.

∴ Total frictional torque acting on the friction surface or on the clutch,

$$T = \int_{r_1}^{r_2} 2\pi\mu.p.r^2.dr = 2\pi\mu\, p\left[\frac{r^3}{3}\right]_{r_2}^{r_1} = 2\pi\mu\, p\left[\frac{(r_1)^3 - (r_2)^3}{3}\right]$$

Substituting the value of p from equation (i),

$$T = 2\pi\mu \times \frac{W}{\pi[(r_1)^2 - (r_2)^2]} \times \frac{(r_1)^3 - (r_2)^3}{3}$$

$$= \frac{2}{3} \times \mu.W\left[\frac{(r_1)^3 - (r_2)^3}{(r_1)^2 - (r_2)^2}\right] = \mu.W.R$$

where R = Mean radius of friction surface

$$= \frac{2}{3}\left[\frac{(r_1)^3 - (r_2)^3}{(r_1)^2 - (r_2)^2}\right]$$

2. *Considering uniform wear*

In Fig. 10.22, let p be the normal intensity of pressure at a distance r from the axis of the clutch. Since the intensity of pressure varies inversely with the distance, therefore

$$p.r = C \text{ (a constant)} \quad \text{or} \quad p = C/r \qquad \qquad ...(i)$$

and the normal force on the ring,

$$\delta W = p.2\pi r.dr = \frac{C}{r} \times 2\pi r.dr = 2\pi C.dr$$

∴ Total force acting on the friction surface,

$$W = \int_{r_2}^{r_1} 2\pi C\, dr = 2\pi C\left[r\right]_{r_2}^{r_1} = 2\pi C(r_1 - r_2)$$

or

$$C = \frac{W}{2\pi(r_1 - r_2)}$$

We know that the frictional torque acting on the ring,

$$T_r = 2\pi\mu.p\, r^2.dr = 2\pi\mu \times \frac{C}{r} \times r^2.dr = 2\pi\mu.C.r.dr$$

$$...(\because\ p = C/r)$$

∴ Total frictional torque on the friction surface,

$$T = \int_{r_2}^{r_1} 2\pi\mu.C.r.dr = 2\pi\mu.C\left[\frac{r^2}{2}\right]_{r_2}^{r_1} = 2\pi\mu.C\left[\frac{(r_1)^2 - (r_2)^2}{2}\right]$$

$$= \pi\mu.C[(r_1)^2 - (r_2)^2] = \pi\mu \times \frac{W}{2\pi(r_1 - r_2)}\left[(r_1)^2 - (r_2)^2\right]$$

$$= \frac{1}{2} \times \mu.W\,(r_1 + r_2) = \mu.W.R$$

where R = Mean radius of the friction surface $= \dfrac{r_1 + r_2}{2}$

Notes : 1. In general, total frictional torque acting on the friction surface (or on the clutch) is given by

$$T = n.\mu.W.R$$

where $\qquad n$ = Number of pairs of friction or contact surfaces, and

$\qquad R$ = Mean radius of friction surface

$$= \frac{2}{3}\left[\frac{(r_1)^3 - (r_2)^3}{(r_1)^2 - (r_2)^2}\right] \qquad\qquad \text{...(For uniform pressure)}$$

$$= \frac{r_1 + r_2}{2} \qquad\qquad\qquad\qquad \text{...(For uniform wear)}$$

2. For a single disc or plate clutch, normally both sides of the disc are effective. Therefore, a single disc clutch has two pairs of surfaces in contact, *i.e.* $n = 2$.

3. Since the intensity of pressure is maximum at the inner radius (r_2) of the friction or contact surface, therefore equation (*i*) may be written as

$$p_{max} \times r_2 = C \qquad \text{or} \qquad p_{max} = C/r_2$$

4. Since the intensity of pressure is minimum at the outer radius (r_1) of the friction or contact surface, therefore equation (*i*) may be written as

$$p_{min} \times r_1 = C \qquad \text{or} \qquad p_{min} = C/r_1$$

5. The average pressure (p_{av}) on the friction or contact surface is given by

$$p_{av} = \frac{\text{Total force on friction surface}}{\text{Cross-sectional area of friction surface}} = \frac{W}{\pi[(r_1)^2 - (r_2)^2]}$$

6. In case of a new clutch, the intensity of pressure is approximately uniform but in an old clutch the uniform wear theory is more approximate.

7. The uniform pressure theory gives a higher frictional torque than the uniform wear theory. Therefore in case of friction clutches, uniform wear should be considered, unless otherwise stated.

10.33. Multiple Disc Clutch

A multiple disc clutch, as shown in Fig. 10.23, may be used when a large torque is to be transmitted. The inside discs (usually of steel) are fastened to the driven shaft to permit axial motion

Dual Disc Clutches.

(except for the last disc). The outside discs (usually of bronze) are held by bolts and are fastened to the housing which is keyed to the driving shaft. The multiple disc clutches are extensively used in motor cars, machine tools etc.

Let $\qquad n_1$ = Number of discs on the driving shaft, and

$\qquad n_2$ = Number of discs on the driven shaft.

∴ Number of pairs of contact surfaces,

$$n = n_1 + n_2 - 1$$

and total frictional torque acting on the friction surfaces or on the clutch,

$$T = n.\mu.W.R$$

where R = Mean radius of the friction surfaces

$$= \frac{2}{3}\left[\frac{(r_1)^3 - (r_2)^3}{(r_1)^2 - (r_2)^2}\right]$$ ...(For uniform pressure)

$$= \frac{r_1 + r_2}{2}$$ ...(For uniform wear)

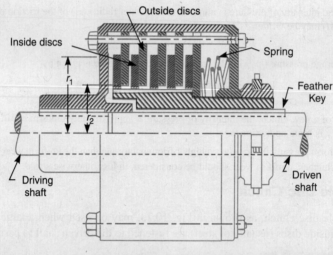

Fig. 10.23. Multiple disc clutch.

Example 10.22. *Determine the maximum, minimum and average pressure in plate clutch when the axial force is 4 kN. The inside radius of the contact surface is 50 mm and the outside radius is 100 mm. Assume uniform wear.*

Solution. Given : $W = 4$ kN $= 4 \times 10^3$ N ; $r_2 = 50$ mm ; $r_1 = 100$ mm

Maximum pressure

Let p_{max} = Maximum pressure.

Since the intensity of pressure is maximum at the inner radius (r_2), therefore

$$p_{max} \times r_2 = C \quad \text{or} \quad C = 50\, p_{max}$$

We know that the total force on the contact surface (W),

$$4 \times 10^3 = 2\,\pi\, C\, (r_1 - r_2) = 2\,\pi \times 50\, p_{max}\, (100 - 50) = 15\,710\, p_{max}$$

∴ $p_{max} = 4 \times 10^3/15\,710 = 0.2546$ N/mm^2 **Ans.**

Minimum pressure

Let p_{min} = Minimum pressure.

Since the intensity of pressure is minimum at the outer radius (r_1), therefore

$$p_{min} \times r_1 = C \quad \text{or} \quad C = 100\, p_{min}$$

We know that the total force on the contact surface (W),

$$4 \times 10^3 = 2 \pi C (r_1 - r_2) = 2\pi \times 100 \, p_{min} (100 - 50) = 31\,420 \, p_{min}$$

$$\therefore \quad p_{min} = 4 \times 10^3/31\,420 = 0.1273 \text{ N/mm}^2 \textbf{ Ans.}$$

Average pressure

We know that average pressure,

$$p_{av} = \frac{\text{Total normal force on contact surface}}{\text{Cross-sectional area of contact surfaces}}$$

$$= \frac{W}{\pi[(r_1)^2 - (r_2)^2]} = \frac{4 \times 10^3}{\pi[(100)^2 - (50)^2]} = 0.17 \text{ N/mm}^2 \textbf{ Ans.}$$

Example 10.23. *A single plate clutch, with both sides effective, has outer and inner diameters 300 mm and 200 mm respectively. The maximum intensity of pressure at any point in the contact surface is not to exceed 0.1 N/mm². If the coefficient of friction is 0.3, determine the power transmitted by a clutch at a speed 2500 r.p.m.*

Solution. Given : $d_1 = 300$ mm or $r_1 = 150$ mm ; $d_2 = 200$ mm or $r_2 = 100$ mm ; $p = 0.1$ N/mm² ; $\mu = 0.3$; $N = 2500$ r.p.m. or $\omega = 2\pi \times 2500/60 = 261.8$ rad/s

Since the intensity of pressure (p) is maximum at the inner radius (r_2), therefore for uniform wear,

$$p.r_2 = C \quad \text{or} \quad C = 0.1 \times 100 = 10 \text{ N/mm}$$

We know that the axial thrust,

$$W = 2 \pi C (r_1 - r_2) = 2 \pi \times 10 (150 - 100) = 3142 \text{ N}$$

and mean radius of the friction surfaces for uniform wear,

$$R = \frac{r_1 + r_2}{2} = \frac{150 + 100}{2} = 125 \text{ mm} = 0.125 \text{ m}$$

We know that torque transmitted,

$$T = n.\mu.W.R = 2 \times 0.3 \times 3142 \times 0.125 = 235.65 \text{ N-m}$$

$$...(\because n = 2, \text{for both sides of plate effective})$$

$\therefore$ Power transmitted by a clutch,

$$P = T.\omega = 235.65 \times 261.8 = 61\,693 \text{ W} = 61.693 \text{ kW Ans.}$$

Example 10.24. *A single plate clutch, effective on both sides, is required to transmit 25 kW at 3000 r.p.m. Determine the outer and inner radii of frictional surface if the coefficient of friction is 0.255, the ratio of radii is 1.25 and the maximum pressure is not to exceed 0.1 N/mm². Also determine the axial thrust to be provided by springs. Assume the theory of uniform wear.*

Solution. Given: $n = 2$; $P = 25$ kW $= 25 \times 10^3$ W ; $N = 3000$ r.p.m. or $\omega = 2\pi \times 3000/60 = 314.2$ rad/s ; $\mu = 0.255$; $r_1/r_2 = 1.25$; $p = 0.1$ N/mm²

Outer and inner radii of frictional surface

Let $\quad r_1$ and r_2 = Outer and inner radii of frictional surfaces, and

$\quad\quad\quad\quad T$ = Torque transmitted.

Since the ratio of radii (r_1/r_2) is 1.25, therefore

$$r_1 = 1.25 \, r_2$$

We know that the power transmitted (P),

$$25 \times 10^3 = T.\omega = T \times 314.2$$

$$\therefore \quad\quad\quad T = 25 \times 10^3/314.2 = 79.6 \text{ N-m} = 79.6 \times 10^3 \text{ N-mm}$$

Since the intensity of pressure is maximum at the inner radius (r_2), therefore

$$p.r_2 = C \quad \text{or} \quad C = 0.1 \, r_2 \text{ N/mm}$$

and the axial thrust transmitted to the frictional surface,

$$W = 2\pi C(r_1 - r_2) = 2\pi \times 0.1 \, r_2 (1.25 \, r_2 - r_2) = 0.157 \, (r_2)^2 \qquad \text{...}(i)$$

We know that mean radius of the frictional surface for uniform wear,

$$R = \frac{r_1 + r_2}{2} = \frac{1.25 \, r_2 + r_2}{2} = 1.125 \, r_2$$

We know that torque transmitted (T),

$$79.6 \times 10^3 = n.\mu.W.R = 2 \times 0.255 \times 0.157 \, (r_2)^2 \times 1.125 \, r_2 = 0.09 \, (r_2)^3$$

∴ $\qquad (r_2)^3 = 79.6 \times 10^3/0.09 = 884 \times 10^3$ or $r_2 = 96$ mm **Ans.**

and $\qquad r_1 = 1.25 \, r_2 = 1.25 \times 96 = 120$ mm **Ans.**

Axial thrust to be provided by springs

We know that axial thrust to be provided by springs,

$$W = 2\pi C(r_1 - r_2) = 0.157 \, (r_2)^2 \qquad \text{...[From equation }(i)]$$

$$= 0.157 \, (96)^2 = 1447 \text{ N } \textbf{Ans.}$$

Example 10.25. *A single dry plate clutch transmits 7.5 kW at 900 r.p.m. The axial pressure is limited to 0.07 N/mm². If the coefficient of friction is 0.25, find 1. Mean radius and face width of the friction lining assuming the ratio of the mean radius to the face width as 4, and 2. Outer and inner radii of the clutch plate.*

Solution. Given : $P = 7.5$ kW $= 7.5 \times 10^3$ W ; $N = 900$ r.p.m or $\omega = 2\pi \times 900/60 = 94.26$ rad/s ; $p = 0.07$ N/mm² ; $\mu = 0.25$

1. *Mean radius and face width of the friction lining*

Let $\qquad R$ = Mean radius of the friction lining in mm, and

$\qquad w$ = Face width of the friction lining in mm,

Ratio of mean radius to the face width,

$$R/w = 4 \qquad \text{...(Given)}$$

We know that the area of friction faces,

$$A = 2\pi R.w$$

∴ Normal or the axial force acting on the friction faces,

$$W = A \times p = 2\pi R.w.p$$

We know that torque transmitted (considering uniform wear),

$$T = n.\mu.W.R = n.\mu \, (2\pi R.w.p) \, R$$

$$= n.\mu\left(2\pi R \times \frac{R}{4} \times p\right) R = \frac{\pi}{2} \times n.\mu.p.R^3 \qquad \text{...}(\because w = R/4)$$

$$= \frac{\pi}{2} \times 2 \times 0.25 \times 0.07 \, R^3 = 0.055 \, R^3 \text{ N-mm} \qquad \text{...}(i)$$

$$\text{...}(\because n = 2, \text{ for single plate clutch})$$

We also know that power transmitted (P),

$$7.5 \times 10^3 = T.\omega = T \times 94.26$$

$\therefore$ $\qquad\qquad T = 7.5 \times 10^3/94.26 = 79.56 \text{ N-m} = 79.56 \times 10^3 \text{ N-mm}$ ...(ii)

From equations (i) and (ii),

$$R^3 = 79.56 \times 10^3/0.055 = 1446.5 \times 10^3 \text{ or } R = 113 \text{ mm Ans.}$$

and $\qquad\qquad w = R/4 = 113/4 = 28.25 \text{mm }$ **Ans.**

2. Outer and inner radii of the clutch plate

Let $\qquad r_1$ and r_2 = Outer and inner radii of the clutch plate respectively.

Since the width of the clutch plate is equal to the difference of the outer and inner radii, therefore

$$w = r_1 - r_2 = 28.25 \text{ mm} \qquad\qquad\qquad ...(iii)$$

Also for uniform wear, the mean radius of the clutch plate,

$$R = \frac{r_1 + r_2}{2} \quad \text{or} \quad r_1 + r_2 = 2R = 2 \times 113 = 226 \text{ mm} \qquad ...(iv)$$

From equations (iii) and (iv),

$$r_1 = 127.125 \text{ mm ; and } r_2 = 98.875 \text{ Ans.}$$

Example 10.26. *A dry single plate clutch is to be designed for an automotive vehicle whose engine is rated to give 100 kW at 2400 r.p.m. and maximum torque 500 N-m. The outer radius of friction plate is 25% more than the inner radius. The intensity of pressure between the plate is not to exceed 0.07 N/mm². The coefficient of friction may be assumed equal to 0.3. The helical springs required by this clutch to provide axial force necessary to engage the clutch are eight. If each spring has stiffness equal to 40 N /mm, determine the initial compression in the springs and dimensions of the friction plate.*

Solution. Given : $P = 100$ kW; [*]$N = 2400$ r.p.m. ; $T = 500$ N-m $= 500 \times 10^3$ N-mm ; $p = 0.07$ N/mm² ; $\mu = 0.3$; Number of springs = 8 ; Stiffness = 40 N/mm

Dimensions of the friction plate

Let $\qquad r_1$ and r_2 = Outer and inner radii of the friction plate respectively.

Since the outer radius of the friction plate is 25% more than the inner radius, therefore

$$r_1 = 1.25 \, r_2$$

We know that, for uniform wear,

$$p.r_2 = C \quad \text{or} \quad C = 0.07 \, r_2 \text{ N/mm}$$

and load transmitted to the friction plate,

$$W = 2\pi C (r_1 - r_2) = 2\pi \times 0.07 \, r_2 (1.125 \, r_2 - r_2) = 0.11 \, (r_2)^2 \text{ N} \qquad ...(i)$$

We know that mean radius of the plate for uniform wear,

$$R = \frac{r_1 + r_2}{2} = \frac{1.25 \, r_2 + r_2}{2} = 1.125 \, r_2$$

$\therefore$ Torque transmitted (T),

$$500 \times 10^3 = n.\mu.W.R = 2 \times 0.3 \times 0.11 \, (r_2)^2 \times 1.125 \, r_2 = 0.074 \, (r_2)^3$$

$$...(\because \; n = 2)$$

$\therefore$ $\qquad\qquad (r_2)^3 = 500 \times 10^3/0.074 = 6757 \times 10^3 \text{ or } r_2 = 190 \text{ mm Ans.}$

[*] Superfluous data.

and $r_1 = 1.25\, r_2 = 1.25 \times 190 = 273.5$ mm **Ans.**

Initial compression of the springs

We know that total stiffness of the springs,

$$s = \text{Stiffness per spring} \times \text{No. of springs} = 40 \times 8 = 320 \text{ N/mm}$$

Axial force required to engage the clutch,

$$W = 0.11\,(r_2)^2 = 0.11\,(190)^2 = 3970 \text{ N} \qquad \text{...[From equation } (i)]$$

∴ Initial compression in the springs

$$= W/s = 3970/320 = 12.5 \text{ mm} \quad \textbf{Ans.}$$

Example 10.27. *A rotor is driven by a co-axial motor through a single plate clutch, both sides of the plate being effective. The external and internal diameters of the plate are respectively 220 mm and 160 mm and the total spring load pressing the plates together is 570 N. The motor armature and shaft has a mass of 800 kg with an effective radius of gyration of 200 mm. The rotor has a mass of 1300 kg with an effective radius of gyration of 180 mm. The coefficient of friction for the clutch is 0.35.*

The driving motor is brought up to a speed of 1250 r.p.m. when the current is switched off and the clutch suddenly engaged. Determine

1. The final speed of motor and rotor, 2. The time to reach this speed, and 3. The kinetic energy lost during the period of slipping.

How long would slipping continue if it is assumed that a constant resisting torque of 60 N-m were present? If instead of a resisting torque, it is assumed that a constant driving torque of 60 N-m is maintained on the armature shaft, what would then be slipping time?

Solution. Given : $d_1 = 220$ mm or $r_1 = 110$ mm ; $d_2 = 160$ mm or $r_2 = 80$ mm ; $W = 570$ N ; $m_1 = 800$ kg ; $k_1 = 200$ mm $= 0.2$ m ; $m_2 = 1300$ kg ; $k_2 = 180$ mm $= 0.18$ m ; $\mu = 0.35$; $N_1 = 1250$ r.p.m. or $\omega_1 = \pi \times 1250/60 = 131$ rad/s

1. Final speed of the motor and rotor

Let $\omega_3 = $ Final speed of the motor and rotor in rad/s.

We know that moment of inertia for the motor armature and shaft,

$$I_1 = m_1\,(k_1)^2 = 800\,(0.2)^2 = 32 \text{ kg-m}^2$$

and moment of inertia for the rotor,

$$I_2 = m_2\,(k_2)^2 = 1300\,(0.18)^2 = 42.12 \text{ kg-m}^2$$

Since the angular momentum before slipping is equal to the angular momentum after slipping, therefore

$$I_1.\omega_1 + I_2.\omega_2 = (I_1 + I_2)\,\omega_3$$
$$32 \times 131 + I_2 \times 0 = (32 + 42.12)\,\omega_3 = 74.12\,\omega_3 \qquad \text{...(}\because \omega_2 = 0)$$
∴ $\omega_3 = 32 \times 131\,/\,74.12 = 56.56$ rad/s **Ans.**

2. Time to reach this speed

Let $t = $ Time to reach this speed *i.e.* 56.56 rad/s.

We know that mean radius of the friction plate,

$$R = \frac{r_1 + r_2}{2} = \frac{110 + 80}{2} = 95 \text{ mm} = 0.095 \text{ m}$$

and total frictional torque,

$$T = n.\mu.W.R = 2 \times 0.35 \times 570 \times 0.095 = 37.9 \text{ N-m} \qquad ...(\because \ n = 2)$$

Considering the rotor, let α_2, ω_I and ω_F be the angular acceleration, initial angular speed and the final angular speed of the rotor respectively.

We know that the torque (T),

$$37.9 = I_2.\alpha_2 = 42.12 \ \alpha_2 \quad \text{or} \quad \alpha_2 = 37.9/42.12 = 0.9 \text{ rad/s}^2$$

Since the angular acceleration is the rate of change of angular speed, therefore

$$\alpha_2 = \frac{\omega_F - \omega_I}{t} \quad \text{or} \quad t = \frac{\omega_F - \omega_I}{\alpha_2} = \frac{56.56 - 0}{0.9} = 62.8 \text{ s } \textbf{ Ans.}$$

$$...(\because \ \omega_F = \omega_3 = 56.56 \text{ rad/s, and } \omega_1 = 0)$$

3. *Kinetic energy lost during the period of slipping*

We know that angular kinetic energy before impact,

$$E_1 = \frac{1}{2} I_1 \, (\omega_1)^2 + \frac{1}{2} I_2 \, (\omega_2)^2 = \frac{1}{2} I_1 \, (\omega_1)^2 \qquad ...(\because \ \omega_2 = 0)$$

$$= \frac{1}{2} \times 32 \, (131)^2 = 274 \ 576 \text{ N-m}$$

and angular kinetic energy after impact,

$$E_2 = \frac{1}{2}(I_1 + I_2)(\omega_3)^2 = \frac{1}{2}(32 + 42.12)(56.56)^2 = 118 \ 556 \text{ N-m}$$

∴ Kinetic energy lost during the period of slipping,

$$= E_1 - E_2 = 274 \ 576 - 118 \ 556 = 156 \ 020 \text{ N-m } \textbf{ Ans.}$$

Time of slipping assuming constant resisting torque

Let t_1 = Time of slipping, and

ω_2 = Common angular speed of armature and rotor shaft = 56.56 rad/s

When slipping has ceased and there is exerted a constant torque of 60 N-m on the armature shaft, then

Torque on armature shaft,

$$T_1 = -60 - 37.9 = -97.9 \text{ N-m}$$

Torque on rotor shaft,

$$T_2 = T = 37.9 \text{ N-m}$$

Considering armature shaft,

$$\omega_3 = \omega_1 + \alpha_1.t_1 = \omega_1 + \frac{T_1}{I_1} \times t_1 = 131 - \frac{97.9}{32} \times t_1 = 131 - 3.06 \ t_1 \qquad ...(i)$$

Considering rotor shaft,

$$\omega_3 = \alpha_2.t_1 = \frac{T_2}{I_2} \times t_1 = \frac{37.9}{42.12} \times t_1 = 0.9 \ t_1 \qquad ...(ii)$$

From equations (*i*) and (*ii*),

$$131 - 3.06 \ t_1 = 0.9 \ t_1 \quad \text{or} \quad 3.96 \ t_1 = 131$$

∴ $$t_1 = 131/3.96 = 33.1 \text{ s} \textbf{Ans.}$$

Time of slipping assuming constant driving torque of 60 N-m

In this case, $T_1 = 60 - 37.9 = 22.1$ N-m

Since $\omega_1 + \dfrac{T_1}{I_1} \times t_1 \; \omega_2 + \dfrac{T_2}{I_2} \times t_1$,   therefore

$$131 + \frac{22.1}{32} \times t_1 = \frac{37.9}{42.12} \times t_1 \quad \text{or} \quad 131 + 0.69\, t_1 = 0.9\, t_1$$

∴ $0.9\, t_1 - 0.69\, t_1 = 131$ or $t_1 = 624$ s **Ans.**

Example 10.28. *A multiple disc clutch has five plates having four pairs of active friction surfaces. If the intensity of pressure is not to exceed 0.127 N/mm², find the power transmitted at 500 r.p.m. The outer and inner radii of friction surfaces are 125 mm and 75 mm respectively. Assume uniform wear and take coefficient of friction = 0.3.*

Solution. Given : $n_1 + n_2 = 5$; $n = 4$; $p = 0.127$ N/mm² ; $N = 500$ r.p.m. or $\omega = 2\pi \times 500/60$ = 52.4 rad/s ; $r_1 = 125$ mm ; $r_2 = 75$ mm ; $\mu = 0.3$

Since the intensity of pressure is maximum at the inner radius r_2, therefore

$$p.r_2 = C \quad \text{or} \quad C = 0.127 \times 75 = 9.525 \text{ N/mm}$$

We know that axial force required to engage the clutch,

$$W = 2\pi C (r_1 - r_2) = 2\pi \times 9.525 (125 - 75) = 2990 \text{ N}$$

and mean radius of the friction surfaces,

$$R = \frac{r_1 + r_2}{2} = \frac{125 + 75}{2} = 100 \text{ mm} = 0.1 \text{ m}$$

We know that torque transmitted,

$$T = n.\mu.W.R = 4 \times 0.3 \times 2990 \times 0.1 = 358.8 \text{ N-m}$$

∴ Power transmitted,

$$P = T.\omega = 358.8 \times 52.4 = 18\,800 \text{ W} = 18.8 \text{ kW }\textbf{ Ans.}$$

Example 10.29. *A multi-disc clutch has three discs on the driving shaft and two on the driven shaft. The outside diameter of the contact surfaces is 240 mm and inside diameter 120 mm. Assuming uniform wear and coefficient of friction as 0.3, find the maximum axial intensity of pressure between the discs for transmitting 25 kW at 1575 r.p.m.*

Solution. Given : $n_1 = 3$; $n_2 = 2$; $d_1 = 240$ mm or $r_1 = 120$ mm ; $d_2 = 120$ mm or $r_2 = 60$ mm ; $\mu = 0.3$; $P = 25$ kW = 25×10^3 W ; $N = 1575$ r.p.m. or $\omega = 2\pi \times 1575/60 = 165$ rad/s

Let T = Torque transmitted in N-m, and

   W = Axial force on each friction surface.

We know that the power transmitted (P),

$$25 \times 10^3 = T.\omega = T \times 165 \quad \text{or} \quad T = 25 \times 10^3/165 = 151.5 \text{ N-m}$$

Number of pairs of friction surfaces,

$$n = n_1 + n_2 - 1 = 3 + 2 - 1 = 4$$

and mean radius of friction surfaces for uniform wear,

$$R = \frac{r_1 + r_2}{2} = \frac{120 + 60}{2} = 90 \text{ mm} = 0.09 \text{ m}$$

We know that torque transmitted (T),

$$151.5 = n.\mu.W.R = 4 \times 0.3 \times W \times 0.09 = 0.108 \, W$$

$\therefore$ $W = 151.5/0.108 = 1403$ N

Let p = Maximum axial intensity of pressure.

Since the intensity of pressure (p) is maximum at the inner radius (r_2), therefore for uniform wear

$$p.r_2 = C \quad \text{or} \quad C = p \times 60 = 60 \, p \text{ N/mm}$$

We know that the axial force on each friction surface (W),

$$1403 = 2 \, \pi.C \, (r_1 - r_2) = 2 \, \pi \times 60 \, p \, (120 - 60) = 22 \, 622 \, p$$

$\therefore$ $p = 1403/22 \, 622 = 0.062$ N/mm^2 **Ans.**

Example 10.30. *A plate clutch has three discs on the driving shaft and two discs on the driven shaft, providing four pairs of contact surfaces. The outside diameter of the contact surfaces is 240 mm and inside diameter 120 mm. Assuming uniform pressure and $\mu = 0.3$; find the total spring load pressing the plates together to transmit 25 kW at 1575 r.p.m.*

If there are 6 springs each of stiffness 13 kN/m and each of the contact surfaces has worn away by 1.25 mm, find the maximum power that can be transmitted, assuming uniform wear.

Solution. Given : $n_1 = 3$; $n_2 = 2$; $n = 4$; $d_1 = 240$ mm or $r_1 = 120$ mm ; $d_2 = 120$ mm or $r_2 = 60$ mm ; $\mu = 0.3$; $P = 25$ kW $= 25 \times 10^3$ W ; $N = 1575$ r.p.m. or $\omega = 2 \, \pi \times 1575/60 = 165$ rad/s

Total spring load

Let W = Total spring load, and

            T = Torque transmitted.

We know that power transmitted (P),

$$25 \times 10^3 = T.\omega = T \times 165 \quad \text{or} \quad T = 25 \times 10^3/165 = 151.5 \text{ N-m}$$

Mean radius of the contact surface, for uniform pressure,

$$R = \frac{2}{3}\left[\frac{(r_1)^3 - (r_2)^3}{(r_1)^2 - (r_2)^2}\right] = \frac{2}{3}\left[\frac{(120)^3 - (60)^3}{(120)^2 - (60)^2}\right] = 93.3 \text{ mm} = 0.0933 \text{ m}$$

and torque transmitted (T),

$$151.5 = n.\mu.W.R = 4 \times 0.3 \, W \times 0.0933 = 0.112 \, W$$

$\therefore$ $W = 151.5/0.112 = 1353$ N **Ans.**

Maximum power transmitted

Given : No of springs = 6

$\therefore$ Contact surfaces of the spring

            = 8

Wear on each contact surface

            = 1.25 mm

$\therefore$ Total wear = 8 × 1.25 = 10 mm = 0.01 m

Stiffness of each spring = 13 kN/m = 13×10^3 N/m

$\therefore$ Reduction in spring force

            = Total wear × Stiffness per spring × No. of springs

            = $0.01 \times 13 \times 10^3 \times 6 = 780$ N

∴ New axial load, $W = 1353 - 780 = 573$ N

We know that mean radius of the contact surfaces for uniform wear,

$$R = \frac{r_1 + r_2}{2} = \frac{120 + 60}{2} = 90 \text{ mm} = 0.09 \text{ m}$$

∴ Torque transmitted,

$$T = n.\mu.W.R = 4 \times 0.3 \times 573 \times 0.09 = 62 \text{ N-m}$$

and maximum power transmitted,

$$P = T.\omega = 62 \times 155 = 10\ 230 \text{ W} = 10.23 \text{ kW } \textbf{Ans.}$$

10.34. Cone Clutch

A cone clutch, as shown in Fig. 10.24, was extensively used in automobiles but now-a-days it has been replaced completely by the disc clutch.

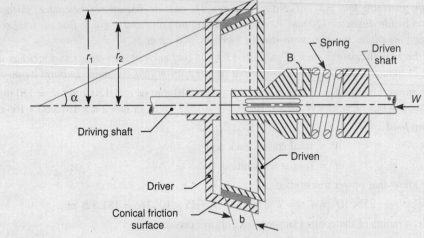

Fig. 10.24. Cone clutch.

It consists of one pair of friction surface only. In a cone clutch, the driver is keyed to the driving shaft by a sunk key and has an inside conical surface or face which exactly fits into the outside conical surface of the driven. The driven member resting on the feather key in the driven shaft, may be shifted along the shaft by a forked lever provided at B, in order to engage the clutch by bringing the two conical surfaces in contact. Due to the frictional resistance set up at this contact surface, the torque is transmitted from one shaft to another. In some cases, a spring is placed around the driven shaft in contact with the hub of the driven. This spring holds the clutch faces in contact and maintains the pressure between them, and the forked lever is used only for disengagement of the clutch. The contact surfaces of the clutch may be metal to metal contact, but more often the driven member is lined with some material like wood, leather, cork or asbestos etc. The material of the clutch faces (*i.e.* contact surfaces) depends upon the allowable normal pressure and the coefficient of friction.

Consider a pair of friction surface as shown in Fig. 10.25 (*a*). Since the area of contact of a pair of friction surface is a frustrum of a cone, therefore the torque transmitted by the cone clutch may be determined in the similar manner as discussed for conical pivot bearings in Art. 10.28.

Let p_n = Intensity of pressure with which the conical friction surfaces are held together (*i.e.* normal pressure between contact surfaces),

r_1 and r_2 = Outer and inner radius of friction surfaces respectively.

R = Mean radius of the friction surface = $\dfrac{r_1 + r_2}{2}$,

α = Semi angle of the cone (also called face angle of the cone) or the angle of the friction surface with the axis of the clutch,

μ = Coefficient of friction between contact surfaces, and

b = Width of the contact surfaces (also known as face width or clutch face).

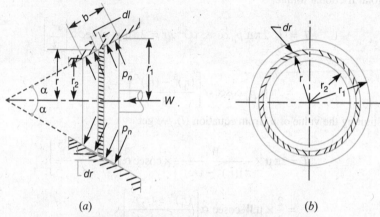

(a) (b)

Fig. 10.25. Friction surfaces as a frustrum of a cone.

Consider a small ring of radius r and thickness dr, as shown in Fig. 10.25 (b). Let dl is length of ring of the friction surface, such that

$$dl = dr.\text{cosec }\alpha$$

$\therefore$ Area of the ring,

$$A = 2\pi\, r.dl = 2\pi\, r.dr \text{ cosec }\alpha$$

We shall consider the following two cases :

1. When there is a uniform pressure, and
2. When there is a uniform wear.

1. *Considering uniform pressure*

We know that normal load acting on the ring,

$$\delta W_n = \text{Normal pressure} \times \text{Area of ring} = p_n \times 2\,\pi\, r.dr.\text{cosec }\alpha$$

and the axial load acting on the ring,

$$\delta W = \text{Horizontal component of } \delta W_n \ (i.e. \text{ in the direction of } W).$$
$$= \delta W_n \times \sin \alpha = p_n \times 2\pi\, r.dr. \text{ cosec }\alpha \times \sin \alpha = 2\pi \times p_n.r.dr$$

$\therefore$ Total axial load transmitted to the clutch or the axial spring force required,

$$W = \int_{r_2}^{r_1} 2\pi\, p_n.r.dr = 2\pi\, p_n \left[\frac{r^2}{2}\right]_{r_2}^{r_1} = 2\pi\, p_n \left[\frac{(r_1)^2 - (r_2)^2}{2}\right]$$

$$= \pi\, p_n \left[(r_1)^2 - (r_2)^2\right]$$

$\therefore$
$$p_n = \frac{W}{\pi[(r_1)^2 - (r_2)^2]} \qquad \qquad ...(i)$$

We know that frictional force on the ring acting tangentially at radius r,

$$F_r = \mu.\delta W_n = \mu.p_n \times 2\pi\, r.dr.\text{cosec}\,\alpha$$

∴ Frictional torque acting on the ring,

$$T_r = F_r \times r = \mu.p_n \times 2\pi\, r.dr.\,\text{cosec}\,\alpha.r = 2\pi\,\mu.p_n.\text{cosec}\,\alpha.r^2\,dr$$

Integrating this expression within the limits from r_2 to r_1 for the total frictional torque on the clutch.

∴ Total frictional torque,

$$T = \int_{r_2}^{r_1} 2\pi\mu.p_n.\text{cosec}\,\alpha.r^2.dr = 2\pi\mu\,p_n.\text{cosec}\,\alpha\left[\frac{r^3}{3}\right]_{r_2}^{r_1}$$

$$= 2\pi\,\mu\,p_n.\text{cosec}\,\alpha\left[\frac{(r_1)^3 - (r_2)^3}{3}\right]$$

Substituting the value of p_n from equation (i), we get

$$T = 2\pi\,\mu \times \frac{W}{\pi\,[(r_1)^2 - (r_2)^2]} \times \text{cosec}\,\alpha\left[\frac{(r_1)^3 - (r_2)^3}{3}\right]$$

$$= \frac{2}{3} \times \mu.W.\text{cosec}\,\alpha\left[\frac{(r_1)^3 - (r_2)^3}{(r_1)^2 - (r_2)^2}\right] \qquad ..(ii)$$

2. Considering uniform wear

In Fig. 10.25, let p_r be the normal intensity of pressure at a distance r from the axis of the clutch. We know that, in case of uniform wear, the intensity of pressure varies inversely with the distance.

∴ $$p_r.r = C \text{ (a constant)} \quad \text{or} \quad p_r = C/r$$

We know that the normal load acting on the ring,

$$\delta W_n = \text{Normal pressure} \times \text{Area of ring} = p_r \times 2\pi r.dr\,\text{cosec}\,\alpha$$

and the axial load acting on the ring ,

$$\delta W = \delta W_n \times \sin\alpha = p_r.2\pi\,r.dr.\text{cosec}\,\alpha\,.\sin\alpha = p_r \times 2\pi\,r.dr$$

$$= \frac{C}{r} \times 2\pi r.dr = 2\pi C.dr \qquad ...(\because\ p_r = C/r)$$

∴ Total axial load transmitted to the clutch,

$$W = \int_{r_2}^{r_1} 2\pi C.dr = 2\pi C[r]_{r_2}^{r_1} = 2\pi C(r_1 - r_2)$$

or $$C = \frac{W}{2\pi(r_1 - r_2)} \qquad ...(iii)$$

We know that frictional force acting on the ring,

$$F_r = \mu.\delta W_n = \mu.p_r \times 2\pi\, r \times dr\,\text{cosec}\,\alpha$$

and frictional torque acting on the ring,

$$T_r = F_r \times r = \mu.p_r \times 2\pi\, r.dr.\text{cosec}\,\alpha \times r$$

$$= \mu \times \frac{C}{r} \times 2\pi r^2.dr.\text{cosec}\,\alpha = 2\pi\mu.C\,\text{cosec}\,\alpha \times r\,dr$$

∴ Total frictional torque acting on the clutch,

$$T = \int_{r_2}^{r_1} 2\pi\mu.C.\text{cosec } \alpha.r\, dr = 2\pi\mu.C.\text{cosec } \alpha\left[\frac{r^2}{2}\right]_{r_2}^{r_1}$$

$$= 2\pi\mu.C.\text{cosec } \alpha\left[\frac{(r_1)^2 - (r_2)^2}{2}\right]$$

Substituting the value of C from equation (iii), we have

$$T = 2\pi\mu \times \frac{W}{2\pi(r_1 - r_2)} \times \text{cosec } \alpha\left[\frac{(r_1)^2 - (r_2)^2}{2}\right]$$

$$= \mu.W \text{ cosec } \alpha\left(\frac{r_1 + r_2}{2}\right) = \mu.W.R \text{ cosec } \alpha \qquad\qquad ...(iv)$$

where $\qquad\qquad R = \dfrac{r_1 + r_2}{2} = $ Mean radius of friction surface

Since the normal force acting on the friction surface, $W_n = W/\sin \alpha$, therefore the equation (iv) may be written as

$$T = \mu.W_n.R \qquad\qquad ...(v)$$

The forces on a friction surface, for steady operation of the clutch and after the clutch is engaged, is shown in Fig. 10.26.

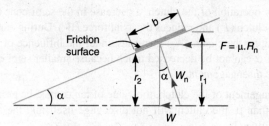

(a) For steady operation of the clutch.

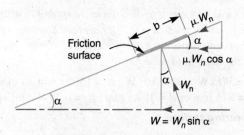

(b) During engagement of the clutch.

Fig. 10.26. Forces on a friction surface.

From Fig. 10.26 (a), we find that

$$r_1 - r_2 = b\sin\alpha; \text{ and } R = \frac{r_1 + r_2}{2} \text{ or } r_1 + r_2 = 2R$$

∴ From equation, (*i*), normal pressure acting on the friction surface,

$$p_n = \frac{W}{\pi[(r_1)^2 - (r_2)^2]} = \frac{W}{\pi(r_1 + r_2)(r_1 - r_2)} = \frac{W}{2\pi R.b.\sin\alpha}$$

or $\qquad\qquad W = p_n \times 2\pi R.b \sin\alpha = W_n \sin\alpha$

where $\qquad\quad W_n$ = Normal load acting on the friction surface = $p_n \times 2\pi R.b$

Now the equation (*iv*) may be written as,

$$T = \mu(p_n \times 2\pi R.b \sin\alpha) R \cosec\alpha = 2\pi\mu.p_n.R^2 b$$

The following points may be noted for a cone clutch :

1. The above equations are valid for steady operation of the clutch and after the clutch is engaged.

2. If the clutch is engaged when one member is stationary and the other rotating (*i.e.* during engagement of the clutch) as shown in Fig. 10.26 (*b*), then the cone faces will tend to slide on each other due to the presence of relative motion. Thus an additional force (of magnitude equal to $\mu.W_n.\cos\alpha$) acts on the clutch which resists the engagement and the axial force required for engaging the clutch increases.

∴ Axial force required for engaging the clutch,

$$W_e = W + \mu.W_n \cos\alpha = W_n \sin\alpha + \mu.W_n \cos\alpha$$
$$= W_n (\sin\alpha + \mu\cos\alpha)$$

3. Under steady operation of the clutch, a decrease in the semi-cone angle (α) increases the torque produced by the clutch (T) and reduces the axial force (W). During engaging period, the axial force required for engaging the clutch (W_e) increases under the influence of friction as the angle α decreases. The value of α can not be decreased much because smaller semi-cone angle (α) requires larger axial force for its disengagement.

For free disengagement of the clutch, the value of $\tan\alpha$ must be greater than μ. In case the value of $\tan\alpha$ is less than μ, the clutch will not disengage itself and the axial force required to disengage the clutch is given by

$$W_d = W_n (\mu\cos\alpha - \sin\alpha)$$

Example 10.31. *A conical friction clutch is used to transmit 90 kW at 1500 r.p.m. The semi-cone angle is 20° and the coefficient of friction is 0.2. If the mean diameter of the bearing surface is 375 mm and the intensity of normal pressure is not to exceed 0.25 N/mm², find the dimensions of the conical bearing surface and the axial load required.*

Solution. Given : P = 90 kW = 90 × 10³ W ; N = 1500 r.p.m. or ω = 2 π × 1500/60 = 156 rad/s ; α = 20° ; μ = 0.2 ; D = 375 mm or R = 187.5 mm ; p_n = 0.25 N/mm²

Dimensions of the conical bearing surface

Let $\qquad\qquad r_1$ and r_2 = External and internal radii of the bearing surface respectively,

$\qquad\qquad\qquad b$ = Width of the bearing surface in mm, and

$\qquad\qquad\qquad T$ = Torque transmitted.

We know that power transmitted (P),

$$90 \times 10^3 = T.\omega = T \times 156$$

∴ $\qquad\qquad T = 90 \times 10^3/156 = 577 \text{ N-m} = 577 \times 10^3 \text{ N-mm}$

and the torque transmitted (T),

$$577 \times 10^3 = 2\,\pi\,\mu\,p_n.R^2.b = 2\pi \times 0.2 \times 0.25\,(187.5)^2\,b = 11\,046\,b$$

∴ $b = 577 \times 10^3/11\,046 = 52.2$ mm **Ans.**

We know that $r_1 + r_2 = 2R = 2 \times 187.5 = 375$ mm   ...(*i*)

and $r_1 - r_2 = b \sin \alpha = 52.2 \sin 20° = 18$ mm   ...(*ii*)

From equations (*i*) and (*ii*),

$$r_1 = 196.5 \text{ mm, and } r_2 = 178.5 \text{ mm}\ \textbf{Ans.}$$

Axial load required

Since in case of friction clutch, uniform wear is considered and the intensity of pressure is maximum at the minimum contact surface radius (r_2), therefore

$$p_n.r_2 = C\ (\text{a constant}) \text{ or } C = 0.25 \times 178.5 = 44.6 \text{ N/mm}$$

We know that the axial load required,

$$W = 2\pi C\,(r_1 - r_2) = 2\pi \times 44.6\,(196.5 - 178.5) = 5045 \text{ N}\ \textbf{Ans.}$$

Example 10.32. *An engine developing 45 kW at 1000 r.p.m. is fitted with a cone clutch built inside the flywheel. The cone has a face angle of 12.5° and a maximum mean diameter of 500 mm. The coefficient of friction is 0.2. The normal pressure on the clutch face is not to exceed 0.1 N/mm². Determine : 1. the axial spring force necessary to engage to clutch, and 2. the face width required.*

Solution. Given : $P = 45$ kW $= 45 \times 10^3$ W ; $N = 1000$ r.p.m. or $\omega = 2\pi \times 1000/60 = 104.7$ rad/s ; $\alpha = 12.5°$; $D = 500$ mm or $R = 250$ mm $= 0.25$ m ; $\mu = 0.2$; $p_n = 0.1$ N/mm²

1. *Axial spring force necessary to engage the clutch*

First of all, let us find the torque (T) developed by the clutch and the normal load (W_n) acting on the friction surface.

We know that power developed by the clutch (P),

$$45 \times 10^3 = T.\omega = T \times 104.7 \text{ or } T = 45 \times 10^3/104.7 = 430 \text{ N-m}$$

We also know that the torque developed by the clutch (T),

$$430 = \mu.W_n.R = 0.2 \times W_n \times 0.25 = 0.05\,W_n$$

∴ $W_n = 430/0.05 = 8600$ N

and axial spring force necessary to engage the clutch,

$$W_e = W_n\,(\sin \alpha + \mu \cos \alpha)$$
$$= 8600\,(\sin 12.5° + 0.2 \cos 12.5°) = 3540 \text{ N}\ \textbf{Ans.}$$

2. *Face width required*

Let $b = $ Face width required.

We know that normal load acting on the friction surface (W_n),

$$8600 = p_n \times 2\,\pi\,R.b = 0.1 \times 2\pi \times 250 \times b = 157\,b$$

∴ $b = 8600/157 = 54.7$ mm **Ans.**

Example 10.33. *A leather faced conical clutch has a cone angle of 30°. If the intensity of pressure between the contact surfaces is limited to 0.35 N/mm² and the breadth of the conical surface is not to exceed one-third of the mean radius, find the dimensions of the contact surfaces to transmit 22.5 kW at 2000 r.p.m. Assume uniform rate of wear and take coefficient of friction as 0.15.*

Solution. Given : $2\,\alpha = 30°$ or $\alpha = 15°$; $p_n = 0.35$ N/mm²; $b = R/3$; $P = 22.5$ kW $= 22.5 \times 10^3$ W ; $N = 2000$ r.p.m. or $\omega = 2\,\pi \times 2000/60 = 209.5$ rad/s ; $\mu = 0.15$

Let $r_1 = $ Outer radius of the contact surface in mm,

r_2 = Inner radius of the contact surface in mm,

R = Mean radius of the the contact surface in mm,

b = Face width of the contact surface in mm = $R/3$, and

T = Torque transmitted by the clutch in N-m.

We know that power transmitted (P),

$$22.5 \times 10^3 = T.\omega = T \times 209.5$$

∴ $T = 22.5 \times 10^3/209.5 = 107.4$ N-m = 107.4×10^3 N-mm

We also know that torque transmitted (T),

$$107.4 \times 10^3 = 2\pi \mu \, p_n.R^2. \, b = 2\pi \times 0.15 \times 0.35 \times R^2 \times R/3 = 0.11 \, R^3$$

∴ $R^3 = 107.4 \times 10^3/0.11 = 976.4 \times 10^3$ or $R = 99$ mm   **Ans.**

The dimensions of the contact surface are shown in Fig. 10.27.

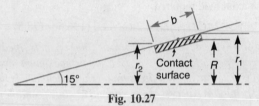

Fig. 10.27

From Fig. 10.27, we find that

$$r_1 - r_2 = b \sin \alpha = \frac{R}{3} \times \sin \alpha = \frac{99}{3} \times \sin 15° = 8.54 \text{ mm} \qquad ...(i)$$

and $$r_1 + r_2 = 2R = 2 \times 99 = 198 \text{ mm} \qquad ...(ii)$$

From equations (i) and (ii),

$$r_1 = 103.27 \text{ mm, and } r_2 = 94.73 \text{ mm} \quad \textbf{Ans.}$$

Example 10.34. *The contact surfaces in a cone clutch have an effective diameter of 75 mm. The semi-angle of the cone is 15°. The coefficient of friction is 0.3. Find the torque required to produce slipping of the clutch if an axial force applied is 180 N.*

This clutch is employed to connect an electric motor running uniformly at 1000 r.p.m. with a flywheel which is initially stationary. The flywheel has a mass of 13.5 kg and its radius of gyration is 150 mm. Calculate the time required for the flywheel to attain full speed and also the energy lost in the slipping of the clutch.

Solution. Given : $D = 75$ mm or $R = 37.5$ mm = 0.0375 m ; $\alpha = 15°$; $\mu = 0.3$; $W = 180$ N ; $N_F = 1000$ r.p.m. or $\omega_F = 2\pi \times 1000/60 = 104.7$ rad/s ; $m = 13.5$ kg ; $k = 150$ mm = 0.15 m

Torque required to produce slipping

We know that torque required to produce slipping,

$$T = \mu.W.R.\text{cosec } \alpha = 0.3 \times 180 \times 0.0375 \times \text{cosec } 15° = 7.8 \text{ N-m} \quad \textbf{Ans.}$$

Time required for the flywheel to attain full speed

Let t_F = Time required for the flywheel to attain full speed in seconds, and

α_F = Angular acceleration of the flywheel in rad/s^2.

We know that the mass moment of inertia of the flywheel,

$$I_F = m.k^2 = 13.5 \times (0.15)^2 = 0.304 \text{ kg-m}^2$$

∴ Torque required (T),

$$7.8 = I_F.\alpha_F = 0.304\ \alpha_F \quad \text{or} \quad \alpha_F = 7.8/0.304 = 25.6\ \text{rad/s}^2$$

and angular speed of the flywheel (ω_F),

$$104.7 = \alpha_F.t_F = 25.6\ t_F \quad \text{or} \quad t_F = 104.7/25.6 = 4.1\ \text{s} \quad \textbf{Ans.}$$

Energy lost in slipping of the clutch

We know that the angle turned through by the motor and flywheel (*i.e.* clutch) in time 4.1 s from rest,

$$\theta = \text{Average angular velocity} \times \text{time} = \frac{1}{2} \times W_F \times t_F = \frac{1}{2} \times 104.7 \times 4.1 = 214.6\ \text{rad}$$

∴ Energy lost in slipping of the clutch,

$$= T.\theta = 7.8 \times 214.6 = 1674\ \text{N-m} \quad \textbf{Ans.}$$

10.35. Centrifugal Clutch

The centrifugal clutches are usually incorporated into the motor pulleys. It consists of a number of shoes on the inside of a rim of the pulley, as shown in Fig. 10.28. The outer surface of the shoes are covered with a friction material. These shoes, which can move radially in guides, are held

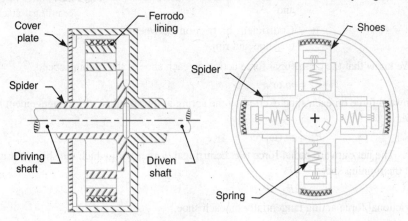

Fig. 10.28. Centrifugal clutch.

against the boss (or spider) on the driving shaft by means of springs. The springs exert a radially inward force which is assumed constant. The mass of the shoe, when revolving, causes it to exert a radially outward force (*i.e.* centrifugal force). The magnitude of this centrifugal force depends upon the speed at which the shoe is revolving. A little consideration will show that when the centrifugal force is less than the spring force, the shoe remains in the same position as when the driving shaft was stationary, but when the centrifugal force is equal to the spring force, the shoe is just floating. When the centrifugal force exceeds the spring force, the shoe moves outward and comes into contact with the driven member and presses against it. The force with which the shoe presses against the driven member is the difference of the centrifugal force and the spring force. The increase of speed causes the shoe to press harder

Centrifugal clutch.

and enables more torque to be transmitted.

In order to determine the mass and size of the shoes, the following procedure is adopted :

1. Mass of the shoes

Consider one shoe of a centrifugal clutch as shown in Fig. 10.29.

Let
m = Mass of each shoe,

n = Number of shoes,

r = Distance of centre of gravity of the shoe from the centre of the spider,

R = Inside radius of the pulley rim,

N = Running speed of the pulley in r.p.m.,

ω = Angular running speed of the pulley in rad/s = $2\pi N/60$ rad/s,

ω_1 = Angular speed at which the engagement begins to take place, and

μ = Coefficient of friction between the shoe and rim.

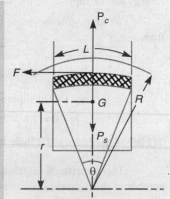

Fig. 10.29. Forces on a shoe of centrifugal clutch.

We know that the centrifugal force acting on each shoe at the running speed,

$$*P_c = m.\omega^2.r$$

and the inward force on each shoe exerted by the spring at the speed at which engagement begins to take place,

$$P_s = m\,(\omega_1)^2\,r$$

∴ The net outward radial force (i.e. centrifugal force) with which the shoe presses against the rim at the running speed

$$= P_c - P_s$$

and the frictional force acting tangentially on each shoe,

$$F = \mu\,(P_c - P_s)$$

∴ Frictional torque acting on each shoe,

$$= F \times R = \mu\,(P_c - P_s)\,R$$

and total frictional torque transmitted,

$$T = \mu\,(P_c - P_s)\,R \times n = n.F.R$$

From this expression, the mass of the shoes (m) may be evaluated.

2. Size of the shoes

Let
l = Contact length of the shoes,

b = Width of the shoes,

---

* The radial clearance between the shoe and the rim being very small as compared to r, therefore it is neglected. If, however, the radial clearance is given, then the operating radius of the mass centre of the shoe from the axis of the clutch,

$r_1 = r + c$, where c = Radial clearance.

Then
$P_c = m.\omega^2.r_1$, and $P_s = m\,(\omega_1)^2\,r_1$

R = Contact radius of the shoes. It is same as the inside radius of the rim of the pulley.

θ = Angle subtended by the shoes at the centre of the spider in radians.

p = Intensity of pressure exerted on the shoe. In order to ensure reasonable life, the intensity of pressure may be taken as 0.1 N/mm².

We know that $\qquad \theta = l/R$ rad $\quad$ or $\quad l = \theta.R$

∴ Area of contact of the shoe,

$$A = l.b$$

and the force with which the shoe presses against the rim

$$= A \times p = l.b.p$$

Since the force with which the shoe presses against the rim at the running speed is $(P_c - P_s)$, therefore

$$l.b.p = P_c - P_s$$

From this expression, the width of shoe (b) may be obtained.

Example 10.35. *A centrifugal clutch is to transmit 15 kW at 900 r.p.m. The shoes are four in number. The speed at which the engagement begins is 3/4th of the running speed. The inside radius of the pulley rim is 150 mm and the centre of gravity of the shoe lies at 120 mm from the centre of the spider. The shoes are lined with Ferrodo for which the coefficient of friction may be taken as 0.25. Determine : 1. Mass of the shoes, and 2. Size of the shoes, if angle subtended by the shoes at the centre of the spider is 60° and the pressure exerted on the shoes is 0.1 N/mm².*

Solution. Given : $P = 15$ kW $= 15 \times 10^3$ W ; $N = 900$ r.p.m. or $\omega = 25 \times 900/60 = 94.26$ rad/s ; $n = 4$; $R = 150$ mm $= 0.15$ m ; $r = 120$ mm $= 0.12$ m ; $\mu = 0.25$

Since the speed at which the engagement begins (*i.e.* ω_1) is 3/4th of the running speed (*i.e.* ω), therefore

$$\omega_1 = \frac{3}{4}\,\omega = \frac{3}{4} \times 94.26 = 70.7 \text{ rad/s}$$

Let $\qquad\qquad T$ = Torque transmitted at the running speed.

We know that power transmitted (P),

$$15 \times 10^3 = T.\omega = T \times 94.26 \quad \text{or} \quad T = 15 \times 10^3/94.26 = 159 \text{ N-m}$$

1. Mass of the shoes

Let $\qquad\qquad m$ = Mass of the shoes in kg.

We know that the centrifugal force acting on each shoe,

$$P_c = m.\omega^2.r = m\,(94.26)^2 \times 0.12 = 1066\,m \text{ N}$$

and the inward force on each shoe exerted by the spring *i.e.* the centrifugal force at the engagement speed ω_1,

$$P_s = m\,(\omega_1)^2\,r = m\,(70.7)^2 \times 0.12 = 600\,m \text{ N}$$

∴ Frictional force acting tangentially on each shoe,

$$F = \mu\,(P_c - P_s) = 0.25\,(1066\,m - 600\,m) = 116.5\,m \text{ N}$$

We know that the torque transmitted (T),

$$159 = n.F.R = 4 \times 116.5\,m \times 0.15 = 70\,m \quad \text{or} \quad m = 2.27 \text{ kg} \text{ **Ans.**}$$

2. Size of the shoes

Let $\qquad\qquad l$ = Contact length of shoes in mm,

$\qquad\qquad\qquad b$ = Width of the shoes in mm,

θ = Angle subtended by the shoes at the centre of the spider in radians

= 60° = $\pi/3$ rad, and ...(Given)

p = Pressure exerted on the shoes in N/mm² = 0.1 N/mm² ...(Given)

We know that $l = \theta . R = \dfrac{\pi}{3} \times 150 = 157.1$ mm

and $l.b.p = P_c - P_s = 1066\,m - 600\,m = 466\,m$

$\therefore$ $157.1 \times b \times 0.1 = 466 \times 2.27 = 1058$

or $b = 1058/157.1 \times 0.1 = 67.3$ mm **Ans.**

Example 10.36. *A centrifugal clutch has four shoes which slide radially in a spider keyed to the driving shaft and make contact with the internal cylindrical surface of a rim keyed to the driven shaft. When the clutch is at rest, each shoe is pulled against a stop by a spring so as to leave a radial clearance of 5 mm between the shoe and the rim. The pull exerted by the spring is then 500 N. The mass centre of the shoe is 160 mm from the axis of the clutch.*

If the internal diameter of the rim is 400 mm, the mass of each shoe is 8 kg, the stiffness of each spring is 50 N/mm and the coefficient of friction between the shoe and the rim is 0.3 ; find the power transmitted by the clutch at 500 r.p.m.

Solution. Given : $n = 4$; $c = 5$ mm ; $S = 500$ N ; $r = 160$ mm ; $D = 400$ mm or $R = 200$ mm = 0.2 m ; $m = 8$ kg ; $s = 50$ N/mm ; $\mu = 0.3$; $N = 500$ r.p.m. or $\omega = 2\,\pi \times 500/60 = 52.37$ rad/s

We know that the operating radius,

$r_1 = r + c = 160 + 5 = 165$ mm = 0.165 m

Centrifugal force on each shoe,

$P_c = m.\omega^2.r_1 = 8\,(52.37)^2 \times 0.165 = 3620$ N

and the inward force exerted by the spring,

$P_s = S + c.s = 500 + 5 \times 50 = 750$ N

$\therefore$ Frictional force acting tangentially on each shoe,

$F = \mu\,(P_c - P_s) = 0.3\,(3620 - 750) = 861$ N

We know that total frictional torque transmitted by the clutch,

$T = n.F.R = 4 \times 861 \times 0.2 = 688.8$ N-m

$\therefore$ Power transmitted,

$P = T.\omega = 688.8 \times 52.37 = 36\,100$ W = 36.1 kW **Ans.**

EXERCISES

1. Find the force required to move a load of 300 N up a rough plane, the force being applied parallel to the plane. The inclination of the plane is such that a force of 60 N inclined at 30° to a similar smooth plane would keep the same load in equilibrium. The coefficient of friction is 0.3. **[Ans. 146 N]**

2. A square threaded screw of mean diameter 25 mm and pitch of thread 6 mm is utilised to lift a weight of 10 kN by a horizontal force applied at the circumference of the screw. Find the magnitude of the force if the coefficient of friction between the nut and screw is 0.02. **[Ans. 966 N]**

3. A bolt with a square threaded screw has mean diameter of 25 mm and a pitch of 3 mm. It carries an axial thrust of 10 kN on the bolt head of 25 mm mean radius. If $\mu = 0.12$, find the force required at the end of a spanner 450 mm long, in tightening up the bolt. **[Ans. 110.8 N]**

4. A turn buckle, with right and left hand threads is used to couple two railway coaches. The threads which are square have a pitch of 10 mm and a mean diameter of 30 mm and are of single start type. Taking the coefficient of friction as 0.1, find the work to be done in drawing the coaches together a distance of 200 mm against a steady load of 20 kN. **[Ans. 3927 N-m]**

5. A vertical two start square threaded screw of a 100 mm mean diameter and 20 mm pitch supports a vertical load of 18 kN. The axial thrust on the screw is taken by a collar bearing of 250 mm outside diameter and 100 mm inside diameter. Find the force required at the end of a lever which is 400 mm long in order to lift and lower the load. The coefficient of friction for the vertical screw and nut is 0.15 and that for collar bearing is 0.20.

[Ans. 1423 N ; 838 N]

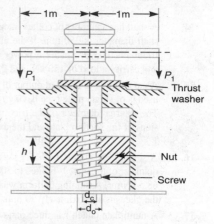

Fig. 10.30

6. A sluice gate weighing 18 kN is raised and lowered by means of square threaded screws, as shown in Fig.10.30. The frictional resistance induced by water pressure against the gate when it is in its lowest position is 4000 N.

The outside diameter of the screw is 60 mm and pitch is 10 mm. The outside and inside diameter of washer is 150 mm and 50 mm respectively. The coefficient of friction between the screw and nut is 0.1 and for the washer and seat is 0.12. Find :

1. The maximum force to be exerted at the ends of the lever for raising and lowering the gate, and

2. Efficiency of the arrangement.   **[Ans. 114 N ; 50 N ; 15.4%]**

7. The spindle of a screw jack has single start square threads with an outside diameter of 45 mm and a pitch of 10 mm. The spindle moves in a fixed nut. The load is carried on a swivel head but is not free to rotate. The bearing surface of the swivel head has a mean diameter of 60 mm. The coefficient of friction between the nut and screw is 0.12 and that between the swivel head and the spindle is 0.10. Calculate the load which can be raised by efforts of 100 N each applied at the end of two levers each of effective length of 350 mm. Also determine the velocity ratio and the efficiency of the lifting arrangement.   **[Ans. 9943 N ; 218.7 N ; 39.6%]**

8. The lead screw of a lathe has acme threads of 50 mm outside diameter and 10 mm pitch. The included angle of the thread is 29°. It drives a tool carriage and exerts an axial pressure of 2500 N. A collar bearing with outside diameter 100 mm and inside diameter 50 mm is provided to take up the thrust. If the lead screw rotates at 30 r.p.m., find the efficiency and the power required to drive the screw. The coefficient of friction for screw threads is 0.15 and for the collar is 0.12.   **[Ans. 16.3% ; 75.56 W]**

9. A flat foot step bearing 225 mm in diameter supports a load of 7.5 kN. If the coefficient of friction is 0.09 and r.p.m is 60, find the power lost in friction, assuming 1. Uniform pressure, and 2. Uniform wear.   **[Ans. 318 W ; 239 W]**

10. A conical pivot bearing 150 mm in diameter has a cone angle of 120°. If the shaft supports an axial load of 20 kN and the coefficient of friction is 0.03, find the power lost in friction when the shaft rotates at 200 r.p.m., assuming 1. Uniform pressure, and 2. uniform wear.

[Ans. 727.5 W ; 545.6 W]

11. A vertical shaft supports a load of 20 kN in a conical pivot bearing. The external radius of the cone is 3 times the internal radius and the cone angle is 120°. Assuming uniform intensity of pressure as 0.35 MN/m^2, determine the dimensions of the bearing.

If the coefficient of friction between the shaft and bearing is 0.05 and the shaft rotates at 120 r.p.m., find the power absorbed in friction.   **[Ans. 47.7 mm ; 143 mm ; 1.50 kW]**

12. A plain collar type thrust bearing having inner and outer diameters of 200 mm and 450 mm is subjected to an axial thrust of 40 kN. Assuming coefficient of friction between the thrust surfaces as 0.025, find the power absorbed in overcoming friction at a speed of 120 r.p.m. The rate of wear is considered to be proportional to the pressure and rubbing speed.   **[Ans. 4.1 kW]**

13. The thrust on the propeller shaft of a marine engine is taken up by 8 collars whose external and internal diameters are 660 mm and 420 mm respectively. The thrust pressure is 0.4 MN/m^2 and may

be assumed uniform. The coefficient of friction between the shaft and collars is 0.04. If the shaft rotates at 90 r.p.m. ; find 1. total thrust on the collars ; and 2. power absorbed by friction at the bearing.

[Ans. 651 kN ; 68 kW]

14. A shaft has a number of collars integral with it. The external diameter of the collars is 400 mm and the shaft diameter is 250 mm. If the uniform intensity of pressure is 0.35 N/mm^2 and its coefficient of friction is 0.05, estimate : 1. power absorbed in overcoming friction when the shaft runs at 105 r.p.m. and carries a load of 150 kN, and 2. number of collars required. **[Ans. 13.4 kW ; 6]**

15. A car engine has its rated output of 12 kW. The maximum torque developed is 100 N-m. The clutch used is of single plate type having two active surfaces. The axial pressure is not to exceed 85 kN/m^2. The external diameter of the friction plate is 1.25 times the internal diameter. Determine the dimensions of the friction plate and the axial force exerted by the springs. Coefficient of friction = 0.3.

[Ans. 129.5 mm ; 103.6 mm ; 1433 N]

16. A single plate clutch (both sides effective) is required to transmit 26.5 kW at 1600 r.p.m. The outer diameter of the plate is limited to 300 mm and intensity of pressure between the plates is not to exceed 68.5 kN/m^2. Assuming uniform wear and a coefficient of friction 0.3, show that the inner diameter of the plates is approximately 90 mm.

17. A multiplate clutch has three pairs of contact surfaces. The outer and inner radii of the contact surfaces are 100 mm and 50 mm respectively. The maximum axial spring force is limited to 1 kN. If the coefficient of friction is 0.35 and assuming uniform wear, find the power transmitted by the clutch at 1500 r.p.m. **[Ans. 12.37 kW]**

18. A cone clutch is to transmit 7.5 kW at 900 r.p.m. The cone has a face angle of 12°. The width of the face is half of the mean radius and the normal pressure between the contact faces is not to exceed 0.09 N/mm^2. Assuming uniform wear and the coefficient of friction between contact faces as 0.2, find the main dimensions of the clutch and the axial force required to engage the clutch.

[Ans. R = 112 mm, b = 56 mm, r_1 = 117.8 mm, r_2 = 106.2 mm ; 1433 N]

19. A cone clutch with cone angle 20° is to transmit 7.5 kW at 750 r.p.m. The normal intensity of pressure between the contact faces is not to exceed 0.12 N/mm^2. The coefficient of friction is 0.2. If face width is $\frac{1}{5}$ th of mean diameter, find : 1. the main dimensions of the clutch, and 2. axial force required while running. **[Ans. R = 117 mm ; b = 46.8 mm ; r_1 = 125 mm ; r_2 = 109 mm ; 1395 N]**

20. A centrifugal friction clutch has a driving member consisting of a spider carrying four shoes which are kept from contact with the clutch case by means of flat springs until increase of centrifugal force overcomes the resistance of the springs and the power is transmitted by friction between the shoes and the case.

Determine the necessary mass of each shoe if 22.5 kW is to be transmitted at 750 r.p.m. with engagement beginning at 75% of the running speed. The inside diameter of the drum is 300 mm and the radial distance of the centre of gravity of each shoe from the shaft axis is 125 mm. Assume μ = 0.25. **[Ans. 5.66 kg]**

DO YOU KNOW ?

1. Discuss briefly the various types of friction experienced by a body.

2. State the laws of
   (i) Static friction ;   (ii) Dynamic friction ;
   (iii) Solid friction ; and   (iv) Fluid friction.

3. Explain the following :
   (i) Limiting friction,   (ii) Angle of friction, and
   (iii) Coefficient of friction.

4. Derive from first principles an expression for the effort required to raise a load with a screw jack taking friction into consideration.

5. Neglecting collar friction, derive an expression for mechanical advantage of a square threaded screw moving in a nut, in terms of helix angle of the screw and friction angle.

6. In a screw jack, the helix angle of thread is α and the angle of friction is ϕ. Show that its efficiency is maximum, when $2\alpha = (90° - \phi)$.

7. For a screw jack having the nut fixed, derive the equation (with usual notations),

$$\eta = \frac{\tan \alpha}{\tan (\alpha + \phi) + \mu.r_m.r}.$$

8. Neglecting collar friction, from first principles, prove that the maximum efficiency of a square threaded screw moving in a nut is $\dfrac{1 - \sin \phi}{1 + \sin \phi}$, where ϕ is the friction angle.

9. Write a short note on journal bearing.

10. What is meant by the expression 'friction circle'? Deduce an expression for the radius of friction circle in terms of the radius of the journal and the angle of friction.

11. From first principles, deduce an expression for the friction moment of a collar thrust bearing, stating clearly the assumptions made.

12. Derive an expression for the friction moment for a flat collar bearing in terms of the inner radius r_1, outer radius r_2, axial thrust W and coefficient of friction μ. Assume uniform intensity of pressure.

13. Derive from first principles an expression for the friction moment of a conical pivot assuming (*i*) Uniform pressure, and (*ii*) Uniform wear.

14. A truncated conical pivot of cone angle ϕ rotating at speed N supports a load W. The smallest and largest diameter of the pivot over the contact area are 'd' and 'D' respectively. Assuming uniform wear, derive the expression for the frictional torque.

15. Describe with a neat sketch the working of a single plate friction clutch.

16. Establish a formula for the maximum torque transmitted by a single plate clutch of external and internal radii r_1 and r_2, if the limiting coefficient of friction is μ and the axial spring load is W. Assume that the pressure intensity on the contact faces is uniform.

17. Which of the two assumptions-uniform intensity of pressure or uniform rate of wear, would you make use of in designing friction clutch and why ?

18. Describe with a neat sketch a centrifugal clutch and deduce an equation for the total torque transmitted.

OBJECTIVE TYPE QUESTIONS

1. The angle of inclination of the plane, at which the body begins to move down the plane, is called

    (*a*) angle of friction   (*b*) angle of repose   (*c*) angle of projection

2. In a screw jack, the effort required to lift the load W is given by

    (*a*) $P = W \tan (\alpha - \phi)$ (*b*) $P = W \tan (\alpha + \phi)$

    (*c*) $P = W \cos (\alpha - \phi)$ (*d*) $P = W \cos (\alpha + \phi)$

    where α = Helix angle, and

           ϕ = Angle of friction.

3. The efficiency of a screw jack is given by

    (*a*) $\dfrac{\tan (\alpha + \phi)}{\tan \alpha}$ (*b*) $\dfrac{\tan \alpha}{\tan (\alpha + \phi)}$

    (*c*) $\dfrac{\tan (\alpha - \phi)}{\tan \alpha}$ (*d*) $\dfrac{\tan \alpha}{\tan (\alpha - \phi)}$

4. The radius of a friction circle for a shaft of radius r rotating inside a bearing is

    (*a*) $r \sin \phi$ (*b*) $r \cos \phi$ (*c*) $r \tan \phi$ (*d*) $r \cot \phi$

5.   The efficiency of a screw jack is maximum, when

   (a) $\alpha = 45° + \dfrac{\phi}{2}$ (b) $\alpha = 45° - \dfrac{\phi}{2}$ (c) $\alpha = 90° + \phi$ (d) $\alpha = 90° - \phi$

6.   The maximum efficiency of a screw jack is

   (a) $\dfrac{1 - \sin \phi}{1 + \sin \phi}$ (b) $\dfrac{1 + \sin \phi}{1 - \sin \phi}$ (c) $\dfrac{1 - \tan \phi}{1 + \tan \phi}$ (d) $\dfrac{1 + \tan \phi}{1 - \tan \phi}$

7.   The frictional torque transmitted in a flat pivot bearing, considering uniform pressure, is

   (a) $\dfrac{1}{2} \times \mu.W.R$ (b) $\dfrac{2}{3} \times \mu.W.R$ (c) $\dfrac{3}{4} \times \mu.W.R$ (d) $\mu.W.R$

   where μ = Coefficient of friction,

   W = Load over the bearing, and

   R = Radius of the bearing surface.

8.   The frictional torque transmitted in a conical pivot bearing, considering uniform wear, is

   (a) $\dfrac{1}{2} \times \mu.W.R \, \text{cosec} \, \alpha$ (b) $\dfrac{2}{3} \times \mu.W.R \, \text{cosec} \, \alpha$

   (c) $\dfrac{3}{4} \times \mu.W.R \, \text{cosec} \, \alpha$ (d) $\mu.W.R \, \text{cosec} \, \alpha$

   where R = Radius of the shaft, and

   α = Semi-angle of the cone.

9.   The frictional torque transmitted by a disc or plate clutch is same as that of

   (a)   flat pivot bearing   (b)   flat collar bearing

   (c)   conical pivot bearing   (d)   trapezoidal pivot bearing

10.   The frictional torque transmitted by a cone clutch is same as that of

   (a)   flat pivot bearing   (b)   flat collar bearing

   (c)   conical pivot bearing   (d)   trapezoidal pivot bearing

ANSWERS

1. (a)	2. (b)	3. (b)	4. (a)	5. (b)
6. (a)	7. (b)	8. (a)	9. (b)	10. (d)

11

Belt, Rope and Chain Drives

11.1. Introduction

The belts or ropes are used to transmit power from one shaft to another by means of pulleys which rotate at the same speed or at different speeds. The amount of power transmitted depends upon the following factors :

1. The velocity of the belt.

2. The tension under which the belt is placed on the pulleys.

3. The arc of contact between the belt and the smaller pulley.

4. The conditions under which the belt is used.

It may be noted that

(a) The shafts should be properly in line to insure uniform tension across the belt section.

(b) The pulleys should not be too close together, in order that the arc of contact on the smaller pulley may be as large as possible.

(c) The pulleys should not be so far apart as to cause the belt to weigh heavily on the shafts, thus increasing the friction load on the bearings.

(d) A long belt tends to swing from side to side, causing the belt to run out of the pulleys, which in turn develops crooked spots in the belt.

(e) The tight side of the belt should be at the bottom, so that whatever sag is present on the loose side will increase the arc of contact at the pulleys.

(f) In order to obtain good results with flat belts, the maximum distance between the shafts should not exceed 10 metres and the minimum should not be less than 3.5 times the diameter of the larger pulley.

11.2. Selection of a Belt Drive

Following are the various important factors upon which the selection of a belt drive depends:

1. Speed of the driving and driven shafts,
2. Speed reduction ratio,
3. Power to be transmitted,
4. Centre distance between the shafts,
5. Positive drive requirements,
6. Shafts layout,
7. Space available, and
8. Service conditions.

11.3. Types of Belt Drives

The belt drives are usually classified into the following three groups :

1. *Light drives.* These are used to transmit small powers at belt speeds upto about 10 m/s, as in agricultural machines and small machine tools.

2. *Medium drives.* These are used to transmit medium power at belt speeds over 10 m/s but up to 22 m/s, as in machine tools.

3. *Heavy drives.* These are used to transmit large powers at belt speeds above 22 m/s, as in compressors and generators.

11.4. Types of Belts

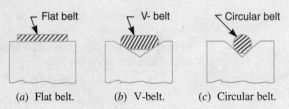

(a) Flat belt. (b) V-belt. (c) Circular belt.

Fig. 11.1. Types of belts.

Though there are many types of belts used these days, yet the following are important from the subject point of view :

1. *Flat belt.* The flat belt, as shown in Fig. 11.1 (a), is mostly used in the factories and workshops, where a moderate amount of power is to be transmitted, from one pulley to another when the two pulleys are not more than 8 metres apart.

2. *V-belt.* The V-belt, as shown in Fig. 11.1 (b), is mostly used in the factories and work-shops, where a moderate amount of power is to be transmitted, from one pulley to another, when the two pulleys are very near to each other.

3. *Circular belt or rope.* The circular belt or rope, as shown in Fig. 11.1 (c), is mostly used in the factories and workshops, where a great amount of power is to be transmitted, from one pulley to another, when the two pulleys are more than 8 meters apart.

If a huge amount of power is to be transmitted, then a single belt may not be sufficient. In such a case, wide pulleys (for V-belts or circular belts) with a number of grooves are used. Then a belt in each groove is provided to transmit the required amount of power from one pulley to another.

11.5. Material used for Belts

The material used for belts and ropes must be strong, flexible, and durable. It must have a high coefficient of friction. The belts, according to the material used, are classified as follows :

1. *Leather belts*. The most important material for the belt is leather. The best leather belts are made from 1.2 metres to 1.5 metres long strips cut from either side of the back bone of the top grade steer hides. The hair side of the leather is smoother and harder than the flesh side, but the flesh side is stronger. The fibres on the hair side are perpendicular to the surface, while those on the flesh side are interwoven and parallel to the surface. Therefore for these reasons, the hair side of a belt should be in contact with the pulley surface, as shown in Fig. 11.2. This gives a more intimate contact between the belt and the pulley and places the greatest tensile strength of the belt section on the outside, where the tension is maximum as the belt passes over the pulley.

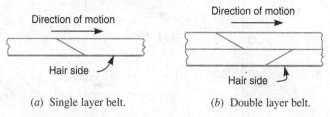

(*a*) Single layer belt.   (*b*) Double layer belt.

Fig. 11.2. Leather belts.

The leather may be either oak-tanned or mineral salt tanned *e.g.* chrome tanned. In order to increase the thickness of belt, the strips are cemented together. The belts are specified according to the number of layers *e.g.* single, double or triple ply and according to the thickness of hides used *e.g.* light, medium or heavy.

The leather belts must be periodically cleaned and dressed or treated with a compound or dressing containing neats foot or other suitable oils so that the belt will remain soft and flexible.

2. *Cotton or fabric belts*. Most of the fabric belts are made by folding canvass or cotton duck to three or more layers (depending upon the thickness desired) and stitching together. These belts are woven also into a strip of the desired width and thickness. They are impregnated with some filler like linseed oil in order to make the belts water proof and to prevent injury to the fibres. The cotton belts are cheaper and suitable in warm climates, in damp atmospheres and in exposed positions. Since the cotton belts require little attention, therefore these belts are mostly used in farm machinery, belt conveyor etc.

3. *Rubber belt*. The rubber belts are made of layers of fabric impregnated with rubber com position and have a thin layer of rubber on the faces. These belts are very flexible but are quickly destroyed if allowed to come into contact with heat, oil or grease. One of the principal advantage of these belts is that they may be easily made endless. These belts are found suitable for saw mills, paper mills where they are exposed to moisture.

4. *Balata belts*. These belts are similar to rubber belts except that balata gum is used in place of rubber. These belts are acid proof and water proof and it is not effected by animal oils or alkalies. The balata belts should not be at temperatures above 40° C because at this temperature the balata begins to soften and becomes sticky. The strength of balata belts is 25 per cent higher than rubber belts.

11.6. Types of Flat Belt Drives

The power from one pulley to another may be transmitted by any of the following types of belt drives:

1. *Open belt drive.* The open belt drive, as shown in Fig. 11.3, is used with shafts arranged parallel and rotating in the same direction. In this case, the driver A pulls the belt from one side (*i.e.* lower side RQ) and delivers it to the other side (*i.e.* upper side LM). Thus the tension in the lower side belt will be more than that in the upper side belt. The lower side belt (because of more tension) is known as *tight side* whereas the upper side belt (because of less tension) is known as *slack side*, as shown in Fig. 11.3.

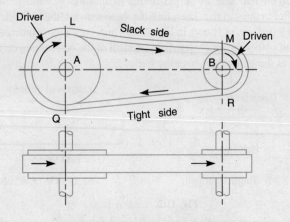

Fig. 11.3. Open belt drive.

2. *Crossed or twist belt drive.* The crossed or twist belt drive, as shown in Fig. 11.4, is used with shafts arranged parallel and rotating in the opposite directions.

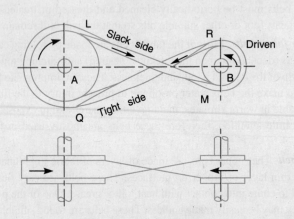

Fig. 11.4. Crossed or twist belt drive.

In this case, the driver pulls the belt from one side (*i.e. RQ*) and delivers it to the other side (*i.e. LM*). Thus the tension in the belt RQ will be more than that in the belt LM. The belt RQ (because of more tension) is known as *tight side,* whereas the belt LM (because of less tension) is known as *slack side*, as shown in Fig. 11.4.

A little consideration will show that at a point where the belt crosses, it rubs against each other and there will be excessive wear and tear. In order to avoid this, the shafts should be placed at a maximum distance of 20 *b*, where *b* is the width of belt and the speed of the belt should be less than 15 m/s.

3. *Quarter turn belt drive.* The quarter turn belt drive also known as right angle belt drive, as shown in Fig. 11.5 (*a*), is used with shafts arranged at right angles and rotating in one definite direction. In order to prevent the belt from leaving the pulley, the width of the face of the pulley should be greater or equal to 1.4 *b*, where *b* is the width of belt.

In case the pulleys cannot be arranged, as shown in Fig. 11.5 (*a*), or when the reversible motion is desired, then a *quarter turn belt drive with guide pulley*, as shown in Fig. 11.5 (*b*), may be used.

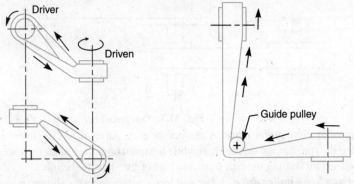

(*a*) Quarter turn belt drive.   (*b*) Quarter turn belt drive with guide pulley.

Fig. 11.5

4. *Belt drive with idler pulleys.* A belt drive with an idler pulley, as shown in Fig. 11.6 (*a*), is used with shafts arranged parallel and when an open belt drive cannot be used due to small angle of contact on the smaller pulley. This type of drive is provided to obtain high velocity ratio and when the required belt tension cannot be obtained by other means.

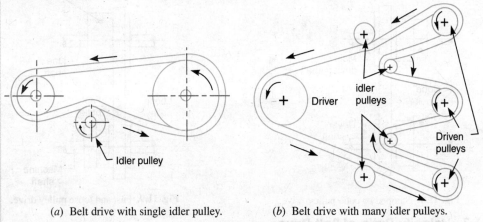

(*a*) Belt drive with single idler pulley.   (*b*) Belt drive with many idler pulleys.

Fig. 11.6

When it is desired to transmit motion from one shaft to several shafts, all arranged in parallel, a belt drive with many idler pulleys, as shown in Fig. 11.6 (*b*), may be employed.

5. *Compound belt drive*. A compound belt drive, as shown in Fig. 11.7, is used when power is transmitted from one shaft to another through a number of pulleys.

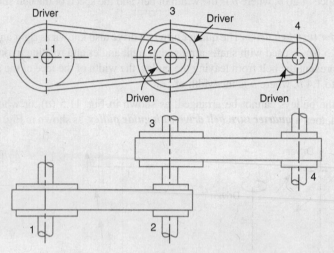

Fig. 11.7. Compound belt brive.

6. *Stepped or cone pulley drive*. A stepped or cone pulley drive, as shown in Fig. 11.8, is used for changing the speed of the driven shaft while the main or driving shaft runs at constant speed. This is accomplished by shifting the belt from one part of the steps to the other.

7. *Fast and loose pulley drive*. A fast and loose pulley drive, as shown in Fig. 11.9, is used when the driven or machine shaft is to be started or stopped when ever desired without interfering with the driving shaft. A pulley which is keyed to the machine shaft is called *fast pulley* and runs at the same speed as that of machine shaft. A loose pulley runs freely over the machine shaft and is incapable of transmitting any power. When the driven shaft is required to be stopped, the belt is pushed on to the loose pulley by means of sliding bar having belt forks.

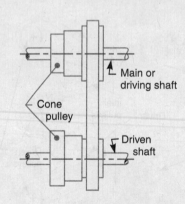

Fig. 11.8. Stepped or cone pulley drive.

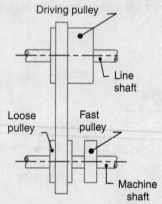

Fig. 11.9. Fast and loose pulley drive.

11.7. Velocity Ratio of Belt Drive

It is the **ratio between the velocities of the driver and the follower or driven.** It may be expressed, mathematically, as discussed below :

Let d_1 = Diameter of the driver,

d_2 = Diameter of the follower,

N_1 = Speed of the driver in r.p.m., and

N_2 = Speed of the follower in r.p.m.

∴ Length of the belt that passes over the driver, in one minute

$$= \pi\, d_1.N_1$$

Similarly, length of the belt that passes over the follower, in one minute

$$= \pi\, d_2.N_2$$

Since the length of belt that passes over the driver in one minute is equal to the length of belt that passes over the follower in one minute, therefore

$$\pi\, d_1.N_1 = \pi\, d_2.N_2$$

∴ Velocity ratio, $\dfrac{N_2}{N_1} = \dfrac{d_1}{d_2}$

When the thickness of the belt (t) is considered, then velocity ratio,

$$\frac{N_2}{N_1} = \frac{d_1 + t}{d_2 + t}$$

Note: The velocity ratio of a belt drive may also be obtained as discussed below :

We know that peripheral velocity of the belt on the driving pulley,

$$v_1 = \frac{\pi\, d_1.N_1}{60} \text{ m/s}$$

and peripheral velocity of the belt on the driven or follower pulley,

$$v_2 = \frac{\pi\, d_2.N_2}{60} \text{ m/s}$$

When there is no slip, then $v_1 = v_2$.

$$\therefore \quad \frac{\pi\, d_1.N_1}{60} = \frac{\pi\, d_2.N_2}{60} \quad \text{or} \quad \frac{N_2}{N_1} = \frac{d_1}{d_2}$$

11.8. Velocity Ratio of a Compound Belt Drive

Sometimes the power is transmitted from one shaft to another, through a number of pulleys as shown in Fig. 11.7. Consider a pulley 1 driving the pulley 2. Since the pulleys 2 and 3 are keyed to the same shaft, therefore the pulley 1 also drives the pulley 3 which, in turn, drives the pulley 4.

Let $\qquad d_1$ = Diameter of the pulley 1,

$\qquad\qquad N_1$ = Speed of the pulley 1 in r.p.m.,

$d_2, d_3, d_4,$ and N_2, N_3, N_4 = Corresponding values for pulleys 2, 3 and 4.

We know that velocity ratio of pulleys 1 and 2,

$$\frac{N_2}{N_1} = \frac{d_1}{d_2} \qquad\qquad ...(i)$$

Similarly, velocity ratio of pulleys 3 and 4,

$$\frac{N_4}{N_3} = \frac{d_3}{d_4} \qquad\qquad ...(ii)$$

Multiplying equations (i) and (ii),

$$\frac{N_2}{N_1} \times \frac{N_4}{N_3} = \frac{d_1}{d_2} \times \frac{d_3}{d_4}$$

or
$$\frac{N_4}{N_1} = \frac{d_1 \times d_3}{d_2 \times d_4} \quad ...(\because N_2 = N_3, \text{ being keyed to the same shaft})$$

A little consideration will show, that if there are six pulleys, then
$$\frac{N_6}{N_1} = \frac{d_1 \times d_3 \times d_5}{d_2 \times d_4 \times d_6}$$

or
$$\frac{\text{Speed of last driven}}{\text{Speed of first driver}} = \frac{\text{Product of diameters of drivers}}{\text{Product of diameters of drivens}}$$

11.9. Slip of Belt

In the previous articles, we have discussed the motion of belts and shafts assuming a firm frictional grip between the belts and the shafts. But sometimes, the frictional grip becomes insufficient. This may cause some forward motion of the driver without carrying the belt with it. This may also cause some forward motion of the belt without carrying the driven pulley with it. This is called *slip of the belt* and is generally expressed as a percentage.

The result of the belt slipping is to reduce the velocity ratio of the system. As the slipping of the belt is a common phenomenon, thus the belt should never be used where a definite velocity ratio is of importance (as in the case of hour, minute and second arms in a watch).

Let $s_1 \%$ = Slip between the driver and the belt, and

$s_2 \%$ = Slip between the belt and the follower.

∴ Velocity of the belt passing over the driver per second

$$v = \frac{\pi d_1 . N_1}{60} - \frac{\pi d_1 . N_1}{60} \times \frac{s_1}{100} = \frac{\pi d_1 . N_1}{60} \left(1 - \frac{s_1}{100}\right) \qquad ...(i)$$

and velocity of the belt passing over the follower per second,

$$\frac{\pi d_2 . N_2}{60} = v - v \times \frac{s_2}{100} = v \left(1 - \frac{s_2}{100}\right)$$

Substituting the value of v from equation (i),

$$\frac{\pi d_2 N_2}{60} = \frac{\pi d_1 N_1}{60} \left(1 - \frac{s_1}{100}\right)\left(1 - \frac{s_2}{100}\right)$$

$$\frac{N_2}{N_1} = \frac{d_1}{d_2} \left(1 - \frac{s_1}{100} - \frac{s_2}{100}\right) \qquad ...\left(\text{Neglecting } \frac{s_1 \times s_2}{100 \times 100}\right)$$

$$= \frac{d_1}{d_2}\left(1 - \frac{s_1 + s_2}{100}\right) = \frac{d_1}{d_2}\left(1 - \frac{s}{100}\right)$$

$$... \text{(where } s = s_1 + s_2, \text{ i.e. total percentage of slip)}$$

If thickness of the belt (t) is considered, then

$$\frac{N_2}{N_1} = \frac{d_1 + t}{d_2 + t}\left(1 - \frac{s}{100}\right)$$

Example 11.1. *An engine, running at 150 r.p.m., drives a line shaft by means of a belt. The engine pulley is 750 mm diameter and the pulley on the line shaft being 450 mm. A 900 mm diameter pulley on the line shaft drives a 150 mm diameter pulley keyed to a dynamo shaft. Find the speed of the dynamo shaft, when 1. there is no slip, and 2. there is a slip of 2% at each drive.*

Solution. Given : $N_1 = 150$ r.p.m. ; $d_1 = 750$ mm ; $d_2 = 450$ mm ; $d_3 = 900$ mm ; $d_4 = 150$ mm

The arrangement of belt drive is shown in Fig. 11.10.

Let $N_4 =$ Speed of the dynamo shaft .

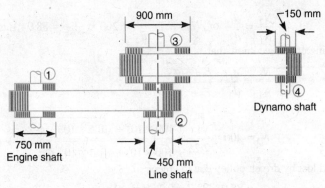

Fig. 11.10

1. When there is no slip

We know that $\dfrac{N_4}{N_1} = \dfrac{d_1 \times d_3}{d_2 \times d_4}$ or $\dfrac{N_4}{150} = \dfrac{750 \times 900}{450 \times 150} = 10$

∴ $N_4 = 150 \times 10 = 1500$ r.p.m. **Ans.**

2. When there is a slip of 2% at each drive

We know that $\dfrac{N_4}{N_1} = \dfrac{d_1 \times d_3}{d_2 \times d_4}\left(1 - \dfrac{s_1}{100}\right)\left(1 - \dfrac{s_2}{100}\right)$

$\dfrac{N_4}{150} = \dfrac{750 \times 900}{450 \times 150}\left(1 - \dfrac{2}{100}\right)\left(1 - \dfrac{2}{100}\right) = 9.6$

∴ $N_4 = 150 \times 9.6 = 1440$ r.p.m. **Ans.**

11.10. Creep of Belt

When the belt passes from the slack side to the tight side, a certain portion of the belt extends and it contracts again when the belt passes from the tight side to slack side. Due to these changes of length, there is a relative motion between the belt and the pulley surfaces. This relative motion is termed as *creep.* The total effect of creep is to reduce slightly the speed of the driven pulley or follower. Considering creep, the velocity ratio is given by

$$\frac{N_2}{N_1} = \frac{d_1}{d_2} \times \frac{E + \sqrt{\sigma_2}}{E + \sqrt{\sigma_1}}$$

where σ_1 and $\sigma_2 =$ Stress in the belt on the tight and slack side respectively, and

$E =$ Young's modulus for the material of the belt.

Example 11.2. *The power is transmitted from a pulley 1 m diameter running at 200 r.p.m. to a pulley 2.25 m diameter by means of a belt. Find the speed lost by the driven pulley as a result of creep, if the stress on the tight and slack side of the belt is 1.4 MPa and 0.5 MPa respectively. The Young's modulus for the material of the belt is 100 MPa.*

Solution. Given : $d_1 = 1$ m ; $N_1 = 200$ r.p.m. ; $d_2 = 2.25$ m ; $\sigma_1 = 1.4$ MPa $= 1.4 \times 10^6$ N/m²; $\sigma_2 = 0.5$ MPa $= 0.5 \times 10^6$ N/m² ; $E = 100$ MPa $= 100 \times 10^6$ N/m²

Let N_2 = Speed of the driven pulley.

Neglecting creep, we know that

$$\frac{N_2}{N_1} = \frac{d_1}{d_2} \quad \text{or} \quad N_2 = N_1 \times \frac{d_1}{d_2} = 200 \times \frac{1}{2.25} = 88.9 \text{ r.p.m.}$$

Considering creep, we know that

$$\frac{N_2}{N_1} = \frac{d_1}{d_2} \times \frac{E + \sqrt{\sigma_2}}{E + \sqrt{\sigma_1}}$$

or

$$N_2 = 200 \times \frac{1}{2.25} \times \frac{100 \times 10^6 + \sqrt{0.5 \times 10^6}}{100 \times 10^6 + \sqrt{1.4 \times 10^6}} = 88.7 \text{ r.p.m.}$$

∴ Speed lost by driven pulley due to creep

$$= 88.9 - 88.7 = 0.2 \text{ r.p.m. } \textbf{Ans.}$$

11.11. Length of an Open Belt Drive

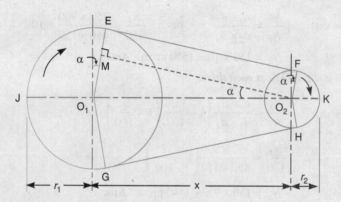

Fig. 11.11. Length of an open belt drive.

We have already discussed in Art. 11.6 that in an open belt drive, both the pulleys rotate in the *same* direction as shown in Fig. 11.11.

Let r_1 and r_2 = Radii of the larger and smaller pulleys,

x = Distance between the centres of two pulleys (*i.e.* $O_1 O_2$), and

L = Total length of the belt.

Let the belt leaves the larger pulley at E and G and the smaller pulley at F and H as shown in Fig. 11.11. Through O_2, draw $O_2 M$ parallel to FE.

From the geometry of the figure, we find that $O_2 M$ will be perpendicular to $O_1 E$.

Let the angle $MO_2 O_1 = \alpha$ radians.

We know that the length of the belt,

$$L = \text{Arc } GJE + EF + \text{Arc } FKH + HG$$

$$= 2 \, (\text{Arc } JE + EF + \text{Arc } FK) \qquad \qquad ...(i)$$

From the geometry of the figure, we find that

$$\sin \alpha = \frac{O_1 M}{O_1 O_2} = \frac{O_1 E - EM}{O_1 O_2} = \frac{r_1 - r_2}{x}$$

Since α is very small, therefore putting

$$\sin \alpha = \alpha \text{ (in radians)} = \frac{r_1 - r_2}{x} \qquad \qquad ...(ii)$$

$\therefore \qquad \qquad \text{Arc } JE = r_1 \left(\frac{\pi}{2} + \alpha \right) \qquad \qquad ...(iii)$

Similarly $\qquad \text{Arc } FK = r_2 \left(\frac{\pi}{2} - \alpha \right) \qquad \qquad ...(iv)$

and $\qquad \qquad EF = MO_2 = \sqrt{(O_1 O_2)^2 - (O_1 M)^2} = \sqrt{x^2 - (r_1 - r_2)^2}$

$$= x \sqrt{1 - \left(\frac{r_1 - r_2}{x} \right)^2}$$

Expanding this equation by binomial theorem,

$$EF = x \left[1 - \frac{1}{2} \left(\frac{r_1 - r_2}{x} \right)^2 + ... \right] = x - \frac{(r_1 - r_2)^2}{2x} \qquad \qquad ...(v)$$

Substituting the values of arc JE from equation (iii), arc FK from equation (iv) and EF from equation (v) in equation (i), we get

$$L = 2 \left[r_1 \left(\frac{\pi}{2} + \alpha \right) + x - \frac{(r_1 - r_2)^2}{2x} + r_2 \left(\frac{\pi}{2} - \alpha \right) \right]$$

$$= 2 \left[r_1 \times \frac{\pi}{2} + r_1 . \alpha + x - \frac{(r_1 - r_2)^2}{2x} + r_2 \times \frac{\pi}{2} - r_2 . \alpha \right]$$

$$= 2 \left[\frac{\pi}{2} (r_1 + r_2) + \alpha (r_1 - r_2) + x - \frac{(r_1 - r_2)^2}{2x} \right]$$

$$= \pi (r_1 + r_2) + 2\alpha (r_1 - r_2) + 2x - \frac{(r_1 - r_2)^2}{x}$$

Substituting the value of $\alpha = \frac{r_1 - r_2}{x}$ from equation (ii),

$$L = \pi (r_1 + r_2) + 2 \times \frac{(r_1 - r_2)}{x} \times (r_1 - r_2) + 2x - \frac{(r_1 - r_2)^2}{x}$$

$$= \pi (r_1 + r_2) + \frac{2(r_1 - r_2)^2}{x} + 2x - \frac{(r_1 - r_2)^2}{x}$$

$$= \pi (r_1 + r_2) + 2x + \frac{(r_1 - r_2)^2}{x} \qquad \qquad ...(\text{In terms of pulley radii})$$

$$= \frac{\pi}{2} (d_1 + d_2) + 2x + \frac{(d_1 - d_2)^2}{4x} \qquad \qquad ...(\text{In terms of pulley diameters})$$

11.12. Length of a Cross Belt Drive

We have already discussed in Art. 11.6 that in a cross belt drive, both the pulleys rotate in *opposite* directions as shown in Fig. 11.12.

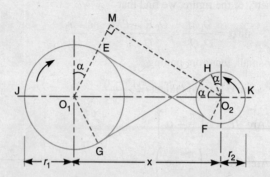

Fig. 11.12. Length of a cross belt drive.

Let r_1 and r_2 = Radii of the larger and smaller pulleys,

x = Distance between the centres of two pulleys (*i.e.* $O_1 O_2$), and

L = Total length of the belt.

Let the belt leaves the larger pulley at E and G and the smaller pulley at F and H, as shown in Fig. 11.12. Through O_2, draw O_2M parallel to FE.

From the geometry of the figure, we find that O_2M will be perpendicular to O_1E.

Let the angle $MO_2 O_1 = \alpha$ radians.

We know that the length of the belt,

$$L = \text{Arc } GJE + EF + \text{Arc } FKH + HG$$

$$= 2 \,(\text{Arc } JE + EF + \text{Arc } FK) \qquad \qquad \dots (i)$$

From the geometry of the figure, we find that

$$\sin \alpha = \frac{O_1 M}{O_1 O_2} = \frac{O_1 E + EM}{O_1 O_2} = \frac{r_1 + r_2}{x}$$

Since α is very small, therefore putting

$$\sin \alpha = \alpha \text{ (in radians)} = \frac{r_1 + r_2}{x} \qquad \qquad \dots (ii)$$

$\therefore$ $\qquad \qquad$ Arc $JE = r_1 \left(\dfrac{\pi}{2} + \alpha \right)$ $\qquad \qquad \dots (iii)$

Similarly $\quad$ Arc $FK = r_2 \left(\dfrac{\pi}{2} + \alpha \right)$ $\qquad \qquad \dots (iv)$

and $\qquad \qquad EF = MO_2 = \sqrt{(O_1O_2)^2 - (O_1 M)^2} = \sqrt{x^2 - (r_1 + r_2)^2}$

$$= x \sqrt{1 - \left(\frac{r_1 + r_2}{x} \right)^2}$$

Expanding this equation by binomial theorem,

$$EF = x\left[1 - \frac{1}{2}\left(\frac{r_1 + r_2}{x}\right)^2 + \ldots\right] = x - \frac{(r_1 + r_2)^2}{2x} \qquad \ldots(v)$$

Substituting the values of arc *JE* from equation (*iii*), arc *FK* from equation (*iv*) and *EF* from equation (*v*) in equation (*i*), we get

$$L = 2\left[r_1\left(\frac{\pi}{2} + \alpha\right) + x - \frac{(r_1 + r_2)^2}{2x} + r_2\left(\frac{\pi}{2} + \alpha\right)\right]$$

$$= 2\left[r_1 \times \frac{\pi}{2} + r_1 . \alpha + x - \frac{(r_1 + r_2)^2}{2x} + r_2 \times \frac{\pi}{2} + r_2 . \alpha\right]$$

$$= 2\left[\frac{\pi}{2}(r_1 + r_2) + \alpha(r_1 + r_2) + x - \frac{(r_1 + r_2)^2}{2x}\right]$$

$$= \pi(r_1 + r_2) + 2\alpha(r_1 + r_2) + 2x - \frac{(r_1 + r_2)^2}{x}$$

Substituting the value of $\alpha = \dfrac{r_1 + r_2}{x}$ from equation (*ii*),

$$L = \pi(r_1 + r_2) + \frac{2(r_1 + r_2)}{x} \times (r_1 + r_2) + 2x - \frac{(r_1 + r_2)^2}{x}$$

$$= \pi(r_1 + r_2) + \frac{2(r_1 + r_2)^2}{x} + 2x - \frac{(r_1 + r_2)^2}{x}$$

$$= \pi(r_1 + r_2) + 2x + \frac{(r_1 + r_2)^2}{x} \qquad \ldots\text{(In terms of pulley radii)}$$

$$= \frac{\pi}{2}(d_1 + d_2) + 2x + \frac{(d_1 + d_2)^2}{4x} \qquad \ldots\text{(In terms of pulley diameters)}$$

It may be noted that the above expression is a function of $(r_1 + r_2)$. It is thus obvious that if sum of the radii of the two pulleys be constant, then length of the belt required will also remain constant, provided the distance between centres of the pulleys remain unchanged.

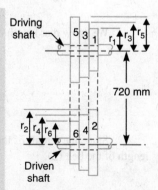

Fig. 11.13.

Example 11.3. *A shaft which rotates at a constant speed of 160 r.p.m. is connected by belting to a parallel shaft 720 mm apart, which has to run at 60, 80 and 100 r.p.m. The smallest pulley on the driving shaft is 40 mm in radius. Determine the remaining radii of the two stepped pulleys for 1. a crossed belt, and 2. an open belt. Neglect belt thickness and slip.*

Solution. Given : $N_1 = N_3 = N_5 = 160$ r.p.m. ; $x = 720$ mm ; $N_2 = 60$ r.p.m.; $N_4 = 80$ r.p.m.; $N_6 = 100$ r.p.m. ; $r_1 = 40$ mm

Let r_2, r_3, r_4, r_5 and r_6 be the radii of the pulleys 2, 3, 4, 5, and 6 respectively, as shown in Fig. 11.13.

1. For a crossed belt

We know that for pulleys 1 and 2,

$$\frac{N_2}{N_1} = \frac{r_1}{r_2}$$

or

$$r_2 = r_1 \times \frac{N_1}{N_2} = 40 \times \frac{160}{60} = 106.7 \text{ mm } \textbf{Ans.}$$

and for pulleys 3 and 4,

$$\frac{N_4}{N_3} = \frac{r_3}{r_4} \quad \text{or} \quad r_4 = r_3 \times \frac{N_3}{N_4} = r_3 \times \frac{160}{80} = 2\, r_3$$

We know that for a crossed belt drive,

$$r_1 + r_2 = r_3 + r_4 = r_5 + r_6 = 40 + 106.7 = 146.7 \text{ mm} \qquad \text{...}(i)$$

$\therefore$

$$r_3 + 2\, r_3 = 146.7 \quad \text{or} \quad r_3 = 146.7/3 = 48.9 \text{ mm } \textbf{Ans.}$$

and

$$r_4 = 2\, r_3 = 2 \times 48.9 = 97.8 \text{ mm } \textbf{Ans.}$$

Now for pulleys 5 and 6,

$$\frac{N_6}{N_5} = \frac{r_5}{r_6} \quad \text{or} \quad r_6 = r_5 \times \frac{N_5}{N_6} = r_5 \times \frac{160}{100} = 1.6\, r_5$$

From equation (i),

$$r_5 + 1.6\, r_5 = 146.7 \quad \text{or} \quad r_5 = 146.7/2.6 = 56.4 \text{ mm } \textbf{Ans.}$$

and

$$r_6 = 1.6\, r_5 = 1.6 \times 56.4 = 90.2 \text{ mm } \textbf{Ans.}$$

2. For an open belt

We know that for pulleys 1 and 2,

$$\frac{N_2}{N_1} = \frac{r_1}{r_2} \quad \text{or} \quad r_2 = r_1 \times \frac{N_1}{N_2} = 40 \times \frac{160}{60} = 106.7 \text{ mm } \textbf{Ans.}$$

and for pulleys 3 and 4,

$$\frac{N_4}{N_3} = \frac{r_3}{r_4} \quad \text{or} \quad r_4 = r_3 \times \frac{N_3}{N_4} = r_3 \times \frac{160}{80} = 2\, r_3$$

We know that length of belt for an open belt drive,

$$L = \pi(r_1 + r_2) + \frac{(r_2 - r_1)^2}{x} + 2x$$

$$= \pi(40 + 106.7) + \frac{(106.7 - 40)^2}{720} + 2 \times 720 = 1907 \text{ mm}$$

Since the length of the belt in an open belt drive is constant, therefore for pulleys 3 and 4, length of the belt (L),

$$1907 = \pi(r_3 + r_4) + \frac{(r_4 - r_3)^2}{x} + 2x$$

$$= \pi(r_3 + 2r_3) + \frac{(2r_3 - r_3)^2}{720} + 2 \times 720$$

$$= 9.426 \, r_3 + 0.0014 \, (r_3)^2 + 1440$$

or $\quad 0.0014 \, (r_3)^2 + 9.426 \, r_3 - 467 = 0$

$$\therefore \quad r_3 = \frac{-9.426 \pm \sqrt{(9.426)^2 + 4 \times 0.0014 \times 467}}{2 \times 0.0014}$$

$$= \frac{-9.426 \pm 9.564}{0.0028} = 49.3 \text{ mm } \textbf{Ans.}$$

...(Taking +ve sign)

and $\quad r_4 = 2 \, r_3 = 2 \times 49.3 = 98.6 \text{ mm } \textbf{Ans.}$

Now for pulleys 5 and 6,

$$\frac{N_6}{N_5} = \frac{r_5}{r_6} \quad \text{or}$$

$$r_6 = \frac{N_5}{N_6} \times r_5 = \frac{160}{100} \times r_5 = 1.6 \, r_5$$

and length of the belt (L),

$$1907 = \pi(r_5 + r_6) + \frac{(r_6 - r_5)^2}{x} + 2x$$

$$= \pi(r_5 + 1.6 \, r_5) + \frac{(1.6 \, r_5 - r_5)^2}{720} + 2 \times 720$$

$$= 8.17 \, r_5 + 0.0005 \, (r_5)^2 + 1440$$

or $\quad 0.0005 \, (r_5)^2 + 8.17 \, r_5 - 467 = 0$

$$\therefore \quad r_5 = \frac{-8.17 \pm \sqrt{(8.17)^2 + 4 \times 0.0005 \times 467}}{2 \times 0.0005}$$

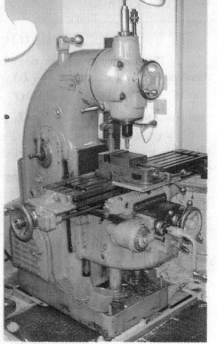

Milling machine is used for dressing surfaces by rotary cutters.

Note : This picture is given as additional information.

$$= \frac{-8.17 \pm 8.23}{0.001} = 60 \text{ mm } \textbf{Ans.}$$

...(Taking +ve sign)

and $\quad r_6 = 1.6 \, r_5 = 1.6 \times 60 = 96 \text{ mm } \textbf{Ans.}$

11.13. Power Transmitted by a Belt

Fig. 11.14 shows the driving pulley (or driver) *A* and the driven pulley (or follower) *B*. We have already discussed that the driving pulley pulls the belt from one side and delivers the same to the other side. It is thus obvious that the tension on the former side (*i.e.* tight side) will be greater than the latter side (*i.e.* slack side) as shown in Fig. 11.14.

Let $\quad T_1$ and T_2 = Tensions in the tight and slack side of the belt respectively in newtons,

r_1 and r_2 = Radii of the driver and follower respectively, and

v = Velocity of the belt in m/s.

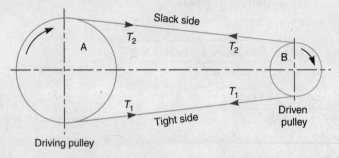

Fig. 11.14. Power transmitted by a belt.

The effective turning (driving) force at the circumference of the follower is the difference between the two tensions (*i.e.* $T_1 - T_2$).

∴ Work done per second = $(T_1 - T_2) v$ N-m/s

and power transmitted, $\qquad P = (T_1 - T_2) v$ W $\qquad \qquad$ ...($∵$ 1 N-m/s = 1 W)

A little consideration will show that the torque exerted on the driving pulley is $(T_1 - T_2) r_1$. Similarly, the torque exerted on the driven pulley *i.e.* follower is $(T_1 - T_2) r_2$.

11.14. Ratio of Driving Tensions For Flat Belt Drive

Consider a driven pulley rotating in the clockwise direction as shown in Fig. 11.15.

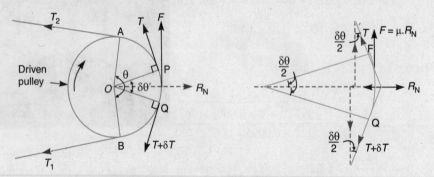

Fig. 11.15. Ratio of driving tensions for flat belt.

Let $\qquad T_1$ = Tension in the belt on the tight side,

$\qquad \qquad T_2$ = Tension in the belt on the slack side, and

$\qquad \qquad \theta$ = Angle of contact in radians (*i.e.* angle subtended by the arc *AB*, along which the belt touches the pulley at the centre).

Now consider a small portion of the belt *PQ*, subtending an angle $\delta\theta$ at the centre of the pulley as shown in Fig. 11.15. The belt *PQ* is in equilibrium under the following forces :

1. Tension T in the belt at P,
2. Tension $(T + \delta T)$ in the belt at Q,
3. Normal reaction R_N, and
4. Frictional force, $F = \mu \times R_N$, where μ is the coefficient of friction between the belt and pulley.

Resolving all the forces horizontally and equating the same,

$$R_N = (T + \delta T) \sin \frac{\delta \theta}{2} + T \sin \frac{\delta \theta}{2} \qquad ...(i)$$

Since the angle $\delta \theta$ is very small, therefore putting $\sin \delta \theta / 2 = \delta \theta / 2$ in equation (i),

$$R_N = (T + \delta T) \frac{\delta \theta}{2} + T \times \frac{\delta \theta}{2} = \frac{T.\delta \theta}{2} + \frac{\delta T.\delta \theta}{2} + \frac{T.\delta \theta}{2} = T.\delta \theta \qquad ...(ii)$$

$$...\left(\text{Neglecting } \frac{\delta T.\delta \theta}{2} \right)$$

Now resolving the forces vertically, we have

$$\mu \times R_N = (T + \delta T) \cos \frac{\delta \theta}{2} - T \cos \frac{\delta \theta}{2} \qquad ...(iii)$$

Since the angle $\delta \theta$ is very small, therefore putting $\cos \delta \theta / 2 = 1$ in equation (iii),

$$\mu \times R_N = T + \delta T - T = \delta T \quad \text{or} \quad R_N = \frac{\delta T}{\mu} \qquad ...(iv)$$

Equating the values of R_N from equations (ii) and (iv),

$$T.\delta \theta = \frac{\delta T}{\mu} \quad \text{or} \quad \frac{\delta T}{T} = \mu.\delta \theta$$

Integrating both sides between the limits T_2 and T_1 and from 0 to θ respectively,

i.e.
$$\int_{T_2}^{T_1} \frac{\delta T}{T} = \mu \int_0^\theta \delta \theta \qquad \text{or} \qquad \log_e \left(\frac{T_1}{T_2} \right) = \mu.\theta \quad \text{or} \quad \frac{T_1}{T_2} = e^{\mu.\theta} \qquad ...(v)$$

Equation (v) can be expressed in terms of corresponding logarithm to the base 10, *i.e.*

$$2.3 \log \left(\frac{T_1}{T_2} \right) = \mu.\theta$$

The above expression gives the relation between the tight side and slack side tensions, in terms of coefficient of friction and the angle of contact.

11.15. Determination of Angle of Contact

When the two pulleys of different diameters are connected by means of an open belt as shown in Fig. 11.16 (a), then the angle of contact or lap (θ) at the smaller pulley must be taken into consideration.

Let r_1 = Radius of larger pulley,

r_2 = Radius of smaller pulley, and

x = Distance between centres of two pulleys (*i.e.* $O_1 O_2$).

From Fig. 11.16 (a),

$$\sin \alpha = \frac{O_1 M}{O_1 O_2} = \frac{O_1 E - ME}{O_1 O_2} = \frac{r_1 - r_2}{x} \qquad ...(\because ME = O_2 F = r_2)$$

∴ Angle of contact or lap,

$$\theta = (180° - 2\alpha) \frac{\pi}{180} \text{ rad}$$

A little consideration will show that when the two pulleys are connected by means of a crossed belt as shown in Fig. 11.16 (b), then the angle of contact or lap (θ) on both the pulleys is same. From Fig. 11.16 (b),

$$\sin \alpha = \frac{O_1 M}{O_1 O_2} = \frac{O_1 E + ME}{O_1 O_2} = \frac{r_1 + r_2}{x}$$

∴ Angle of contact or lap, $\theta = (180° + 2\alpha) \dfrac{\pi}{180}$ rad

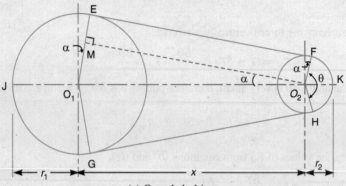

(a) Open belt drive.

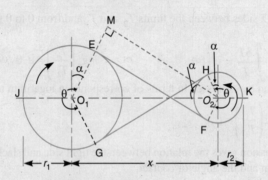

(b) Crossed belt drive.

Fig. 11.16.

Example 11.4. *Find the power transmitted by a belt running over a pulley of 600 mm diameter at 200 r.p.m. The coefficient of friction between the belt and the pulley is 0.25, angle of lap 160° and maximum tension in the belt is 2500 N.*

Solution. Given : $d = 600$ mm $= 0.6$ m ; $N = 200$ r.p.m. ; $\mu = 0.25$; $\theta = 160° = 160 \times \pi / 180$ $= 2.793$ rad ; $T_1 = 2500$ N

We know that velocity of the belt,

$$v = \frac{\pi d . N}{60} = \frac{\pi \times 0.6 \times 200}{60} = 6.284 \text{ m/s}$$

Let $T_2 =$ Tension in the slack side of the belt.

We know that $2.3 \log \left(\dfrac{T_1}{T_2} \right) = \mu . \theta = 0.25 \times 2.793 = 0.6982$

$$\log\left(\frac{T_1}{T_2}\right) = \frac{0.6982}{2.3} = 0.3036$$

∴ $$\frac{T_1}{T_2} = 2.01 \qquad \text{...(Taking antilog of 0.3036)}$$

and $$T_2 = \frac{T_1}{2.01} = \frac{2500}{2.01} = 1244 \, \text{N}$$

We know that power transmitted by the belt,

$$P = (T_1 - T_2) \, v = (2500 - 1244) \, 6.284 = 7890 \, \text{W}$$

$$= 7.89 \, \text{kW} \quad \textbf{Ans.}$$

Another model of milling machine.

Note : This picture is given as additional information.

Example 11.5. *A casting weighing 9 kN hangs freely from a rope which makes 2.5 turns round a drum of 300 mm diameter revolving at 20 r.p.m. The other end of the rope is pulled by a man. The coefficient of friction is 0.25. Determine 1. The force required by the man, and 2. The power to raise the casting.*

Solution. Given : $W = T_1 = 9 \, \text{kN} = 9000 \, \text{N}$; $d = 300 \, \text{mm} = 0.3 \, \text{m}$; $N = 20 \, \text{r.p.m.}$; $\mu = 0.25$

1. *Force required by the man*

Let T_2 = Force required by the man.

Since the rope makes 2.5 turns round the drum, therefore angle of contact,

$$\theta = 2.5 \times 2\pi = 5\pi \, \text{rad}$$

We know that
$$2.3 \log\left(\frac{T_1}{T_2}\right) = \mu.\theta = 0.25 \times 5\pi = 3.9275$$

$$\log\left(\frac{T_1}{T_2}\right) = \frac{3.9275}{2.3} = 1.71 \quad \text{or} \quad \frac{T_1}{T_2} = 51$$

...(Taking antilog of 1.71)

$$\therefore \qquad T_2 = \frac{T_1}{51} = \frac{9000}{51} = 176.47 \text{ N} \text{ Ans.}$$

2. *Power to raise the casting*

We know that velocity of the rope,

$$v = \frac{\pi d.N}{60} = \frac{\pi \times 0.3 \times 20}{60} = 0.3142 \text{ m/s}$$

∴ Power to raise the casting,

$$P = (T_1 - T_2) \, v = (9000 - 176.47) \, 0.3142 = 2772 \text{ W}$$

$$= 2.772 \text{ kW} \text{ Ans.}$$

Example 11.6. *Two pulleys, one 450 mm diameter and the other 200 mm diameter are on parallel shafts 1.95 m apart and are connected by a crossed belt. Find the length of the belt required and the angle of contact between the belt and each pulley.*

What power can be transmitted by the belt when the larger pulley rotates at 200 rev/min, if the maximum permissible tension in the belt is 1 kN, and the coefficient of friction between the belt and pulley is 0.25 ?

Solution. Given : d_1 = 450 mm = 0.45 m or r_1 = 0.225 m ; d_2 = 200 mm = 0.2 m or r_2 = 0.1 m ; x = 1.95 m ; N_1 = 200 r.p.m. ; T_1 = 1 kN = 1000 N ; μ = 0.25

We know that speed of the belt,

$$v = \frac{\pi d_1.N_1}{60} = \frac{\pi \times 0.45 \times 200}{60} = 4.714 \text{ m/s}$$

Length of the belt

We know that length of the crossed belt,

$$L = \pi(r_1 + r_2) + 2x + \frac{(r_1 + r_2)^2}{x}$$

$$= \pi(0.225 + 0.1) + 2 \times 1.95 + \frac{(0.225 + 0.1)^2}{1.95} = 4.975 \text{ m} \text{ Ans.}$$

Angle of contact between the belt and each pulley

Let $\qquad \theta$ = Angle of contact between the belt and each pulley.

We know that for a crossed belt drive,

$$\sin\alpha = \frac{r_1 + r_2}{x} = \frac{0.225 + 0.1}{1.95} = 0.1667 \quad \text{or} \quad \alpha = 9.6°$$

$$\therefore \qquad \theta = 180° + 2\alpha = 180° + 2 \times 9.6° = 199.2°$$

$$= 199.2 \times \frac{\pi}{180} = 3.477 \text{ rad} \text{ Ans.}$$

Power transmitted

Let T_2 = Tension in the slack side of the belt.

We know that

$$2.3 \log\left(\frac{T_1}{T_2}\right) = \mu.\theta = 0.25 \times 3.477 = 0.8692$$

$$\log\left(\frac{T_1}{T_2}\right) = \frac{0.8692}{2.3} = 0.378 \quad \text{or} \quad \frac{T_1}{T_2} = 2.387 \qquad ...(\text{Taking antilog of } 0.378)$$

$$\therefore \qquad T_2 = \frac{T_1}{2.387} = \frac{1000}{2.387} = 419 \text{ N}$$

We know that power transmitted,

$$P = (T_1 - T_2)\, v = (1000 - 419)\, 4.714 = 2740 \text{ W} = 2.74 \text{ kW} \quad \textbf{Ans.}$$

11.16. Centrifugal Tension

Since the belt continuously runs over the pulleys, therefore, some centrifugal force is caused, whose effect is to increase the tension on both, tight as well as the slack sides. The tension caused by centrifugal force is called *centrifugal tension*. At lower belt speeds (less than 10 m/s), the centrifugal tension is very small, but at higher belt speeds (more than 10 m/s), its effect is considerable and thus should be taken into account.

Consider a small portion *PQ* of the belt subtending an angle *d*θ the centre of the pulley as shown in Fig. 11.17.

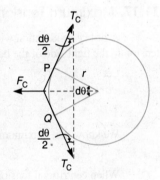

Fig. 11.17. Centrifugal tension.

Let m = Mass of the belt per unit length in kg,

v = Linear velocity of the belt in m/s,

r = Radius of the pulley over which the belt runs in metres, and

T_C = Centrifugal tension acting tangentially at *P* and *Q* in newtons.

We know that length of the belt *PQ*

$$= r.\, d\theta$$

and mass of the belt *PQ* $= m.\, r.\, d\theta$

∴ Centrifugal force acting on the belt *PQ*,

$$F_C = (m.r.d\theta)\frac{v^2}{r} = m.d\theta.v^2$$

The centrifugal tension T_C acting tangentially at *P* and *Q* keeps the belt in equilibrium.

Now resolving the forces (*i.e.* centrifugal force and centrifugal tension) horizontally and equating the same, we have

$$T_C \sin\left(\frac{d\theta}{2}\right) + T_C \sin\left(\frac{d\theta}{2}\right) = F_C = m.d\theta.v^2$$

Since the angle *d*θ is very small, therefore, putting $\sin\left(\frac{d\theta}{2}\right) = \frac{d\theta}{2}$, in the above expression,

$$2T_C \left(\frac{d\theta}{2} \right) = m.d\theta.v^2 \quad \text{or} \quad T_C = m \cdot v^2$$

Notes : 1. When the centrifugal tension is taken into account, then total tension in the tight side,

$$T_{t1} = T_1 + T_C$$

and total tension in the slack side,

$$T_{t2} = T_2 + T_C$$

2. Power transmitted, $\quad P = (T_{t1} - T_{t2})\, v$ ...(in watts)

$$= [(T_1 + T_C) - (T_2 + T_C)]\, v = (T_1 - T_2)\, v \quad \text{...(same as before)}$$

Thus we see that centrifugal tension has no effect on the power transmitted.

3. The ratio of driving tensions may also be written as

$$2.3 \log \left(\frac{T_{t1} - T_C}{T_{t2} - T_C} \right) = \mu.\theta$$

where T_{t1} = Maximum or total tension in the belt.

11.17. Maximum Tension in the Belt

A little consideration will show that the maximum tension in the belt (T) is equal to the total tension in the tight side of the belt (T_{t1}).

    Let σ = Maximum safe stress in N/mm^2,

                   b = Width of the belt in mm, and

                   t = Thickness of the belt in mm.

We know that maximum tension in the belt,

        T = Maximum stress × cross-sectional area of belt = $\sigma. b. t$

When centrifugal tension is neglected, then

        T (or T_{t1}) = T_1, *i.e.* Tension in the tight side of the belt

and when centrifugal tension is considered, then

        T (or T_{t1}) = $T_1 + T_C$

11.18. Condition For the Transmission of Maximum Power

We know that power transmitted by a belt,

$$P = (T_1 - T_2)\, v \quad \text{...(}i\text{)}$$

where T_1 = Tension in the tight side of the belt in newtons,

               T_2 = Tension in the slack side of the belt in newtons, and

               v = Velocity of the belt in m/s.

From Art. 11.14, we have also seen that the ratio of driving tensions is

$$\frac{T_1}{T_2} = e^{\mu.\theta} \quad \text{or} \quad T_2 = \frac{T_1}{e^{\mu.\theta}} \quad \text{...(}ii\text{)}$$

Substituting the value of T_2 in equation (i),

$$P = \left(T_1 - \frac{T_1}{e^{\mu.\theta}} \right) v = T_1 \left(1 - \frac{1}{e^{\mu.\theta}} \right) v = T_1.v.C \quad \text{...(}iii\text{)}$$

where
$$C = 1 - \frac{1}{e^{\mu.\theta}}$$

We know that
$$T_1 = T - T_C$$

where
$$T = \text{Maximum tension to which the belt can be subjected in newtons, and}$$

$$T_C = \text{Centrifugal tension in newtons.}$$

Substituting the value of T_1 in equation (*iii*),

$$P = (T - T_C) v.C$$
$$= (T - m.v^2) v.C = (T.v - m v^3) C \quad \text{... (Substituting } T_C = m. v^2)$$

For maximum power, differentiate the above expression with respect to v and equate to zero,
i.e.

$$\frac{dP}{dv} = 0 \quad \text{or} \quad \frac{d}{dv}(T.v - mv^3)C = 0$$

$$\therefore \quad T - 3 m . v^2 = 0$$

or
$$T - 3 T_C = 0 \text{ or } T = 3 T_C \qquad \qquad \text{...(iv)}$$

It shows that when the power transmitted is maximum, 1/3rd of the maximum tension is absorbed as centrifugal tension.

Notes : 1. We know that $T_1 = T - T_C$ and for maximum power, $T_C = \dfrac{T}{3}$.

$$\therefore \qquad T_1 = T - \frac{T}{3} = \frac{2T}{3}$$

2. From equation (*iv*), the velocity of the belt for the maximum power,

$$v = \sqrt{\frac{T}{3m}}$$

Example. 11.7. *A shaft rotating at 200 r.p.m. drives another shaft at 300 r.p.m. and transmits 6 kW through a belt. The belt is 100 mm wide and 10 mm thick. The distance between the shafts is 4m. The smaller pulley is 0.5 m in diameter. Calculate the stress in the belt, if it is 1. an open belt drive, and 2. a cross belt drive. Take* μ *= 0.3.*

Solution. Given : N_1 = 200 r.p.m. ; N_2 = 300 r.p.m. ; P = 6 kW = 6 × 10³ W ; b = 100 mm ; t = 10 mm ; x = 4 m ; d_2 = 0.5 m ; μ = 0.3

Let
$$σ = \text{Stress in the belt.}$$

1. *Stress in the belt for an open belt drive*

First of all, let us find out the diameter of larger pulley (d_1). We know that

$$\frac{N_2}{N_1} = \frac{d_1}{d_2} \quad \text{or} \quad d_1 = \frac{N_2.d_2}{N_1} = \frac{300 \times 0.5}{200} = 0.75\,\text{m}$$

and velocity of the belt,
$$v = \frac{\pi d_2.N_2}{60} = \frac{\pi \times 0.5 \times 300}{60} = 7.855 \text{ m/s}$$

Now let us find the angle of contact on the smaller pulley. We know that, for an open belt drive,

$$\sin α = \frac{r_1 - r_2}{x} = \frac{d_1 - d_2}{2x} = \frac{0.75 - 0.5}{2 \times 4} = 0.03125 \text{ or } α = 1.8°$$

∴ Angle of contact, $\theta = 180° - 2\alpha = 180 - 2 \times 1.8 = 176.4°$

$$= 176.4 \times \pi / 180 = 3.08 \text{ rad}$$

Let T_1 = Tension in the tight side of the belt, and

T_2 = Tension in the slack side of the belt.

We know that

$$2.3 \log\left(\frac{T_1}{T_2}\right) = \mu.\theta = 0.3 \times 3.08 = 0.924$$

∴

$$\log\left(\frac{T_1}{T_2}\right) = \frac{0.924}{2.3} = 0.4017 \text{ or } \frac{T_1}{T_2} = 2.52 \qquad ...(i)$$

...(Taking antilog of 0.4017)

We also know that power transmitted (P),

$$6 \times 10^3 = (T_1 - T_2)\, v = (T_1 - T_2)\, 7.855$$

∴ $\qquad T_1 - T_2 = 6 \times 10^3 / 7.855 = 764 \text{ N} \qquad ...(ii)$

From equations (i) and (ii),

$$T_1 = 1267 \text{ N, and } T_2 = 503 \text{ N}$$

We know that maximum tension in the belt (T_1),

$$1267 = \sigma.\, b.\, t = \sigma \times 100 \times 10 = 1000\,\sigma$$

∴ $\qquad \sigma = 1267 / 1000 = 1.267 \text{ N/mm}^2 = 1.267 \text{ MPa } \textbf{Ans.}$

...[∵ 1 MPa = 1 MN/m² = 1 N/mm²]

Stress in the belt for a cross belt drive

We know that for a cross belt drive,

$$\sin\alpha = \frac{r_1 + r_2}{x} = \frac{d_1 + d_2}{2x} = \frac{0.75 + 0.5}{2 \times 4} = 0.1562 \text{ or } \alpha = 9°$$

∴ Angle of contact, $\theta = 180° + 2\alpha = 180 + 2 \times 9 = 198°$

$$= 198 \times \pi / 180 = 3.456 \text{ rad}$$

We know that

$$2.3 \log\left(\frac{T_1}{T_2}\right) = \mu.\theta = 0.3 \times 3.456 = 1.0368$$

$$\log\left(\frac{T_1}{T_2}\right) = \frac{1.0368}{2.3} = 0.4508 \text{ or } \frac{T_1}{T_2} = 2.82 \qquad ...(iii)$$

...(Taking antilog of 0.4508)

From equations (ii) and (iii),

$$T_1 = 1184 \text{ N and } T_2 = 420 \text{ N}$$

We know that maximum tension in the belt (T_1),

$$1184 = \sigma.\, b.\, t = \sigma \times 100 \times 10 = 1000\,\sigma$$

∴ $\qquad \sigma = 1184 / 1000 = 1.184 \text{ N/mm}^2 = 1.184 \text{ MPa } \textbf{Ans.}$

Example 11.8. *A leather belt is required to transmit 7.5 kW from a pulley 1.2 m in diameter, running at 250 r.p.m. The angle embraced is 165° and the coefficient of friction between the belt and the pulley is 0.3. If the safe working stress for the leather belt is 1.5 MPa, density of leather 1 Mg/m³ and thickness of belt 10 mm, determine the width of the belt taking centrifugal tension into account.*

Solution. Given : $P = 7.5$ kW $= 7500$ W ; $d = 1.2$ m ; $N = 250$ r.p.m. ; $\theta = 165° = 165 \times \pi / 180$ $= 2.88$ rad ; $\mu = 0.3$; $\sigma = 1.5$ MPa $= 1.5 \times 10^6$ * N/m² ; $\rho = 1$ Mg/m³ $= 1 \times 10^6$ g/m³ $= 1000$ kg/m³; $t = 10$ mm $= 0.01$ m

Let $\qquad b$ = Width of belt in metres,

$\qquad\qquad T_1$ = Tension in the tight side of the belt in N, and

$\qquad\qquad T_2$ = Tension in the slack side of the belt in N.

We know that velocity of the belt,

$$v = \pi d . N / 60 = \pi \times 1.2 \times 250/60 = 15.71 \text{ m/s}$$

and power transmitted (P),

$$7500 = (T_1 - T_2) v = (T_1 - T_2) 15.71$$

$\therefore \qquad\qquad T_1 - T_2 = 7500 / 15.71 = 477.4 \text{ N}$ $\qquad\qquad$ ...(*i*)

We know that

$$2.3 \log\left(\frac{T_1}{T_2}\right) = \mu.\theta = 0.3 \times 2.88 = 0.864$$

$$\log\left(\frac{T_1}{T_2}\right) = \frac{0.864}{2.3} = 0.3756 \quad \text{or} \quad \frac{T_1}{T_2} = 2.375 \qquad ...(ii)$$

$\qquad\qquad\qquad\qquad\qquad\qquad\qquad\qquad\qquad\qquad$ ...(Taking antilog of 0.3756)

From equations (*i*) and (*ii*),

$$T_1 = 824.6 \text{ N}, \quad \text{and} \quad T_2 = 347.2 \text{ N}$$

We know that mass of the belt per metre length,

$$m = \text{Area} \times \text{length} \times \text{density} = b.t.l.\rho$$

$$= b \times 0.01 \times 1 \times 1000 = 10 \, b \text{ kg}$$

$\therefore$ Centrifugal tension,

$$T_C = m. v^2 = 10 \, b \, (15.71)^2 = 2468 \, b \text{ N}$$

and maximum tension in the belt,

$$T = \sigma. b. t = 1.5 \times 10^6 \times b \times 0.01 = 15 \, 000 \, b \text{ N}$$

We know that $\qquad\qquad T = T_1 + T_C$ or $15000 \, b = 824.6 + 2468 \, b$

$15 \, 000 \, b - 2468 \, b = 824.6$ or $12 \, 532 \, b = 824.6$

$\therefore \qquad\qquad b = 824.6 / 12532 = 0.0658 \text{ m} = 65.8 \text{ mm}$ **Ans.**

Example. 11.9. *Determine the width of a 9.75 mm thick leather belt required to transmit 15 kW from a motor running at 900 r.p.m. The diameter of the driving pulley of the motor is 300 mm. The driven pulley runs at 300 r.p.m. and the distance between the centre of two pulleys is 3 metres. The density of the leather is 1000 kg/m³. The maximum allowable stress in the leather is 2.5 MPa. The coefficient of friction between the leather and pulley is 0.3. Assume open belt drive and neglect the sag and slip of the belt.*

Solution. Given : $t = 9.75$ mm $= 9.75 \times 10^{-3}$ m ; $P = 15$ kW $= 15 \times 10^3$ W ; $N_1 = 900$ r.p.m. ; $d_1 = 300$ mm $= 0.3$ m ; $N_2 = 300$ r.p.m. ; $x = 3$m ; $\rho = 1000$ kg/m³ ; $\sigma = 2.5$ MPa $= 2.5 \times 10^6$ N/m² ; $\mu = 0.3$

---

* $\quad 1$ MPa $= 1 \times 10^6$ N/m²

First of all, let us find out the diameter of the driven pulley (d_2). We know that

$$\frac{N_2}{N_1} = \frac{d_1}{d_2} \quad \text{or} \quad d_2 = \frac{N_1 \times d_1}{N_2} = \frac{900 \times 0.3}{300} = 0.9 \text{ m}$$

and velocity of the belt,

$$v = \frac{\pi d_1 N_1}{60} = \frac{\pi \times 0.3 \times 900}{60} = 14.14 \text{ m/s}$$

For an open belt drive,

$$\sin \alpha = \frac{r_2 - r_1}{x} = \frac{d_2 - d_1}{2x} = \frac{0.9 - 0.3}{2 \times 3} = 0.1 \qquad ...(\because d_2 > d_1)$$

or

$$\alpha = 5.74°$$

∴ Angle of lap, $\theta = 180° - 2\alpha = 180 - 2 \times 5.74 = 168.52°$

$$= 168.52 \times \pi / 180 = 2.94 \text{ rad}$$

Let T_1 = Tension in the tight side of the belt, and

T_2 = Tension in the slack side of the belt.

We know that

$$2.3 \log\left(\frac{T_1}{T_2}\right) = \mu.\theta = 0.3 \times 2.94 = 0.882$$

$$\log\left(\frac{T_1}{T_2}\right) = \frac{0.882}{2.3} = 0.3835 \quad \text{or} \quad \frac{T_1}{T_2} = 2.42 \qquad ...(i)$$

... (Taking antilog of 0.3835)

We also know that power transmitted (P),

$$15 \times 10^3 = (T_1 - T_2) v = (T_1 - T_2) 14.14$$

∴ $T_1 - T_2 = 15 \times 10^3 / 14.14 = 1060 \text{ N}$ .... (ii)

From equations (i) and (ii),

$$T_1 = 1806 \text{ N}$$

Let b = Width of the belt in metres.

We know that mass of the belt per metre length,

$$m = \text{Area} \times \text{length} \times \text{density} = b.t.l.\rho$$

$$= b \times 9.75 \times 10^{-3} \times 1 \times 1000 = 9.75 \, b \text{ kg}$$

∴ Centrifugal tension,

$$T_C = m.v^2 = 9.75 \, b \, (14.14)^2 = 1950 \, b \text{ N}$$

Maximum tension in the belt,

$$T = \sigma. b. t = 2.5 \times 10^6 \times b \times 9.75 \times 10^{-3} = 24\,400 \, b \text{ N}$$

We know that $T = T_1 + T_C$ or $T - T_C = T_1$

$$24\,400 \, b - 1950 \, b = 1806 \quad \text{or} \quad 22\,450 \, b = 1806$$

∴ $b = 1806 / 22\,450 = 0.080 \text{ m} = 80 \text{ mm}$ **Ans.**

Example. 11.10. *A pulley is driven by a flat belt, the angle of lap being 120°. The belt is 100 mm wide by 6 mm thick and density 1000 kg/m³. If the coefficient of friction is 0.3 and the maximum stress in the belt is not to exceed 2 MPa, find the greatest power which the belt can transmit and the corresponding speed of the belt.*

Solution. Given : $\theta = 120° = 120 \times \pi / 180 = 2.1$ rad ; $b = 100$ mm $= 0.1$ m ; $t = 6$ mm $= 0.006$ m ; $\rho = 1000$ kg / m³ ; $\mu = 0.3$; $\sigma = 2$ MPa $= 2 \times 10^6$ N/m²

Speed of the belt for greatest power

We know that maximum tension in the belt,

$$T = \sigma . b . t = 2 \times 10^6 \times 0.1 \times 0.006 = 1200 \text{ N}$$

and mass of the belt per metre length,

$$m = \text{Area} \times \text{length} \times \text{density} = b. t. l. \rho$$
$$= 0.1 \times 0.006 \times 1 \times 1000 = 0.6 \text{ kg/m}$$

∴ Speed of the belt for greatest power,

$$v = \sqrt{\frac{T}{3m}} = \sqrt{\frac{1200}{3 \times 0.6}} = 25.82 \text{ m/s} \qquad \textbf{Ans.}$$

Greatest power which the belt can transmit

We know that for maximum power to be transmitted, centrifugal tension,

$$T_C = T/3 = 1200/3 = 400 \text{ N}$$

and tension in the tight side of the belt,

$$T_1 = T - T_C = 1200 - 400 = 800 \text{ N}$$

Let $\qquad T_2 =$Tension in the slack side of the belt.

We know that

$$2.3 \log\left(\frac{T_1}{T_2}\right) = \mu.\theta = 0.3 \times 2.1 = 0.63$$

$$\log\left(\frac{T_1}{T_2}\right) = \frac{0.63}{2.3} = 0.2739 \text{ or } \frac{T_1}{T_2} = 1.88 \qquad \text{...(Taking antilog of 0.2739)}$$

and $\qquad T_2 = \dfrac{T_1}{1.88} = \dfrac{800}{1.88} = 425.5 \text{ N}$

∴ Greatest power which the belt can transmit,

$$P = (T_1 - T_2) v = (800 - 425.5) 25.82 = 9670 \text{ W} = 9.67 \text{ kW} \quad \textbf{Ans.}$$

Example 11.11. *An open belt drive connects two pulleys 1.2 m and 0.5 m diameter, on parallel shafts 4 metres apart. The mass of the belt is 0.9 kg per metre length and the maximum tension is not to exceed 2000 N.The coefficient of friction is 0.3. The 1.2 m pulley, which is the driver, runs at 200 r.p.m. Due to belt slip on one of the pulleys, the velocity of the driven shaft is only 450 r.p.m. Calculate the torque on each of the two shafts, the power transmitted, and power lost in friction. What is the efficiency of the drive ?*

Solution. Given : $d_1 = 1.2$ m or $r_1 = 0.6$ m ; $d_2 = 0.5$ m or $r_2 = 0.25$ m ; $x = 4$ m ; $m = 0.9$ kg/m; $T = 2000$ N ; $\mu = 0.3$; $N_1 = 200$ r.p.m. ; $N_2 = 450$ r.p.m.

We know that velocity of the belt,

$$v = \frac{\pi d_1 . N_1}{60} = \frac{\pi \times 1.2 \times 200}{60} = 12.57 \text{ m/s}$$

and centrifugal tension, $\qquad T_C = m.v^2 = 0.9 (12.57)^2 = 142 \text{ N}$

∴ Tension in the tight side of the belt,

$$T_1 = T - T_C = 2000 - 142 = 1858 \text{ N}$$

We know that for an open belt drive,

$$\sin \alpha = \frac{r_1 - r_2}{x} = \frac{0.6 - 0.25}{4} = 0.0875 \quad \text{or} \quad \alpha = 5.02°$$

∴ Angle of lap on the smaller pulley,

$$\theta = 180° - 2\,\alpha = 180° - 2 \times 5.02° = 169.96°$$

$$= 169.96 \times \pi \,/\, 180 = 2.967 \text{ rad}$$

Let T_2 = Tension in the slack side of the belt.

We know that

$$2.3 \log\left(\frac{T_1}{T_2}\right) = \mu.\theta = 0.3 \times 2.967 = 0.8901$$

$$\log\left(\frac{T_1}{T_2}\right) = \frac{0.8901}{2.3} = 0.387 \quad \text{or} \quad \frac{T_1}{T_2} = 2.438$$

...(Taking antilog of 0.387)

∴

$$T_2 = \frac{T_1}{2.438} = \frac{1858}{2.438} = 762 \text{ N}$$

Torque on the shaft of larger pulley

We know that torque on the shaft of larger pulley,

$$T_L = (T_1 - T_2)\,r_1 = (1858 - 762)\,0.6 = 657.6 \text{ N-m} \quad \textbf{Ans.}$$

Torque on the shaft of smaller pulley

We know that torque on the shaft of smaller pulley,

$$T_S = (T_1 - T_2)\,r_2 = (1858 - 762)\,0.25 = 274 \text{ N-m} \quad \textbf{Ans.}$$

Power transmitted

We know that the power transmitted,

$$P = (T_1 - T_2)\,v = (1858 - 762)\,12.57 = 13780 \text{ W}$$

$$= 13.78 \text{ kW} \quad \textbf{Ans.}$$

Power lost in friction

We know that input power,

$$P_1 = \frac{T_L \times 2\pi N_1}{60} = \frac{657.6 \times 2\pi \times 200}{60} = 13\ 780 \text{ W} = 13.78 \text{ kW}$$

and output power, $$P_2 = \frac{T_S \times 2\pi N_2}{60} = \frac{274 \times 2\pi \times 450}{60} = 12\ 910 \text{ W} = 12.91 \text{ kW}$$

∴ Power lost in friction = $P_1 - P_2$ = 13.78 − 12.91 = 0.87 kW **Ans.**

Efficiency of the drive

We know that efficiency of the drive,

$$\eta = \frac{\text{Output power}}{\text{Input power}} = \frac{12.91}{13.78} = 0.937 \text{ or } 93.7\% \quad \textbf{Ans.}$$

11.19. Initial Tension in the Belt

When a belt is wound round the two pulleys (*i.e.* driver and follower), its two ends are joined together ; so that the belt may continuously move over the pulleys, since the motion of the belt from the driver and the follower is governed by a firm grip, due to friction between the belt and the pulleys. In order to increase this grip, the belt is tightened up. At this stage, even when the pulleys are stationary, the belt is subjected to some tension, called *initial tension*.

When the driver starts rotating, it pulls the belt from one side (increasing tension in the belt on this side) and delivers it to the other side (decreasing the tension in the belt on that side). The increased tension in one side of the belt is called tension in tight side and the decreased tension in the other side of the belt is called tension in the slack side.

Let T_0 = Initial tension in the belt,

T_1 = Tension in the tight side of the belt,

T_2 = Tension in the slack side of the belt, and

α = Coefficient of increase of the belt length per unit force.

A little consideration will show that the increase of tension in the tight side

$$= T_1 - T_0$$

and increase in the length of the belt on the tight side

$$= \alpha\,(T_1 - T_0) \qquad\qquad ...(i)$$

Similarly, decrease in tension in the slack side

$$= T_0 - T_2$$

and decrease in the length of the belt on the slack side

$$= \alpha\,(T_0 - T_2) \qquad\qquad ...(ii)$$

Assuming that the belt material is perfectly elastic such that the length of the belt remains constant, when it is at rest or in motion, therefore increase in length on the tight side is equal to decrease in the length on the slack side. Thus, equating equations (*i*) and (*ii*),

$$\alpha\,(T_1 - T_0) = \alpha\,(T_0 - T_2) \quad \text{or} \quad T_1 - T_0 = T_0 - T_2$$

$\therefore \qquad\qquad T_0 = \dfrac{T_1 + T_2}{2} \qquad\qquad$ ...(Neglecting centrifugal tension)

$$\qquad\qquad = \dfrac{T_1 + T_2 + 2T_C}{2} \qquad\qquad \text{...(Considering centrifugal tension)}$$

Example. 11.12. *In a flat belt drive the initial tension is 2000 N. The coefficient of friction between the belt and the pulley is 0.3 and the angle of lap on the smaller pulley is 150°. The smaller pulley has a radius of 200 mm and rotates at 500 r.p.m. Find the power in kW transmitted by the belt.*

Solution. Given : $T_0 = 2000$ N ; $\mu_0 = 0.3$; $\theta = 150° = 150° \times \pi / 180 = 2.618$ rad ; $r_2 = 200$ mm or $d_2 = 400$ mm $= 0.4$ m ; $N_2 = 500$ r.p.m.

We know that velocity of the belt,

$$v = \frac{\pi d_2.N_2}{60} = \frac{\pi \times 0.4 \times 500}{60} = 10.47 \text{ m/s}$$

Let T_1 = Tension in the tight side of the belt, and

T_2 = Tension in the slack side of the belt.

We know that initial tension (T_0),

$$2000 = \frac{T_1 + T_2}{2} \quad \text{or} \quad T_1 + T_2 = 4000 \text{ N} \qquad \text{...}(i)$$

We also know that

$$2.3 \log\left(\frac{T_1}{T_2}\right) = \mu.\theta = 0.3 \times 2.618 = 0.7854$$

$$\log\left(\frac{T_1}{T_2}\right) = \frac{0.7854}{2.3} = 0.3415$$

or

$$\frac{T_1}{T_2} = 2.2 \quad \text{...}(ii)$$

...(Taking antilog of 0.3415)

From equations (i) and (ii),

$$T_1 = 2750 \text{ N};$$

and

$$T_2 = 1250 \text{ N}$$

$\therefore$ Power transmitted, $P = (T_1 - T_2) v$

A military tank uses chain, belt and gear drives
for its movement and operation.

$$= (2750 - 1250) \, 10.47$$

$$= 15\,700 \text{ W} = 15.7 \text{ kW} \quad \textbf{Ans.}$$

Example 11.13. *Two parallel shafts whose centre lines are 4.8 m apart, are connected by open belt drive. The diameter of the larger pulley is 1.5 m and that of smaller pulley 1 m. The initial tension in the belt when stationary is 3 kN. The mass of the belt is 1.5 kg / m length. The coefficient of friction between the belt and the pulley is 0.3. Taking centrifugal tension into account, calculate the power transmitted, when the smaller pulley rotates at 400 r.p.m.*

Solution. Given : $x = 4.8$ m ; $d_1 = 1.5$ m ; $d_2 = 1$ m ; $T_0 = 3$ kN $= 3000$ N ; $m = 1.5$ kg / m ; $\mu = 0.3$; $N_2 = 400$ r.p.m.

We know that velocity of the belt,

$$v = \frac{\pi d_2 . N_2}{60} = \frac{\pi \times 1 \times 400}{60} = 21 \text{m/s}$$

and centrifugal tension, $\quad T_C = m.v^2 = 1.5 \, (21)^2 = 661.5$ N

Let $\quad T_1 =$ Tension in the tight side, and

$\quad T_2 =$ Tension in the slack side.

We know that initial tension (T_0),

$$3000 = \frac{T_1 + T_2 + 2T_C}{2} = \frac{T_1 + T_2 + 2 \times 661.5}{2}$$

$\therefore \quad T_1 + T_2 = 3000 \times 2 - 2 \times 661.5 = 4677$ N $\qquad \text{...}(i)$

For an open belt drive,

$$\sin \alpha = \frac{r_1 - r_2}{x} = \frac{d_1 - d_2}{2x} = \frac{1.5 - 1}{2 \times 4.8} = 0.0521 \quad \text{or} \quad \alpha = 3°$$

$\therefore$ Angle of lap on the smaller pulley,

$$\theta = 180° - 2 \, \alpha = 180° - 2 \times 3° = 174°$$

$$= 174° \times \pi / 180 = 3.04 \text{ rad}$$

We know that

$$2.3 \log\left(\frac{T_1}{T_2}\right) = \mu.\theta = 0.3 \times 3.04 = 0.912$$

$$\log\left(\frac{T_1}{T_2}\right) = \frac{0.912}{2.3} = 0.3965 \quad \text{or} \quad \frac{T_1}{T_2} = 2.5 \qquad \qquad ...(ii)$$

...(Taking antilog of 0.3965)

From equations (*i*) and (*ii*),

$$T_1 = 3341 \text{ N} ; \text{ and } T_2 = 1336 \text{ N}$$

∴ Power transmitted,

$$P = (T_1 - T_2) \, v = (3341 - 1336) \, 21 = 42 \, 100 \text{ W} = 42.1 \text{ kW Ans.}$$

Example 11.14. *An open flat belt drive connects two parallel shafts 1.2 metres apart. The driving and the driven shafts rotate at 350 r.p.m. and 140 r.p.m. respectively and the driven pulley is 400 mm in diameter. The belt is 5 mm thick and 80 mm wide. The coefficient of friction between the belt and pulley is 0.3 and the maximum permissible tension in the belting is 1.4 MN/m². Determine:*

1. diameter of the driving pulley, 2. maximum power that may be transmitted by the belting, and 3. required initial belt tension.

Solution. Given : $x = 1.2$ m ; $N_1 = 350$ r.p.m. ; $N_2 = 140$ r.p.m. ; $d_2 = 400$ mm = 0.4 m ; $t = 5$ mm = 0.005 m ; $b = 80$ mm = 0.08 m ; $\mu = 0.3$; $\sigma = 1.4$ MN/m² = 1.4×10^6 N/m²

1. *Diameter of the driving pulley*

Let d_1 = Diameter of the driving pulley.

We know that $\dfrac{N_2}{N_1} = \dfrac{d_1}{d_2}$ or $d_1 = \dfrac{N_2.d_2}{N_1} = \dfrac{140 \times 0.4}{350} = 0.16$ m **Ans.**

2. *Maximum power transmitted by the belting*

First of all, let us find the angle of contact of the belt on the smaller pulley (or driving pulley).

Let θ = Angle of contact of the belt on the driving pulley.

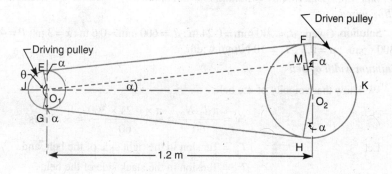

Fig. 11.18

From Fig. 11.18, we find that

$$\sin \alpha = \frac{O_2 M}{O_1 O_2} = \frac{r_2 - r_1}{x} = \frac{d_2 - d_1}{2x} = \frac{0.4 - 0.16}{2 \times 1.2} = 0.1$$

or

$$\alpha = 5.74°$$

∴

$$\theta = 180° - 2\alpha = 180° - 2 \times 5.74° = 168.52°$$
$$= 168.52 \times \pi / 180 = 2.94 \text{ rad}$$

Let

T_1 = Tension in the tight side of the belt, and

T_2 = Tension in the slack side of the belt.

We know that

$$2.3 \log\left(\frac{T_1}{T_2}\right) = \mu.\theta = 0.3 \times 2.94 = 0.882$$

$$\log\left(\frac{T_1}{T_2}\right) = \frac{0.882}{2.3} = 0.3835 \text{ or } \frac{T_1}{T_2} = 2.42 \qquad ...(i)$$

...(Taking antilog of 0.3835)

We know that maximum tension to which the belt can be subjected,

$$T_1 = \sigma \times b \times t = 1.4 \times 10^6 \times 0.08 \times 0.005 = 560 \text{ N}$$

∴

$$T_2 = \frac{T_1}{2.42} = \frac{560}{2.42} = 231.4 \text{ N} \qquad ...\text{[From equation } (i)\text{]}$$

Velocity of the belt,

$$v = \frac{\pi d_1.N_1}{60} = \frac{\pi \times 0.16 \times 350}{60} = 2.93 \text{ m/s}$$

∴ Power transmitted,

$$P = (T_1 - T_2)\, v = (560 - 231.4)\, 2.93 = 963 \text{ W} = 0.963 \text{ kW} \textbf{ Ans.}$$

3. Required initial belt tension

We know that the initial belt tension,

$$T_0 = \frac{T_1 + T_2}{2} = \frac{560 + 231.4}{2} = 395.7 \text{ N Ans.}$$

Example 11.15. *An open belt running over two pulleys 240 mm and 600 mm diameter connects two parallel shafts 3 metres apart and transmits 4 kW from the smaller pulley that rotates at 300 r.p.m. Coefficient of friction between the belt and the pulley is 0.3 and the safe working tension is 10N per mm width. Determine : 1. minimum width of the belt, 2. initial belt tension, and 3. length of the belt required.*

Solution. Given : $d_2 = 240$ mm $= 0.24$ m ; $d_1 = 600$ mm $= 0.6$ m ; $x = 3$ m ; $P = 4$ kW $= 4000$ W; $N_2 = 300$ r.p.m. ; $\mu = 0.3$; $T_1 = 10$ N/mm width

1. Minimum width of belt

We know that velocity of the belt,

$$v = \frac{\pi d_2.N_2}{60} = \frac{\pi \times 0.24 \times 300}{60} = 3.77 \text{ m/s}$$

Let

T_1 = Tension in the tight side of the belt, and

T_2 = Tension in the slack side of the belt.

∴ Power transmitted (P),

$$4000 = (T_1 - T_2)\, v = (T_1 - T_2)\, 3.77$$

or

$$T_1 - T_2 = 4000 / 3.77 = 1061 \text{ N} \qquad ...(i)$$

We know that for an open belt drive,

$$\sin \alpha = \frac{r_1 - r_2}{x} = \frac{d_1 - d_2}{2x} = \frac{0.6 - 0.24}{2 \times 3} = 0.06 \quad \text{or} \quad \alpha = 3.44°$$

and angle of lap on the smaller pulley,

$$\theta = 180° - 2\alpha = 180° - 2 \times 3.44° = 173.12°$$
$$= 173.12 \times \pi / 180 = 3.022 \text{ rad}$$

We know that

$$2.3 \log\left(\frac{T_1}{T_2}\right) = \mu.\theta = 0.3 \times 3.022 = 0.9066$$

$$\log\left(\frac{T_1}{T_2}\right) = \frac{0.9066}{2.3} = 0.3942 \quad \text{or} \quad \frac{T_1}{T_2} = 2.478 \qquad \text{...(ii)}$$

...(Taking antilog of 0.3942)

From equations (*i*) and (*ii*),

$$T_1 = 1779 \text{ N, and } T_2 = 718 \text{ N}$$

Since the safe working tension is 10 N per mm width, therefore minimum width of the belt,

$$b = \frac{T_1}{10} = \frac{1779}{10} = 177.9 \text{ mm} \quad \textbf{Ans.}$$

2. Initial belt tension

We know that initial belt tension,

$$T_0 = \frac{T_1 + T_2}{2} = \frac{1779 + 718}{2} = 1248.5 \text{ N} \quad \textbf{Ans.}$$

3. Length of the belt required

We know that length of the belt required,

$$L = \frac{\pi}{2}(d_1 - d_2) + 2x + \frac{(d_1 - d_2)^2}{4x}$$

$$= \frac{\pi}{2}(0.6 + 0.24) + 2 \times 3 + \frac{(0.6 - 0.24)^2}{4 \times 3}$$

$$= 1.32 + 6 + 0.01 = 7.33 \text{ m} \quad \textbf{Ans.}$$

Example 11.16. *The following data refer to an open belt drive :*

Diameter of larger pulley = 400 mm ; Diameter of smaller pulley = 250 mm ; Distance between two pulleys = 2 m ; Coefficient of friction between smaller pulley surface and belt = 0.4 ; Maximum tension when the belt is on the point of slipping = 1200 N.

Find the power transmitted at speed of 10 m/s. It is desired to increase the power. Which of the following two methods you will select ?

1. Increasing the initial tension in the belt by 10 per cent.

2. Increasing the coefficient of friction between the smaller pulley surface and belt by 10 per cent by the application of suitable dressing on the belt.

Find, also, the percentage increase in power possible in each case.

Solution. Given : $d_1 = 400$ mm $= 0.4$ m ; $d_2 = 250$ mm $= 0.25$ m ; $x = 2$ m ; $\mu = 0.4$; $T = 1200$ N ; $v = 10$ m/s

Power transmitted

We know that for an open belt drive,

$$\sin \alpha = \frac{r_1 - r_2}{x} = \frac{d_1 - d_2}{2x} = \frac{0.4 - 0.25}{2 \times 2} = 0.0375 \text{ or } \alpha = 2.15°$$

∴ Angle of contact,

$$\theta = 180° - 2\alpha = 180° - 2 \times 2.15° = 175.7°$$

$$= 175.7 \times \pi / 180 = 3.067 \text{ rad}$$

Let T_1 = Tension in the tight side of the belt, and

T_2 = Tension in the slack side of the belt.

Neglecting centrifugal tension,

$$T_1 = T = 1200 \text{ N} \hspace{3cm} ...\text{(Given)}$$

We know that

$$2.3 \log \left(\frac{T_1}{T_2} \right) = \mu . \theta = 0.4 \times 3.067 = 1.2268$$

$$\log \left(\frac{T_1}{T_2} \right) = \frac{1.2268}{2.3} = 0.5334 \text{ or } \frac{T_1}{T_2} = 3.41$$

$$...\text{(Taking antilog of 0.5334)}$$

and

$$T_2 = \frac{T_1}{3.41} = \frac{1200}{3.41} = 352 \text{ N}$$

We know that power transmitted,

$$P = (T_1 - T_2) v = (1200 - 352) \, 10 = 8480 \text{ W} = 8.48 \text{ kW} \textbf{ Ans.}$$

Power transmitted when initial tension is increased by 10%

We know that initial tension,

$$T_0 = \frac{T_1 + T_2}{2} = \frac{1200 + 352}{2} = 776 \text{ N}$$

∴ Increased initial tension,

$$T_0' = 776 + \frac{776 \times 10}{100} = 853.6 \text{ N}$$

Let T_1 and T_2 be the corresponding tensions in the tight side and slack side of the belt respectively.

∴

$$T_0' = \frac{T_1 + T_2}{2}$$

or

$$T_1 + T_2 = 2 \, T_0' = 2 \times 853.6 = 1707.2 \text{ N} \hspace{2cm} ...(i)$$

Since the ratio of tensions is constant, therefore

$$\frac{T_1}{T_2} = 3.41 \hspace{4cm} ...(ii)$$

From equations (*i*) and (*ii*),

$$T_1 = 1320.2 \text{ N} \text{ ; and } T_2 = 387 \text{ N}$$

∴ Power transmitted, $P = (T_1 - T_2) v = (1320.2 - 387) 10 = 9332 \text{ W} = 9.332 \text{ kW}$

Power transmitted when coefficient of friction is increased by 10%

We know that coefficient of friction,

$$\mu = 0.4$$

∴ Increased coefficient of friction,

$$\mu' = 0.4 + 0.4 \times \frac{10}{100} = 0.44$$

Let T_1 and T_2 be the corresponding tensions in the tight side and slack side respectively.
We know that

$$2.3 \log \left(\frac{T_1}{T_2} \right) = \mu'.\theta = 0.44 \times 3.067 = 1.3495$$

$$\log \left(\frac{T_1}{T_2} \right) = \frac{1.3495}{2.3} = 0.5867 \text{ or } \frac{T_1}{T_2} = 3.86 \qquad ...(iii)$$

... (Taking antilog of 0.5867)

Here the initial tension is constant, *i.e.*

$$T_0 = \frac{T_1 + T_2}{2} \text{ or } T_1 + T_2 = 2 T_0 = 2 \times 776 = 1552 \text{ N} \qquad ...(iv)$$

From equations (*iii*) and (*iv*),

$$T = 1232.7 \text{ N and } T_2 = 319.3 \text{ N}$$

∴ Power transmitted,

$$P = (T_1 - T_2) v = (1232.7 - 319.3) 10 = 9134 \text{ W} = 9.134 \text{ kW}$$

Since the power transmitted by increasing the initial tension is more, therefore in order to increase the power transmitted we shall adopt the method of increasing the initial tension. **Ans.**

Percentage increase in power

We know that percentage increase in power when the initial tension is increased

$$= \frac{9.332 - 8.48}{8.48} \times 100 = 10.05\% \quad \textbf{Ans.}$$

and percentage increase in power when coefficient of friction is increased

$$= \frac{9.134 - 8.48}{8.48} \times 100 = 7.7\% \quad \textbf{Ans.}$$

11.20. V-belt drive

We have already discussed that a V-belt is mostly used in factories and workshops where a great amount of power is to be transmitted from one pulley to another when the two pulleys are very near to each other.

The V-belts are made of fabric and cords moulded in rubber and covered with fabric and rubber, as shown in Fig. 11.19 (*a*). These belts are moulded to a trapezoidal shape and are made endless. These are particularly suitable for short drives *i.e.* when the shafts are at a short distance apart. The included angle for the V-belt is usually from 30° – 40°. In case of flat belt drive, the belt runs over the pulleys whereas in case of V-belt drive, the rim of the pulley is grooved in which the V-belt runs. The effect of the groove is to increase the frictional grip of the V-belt on the pulley and thus to reduce the tendency of slipping. In order to have a good grip on the pulley, the V-belt is in contact with the side faces of the groove and not at the bottom. The power is transmitted by the *wedging action between the belt and the V-groove in the pulley.

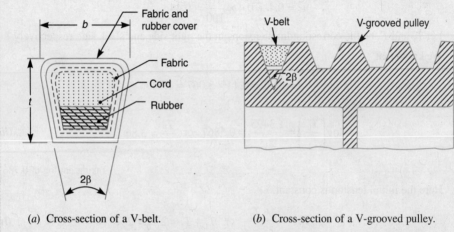

    (*a*) Cross-section of a V-belt.   (*b*) Cross-section of a V-grooved pulley.

Fig. 11.19. V-belt and V-grooved pulley.

A clearance must be provided at the bottom of the groove, as shown in Fig. 11.19 (*b*), in order to prevent touching to the bottom as it becomes narrower from wear. The V-belt drive, may be inclined at any angle with tight side either at top or bottom. In order to increase the power output, several V- belts may be operated side by side. It may be noted that in multiple V-belt drive, all the belts should stretch at the same rate so that the load is equally divided between them. When one of the set of belts break, the entire set should be replaced at the same time. If only one belt is replaced, the new unworn and unstressed belt will be more tightly stretched and will move with different velocity.

11.21. Advantages and Disadvantages of V-belt Drive Over Flat Belt Drive

Following are the advantages and disadvantages of the V-belt drive over flat belt drive.

Advantages

1. The V-belt drive gives compactness due to the small distance between the centres of pulleys.

2. The drive is positive, because the slip between the belt and the pulley groove is negligible.

3. Since the V-belts are made endless and there is no joint trouble, therefore the drive is smooth.

4. It provides longer life, 3 to 5 years.

---

*   The wedging action of the V-belt in the groove of the pulley results in higher forces of friction. A little consideration will show that the wedging action and the transmitted torque will be more if the groove angle of the pulley is small. But a smaller groove angle will require more force to pull the belt out of the groove which will result in loss of power and excessive belt wear due to friction and heat. Hence a selective groove angle is a compromise between the two. Usually the groove angles of 32° to 38° are used.

5. It can be easily installed and removed.

6. The operation of the belt and pulley is quiet.

7. The belts have the ability to cushion the shock when machines are started.

8. The high velocity ratio (maximum 10) may be obtained.

9. The wedging action of the belt in the groove gives high value of limiting ratio of tensions. Therefore the power transmitted by V-belts is more than flat belts for the same coefficient of friction, arc of contact and allowable tension in the belts.

10. The V-belt may be operated in either direction with tight side of the belt at the top or bottom. The centre line may be horizontal, vertical or inclined.

Disadvantages

1. The V-belt drive cannot be used with large centre distances.

2. The V-belts are not so durable as flat belts.

3. The construction of pulleys for V-belts is more complicated than pulleys for flat belts.

4. Since the V-belts are subjected to certain amount of creep, therefore these are not suitable for constant speed application such as synchronous machines, and timing devices.

5. The belt life is greatly influenced with temperature changes, improper belt tension and mismatching of belt lengths.

6. The centrifugal tension prevents the use of V-belts at speeds below 5 m/s and above 50m/s.

11.22. Ratio of Driving Tensions for V-belt

A V-belt with a grooved pulley is shown in Fig. 11.20.

Let R_1 = Normal reaction between the belt and sides of the groove.

R = Total reaction in the plane of the groove.

2β = Angle of the groove.

μ = Coefficient of friction between the belt and sides of the groove.

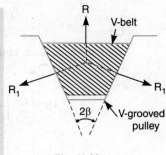

Fig. 11.20.

Resolving the reactions vertically to the groove,

$$R = R_1 \sin\beta + R_1 \sin\beta = 2 R_1 \sin\beta$$

or $$R_1 = \frac{R}{2\sin\beta}$$

We know that the frictional force

$$= 2\mu . R_1 = 2\mu \times \frac{R}{2\sin\beta} = \frac{\mu . R}{\sin\beta} = \mu . R \cosec\beta$$

Consider a small portion of the belt, as in Art. 11.14, subtending an angle $\delta\theta$ at the centre. The tension on one side will be T and on the other side $T + \delta T$. Now proceeding as in Art. 11.14, we get the frictional resistance equal to $\mu . R \cosec\beta$ instead of $\mu . R$. Thus the relation between T_1 and T_2 for the V-belt drive will be

$$2.3 \log\left(\frac{T_1}{T_2}\right) = \mu . \theta \cosec\beta$$

Example 11.17. *A belt drive consists of two V-belts in parallel, on grooved pulleys of the same size. The angle of the groove is 30°. The cross-sectional area of each belt is 750 mm² and μ. = 0.12. The density of the belt material is 1.2 Mg/m³ and the maximum safe stress in the material is 7 MPa. Calculate the power that can be transmitted between pulleys 300 mm diameter rotating at 1500 r.p.m. Find also the shaft speed in r.p.m. at which the power transmitted would be maximum.*

Solution. Given : $2\beta = 30°$ or $\beta = 15°$; $\alpha = 750$ mm² $= 750 \times 10^{-6}$ m² ; $\mu = 0.12$; $\rho = 1.2$ Mg/m³ $= 1200$ kg/m³ ; $\sigma = 7$ MPa $= 7 \times 10^6$ N/m² ; $d = 300$ mm $= 0.3$ m ; $N = 1500$ r.p.m.

Power transmitted

We know that velocity of the belt,

$$v = \frac{\pi d.N}{60} = \frac{\pi \times 0.3 \times 1500}{60} = 23.56 \text{ m/s}$$

and mass of the belt per metre length,

$$m = \text{Area} \times \text{length} \times \text{density} = 750 \times 10^{-6} \times 1 \times 1200 = 0.9 \text{ kg/m}$$

∴ Centrifugal tension,

$$T_C = m.v^2 = 0.9 \, (23.56)^2 = 500 \text{ N}$$

We know that maximum tension in the belt,

$$T = \text{Maximum stress} \times \text{cross-sectional area of belt} = \sigma \times a$$
$$= 7 \times 10^6 \times 750 \times 10^{-6} = 5250 \text{ N}$$

∴ Tension in the tight side of the belt,

$$T_1 = T - T_C = 5250 - 500 = 4750 \text{ N}$$

Let $\qquad T_2 = $ Tension in the slack side of the belt.

Since the pulleys are of the same size, therefore angle of contact, $\theta = 180° = \pi$ rad.

We know that

$$2.3 \log\left(\frac{T_1}{T_2}\right) = \mu.\theta \, \text{cosec}\,\beta = 0.12 \times \pi \times \text{cosec}\,15° = 1.457$$

$$\log\left(\frac{T_1}{T_2}\right) = \frac{1.457}{2.3} = 0.6334 \quad \text{or} \quad \frac{T_1}{T_2} = 4.3$$

...(Taking antilog of 0.6334)

and $\qquad T_2 = \dfrac{T_1}{4.3} = \dfrac{4750}{4.3} = 1105 \text{ N}$

We know that power transmitted,

$$P = (T_1 - T_2) \, v \times 2 \qquad\qquad \text{...(}\because \text{No. of belts} = 2\text{)}$$
$$= (4750 - 1105) \, 23.56 \times 2 = 171\ 752 \text{ W} = 171.752 \text{ kW} \textbf{ Ans.}$$

Shaft speed

Let $\qquad N_1 = $ Shaft speed in r.p.m., and

$\qquad v_1 = $ Belt speed in m/s.

We know that for maximum power, centrifugal tension,

$$T_C = T/3 \quad \text{or} \quad m\,(v_1)^2 = T/3 \quad \text{or} \quad 0.9\,(v_1)^2 = 5250/3 = 1750$$

∴ $\qquad (v_1)^2 = 1750/0.9 = 1944.4 \quad \text{or} \quad v_1 = 44.1 \text{ m/s}$

We know that belt speed (v_1),

$$44.1 = \frac{\pi d . N_1}{60} = \frac{\pi \times 0.3 \times N_1}{60} = 0.0157 N_1$$

$\therefore$ $N_1 = 44.1 / 0.0157 = 2809$ r.p.m. **Ans.**

Example 11.18. *Power is transmitted using a V-belt drive. The included angle of V-groove is 30°. The belt is 20 mm deep and maximum width is 20 mm. If the mass of the belt is 0.35 kg per metre length and maximum allowable stress is 1.4 MPa, determine the maximum power transmitted when the angle of lap is 140°. μ = 0.15.*

Solution. Given : $2\beta = 30°$ or $\beta = 15°$; $t = 20$ mm $= 0.02$ m ; $b = 20$ mm $= 0.02$ m ; $m = 0.35$ kg/m ; $\sigma = 1.4$ MPa $= 1.4 \times 10^6$ N/m² ; $\theta = 140° = 140° \times \pi / 180 = 2.444$ rad ; $\mu = 0.15$

We know that maximum tension in the belt,

$$T = \sigma . b . t = 1.4 \times 10^6 \times 0.02 \times 0.02 = 560 \text{ N}$$

and for maximum power to be transmitted, velocity of the belt,

$$v = \sqrt{\frac{T}{3m}} = \sqrt{\frac{560}{3 \times 0.35}} = 23.1 \text{ m/s}$$

Let T_1 = Tension in the tight side of the belt, and

T_2 = Tension in the slack side of the belt.

We know that

$$2.3 \log\left(\frac{T_1}{T_2}\right) = \mu . \theta \operatorname{cosec}\beta = 0.15 \times 2.444 \times \operatorname{cosec} 15° = 1.416$$

$$\log\left(\frac{T_1}{T_2}\right) = \frac{1.416}{2.3} = 0.616 \text{ or } \frac{T_1}{T_2} = 4.13 \qquad ...(i)$$

...(Taking antilog of 0.616)

Centrifugal tension, $T_C = \dfrac{T}{3} = \dfrac{560}{3} = 187$ N

and $T_1 = T - T_C = 560 - 187 = 373$ N

$$T_2 = \frac{T_1}{4.13} = \frac{373}{4.13} = 90.3 \text{ N} \qquad ...[\text{From equation } (i)]$$

We know that maximum power transmitted,

$$P = (T_1 - T_2) v = (373 - 90.3) \, 23.1 = 6530 \text{ W} = 6.53 \text{ kW } \textbf{Ans.}$$

Example 11.19. *A compressor, requiring 90 kW is to run at about 250 r.p.m. The drive is by V-belts from an electric motor running at 750 r.p.m. The diameter of the pulley on the compressor shaft must not be greater than 1 metre while the centre distance between the pulleys is limited to 1.75 metre. The belt speed should not exceed 1600 m/min.*

Determine the number of V-belts required to transmit the power if each belt has a cross-sectional area of 375 mm², density 1000 kg/m³ and an allowable tensile stress of 2.5 MPa. The groove angle of the pulley is 35°. The coefficient of friction between the belt and the pulley is 0.25. Calculate also the length required of each belt.

Solution. Given : $P = 90$ kW ; $N_2 = 250$ r.p.m. ; $N_1 = 750$ r.p.m. ; $d_2 = 1$ m ; $x = 1.75$ m ; $v = 1600$ m/min $= 26.67$ m/s ; $a = 375$ mm² $= 375 \times 10^{-6}$ m² ; $\rho = 1000$ kg/m³ ; $\sigma = 2.5$ MPa $= 2.5 \times 10^6$ N/m² ; $2\beta = 35°$ or $\beta = 17.5°$; $\mu = 0.25$

First of all, let us find the diameter of pulley on the motor shaft (d_1). We know that

$$\frac{N_2}{N_1} = \frac{d_1}{d_2} \quad \text{or} \quad d_1 = \frac{N_2 . d_2}{N_1} = \frac{250 \times 1}{750} = 0.33 \,\text{m}$$

We know that the mass of the belt per metre length,

$$m = \text{Area} \times \text{length} \times \text{density}$$
$$= 375 \times 10^{-6} \times 1 \times 1000 = 0.375 \,\text{kg}$$

∴ Centrifugal tension, $\quad T_C = m.v^2 = 0.375 \,(26.67)^2 = 267 \,\text{N}$

and maximum tension in the belt,

$$T = \sigma . a = 2.5 \times 10^6 \times 375 \times 10^{-6} = 937.5 \,\text{N}$$

∴ Tension in the tight side of the belt,

$$T_1 = T - T_C = 937.5 - 267 = 670.5 \,\text{N}$$

Let $\qquad T_2 = $ Tension in the slack side of the belt.

For an open belt drive, as shown in Fig. 11.21,

$$\sin \alpha = \frac{O_2 M}{O_1 O_2} = \frac{r_2 - r_1}{x} = \frac{d_2 - d_1}{2x} = \frac{1 - 0.33}{2 \times 1.75} = 0.1914$$

∴ $\qquad \alpha = 11°$

and angle of lap on smaller pulley (*i.e.* pulley on motor shaft),

$$\theta = 180° - 2\alpha = 180° - 2 \times 11° = 158°$$
$$= 158 \times \pi / 180 = 2.76 \,\text{rad}$$

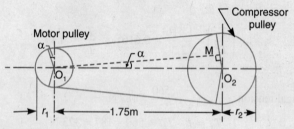

Fig. 11.21

We know that

$$2.3 \log\left(\frac{T_1}{T_2}\right) = \mu . \theta \operatorname{cosec} \beta = 0.25 \times 2.76 \times \operatorname{cosec} 17.5° = 2.295$$

$$\log\left(\frac{T_1}{T_2}\right) = \frac{2.295}{2.3} = 0.998 \quad \text{or} \quad \frac{T_1}{T_2} = 9.954 \qquad \text{...(Taking antilog of 0.998)}$$

and $\qquad T_2 = \dfrac{T_1}{9.954} = \dfrac{670.5}{9.954} = 67.36 \,\text{N}$

Number of V-belts

We know that power transmitted per belt

$$= (T_1 - T_2) \, v = (670.5 - 67.36) \, 26.67 = 16\ 086 \,\text{W}$$
$$= 16.086 \,\text{kW}$$

∴ $\qquad$ Number of V-belts $= \dfrac{\text{Total power transmitted}}{\text{Power transmitted per belt}} = \dfrac{90}{16.086} = 5.6 \text{ or } 6 \textbf{ Ans.}$

Length of each belt

We know that length of belt for an open belt drive,

$$L = \frac{\pi}{2}(d_2 + d_1) + 2x + \frac{(d_2 - d_1)^2}{4x}$$

$$= \frac{\pi}{2}(1 + 0.33) + 2 \times 1.75 + \frac{(1 - 0.33)^2}{4 \times 1.75}$$

$$= 2.1 + 3.5 + 0.064 = 5.664 \text{ m } \textbf{Ans.}$$

11.23. Rope Drive

The rope drives are widely used where a large amount of power is to be transmitted, from one pulley to another, over a considerable distance. It may be noted that the use of flat belts is limited for the transmission of moderate power from one pulley to another when the two pulleys are not more than 8 metres apart. If large amounts of power are to be transmitted by the flat belt, then it would result in excessive belt cross-section. It may be noted that frictional grip in case of rope drives is more than that in V-drive. One of the main advantage of rope drives is that a number of separate drives may be taken from the one driving pulley. For example, in many spinning mills, the line shaft on each floor is driven by ropes passing directly from the main engine pulley on the ground floor.

The rope drives use the following two types of ropes :

1. Fibre ropes, and **2.** Wire ropes.

The fibre ropes operate successfully when the pulleys are about 60 metres apart, while the wire ropes are used when the pulleys are upto 150 metres apart.

11.24. Fibre Ropes

The ropes for transmitting power are usually made from fibrous materials such as hemp, manila and cotton. Since the hemp and manila fibres are rough, therefore the ropes made from these fibres are not very flexible and possesses poor mechanical properties. The hemp ropes have less strength as compared to manila ropes. When the hemp and manila ropes are bent over the sheave (or pulley), there is some sliding of fibres, causing the rope to wear and chafe internally. In order to minimise this defect, the rope fibres are lubricated with a tar, tallow or graphite. The lubrication also makes the rope moisture proof. The hemp ropes are suitable only for hand operated hoisting machinery and as tie ropes for lifting tackle, hooks etc.

The cotton ropes are very soft and smooth. The lubrication of cotton ropes is not necessary. But if it is done, it reduces the external wear between the rope and the grooves of its sheaves. It may be noted that manila ropes are more durable and stronger than cotton ropes. The cotton ropes are costlier than manila ropes.

Note : The diameter of manila and cotton ropes usually ranges from 38 mm to 50 mm. The size of the rope is usually designated by its circumference or **'girth'.**

11.25. Advantages of Fibre Rope Drives

The fibre rope drives have the following advantages :

1. They give smooth, steady and quiet service.

2. They are little affected by out door conditions.

3. The shafts may be out of strict alignment.

4. The power may be taken off in any direction and in fractional parts of the whole amount.

5. They give high mechanical efficiency.

11.26. Sheave for Fibre Ropes

The fibre ropes are usually circular in cross-section as shown in Fig. 11.22 (*a*). The sheave for the fibre ropes is shown in Fig. 11.22 (*b*). The groove angle of the pulley for rope drives is usually 45°. The grooves in the pulleys are made narrow at the bottom and the rope is pinched between the edges of the V-groove to increase the holding power of the rope on the pulley.

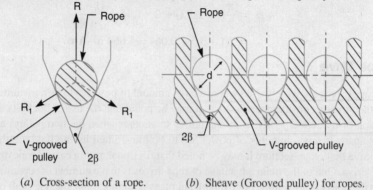

(*a*) Cross-section of a rope.　　　(*b*) Sheave (Grooved pulley) for ropes.

Fig. 11.22. Rope and sheave.

11.27. Wire Ropes

When a large amount of power is to be transmitted over long distances from one pulley to another (*i.e.* when the pulleys are upto 150 metres apart), then wire ropes are used. The wire ropes are

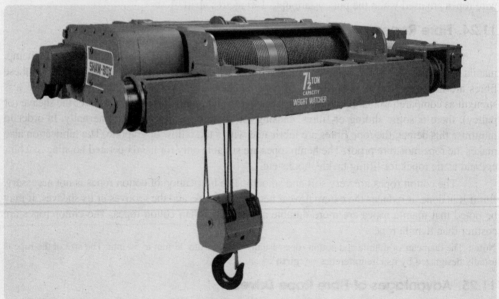

This electric hoist uses wire ropes.

widely used in elevators, mine hoists, cranes, conveyors, hauling devices and suspension bridges. The wire ropes run on grooved pulleys but they rest on the bottom of the *grooves and are not wedged between the sides of the grooves. The wire ropes have the following advantage over cotton ropes.

---

*　The fibre ropes do not rest at the bottom of the groove.

1. These are lighter in weight, **2.** These offer silent operation, **3.** These can withstand shock loads, **4.** These are more reliable, **5.** They do not fail suddenly, **6.** These are more durable, **7.** The efficiency is high, and **8.** The cost is low.

11.28. Ratio of Driving Tensions for Rope Drive

The ratio of driving tensions for the rope drive may be obtained in the similar way as V-belts. We have discussed in Art. 11.22, that the ratio of driving tensions is

$$2.3 \log\left(\frac{T_1}{T_2}\right) = \mu . \theta \cosec \beta$$

where, μ, θ and β have usual meanings.

Example 11.20. *A rope drive transmits 600 kW from a pulley of effective diameter 4 m, which runs at a speed of 90 r.p.m. The angle of lap is 160° ; the angle of groove 45° ; the coefficient of friction 0.28 ; the mass of rope 1.5 kg / m and the allowable tension in each rope 2400 N. Find the number of ropes required.*

Solution. Given : $P = 600$ kW ; $d = 4$ m ; $N = 90$ r.p.m. ; $\theta = 160° = 160 \times \pi / 180 = 2.8$ rad; $2\beta = 45°$ or $\beta = 22.5°$; $\mu = 0.28$; $m = 1.5$ kg / m ; $T = 2400$ N

We know that velocity of the rope,

$$v = \frac{\pi d . N}{60} = \frac{\pi \times 4 \times 90}{60} = 18.85 \text{ m/s}$$

∴ Centrifugal tension, $T_C = m.v^2 = 1.5 (18.85)^2 = 533$ N

and tension in the tight side of the rope,

$$T_1 = T - T_C = 2400 - 533 = 1867 \text{ N}$$

Let $T_2 =$ Tension in the slack side of the rope.

We know that

$$2.3 \log\left(\frac{T_1}{T_2}\right) = \mu . \theta \cosec \beta = 0.28 \times 2.8 \times \cosec 22.5° = 2.05$$

$$\log\left(\frac{T_1}{T_2}\right) = \frac{2.05}{2.3} = 0.8913 \quad \text{or} \quad \frac{T_1}{T_2} = 7.786$$

...(Taking antilog of 0.8913)

and

$$T_2 = \frac{T_1}{7.786} = \frac{1867}{7.786} = 240 \text{ N}$$

We know that power transmitted per rope

$$= (T_1 - T_2) v = (1867 - 240) \, 18.85 = 30\ 670 \text{ W} = 30.67 \text{ kW}$$

∴ Number of ropes $= \dfrac{\text{Total power transmitted}}{\text{Power transmitted per rope}} = \dfrac{600}{30.67} = 19.56$ or 20 **Ans.**

Example 11.21. *A pulley used to transmit power by means of ropes has a diameter of 3.6 metres and has 15 grooves of 45° angle. The angle of contact is 170° and the coefficient of friction between the ropes and the groove sides is 0.28. The maximum possible tension in the ropes is 960 N and the mass of the rope is 1.5 kg per metre length. What is the speed of pulley in r.p.m. and the power transmitted if the condition of maximum power prevail ?*

Solution. Given : $d = 3.6$ m ; No. of grooves $= 15$; $2\beta = 45°$ or $\beta = 22.5°$; $\theta = 170°$ $= 170 \, \pi \times 180 = 2.967$ rad ; $\mu = 0.28$; $T = 960$ N ; $m = 1.5$ kg/m

Speed of the pulley

Let N = Speed of the pulley in r.p.m.

We know that for maximum power, velocity of the rope or pulley,

$$v = \sqrt{\frac{T}{3m}} = \sqrt{\frac{960}{3 \times 1.5}} = 14.6 \text{ m/s}$$

∴ $$N = \frac{v \times 60}{\pi d} = \frac{14.6 \times 60}{\pi \times 3.6} = 77.5 \text{ r.p.m.} \quad \textbf{Ans.} \quad \dots \left(\because v = \frac{\pi d N}{60} \right)$$

Power transmitted

We know that for maximum power, centrifugal tension,

$$T_C = T / 3 = 960 / 3 = 320 \text{ N}$$

∴ Tension in the tight side of the rope,

$$T_1 = T - T_C = 960 - 320 = 640 \text{ N}$$

Let T_2 = Tension in the slack side of the rope.

We know that $$2.3 \log \left(\frac{T_1}{T_2} \right) = \mu . \theta \operatorname{cosec} \beta = 0.28 \times 2.967 \times \operatorname{cosec} 22.5° = 2.17$$

$$\log \left(\frac{T_1}{T_2} \right) = \frac{2.17}{2.3} = 0.9438 \quad \text{or} \quad \frac{T_1}{T_2} = 8.78$$

...(Taking antilog of 0.9438)

and $$T_2 = \frac{T_1}{8.78} = \frac{640}{8.78} = 73 \text{ N}$$

∴ Power transmitted per rope = $(T_1 - T_2) v = (640 - 73) 14.6 = 8278 \text{ W} = 8.278 \text{ kW}$

Since the number of grooves are 15, therefore total power transmitted

$$= 8.278 \times 15 = 124.17 \text{ kW} \quad \textbf{Ans.}$$

Example 11.22. *Following data is given for a rope pulley transmitting 24 kW :*

Diameter of pulley = 400 mm ; Speed = 110 r.p.m.; angle of groove = 45° ; Angle of lap on smaller pulley = 160° ; Coefficient of friction = 0.28 ; Number of ropes = 10 ; Mass in kg/m length of ropes = 53 C² ; and working tension is limited to 122 C² kN, where C is girth of rope in metres.

Find initial tension and diameter of each rope.

Solution. Given : $P_T = 24$ kW ; $d = 400$ mm $= 0.4$ m ; $N = 110$ r.p.m. ; $2\beta = 45°$ or $\beta = 22.5°$; $\theta = 160° = 160 \times \pi / 180 = 2.8$ rad ; $n = 0.28$; $n = 10$; $m = 53 \, C^2$ kg/m ; $T = 122 \, C^2$ kN $= 122 \times 10^3 \, C^2$ N

Initial tension

We know that power transmitted per rope,

$$P = \frac{\text{Total power transmitted}}{\text{No. of ropes}} = \frac{P_T}{n} = \frac{24}{10} = 2.4 \text{ kW} = 2400 \text{ W}$$

and velocity of the rope, $$v = \frac{\pi d . N}{60} = \frac{\pi \times 0.4 \times 110}{60} = 2.3 \text{ m/s}$$

Let T = Tension in the tight side of the rope, and

T_2 = Tension in the slack side of the rope.

We know that power transmitted per rope (P)

$$2400 = (T_1 - T_2) v = (T_1 - T_2) 2.3$$

$$\therefore \qquad T_1 - T_2 = 2400 / 2.3 = 1043.5 \text{ N} \qquad \qquad ...(i)$$

We know that

$$2.3 \log\left(\frac{T_1}{T_2}\right) = \mu \cdot \theta \operatorname{cosec}\beta = 0.28 \times 2.8 \times \operatorname{cosec} 22.5° = 2.05$$

$$\log\left(\frac{T_1}{T_2}\right) = \frac{2.05}{2.3} = 0.8913 \quad \text{or} \quad \frac{T_1}{T_2} = 7.786 \qquad \qquad ...(ii)$$

...(Taking antilog of 0.8913)

From equations (*i*) and (*ii*),

$$T_1 = 1197.3 \text{ N, and } T_2 = 153.8 \text{ N}$$

We know that initial tension in each rope,

$$T_0 = \frac{T_1 + T_2}{2} = \frac{1197.3 + 153.8}{2} = 675.55 \text{ N} \quad \textbf{Ans.}$$

Diameter of each rope

Let $\qquad d_1$ = Diameter of each rope,

We know that centrifugal tension,

$$T_C = m.v^2 = 53 \, C^2 \, (2.3)^2 = 280.4 \, C^2 \text{ N}$$

and working tension (T),

$$122 \times 10^3 \, C^2 = T_1 + T_C = 1197.3 + 280.4 \, C^2$$

$$122 \times 10^3 \, C^2 - 280.4 \, C^2 = 1197.3$$

$$\therefore \qquad C^2 = 9.836 \times 10^{-3} \text{ or } C = 0.0992 \text{ m} = 99.2 \text{ mm}$$

We know that girth (*i.e.* circumference) of rope (*C*),

$$99.2 = \pi \, d_1 \text{ or } d_1 = 99.2 / \pi = 31.57 \text{ mm} \quad \textbf{Ans.}$$

11.29. Chain Drives

We have seen in belt and rope drives that slipping may occur. In order to avoid slipping, steel chains are used. The chains are made up of rigid links which are hinged together in order to provide the necessary flexibility for warping around the driving and driven wheels. The wheels have projecting teeth and fit into the corresponding recesses, in the links of the chain as shown in Fig. 11.23. The wheels and the chain are thus constrained to move together without slipping and ensures perfect velocity ratio. The toothed wheels are known as *sprocket wheels* or simply *sprockets*. These wheels resemble to spur gears.

The chains are mostly used to transmit motion and power from one shaft to another, when the distance between the centres of the shafts is short such as in bicycles, motor cycles, agricultural machinery, road rollers, etc.

11.30. Advantages and Disadvantages of Chain Drive Over Belt or Rope Drive

Following are the advantages and disadvantages of chain drive over belt or rope drive :

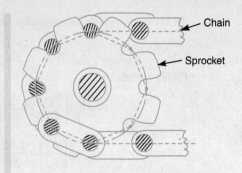

Fig. 11.23. Sprocket and chain.

Advantages

1. As no slip takes place during chain drive, hence perfect velocity ratio is obtained.

2. Since the chains are made of metal, therefore they occupy less space in width than a belt or rope drive.

3. The chain drives may be used when the distance between the shafts is less.

4. The chain drive gives a high transmission efficiency (upto 98 per cent).

5. The chain drive gives less load on the shafts.

6. The chain drive has the ability of transmitting motion to several shafts by one chain only.

Disadvantages

1. The production cost of chains is relatively high.

2. The chain drive needs accurate mounting and careful maintenance.

3. The chain drive has velocity fluctuations especially when unduly stretched.

11.31. Terms Used in Chain Drive

The following terms are frequently used in chain drive.

1. *Pitch of the chain* : It is the distance between the hinge centre of a link and the corresponding hinge centre of the adjacent link as shown in Fig. 11.24. It is usually denoted by p.

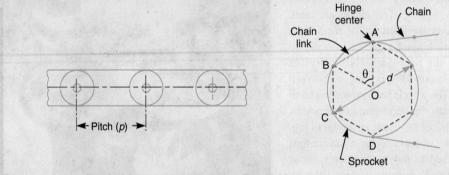

Fig. 11.24. Pitch of the chain.   **Fig. 11.25.** Pitch circle diameter of the chain sprocket.

2. *Pitch circle diameter of the chain sprocket.* It is the diameter of the circle on which the hinge centres of the chain lie, when the chain is wrapped round a sprocket as shown in Fig. 11.25. The points A, B, C, and D are the hinge centres of the chain and the circle drawn through these centres is called pitch circle and its diameter (d) is known as pitch circle diameter.

11.32. Relation Between Pitch and Pitch Circle Diameter

A chain wrapped round the sprocket is shown in Fig. 11.25. Since the links of the chain are rigid, therefore pitch of the chain does not lie on the arc of the pitch circle. The pitch length becomes a chord. Consider one pitch length *AB* of the chain subtending an angle θ at the centre of sprocket (or pitch circle).

Let
d = Diameter of the pitch circle, and

T = Number of teeth on the sprocket.

From Fig. 11.25, we find that pitch of the chain,

$$p = AB = 2\,AO\sin\left(\frac{\theta}{2}\right) = 2 \times \frac{d}{2}\sin\left(\frac{\theta}{2}\right) = d\sin\left(\frac{\theta}{2}\right)$$

We know that
$$\theta = \frac{360°}{T}$$

∴
$$p = d\sin\left(\frac{360°}{2T}\right) = d\sin\left(\frac{180°}{T}\right)$$

or
$$d = p\cosec\left(\frac{180°}{T}\right)$$

11.33. Relation Between Chain Speed and Angular Velocity of Sprocket

Since the links of the chain are rigid, therefore they will have different positions on the sprocket at different instants. The relation between the chain speed (*v*) and angular velocity of the sprocket (ω) also varies with the angular position of the sprocket. The extreme positions are shown in Fig. 11.26 (*a*) and (*b*).

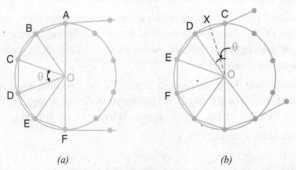

(a) (b)

Fig. 11.26. Relation between chain speed and angular velocity of sprocket.

For the angular position of the sprocket as shown in Fig. 11.26 (*a*),

$$v = \omega \times OA$$

and for the angular position of the sprocket as shown in Fig. 11.26 (*b*),

$$v = \omega \times OX = \omega \times OC \cos\left(\frac{\theta}{2}\right) = \omega \times OA \cos\left(\frac{\theta}{2}\right) \qquad ...(\because OC = OA)$$

11.34. Kinematic of Chain Drive

Fig. 11.27 shows an arrangement of a chain drive in which the smaller or driving sprocket has 6 teeth and the larger or driven sprocket has 9 teeth. Though this is an impracticable case, but this is considered to bring out clearly the kinematic conditions of a chain drive. Let both the sprockets rotate anticlockwise and the angle subtended by the chain pitch at the centre of the driving and driven sprockets be α and ϕ respectively. The lines AB and A_1B_1 show the positions of chain having minimum and maximum inclination respectively with the line of centres O_1O_2 of the sprockets. The points A, B_2 and B are in one straight line and the points A_1, C and B_1 are in one straight line. It may be noted that the straight length of the chain between the two sprockets must be equal to exact number of pitches.

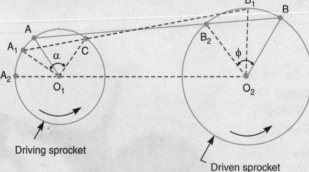

Fig. 11.27. Kinematic of chain drive.

Let us now consider the pin centre on the driving sprocket in position A. The length of the chain AB will remain straight as the sprockets rotate, until A reaches A_1 and B reaches B_1. As the driving sprocket continues to turn, the link A_1C of the chain turns about the pin centre C and the straight length of the chain between the two sprockets reduces to CB_1. When the pin centre C moves to the position A_1, the pin centre A_1 moves to the position A_2. During this time, each of the sprockets rotate from its original position by an angle corresponding to one chain pitch. During the first part of the angular displacement, the radius O_1A moves to O_1A_1 and the radius O_2B moves to O_2B_1. This arrangement is kinematically equivalent to the four bar chain O_1ABO_2.

During the second part of the angular displacement, the radius O_1A_1 moves to O_1A_2 and the radius O_2B_1 moves to O_2B_2. This arrangement is kinematically equivalent to the four bar chain $O_1CB_1O_2$. The ratio of the angular velocities, under these circumstances, cannot be constant. This may be easily shown as discussed below :

First of all, let us find the instantaneous centre for the two links O_1A and O_2B. This lies at point I which is the intersection of BA and O_2O_1 produced as shown in Fig. 11.28. If ω_1 is the angular velocity of the driving sprocket and ω_2 is the angular velocity of the driven sprocket, then

$$\omega_1 \times O_1I = \omega_2 \times O_2I$$

or

$$\frac{\omega_1}{\omega_2} = \frac{O_2I}{O_1I} = \frac{O_2O_1 + O_1I}{O_1I} = 1 + \frac{O_2O_1}{O_1I}.$$

The distance between the centres of two sprockets $O_1 O_2$ is constant for a given chain drive, but the distance $O_1 I$ varies periodically as the two sprockets rotate. This period corresponds to a rotation of the driving sprocket by an angle α. It is clear from the figure that the line AB has minimum inclination with line $O_1 O_2$. Therefore the distance $O_1 I$ is maximum and thus velocity ratio (ω_1 / ω_2) is minimum. When the chain occupies the position $A_1 B_1$, the inclination of line $A_1 B_1$ is maximum with the line $O_1 O_2$. Therefore the distance $O_1 I_1$ is minimum and thus the velocity ratio (ω_1 / ω_2) is maximum.

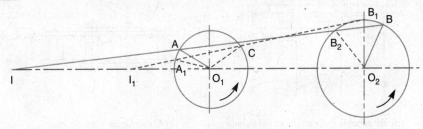

Fig. 11.28. Angular velocities of the two sprockets.

In actual practice, the smaller sprocket have a minimum of 18 teeth and hence the actual variation of velocity ratio (ω_1/ω_2) from the mean value is very small.

11.35. Classification of Chains

The chains, on the basis of their use, are classified into the following three groups :

1. Hoisting and hauling (or crane) chains,
2. Conveyor (or tractive) chains, and
3. Power transmitting (or driving) chains.

These chains are discussed, in detail, in the following pages.

11.36. Hoisting and Hauling Chains

These chains are used for hoisting and hauling purposes. The hoisting and hauling chains are of the following two types :

1. *Chain with oval links.* The links of this type of chain are of oval shape, as shown in Fig. 11.29 (*a*). The joint of each link is welded. The sprockets which are used for this type of chain have receptacles to receive the links. Such type of chains are used only at low speeds such as in chain hoists and in anchors for marine works.

(*a*) Chain with oval links.   (*b*) Chain with square links.

Fig. 11.29. Hoisting and hauling chains.

2. *Chain with square links.* The links of this type of chain are of square shape, as shown in Fig. 11.29 (*b*). Such type of chains are used in hoists, cranes, dredges. The manufacturing cost of this type of chain is less than that of chain with oval links, but in these chains, the kinking occurs easily on overloading.

11.37. Conveyor Chains

These chains are used for elevating and conveying the materials continuously. The conveyor chains are of the following two types :

1. Detachable or hook joint type chain, as shown in Fig. 11.30 (*a*), and

2. Closed joint type chain, as shown in Fig. 11.30 (*b*).

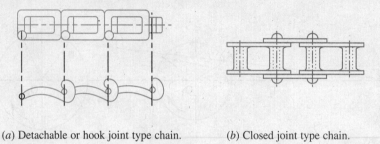

(*a*) Detachable or hook joint type chain.　　(*b*) Closed joint type chain.

Fig. 11.30. Conveyor chains.

The conveyor chains are usually made of malleable cast iron. These chains do not have smooth running qualities. The conveyor chains run at slow speeds of about 3 to 12 km.p.h.

11.38. Power Transmitting Chains

These chains are used for transmission of power, when the distance between the centres of shafts is short. These chains have provision for efficient lubrication. The power transmitting chains are of the following three types.

1. *Block chain.* A block chain, as shown in Fig. 11.31, is also known as **bush chain.** This type of chain was used in the early stages of development in the power transmission.

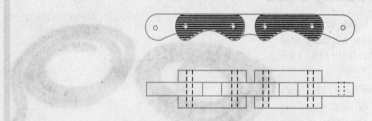

Fig. 11.31. Block chain.

It produces noise when approaching or leaving the teeth of the sprocket because of rubbing between the teeth and the links. Such type of chains are used to some extent as conveyor chain at small speed.

2. *Bush roller chain.* A bush roller chain, as shown in Fig. 11.32, consists of outer plates or pin link plates, inner plates or roller link plates, pins, bushes and rollers. A pin passes through the bush which is secured in the holes of the roller between the two sides of the chain. The rollers are free to rotate on the bush which protect the sprocket wheel teeth against wear.

A bush roller chain is extremely strong and simple in construction. It gives good service under severe conditions. There is a little noise with this chain which is due to impact of the rollers on the sprocket wheel teeth. This chain may be used where there is a little lubrication. When one of these chains elongates slightly due to wear and stretching of the parts, then the extended chain is of greater pitch than the pitch of the sprocket wheel teeth. The rollers then fit unequally into the cavities of the wheel. The result is that the total load falls on one teeth or on a few teeth. The stretching of the parts increase wear of the surfaces of the roller and of the sprocket wheel teeth.

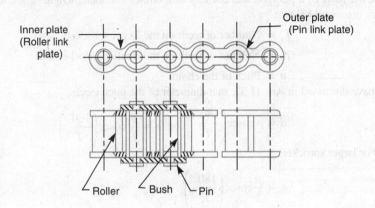

Inner plate
(Roller link
plate)

Outer plate
(Pin link plate)

Roller   Bush   Pin

Fig. 11.32. Bush roller chain.

3. *Inverted tooth or silent chain*. An inverted tooth or silent chain is shown in Fig. 11.33. It is designed to eliminate the evil effects caused by stretching and to produce noiseless running. When the chain stretches and the pitch of the chain increases, the links ride on the teeth of the sprocket wheel at a slightly increased radius. This automatically corrects the small change in the pitch. There is no relative sliding between the teeth of the inverted tooth chain and the sprocket wheel teeth. When properly lubricated, this chain gives durable service and runs very smoothly and quietly.

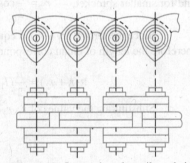

Fig. 11.33. Inverted tooth or silent chain.

11.39. Length of Chain

An open chain drive system connecting the two sprockets is shown in Fig. 11.34. We have already discussed in Art. 11.11 that the length of belt for an open belt drive connecting the two pulleys of radii r_1 and r_2 and a centre distance x, is

$$L = \pi(r_1 + r_2) + 2x + \frac{(r_1 - r_2)^2}{x}$$

(*i*)

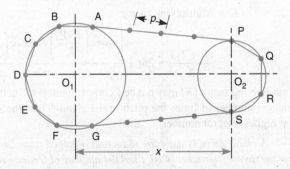

Fig. 11.34. Length of chain

If this expression is used for determining the length of chain, the result will be slightly greater than the required length. This is due to the fact that the pitch lines $A\,B\,C\,D\,E\,F\,G$ and $P\,Q\,R\,S$ of the sprockets are the parts of a polygon and not that of a circle. The exact length of the chain may be determined as discussed below :

Let $\qquad T_1$ = Number of teeth on the larger sprocket,

$\qquad\qquad T_2$ = Number of teeth on the smaller sprocket, and

$\qquad\qquad p$ = Pitch of the chain.

We have discussed in Art. 11.32, that diameter of the pitch circle,

$$d = p\,\mathrm{cosec}\left(\frac{180°}{T}\right) \quad \text{or} \quad r = \frac{p}{2}\,\mathrm{cosec}\left(\frac{180°}{T}\right)$$

∴ For larger sprocket,

$$r_1 = \frac{p}{2}\,\mathrm{cosec}\left(\frac{180°}{T_1}\right)$$

and for smaller sprocket, $\qquad r_2 = \dfrac{p}{2}\,\mathrm{cosec}\left(\dfrac{180°}{T_2}\right)$

Since the term $\pi\,(r_1 + r_2)$ is equal to half the sum of the circumferences of the pitch circles, therefore the length of chain corresponding to

$$\pi\,(r_1 + r_2) = \frac{p}{2}\,(T_1 + T_2)$$

Substituting the values of r_1, r_2 and $\pi\,(r_1 + r_2)$ in equation (i), the length of chain is given by

$$L = \frac{p}{2}\,(T_1 + T_2) + 2x + \frac{\left[\dfrac{p}{2}\,\mathrm{cosec}\left(\dfrac{180°}{T_1}\right) - \dfrac{p}{2}\,\mathrm{cosec}\left(\dfrac{180°}{T_2}\right)\right]^2}{x}$$

If $x = m.p$, then

$$L = p\left[\frac{(T_1 + T_2)}{2} + 2m + \frac{\left[\mathrm{cosec}\left(\dfrac{180°}{T_1}\right) - \mathrm{cosec}\left(\dfrac{180°}{T_2}\right)\right]^2}{4\,m}\right] = p.K$$

where $\qquad\qquad K$ = Multiplying factor

$$= \frac{(T_1 + T_2)}{2} + 2m + \frac{\left[\mathrm{cosec}\left(\dfrac{180°}{T_1}\right) - \mathrm{cosec}\left(\dfrac{180°}{T_2}\right)\right]^2}{4\,m}$$

The value of multiplying factor (K) may not be a complete integer. But the length of the chain must be equal to an integer number of times the pitch of the chain. Thus, the value of K should be rounded off to the next higher integral number.

Example 11.23. *A chain drive is used for reduction of speed from 240 r.p.m. to 120 r.p.m. The number of teeth on the driving sprocket is 20. Find the number of teeth on the driven sprocket. If the pitch circle diameter of the driven sprocket is 600 mm and centre to centre distance between the two sprockets is 800 mm, determine the pitch and length of the chain.*

Solution. Given : N_1 = 240 r.p.m ; N_2 = 120 r.p.m ; T_1 = 20 ; d_2 = 600 mm or r_2 = 300 mm = 0.3 m ; x = 800 mm = 0.8 m

Number of teeth on the driven sprocket

Let T_2 = Number of teeth on the driven sprocket.

We know that

$$N_1.T_1 = N_2.T_2 \qquad \text{or} \qquad T_2 = \frac{N_1.T_1}{N_2} = \frac{240 \times 20}{120} = 40 \quad \textbf{Ans.}$$

Pitch of the chain

Let p = Pitch of the chain.

We know that pitch circle radius of the driven sprocket (r_2),

$$0.3 = \frac{p}{2} \operatorname{cosec}\left(\frac{180°}{T_2}\right) = \frac{p}{2} \operatorname{cosec}\left(\frac{180°}{40}\right) = 6.37\,p$$

∴ $p = 0.3 / 6.37 = 0.0471$ m = 47.1 mm **Ans.**

Length of the chain

We know that pitch circle radius of the driving sprocket,

$$r_1 = \frac{p}{2} \operatorname{cosec}\left(\frac{180°}{T_1}\right) = \frac{47.1}{2} \operatorname{cosec}\left(\frac{180°}{20}\right) = 150.5\,\text{mm}$$

and $x = m.p \qquad \text{or} \quad m = x / p = 800 / 47.1 = 16.985$

We know that multiplying factor,

$$K = \frac{(T_1 + T_2)}{2} + 2m + \frac{\left[\operatorname{cosec}\left(\dfrac{180°}{T_1}\right) - \operatorname{cosec}\left(\dfrac{180°}{T_2}\right)\right]^2}{4m}$$

$$= \frac{(20 + 40)}{2} + 2 \times 16.985 + \frac{\left[\operatorname{cosec}\left(\dfrac{180°}{20}\right) - \operatorname{cosec}\left(\dfrac{180°}{40}\right)\right]^2}{4 \times 16.985}$$

$$= 30 + 33.97 + \frac{(6.392 - 12.745)^2}{67.94} = 64.56 \text{ say } 65$$

∴ Length of the chain,

$$L = p.K = 47.1 \times 65 = 3061.5 \text{ mm} = 3.0615 \text{ m} \quad \textbf{Ans.}$$

EXERCISES

1. An engine shaft running at 120 r.p.m. is required to drive a machine shaft by means of a belt. The pulley on the engine shaft is of 2 m diameter and that of the machine shaft is 1 m diameter. If the belt thickness is 5 mm ; determine the speed of the machine shaft, when 1. there is no slip ; and 2. there is a slip of 3%. **[Ans. 239.4 r.p.m. ; 232.3 r.p.m.]**

2. Two parallel shafts 6 metres apart are provided with 300 mm and 400 mm diameter pulleys and are connected by means of a cross belt. The direction of rotation of the follower pulley is to be reversed by changing over to an open belt drive. How much length of the belt has to be reduced ?

   [Ans. 203.6 mm]

3. A pulley is driven by a flat belt running at a speed of 600 m/min. The coefficient of friction between the pulley and the belt is 0.3 and the angle of lap is 160°. If the maximum tension in the belt is 700 N ; find the power transmitted by a belt. **[Ans. 3.983 kW]**

4. Find the width of the belt, necessary to transmit 7.5 kW to a pulley 300 mm diameter, if the pulley makes 1600 r.p.m and the coefficient of friction between the belt and the pulley is 0.22. Assume the angle of contact as 210° and the maximum tension in the belt is not to exceed 8 N/mm width.

[Ans. 67.4 mm]

5. An open belt 100 mm wide connects two pulleys mounted on parallel shafts with their centres 2.4 m apart. The diameter of the larger pulley is 450 mm and that of the smaller pulley 300 mm. The coefficient of friction between the belt and the pulley is 0.3 and the maximum stress in the belt is limited to 14 N/mm width. If the larger pulley rotates at 120 r.p.m., find the maximum power that can be transmitted.

[Ans. 2.39 kW]

6. A leather belt 125 mm wide and 6 mm thick, transmits power from a pulley 750 mm diameter which runs at 500 r.p.m. The angle of lap is 150° and $\mu = 0.3$. If the mass of 1 m^3 of leather is 1 Mg and the stress in the belt is not to exceed 2.75 MPa, find the maximum power that can be transmitted.

[Ans. 19 kW]

7. A flat belt is required to transmit 35 kW from a pulley of 1.5 m effective diameter running at 300 r.p.m. The angle of contact is spread over 11/24 of the circumference and the coefficient of friction between belt and pulley surface is 0.3. Determine, taking centrifugal tension into account, width of the belt required. It is given that the belt thickness is 9.5 mm, density of its material is 1.1 Mg/m^3 and the related permissible working stress is 2.5 MPa.

[Ans. 143 mm]

8. A blower is driven by an electric motor though a belt drive. The motor runs at 750 r.p.m. For this power transmission, a flat belt of 8 mm thickness and 250 mm width is used. The diameter of the motor pulley is 350 mm and that of the blower pulley 1350 mm. The centre distance between these pulleys is 1350 mm and an open belt configuration is adopted. The pulleys are made out of cast iron. The frictional coefficient between the belt and pulley is 0.35 and the permissible stress for the belt material can be taken as 2.5 N/mm^2 with sufficient factor of safety. The mass of a belt is 2 kg per metre length. Find the maximum power transmitted without belt slipping in any one of the pulleys.

[Ans. 35.9 kW]

9. An open belt drive connects two pulleys 1.2 m and 0.5 m diameter on parallel shafts 3.6 m apart. The belt has a mass of 1 kg/m length and the maximum tension in it is not to exceed 2 kN. The 1.2 m pulley, which is the driver, runs at 200 r.p.m. Due to the belt slip on one of the pulleys, the velocity of the driven shaft is only 450 r.p.m. If the coefficient of friction between the belt and the pulley is 0.3, find : 1. Torque on each of the two shafts, 2. Power transmitted, 3. Power lost in friction, and 4. Efficiency of the drive. **[Ans. 648.6 N-m, 270.25 N-m ; 13.588 kW ; 0.849 kW ; 93.75%]**

10. The power transmitted between two shafts 3.5 metres apart by a cross belt drive round the two pulleys 600 mm and 300 mm in diameters, is 6 kW. The speed of the larger pulley (driver) is 220 r.p.m. The permissible load on the belt is 25 N/mm width of the belt which is 5 mm thick. The coefficient of friction between the smaller pulley surface and the belt is 0.35. Determine : 1. necessary length of the belt ; 2. width of the belt, and 3. necessary initial tension in the belt.

[Ans. 8.472 m ; 53 mm ; 888 N]

11. A flat belt, 8 mm thick and 100 mm wide transmits power between two pulleys, running at 1600 m/min. The mass of the belt is 0.9 kg/m length. The angle of lap in the smaller pulley is 165° and the coefficient of friction between the belt and pulley is 0.3. If the maximum permissible stress in the belt is 2 MN/m^2, find : 1. maximum power transmitted ; and 2. initial tension in the belt

[Ans. 14.83 kW ; 1002 N]

12. An open belt connects two flat pulleys. The smaller pulley is 400 mm diameter and runs at 200 r.p.m. The angle of lap on this pulley is 160° and the coefficient of friction between the belt and pulley face is 0.25. The belt is on the point of slipping when 3 kW is being transmitted. Which of the following two alternatives would be more effective in order to increase the power :

1. Increasing the initial tension in the belt by 10 per cent, and

2. Increasing the coefficient of friction by 10 per cent by the application of a suitable dressing to the belt? **[Ans. First method is more effective]**

13. A V-belt drive consists of three V-belts in parallel on grooved pulleys of the same size. The angle of groove is 30° and the coefficient of friction 0.12. The cross-sectional area of each belt is 800 mm² and the permissible safe stress in the material is 3 MPa. Calculate the power that can be transmitted between two pulleys 400 mm in diameter rotating at 960 r.p.m. **[Ans. 111.12 kW]**

14. Power is transmitted between two shafts by a V-belt whose mass is 0.9 kg/m length. The maximum permissible tension in the belt is limited to 2.2 kN. The angle of lap is 170° and the groove angle 45°. If the coefficient of friction between the belt and pulleys is 0.17, find : 1. velocity of the belt for maximum power ; and 2. power transmitted at this velocity. **[Ans. 28.54 m/s ; 30.7 kW]**

15. Two shafts whose centres are 1 m apart are connected by a V-belt drive. The driving pulley is supplied with 100 kW and has an effective diameter of 300 mm. It runs at 1000 r.p.m. while the driven pulley runs at 375 r.p.m. The angle of groove on the pulleys is 40°. The permissible tension in 400 mm² cross-sectional area belt is 2.1 MPa. The density of the belt is 1100 kg/m³. The coefficient of friction between the belt and pulley is 0.28. Estimate the number of belts required. **[Ans. 10]**

16. A rope drive is required to transmit 230 kW from a pulley of 1 metre diameter running at 450 r.p.m. The safe pull in each rope is 800 N and the mass of the rope is 0.46 kg per metre length. The angle of lap and the groove angle is 160° and 45° respectively. If the coefficient of friction between the rope and the pulley is 0.3, find the number of ropes required. **[Ans. 21]**

17. Power is transmitted between two shafts, 3 metres apart by an open wire rope passing round two pulleys of 3 metres and 2 metres diameters respectively, the groove angle being 40°. If the rope has a mass of 3.7 kg per metre length and the maximum working tension in rope is 20 kN, determine the maximum power that the rope can transmit and the corresponding speed of the smaller pulley. The coefficient of friction being 0.15. **[Ans. 400 kW ; 403.5 r.p.m.]**

18. A rope drive transmits 75 kW through a 1.5 m diameter, 45° grooved pulley rotating at 200 r.p.m. The coefficient of friction between the ropes and the pulley grooves is 0.3 and the angle of lap is 160°. Each rope has a mass of 0.6 kg/m and can safely take a pull of 800 N. Taking centrifugal tension into account determine : 1. the number of ropes required for the drive, and 2. initial rope tension.

[Ans. 9 ; 510.2 N]

19. The reduction of speed from 360 r.p.m. to 120 r.p.m. is desired by the use of chain drive. The driving sprocket has 10 teeth. Find the number of teeth on the driven sprocket. If the pitch radius of the driven sprocket is 250 mm and the centre to centre distance between the two sprocket is 400 mm, find the pitch and length of the chain. **[Ans. 30 ; 52.25 mm ; 1.93 m]**

DO YOU KNOW ?

1. Discuss briefly the various types of belts used for the transmission of power.

2. How does the velocity ratio of a belt drive effect, when some slip is taking place between the belt and the two pulleys ?

3. Obtain an expression for the length of a belt in 1. an open belt drive ; and 2. a cross belt drive.

4. Explain the phenomena of 'slip' and 'creep' in a belt drive.

5. For a flat belt, prove that $\dfrac{T_1}{T_2} = e^{\mu\theta}$, where

T_1 = Tension in the tight side of the belt,

T_2 = Tension in the slack side of the belt,

μ = Coefficient of friction between the belt and the pulley, and

θ = Angle of contact between the belt and the pulley (in radians.)

6. What is centrifugal tension in a belt ? How does it affect the power transmitted.

7. Derive the condition for transmitting the maximum power in a flat belt drive.

8. It is stated that the speed at which a belt or rope should be run to transmit maximum power is that at which the maximum allowable tension is three times the centrifugal tension in the belt or rope at that speed. Prove the statement.

9. Explain what do you understand by 'initial tension in a belt'.

10. Derive an expression for the ratio of the driving tensions in a rope drive assuming the angle of the groove of the pulley to be as 2β.

11. Discuss relative merits and demerits of belt, rope and chain drive for transmission of power.

12. What are different types of chains ? Explain, with neat sketches, the power transmission chains.

13. Obtain an expression for the length of a chain.

OBJECTIVE TYPE QUESTIONS

1. The velocity ratio of two pulleys connected by an open belt or crossed belt is

   (a) directly proportional to their diameters

   (b) inversely proportional to their diameters

   (c) directly proportional to the square of their diameters

   (d) inversely proportional to the square of their diameters

2. Two pulleys of diameters d_1 and d_2 and at distance x apart are connected by means of an open belt drive. The length of the belt is

   (a) $\dfrac{\pi}{2}(d_1 + d_2) + 2x + \dfrac{(d_1 + d_2)^2}{4x}$ (b) $\dfrac{\pi}{2}(d_1 - d_2) + 2x + \dfrac{(d_1 - d_2)^2}{4x}$

   (c) $\dfrac{\pi}{2}(d_1 + d_2) + 2x + \dfrac{(d_1 - d_2)^2}{4x}$ (d) $\dfrac{\pi}{2}(d_1 - d_2) + 2x + \dfrac{(d_1 + d_2)^2}{4x}$

3. In a cone pulley, if the sum of radii of the pulleys on the driving and driven shafts is constant, then

   (a) open belt drive is recommended

   (b) cross belt drive is recommended

   (c) both open belt drive and cross belt drive are recommended

   (d) the drive is recommended depending upon the torque transmitted

4. Due to slip of the belt, the velocity ratio of the belt drive

   (a) decreases   (b) increases   (c) does not change

5. When two pulleys of different diameters are connected by means of an open belt drive, then the angle of contact taken into consideration should be of the

   (a) larger pulley   (b) smaller pulley   (c) average of two pulleys

6. The power transmitted by a belt is maximum when the maximum tension in the belt (T) is equal to

   (a) T_C (b) $2T_C$ (c) $3T_C$ (d) $4T_C$

   where T_C = Centrifugal tension.

7. The velocity of the belt for maximum power is

   (a) $\sqrt{\dfrac{T}{3m}}$ (b) $\sqrt{\dfrac{T}{4m}}$ (c) $\sqrt{\dfrac{T}{5m}}$ (d) $\sqrt{\dfrac{T}{6m}}$

   where m = Mass of the belt in kg per metre length.

8. The centrifugal tension in belts

   (*a*) increases power transmitted

   (*b*) decreases power transmitted

   (*c*) have no effect on the power transmitted

   (*d*) increases power transmitted upto a certain speed and then decreases

9. When the belt is stationary, it is subjected to some tension, known as initial tension. The value of this tension is equal to the

   (*a*) tension in the tight side of the belt

   (*b*) tension in the slack side of the belt

   (*c*) sum of the tensions in the tight side and slack side of the belt

   (*d*) average tension of the tight side and slack side of the belt

10. The relation between the pitch of the chain (*p*) and pitch circle diameter of the sprocket (*d*) is given by

   (*a*) $p = d \sin\left(\dfrac{60°}{T}\right)$

   (*b*) $p = d \sin\left(\dfrac{90°}{T}\right)$

   (*c*) $p = d \sin\left(\dfrac{120°}{T}\right)$

   (*d*) $p = d \sin\left(\dfrac{180°}{T}\right)$

   where   *T* = Number of teeth on the sprocket.

ANSWERS

1. (*b*)	2. (*c*)	3. (*b*)	4. (*a*)	5. (*b*)
6. (*c*)	7. (*a*)	8. (*c*)	9. (*d*)	10. (*d*)

Features

12

Toothed Wheels

12.1. Introduction

We have discussed in the previous chapter, that the slipping of a belt or rope is a common phenomenon, in the transmission of motion or power between two shafts. The effect of slipping is to reduce the velocity ratio of the system. In precision machines, in which a definite velocity ratio is of importance (as in watch mechanism), the only positive drive is by means of *gears* or *toothed wheels*. A gear drive is also provided, when the distance between the driver and the follower is very small.

12.2. Friction Wheels

The motion and power transmitted by gears is kinematically equivalent to that transmitted by friction wheels or discs. In order to understand how the motion can be transmitted by two toothed wheels, consider two plain circular wheels A and B mounted on  shafts, having sufficient rough surfaces and pressing against each other as shown in Fig. 12.1 (a).

Let the wheel *A* be keyed to the rotating shaft and the wheel *B* to the shaft, to be rotated. A little consideration will show, that when the wheel *A* is rotated by a rotating shaft, it will rotate the wheel *B* in the opposite direction as shown in Fig. 12.1 (*a*).

The wheel *B* will be rotated (by the wheel *A*) so long as the tangential force exerted by the wheel *A* does not exceed the maximum frictional resistance between the two wheels. But when the tangential force (*P*) exceeds the *frictional resistance (*F*), slipping will take place between the two wheels. Thus the friction drive is not a positive drive.

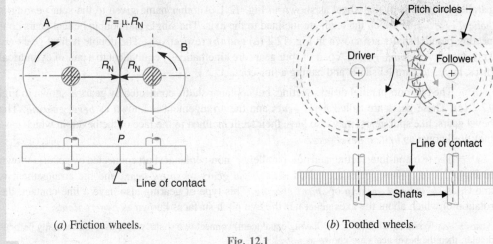

(*a*) Friction wheels. (*b*) Toothed wheels.

Fig. 12.1

In order to avoid the slipping, a number of projections (called teeth) as shown in Fig. 12.1 (*b*), are provided on the periphery of the wheel *A*, which will fit into the corresponding recesses on the periphery of the wheel *B*. A friction wheel with the teeth cut on it is known as *toothed wheel* or *gear*. The usual connection to show the toothed wheels is by their **pitch circles.

Note : Kinematically, the friction wheels running without slip and toothed gearing are identical. But due to the possibility of slipping of wheels, the friction wheels can only be used for transmission of small powers.

12.3. Advantages and Disadvantages of Gear Drive

The following are the advantages and disadvantages of the gear drive as compared to belt, rope and chain drives :

Advantages

1. It transmits exact velocity ratio.
2. It may be used to transmit large power.
3. It has high efficiency.
4. It has reliable service.
5. It has compact layout.

Disadvantages

1. The manufacture of gears require special tools and equipment.
2. The error in cutting teeth may cause vibrations and noise during operation.

---

*   The frictional force *F* is equal to $\mu . R_N$, where μ = Coefficient of friction between the rubbing surface of two wheels, and R_N = Normal reaction between the two rubbing surfaces.

** For details, please refer to Art. 12.4.

12.4. Classification of Toothed Wheels

The gears or toothed wheels may be classified as follows :

1. *According to the position of axes of the shafts.* The axes of the two shafts between which the motion is to be transmitted, may be

(*a*) Parallel, (*b*) Intersecting, and (*c*) Non-intersecting and non-parallel.

The two parallel and co-planar shafts connected by the gears is shown in Fig. 12.1. These gears are called *spur gears* and the arrangement is known as *spur gearing*. These gears have teeth parallel to the axis of the wheel as shown in Fig. 12.1. Another name given to the spur gearing is *helical gearing*, in which the teeth are inclined to the axis. The single and double helical gears connecting parallel shafts are shown in Fig. 12.2 (*a*) and (*b*) respectively. The double helical gears are known as *herringbone gears*. A pair of spur gears are kinematically equivalent to a pair of cylindrical discs, keyed to parallel shafts and having a line contact.

The two non-parallel or intersecting, but coplanar shafts connected by gears is shown in Fig. 12.2 (*c*). These gears are called *bevel gears* and the arrangement is known as *bevel gearing*. The bevel gears, like spur gears, may also have their teeth inclined to the face of the bevel, in which case they are known as *helical bevel gears*.

The two non-intersecting and non-parallel *i.e.* non-coplanar shaft connected by gears is shown in Fig. 12.2 (*d*). These gears are called *skew bevel gears* or *spiral gears* and the arrangement is known as *skew bevel gearing* or *spiral gearing*. This type of gearing also have a line contact, the rotation of which about the axes generates the two pitch surfaces known as *hyperboloids*.

Notes : (*a*) When equal bevel gears (having equal teeth) connect two shafts whose axes are mutually perpendicular, then the bevel gears are known as *mitres*.

(*b*) A hyperboloid is the solid formed by revolving a straight line about an axis (not in the same plane), such that every point on the line remains at a constant distance from the axis.

(*c*) The worm gearing is essentially a form of spiral gearing in which the shafts are usually at right angles.

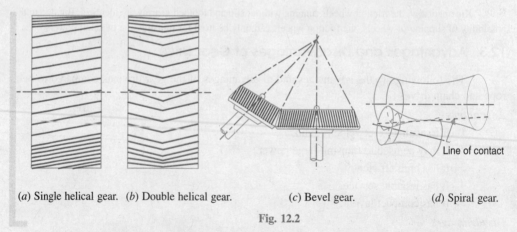

(*a*) Single helical gear. (*b*) Double helical gear.   (*c*) Bevel gear.   (*d*) Spiral gear.

Fig. 12.2

2. *According to the peripheral velocity of the gears.* The gears, according to the peripheral velocity of the gears may be classified as :

(*a*) Low velocity, (*b*) Medium velocity, and (*c*) High velocity.

The gears having velocity less than 3 m/s are termed as *low velocity* gears and gears having velocity between 3 and 15 m/s are known as *medium velocity gears*. If the velocity of gears is more than 15 m/s, then these are called *high speed gears*.

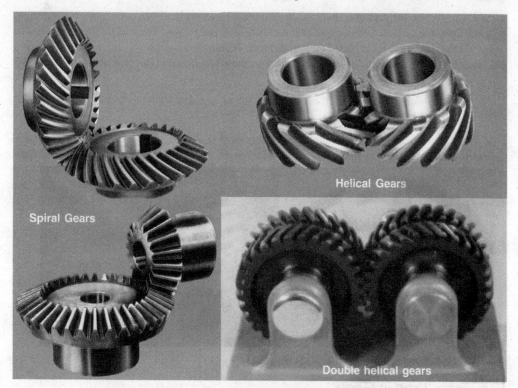

Spiral Gears

Helical Gears

Double helical gears

3. *According to the type of gearing.* The gears, according to the type of gearing may be classified as :

(*a*) External gearing, (*b*) Internal gearing, and (*c*) Rack and pinion.

In *external gearing*, the gears of the two shafts mesh externally with each other as shown in Fig. 12.3 (*a*). The larger of these two wheels is called *spur wheel* and the smaller wheel is called **pinion.** In an external gearing, the motion of the two wheels is always *unlike*, as shown in Fig. 12.3 (*a*).

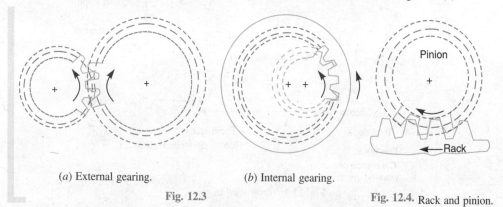

(*a*) External gearing.

(*b*) Internal gearing.

Pinion

Rack

Fig. 12.3

Fig. 12.4. Rack and pinion.

In *internal gearing*, the gears of the two shafts mesh *internally* with each other as shown in Fig. 12.3 (*b*). The larger of these two wheels is called *annular wheel* and the smaller wheel is called *pinion*. In an internal gearing, the motion of the two wheels is always *like*, as shown in Fig. 12.3 (*b*).

Sometimes, the gear of a shaft meshes externally and internally with the gears in a *straight line, as shown in Fig. 12.4. Such type of gear is called *rack and pinion*. The straight line gear is called rack and the circular wheel is called pinion. A little consideration will show that with the help of a rack and pinion, we can convert linear motion into rotary motion and *vice-versa* as shown in Fig. 12.4.

  4. *According to position of teeth on the gear surface.* The teeth on the gear surface may be (*a*) straight, (*b*) inclined, and (*c*) curved.

  We have discussed earlier that the spur gears have straight teeth where as helical gears have their teeth inclined to the wheel rim. In case of spiral gears, the teeth are curved over the rim surface.

Internal gears   Rack and pinion

12.5. Terms Used in Gears

  The following terms, which will be mostly used in this chapter, should be clearly understood at this stage. These terms are illustrated in Fig. 12.5.

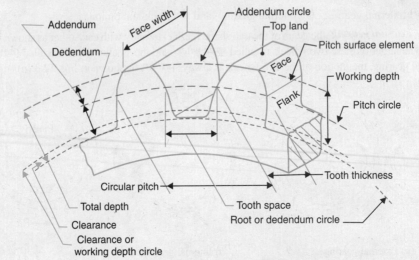

Fig. 12.5. Terms used in gears.

  1. *Pitch circle.* It is an imaginary circle which by pure rolling action, would give the same motion as the actual gear.

---

* A straight line may also be defined as a wheel of infinite radius.

2. *Pitch circle diameter*. It is the diameter of the pitch circle. The size of the gear is usually specified by the pitch circle diameter. It is also known as *pitch diameter*.

3. *Pitch point*. It is a common point of contact between two pitch circles.

4. *Pitch surface*. It is the surface of the rolling discs which the meshing gears have replaced at the pitch circle.

5. *Pressure angle or angle of obliquity*. It is the angle between the common normal to two gear teeth at the point of contact and the common tangent at the pitch point. It is usually denoted by φ. The standard pressure angles are $14\frac{1}{2}°$ and 20°.

6. *Addendum*. It is the radial distance of a tooth from the pitch circle to the top of the tooth.

7. *Dedendum*. It is the radial distance of a tooth from the pitch circle to the bottom of the tooth.

8. *Addendum circle*. It is the circle drawn through the top of the teeth and is concentric with the pitch circle.

9. *Dedendum circle*. It is the circle drawn through the bottom of the teeth. It is also called root circle.

Note : Root circle diameter = Pitch circle diameter × cos φ, where φ is the pressure angle.

10. *Circular pitch*. It is the distance measured on the circumference of the pitch circle from a point of one tooth to the corresponding point on the next tooth. It is usually denoted by p_c. Mathematically,

Circular pitch, $p_c = \pi D/T$

where

D = Diameter of the pitch circle, and

T = Number of teeth on the wheel.

A little consideration will show that the two gears will mesh together correctly, if the two wheels have the same circular pitch.

Note : If D_1 and D_2 are the diameters of the two meshing gears having the teeth T_1 and T_2 respectively, then for them to mesh correctly,

$$p_c = \frac{\pi D_1}{T_1} = \frac{\pi D_2}{T_2} \quad \text{or} \quad \frac{D_1}{D_2} = \frac{T_1}{T_2}$$

11. *Diametral pitch*. It is the ratio of number of teeth to the pitch circle diameter in millimetres. It is denoted by p_d. Mathematically,

Diametral pitch, $p_d = \dfrac{T}{D} = \dfrac{\pi}{p_c}$ $\qquad \ldots\left(\because p_c = \dfrac{\pi D}{T}\right)$

where

T = Number of teeth, and

D = Pitch circle diameter.

12. *Module*. It is the ratio of the pitch circle diameter in millimeters to the number of teeth. It is usually denoted by m. Mathematically,

Module, $m = D/T$

Note : The recommended series of modules in Indian Standard are 1, 1.25, 1.5, 2, 2.5, 3, 4, 5, 6, 8, 10, 12, 16, and 20. The modules 1.125, 1.375, 1.75, 2.25, 2.75, 3.5, 4.5, 5.5, 7, 9, 11, 14 and 18 are of second choice.

13. *Clearance*. It is the radial distance from the top of the tooth to the bottom of the tooth, in a meshing gear. A circle passing through the top of the meshing gear is known as *clearance circle*.

14. *Total depth*. It is the radial distance between the addendum and the dedendum circles of a gear. It is equal to the sum of the addendum and dedendum.

15. *Working depth*. It is the radial distance from the addendum circle to the clearance circle. It is equal to the sum of the addendum of the two meshing gears.

16. *Tooth thickness*. It is the width of the tooth measured along the pitch circle.

17. *Tooth space* . It is the width of space between the two adjacent teeth measured along the pitch circle.

18. *Backlash*. It is the difference between the tooth space and the tooth thickness, as measured along the pitch circle. Theoretically, the backlash should be zero, but in actual practice some backlash must be allowed to prevent jamming of the teeth due to tooth errors and thermal expansion.

19. *Face of tooth*. It is the surface of the gear tooth above the pitch surface.

20. *Flank of tooth*. It is the surface of the gear tooth below the pitch surface.

21. *Top land*. It is the surface of the top of the tooth.

22. *Face width*. It is the width of the gear tooth measured parallel to its axis.

23. *Profile*. It is the curve formed by the face and flank of the tooth.

24. *Fillet radius*. It is the radius that connects the root circle to the profile of the tooth.

25. *Path of contact*. It is the path traced by the point of contact of two teeth from the beginning to the end of engagement.

26. **Length of the path of contact*. It is the length of the common normal cut-off by the addendum circles of the wheel and pinion.

27. ** *Arc of contact*. It is the path traced by a point on the pitch circle from the beginning to the end of engagement of a given pair of teeth. The arc of contact consists of two parts, *i.e.*

(*a*) **Arc of approach.** It is the portion of the path of contact from the beginning of the engagement to the pitch point.

(*b*) **Arc of recess.** It is the portion of the path of contact from the pitch point to the end of the engagement of a pair of teeth.

Note : The ratio of the length of arc of contact to the circular pitch is known as *contact ratio i.e.* number of pairs of teeth in contact.

12.6. Gear Materials

The material used for the manufacture of gears depends upon the strength and service conditions like wear, noise etc. The gears may be manufactured from metallic or non-metallic materials. The metallic gears with cut teeth are commercially obtainable in cast iron, steel and bronze. The non-metallic materials like wood, raw hide, compressed paper and synthetic resins like nylon are used for gears, especially for reducing noise.

The cast iron is widely used for the manufacture of gears due to its good wearing properties, excellent machinability and case of producing complicated shapes by casting method. The cast iron gears with cut teeth may be employed, where smooth action is not important.

The steel is used for high strength gears and steel may be plain carbon steel or alloy steel. The steel gears are usually heat treated in order to combine properly the toughness and tooth hardness.

The phosphor bronze is widely used for worm gears in order to reduce wear of the worms which will be excessive with cast iron or steel.

12.7. Condition for Constant Velocity Ratio of Toothed Wheels–Law of Gearing

Consider the portions of the two teeth, one on the wheel 1 (or pinion) and the other on the

---

*   For details, see Art. 12.16.
**   For details, see Art. 12.17.

wheel 2, as shown by thick line curves in Fig. 12.6. Let the two teeth come in contact at point Q, and the wheels rotate in the directions as shown in the figure.

Let T T be the common tangent and MN be the common normal to the curves at the point of contact Q. From the centres O_1 and O_2, draw O_1M and O_2N perpendicular to MN. A little consideration will show that the point Q moves in the direction QC, when considered as a point on wheel 1, and in the direction QD when considered as a point on wheel 2.

Let v_1 and v_2 be the velocities of the point Q on the wheels 1 and 2 respectively. If the teeth are to remain in contact, then the components of these velocities along the common normal MN must be equal.

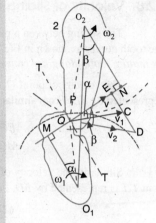

Fig. 12.6. Law of gearing.

$$\therefore \qquad v_1 \cos \alpha = v_2 \cos \beta$$

or $$(\omega_1 \times O_1 Q) \cos \alpha = (\omega_2 \times O_2 Q) \cos \beta$$

$$(\omega_1 \times O_1 Q) \frac{O_1 M}{O_1 Q} = (\omega_2 \times O_2 Q) \frac{O_2 N}{O_2 Q} \quad \text{or} \quad \omega_1 \times O_1M = \omega_2 \times O_2N$$

$$\therefore \qquad \frac{\omega_1}{\omega_2} = \frac{O_2 N}{O_1 M} \qquad \qquad \dots(i)$$

Also from similar triangles O_1MP and O_2NP,

$$\frac{O_2 N}{O_1 M} = \frac{O_2 P}{O_1 P} \qquad \qquad \dots(ii)$$

Combining equations (i) and (ii), we have

$$\frac{\omega_1}{\omega_2} = \frac{O_2 N}{O_1 M} = \frac{O_2 P}{O_1 P} \qquad \qquad \dots(iii)$$

From above, we see that the angular velocity ratio is inversely proportional to the ratio of the distances of the point P from the centres O_1 and O_2, or the common normal to the two surfaces at the point of contact Q intersects the line of centres at point P which divides the centre distance inversely as the ratio of angular velocities.

Therefore in order to have a constant angular velocity ratio for all positions of the wheels, the point P must be the fixed point (called pitch point) for the two wheels. In other words, *the common normal at the point of contact between a pair of teeth must always pass through the pitch point.* This is the fundamental condition which must be satisfied while designing the profiles for the teeth of gear wheels. It is also known as *law of gearing.*

Notes : 1. The above condition is fulfilled by teeth of involute form, provided that the root circles from which the profiles are generated are tangential to the common normal.

2. If the shape of one tooth profile is arbitrarily chosen and another tooth is designed to satisfy the above condition, then the second tooth is said to be conjugate to the first. The conjugate teeth are not in common use because of difficulty in manufacture, and cost of production.

3. If D_1 and D_2 are pitch circle diameters of wheels 1 and 2 having teeth T_1 and T_2 respectively, then velocity ratio,

$$\frac{\omega_1}{\omega_2} = \frac{O_2 P}{O_1 P} = \frac{D_2}{D_1} = \frac{T_2}{T_1}$$

12.8. Velocity of Sliding of Teeth

The sliding between a pair of teeth in contact at Q occurs along the common tangent TT to the tooth curves as shown in Fig. 12.6. *The velocity of sliding is the velocity of one tooth relative to its mating tooth along the common tangent at the point of contact.*

The velocity of point Q, considered as a point on wheel 1, along the common tangent TT is represented by EC. From similar triangles QEC and O_1MQ,

$$\frac{EC}{MQ} = \frac{v}{O_1Q} = \omega_1 \quad \text{or} \quad EC = \omega_1.MQ$$

Similarly, the velocity of point Q, considered as a point on wheel 2, along the common tangent TT is represented by ED. From similar triangles QCD and O_2NQ,

$$\frac{ED}{QN} = \frac{v_2}{O_2Q} = \omega_2 \quad \text{or} \quad ED = \omega_2.QN$$

Let $\qquad\qquad v_S$ = Velocity of sliding at Q.

$\therefore\qquad\qquad$
$$v_S = ED - EC = \omega_2.QN - \omega_1.MQ$$

$$= \omega_2 (QP + PN) - \omega_1 (MP - QP)$$

$$= (\omega_1 + \omega_2) QP + \omega_2.PN - \omega_1.MP \qquad\qquad ...(i)$$

Since $\dfrac{\omega_1}{\omega_2} = \dfrac{O_2P}{O_1P} = \dfrac{PN}{MP}$ $\quad$ or $\quad \omega_1.MP = \omega_2.PN$, therefore equation ($i$) becomes

$$v_S = (\omega_1 + \omega_2) QP \qquad\qquad ...(ii)$$

Notes : 1. We see from equation (ii), that the velocity of sliding is proportional to the distance of the point of contact from the pitch point.

2. Since the angular velocity of wheel 2 relative to wheel 1 is $(\omega_1 + \omega_2)$ and P is the instantaneous centre for this relative motion, therefore the value of v_s may directly be written as v_s $(\omega_1 + \omega_2) QP$, without the above analysis.

12.9. Forms of Teeth

We have discussed in Art. 12.7 (Note 2) that conjugate teeth are not in common use. Therefore, in actual practice following are the two types of teeth commonly used :

1. *Cycloidal* teeth ; and 2. Involute teeth.

We shall discuss both the above mentioned types of teeth in the following articles. Both these forms of teeth satisfy the conditions as discussed in Art. 12.7.

12.10. Cycloidal Teeth

A *cycloid* is the curve traced by a point on the circumference of a circle which rolls without slipping on a fixed straight line. When a circle rolls without slipping on the outside of a fixed circle, the curve traced by a point on the circumference of a circle is known as *epi-cycloid*. On the other hand, if a circle rolls without slipping on the inside of a fixed circle, then the curve traced by a point on the circumference of a circle is called *hypo-cycloid*.

In Fig. 12.7 (*a*), the fixed line or pitch line of a rack is shown. When the circle *C* rolls without slipping above the pitch line in the direction as indicated in Fig. 12.7 (*a*), then the point *P* on the circle traces epi-cycloid *PA*. This represents the face of the cycloidal tooth profile. When the circle *D* rolls without slipping below the pitch line, then the point *P* on the circle *D* traces hypo-cycloid *PB*, which represents the flank of the cycloidal tooth. The profile *BPA* is one side of the cycloidal rack tooth. Similarly, the two curves *P′ A′* and *P′B′* forming the opposite side of the tooth profile are traced by the point *P′* when the circles *C* and *D* roll in the opposite directions.

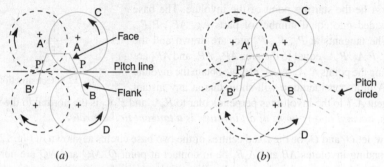

Fig. 12.7. Construction of cycloidal teeth of a gear.

In the similar way, the cycloidal teeth of a gear may be constructed as shown in Fig. 12.7 (*b*). The circle *C* is rolled without slipping on the outside of the pitch circle and the point *P* on the circle *C* traces epi-cycloid *PA*, which represents the face of the cycloidal tooth. The circle *D* is rolled on the inside of pitch circle and the point *P* on the circle *D* traces hypo-cycloid *PB*, which represents the flank of the tooth profile. The profile *BPA* is one side of the cycloidal tooth. The opposite side of the tooth is traced as explained above.

The construction of the two mating cycloidal teeth is shown in Fig. 12.8. A point on the circle *D* will trace the flank of the tooth T_1 when circle *D* rolls without slipping on the inside of pitch circle of wheel 1 and face of tooth T_2 when the circle *D* rolls without slipping on the outside of pitch circle of wheel 2. Similarly, a point on the circle *C* will trace the face of tooth T_1 and flank of tooth T_2. The rolling circles *C* and *D* may have unequal diameters, but if several wheels are to be interchangeable, they must have rolling circles of equal diameters.

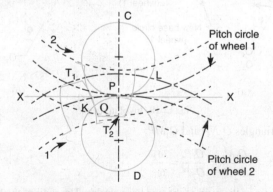

Fig. 12.8. Construction of two mating cycloidal teeth.

A little consideration will show, that the common normal *XX* at the point of contact between two cycloidal teeth always passes through the pitch point, which is the fundamental condition for a constant velocity ratio.

12.11. Involute Teeth

An involute of a circle is a plane curve generated by a point on a tangent, which rolls on the circle without slipping or by a point on a taut string which in unwrapped from a reel as shown in Fig. 12.9. In connection with toothed wheels, the circle is known as base circle. The involute is traced as follows :

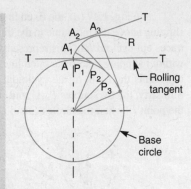

Fig. 12.9. Construction of involute.

Let A be the starting point of the involute. The base circle is divided into equal number of parts *e.g.* AP_1, P_1P_2, P_2P_3 etc. The tangents at P_1, P_2, P_3 etc. are drawn and the length P_1A_1, P_2A_2, P_3A_3 equal to the arcs AP_1, AP_2 and AP_3 are set off. Joining the points A, A_1, A_2, A_3 etc. we obtain the involute curve AR. A little consideration will show that at any instant A_3, the tangent A_3T to the involute is perpendicular to P_3A_3 and P_3A_3 is the normal to the involute. In other words, *normal at any point of an involute is a tangent to the circle.*

Now, let O_1 and O_2 be the fixed centres of the two base circles as shown in Fig. 12.10 (*a*). Let the corresponding involutes AB and A_1B_1 be in contact at point Q. MQ and NQ are normals to the involutes at Q and are tangents to base circles. Since the normal of an involute at a given point is the tangent drawn from that point to the base circle, therefore the common normal MN at Q is also the common tangent to the two base circles. We see that the common normal MN intersects the line of centres O_1O_2 at the fixed point P (called pitch point). Therefore the involute teeth satisfy the fundamental condition of constant velocity ratio.

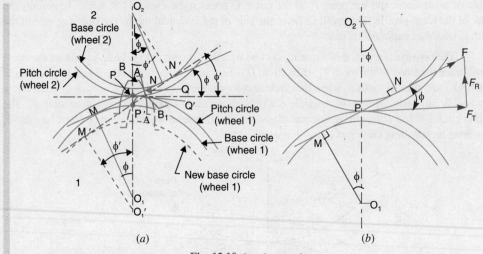

Fig. 12.10. Involute teeth.

From similar triangles O_2NP and O_1MP,

$$\frac{O_1M}{O_2N} = \frac{O_1P}{O_2P} = \frac{\omega_2}{\omega_1} \qquad \qquad ...(i)$$

which determines the ratio of the radii of the two base circles. The radii of the base circles is given by

$$O_1M = O_1P\cos\phi, \quad \text{and} \quad O_2N = O_2P\cos\phi$$

Also the centre distance between the base circles,

$$O_1O_2 = O_1P + O_2P = \frac{O_1M}{\cos\phi} + \frac{O_2N}{\cos\phi} = \frac{O_1M + O_2N}{\cos\phi}$$

where ϕ is the pressure angle or the angle of obliquity. It is the angle which the common normal to the base circles (*i.e. MN*) makes with the common tangent to the pitch circles.

When the power is being transmitted, the maximum tooth pressure (neglecting friction at the teeth) is exerted along the common normal through the pitch point. This force may be resolved into tangential and radial or normal components. These components act along and at right angles to the common tangent to the pitch circles.

If F is the maximum tooth pressure as shown in Fig. 12.10 (*b*), then

Tangential force, $\qquad F_T = F \cos \phi$

and radial or normal force, $\qquad F_R = F \sin \phi$.

$\therefore$ Torque exerted on the gear shaft

$$= F_T \times r, \text{ where } r \text{ is the pitch circle radius of the gear.}$$

Note : The tangential force provides the driving torque and the radial or normal force produces radial deflection of the rim and bending of the shafts.

12.12. Effect of Altering the Centre Distance on the Velocity Ratio for Involute Teeth Gears

In the previous article, we have seen that the velocity ratio for the involute teeth gears is given by

$$\frac{O_1 M}{O_2 N} = \frac{O_1 P}{O_2 P} = \frac{\omega_2}{\omega_1} \qquad \qquad ...(i)$$

Let, in Fig. 12.10 (*a*), the centre of rotation of one of the gears (say wheel 1) is shifted from O_1 to $O_1{}'$. Consequently the contact point shifts from Q to Q '. The common normal to the teeth at the point of contact Q ' is the tangent to the base circle, because it has a contact between two involute curves and they are generated from the base circle. Let the tangent $M'N'$ to the base circles intersects $O_1' O_2$ at the pitch point P'. As a result of this, the wheel continues to work* correctly.

Now from similar triangles O_2NP and O_1MP,

$$\frac{O_1 M}{O_2 N} = \frac{O_1 P}{O_2 P} \qquad \qquad ...(ii)$$

and from similar triangles $O_2N'P'$ and $O_1'M'P'$,

$$\frac{O_1'M'}{O_2 N'} = \frac{O_1'P'}{O_2 P'} \qquad \qquad ...(iii)$$

But $O_2 N = O_2 N'$, and $O_1 M = O_1' M'$. Therefore from equations (*ii*) and (*iii*),

$$\frac{O_1 P}{O_2 P} = \frac{O_1'P'}{O_2 P'} \qquad \qquad ...[\text{Same as equation } (i)]$$

Thus we see that if the centre distance is changed within limits, the velocity ratio remains unchanged. However, the pressure angle increases (from ϕ to ϕ') with the increase in the centre distance.

Example 12.1. *A single reduction gear of 120 kW with a pinion 250 mm pitch circle diameter and speed 650 r.p.m. is supported in bearings on either side. Calculate the total load due to the power transmitted, the pressure angle being 20°.*

Solution. Given : $P = 120$ kW $= 120 \times 10^3$ W ; $d = 250$ mm or $r = 125$ mm $= 0.125$ m ; $N = 650$ r.p.m. or $\omega = 2\pi \times 650/60 = 68$ rad/s ; $\phi = 20°$

---

* It is not the case with cycloidal teeth.

Let T = Torque transmitted in N-m.

We know that power transmitted (P),

$$120 \times 10^3 = T.\omega = T \times 68 \qquad \text{or} \quad T = 120 \times 10^3/68 = 1765 \text{ N-m}$$

and tangential load on the pinion,

$$F_T = T/r = 1765 / 0.125 = 14\ 120 \text{ N}$$

∴ Total load due to power transmitted,

$$F = F_T / \cos \phi = 14\ 120 / \cos 20° = 15\ 026 \text{ N} = 15.026 \text{ kN Ans.}$$

12.13. Comparison Between Involute and Cycloidal Gears

In actual practice, the involute gears are more commonly used as compared to cycloidal gears, due to the following advantages :

Advantages of involute gears

Following are the advantages of involute gears :

1. The most important advantage of the involute gears is that the centre distance for a pair of involute gears can be varied within limits without changing the velocity ratio. This is not true for cycloidal gears which requires exact centre distance to be maintained.

2. In involute gears, the pressure angle, from the start of the engagement of teeth to the end of the engagement, remains constant. It is necessary for smooth running and less wear of gears. But in cycloidal gears, the pressure angle is maximum at the beginning of engagement, reduces to zero at pitch point, starts decreasing and again becomes maximum at the end of engagement. This results in less smooth running of gears.

3. The face and flank of involute teeth are generated by a single curve where as in cycloidal gears, double curves (*i.e.* epi-cycloid and hypo-cycloid) are required for the face and flank respectively. Thus the involute teeth are easy to manufacture than cycloidal teeth. In involute system, the basic rack has straight teeth and the same can be cut with simple tools.

Note : The only disadvantage of the involute teeth is that the interference occurs (Refer Art. 12.19) with pinions having smaller number of teeth. This may be avoided by altering the heights of addendum and dedendum of the mating teeth or the angle of obliquity of the teeth.

Advantages of cycloidal gears

Following are the advantages of cycloidal gears :

1. Since the cycloidal teeth have wider flanks, therefore the cycloidal gears are stronger than the involute gears, for the same pitch. Due to this reason, the cycloidal teeth are preferred specially for cast teeth.

2. In cycloidal gears, the contact takes place between a convex flank and concave surface, whereas in involute gears, the convex surfaces are in contact. This condition results in less wear in cycloidal gears as compared to involute gears. However the difference in wear is negligible.

3. In cycloidal gears, the interference does not occur at all. Though there are advantages of cycloidal gears but they are outweighed by the greater simplicity and flexibility of the involute gears.

12.14. Systems of Gear Teeth

The following four systems of gear teeth are commonly used in practice :

1. $14\frac{1}{2}°$ Composite system, **2.** $14\frac{1}{2}°$ Full depth involute system, **3.** 20° Full depth involute system, and **4.** 20° Stub involute system.

The $14\frac{1}{2}°$ *composite system* is used for general purpose gears. It is stronger but has no interchangeability. The tooth profile of this system has cycloidal curves at the top and bottom and involute curve at the middle portion. The teeth are produced by formed milling cutters or hobs. The tooth profile of the $14\frac{1}{2}°$ *full depth involute system* was developed for use with gear hobs for spur and helical gears.

The tooth profile of the $20°$ *full depth involute system* may be cut by hobs. The increase of the pressure angle from $14\frac{1}{2}°$ to $20°$ results in a stronger tooth, because the tooth acting as a beam is wider at the base. The $20°$ *stub involute system* has a strong tooth to take heavy loads.

12.15. Standard Proportions of Gear Systems

The following table shows the standard proportions in module (m) for the four gear systems as discussed in the previous article.

Table 12.1. Standard proportions of gear systems.

S. No.	Particulars	$14\frac{1}{2}°$ composite or full depth involute system	$20°$ full depth involute system	$20°$ stub involute system
1.	Addenddm	1 m	1 m	0.8 m
2.	Dedendum	1.25 m	1.25 m	1 m
3.	Working depth	2 m	2 m	1.60 m
4.	Minimum total depth	2.25 m	2.25 m	1.80 m
5.	Tooth thickness	1.5708 m	1.5708 m	1.5708 m
6.	Minimum clearance	0.25 m	0.25 m	0.2 m
7.	Fillet radius at root	0.4 m	0.4 m	0.4 m

12.16. Length of Path of Contact

Consider a pinion driving the wheel as shown in Fig. 12.11. When the pinion rotates in clockwise direction, the contact between a pair of involute teeth begins at K (on the flank near the base circle of pinion or the outer end of the tooth face on the wheel) and* ends at L (outer end of the tooth face on the pinion or on the flank near the base circle of wheel). MN is the common normal at the point of contacts and the common tangent to the base circles. The point K is the intersection of the addendum circle of wheel and the common tangent. The point L is the intersection of the addendum circle of pinion and common tangent.

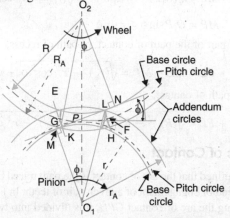

Fig. 12.11. Length of path of contact.

---

* If the wheel is made to act as a driver and the directions of motion are reversed, then the contact between a pair of teeth begins at L and ends at K.

We have discussed in Art. 12.4 that the length of path of contact is the length of common normal cut-off by the addendum circles of the wheel and the pinion. Thus the length of path of contact is KL which is the sum of the parts of the path of contacts KP and PL. The part of the path of contact KP is known as *path of approach* and the part of the path of contact PL is known as *path of recess*.

Bevel gear

Let $r_A = O_1L$ = Radius of addendum circle of pinion,

$R_A = O_2K$ = Radius of addendum circle of wheel,

$r = O_1P$ = Radius of pitch circle of pinion, and

$R = O_2P$ = Radius of pitch circle of wheel.

From Fig. 12.11, we find that radius of the base circle of pinion,
$$O_1M = O_1P \cos \phi = r \cos \phi$$
and radius of the base circle of wheel,
$$O_2N = O_2P \cos \phi = R \cos \phi$$
Now from right angled triangle O_2KN,

$$KN = \sqrt{(O_2K)^2 - (O_2N)^2} = \sqrt{(R_A)^2 - R^2 \cos^2 \phi}$$

and $$PN = O_2P \sin \phi = R \sin \phi$$

∴ Length of the part of the path of contact, or the path of approach,

$$KP = KN - PN = \sqrt{(R_A)^2 - R^2 \cos^2 \phi} - R \sin \phi$$

Similarly from right angled triangle O_1ML,

$$ML = \sqrt{(O_1L)^2 - (O_1M)^2} = \sqrt{(r_A)^2 - r^2 \cos^2 \phi}$$

and $$MP = O_1P \sin \phi = r \sin \phi$$

∴ Length of the part of the path of contact, or path of recess,

$$PL = ML - MP = \sqrt{(r_A)^2 - r^2 \cos^2 \phi} - r \sin \phi$$

∴ Length of the path of contact,

$$KL = KP + PL = \sqrt{(R_A)^2 - R^2 \cos^2 \phi} + \sqrt{(r_A)^2 - r^2 \cos^2 \phi} - (R + r) \sin \phi$$

12.17. Length of Arc of Contact

We have already defined that the arc of contact is the path traced by a point on the pitch circle from the beginning to the end of engagement of a given pair of teeth. In Fig. 12.11, the arc of contact is EPF or GPH. Considering the arc of contact GPH, it is divided into two parts *i.e.* arc GP and arc PH. The arc GP is known as **arc of approach** and the arc PH is called **arc of recess**. The angles subtended by these arcs at O_1 are called **angle of approach** and **angle of recess** respectively.

We know that the length of the arc of approach (arc *GP*)

$$= \frac{\text{Length of path of approach}}{\cos\phi} = \frac{KP}{\cos\phi}$$

and the length of the arc of recess (arc *PH*)

$$= \frac{\text{Length of path of recess}}{\cos\phi} = \frac{PL}{\cos\phi}$$

Since the length of the arc of contact *GPH* is equal to the sum of the length of arc of approach and arc of recess, therefore,

Length of the arc of contact

$$= \text{arc } GP + \text{arc } PH = \frac{KP}{\cos\phi} + \frac{PL}{\cos\phi} = \frac{KL}{\cos\phi}$$

$$= \frac{\text{Length of path of contact}}{\cos\phi}$$

12.18. Contact Ratio (or Number of Pairs of Teeth in Contact)

The contact ratio or the number of pairs of teeth in contact is defined as the **ratio of the length of the arc of contact to the circular pitch.** Mathematically,

Contact ratio or number of pairs of teeth in contact

$$= \frac{\text{Length of the arc of contact}}{p_c}$$

where p_c = Circular pitch = πm, and

m = Module.

Notes : **1.** The contact ratio, usually, is not a whole number. For example, if the contact ratio is 1.6, it does not mean that there are 1.6 pairs of teeth in contact. It means that there are alternately one pair and two pairs of teeth in contact and on a time basis the average is 1.6.

2. The theoretical minimum value for the contact ratio is one, that is there must always be at least one pair of teeth in contact for continuous action.

3. Larger the contact ratio, more quietly the gears will operate.

Example 12.2. *The number of teeth on each of the two equal spur gears in mesh are 40. The teeth have 20° involute profile and the module is 6 mm. If the arc of contact is 1.75 times the circular pitch, find the addendum.*

Solution. Given : $T = t = 40$; $\phi = 20°$; $m = 6$ mm

We know that the circular pitch,

$$p_c = \pi m = \pi \times 6 = 18.85 \text{ mm}$$

∴ Length of arc of contact

$$= 1.75 \, p_c = 1.75 \times 18.85 = 33 \text{ mm}$$

and length of path of contact

$$= \text{Length of arc of contact} \times \cos\phi = 33 \cos 20° = 31 \text{ mm}$$

Let $R_A = r_A$ = Radius of the addendum circle of each wheel.

We know that pitch circle radii of each wheel,

$$R = r = m.T / 2 = 6 \times 40/2 = 120 \text{ mm}$$

and length of path of contact

$$31 = \sqrt{(R_A)^2 - R^2 \cos^2 \phi} + \sqrt{(r_A)^2 - r^2 \cos^2 \phi} - (R + r) \sin \phi$$

$$= 2\left[\sqrt{(R_A)^2 - R^2 \cos^2 \phi} - R \sin \phi\right] \quad ...(\because R = r, \text{ and } R_A = r_A)$$

$$\frac{31}{2} = \sqrt{(R_A)^2 - (120)^2 \cos^2 20°} - 120 \sin 20°$$

$$15.5 = \sqrt{(R_A)^2 - 12\ 715} - 41$$

$$(15.5 + 41)^2 = (R_A)^2 - 12\ 715$$

$$3192 + 12\ 715 = (R_A)^2 \qquad \text{or} \qquad R_A = 126.12 \text{ mm}$$

We know that the addendum of the wheel,

$$= R_A - R = 126.12 - 120 = 6.12 \text{ mm Ans.}$$

Example 12.3. *A pinion having 30 teeth drives a gear having 80 teeth. The profile of the gears is involute with 20° pressure angle, 12 mm module and 10 mm addendum. Find the length of path of contact, arc of contact and the contact ratio.*

Solution. Given : $t = 30$; $T = 80$; $\phi = 20°$; $m = 12$ mm ; Addendum = 10 mm

Length of path of contact

We know that pitch circle radius of pinion,

$$r = m.t / 2 = 12 \times 30 / 2 = 180 \text{ mm}$$

and pitch circle radius of gear,

$$R = m.T / 2 = 12 \times 80 / 2 = 480 \text{ mm}$$

∴ Radius of addendum circle of pinion,

$$r_A = r + \text{Addendum} = 180 + 10 = 190 \text{ mm}$$

and radius of addendum circle of gear,

$$R_A = R + \text{Addendum} = 480 + 10 = 490 \text{ mm}$$

We know that length of the path of approach,

$$KP = \sqrt{(R_A)^2 - R^2 \cos^2 \phi} - R \sin \phi \qquad ...(\text{Refer Fig. 12.11})$$

$$= \sqrt{(490)^2 - (480)^2 \cos^2 20°} - 480 \sin 20° = 191.5 - 164.2 = 27.3 \text{ mm}$$

and length of the path of recess,

$$PL = \sqrt{(r_A)^2 - r^2 \cos^2 \phi} - r \sin \phi$$

$$= \sqrt{(190)^2 - (180)^2 \cos^2 20°} - 180 \sin 20° = 86.6 - 61.6 = 25 \text{ mm}$$

We know that length of path of contact,

$$KL = KP + PL = 27.3 + 25 = 52.3 \text{ mm} \textbf{ Ans.}$$

Worm.

Length of arc of contact

We know that length of arc of contact

$$= \frac{\text{Length of path of contact}}{\cos\phi} = \frac{52.3}{\cos 20°} = 55.66 \text{ mm} \text{ Ans.}$$

Contact ratio

We know that circular pitch,

$$p_c = \pi.m = \pi \times 12 = 37.7 \text{ mm}$$

∴   Contact ratio $= \dfrac{\text{Length of arc of contact}}{p_c} = \dfrac{55.66}{37.7} = 1.5 \text{ say } 2 \text{ Ans.}$

Example 12.4. *Two involute gears of 20° pressure angle are in mesh. The number of teeth on pinion is 20 and the gear ratio is 2. If the pitch expressed in module is 5 mm and the pitch line speed is 1.2 m/s, assuming addendum as standard and equal to one module, find :*

1. The angle turned through by pinion when one pair of teeth is in mesh ; and

2. The maximum velocity of sliding.

Solution. Given : $\phi = 20°$; $t = 20$; $G = T/t = 2$; $m = 5$ mm ; $v = 1.2$ m/s ; addendum = 1 module = 5 mm

1. *Angle turned through by pinion when one pair of teeth is in mesh*

We know that pitch circle radius of pinion,

$$r = m.t / 2 = 5 \times 20 / 2 = 50 \text{ mm}$$

and pitch circle radius of wheel,

$$R = m.T / 2 = m.G.t / 2 = 5 \times 2 \times 20 \times 5 / 2 = 100 \text{ mm} \qquad ... (\because T = G.t)$$

∴ Radius of addendum circle of pinion,

$$r_A = r + \text{Addendum} = 50 + 5 = 55 \text{ mm}$$

and radius of addendum circle of wheel,

$$R_A = R + \text{Addendum} = 100 + 5 = 105 \text{ mm}$$

We know that length of the path of approach (*i.e.* the path of contact when engagement occurs),

$$KP = \sqrt{(R_A)^2 - R^2 \cos^2 \phi} - R \sin\phi \qquad ...(\text{Refer Fig. 12.11})$$

$$= \sqrt{(105)^2 - (100)^2 \cos^2 20°} - 100 \sin 20°$$

$$= 46.85 - 34.2 = 12.65 \text{ mm}$$

and the length of path of recess (*i.e.* the path of contact when disengagement occurs),

$$PL = \sqrt{(r_A)^2 - r^2 \cos^2 \phi} - r \sin\phi$$

$$= \sqrt{(55)^2 - (50)^2 \cos^2 20°} - 50 \sin 20° = 28.6 - 17.1 = 11.5 \text{ mm}$$

∴ Length of the path of contact,

$$KL = KP + PL = 12.65 + 11.5 = 24.15 \text{ mm}$$

and length of the arc of contact

$$= \frac{\text{Length of path of contact}}{\cos\phi} = \frac{24.15}{\cos 20°} = 25.7 \text{ mm}$$

We know that angle turned through by pinion

$$= \frac{\text{Length of arc of contact} \times 360°}{\text{Circumference of pinion}} = \frac{25.7 \times 360°}{2\pi \times 50} = 29.45° \text{ Ans.}$$

2. *Maximum velocity of sliding*

Let ω_1 = Angular speed of pinion, and

ω_2 = Angular speed of wheel.

We know that pitch line speed,

$$v = \omega_1.r = \omega_2.R$$

∴ $$\omega_1 = v/r = 120/5 = 24 \text{ rad/s}$$

and $$\omega_2 = v/R = 120/10 = 12 \text{ rad/s}$$

∴ Maximum velocity of sliding,

$$v_S = (\omega_1 + \omega_2) \, KP \qquad\qquad ...(\because KP > PL)$$

$$= (24 + 12) \, 12.65 = 455.4 \text{ mm/s } \text{Ans.}$$

Example 12.5. *A pair of gears, having 40 and 20 teeth respectively, are rotating in mesh, the speed of the smaller being 2000 r.p.m. Determine the velocity of sliding between the gear teeth faces at the point of engagement, at the pitch point, and at the point of disengagement if the smaller gear is the driver. Assume that the gear teeth are 20° involute form, addendum length is 5 mm and the module is 5 mm.*

Also find the angle through which the pinion turns while any pairs of teeth are in contact.

Solution. Given : $T = 40$; $t = 20$; $N_1 = 2000$ r.p.m. ; $\phi = 20°$; addendum = 5 mm ; $m = 5$ mm

We know that angular velocity of the smaller gear,

$$\omega_1 = \frac{2\pi N_1}{60} = \frac{2\pi \times 2000}{60} = 209.5 \text{ rad/s}$$

and angular velocity of the larger gear,

$$\omega_2 = \omega_1 \times \frac{t}{T} = 209.5 \times \frac{20}{40} = 104.75 \text{ rad/s} \qquad ...\left(\because \frac{\omega_2}{\omega_1} = \frac{t}{T}\right)$$

Pitch circle radius of the smaller gear,

$$r = m.t\,/\,2 = 5 \times 20/2 = 50 \text{ mm}$$

and pitch circle radius of the larger gear,

$$R = m.T\,/\,2 = 5 \times 40/2 = 100 \text{ mm}$$

∴ Radius of addendum circle of smaller gear,

$$r_A = r + \text{Addendum} = 50 + 5 = 55 \text{ mm}$$

and radius of addendum circle of larger gear,

$$R_A = R + \text{Addendum} = 100 + 5 = 105 \text{ mm}$$

The engagement and disengagement of the gear teeth is shown in Fig. 12.11. The point K is the point of engagement, P is the pitch point and L is the point of disengagement. MN is the common tangent at the points of contact.

We know that the distance of point of engagement K from the pitch point P or the length of the path of approach,

$$KP = \sqrt{(R_A)^2 - R^2 \cos^2 \phi} - R \sin \phi$$

$$= \sqrt{(105)^2 - (100)^2 \cos^2 20°} - 100 \sin 20°$$

$$= 46.85 - 34.2 = 12.65 \text{ mm}$$

and the distance of the pitch point P from the point of disengagement L or the length of the path of recess,

$$PL = \sqrt{(r_A)^2 - r^2 \cos^2 \phi} - r \sin \phi$$

$$= \sqrt{(55)^2 - (50)^2 \cos^2 20°} - 50 \sin 20° = 28.6 - 17.1 = 11.5 \text{ mm}$$

Velocity of sliding at the point of engagement

We know that velocity of sliding at the point of engagement K,

$$v_{SK} = (\omega_1 + \omega_2) \, KP = (209.5 + 104.75) \, 12.65 = 3975 \text{ mm/s} \quad \textbf{Ans.}$$

Velocity of sliding at the pitch point

Since the velocity of sliding is proportional to the distance of the contact point from the pitch point, therefore the velocity of sliding at the pitch point is zero. **Ans.**

Velocity of sliding at the point of disengagement

We know that velocity of sliding at the point of disengagement L,

$$v_{SL} = (\omega_1 + \omega_2) \, PL = (209.5 + 104.75) \, 11.5 = 3614 \text{ mm/s} \quad \textbf{Ans.}$$

Angle through which the pinion turns

We know that length of the path of contact,

$$KL = KP + PL = 12.65 + 11.5 = 24.15 \text{ mm}$$

and length of arc of contact $= \dfrac{KL}{\cos \phi} = \dfrac{24.15}{\cos 20°} = 25.7 \text{ mm}$

Circumference of the smaller gear or pinion

$$= 2 \pi r = 2\pi \times 50 = 314.2 \text{ mm}$$

∴ Angle through which the pinion turns

$$= \text{Length of arc of contact} \times \dfrac{360°}{\text{Circumference of pinion}}$$

$$= 25.7 \times \dfrac{360°}{314.2} = 29.45° \quad \textbf{Ans.}$$

Example 12.6. *The following data relate to a pair of 20° involute gears in mesh :*

Module = 6 mm, Number of teeth on pinion = 17, Number of teeth on gear = 49 ; Addenda on pinion and gear wheel = 1 module.

Find : 1. The number of pairs of teeth in contact ; 2. The angle turned through by the pinion and the gear wheel when one pair of teeth is in contact, and 3. The ratio of sliding to rolling motion when the tip of a tooth on the larger wheel (i) is just making contact, (ii) is just leaving contact with its mating tooth, and (iii) is at the pitch point.

Solution. Given : $\phi = 20°$; $m = 6$ mm ; $t = 17$; $T = 49$; Addenda on pinion and gear wheel = 1 module = 6 mm

1. *Number of pairs of teeth in contact*

We know that pitch circle radius of pinion,

$$r = m.t \, / \, 2 = 6 \times 17 \, / \, 2 = 51 \text{ mm}$$

and pitch circle radius of gear,

$$r = m.T \, / \, 2 = 6 \times 49 \, / \, 2 = 147 \text{ mm}$$

∴ Radius of addendum circle of pinion,

$$r_A = r + \text{Addendum} = 51 + 6 = 57 \text{ mm}$$

and radius of addendum circle of gear,

$$R_A = R + \text{Addendum} = 147 + 6 = 153 \text{ mm}$$

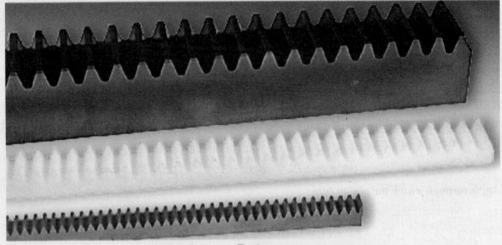

Racks

We know that the length of path of approach (*i.e.* the path of contact when engagement occurs),

$$KP = \sqrt{(R_A)^2 - R^2 \cos^2 \phi} - R \sin \phi \qquad \text{...(Refer Fig. 12.11)}$$

$$= \sqrt{(153)^2 - (147)^2 \cos^2 20°} - 147 \sin 20°$$

$$= 65.8 - 50.3 = 15.5 \text{ mm}$$

and length of path of recess (*i.e.* the path of contact when disengagement occurs),

$$PL = \sqrt{(r_A)^2 - r^2 \cos^2 \phi} - r \sin \phi$$

$$= \sqrt{(57)^2 - (51)^2 \cos^2 20°} - 51 \sin 20°$$

$$= 30.85 - 17.44 = 13.41 \text{ mm}$$

∴ Length of path of contact,

$$KL = KP + PL = 15.5 + 13.41 = 28.91 \text{ mm}$$

and length of arc of contact $= \dfrac{\text{Length of path of contact}}{\cos \phi} = \dfrac{28.91}{\cos 20°} = 30.8$ mm

We know that circular pitch,

$$p_c = \pi.m = \pi \times 6 = 18.852 \text{ mm}$$

∴ Number of pairs of teeth in contact (or contact ratio)

$$= \dfrac{\text{Length of arc of contact}}{\text{Circular pitch}} = \dfrac{30.8}{18.852} = 1.6 \text{ say } 2 \text{ Ans.}$$

2. *Angle turned through by the pinion and gear wheel when one pair of teeth is in contact*

We know that angle turned through by the pinion

$$= \dfrac{\text{Length of arc of contact} \times 360°}{\text{Circumference of pinion}} = \dfrac{30.8 \times 360}{2\pi \times 51} = 34.6° \text{ Ans.}$$

and angle turned through by the gear wheel

$$= \dfrac{\text{Length of arc of contact} \times 360°}{\text{Circumference of gear}} = \dfrac{30.8 \times 360}{2\pi \times 147} = 12° \text{ Ans.}$$

3. *Ratio of sliding to rolling motion*

Let ω_1 = Angular velocity of pinion, and

ω_2 = Angular velocity of gear wheel.

We know that $\omega_1 / \omega_2 = T / t$ or $\omega_2 = \omega_1 \times t / T = \omega_1 \times 17/49 = 0.347 \, \omega_1$

and rolling velocity, $v_R = \omega_1.r = \omega_2.R = \omega_1 \times 51 = 51 \, \omega_1$ mm/s

(*i*) At the instant when the tip of a tooth on the larger wheel is just making contact with its mating teeth (*i.e.* when the engagement commences), the sliding velocity

$$v_S = (\omega_1 + \omega_2) \, KP = (\omega_1 + 0.347 \, \omega_1) \, 15.5 = 20.88 \, \omega_1 \text{ mm/s}$$

∴ Ratio of sliding velocity to rolling velocity,

$$\dfrac{v_S}{v_R} = \dfrac{20.88 \, \omega_1}{51 \omega_1} = 0.41 \text{ Ans.}$$

(*ii*) At the instant when the tip of a tooth on the larger wheel is just leaving contact with its mating teeth (*i.e.* when engagement terminates), the sliding velocity,

$$v_S = (\omega_1 + \omega_2) \, PL = (\omega_1 + 0.347\omega_1) \, 13.41 = 18.1 \, \omega_1 \text{ mm/s}$$

∴ Ratio of sliding velocity to rolling velocity

$$\dfrac{v_S}{v_R} = \dfrac{18.1 \, \omega_1}{51 \, \omega_1} = 0.355 \text{ Ans.}$$

(*iii*) Since at the pitch point, the sliding velocity is zero, therefore the ratio of sliding velocity to rolling velocity is zero. **Ans.**

Example 12.7. *A pinion having 18 teeth engages with an internal gear having 72 teeth. If the gears have involute profiled teeth with 20° pressure angle, module of 4 mm and the addenda on pinion and gear are 8.5 mm and 3.5 mm respectively, find the length of path of contact.*

Solution. Given : $t = 18$; $T = 72$; $\phi = 20°$; $m = 4$ mm ; Addendum on pinion = 8.5 mm ; Addendum on gear = 3.5 mm

Fig. 12.12 shows a pinion with centre O_1, in mesh with internal gear of centre O_2. It may be noted that the internal gears have the addendum circle and the tooth faces *inside* the pitch circle.

We know that the length of path of contact is the length of the common tangent to the two base circles cut by the addendum circles. From Fig. 12.12, we see that the addendum circles cut the common tangents at points K and L. Therefore the length of path of contact is KL which is equal to the sum of KP (*i.e.* path of approach) and PL (*i.e.* path of recess).

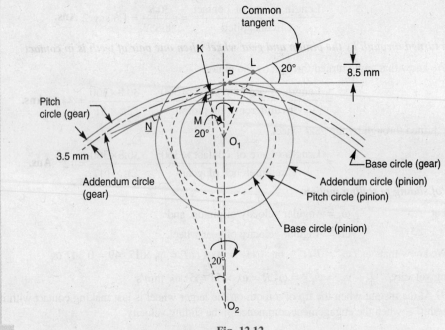

Fig. 12.12

We know that pitch circle radius of the pinion,

$$r = O_1P = m.t/2 = 4 \times 18/2 = 36 \text{ mm}$$

and pitch circle radius of the gear,

$$R = O_2P = m.T/2 = 4 \times 72/2 = 144 \text{ mm}$$

∴ Radius of addendum circle of the pinion,

$$r_A = O_1L = O_1P + \text{ Addendum on pinion} = 36 + 8.5 = 44.5 \text{ mm}$$

and radius of addendum circle of the gear,

$$R_A = O_2K = O_2P - \text{ Addendum on wheel} = 144 - 3.5 = 140.5 \text{ mm}$$

From Fig. 12.12, radius of the base circle of the pinion,

$$O_1M = O_1P \cos \phi = r \cos \phi = 36 \cos 20° = 33.83 \text{ mm}$$

and radius of the base circle of the gear,

$$O_2N = O_2P \cos \phi = R \cos \phi = 144 \cos 20° = 135.32 \text{ mm}$$

We know that length of the path of approach,

$$KP = PN - KN = O_2 P \sin 20° - \sqrt{(O_2K)^2 - (O_2N)^2}$$

$$= 144 \times 0.342 - \sqrt{(140.5)^2 - (135.32)^2} = 49.25 - 37.8 = 11.45 \text{ mm}$$

and length of the path of recess,

$$PL = ML - MP = \sqrt{(O_1L)^2 - (O_1M)^2} - O_1P \sin 20°$$

$$= \sqrt{(44.5)^2 - (33.83)^2} - 36 \times 0.342 = 28.9 - 12.3 = 16.6 \text{ mm}$$

∴ Length of the path of contact,

$$KL = KP + PL = 11.45 + 16.6 = 28.05 \text{ mm} \quad \textbf{Ans.}$$

12.19. Interference in Involute Gears

Fig. 12.13 shows a pinion with centre O_1, in mesh with wheel or gear with centre O_2. MN is the common tangent to the base circles and KL is the path of contact between the two mating teeth.

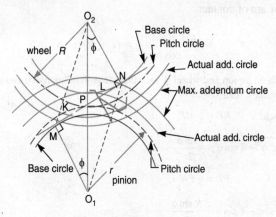

Fig. 12.13. Interference in involute gears.

A little consideration will show, that if the radius of the addendum circle of pinion is increased to O_1N, the point of contact L will move from L to N. When this radius is further increased, the point of contact L will be on the inside of base circle of wheel and not on the involute profile of tooth on wheel. The tip of tooth on the pinion will then undercut the tooth on the wheel at the root and remove part of the involute profile of tooth on the wheel. This effect is known as *interference*, and occurs when the teeth are being cut. In brief, *the phenomenon when the tip of tooth undercuts the root on its mating gear is known as interference.*

Similarly, if the radius of the addendum circle of the wheel increases beyond O_2M, then the tip of tooth on wheel will cause interference with the tooth on pinion. The points M and N are called *interference points.* Obviously, interference may be avoided if the path of contact does not extend beyond interference points. The limiting value of the radius of the addendum circle of the pinion is *O_1N and of the wheel is O_2M.

From the above discussion, we conclude that the interference may only be avoided, if the point of contact between the two teeth is always on the involute profiles of both the teeth. In other

---

* From Fig. 12.13, we see that

$$O_1N = \sqrt{(O_1M)^2 + (MN)^2} = \sqrt{(r_b)^2 + [(r + R)\sin\phi]^2}$$

where r_b = Radius of base circle of pinion = $O_1P \cos\phi = r \cos\phi$

and $O_2M = \sqrt{(O_2N)^2 + (MN)^2} = \sqrt{(R_b)^2 + [(r + R)\sin\phi]^2}$

where R_b = Radius of base circle of wheel = $O_2P \cos\phi = R \cos\phi$

words, *interference may only be prevented, if the addendum circles of the two mating gears cut the common tangent to the base circles between the points of tangency.*

When interference is just avoided, the maximum length of path of contact is *MN* when the maximum addendum circles for pinion and wheel pass through the points of tangency *N* and *M* respectively as shown in Fig. 12.13. In such a case,

Maximum length of path of approach,

$$MP = r \sin \phi$$

and maximum length of path of recess,

$$PN = R \sin \phi$$

∴ Maximum length of path of contact,

$$MN = MP + PN = r \sin \phi + R \sin \phi = (r + R) \sin \phi$$

and maximum length of arc of contact

$$= \frac{(r + R) \sin \phi}{\cos \phi} = (r + R) \tan \phi$$

Note : In case the addenda on pinion and wheel is such that the path of approach and path of recess are half of their maximum possible values, then

Path of approach, $\qquad KP = \frac{1}{2} MP$

or $\qquad \sqrt{(R_A)^2 - R^2 \cos^2 \phi} - R \sin \phi = \dfrac{r \sin \phi}{2}$

and path of recess, $\qquad PL = \frac{1}{2} PN$

or $\qquad \sqrt{(r_A)^2 - r^2 \cos^2 \phi} - r \sin \phi = \dfrac{R \sin \phi}{2}$

∴ Length of the path of contact

$$= KP + PL = \frac{1}{2} MP + \frac{1}{2} PN = \frac{(r + R) \sin \phi}{2}$$

Example 12.8. *Two mating gears have 20 and 40 involute teeth of module 10 mm and 20° pressure angle. The addendum on each wheel is to be made of such a length that the line of contact on each side of the pitch point has half the maximum possible length. Determine the addendum height for each gear wheel, length of the path of contact, arc of contact and contact ratio.*

Solution. Given : $t = 20$; $T = 40$; $m = 10$ mm ; $\phi = 20°$

Addendum height for each gear wheel

We know that the pitch circle radius of the smaller gear wheel,

$$r = m.t \,/\, 2 = 10 \times 20 \,/\, 2 = 100 \text{ mm}$$

and pitch circle radius of the larger gear wheel,

$$R = m.T \,/\, 2 = 10 \times 40 \,/\, 2 = 200 \text{ mm}$$

Let $\qquad R_A$ = Radius of addendum circle for the larger gear wheel, and

$\qquad r_A$ = Radius of addendum circle for the smaller gear wheel.

Since the addendum on each wheel is to be made of such a length that the line of contact on each side of the pitch point (*i.e.* the path of approach and the path of recess) has half the maximum possible length, therefore

Path of approach, $\quad KP = \frac{1}{2}MP$ ...(Refer Fig. 12.13)

or $\quad \sqrt{(R_A)^2 - R^2 \cos^2 \phi} - R \sin \phi = \dfrac{r.\sin \phi}{2}$

or $\quad \sqrt{(R_A)^2 - (200)^2 \cos^2 20°} - 200 \sin 20° = \dfrac{100 \times \sin 20°}{2} = 50 \sin 20°$

$$\sqrt{(R_A)^2 - 35\,320} = 50 \sin 20° + 200 \sin 20° = 250 \times 0.342 = 85.5$$

$$(R_A)^2 - 35\,320 = (85.5)^2 = 7310 \qquad \text{...(Squaring both sides)}$$

$$(R_A)^2 = 7310 + 35\,320 = 42\,630 \quad \text{or} \quad R_A = 206.5 \text{ mm}$$

∴ Addendum height for larger gear wheel

$$= R_A - R = 206.5 - 200 = 6.5 \text{ mm \textbf{Ans.}}$$

Now path of recess, $\quad PL = \frac{1}{2}PN$

or $\quad \sqrt{(r_A)^2 - r^2 \cos^2 \phi} - r \sin \phi = \dfrac{R.\sin \phi}{2}$

or $\quad \sqrt{(r_A)^2 - (100)^2 \cos^2 20°} - 100 \sin 20° = \dfrac{200 \sin 20°}{2} = 100 \sin 20°$

$$\sqrt{(r_A)^2 - (100)^2 \cos^2 20°} = 100 \sin 20° + 100 \sin 20° = 200 \times 0.342 = 68.4$$

$$(r_A)^2 - 8830 = (68.4)^2 = 4680 \qquad \text{...(Squaring both sides)}$$

$$(r_A)^2 = 4680 + 8830 = 13\,510 \quad \text{or} \quad r_A = 116.2 \text{ mm}$$

∴ Addendum height for smaller gear wheel

$$= r_A - r = 116.2 - 100 = 16.2 \text{ mm \textbf{Ans.}}$$

Length of the path of contact

We know that length of the path of contact

$$= KP + PL = \frac{1}{2}MP + \frac{1}{2}PN = \frac{(r + R)\sin \phi}{2}$$

$$= \frac{(100 + 200) \sin 20°}{2} = 51.3 \text{ mm \textbf{Ans.}}$$

Length of the arc of contact

We know that length of the arc of contact

$$= \frac{\text{Length of the path of contact}}{\cos \phi} = \frac{51.3}{\cos 20°} = 54.6 \text{ mm \textbf{Ans.}}$$

Contact ratio

We know that circular pitch,

$$P_c = \pi\, m = \pi \times 10 = 31.42 \text{ mm}$$

∴ $\qquad$ Contact ratio $= \dfrac{\text{Length of the path of contact}}{p_c} = \dfrac{54.6}{31.42} = 1.74 \text{ say } 2\,\textbf{Ans.}$

12.20. Minimum Number of Teeth on the Pinion in Order to Avoid Interference

We have already discussed in the previous article that in order to avoid interference, the addendum circles for the two mating gears must cut the common tangent to the base circles between the points of tangency. The limiting condition reaches, when the addendum circles of pinion and wheel pass through points N and M (see Fig. 12.13) respectively.

Let
t = Number of teeth on the pinion,,

T = Number of teeth on the wheel,

m = Module of the teeth,

r = Pitch circle radius of pinion = $m.t / 2$

G = Gear ratio = $T / t = R / r$

ϕ = Pressure angle or angle of obliquity.

From triangle O_1NP,

$$(O_1N)^2 = (O_1P)^2 + (PN)^2 - 2 \times O_1P \times PN \cos O_1PN$$

$$= r^2 + R^2 \sin^2 \phi - 2r.R \sin \phi \cos (90° + \phi)$$

$$\qquad\qquad ...(\because PN = O_2P \sin \phi = R \sin \phi)$$

$$= r^2 + R^2 \sin^2 \phi + 2r.R \sin^2 \phi$$

$$= r^2 \left[1 + \frac{R^2 \sin^2 \phi}{r^2} + \frac{2R \sin^2 \phi}{r}\right] = r^2 \left[1 + \frac{R}{r}\left(\frac{R}{r} + 2\right) \sin^2 \phi\right]$$

$\therefore$ Limiting radius of the pinion addendum circle,

$$O_1N = r \sqrt{1 + \frac{R}{r}\left(\frac{R}{r} + 2\right) \sin^2 \phi} = \frac{m.t}{2} \sqrt{1 + \frac{T}{t}\left[\frac{T}{t} + 2\right] \sin^2 \phi}$$

Let
$A_P.m$ = Addendum of the pinion, where A_P is a fraction by which the standard addendum of one module for the pinion should be multiplied in order to avoid interference.

We know that the addendum of the pinion

$$= O_1N - O_1P$$

$\therefore$
$$A_P.m = \frac{m.t}{2} \sqrt{1 + \frac{T}{t}\left(\frac{T}{t} + 2\right) \sin^2 \phi} - \frac{m.t}{2} \qquad\qquad ...(\because O_1P = r = m.t/2)$$

$$= \frac{m.t}{2}\left[\sqrt{1 + \frac{T}{t}\left(\frac{T}{t} + 2\right) \sin^2 \phi} - 1\right]$$

or
$$A_P = \frac{t}{2}\left[\sqrt{1 + \frac{T}{t}\left(\frac{T}{t} + 2\right) \sin^2 \phi} - 1\right]$$

$\therefore$
$$t = \frac{2 A_P}{\sqrt{1 + \frac{T}{t}\left(\frac{T}{t} + 2\right) \sin^2 \phi} - 1} = \frac{2 A_P}{\sqrt{1 + G(G + 2)\sin^2 \phi} - 1}$$

This equation gives the minimum number of teeth required on the pinion in order to avoid interference.

Notes : 1. If the pinion and wheel have equal teeth, then $G = 1$. Therefore the above equation reduces to

$$t = \frac{2A_p}{\sqrt{1 + 3\sin^2\phi - 1}}$$

2. The minimum number of teeth on the pinion which will mesh with any gear (also rack) without interference are given in the following table :

Table 12.2. Minimum number of teeth on the pinion

S. No.	System of gear teeth	Minimum number of teeth on the pinion
1.	$14\frac{1}{2}°$ Composite	12
2.	$14\frac{1}{2}°$ Full depth involute	32
3.	$20°$ Full depth involute	18
4.	$20°$ Stub involute	14

12.21. Minimum Number of Teeth on the Wheel in Order to Avoid Interference

Let T = Minimum number of teeth required on the wheel in order to avoid interference,

and $A_w.m$ = Addendum of the wheel, where A_w is a fraction by which the standard addendum for the wheel should be multiplied.

Using the same notations as in Art. 12.20, we have from triangle O_2MP

$$(O_2M)^2 = (O_2P)^2 + (PM)^2 - 2 \times O_2P \times PM \cos O_2PM$$

$$= R^2 + r^2 \sin^2\phi - 2 R.r \sin\phi \cos(90° + \phi)$$

$$...(\because PM = O_1P \sin\phi = r)$$

$$= R^2 + r^2 \sin^2\phi + 2R.r \sin^2\phi$$

$$= R^2\left[1 + \frac{r^2\sin^2\phi}{R^2} + \frac{2r\sin^2\phi}{R}\right] = R^2\left[1 + \frac{r}{R}\left(\frac{r}{R} + 2\right)\sin^2\phi\right]$$

$\therefore$ Limiting radius of wheel addendum circle,

$$O_2M = R\sqrt{1 + \frac{r}{R}\left(\frac{r}{R} + 2\right)\sin^2\phi} = \frac{m.T}{2}\sqrt{1 + \frac{t}{T}\left(\frac{t}{T} + 2\right)\sin^2\phi}$$

We know that the addendum of the wheel

$$= O_2M - O_2P$$

$\therefore$

$$A_w m = \frac{m.T}{2}\sqrt{1 + \frac{t}{T}\left(\frac{t}{T} + 2\right)\sin^2\phi} - \frac{m.T}{2} \qquad ...(\because O_2P = R = m.T/2)$$

$$= \frac{m.T}{2}\left[\sqrt{1 + \frac{t}{T}\left(\frac{t}{T} + 2\right)\sin^2\phi} - 1\right]$$

or

$$A_w = \frac{T}{2}\left[\sqrt{1 + \frac{t}{T}\left(\frac{t}{T} + 2\right)\sin^2\phi} - 1\right]$$

$$\therefore \quad T = \frac{2\,A_W}{\sqrt{1 + \dfrac{t}{T}\left(\dfrac{t}{T} + 2\right)\sin^2 \phi} - 1} = \frac{2\,A_W}{\sqrt{1 + \dfrac{1}{G}\left(\dfrac{1}{G} + 2\right)\sin^2 \phi} - 1}$$

Notes : 1. From the above equation, we may also obtain the minimum number of teeth on pinion.

Multiplying both sides by $\dfrac{t}{T}$,

$$T \times \frac{t}{T} = \frac{2\,A_W \times \dfrac{t}{T}}{\sqrt{1 + \dfrac{1}{G}\left(\dfrac{1}{G} + 2\right)\sin^2 \phi} - 1}$$

$$t = \frac{2\,A_W}{G\left[\sqrt{1 + \dfrac{1}{G}\left(\dfrac{1}{G} + 2\right)\sin^2 \phi} - 1\right]}$$

2. If wheel and pinion have equal teeth, then $G = 1$, and

$$T = \frac{2\,A_W}{\sqrt{1 + 3\sin^2 \phi} - 1}$$

Example 12.9. *Determine the minimum number of teeth required on a pinion, in order to avoid interference which is to gear with,*
1. a wheel to give a gear ratio of 3 to 1 ; and 2. an equal wheel.

The pressure angle is 20° and a standard addendum of 1 module for the wheel may be assumed.

Solution. Given : $G = T/t = 3$; $\phi = 20°$; $A_W = 1$ module

1. *Minimum number of teeth for a gear ratio of 3 : 1*

We know that minimum number of teeth required on a pinion,

$$t = \frac{2 \times A_W}{G\left[\sqrt{1 + \dfrac{1}{G}\left(\dfrac{1}{G} + 2\right)\sin^2 \phi} - 1\right]}$$

$$= \frac{2 \times 1}{3\left[\sqrt{1 + \dfrac{1}{3}\left(\dfrac{1}{3} + 2\right)\sin^2 20°} - 1\right]} = \frac{2}{0.133} = 15.04 \text{ or } 16 \quad \textbf{Ans.}$$

2. *Minimum number of teeth for equal wheel*

We know that minimum number of teeth for equal wheel,

$$t = \frac{2 \times A_W}{\sqrt{1 + 3\sin^2 \phi} - 1} = \frac{2 \times 1}{\sqrt{1 + 3\sin^2 20°} - 1} = \frac{2}{0.162}$$

$$= 12.34 \text{ or } 13 \quad \textbf{Ans.}$$

Example 12.10. *A pair of spur gears with involute teeth is to give a gear ratio of 4 : 1. The arc of approach is not to be less than the circular pitch and smaller wheel is the driver. The angle of pressure is 14.5°. Find : 1. the least number of teeth that can be used on each wheel, and 2. the addendum of the wheel in terms of the circular pitch ?*

Solution. *Given :* $G = T/t = R/r = 4$; $\phi = 14.5°$

1. *Least number of teeth on each wheel*

Let
t = Least number of teeth on the smaller wheel *i.e.* pinion,

T = Least number of teeth on the larger wheel *i.e.* gear, and

r = Pitch circle radius of the smaller wheel *i.e.* pinion.

We know that the maximum length of the arc of approach

$$= \frac{\text{Maximum length of the path of approach}}{\cos\phi} = \frac{r\sin\phi}{\cos\phi} = r\tan\phi$$

and circular pitch,
$$p_c = \pi m = \frac{2\pi r}{t} \qquad \qquad ...\left(\because m = \frac{2r}{t}\right)$$

Since the arc of approach is not to be less than the circular pitch, therefore

$$r\tan\phi = \frac{2\pi r}{t} \quad \text{or} \quad t = \frac{2\pi}{\tan\phi} = \frac{2\pi}{\tan 14.5°} = 24.3 \text{ say } 25 \text{ Ans.}$$

and
$$T = G.t = 4 \times 25 = 100 \text{ Ans.} \qquad ...(\because G = T/t)$$

2. *Addendum of the wheel*

We know that addendum of the wheel

$$= \frac{m.T}{2}\left[\sqrt{1 + \frac{t}{T}\left(\frac{t}{T} + 2\right)\sin^2\phi} - 1\right]$$

$$= \frac{m \times 100}{2}\left[\sqrt{1 + \frac{25}{100}\left(\frac{25}{100} + 2\right)\sin^2 14.5°} - 1\right]$$

$$= 50m \times 0.017 = 0.85\, m = 0.85 \times p_c/\pi = 0.27\, p_c \text{ Ans.}$$

$$...(\because m = p_c/\pi)$$

Example 12.11. *A pair of involute spur gears with 16° pressure angle and pitch of module 6 mm is in mesh. The number of teeth on pinion is 16 and its rotational speed is 240 r.p.m. When the gear ratio is 1.75, find in order that the interference is just avoided ; 1. the addenda on pinion and gear wheel ; 2. the length of path of contact ; and 3. the maximum velocity of sliding of teeth on either side of the pitch point.*

Solution. Given : $\phi = 16°$; $m = 6$ mm ; $t = 16$; $N_1 = 240$ r.p.m. or $\omega_1 = 2\pi \times 240/60$ $= 25.136$ rad/s ; $G = T/t = 1.75$ or $T = G.t = 1.75 \times 16 = 28$

1. *Addenda on pinion and gear wheel*

We know that addendum on pinion

$$= \frac{m.t}{2}\left[\sqrt{1 + \frac{T}{t}\left(\frac{T}{t} + 2\right)\sin^2\phi} - 1\right]$$

$$= \frac{6 \times 16}{2}\left[\sqrt{1 + \frac{28}{16}\left(\frac{28}{16} + 2\right)\sin^2 16°} - 1\right]$$

$$= 48\,(1.224 - 1) = 10.76 \text{ mm Ans.}$$

and addendum on wheel
$$= \frac{m.T}{2}\left[\sqrt{1 + \frac{t}{T}\left(\frac{t}{T} + 2\right)\sin^2\phi} - 1\right]$$

$$= \frac{6 \times 28}{2} \left[\sqrt{1 + \frac{16}{28} \left(\frac{16}{28} + 2 \right) \sin^2 16°} - 1 \right]$$

$$= 84 \, (1.054 - 1) = 4.56 \text{ mm} \textbf{ Ans.}$$

2. Length of path of contact

We know that the pitch circle radius of wheel,

$$R = m.T / 2 = 6 \times 28 / 2 = 84 \text{ mm}$$

and pitch circle radius of pinion,

$$r = m.t / 2 = 6 \times 16 / 2 = 48 \text{ mm}$$

∴ Addendum circle radius of wheel,

$$R_A = R + \text{Addendum of wheel} = 84 + 10.76 = 94.76 \text{ mm}$$

and addendum circle radius of pinion,

$$r_A = r + \text{Addendum of pinion} = 48 + 4.56 = 52.56 \text{ mm}$$

We know that the length of path of approach,

$$KP = \sqrt{(R_A)^2 - R^2 \cos^2 \phi} - R \sin \phi \qquad \text{...(Refer Fig. 12.11)}$$

$$= \sqrt{(94.76)^2 - (84)^2 \cos^2 16°} - 84 \sin 16°$$

$$= 49.6 - 23.15 = 26.45 \text{ mm}$$

and the length of the path of recess,

$$PL = \sqrt{(r_A)^2 - r^2 \cos^2 \phi} - r \sin \phi$$

$$= \sqrt{(52.56)^2 - (48)^2 \cos^2 16°} - 48 \sin 16°$$

$$= 25.17 - 13.23 = 11.94 \text{ mm}$$

∴ Length of the path of contact,

$$KL = KP + PL = 26.45 + 11.94 = 38.39 \text{ mm} \textbf{ Ans.}$$

3. Maximum velocity of sliding of teeth on either side of pitch point

Let ω_2 = Angular speed of gear wheel.

We know that $\dfrac{\omega_1}{\omega_2} = \dfrac{T}{t} = 1.75$ or $\omega_2 = \dfrac{\omega_1}{1.75} = \dfrac{25.136}{1.75} = 14.28 \text{ rad/s}$

∴ Maximum velocity of sliding of teeth on the left side of pitch point *i.e.* at point K

$$= (\omega_1 + \omega_2) \, KP = (25.136 + 14.28) \, 26.45 = 1043 \text{ mm/s} \textbf{ Ans.}$$

and maximum velocity of sliding of teeth on the right side of pitch point *i.e.* at point L

$$= (\omega_1 + \omega_2) \, PL = (25.136 + 14.28) \, 11.94 = 471 \text{ mm/s} \textbf{ Ans.}$$

Example 12.12. *A pair of 20° full depth involute spur gears having 30 and 50 teeth respectively of module 4 mm are in mesh. The smaller gear rotates at 1000 r.p.m. Determine : 1. sliding velocities at engagement and at disengagement of pair of a teeth, and 2. contact ratio.*

Solution. Given: $\phi = 20°$; $t = 30$; $T = 50$; $m = 4$; $N_1 = 1000$ r.p.m. or $\omega_1 = 2\pi \times 1000/60 = 104.7$ rad/s

1. *Sliding velocities at engagement and at disengagement of pair of a teeth*

First of all, let us find the radius of addendum circles of the smaller gear and the larger gear. We know that

Addendum of the smaller gear,

$$= \frac{m.t}{2} \left[\sqrt{1 + \frac{T}{t}\left(\frac{T}{t} + 2\right) \sin^2 \phi} - 1 \right]$$

$$= \frac{4 \times 30}{2} \left[\sqrt{1 + \frac{50}{30}\left(\frac{50}{30} + 2\right) \sin^2 20°} - 1 \right]$$

$$= 60(1.31 - 1) = 18.6 \text{ mm}$$

and addendum of the larger gear,

$$= \frac{m.T}{2} \left[\sqrt{1 + \frac{t}{T}\left(\frac{t}{T} + 2\right) \sin^2 \phi} - 1 \right]$$

$$= \frac{4 \times 50}{2} \left[\sqrt{1 + \frac{30}{50}\left(\frac{30}{50} + 2\right) \sin^2 20°} - 1 \right]$$

$$= 100(1.09 - 1) = 9 \text{ mm}$$

Pitch circle radius of the smaller gear,

$$r = m.t / 2 = 4 \times 30/2 = 60 \text{ mm}$$

∴ Radius of addendum circle of the smaller gear,

$$r_A = r + \text{Addendum of the smaller gear} = 60 + 18.6 = 78.6 \text{ mm}$$

Pitch circle radius of the larger gear,

$$R = m.T / 2 = 4 \times 50 / 2 = 100 \text{ mm}$$

∴ Radius of addendum circle of the larger gear,

$$R_A = R + \text{Addendum of the larger gear} = 100 + 9 = 109 \text{ mm}$$

We know that the path of approach (*i.e.* path of contact when engagement occurs),

$$KP = \sqrt{(R_A)^2 - R^2 \cos^2 \phi} - R\sin\phi \qquad \text{...(Refer Fig. 12.11)}$$

$$= \sqrt{(109)^2 - (100)^2 \cos^2 20°} - 100 \sin 20° = 55.2 - 34.2 = 21 \text{ mm}$$

and the path of recess (*i.e.* path of contact when disengagement occurs),

$$PL = \sqrt{(r_A)^2 - r^2 \cos^2 \phi} - r\sin\phi$$

$$= \sqrt{(78.6)^2 - (60)^2 \cos^2 20°} - 60 \sin 20° = 54.76 - 20.52 = 34.24 \text{ mm}$$

Let ω_2 = Angular speed of the larger gear in rad/s.

We know that $\dfrac{\omega_1}{\omega_2} = \dfrac{T}{t}$ or $\omega_2 = \dfrac{\omega_1 \times t}{T} = \dfrac{10.47 \times 30}{50} = 62.82 \text{ rad/s}$

∴ Sliding velocity at engagement of a pair of teeth

$$= (\omega_1 + \omega_2) KP = (104.7 + 62.82) 21 = 3518 \text{ mm/s}$$

$$= 3.518 \text{ m/s} \textbf{ Ans.}$$

and sliding velocity at disengagement of a pair of teeth

$$= (\omega_1 + \omega_2) PL = (104.7 + 62.82)34.24 = 5736 \text{ mm/s}$$

$$= 5.736 \text{ m/s} \textbf{ Ans.}$$

2. Contact ratio

We know that the length of the arc of contact

$$= \frac{\text{Length of the path of contact}}{\cos\phi} = \frac{KP + PL}{\cos\phi} = \frac{21 + 34.24}{\cos 20°}$$

$$= 58.78 \text{ mm}$$

and   Circular pitch $= \pi \times m = 3.142 \times 4 = 12.568 \text{ mm}$

∴   Contact ratio $= \dfrac{\text{Length of arc of contact}}{\text{Circular pitch}} = \dfrac{58.78}{12.568} = 4.67 \text{ say } 5 \textbf{ Ans.}$

Example 12.13. *Two gear wheels mesh externally and are to give a velocity ratio of 3 to 1. The teeth are of involute form ; module = 6 mm, addendum = one module, pressure angle = 20°. The pinion rotates at 90 r.p.m. Determine : 1. The number of teeth on the pinion to avoid interference on it and the corresponding number of teeth on the wheel, 2. The length of path and arc of contact, 3.The number of pairs of teeth in contact, and 4. The maximum velocity of sliding.*

Solution. Given : $G = T/t = 3$; $m = 6$ mm ; $A_P = A_W = 1$ module $= 6$ mm ; $\phi = 20°$; $N_1 = 90$ r.p.m. or $\omega_1 = 2\pi \times 90 / 60 = 9.43$ rad/s

1. Number of teeth on the pinion to avoid interference on it and the corresponding number of teeth on the wheel

We know that number of teeth on the pinion to avoid interference,

$$t = \frac{2 A_P}{\sqrt{1 + G(G+2)\sin^2\phi} - 1} = \frac{2 \times 6}{\sqrt{1 + 3(3+2)\sin^2 20°} - 1}$$

$$= 18.2 \text{ say } 19 \textbf{ Ans.}$$

and corresponding number of teeth on the wheel,

$$T = G.t = 3 \times 19 = 57 \textbf{ Ans.}$$

2. Length of path and arc of contact

We know that pitch circle radius of pinion,

$$r = m.t / 2 = 6 \times 19/2 = 57 \text{ mm}$$

∴ Radius of addendum circle of pinion,

$$r_A = r + \text{Addendum on pinion } (A_P) = 57 + 6 = 63 \text{ mm}$$

and pitch circle radius of wheel,

$$R = m.T / 2 = 6 \times 57 / 2 = 171 \text{ mm}$$

∴ Radius of addendum circle of wheel,

$$R_A = R + \text{Addendum on wheel } (A_W) = 171 + 6 = 177 \text{ mm}$$

We know that the path of approach (*i.e.* path of contact when engagement occurs),

$$KP = \sqrt{(R_A)^2 - R^2 \cos^2\phi} - R \sin\phi \qquad \text{...(Refer Fig. 12.11)}$$

$$= \sqrt{(177)^2 - (171)^2 \cos^2 20°} - 171 \sin 20° = 74.2 - 58.5 = 15.7 \text{ mm}$$

and the path of recess (*i.e.* path of contact when disengagement occurs),

$$PL = \sqrt{(r_A)^2 - r^2 \cos^2 \phi} - r \sin \phi$$

$$= \sqrt{(63)^2 - (57)^2 \cos^2 20°} - 57 \sin 20° = 33.17 - 19.5 = 13.67 \text{ mm}$$

∴ Length of path of contact,

$$KL = KP + PL = 15.7 + 13.67 = 29.37 \text{ mm} \textbf{ Ans.}$$

We know that length of arc of contact

$$= \frac{\text{Length of path of contact}}{\cos \phi} = \frac{29.37}{\cos 20°} = 31.25 \text{ mm} \textbf{ Ans.}$$

3. *Number of pairs of teeth in contact*

We know that circular pitch,

$$p_c = \pi \times m = \pi \times 6 = 18.852 \text{ mm}$$

∴ Number of pairs of teeth in contact

$$= \frac{\text{Length of arc of contact}}{p_c} = \frac{31.25}{18.852} = 1.66 \text{ say } 2 \textbf{ Ans.}$$

4. *Maximum velocity of sliding*

Let ω_2 = Angular speed of wheel in rad/s.

We know that $\dfrac{\omega_1}{\omega_2} = \dfrac{T}{t}$ or $\omega_2 = \omega_1 \times \dfrac{t}{T} = 9.43 \times \dfrac{19}{57} = 3.14$ rad/s

∴ Maximum velocity of sliding,

$$v_S = (\omega_1 + \omega_2)\, KP \qquad\qquad ...(\because KP > PL)$$

$$= (9.43 + 3.14)\, 15.7 = 197.35 \text{ mm/s} \textbf{ Ans.}$$

12.22. Minimum Number of Teeth on a Pinion for Involute Rack in Order to Avoid Interference

A rack and pinion in mesh is shown in Fig. 12.14.

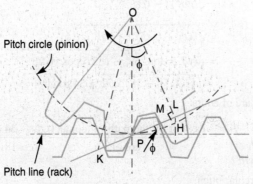

Pitch circle (pinion)

Pitch line (rack)

Fig. 12.14. Rack and pinion in mesh.

Let t = Minimum number of teeth on the pinion,

r = Pitch circle radius of the pinion = $m.t / 2$, and

ϕ = Pressure angle or angle of obliquity, and

$A_R.m$ = Addendum for rack, where A_R is the fraction by which the standard addendum of one module for the rack is to be multiplied.

We know that a rack is a part of toothed wheel of infinite diameter. Therefore its base circle diameter and the profiles of the involute teeth are straight lines. Since these straight profiles are tangential to the pinion profiles at the point of contact, therefore they are perpendicular to the tangent *PM*. The point *M* is the interference point.

Addendum for rack,

$$A_R.m = LH = PL \sin\phi$$

$$= (OP \sin\phi) \sin\phi = OP \sin^2\phi \qquad ...(\because PL = OP \sin\phi)$$

$$= r\sin^2\phi = \frac{m.t}{2} \times \sin^2\phi$$

$$\therefore \qquad t = \frac{2 A_R}{\sin^2\phi}$$

Example 12.14. *A pinion of 20 involute teeth and 125 mm pitch circle diameter drives a rack. The addendum of both pinion and rack is 6.25 mm. What is the least pressure angle which can be used to avoid interference ? With this pressure angle, find the length of the arc of contact and the minimum number of teeth in contact at a time.*

Solution. Given : $T = 20$; $d = 125$ mm or $r = OP = 62.5$ mm ; $LH = 6.25$ mm

Least pressure angle to avoid interference

Let ϕ = Least pressure angle to avoid interference.

We know that for no interference, rack addendum,

$$LH = r\sin^2\phi \qquad \text{or} \qquad \sin^2\phi = \frac{LH}{r} = \frac{6.25}{6.25} = 0.1$$

$$\therefore \qquad \sin\phi = 0.3162 \qquad \text{or} \qquad \phi = 18.435° \quad \textbf{Ans.}$$

Length of the arc of contact

We know that length of the path of contact,

$$KL = \sqrt{(OK)^2 - (OL)^2} \qquad ...(\text{Refer Fig. 12.14})$$

$$= \sqrt{(OP + 6.25)^2 - (OP \cos\phi)^2}$$

$$= \sqrt{(62.5 + 6.25)^2 - (62.5 \cos 18.435°)^2}$$

$$= \sqrt{4726.56 - 3515.62} = 34.8 \text{ mm}$$

$\therefore$ Length of the arc of contact

$$= \frac{\text{Length of the path of contact}}{\cos\phi} = \frac{34.8}{\cos 18.435°} = 36.68 \text{ mm} \quad \textbf{Ans.}$$

Minimum number of teeth

We know that circular pitch,

$$p_c = \pi d / T = \pi \times 125 / 20 = 19.64 \text{ mm}$$

and the number of pairs of teeth in contact

$$= \frac{\text{Length of the arc of contact}}{\text{Circular pitch } (p_c)} = \frac{36.68}{19.64} = 1.87$$

∴ Minimum number of teeth in contact

$$= 2 \text{ or one pair } \textbf{Ans.}$$

12.23. Helical Gears

A helical gear has teeth in the form of helix around the gear. Two such gears may be used to connect two parallel shafts in place of spur gear. The helixes may be right handed on one wheel and left handed on the other. The pitch surfaces are cylindrical as in spur gearing, but the teeth instead of being parallel to the axis, wind around the cylinders helically like screw threads. The teeth of helical gears with parallel axis have line contact, as in spur gearing. This provides gradual

Crossed helical gears.

engagement and continuous contact of the engaging teeth. Hence helical gears give smooth drive with a high efficiency of transmission.

We have already discussed that the helical gears may be of single helical type or double helical type. In case of single helical gears, there is some axial thrust between the teeth, which is a disadvantage. In order to eliminate this axial thrust, double helical gears are used. It is equivalent to two single helical gears, in which equal and opposite thrusts are produced on each gear and the resulting axial thrust is zero.

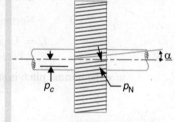

Fig. 12.15. Helical gear.

The following definitions may be clearly understood in connection with a helical gear as shown in Fig. 12.15.

1. *Normal pitch.* It is the distance between similar faces of adjacent teeth, along a helix on the pitch cylinder normal to the teeth. It is denoted by p_N.

2. *Axial pitch.* It is the distance measured parallel to the axis, between similar faces of adjacent teeth. It is the same as circular pitch and is therefore denoted by p_c. If α is the helix angle, then circular pitch,

$$p_c = \frac{p_N}{\cos \alpha}$$

Note : The **helix angle** is also known as **spiral angle** of the teeth.

12.24. Spiral Gears

We have already discussed that spiral gears (also known as **skew gears** or **screw gears**) are used to connect and transmit motion between two non-parallel and non-intersecting shafts. The pitch surfaces of the spiral gears are cylindrical and the teeth have point contact. These gears are only suitable for transmitting small power. We have seen that helical gears, connected on parallel shafts, are of opposite hand. But spiral gears may be of the same hand or of opposite hand.

12.25. Centre Distance for a Pair of Spiral Gears

The centre distance, for a pair of spiral gears, is the shortest distance between the two shafts making any angle between them. A pair of spiral gears 1 and 2, both having left hand helixes (*i.e.* the gears are of the same hand) is shown in Fig. 12.16. The shaft angle θ is the angle through which one of the shafts must be rotated so that it is parallel to the other shaft, also the two shafts be rotating in opposite directions.

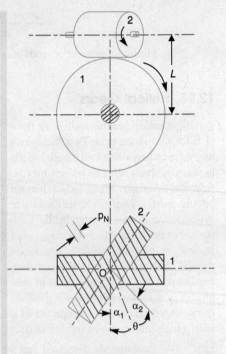

Let α_1 and α_2 = Spiral angles of gear teeth for gears 1 and 2 respectively,

p_{c1} and p_{c2} = Circular pitches of gears 1 and 2,

T_1 and T_2 = Number of teeth on gears 1 and 2,

d_1 and d_2 = Pitch circle diameters of gears 1 and 2,

N_1 and N_2 = Speed of gears 1 and 2,

$$G = \text{Gear ratio} = \frac{T_2}{T_1} = \frac{N_1}{N_2},$$

p_N = Normal pitch, and

L = Least centre distance between the axes of shafts.

Fig. 12.16. Centre distance for a pair of spiral gears.

Since the normal pitch is same for both the spiral gears, therefore

$$p_{c1} = \frac{p_N}{\cos \alpha_1}, \quad \text{and} \quad p_{c2} = \frac{p_N}{\cos \alpha_2}$$

Helical gears

We know that $\qquad p_{c1} = \dfrac{\pi d_1}{T_1}, \quad$ or $\quad d_1 = \dfrac{p_{c1} \times T_1}{\pi}$

and $\qquad p_{c2} = \dfrac{\pi d_2}{T_2}, \quad$ or $\quad d_2 = \dfrac{p_{c2} \times T_2}{\pi}$

$\therefore \qquad L = \dfrac{d_1 + d_2}{2} = \dfrac{1}{2}\left(\dfrac{p_{c1} \times T_1}{\pi} + \dfrac{p_{c2} \times T_2}{\pi}\right)$

$$= \dfrac{T_1}{2\pi}\left(p_{c1} + p_{c2} \times \dfrac{T_2}{T_1}\right) = \dfrac{T_1}{2\pi}\left(\dfrac{p_N}{\cos\alpha_1} + \dfrac{p_N}{\cos\alpha_2} \times G\right)$$

$$= \dfrac{P_N \times T_1}{2\pi}\left(\dfrac{1}{\cos\alpha_1} + \dfrac{G}{\cos\alpha_2}\right)$$

Notes : 1. If the pair of spiral gears have teeth of the same hand, then

$$\theta = \alpha_1 + \alpha_2$$

and for a pair of spiral gears of opposite hand,

$$\theta = \alpha_1 - \alpha_2$$

2. When $\theta = 90°$, then both the spiral gears must have teeth of the same hand.

12.26. Efficiency of Spiral Gears

A pair of spiral gears 1 and 2 in mesh is shown in Fig. 12.17. Let the gear 1 be the driver and the gear 2 the driven. The forces acting on each of a pair of teeth in contact are shown in Fig. 12.17. The forces are assumed to act at the centre of the width of each teeth and in the plane tangential to the pitch cylinders.

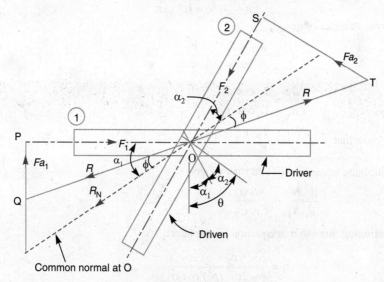

Fig. 12.17. Efficiency of spiral gears.

Let $\qquad F_1$ = Force applied tangentially on the driver,

F_2 = Resisting force acting tangentially on the driven,

F_{a1} = Axial or end thrust on the driver,

F_{a2} = Axial or end thrust on the driven,

R_N = Normal reaction at the point of contact,

ϕ = Angle of friction,

R = Resultant reaction at the point of contact, and

θ = Shaft angle = $\alpha_1 + \alpha_2$

...(∵ Both gears are of the same hand)

From triangle OPQ, $F_1 = R \cos(\alpha_1 - \phi)$

∴ Work input to the driver

$$= F_1 \times \pi d_1.N_1 = R \cos(\alpha_1 - \phi) \pi d_1.N_1$$

From triangle OST, $F_2 = R \cos(\alpha_2 + \phi)$

∴ Work output of the driven

$$= F_2 \times \pi d_2.N_2 = R \cos(\alpha_2 + \phi) \pi d_2.N_2$$

∴ Efficiency of spiral gears,

$$\eta = \frac{\text{Work output}}{\text{Work input}} = \frac{R \cos(\alpha_2 + \phi)\pi d_2.N_2}{R \cos(\alpha_1 - \phi)\pi d_1.N_1}$$

$$= \frac{\cos(\alpha_2 + \phi) d_2.N_2}{\cos(\alpha_1 - \phi) d_1.N_1} \qquad \qquad ...(i)$$

We have discussed in Art. 12.25, that pitch circle diameter of gear 1,

$$d_1 = \frac{p_{c1} \times T_1}{\pi} = \frac{p_N}{\cos \alpha_1} \times \frac{T_1}{\pi}$$

and pitch circle diameter of gear 2,

$$d_2 = \frac{p_{c2} \times T_2}{\pi} = \frac{p_N}{\cos \alpha_2} \times \frac{T_2}{\pi}$$

∴

$$\frac{d_2}{d_1} = \frac{T_2 \cos \alpha_1}{T_1 \cos \alpha_2} \qquad \qquad ...(ii)$$

We know that

$$\frac{N_2}{N_1} = \frac{T_1}{T_2} \qquad \qquad ...(iii)$$

Multiplying equations (ii) and (iii), we get,

$$\frac{d_2.N_2}{d_1.N_1} = \frac{\cos \alpha_1}{\cos \alpha_2}$$

Substituting this value in equation (i), we have

$$\eta = \frac{\cos(\alpha_2 + \phi) \cos \alpha_1}{\cos(\alpha_1 - \phi) \cos \alpha_2} \qquad \qquad ...(iv)$$

$$= \frac{\cos(\alpha_1 + \alpha_2 + \phi) + \cos(\alpha_1 - \alpha_2 - \phi)}{\cos(\alpha_2 + \alpha_1 - \phi) + \cos(\alpha_2 - \alpha_1 + \phi)}$$

$$...\left(\because \cos A \cos B = \frac{1}{2}[\cos(A + B) + \cos(A - B)] \right)$$

$$= \frac{\cos (\theta + \phi) + \cos (\alpha_1 - \alpha_2 - \phi)}{\cos (\theta - \phi) + \cos (\alpha_2 - \alpha_1 + \phi)} \qquad ...(v)$$

$$...(\because \theta = \alpha_1 + \alpha_2)$$

Since the angles θ and ϕ are constants, therefore the efficiency will be maximum, when $\cos (\alpha_1 - \alpha_2 - \phi)$ is maximum, *i.e.*

$$\cos (\alpha_1 - \alpha_2 - \phi) = 1 \quad \text{or} \quad \alpha_1 - \alpha_2 - \phi = 0$$

$$\therefore \qquad \alpha_1 = \alpha_2 + \phi \quad \text{and} \quad \alpha_2 = \alpha_1 - \phi$$

Since $\alpha_1 + \alpha_2 = \theta$, therefore

$$\alpha_1 = \theta - \alpha_2 = \theta - \alpha_1 + \phi \text{ or } \alpha_1 = \frac{\theta + \phi}{2}$$

Similarly, $$\alpha_2 = \frac{\theta - \phi}{2}$$

Substituting $\alpha_1 = \alpha_2 + \phi$ and $\alpha_2 = \alpha_1 - \phi$, in equation (v), we get

$$\eta_{max} = \frac{\cos (\theta + \phi) + 1}{\cos (\theta - \phi) + 1} \qquad ...(vi)$$

Note: From Fig. 12.17, we find that $\quad R_N = \dfrac{F_1}{\cos \alpha_1} = \dfrac{F_2}{\cos \alpha_2}$

$$\therefore \text{ Axial thrust on the driver, } F_{a1} = R_N.\sin \alpha_1 = F_1.\tan \alpha_1$$

and axial thrust on the driven, $\qquad F_{a2} = R_N.\sin \alpha_2 = F_2.\tan \alpha_2$

Example 12.15. *A pair of spiral gears is required to connect two shafts 175 mm apart, the shaft angle being 70°. The velocity ratio is to be 1.5 to 1, the faster wheel having 80 teeth and a pitch circle diameter of 100 mm. Find the spiral angles for each wheel. If the torque on the faster wheel is 75 N-m ; find the axial thrust on each shaft, neglecting friction.*

Solution. Given : $L = 175$ mm $= 0.175$ m ; $\theta = 70°$; $G = 1.5$; $T_2 = 80$; $d_2 = 100$ mm $= 0.1$ m or $r_2 = 0.05$ m ; Torque on faster wheel $= 75$ N-m

Spiral angles for each wheel

Let $\qquad \alpha_1$ = Spiral angle for slower wheel, and

$\qquad \alpha_2$ = Spiral angle for faster wheel.

We know that velocity ratio, $G = \dfrac{N_2}{N_1} = \dfrac{T_1}{T_2} = 1.5$

$\therefore$ No. of teeth on slower wheel,

$$T_1 = T_2 \times 1.5 = 80 \times 1.5 = 120$$

We also know that the centre distance between shafts (L),

$$0.175 = \frac{d_1 + d_2}{2} = \frac{d_1 + 0.1}{2}$$

$$\therefore \qquad d_1 = 2 \times 0.175 - 0.1 = 0.25 \text{ m}$$

and $$\frac{d_2}{d_1} = \frac{T_2 \cos \alpha_1}{T_1 \cos \alpha_2} \quad \text{or} \quad \frac{0.1}{0.25} = \frac{80 \cos \alpha_1}{120 \cos \alpha_2} = \frac{2 \cos \alpha_1}{3 \cos \alpha_2}$$

$$\therefore \qquad \frac{\cos \alpha_1}{\cos \alpha_2} = \frac{0.1 \times 3}{0.25 \times 2} = 0.6 \quad \text{or} \quad \cos \alpha_1 = 0.6 \cos \alpha_2 \qquad \qquad ...(i)$$

We know that, $\qquad \alpha_1 + \alpha_2 = \theta = 70° \quad \text{or} \quad \alpha_2 = 70° - \alpha_1$

Substituting the value of α_2 in equation (i),

$$\cos \alpha_1 = 0.6 \cos (70° - \alpha_1) = 0.6 (\cos 70° \cos \alpha_1 + \sin 70° \sin \alpha_1)$$

$$...[\because \cos(A - B) = \cos A \cos B + \sin A \sin B]$$

$$= 0.2052 \cos \alpha_1 + 0.5638 \sin \alpha_1$$

$$\cos \alpha_1 - 0.2052 \cos \alpha_1 = 0.5638 \sin \alpha_1$$

$$0.7948 \cos \alpha_1 = 0.5638 \sin \alpha_1$$

$$\therefore \qquad \tan \alpha_1 = \frac{\sin \alpha_1}{\cos \alpha_1} = \frac{0.7948}{0.5638} = 1.4097 \quad \text{or} \quad \alpha_1 = 54.65°$$

and $\qquad\qquad\qquad \alpha_2 = 70° - 54.65° = 15.35° \text{ Ans.}$

Axial thrust on each shaft

We know that $\qquad$ Torque = Tangential force × Pitch circle radius

$\therefore$ Tangential force at faster wheel,

$$F_2 = \frac{\text{Torque on the faster wheel}}{\text{Pitch circle radius } (r_2)} = \frac{75}{0.05} = 1500 \text{ N}$$

and normal reaction at the point of contact,

$$R_N = F_2 / \cos \alpha_2 = 1500/\cos 15.35° = 1556 \text{ N}$$

We know that axial thrust on the shaft of slower wheel,

$$F_{a1} = R_N. \sin \alpha_1 = 1556 \times \sin 54.65° = 1269 \text{ N Ans.}$$

and axial thrust on the shaft of faster wheel,

$$F_{a2} = R_N. \sin \alpha_2 = 1556 \times \sin 15.35° = 412 \text{ N Ans.}$$

Example 12.16. *In a spiral gear drive connecting two shafts, the approximate centre distance is 400 mm and the speed ratio = 3. The angle between the two shafts is 50° and the normal pitch is 18 mm. The spiral angle for the driving and driven wheels are equal. Find : 1. Number of teeth on each wheel, 2. Exact centre distance, and 3. Efficiency of the drive, if friction angle = 6°.*

Solution. Given : $L = 400$ mm $= 0.4$ m ; $G = T_2 / T_1 = 3$; $\theta = 50°$; $p_N = 18$ mm ; $\phi = 6°$

1. *Number of teeth on each wheel*

Let $\qquad\qquad\qquad T_1 =$ Number of teeth on wheel 1 (*i.e.* driver), and

$\qquad\qquad\qquad\qquad T_2 =$ Number of teeth on wheel 2 (*i.e.* driven).

Since the spiral angle α_1 for the driving wheel is equal to the spiral angle α_2 for the driven wheel, therefore

$$\alpha_1 = \alpha_2 = \theta/2 = 25° \qquad\qquad ...(\because \alpha_1 + \alpha_2 = \theta = 50°)$$

We know that centre distance between two shafts (L),

$$400 = \frac{p_N. T_1}{2\pi} \left(\frac{1}{\cos \alpha_1} + \frac{G}{\cos \alpha_2} \right) = \frac{p_N. T_1}{2\pi} \left(\frac{1 + G}{\cos \alpha_1} \right) \qquad ...(\because \alpha_1 = \alpha_2)$$

$$= \frac{18 \times T_1}{2\pi} \left(\frac{1+3}{\cos 25°} \right) = 12.64 \, T_1$$

∴ $T_1 = 400/12.64 = 31.64$ or 32 **Ans.**

and $T_2 = G.T_1 = 3 \times 32 = 96$ **Ans.**

2. *Exact centre distance*

We know that exact centre distance,

$$L_1 = \frac{p_N.T_1}{2\pi} \left(\frac{1}{\cos\alpha_1} + \frac{G}{\cos\alpha_2} \right) = \frac{p_N.T_1}{2\pi} \left(\frac{1+G}{\cos\alpha_1} \right) \qquad ...(\because \alpha_1 = \alpha_2)$$

$$= \frac{18 \times 32}{2\pi} \left(\frac{1+3}{\cos 25°} \right) = 404.5 \text{ mm } \textbf{Ans.}$$

3. *Efficiency of the drive*

We know that efficiency of the drive,

$$\eta = \frac{\cos(\alpha_2 + \phi)\cos\alpha_1}{\cos(\alpha_1 - \phi)\cos\alpha_2} = \frac{\cos(\alpha_1 + \phi)}{\cos(\alpha_1 - \phi)} \qquad ...(\because \alpha_1 = \alpha_2)$$

$$= \frac{\cos(25° + 6°)}{\cos(25° - 6°)} = \frac{\cos 31°}{\cos 19°} = \frac{0.8572}{0.9455} = 0.907 = 90.7\% \text{ } \textbf{Ans.}$$

Example 12.17. *A drive on a machine tool is to be made by two spiral gear wheels, the spirals of which are of the same hand and has normal pitch of 12.5 mm. The wheels are of equal diameter and the centre distance between the axes of the shafts is approximately 134 mm. The angle between the shafts is 80° and the speed ratio 1.25. Determine : 1. the spiral angle of each wheel, 2. the number of teeth on each wheel, 3. the efficiency of the drive, if the friction angle is 6°, and 4. the maximum efficiency.*

Solution. Given : $p_N = 12.5$ mm ; $L = 134$ mm ; $\theta = 80°$; $G = N_2 / N_1 = T_1 / T_2 = 1.25$

1. *Spiral angle of each wheel*

Let α_1 and α_2 = Spiral angles of wheels 1 and 2 respectively, and

            d_1 and d_2 = Pitch circle diameter of wheels 1 and 2 respectively.

We know that $\dfrac{d_2}{d_1} = \dfrac{T_2 \cos\alpha_1}{T_1 \cos\alpha_2}$ or $T_1 \cos\alpha_2 = T_2 \cos\alpha_1$ $...(\because d_1 = d_2)$

∴ $\dfrac{\cos\alpha_1}{\cos\alpha_2} = \dfrac{T_1}{T_2} = 1.25$ or $\cos\alpha_1 = 1.25 \cos\alpha_2$ $...(i)$

We also know that

            $\alpha_1 + \alpha_2 = \theta = 80°$ or $\alpha_2 = 80° - \alpha_1$

Substituting the value of α_2 in equation (i),

       $\cos\alpha_1 = 1.25 \cos(80° - \alpha_1) = 1.25 (\cos 80° \cos\alpha_1 + \sin 80° \sin\alpha_1)$

             $= 1.25 (0.1736 \cos\alpha_1 + 0.9848 \sin\alpha_1)$

             $= 0.217 \cos\alpha_1 + 1.231 \sin\alpha_1$

   $\cos\alpha_1 - 0.217 \cos\alpha_1 = 1.231 \sin\alpha_1$ or $0.783 \cos\alpha_1 = 1.231 \sin\alpha_1$

∴ $\tan\alpha_1 = \sin\alpha_1 / \cos\alpha_1 = 0.783 / 1.231 = 0.636$ or $\alpha_1 = 32.46°$ **Ans.**

and $\alpha_2 = 80° - 32.46° = 47.54°$ **Ans.**

2. Number of teeth on each wheel

Let T_1 = Number of teeth on wheel 1, and

T_2 = Number of teeth on wheel 2.

We know that centre distance between the two shafts (L),

$$134 = \frac{d_1 + d_2}{2} \quad \text{or} \quad d_1 = d_2 = 134 \text{ mm} \quad ...(\because d_1 = d_2)$$

We know that $d_1 = \frac{p_{c1} \cdot T_1}{\pi} = \frac{p_N \cdot T_1}{\pi \cos \alpha_1}$

$\therefore \quad T_1 = \frac{\pi d_1 \cdot \cos \alpha_1}{p_N} = \frac{\pi \times 134 \times \cos 32.46°}{12.5} = 28.4 \text{ or } 30 \quad \textbf{Ans.}$

and $\quad T_2 = \frac{T_1}{1.25} = \frac{30}{1.25} = 24 \quad \textbf{Ans.}$

3. Efficiency of the drive

We know that efficiency of the drive,

$$\eta = \frac{\cos(\alpha_2 + \phi) \cos \alpha_1}{\cos(\alpha_1 - \phi) \cos \alpha_2} = \frac{\cos(47.54° + 6°) \cos 32.46°}{\cos(32.46° - 6°) \cos 47.54°}$$

$$= \frac{0.5943 \times 0.8437}{0.8952 \times 0.6751} = 0.83 \quad \text{or} \quad 83\% \textbf{ Ans.}$$

4. Maximum efficiency

We know that maximum efficiency,

$$\eta_{max} = \frac{\cos(\theta + \phi) + 1}{\cos(\theta - \phi) + 1} = \frac{\cos(80° + 6°) + 1}{\cos(80° - 6°) + 1} = \frac{1.0698}{1.2756}$$

$$= 0.838 \quad \text{or} \quad 83.8\% \textbf{ Ans.}$$

EXERCISES

1. The pitch circle diameter of the smaller of the two spur wheels which mesh externally and have involute teeth is 100 mm. The number of teeth are 16 and 32. The pressure angle is 20° and the addendum is 0.32 of the circular pitch. Find the length of the path of contact of the pair of teeth.

   [Ans. 29.36 mm]

2. A pair of gears, having 40 and 30 teeth respectively are of 25° involute form. The addendum length is 5 mm and the module pitch is 2.5 mm. If the smaller wheel is the driver and rotates at 1500 r.p.m., find the velocity of sliding at the point of engagement and at the point of disengagement.

   [Ans. 2.8 m/s ; 2.66 m/s]

3. Two gears of module 4mm have 24 and 33 teeth. The pressure angle is 20° and each gear has a standard addendum of one module. Find the length of arc of contact and the maximum velocity of sliding if the pinion rotates at 120 r.p.m. **[Ans. 20.58 mm ; 0.2147 m/s]**

4. The number of teeth in gears 1 and 2 are 60 and 40 ; module = 3 mm ; pressure angle = 20° and addendum = 0.318 of the circular pitch. Determine the velocity of sliding when the contact is at the tip of the teeth of gear 2 and the gear 2 rotates at 800 r.p.m. **[Ans. 1.06 m/s]**

5. Two spur gears of 24 teeth and 36 teeth of 8 mm module and 20° pressure angle are in mesh. Addendum of each gear is 7.5 mm. The teeth are of involute form. Determine : 1. the angle through which the pinion turns while any pair of teeth are in contact, and 2. the velocity of sliding between the teeth when the contact on the pinion is at a radius of 102 mm. The speed of the pinion is 450 r.p.m.

   [Ans. 20.36°, 1.16 m/s]

6. A pinion having 20 involute teeth of module pitch 6 mm rotates at 200 r.p.m. and transmits 1.5 kW to a gear wheel having 50 teeth. The addendum on both the wheels is 1/4 of the circular pitch. The angle of obliquity is 20°. Find (*a*) the length of the path of approach ; (*b*) the length of the arc of approach; (*c*) the normal force between the teeth at an instant where there is only pair of teeth in contact.

[Ans. 13.27 mm ; 14.12 mm ; 1193 N]

7. Two mating involute spur gear of 20° pressure angle have a gear ratio of 2. The number of teeth on the pinion is 20 and its speed is 250 r.p.m. The module pitch of the teeth is 12 mm.

If the addendum on each wheel is such that the path of approach and the path of recess on each side are half the maximum possible length, find : 1. the addendum for pinion and gear wheel ; 2. the length of the arc of contact ; and 3. the maximum velocity of sliding during approach and recess.

Assume pinion to be the driver. **[Ans. 19.5 mm, 7.8 mm ; 65.5 mm ; 807.5 mm/s, 1615 mm/s]**

8. Two mating gears have 20 and 40 involute teeth of module 10 mm and 20° pressure angle. If the addendum on each wheel is such that the path of contact is maximum and interference is just avoided, find the addendum for each gear wheel, path of contact, arc of contact and contact ratio.

[Ans. 14 mm ; 39 mm ; 102.6 mm ; 109.3 mm ; 4]

9. A 20° involute pinion with 20 teeth drives a gear having 60 teeth. Module is 8 mm and addendum of each gear is 10 mm.

1. State whether interference occurs or not. Give reasons.
2. Find the length of path of approach and arc of approach if pinion is the driver.

[Ans. Interference does not occur ; 25.8 mm, 27.45 mm]

10. A pair of spur wheels with involute teeth is to give a gear ratio of 3 to 1. The arc of approach is not to be less than the circular pitch and the smaller wheel is the driver. The pressure angle is 20°. What is the least number of teeth that can be used on each wheel ? What is the addendum of the wheel in terms of the circular pitch ? **[Ans. 18, 54 ; 0.382 P_c]**

11. Two gear wheels mesh externally and are to give a velocity ratio of 3. The teeth are of involute form of module 6. The standard addendum is 1 module. If the pressure angle is 18° and pinion rotates at 90 r.p.m., find : 1. the number of teeth on each wheel, so that the interference is just avoided, 2. the length of the path of contact, and 3. the maximum velocity of sliding between the teeth.

[Ans. 19, 57 ; 31.5 mm ; 213.7 mm/s]

12. A pinion with 24 involute teeth of 150 mm of pitch circle diameter drives a rack. The addendum of the pinion and rack is 6 mm. Find the least pressure angle which can be used if under cutting of the teeth is to be avoided. Using this pressure angle, find the length of the arc of contact and the minimum number of teeth in contact at one time. **[Ans. 16.8° ; 40 mm ; 2 pairs of teeth]**

13. Two shafts, inclined at an angle of 65° and with a least distance between them of 175 mm are to be connected by spiral gears of normal pitch 15 mm to give a reduction ratio 3 : 1. Find suitable diameters and numbers of teeth. Determine, also, the efficiency if the spiral angles are determined by the condition of maximum efficiency. The friction angle is 7°.

[Ans. 88.5 mm ; 245.7 mm ; 15, 45 ; 85.5 %]

14. A spiral wheel reduction gear, of ratio 3 to 2, is to be used on a machine, with the angle between the shafts 80°. The approximate centre distance between the shafts is 125 mm. The normal pitch of the teeth is 10 mm and the wheel diameters are equal. Find the number of teeth on each wheel, pitch circle diameters and spiral angles. Find the efficiency of the drive if the friction angle is 5°.

[Ans. 24, 36 ; 128 mm ; 53.4°, 26.6° ; 85.5 %]

15. A right angled drive on a machine is to be made by two spiral wheels. The wheels are of equal diameter with a normal pitch of 10 mm and the centre distance is approximately 150 mm. If the speed ratio is 2.5 to 1, find : 1. the spiral angles of the teeth, 2. the number of teeth on each wheel, 3. the exact centre distance, and 4. transmission efficiency, if the friction angle is 6°.

[Ans. 21.8°, 68.2° ; 18 , 45 ; 154 mm ; 75.8 %]

DO YOU KNOW ?

1. Explain the terms : (*i*) Module, (*ii*) Pressure angle, and (*iii*) Addendum.
2. State and prove the law of gearing. Show that involute profile satisfies the conditions for correct gearing.
3. Derive an expression for the velocity of sliding between a pair of involute teeth. State the advantages of involute profile as a gear tooth profile.

4. Prove that the velocity of sliding is proportional to the distance of the point of contact from the pitch point.

5. Prove that for two involute gear wheels in mesh, the angular velocity ratio does not change if the centre distance is increased within limits, but the pressure angle increases.

6. Derive an expression for the length of the arc of contact in a pair of meshed spur gears.

7. What do you understand by the term 'interference' as applied to gears?

8. Derive an expression for the minimum number of teeth required on the pinion in order to avoid interference in involute gear teeth when it meshes with wheel.

9. Derive an expression for minimum number of teeth required on a pinion to avoid interference when it gears with a rack.

10. Define (i) normal pitch, and (ii) axial pitch relating to helical gears.

11. Derive an expression for the centre distance of a pair of spiral gears.

12. Show that, in a pair of spiral gears connecting inclined shafts, the efficiency is maximum when the spiral angle of the driving wheel is half the sum of the shaft and friction angles.

OBJECTIVE TYPE QUESTIONS

1. The two parallel and coplanar shafts are connected by gears having teeth parallel to the axis of the shaft. This arrangement is called
   (a) spur gearing   (b) helical gearing   (c) bevel gearing   (d) spiral gearing

2. The type of gears used to connect two non-parallel non-intersecting shafts are
   (a) spur gears   (b) helical gears   (c) spiral gears   (d) none of these

3. An imaginary circle which by pure rolling action, gives the same motion as the actual gear, is called
   (a) addendum circle   (b) dedendum circle   (c) pitch circle   (d) clearance circle

4. The size of a gear is usually specified by
   (a) pressure angle   (b) circular pitch   (c) diametral pitch   (d) pitch circle diameter

5. The radial distance of a tooth from the pitch circle to the bottom of the tooth, is called
   (a) dedendum   (b) addendum   (c) clearance   (d) working depth

6. The product of the diametral pitch and circular pitch is equal to
   (a) 1   (b) $1/\pi$ (c) π (d) 2π

7. The module is the reciprocal of
   (a) diametral pitch   (b) circular pitch   (c) pitch diameter   (d) none of these

8. Which is the incorrect relationship of gears?
   (a) Circular pitch × Diametral pitch = π (b) Module = P.C.D/No.of teeth
   (c) Dedendum = 1.157 module   (d) Addendum = 2.157 module

9. If the module of a gear be m, the number of teeth T and pitch circle diameter D, then
   (a) $m = D/T$ (b) $D = T/m$ (c) $m = D/2T$ (d) none of these

10. Mitre gears are used for
    (a) great speed reduction   (b) equal speed
    (c) minimum axial thrust   (d) minimum backlash

11. The condition of correct gearing is
    (a) pitch line velocities of teeth be same
    (b) radius of curvature of two profiles be same
    (c) common normal to the pitch surface cuts the line of centres at a fixed point
    (d) none of the above

12. Law of gearing is satisfied if
    (a) two surfaces slide smoothly
    (b) common normal at the point of contact passes through the pitch point on the line joining the centres of rotation
    (c) number of teeth = P.C.D. / module
    (d) addendum is greater than dedendum

13. Involute profile is preferred to cycloidal because
    (a) the profile is easy to cut
    (b) only one curve is required to cut
    (c) the rack has straight line profile and hence can be cut accurately
    (d) none of the above
14. The contact ratio for gears is
    (a) zero   (b) less than one   (c) greater than one
15. The maximum length of arc of contact for two mating gears, in order to avoid interference, is
    (a) $(r + R) \sin \phi$ (b) $(r + R) \cos \phi$ (c) $(r + R) \tan \phi$ (d) none of these
    where r = Pitch circle radius of pinion,
            R = Pitch circle radius of driver, and
            ϕ = Pressure angle.
16. When the addenda on pinion and wheel is such that the path of approach and path of recess are half of their maximum possible values, then the length of the path of contact is given by
    (a) $\dfrac{(r + R) \sin \phi}{2}$ (b) $\dfrac{(r + R) \cos \phi}{2}$ (c) $\dfrac{(r + R) \tan \phi}{2}$ (d) none of these
17. Interference can be avoided in involute gears with 20° pressure angle by
    (a) cutting involute correctly
    (b) using as small number of teeth as possible
    (c) using more than 20 teeth
    (d) using more than 8 teeth
18. The ratio of face width to transverse pitch of a helical gear with α as the helix angle is normally
    (a) more than 1.15/tan α (b) more than 1.05/tan α
    (c) more than 1/tan α (d) none of these
19. The maximum efficiency for spiral gears is
    (a) $\dfrac{\sin (\theta + \phi) + 1}{\cos (\theta - \phi) + 1}$ (b) $\dfrac{\cos (\theta - \phi) + 1}{\sin (\theta + \phi) + 1}$
    (c) $\dfrac{\cos (\theta + \phi) + 1}{\cos (\theta - \phi) + 1}$ (d) $\dfrac{\cos (\theta - \phi) + 1}{\cos (\theta + \phi) + 1}$
    where θ = Shaft angle, and ϕ = Friction angle.
20. For a speed ratio of 100, smallest gear box is obtained by using
    (a) a pair of spur gears
    (b) a pair of helical and a pair of spur gear compounded
    (c) a pair of bevel and a pair of spur gear compounded
    (d) a pair of helical and a pair of worm gear compounded

ANSWERS

1. (a)	2. (c)	3. (c)	4. (d)	5. (a)
6. (c)	7. (a)	8. (d)	9. (a)	10. (b)
11. (c)	12. (b)	13. (b)	14. (c)	15. (c)
16. (a)	17. (c)	18. (a)	19. (c)	20. (d)

13

Gear Trains

13.1. Introduction

Sometimes, two or more gears are made to mesh with each other to transmit power from one shaft to another. Such a combination is called *gear train* or *train of toothed wheels*. The nature of the train used depends upon the velocity ratio required and the relative position of the axes of shafts. A gear train may consist of spur, bevel or spiral gears.

13.2. Types of Gear Trains

Following are the different types of gear trains, depending upon the arrangement of wheels :

1. Simple gear train, **2.** Compound gear train, **3.** Reverted gear train, and **4.** Epicyclic gear train.

In the first three types of gear trains, the axes of the shafts over which the gears are mounted are fixed relative to each other. But in case of epicyclic gear trains, the axes of the shafts on which the gears are mounted may move relative to a fixed axis.

13.3. Simple Gear Train

When there is only one gear on each shaft, as shown in Fig. 13.1, it is known as *simple gear train*. The gears are represented by their pitch circles.

When the distance between the two shafts is small, the two gears 1 and 2 are made to mesh with each other to transmit motion from one shaft to the other, as shown in Fig. 13.1 (*a*). Since the gear 1 drives the gear 2, therefore gear 1 is called the ***driver*** and the gear 2 is called the ***driven*** or ***follower.*** It may be noted that the motion of the driven gear is opposite to the motion of driving gear.

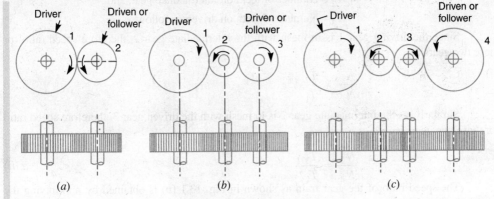

(*a*)   (*b*)   (*c*)

Fig. 13.1. Simple gear train.

Let N_1 = Speed of gear 1(or driver) in r.p.m.,

N_2 = Speed of gear 2 (or driven or follower) in r.p.m.,

T_1 = Number of teeth on gear 1, and

T_2 = Number of teeth on gear 2.

Since the speed ratio (or velocity ratio) of gear train is the ratio of the speed of the driver to the speed of the driven or follower and ratio of speeds of any pair of gears in mesh is the inverse of their number of teeth, therefore

$$\text{Speed ratio} = \frac{N_1}{N_2} = \frac{T_2}{T_1}$$

It may be noted that ratio of the speed of the driven or follower to the speed of the driver is known as ***train value*** of the gear train. Mathematically,

$$\text{Train value} = \frac{N_2}{N_1} = \frac{T_1}{T_2}$$

From above, we see that the train value is the reciprocal of speed ratio.

Sometimes, the distance between the two gears is large. The motion from one gear to another, in such a case, may be transmitted by either of the following two methods :

1. By providing the large sized gear, or **2.** By providing one or more intermediate gears.

A little consideration will show that the former method (*i.e.* providing large sized gears) is very inconvenient and uneconomical method ; whereas the latter method (*i.e.* providing one or more intermediate gear) is very convenient and economical.

It may be noted that when the number of intermediate gears are *odd*, the motion of both the gears (*i.e.* driver and driven or follower) is *like* as shown in Fig. 13.1 (*b*).

But if the number of intermediate gears are *even*, the motion of the driven or follower will be in the opposite direction of the driver as shown in Fig. 13.1 (*c*).

Now consider a simple train of gears with one intermediate gear as shown in Fig. 13.1 (*b*).

Let N_1 = Speed of driver in r.p.m.,

N_2 = Speed of intermediate gear in r.p.m.,

N_3 = Speed of driven or follower in r.p.m.,

T_1 = Number of teeth on driver,

T_2 = Number of teeth on intermediate gear, and

T_3 = Number of teeth on driven or follower.

Since the driving gear 1 is in mesh with the intermediate gear 2, therefore speed ratio for these two gears is

$$\frac{N_1}{N_2} = \frac{T_2}{T_1} \qquad \qquad \dots(i)$$

Similarly, as the intermediate gear 2 is in mesh with the driven gear 3, therefore speed ratio for these two gears is

$$\frac{N_2}{N_3} = \frac{T_3}{T_2} \qquad \qquad \dots(ii)$$

The speed ratio of the gear train as shown in Fig. 13.1 (b) is obtained by multiplying the equations (i) and (ii).

∴ $$\frac{N_1}{N_2} \times \frac{N_2}{N_3} = \frac{T_2}{T_1} \times \frac{T_3}{T_2} \qquad \text{or} \qquad \frac{N_1}{N_3} = \frac{T_3}{T_1}$$

i.e.

$$\text{Speed ratio} = \frac{\text{Speed of driver}}{\text{Speed of driven}} = \frac{\text{No. of teeth on driven}}{\text{No. of teeth on driver}}$$

and

$$\text{Train value} = \frac{\text{Speed of driven}}{\text{Speed of driver}} = \frac{\text{No. of teeth on driver}}{\text{No. of teeth on driven}}$$

Similarly, it can be proved that the above equation holds good even if there are any number of intermediate gears. From above, we see that the speed ratio and the train value, in a simple train of gears, is independent of the size and number of intermediate gears. These intermediate gears are called *idle gears*, as they do not effect the speed ratio or train value of the system. The idle gears are used for the following two purposes :

1. To connect gears where a large centre distance is required, and

2. To obtain the desired direction of motion of the driven gear (*i.e.* clockwise or anticlockwise).

Gear trains inside a mechanical watch

13.4. Compound Gear Train

When there are more than one gear on a shaft, as shown in Fig. 13.2, it is called a *compound train of gear.*

We have seen in Art. 13.3 that the idle gears, in a simple train of gears do not effect the speed ratio of the system. But these gears are useful in bridging over the space between the driver and the driven.

But whenever the distance between the driver and the driven or follower has to be bridged over by intermediate gears and at the same time a great (or much less) speed ratio is required, then the advantage of intermediate gears is intensified by providing compound gears on intermediate shafts. In this case, each intermediate shaft has two gears rigidly fixed to it so that they may have the same speed. One of these two gears meshes with the driver and the other with the driven or follower attached to the next shaft as shown in Fig.13.2.

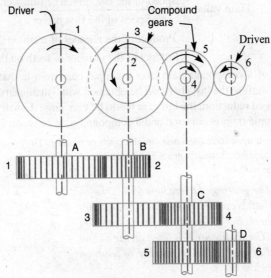

Fig. 13.2. Compound gear train.

In a compound train of gears, as shown in Fig. 13.2, the gear 1 is the driving gear mounted on shaft *A*, gears 2 and 3 are compound gears which are mounted on shaft *B*. The gears 4 and 5 are also compound gears which are mounted on shaft *C* and the gear 6 is the driven gear mounted on shaft *D*.

Let
$$N_1 = \text{Speed of driving gear 1,}$$
$$T_1 = \text{Number of teeth on driving gear 1,}$$
$$N_2, N_3 ..., N_6 = \text{Speed of respective gears in r.p.m., and}$$
$$T_2, T_3..., T_6 = \text{Number of teeth on respective gears.}$$

Since gear 1 is in mesh with gear 2, therefore its speed ratio is

$$\frac{N_1}{N_2} = \frac{T_2}{T_1} \qquad ...(i)$$

Similarly, for gears 3 and 4, speed ratio is

$$\frac{N_3}{N_4} = \frac{T_4}{T_3} \qquad ...(ii)$$

and for gears 5 and 6, speed ratio is

$$\frac{N_5}{N_6} = \frac{T_6}{T_5} \qquad ...(iii)$$

The speed ratio of compound gear train is obtained by multiplying the equations (*i*), (*ii*) and (*iii*),

$$\therefore \qquad \frac{N_1}{N_2} \times \frac{N_3}{N_4} \times \frac{N_5}{N_6} = \frac{T_2}{T_1} \times \frac{T_4}{T_3} \times \frac{T_6}{T_5} \qquad \text{or} \qquad {}^*\frac{N_1}{N_6} = \frac{T_2 \times T_4 \times T_6}{T_1 \times T_3 \times T_5}$$

---

* Since gears 2 and 3 are mounted on one shaft *B*, therefore $N_2 = N_3$. Similarly gears 4 and 5 are mounted on shaft *C*, therefore $N_4 = N_5$.

i.e.

$$\text{Speed ratio} = \frac{\text{Speed of the first driver}}{\text{Speed of the last driven or follower}}$$

$$= \frac{\text{Product of the number of teeth on the drivens}}{\text{Product of the number of teeth on the drivers}}$$

and

$$\text{Train value} = \frac{\text{Speed of the last driven or follower}}{\text{Speed of the first driver}}$$

$$= \frac{\text{Product of the number of teeth on the drivers}}{\text{Product of the number of teeth on the drivens}}$$

The advantage of a compound train over a simple gear train is that a much larger speed reduction from the first shaft to the last shaft can be obtained with small gears. If a simple gear train is used to give a large speed reduction, the last gear has to be very large. Usually for a speed reduction in excess of 7 to 1, a simple train is not used and a compound train or worm gearing is employed.

Note: The gears which mesh must have the same circular pitch or module. Thus gears 1 and 2 must have the same module as they mesh together. Similarly gears 3 and 4, and gears 5 and 6 must have the same module.

Example 13.1. *The gearing of a machine tool is shown in Fig. 13.3. The motor shaft is connected to gear A and rotates at 975 r.p.m. The gear wheels B, C, D and E are fixed to parallel shafts rotating together. The final gear F is fixed on the output shaft. What is the speed of gear F ? The number of teeth on each gear are as given below :*

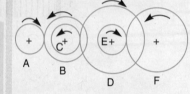

Fig. 13.3

Gear	A	B	C	D	E	F
No. of teeth	20	50	25	75	26	65

Solution. Given : $N_A = 975$ r.p.m. ; $T_A = 20$; $T_B = 50$; $T_C = 25$; $T_D = 75$; $T_E = 26$; $T_F = 65$

From Fig. 13.3, we see that gears A, C and E are drivers while the gears B, D and F are driven or followers. Let the gear A rotates in clockwise direction. Since the gears B and C are mounted on the same shaft, therefore it is a compound gear and the direction or rotation of both these gears is same (*i.e.* anticlockwise). Similarly, the gears D and E are mounted on the same shaft, therefore it is also a compound gear and the direction of rotation of both these gears is same (*i.e.* clockwise). The gear F will rotate in anticlockwise direction.

Battery Car: Even though it is run by batteries, the power transmission, gears, clutches, brakes, etc. remain mechanical in nature.

Note : This picture is given as additional information.

Let N_F = Speed of gear F, *i.e.* last driven or follower.

We know that

$$\frac{\text{Speed of the first driver}}{\text{Speed of the last driven}} = \frac{\text{Product of no. of teeth on drivens}}{\text{Product of no. of teeth on drivers}}$$

or
$$\frac{N_A}{N_F} = \frac{T_B \times T_D \times T_F}{T_A \times T_C \times T_E} = \frac{50 \times 75 \times 65}{20 \times 25 \times 26} = 18.75$$

∴
$$N_F = \frac{N_A}{18.75} = \frac{975}{18.75} = 52 \text{ r. p. m. } \textbf{Ans.}$$

13.5. Design of Spur Gears

Sometimes, the spur gears (*i.e.* driver and driven) are to be designed for the given velocity ratio and distance between the centres of their shafts.

Let
x = Distance between the centres of two shafts,

N_1 = Speed of the driver,

T_1 = Number of teeth on the driver,

d_1 = Pitch circle diameter of the driver,

N_2, T_2 and d_2 = Corresponding values for the driven or follower, and

p_c = Circular pitch.

We know that the distance between the centres of two shafts,

$$x = \frac{d_1 + d_2}{2} \qquad \qquad ...(i)$$

and speed ratio or velocity ratio,

$$\frac{N_1}{N_2} = \frac{d_2}{d_1} = \frac{T_2}{T_1} \qquad \qquad ...(ii)$$

From the above equations, we can conveniently find out the values of d_1 and d_2 (or T_1 and T_2) and the circular pitch (p_c). The values of T_1 and T_2, as obtained above, may or may not be whole numbers. But in a gear since the number of its teeth is always a whole number, therefore a slight alterations must be made in the values of x, d_1 and d_2, so that the number of teeth in the two gears may be a complete number.

Example 13.2. *Two parallel shafts, about 600 mm apart are to be connected by spur gears. One shaft is to run at 360 r.p.m. and the other at 120 r.p.m. Design the gears, if the circular pitch is to be 25 mm.*

Solution. Given : x = 600 mm ; N_1 = 360 r.p.m. ; N_2 = 120 r.p.m. ; p_c = 25 mm

Let
d_1 = Pitch circle diameter of the first gear, and

d_2 = Pitch circle diameter of the second gear.

We know that speed ratio,

$$\frac{N_1}{N_2} = \frac{d_2}{d_1} = \frac{360}{120} = 3 \quad \text{or} \quad d_2 = 3d_1 \qquad \qquad ...(i)$$

and centre distance between the shafts (x),

$$600 = \frac{1}{2}(d_1 + d_2) \quad \text{or} \quad d_1 + d_2 = 1200 \qquad \qquad ...(ii)$$

From equations (*i*) and (*ii*), we find that

$$d_1 = 300 \text{ mm, and } d_2 = 900 \text{ mm}$$

∴ Number of teeth on the first gear,

$$T_1 = \frac{\pi d_2}{p_c} = \frac{\pi \times 300}{25} = 37.7$$

and number of teeth on the second gear,

$$T_2 = \frac{\pi d_2}{p_c} = \frac{\pi \times 900}{25} = 113.1$$

Since the number of teeth on both the gears are to be in complete numbers, therefore let us make the number of teeth on the first gear as 38. Therefore for a speed ratio of 3, the number of teeth on the second gear should be $38 \times 3 = 114$.

Now the exact pitch circle diameter of the first gear,

$$d_1' = \frac{T_1 \times p_c}{\pi} = \frac{38 \times 25}{\pi} = 302.36 \text{ mm}$$

and the exact pitch circle diameter of the second gear,

$$d_2' = \frac{T_2 \times p_c}{\pi} = \frac{114 \times 25}{\pi} = 907.1 \text{ mm}$$

∴ Exact distance between the two shafts,

$$x' = \frac{d_1' + d_2'}{2} = \frac{302.36 + 907.1}{2} = 604.73 \text{ mm}$$

Hence the number of teeth on the first and second gear must be 38 and 114 and their pitch circle diameters must be 302.36 mm and 907.1 mm respectively. The exact distance between the two shafts must be 604.73 mm. **Ans.**

13.6. Reverted Gear Train

When the axes of the first gear (*i.e.* first driver) and the last gear (*i.e.* last driven or follower) are co-axial, then the gear train is known as *reverted gear* **train** as shown in Fig. 13.4.

We see that gear 1 (*i.e.* first driver) drives the gear 2 (*i.e.* first driven or follower) in the opposite direction. Since the gears 2 and 3 are mounted on the same shaft, therefore they form a compound gear and the gear 3 will rotate in the same direction as that of gear 2. The gear 3 (which is now the second driver) drives the gear 4 (*i.e.* the last driven or follower) in the same direction as that of gear 1. Thus we see that in a reverted gear train, the motion of the first gear and the last gear is *like*.

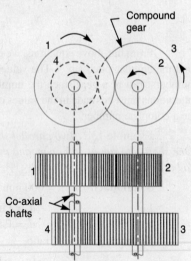

Fig. 13.4. Reverted gear train.

Let T_1 = Number of teeth on gear 1,

r_1 = Pitch circle radius of gear 1, and

N_1 = Speed of gear 1 in r.p.m.

Similarly,

T_2, T_3, T_4 = Number of teeth on respective gears,

r_2, r_3, r_4 = Pitch circle radii of respective gears, and

N_2, N_3, N_4 = Speed of respective gears in r.p.m.

Since the distance between the centres of the shafts of gears 1 and 2 as well as gears 3 and 4 is same, therefore

$$r_1 + r_2 = r_3 + r_4 \qquad \qquad ...(i)$$

Also, the circular pitch or module of all the gears is assumed to be same, therefore number of teeth on each gear is directly proportional to its circumference or radius.

$$\therefore \qquad \qquad *T_1 + T_2 = T_3 + T_4 \qquad \qquad ...(ii)$$

and
$$\text{Speed ratio} = \frac{\text{Product of number of teeth on drivens}}{\text{Product of number of teeth on drivers}}$$

or
$$\frac{N_1}{N_4} = \frac{T_2 \times T_4}{T_1 \times T_3} \qquad \qquad ... (iii)$$

From equations (*i*), (*ii*) and (*iii*), we can determine the number of teeth on each gear for the given centre distance, speed ratio and module only when the number of teeth on one gear is chosen arbitrarily.

The reverted gear trains are used in automotive transmissions, lathe back gears, industrial speed reducers, and in clocks (where the minute and hour hand shafts are co-axial).

Example 13.3. *The speed ratio of the reverted gear train, as shown in Fig. 13.5, is to be 12. The module pitch of gears A and B is 3.125 mm and of gears C and D is 2.5 mm. Calculate the suitable numbers of teeth for the gears. No gear is to have less than 24 teeth.*

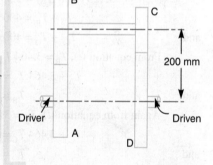

Fig. 13.5

Solution. Given : Speed ratio, $N_A/N_D = 12$; $m_A = m_B = 3.125$ mm ; $m_C = m_D = 2.5$ mm

Let N_A = Speed of gear A,

T_A = Number of teeth on gear A,

r_A = Pitch circle radius of gear A,

N_B, N_C, N_D = Speed of respective gears,

T_B, T_C, T_D = Number of teeth on respective gears, and

r_B, r_C, r_D = Pitch circle radii of respective gears.

---

* We know that circular pitch,

$$p_c = \frac{2\pi r}{T} = \pi m \qquad \text{or} \qquad r = \frac{m.T}{2} \text{ , where } m \text{ is the module.}$$

$$\therefore \qquad r_1 = \frac{m.T_1}{2} \ ; \ r_2 = \frac{m.T_2}{2} \ ; \ r_3 = \frac{m.T_3}{2} \ ; \ r_4 = \frac{m.T_4}{2}$$

Now from equation (*i*),

$$\frac{m.T_1}{2} + \frac{m.T_2}{2} = \frac{m.T_3}{2} + \frac{m.T_4}{2}$$

$$T_1 + T_2 = T_3 + T_4$$

Since the speed ratio between the gears A and B and between the gears C and D are to be same, therefore

$$* \frac{N_A}{N_B} = \frac{N_C}{N_D} = \sqrt{12} = 3.464$$

Also the speed ratio of any pair of gears in mesh is the inverse of their number of teeth, therefore

$$\frac{T_B}{T_A} = \frac{T_D}{T_C} = 3.464 \qquad \qquad ...(i)$$

We know that the distance between the shafts

$$x = r_A + r_B = r_C + r_D = 200 \text{ mm}$$

or $\qquad \dfrac{m_A . T_A}{2} + \dfrac{m_B . T_B}{2} = \dfrac{m_C . T_C}{2} + \dfrac{m_D . T_D}{2} = 200 \qquad \qquad ...\left(\because r = \dfrac{m.T}{2} \right)$

$$3.125 \,(T_A + T_B) = 2.5 \,(T_C + T_D) = 400 \qquad \qquad ...(\because m_A = m_B, \text{ and } m_C = m_D)$$

$\therefore \qquad \qquad T_A + T_B = 400 / 3.125 = 128 \qquad \qquad ...(ii)$

and $\qquad \qquad T_C + T_D = 400 / 2.5 = 160 \qquad \qquad ...(iii)$

From equation (i), $T_B = 3.464 \, T_A$. Substituting this value of T_B in equation (ii),

$$T_A + 3.464 \, T_A = 128 \quad \text{ or } \quad T_A = 128 / 4.464 = 28.67 \text{ say } 28 \text{ **Ans.**}$$

and $\qquad \qquad T_B = 128 - 28 = 100 \text{ **Ans.**}$

Again from equation (i), $T_D = 3.464 \, T_C$. Substituting this value of T_D in equation (iii),

$$T_C + 3.464 \, T_C = 160 \quad \text{ or } \quad T_C = 160 / 4.464 = 35.84 \text{ say } 36 \text{ **Ans.**}$$

and $\qquad \qquad T_D = 160 - 36 = 124 \text{ **Ans.**}$

Note : The speed ratio of the reverted gear train with the calculated values of number of teeth on each gear is

$$\frac{N_A}{N_D} = \frac{T_B \times T_D}{T_A \times T_C} = \frac{100 \times 124}{28 \times 36} = 12.3$$

13.7. Epicyclic Gear Train

We have already discussed that in an epicyclic gear train, the axes of the shafts, over which the gears are mounted, may move relative to a fixed axis. A simple epicyclic gear train is shown in Fig. 13.6, where a gear A and the arm C have a common axis at O_1 about which they can rotate. The gear B meshes with gear A and has its axis on the arm at O_2, about which the gear B can rotate. If the

---

* $\qquad$ We know that speed ratio $\qquad = \dfrac{\text{Speed of first driver}}{\text{Speed of last driven}} = \dfrac{N_A}{N_D} = 12$

$\qquad$ Also $\qquad \qquad \dfrac{N_A}{N_D} = \dfrac{N_A}{N_B} \times \dfrac{N_C}{N_D} \qquad \qquad ...(N_B = N_C, \text{ being on the same shaft})$

$\qquad$ For $\dfrac{N_A}{N_B}$ and $\dfrac{N_C}{N_D}$ to be same, each speed ratio should be $\sqrt{12}$ so that

$$\frac{N_A}{N_D} = \frac{N_A}{N_B} \times \frac{N_C}{N_D} = \sqrt{12} \times \sqrt{12} = 12$$

arm is fixed, the gear train is simple and gear A can drive gear B or *vice- versa*, but if gear A is fixed and the arm is rotated about the axis of gear A (*i.e.* O_1), then the gear B is forced to rotate **upon** and **around** gear A. Such a motion is called **epicyclic** and the gear trains arranged in such a manner that one or more of their members move upon and around another member are known as **epicyclic gear trains** (*epi.* means upon and *cyclic* means around). The epicyclic gear trains may be *simple* or *compound*.

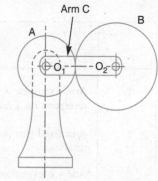

Fig. 13.6. Epicyclic gear train.

The epicyclic gear trains are useful for transmitting high velocity ratios with gears of moderate size in a comparatively lesser space. The epicyclic gear trains are used in the back gear of lathe, differential gears of the automobiles, hoists, pulley blocks, wrist watches etc.

13.8. Velocity Ratio of Epicyclic Gear Train

The following two methods may be used for finding out the velocity ratio of an epicyclic gear train.

1. Tabular method, and 2. Algebraic method.

These methods are discussed, in detail, as follows :

1. *Tabular method.* Consider an epicyclic gear train as shown in Fig. 13.6.

Let

$\qquad\qquad T_A$ = Number of teeth on gear A, and

$\qquad\qquad T_B$ = Number of teeth on gear B.

First of all, let us suppose that the arm is fixed. Therefore the axes of both the gears are also fixed relative to each other. When the gear A makes one revolution anticlockwise, the gear B will make $^*T_A / T_B$ revolutions, clockwise. Assuming the anticlockwise rotation as positive and clockwise as negative, we may say that when gear A makes + 1 revolution, then the gear B will make $(- T_A / T_B)$ revolutions. This statement of relative motion is entered in the first row of the table (see Table 13.1).

Secondly, if the gear A makes + x revolutions, then the gear B will make $- x \times T_A / T_B$ revolutions. This statement is entered in the second row of the table. In other words, multiply the each motion (entered in the first row) by x.

Inside view of a car engine.

Note : This picture is given as additional information.

Thirdly, each element of an epicyclic train is given + y revolutions and entered in the third row. Finally, the motion of each element of the gear train is added up and entered in the fourth row.

---

* We know that $N_B / N_A = T_A / T_B$. Since $N_A = 1$ revolution, therefore $N_B = T_A / T_B$.

Table 13.1. Table of motions

Step No.	Conditions of motion	Revolutions of elements		
		Arm C	Gear A	Gear B
1.	Arm fixed-gear A rotates through + 1 revolution i.e. 1 rev. anticlockwise	0	+ 1	$-\dfrac{T_A}{T_B}$
2.	Arm fixed-gear A rotates through + x revolutions	0	+ x	$-x \times \dfrac{T_A}{T_B}$
3.	Add + y revolutions to all elements	+ y	+ y	+ y
4.	Total motion	+ y	x + y	$y - x \times \dfrac{T_A}{T_B}$

A little consideration will show that when two conditions about the motion of rotation of any two elements are known, then the unknown speed of the third element may be obtained by substituting the given data in the third column of the fourth row.

2. *Algebraic method.* In this method, the motion of each element of the epicyclic train relative to the arm is set down in the form of equations. The number of equations depends upon the number of elements in the gear train. But the two conditions are, usually, supplied in any epicyclic train *viz.* some element is fixed and the other has specified motion. These two conditions are sufficient to solve all the equations ; and hence to determine the motion of any element in the epicyclic gear train.

Let the arm *C* be fixed in an epicyclic gear train as shown in Fig. 13.6. Therefore speed of the gear *A* relative to the arm *C*

$$= N_A - N_C$$

and speed of the gear *B* relative to the arm *C*,

$$= N_B - N_C$$

Since the gears *A* and *B* are meshing directly, therefore they will revolve in *opposite* directions.

∴
$$\frac{N_B - N_C}{N_A - N_C} = -\frac{T_A}{T_B}$$

Since the arm *C* is fixed, therefore its speed, $N_C = 0$.

∴
$$\frac{N_B}{N_A} = -\frac{T_A}{T_B}$$

If the gear *A* is fixed, then $N_A = 0$.

$$\frac{N_B - N_C}{0 - N_C} = -\frac{T_A}{T_B} \quad \text{or} \quad \frac{N_B}{N_C} = 1 + \frac{T_A}{T_B}$$

Note : The tabular method is easier and hence mostly used in solving problems on epicyclic gear train.

Example 13.4. *In an epicyclic gear train, an arm carries two gears A and B having 36 and 45 teeth respectively. If the arm rotates at 150 r.p.m. in the anticlockwise direction about the centre of the gear A which is fixed, determine the speed of gear B. If the gear A instead of being fixed, makes 300 r.p.m. in the clockwise direction, what will be the speed of gear B ?*

Solution. Given : $T_A = 36$; $T_B = 45$; $N_C = 150$ r.p.m. (anticlockwise)

The gear train is shown in Fig. 13.7.

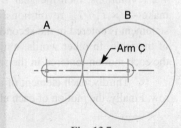

Fig. 13.7

We shall solve this example, first by tabular method and then by algebraic method.

1. *Tabular method*

First of all prepare the table of motions as given below :

Table 13.2. Table of motions.

Step No.	Conditions of motion	Revolutions of elements		
		Arm C	Gear A	Gear B
1.	Arm fixed-gear A rotates through + 1 revolution (*i.e.* 1 rev. anticlockwise)	0	+ 1	$-\dfrac{T_A}{T_B}$
2.	Arm fixed-gear A rotates through + x revolutions	0	+ x	$-x \times \dfrac{T_A}{T_B}$
3.	Add + y revolutions to all elements	+ y	+ y	+ y
4.	Total motion	+ y	x + y	$y - x \times \dfrac{T_A}{T_B}$

Speed of gear B when gear A is fixed

Since the speed of arm is 150 r.p.m. anticlockwise, therefore from the fourth row of the table,

$$y = + 150 \text{ r.p.m.}$$

Also the gear A is fixed, therefore

$$x + y = 0 \qquad \text{or} \qquad x = -y = -150 \text{ r.p.m.}$$

∴ Speed of gear B, $\quad N_B = y - x \times \dfrac{T_A}{T_B} = 150 + 150 \times \dfrac{36}{45} = + 270$ r.p.m.

$$= 270 \text{ r.p.m. (anticlockwise)} \quad \textbf{Ans.}$$

Speed of gear B when gear A makes 300 r.p.m. clockwise

Since the gear A makes 300 r.p.m.clockwise, therefore from the fourth row of the table,

$$x + y = -300 \qquad \text{or} \qquad x = -300 - y = -300 - 150 = -450 \text{ r.p.m.}$$

∴ Speed of gear B,

$$N_B = y - x \times \frac{T_A}{T_B} = 150 + 450 \times \frac{36}{45} = + 510 \text{ r.p.m.}$$

$$= 510 \text{ r.p.m. (anticlockwise)} \qquad \textbf{Ans.}$$

2. *Algebraic method*

Let $\qquad\qquad N_A$ = Speed of gear A.

$\qquad\qquad\qquad N_B$ = Speed of gear B, and

$\qquad\qquad\qquad N_C$ = Speed of arm C.

Assuming the arm C to be fixed, speed of gear A relative to arm C

$$= N_A - N_C$$

and speed of gear B relative to arm $C = N_B - N_C$

Since the gears A and B revolve in *opposite* directions, therefore

$$\frac{N_B - N_C}{N_A - N_C} = -\frac{T_A}{T_B} \qquad \qquad ...(i)$$

Speed of gear B when gear A is fixed

When gear A is fixed, the arm rotates at 150 r.p.m. in the anticlockwise direction, *i.e.*

$$N_A = 0, \quad \text{and} \quad N_C = +150 \text{ r.p.m.}$$

∴ $$\frac{N_B - 150}{0 - 150} = -\frac{36}{45} = -0.8 \qquad ...[\text{From equation } (i)]$$

or $$N_B = -150 \times -0.8 + 150 = 120 + 150 = 270 \text{ r.p.m. } \textbf{Ans.}$$

Speed of gear B when gear A makes 300 r.p.m. clockwise

Since the gear A makes 300 r.p.m. clockwise, therefore

$$N_A = -300 \text{ r.p.m.}$$

∴ $$\frac{N_B - 150}{-300 - 150} = -\frac{36}{45} = -0.8$$

or $$N_B = -450 \times -0.8 + 150 = 360 + 150 = 510 \text{ r.p.m. } \textbf{Ans.}$$

Example 13.5. *In a reverted epicyclic gear train, the arm A carries two gears B and C and a compound gear D - E. The gear B meshes with gear E and the gear C meshes with gear D. The number of teeth on gears B, C and D are 75, 30 and 90 respectively. Find the speed and direction of gear C when gear B is fixed and the arm A makes 100 r.p.m. clockwise.*

Solution. Given : $T_B = 75$; $T_C = 30$; $T_D = 90$; $N_A = 100$ r.p.m. (clockwise)

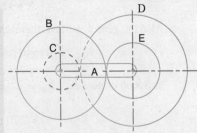

Fig. 13.8

The reverted epicyclic gear train is shown in Fig. 13.8. First of all, let us find the number of teeth on gear E (T_E). Let d_B, d_C, d_D and d_E be the pitch circle diameters of gears B, C, D and E respectively. From the geometry of the figure,

$$d_B + d_E = d_C + d_D$$

Since the number of teeth on each gear, for the same module, are proportional to their pitch circle diameters, therefore

$$T_B + T_E = T_C + T_D$$

∴ $$T_E = T_C + T_D - T_B = 30 + 90 - 75 = 45$$

The table of motions is drawn as follows :

A gear-cutting machine is used to cut gears.
Note : This picture is given as additional information.

Table 13.3. Table of motions.

Step No.	Conditions of motion	Revolutions of elements			
		Arm A	Compound gear D-E	Gear B	Gear C
1.	Arm fixed-compound gear *D-E* rotated through + 1 revolution (*i.e.* 1 rev. anticlockwise)	0	+ 1	$-\dfrac{T_E}{T_B}$	$-\dfrac{T_D}{T_C}$
2.	Arm fixed-compound gear *D-E* rotated through + *x* revolutions	0	+ x	$-x \times \dfrac{T_E}{T_B}$	$-x \times \dfrac{T_D}{T_C}$
3.	Add + y revolutions to all elements	+ y	+ y	+ y	+ y
4.	Total motion	+ y	x + y	$y - x \times \dfrac{T_E}{T_B}$	$y - x \times \dfrac{T_D}{T_C}$

Since the gear *B* is fixed, therefore from the fourth row of the table,

$$y - x \times \frac{T_E}{T_B} = 0 \quad \text{or} \quad y - x \times \frac{45}{75} = 0$$

$$\therefore \qquad\qquad y - 0.6\,x = 0 \qquad\qquad\qquad ...(i)$$

Also the arm *A* makes 100 r.p.m. clockwise, therefore

$$y = -100 \qquad\qquad\qquad ...(ii)$$

Substituting $y = -100$ in equation (i), we get

$$-100 - 0.6\,x = 0 \quad \text{or} \quad x = -100 / 0.6 = -166.67$$

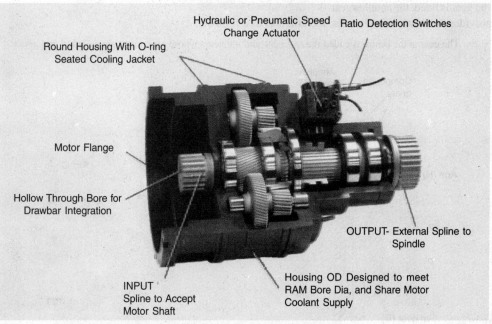

Hydraulic or Pneumatic Speed Change Actuator

Ratio Detection Switches

Round Housing With O-ring Seated Cooling Jacket

Motor Flange

Hollow Through Bore for Drawbar Integration

OUTPUT- External Spline to Spindle

INPUT Spline to Accept Motor Shaft

Housing OD Designed to meet RAM Bore Dia, and Share Motor Coolant Supply

Model of sun and planet gears.

From the fourth row of the table, speed of gear C,

$$N_C = y - x \times \frac{T_D}{T_C} = -100 + 166.67 \times \frac{90}{30} = +400 \text{ r.p.m.}$$

$$= 400 \text{ r.p.m. (anticlockwise) Ans.}$$

13.9. Compound Epicyclic Gear Train—Sun and Planet Gear

A compound epicyclic gear train is shown in Fig. 13.9. It consists of two co-axial shafts S_1 and S_2, an annulus gear A which is fixed, the compound gear (or planet gear) B-C, the sun gear D and the arm H. The annulus gear has internal teeth and the compound gear is carried by the arm and revolves freely on a pin of the arm H. The sun gear is co-axial with the annulus gear and the arm but independent of them.

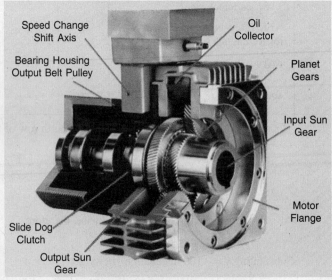

The annulus gear A meshes with the gear B and the sun gear D meshes with the gear C. It may be noted that when the annulus gear is fixed, the sun gear provides the drive and when the sun gear is fixed, the annulus gear provides the drive. In both cases, the arm acts as a follower.

Sun and Planet gears.

Note : The gear at the centre is called the *sun gear* and the gears whose axes move are called *planet gears*.

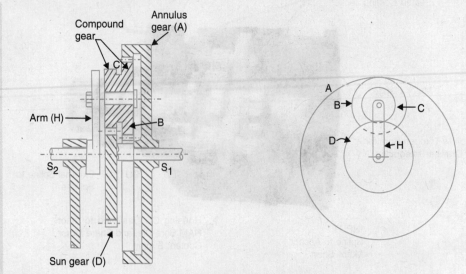

Fig. 13.9. Compound epicyclic gear train.

Let T_A, T_B, T_C, and T_D be the teeth and N_A, N_B, N_C and N_D be the speeds for the gears A, B, C and D respectively. A little consideration will show that when the arm is fixed and the sun gear D is turned anticlockwise, then the compound gear B-C and the annulus gear A will rotate in the clockwise direction.

The motion of rotations of the various elements are shown in the table below.

Table 13.4. Table of motions.

Step No.	Conditions of motion	Revolutions of elements			
		Arm	Gear D	Compound gear B-C	Gear A
1.	Arm fixed-gear D rotates through + 1 revolution	0	+ 1	$-\dfrac{T_D}{T_C}$	$-\dfrac{T_D}{T_C} \times \dfrac{T_B}{T_A}$
2.	Arm fixed-gear D rotates through + x revolutions	0	+ x	$-x \times \dfrac{T_D}{T_C}$	$-x \times \dfrac{T_D}{T_C} \times \dfrac{T_B}{T_A}$
3.	Add + y revolutions to all elements	+ y	+ y	+ y	+ y
4.	Total motion	+ y	$x + y$	$y - x \times \dfrac{T_D}{T_C}$	$y - x \times \dfrac{T_D}{T_C} \times \dfrac{T_B}{T_A}$

Note : If the annulus gear A is rotated through one revolution anticlockwise with the arm fixed, then the compound gear rotates through T_A / T_B revolutions in the same sense and the sun gear D rotates through $T_A / T_B \times T_C / T_D$ revolutions in clockwise direction.

Example 13.6. *An epicyclic gear consists of three gears A, B and C as shown in Fig. 13.10. The gear A has 72 internal teeth and gear C has 32 external teeth. The gear B meshes with both A and C and is carried on an arm EF which rotates about the centre of A at 18 r.p.m.. If the gear A is fixed, determine the speed of gears B and C.*

Solution. Given : $T_A = 72$; $T_C = 32$; Speed of arm $EF = 18$ r.p.m.

Considering the relative motion of rotation as shown in Table 13.5.

Table 13.5. Table of motions.

Step No.	Conditions of motion	Revolutions of elements			
		Arm EF	Gear C	Gear B	Gear A
1.	Arm fixed-gear C rotates through + 1 revolution (*i.e.* 1 rev. anticlockwise)	0	+ 1	$-\dfrac{T_C}{T_B}$	$-\dfrac{T_C}{T_B} \times \dfrac{T_B}{T_A} = -\dfrac{T_C}{T_A}$
2.	Arm fixed-gear C rotates through + x revolutions	0	+ x	$-x \times \dfrac{T_C}{T_B}$	$-x \times \dfrac{T_C}{T_A}$
3.	Add + y revolutions to all elements	+ y	+ y	+ y	+ y
4.	Total motion	+ y	$x + y$	$y - x \times \dfrac{T_C}{T_B}$	$y - x \times \dfrac{T_C}{T_A}$

Speed of gear C

We know that the speed of the arm is 18 r.p.m. therefore,

$$y = 18 \text{ r.p.m.}$$

and the gear A is fixed, therefore

$$y - x \times \frac{T_C}{T_A} = 0 \quad \text{or} \quad 18 - x \times \frac{32}{72} = 0$$

∴ $x = 18 \times 72 / 32 = 40.5$

∴ Speed of gear C $= x + y = 40.5 + 18$

                        $= + 58.5$ r.p.m.

                        $= 58.5$ r.p.m. in the direction
                        of arm. **Ans.**

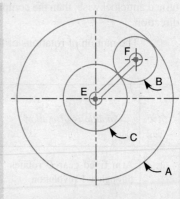

Fig. 13.10

Speed of gear B

Let d_A, d_B and d_C be the pitch circle diameters of gears
A, B and C respectively. Therefore, from the geometry of Fig. 13.10,

$$d_B + \frac{d_C}{2} = \frac{d_A}{2} \quad \text{or} \quad 2\,d_B + d_C = d_A$$

Since the number of teeth are proportional to their pitch circle diameters, therefore

$$2\,T_B + T_C = T_A \quad \text{or} \quad 2\,T_B + 32 = 72 \quad \text{or} \quad T_B = 20$$

∴ Speed of gear B $= y - x \times \dfrac{T_C}{T_B} = 18 - 40.5 \times \dfrac{32}{20} = -46.8$ r.p.m.

                        $= 46.8$ r.p.m. in the opposite direction of arm. **Ans.**

Example 13.7. *An epicyclic train of gears is arranged as shown in Fig.13.11. How many revolutions does the arm, to which the pinions B and C are attached, make :*

1. when A makes one revolution clockwise and D makes half a revolution anticlockwise, and

2. when A makes one revolution clockwise and D is stationary ?

The number of teeth on the gears A and D are 40 and 90 respectively.

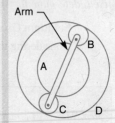

Fig. 13.11

Solution. Given : $T_A = 40$; $T_D = 90$

First of all, let us find the number of teeth on gears B and C (*i.e.* T_B and T_C). Let d_A, d_B, d_C and d_D be the pitch circle diameters of gears A, B, C and D respectively. Therefore from the geometry of the figure,

$$d_A + d_B + d_C = d_D \quad \text{or} \quad d_A + 2\,d_B = d_D \qquad ...(\because d_B = d_C)$$

Since the number of teeth are proportional to their pitch circle diameters, therefore,

$$T_A + 2\,T_B = T_D \quad \text{or} \quad 40 + 2\,T_B = 90$$

∴ $T_B = 25, \quad \text{and} \quad T_C = 25 \qquad ...(\because T_B = T_C)$

The table of motions is given below :

Table 13.6. Table of motions.

Step No.	Conditions of motion	Revolutions of elements			
		Arm	Gear A	Compound gear B-C	Gear D
1.	Arm fixed, gear A rotates through -1 revolution (*i.e.* 1 rev. clockwise)	0	-1	$+\dfrac{T_A}{T_B}$	$+\dfrac{T_A}{T_B} \times \dfrac{T_B}{T_D} = +\dfrac{T_A}{T_D}$
2.	Arm fixed, gear A rotates through $-x$ revolutions	0	$-x$	$+x \times \dfrac{T_A}{T_B}$	$+x \times \dfrac{T_A}{T_D}$
3.	Add $-y$ revolutions to all elements	$-y$	$-y$	$-y$	$-y$
4.	Total motion	$-y$	$-x-y$	$x \times \dfrac{T_A}{T_B} - y$	$x \times \dfrac{T_A}{T_D} - y$

1. *Speed of arm when A makes* **1** *revolution clockwise and D makes half revolution anticlockwise*

Since the gear A makes 1 revolution clockwise, therefore from the fourth row of the table,

$$-x - y = -1 \quad \text{or} \quad x + y = 1 \qquad \qquad ...(i)$$

Also, the gear D makes half revolution anticlockwise, therefore

$$x \times \frac{T_A}{T_D} - y = \frac{1}{2} \quad \text{or} \quad x \times \frac{40}{90} - y = \frac{1}{2}$$

$$\therefore \quad 40\,x - 90\,y = 45 \quad \text{or} \quad x - 2.25\,y = 1.125 \qquad \qquad ...(ii)$$

From equations (*i*) and (*ii*), $x = 1.04$ and $y = -0.04$

$$\therefore \quad \text{Speed of arm} = -y = -(-0.04) = +0.04$$

$$= 0.04 \text{ revolution anticlockwise } \textbf{Ans.}$$

2. *Speed of arm when A makes* **1** *revolution clockwise and D is stationary*

Since the gear A makes 1 revolution clockwise, therefore from the fourth row of the table,

$$-x - y = -1 \quad \text{or} \quad x + y = 1 \qquad \qquad ...(iii)$$

Also the gear D is stationary, therefore

$$x \times \frac{T_A}{T_D} - y = 0 \quad \text{or} \quad x \times \frac{40}{90} - y = 0$$

$$\therefore \quad 40\,x - 90\,y = 0 \quad \text{or} \quad x - 2.25\,y = 0 \qquad \qquad ...(iv)$$

From equations (*iii*) and (*iv*),

$$x = 0.692 \quad \text{and} \quad y = 0.308$$

$$\therefore \quad \text{Speed of arm} = -y = -0.308 = 0.308 \text{ revolution clockwise } \textbf{Ans.}$$

Example 13.8. *In an epicyclic gear train, the internal wheels A and B and compound wheels C and D rotate independently about axis O. The wheels E and F rotate on pins fixed to the arm G. E gears with A and C and F gears with B and D. All the wheels have the same module and the number of teeth are : $T_C = 28$; $T_D = 26$; $T_E = T_F = 18$.*

1. Sketch the arrangement ; 2. Find the number of teeth on A and B ; 3. If the arm G makes 100 r.p.m. clockwise and A is fixed, find the speed of B ; and 4. If the arm G makes 100 r.p.m. clockwise and wheel A makes 10 r.p.m. counter clockwise ; find the speed of wheel B.

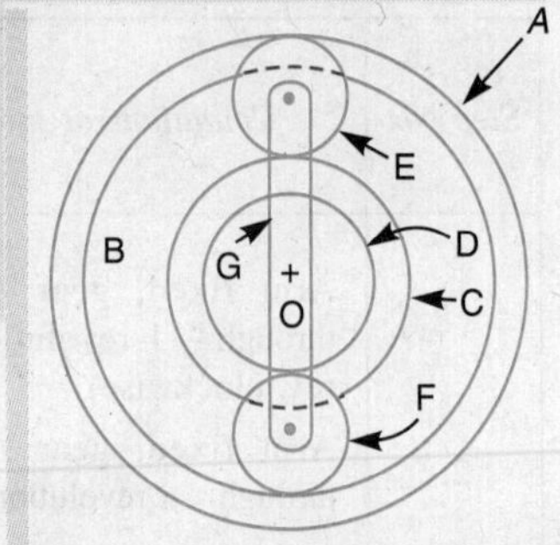

Fig. 13.12

Solution. Given : $T_C = 28$; $T_D = 26$; $T_E = T_F = 18$

1. Sketch the arrangement

The arrangement is shown in Fig. 13.12.

2. Number of teeth on wheels A and B

Let T_A = Number of teeth on wheel *A*, and

T_B = Number of teeth on wheel *B*.

If d_A, d_B, d_C, d_D, d_E and d_F are the pitch circle diameters of wheels *A, B, C, D, E* and *F* respectively, then from the geometry of Fig. 13.12,

$$d_A = d_C + 2\,d_E$$

and
$$d_B = d_D + 2\,d_F$$

Since the number of teeth are proportional to their pitch circle diameters, for the same module, therefore

$$T_A = T_C + 2\,T_E = 28 + 2 \times 18 = 64 \qquad \textbf{Ans.}$$

and
$$T_B = T_D + 2\,T_F = 26 + 2 \times 18 = 62 \qquad \textbf{Ans.}$$

3. Speed of wheel B when arm G makes 100 r.p.m. clockwise and wheel A is fixed

First of all, the table of motions is drawn as given below :

Table 13.7. Table of motions.

Step No.	Conditions of motion	Arm G	Wheel A	Wheel E	Compound wheel C-D	Wheel F	Wheel B
		Revolutions of elements					
1.	Arm fixed- wheel A rotates through + 1 revolution (*i.e.* 1 rev. anticlockwise)	0	+ 1	$+\dfrac{T_A}{T_E}$	$-\dfrac{T_A}{T_E} \times \dfrac{T_E}{T_C}$ $= -\dfrac{T_A}{T_C}$	$+\dfrac{T_A}{T_C} \times \dfrac{T_D}{T_F}$	$+\dfrac{T_A}{T_C} \times \dfrac{T_D}{T_F} \times \dfrac{T_F}{T_B}$ $= +\dfrac{T_A}{T_C} \times \dfrac{T_D}{T_B}$
2.	Arm fixed-wheel A rotates through + x revolutions	0	+ x	$+ x \times \dfrac{T_A}{T_E}$	$- x \times \dfrac{T_A}{T_C}$	$+ x \times \dfrac{T_A}{T_C} \times \dfrac{T_D}{T_F}$	$+ x \times \dfrac{T_A}{T_C} \times \dfrac{T_D}{T_B}$
3.	Add + y revolutions to all elements	+ y	+ y	+ y	+ y	+ y	+ y
4.	Total motion	+ y	x + y	$y + x \times \dfrac{T_A}{T_E}$	$y - x \times \dfrac{T_A}{T_C}$	$y + x \times \dfrac{T_A}{T_C} \times \dfrac{T_D}{T_F}$	$y + x \times \dfrac{T_A}{T_C} \times \dfrac{T_D}{T_B}$

Since the arm G makes 100 r.p.m. clockwise, therefore from the fourth row of the table,

$$y = -100 \qquad \qquad ...(i)$$

Also, the wheel A is fixed, therefore from the fourth row of the table,

$$x + y = 0 \qquad \text{or} \qquad x = -y = 100 \qquad \qquad ...(ii)$$

$$\therefore \quad \text{Speed of wheel } B = y + x \times \frac{T_A}{T_C} \times \frac{T_D}{T_B} = -100 + 100 \times \frac{64}{28} \times \frac{26}{62} = -100 + 95.8 \text{ r.p.m.}$$

$$= -4.2 \text{ r.p.m.} = 4.2 \text{ r.p.m. clockwise } \textbf{Ans.}$$

4. *Speed of wheel B when arm G makes* **100** *r.p.m. clockwise and wheel A makes* **10** *r.p.m. counter clockwise*

Since the arm G makes 100 r.p.m. clockwise, therefore from the fourth row of the table

$$y = -100 \qquad \qquad ...(iii)$$

Also the wheel A makes 10 r.p.m. counter clockwise, therefore from the fourth row of the table,

$$x + y = 10 \qquad \text{or} \qquad x = 10 - y = 10 + 100 = 110 \qquad \qquad ...(iv)$$

$$\therefore \quad \text{Speed of wheel } B = y + x \times \frac{T_A}{T_C} \times \frac{T_D}{T_B} = -100 + 110 \times \frac{64}{28} \times \frac{26}{62} = -100 + 105.4 \text{ r.p.m.}$$

$$= +5.4 \text{ r.p.m.} = 5.4 \text{ r.p.m. counter clockwise } \textbf{Ans.}$$

Example 13.9. *In an epicyclic gear of the 'sun and planet' type shown in Fig. 13.13, the pitch circle diameter of the internally toothed ring is to be 224 mm and the module 4 mm. When the ring D is stationary, the spider A, which carries three planet wheels C of equal size, is to make one revolution in the same sense as the sunwheel B for every five revolutions of the driving spindle carrying the sunwheel B. Determine suitable numbers of teeth for all the wheels.*

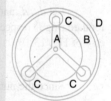

Fig. 13.13

Solution. Given : $\quad d_D = 224$ mm ; $\quad m = 4$ mm ; $\quad N_A = N_B / 5$

Let T_B, T_C and T_D be the number of teeth on the sun wheel B, planet wheels C and the internally toothed ring D. The table of motions is given below :

Table 13.8. Table of motions.

Step No.	Conditions of motion	Revolutions of elements			
		Spider A	Sun wheel B	Planet wheel C	Internal gear D
1.	Spider A fixed, sun wheel B rotates through + 1 revolution (*i.e.* 1 rev. anticlockwise)	0	+ 1	$-\dfrac{T_B}{T_C}$	$-\dfrac{T_B}{T_C} \times \dfrac{T_C}{T_D} = -\dfrac{T_B}{T_D}$
2.	Spider A fixed, sun wheel B rotates through + x revolutions	0	+ x	$-x \times \dfrac{T_B}{T_C}$	$-x \times \dfrac{T_B}{T_D}$
3.	Add + y revolutions to all elements	+ y	+ y	+ y	+ y
4.	Total motion	+ y	$x + y$	$y - x \times \dfrac{T_B}{T_C}$	$y - x \times \dfrac{T_B}{T_D}$

We know that when the sun wheel B makes $+5$ revolutions, the spider A makes $+1$ revolution. Therefore from the fourth row of the table,

$$y = +1 \; ; \; \text{and} \; x + y = +5$$

$$\therefore \quad x = 5 - y = 5 - 1 = 4$$

Since the internally toothed ring D is stationary, therefore from the fourth row of the table,

$$y - x \times \frac{T_B}{T_D} = 0$$

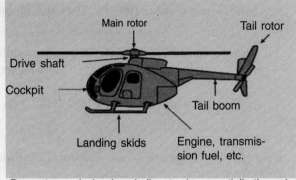

or

$$1 - 4 \times \frac{T_B}{T_D} = 0$$

Power transmission in a helicopter is essentially through gear trains.

Note : This picture is given as additional information.

$$\therefore \qquad \frac{T_B}{T_D} = \frac{1}{4} \quad \text{or} \quad T_D = 4 \, T_B \qquad \qquad \ldots(i)$$

We know that $\qquad T_D = d_D / m = 224 / 4 = 56 \text{ Ans.}$

$\therefore \qquad T_B = T_D / 4 = 56 / 4 = 14 \text{ Ans.}$ $\qquad$ ...[From equation (i)]

Let d_B, d_C and d_D be the pitch circle diameters of sun wheel B, planet wheels C and internally toothed ring D respectively. Assuming the pitch of all the gears to be same, therefore from the geometry of Fig. 13.13,

$$d_B + 2 \, d_C = d_D$$

Since the number of teeth are proportional to their pitch circle diameters, therefore

$$T_B + 2 \, T_C = T_D \qquad \text{or} \qquad 14 + 2 \, T_C = 56$$

$$\therefore \qquad T_C = 21 \text{ Ans.}$$

Example 13.10. *Two shafts A and B are co-axial. A gear C (50 teeth) is rigidly mounted on shaft A. A compound gear D-E gears with C and an internal gear G. D has 20 teeth and gears with C and E has 35 teeth and gears with an internal gear G. The gear G is fixed and is concentric with the shaft axis. The compound gear D-E is mounted on a pin which projects from an arm keyed to the shaft B. Sketch the arrangement and find the number of teeth on internal gear G assuming that all gears have the same module. If the shaft A rotates at 110 r.p.m., find the speed of shaft B.*

Solution. Given : $T_C = 50$; $T_D = 20$; $T_E = 35$; $N_A = 110$ r.p.m.

The arrangement is shown in Fig. 13.14.

Number of teeth on internal gear G

Let d_C, d_D, d_E and d_G be the pitch circle diameters of gears C, D, E and G respectively. From the geometry of the figure,

$$\frac{d_G}{2} = \frac{d_C}{2} + \frac{d_D}{2} + \frac{d_E}{2}$$

or

$$d_G = d_C + d_D + d_E$$

Let T_C, T_D, T_E and T_G be the number of teeth on gears C, D, E and G respectively. Since all the gears have the same module, therefore number of teeth are proportional to their pitch circle diameters.

∴ $$T_G = T_C + T_D + T_E = 50 + 20 + 35 = 105 \text{ Ans.}$$

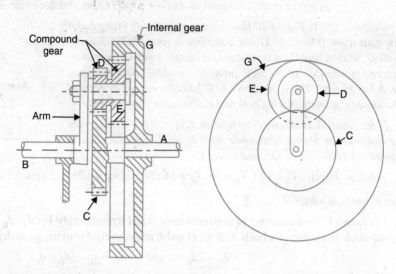

Fig. 13.14

Speed of shaft B

The table of motions is given below :

Table 13.9. Table of motions.

Step No.	Conditions of motion	Arm	Gear C (or shaft A)	Compound gear D-E	Gear G
1.	Arm fixed - gear C rotates through $+1$ revolution	0	$+1$	$-\dfrac{T_C}{T_D}$	$-\dfrac{T_C}{T_D} \times \dfrac{T_E}{T_G}$
2.	Arm fixed - gear C rotates through $+x$ revolutions	0	$+x$	$-x \times \dfrac{T_C}{T_D}$	$-x \times \dfrac{T_C}{T_D} \times \dfrac{T_E}{T_G}$
3.	Add $+y$ revolutions to all elements	$+y$	$+y$	$+y$	$+y$
4.	Total motion	$+y$	$x+y$	$y - x \times \dfrac{T_C}{T_D}$	$y - x \times \dfrac{T_C}{T_D} \times \dfrac{T_E}{T_G}$

Since the gear G is fixed, therefore from the fourth row of the table,

$$y - x \times \frac{T_C}{T_D} \times \frac{T_E}{T_G} = 0 \quad \text{or} \quad y - x \times \frac{50}{20} \times \frac{35}{105} = 0$$

∴ $$y - \frac{5}{6}x = 0 \qquad \qquad ...(i)$$

Since the gear C is rigidly mounted on shaft A, therefore speed of gear C and shaft A is same. We know that speed of shaft A is 110 r.p.m., therefore from the fourth row of the table,

$$x + y = 100 \qquad \qquad ...(ii)$$

From equations (i) and (ii), $x = 60$, and $y = 50$

∴　　　　　Speed of shaft B = Speed of arm = $+ y = 50$ r.p.m. anticlockwise **Ans.**

Example 13.11. *Fig. 13.15 shows diagrammatically a compound epicyclic gear train. Wheels A, D and E are free to rotate independently on spindle O, while B and C are compound and rotate together on spindle P, on the end of arm OP. All the teeth on different wheels have the same module. A has 12 teeth, B has 30 teeth and C has 14 teeth cut externally. Find the number of teeth on wheels D and E which are cut internally.*

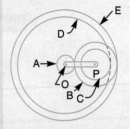

Fig. 13.15

If the wheel A is driven clockwise at 1 r.p.s. while D is driven counter clockwise at 5 r.p.s., determine the magnitude and direction of the angular velocities of arm OP and wheel E.

Solution. Given : $T_A = 12$; $T_B = 30$; $T_C = 14$; $N_A = 1$ r.p.s. ; $N_D = 5$ r.p.s.

Number of teeth on wheels D and E

Let T_D and T_E be the number of teeth on wheels D and E respectively. Let d_A, d_B, d_C, d_D and d_E be the pitch circle diameters of wheels A, B, C, D and E respectively. From the geometry of the figure,

$$d_E = d_A + 2d_B \qquad \text{and} \qquad d_D = d_E - (d_B - d_C)$$

Since the number of teeth are proportional to their pitch circle diameters for the same module, therefore

$$T_E = T_A + 2T_B = 12 + 2 \times 30 = 72 \ \text{ Ans.}$$

and
$$T_D = T_E - (T_B - T_C) = 72 - (30 - 14) = 56 \ \text{ Ans.}$$

Magnitude and direction of angular velocities of arm OP and wheel E

The table of motions is drawn as follows :

Table 13.10. Table of motions.

Step No.	Conditions of motion	Arm	Wheel A	Compound wheel B-C	Wheel D	Wheel E
1.	Arm fixed A rotated through -1 revolution (i.e. 1 revolution clockwise)	0	-1	$+\dfrac{T_A}{T_B}$	$+\dfrac{T_A}{T_B} \times \dfrac{T_C}{T_D}$	$+\dfrac{T_A}{T_B} \times \dfrac{T_B}{T_E}$ $= +\dfrac{T_A}{T_E}$
2.	Arm fixed-wheel A rotated through $-x$ revolutions	0	$-x$	$+x \times \dfrac{T_A}{T_B}$	$+x \times \dfrac{T_A}{T_B} \times \dfrac{T_C}{T_D}$	$+x \times \dfrac{T_A}{T_E}$
3.	Add $-y$ revolutions to all elements	$-y$	$-y$	$-y$	$-y$	$-y$
4.	Total motion	$-y$	$-x-y$	$x \times \dfrac{T_A}{T_B} - y$	$x \times \dfrac{T_A}{T_B} \times \dfrac{T_C}{T_D} - y$	$x \times \dfrac{T_A}{T_E} - y$

Since the wheel *A* makes 1 r.p.s. clockwise, therefore from the fourth row of the table,

$$-x - y = -1 \quad \text{or} \quad x + y = 1 \qquad ...(i)$$

Also, the wheel *D* makes 5 r.p.s. counter clockwise, therefore

$$x \times \frac{T_A}{T_B} \times \frac{T_C}{T_D} - y = 5 \quad \text{or} \quad x \times \frac{12}{30} \times \frac{14}{56} - y = 5$$

$$\therefore \qquad 0.1\, x - y = 5 \qquad ...(ii)$$

From equations (*i*) and (*ii*),

$$x = 5.45 \quad \text{and} \quad y = -4.45$$

∴ Angular velocity of arm *OP*

$$= -y = -(-4.45) = 4.45 \text{ r.p.s}$$

$$= 4.45 \times 2\,\pi = 27.964 \text{ rad/s (counter clockwise)} \textbf{ Ans.}$$

and angular velocity of wheel $E = x \times \dfrac{T_A}{T_E} - y = 5.45 \times \dfrac{12}{72} - (-4.45) = 5.36$ r.p.s.

$$= 5.36 \times 2\,\pi = 33.68 \text{ rad/s (counter clockwise)} \textbf{ Ans.}$$

Example 13.12. *An internal wheel B with 80 teeth is keyed to a shaft F. A fixed internal wheel C with 82 teeth is concentric with B. A compound wheel D-E gears with the two internal wheels; D has 28 teeth and gears with C while E gears with B. The compound wheels revolve freely on a pin which projects from a disc keyed to a shaft A co-axial with F. If the wheels have the same pitch and the shaft A makes 800 r.p.m., what is the speed of the shaft F ? Sketch the arrangement.*

Helicopter
Note : This picture is given as additional information.

Solution. Given : $T_B = 80$; $T_C = 82$; $T_D = 28$; $N_A = 500$ r.p.m.

The arrangement is shown in Fig. 13.16.

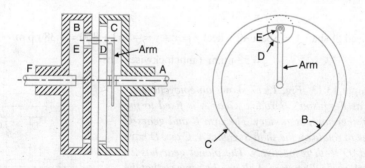

Fig. 13.16

First of all, let us find out the number of teeth on wheel *E* (T_E). Let d_B, d_C, d_D and d_E be the pitch circle diameter of wheels *B, C, D* and *E* respectively. From the geometry of the figure,

$$d_B = d_C - (d_D - d_E)$$

or
$$d_E = d_B + d_D - d_C$$

Since the number of teeth are proportional to their pitch circle diameters for the same pitch, therefore

$$T_E = T_B + T_D - T_C = 80 + 28 - 82 = 26$$

The table of motions is given below :

Table 13.11. Table of motions.

Step No.	Conditions of motion	Revolutions of elements			
		Arm (or shaft A)	Wheel B (or shaft F)	Compound gear D-E	Wheel C
1.	Arm fixed - wheel B rotated through + 1 revolution (i.e. 1 revolution anticlockwise)	0	+ 1	$+\dfrac{T_B}{T_E}$	$+\dfrac{T_B}{T_E} \times \dfrac{T_D}{T_C}$
2.	Arm fixed - wheel B rotated through + x revolutions	0	+ x	$+x \times \dfrac{T_B}{T_E}$	$+x \times \dfrac{T_B}{T_E} \times \dfrac{T_D}{T_C}$
3.	Add + y revolutions to all elements	+ y	+ y	+ y	+ y
4.	Total motion	+ y	x + y	$y + x \times \dfrac{T_B}{T_E}$	$y + x \times \dfrac{T_B}{T_E} \times \dfrac{T_D}{T_C}$

Since the wheel C is fixed, therefore from the fourth row of the table,

$$y + x \times \frac{T_B}{T_E} \times \frac{T_D}{T_C} = 0 \qquad \text{or} \qquad y + x \times \frac{80}{26} \times \frac{28}{82} = 0$$

$$\therefore \qquad y + 1.05\, x = 0 \qquad\qquad\qquad\qquad\qquad ...(i)$$

Also, the shaft A (or the arm) makes 800 r.p.m., therefore from the fourth row of the table,

$$y = 800 \qquad\qquad\qquad\qquad\qquad ...(ii)$$

From equations (i) and (ii),

$$x = -762$$

∴ Speed of shaft F = Speed of wheel B = x + y = – 762 + 800 = + 38 r.p.m.

= 38 r.p.m. (anticlockwise) **Ans.**

Example 13.13. *Fig. 13.17 shows an epicyclic gear train known as Ferguson's paradox. Gear A is fixed to the frame and is, therefore, stationary. The arm B and gears C and D are free to rotate on the shaft S. Gears A, C and D have 100, 101 and 99 teeth respectively. The planet gear has 20 teeth. The pitch circle diameters of all are the same so that the planet gear P meshes with all of them. Determine the revolutions of gears C and D for one revolution of the arm B.*

Solution. Given : $T_A = 100$; $T_C = 101$; $T_D = 99$; $T_P = 20$

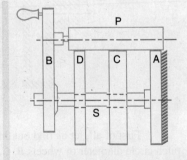

Fig. 13.17

The table of motions is given below :

Table 13.12. Table of motions.

Step No.	Conditions of motion	Revolutions of elements			
		Arm B	Gear A	Gear C	Gear D
1.	Arm B fixed, gear A rotated through $+1$ revolution (*i.e.* 1 revolution anticlockwise)	0	$+1$	$+\dfrac{T_A}{T_C}$	$+\dfrac{T_A}{T_C}\times\dfrac{T_C}{T_D}=+\dfrac{T_A}{T_D}$
2.	Arm B fixed, gear A rotated through $+x$ revolutions	0	$+x$	$+x\times\dfrac{T_A}{T_C}$	$+x\times\dfrac{T_A}{T_D}$
3.	Add $+y$ revolutions to all elements	$+y$	$+y$	$+y$	$+y$
4.	Total motion	$+y$	$x+y$	$y+x\times\dfrac{T_A}{T_C}$	$y+x\times\dfrac{T_A}{T_D}$

The arm B makes one revolution, therefore
$$y = 1$$
Since the gear A is fixed, therefore from the fourth row of the table,
$$x + y = 0 \quad \text{or} \quad x = -y = -1$$
Let N_C and N_D = Revolutions of gears C and D respectively.
From the fourth row of the table, the revolutions of gear C,
$$N_C = y + x \times \frac{T_A}{T_C} = 1 - 1 \times \frac{100}{101} = +\frac{1}{101} \ \text{Ans.}$$
and the revolutions of gear D,
$$N_D = y + x \times \frac{T_A}{T_D} = 1 - \frac{100}{99} = -\frac{1}{99} \ \text{Ans.}$$
From above we see that for one revolution of the arm B, the gear C rotates through 1/101 revolutions in the same direction and the gear D rotates through 1/99 revolutions in the opposite direction.

Example 13.14. *In the gear drive as shown in Fig. 13.18, the driving shaft A rotates at 300 r.p.m. in the clockwise direction, when seen from left hand. The shaft B is the driven shaft. The casing C is held stationary. The wheels E and H are keyed to the central vertical spindle and wheel F can rotate freely on this spindle. The wheels K and L are rigidly fixed to each other and rotate together freely on a pin fitted on the underside of F. The wheel L meshes with internal teeth on the casing C. The numbers of teeth on the different wheels are indicated within brackets in Fig. 13.18.*

Find the number of teeth on wheel C and the speed and direction of rotation of shaft B.

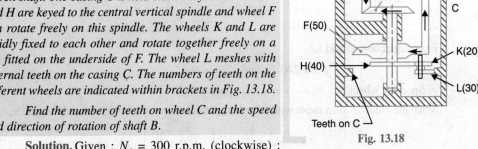

Fig. 13.18

Solution. Given : $N_A = 300$ r.p.m. (clockwise) ; $T_D = 40$; $T_B = 30$; $T_F = 50$; $T_G = 80$; $T_H = 40$; $T_K = 20$; $T_L = 30$

In the arrangement shown in Fig. 13.18, the wheels D and G are auxillary gears and do not form a part of the epicyclic gear train.

Speed of wheel E, $N_E = N_A \times \dfrac{T_D}{T_E} = 300 \times \dfrac{40}{30} = 400$ r.p.m. (clockwise)

Number of teeth on wheel C

Let T_C = Number of teeth on wheel C.

Assuming the same module for all teeth and since the pitch circle diameter is proportional to the number of teeth ; therefore from the geometry of Fig.13.18,

$$T_C = T_H + T_K + T_L = 40 + 20 + 30 = 90 \text{ Ans.}$$

Speed and direction of rotation of shaft B

The table of motions is given below. The wheel F acts as an arm.

Table 13.13. Table of motions.

Step No.	Conditions of motion	Arm or wheel F	Wheel E	Wheel H	Compound wheel K-L	Wheel C
				Revolutions of elements		
1.	Arm fixed-wheel E rotated through -1 revolution (*i.e.* 1 revolution clockwise)	0	-1	$-1(\because E$ and H are on the same shaft)	$+\dfrac{T_H}{T_K}$	$+\dfrac{T_H}{T_K} \times \dfrac{T_L}{T_C}$
2.	Arm fixed-wheel E rotated through $-x$ revolutions	0	$-x$	$-x$	$+x \times \dfrac{T_H}{T_K}$	$+x \times \dfrac{T_H}{T_K} \times \dfrac{T_L}{T_C}$
3.	Add $-y$ revolutions to all elements	$-y$	$-y$	$-y$	$-y$	$-y$
4.	Total motion	$-y$	$-x-y$	$-x-y$	$x \times \dfrac{T_H}{T_K} - y$	$x \times \dfrac{T_H}{T_K} \times \dfrac{T_L}{T_C} - y$

Since the speed of wheel E is 400 r.p.m. (clockwise), therefore from the fourth row of the table,

$$-x - y = -400 \quad \text{or} \quad x + y = 400 \qquad \qquad ...(i)$$

Also the wheel C is fixed, therefore

$$x \times \dfrac{T_H}{T_K} \times \dfrac{T_L}{T_C} - y = 0$$

or

$$x \times \dfrac{40}{20} \times \dfrac{30}{90} - y = 0$$

$$\therefore \qquad \dfrac{2x}{3} - y = 0 \qquad \qquad ...(ii)$$

From equations (*i*) and (*ii*),

$$x = 240 \quad \text{and} \quad y = 160$$

$\therefore$ Speed of wheel F, $N_F = -y = -160$ r.p.m.

Since the wheel F is in mesh with wheel G, therefore speed of wheel G or speed of shaft B

$$= -N_F \times \dfrac{T_F}{T_G} = -\left(-160 \times \dfrac{50}{80}\right) = 100 \text{ r.p.m.}$$

$...(\because$ Wheel G will rotate in opposite direction to that of wheel $F.$)

= 100 r.p.m. anticlockwise *i.e.* in opposite direction of shaft A. **Ans.**

Example 13.15. *Fig. 13.19 shows a compound epicyclic gear in which the casing C contains an epicyclic train and this casing is inside the larger casing D.*

Determine the velocity ratio of the output shaft B to the input shaft A when the casing D is held stationary. The number of teeth on various wheels are as follows :

Wheel on A = 80 ; Annular wheel on B = 160 ; Annular wheel on C = 100 ; Annular wheel on D = 120 ; Small pinion on F = 20 ; Large pinion on F = 66.

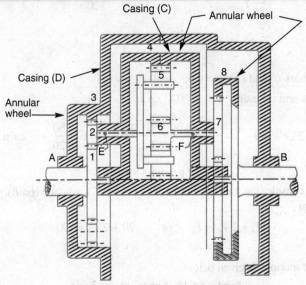

Fig. 13.19

Solution. Given : $T_1 = 80$; $T_8 = 160$; $T_4 = 100$; $T_3 = 120$; $T_6 = 20$; $T_7 = 66$

First of all, let us consider the train of wheel 1 (on A), wheel 2 (on E), annular wheel 3 (on D) and the arm *i.e.* casing C. Since the pitch circle diameters of wheels are proportional to the number of teeth, therefore from the geometry of Fig. 13.19,

$$T_1 + 2\,T_2 = T_3 \quad \text{or} \quad 80 + 2\,T_2 = 120$$

∴ $$T_2 = 20$$

The table of motions for the train considered is given below :

Table 13.14. Table of motions.

Step No.	Conditons of motion	Revolutions of elements			
		Arm	Wheel 1	Wheel 2	Wheel 3
1.	Arm fixed - wheel 1 rotated through + 1 revolution (anticlockwise)	0	+ 1	$-\dfrac{T_1}{T_2}$	$-\dfrac{T_1}{T_2} \times \dfrac{T_2}{T_3} = -\dfrac{T_1}{T_3}$
2.	Arm fixed - wheel 1 rotated through + x revolutions	0	+ x	$-x \times \dfrac{T_1}{T_2}$	$-x \times \dfrac{T_1}{T_3}$
3.	Add + y revolutions to all elements	+ y	+ y	+ y	+ y
4.	Total motion	y	x + y	$y - x \times \dfrac{T_1}{T_2}$	$y - x \times \dfrac{T_1}{T_3}$

Let us assume that wheel 1 makes 1 r.p.s. anticlockwise.

$$\therefore \qquad\qquad x + y = 1 \qquad\qquad\qquad\qquad\qquad \textit{...(i)}$$

Also the wheel 3 is stationary, therefore from the fourth row of the table,

$$y - x \times \frac{T_1}{T_3} = 0 \qquad \text{or} \qquad y - x \times \frac{80}{120} = 0$$

$$\therefore \qquad\qquad y - \frac{2}{3}x = 0 \qquad\qquad\qquad\qquad\qquad \textit{...(ii)}$$

From equations *(i)* and *(ii)*, $x = 0.6$, and $y = 0.4$

∴ Speed of arm or casing $C = y = 0.4$ r.p.s.

and speed of wheel 2 or arm E
$$= y - x \times \frac{T_1}{T_2} = 0.4 - 0.6 \times \frac{80}{20} = -2 \text{ r.p.s.}$$

$$= 2 \text{ r.p.s. (clockwise)}$$

Let us now consider the train of annular wheel 4 (on C), wheel 5 (on E), wheel 6 (on F) and arm E. We know that

$$T_6 + 2T_5 = T_4 \qquad \text{or} \qquad 20 + 2T_5 = 100$$

$$\therefore \qquad\qquad T_5 = 40$$

The table of motions is given below :

Table 13.15. Table of motions.

Step No.	Conditions of motion	Revolutions of elements			
		Arm E or wheel 2	Wheel 6	Wheel 5	Wheel 4
1.	Arm fixed, wheel 6 rotated through + 1 revolution	0	+ 1	$-\dfrac{T_6}{T_5}$	$-\dfrac{T_6}{T_5} \times \dfrac{T_5}{T_4} = -\dfrac{T_6}{T_4}$
2.	Arm fixed, wheel 6 rotated through + x_1 revolutions	0	x_1	$-x_1 \times \dfrac{T_6}{T_5}$	$-x_1 \times \dfrac{T_6}{T_4}$
3.	Add + y_1 revolutions to all elements	$+ y_1$	$+ y_1$	$+ y_1$	$+ y_1$
4.	Total motion	$+ y_1$	$x_1 + y_1$	$y_1 - x_1 \times \dfrac{T_6}{T_5}$	$y_1 - x_1 \times \dfrac{T_6}{T_4}$

We know that speed of arm E = Speed of wheel 2 in the first train

$$\therefore \qquad\qquad y_1 = -2 \qquad\qquad\qquad\qquad\qquad \textit{...(iii)}$$

Also speed of wheel 4 = Speed of arm or casing C in the first train

$$\therefore \qquad y_1 - x_1 \times \frac{T_6}{T_4} = 0.4 \qquad \text{or} \qquad -2 - x_1 \times \frac{20}{100} = 0.4 \qquad\qquad \textit{...(iv)}$$

or
$$x_1 = (-2 - 0.4)\frac{100}{20} = -12$$

∴ Speed of wheel 6 (or F)

$$= x_1 + y_1 = -12 - 2 = -14 \text{ r.p.s.} = 14 \text{ r.p.s. (clockwise)}$$

Now consider the train of wheels 6 and 7 (both on F), annular wheel 8 (on B) and the arm *i.e.* casing C. The table of motions is given below :

Table 13.16. Table of motions.

Step No.	Conditions of motion	Revolutions of elements		
		Arm	Wheel 8	Wheel 7
1.	Arm fixed, wheel 8 rotated through + 1 revolution	0	+ 1	$+\dfrac{T_8}{T_7}$
2.	Arm fixed, wheel 8 rotated through $+ x_2$ revolutions	0	$+ x_2$	$+x_2 \times \dfrac{T_8}{T_7}$
3.	Add $+ y_2$ revolutions to all elements	$+ y_2$	$+ y_2$	$+ y_2$
4.	Total motion	y_2	$x_2 + y_2$	$y_2 + x_2 \times \dfrac{T_8}{T_7}$

We know that the speed of C in the first train is 0.4 r.p.s., therefore

$$y_2 = 0.4 \qquad \qquad ...(v)$$

Also the speed of wheel 7 is equal to the speed of F or wheel 6 in the second train, therefore

$$y_2 + x_2 \times \frac{T_8}{T_7} = -14 \quad \text{or} \quad 0.4 + x_2 \times \frac{160}{66} = -14 \qquad ...(vi)$$

$$\therefore \qquad x_2 = (-14 - 0.4)\frac{66}{160} = -5.94$$

∴ Speed of wheel 8 or of the shaft B

$$x_2 + y_2 = -5.94 + 0.4 = -5.54 \text{ r.p.s.} = 5.54 \text{ r.p.s. (clockwise)}$$

We have already assumed that the speed of wheel 1 or the shaft A is 1 r.p.s. anticlockwise

∴ Velocity ratio of the output shaft B to the input shaft A

$$= -5.54 \text{ Ans.}$$

Note : The – ve sign shows that the two shafts A and B rotate in opposite directions.

13.10. Epicyclic Gear Train with Bevel Gears

The bevel gears are used to make a more compact epicyclic system and they permit a very high speed reduction with few gears. The useful application of the epicyclic gear train with bevel gears is found in Humpage's speed reduction gear and differential gear of an automobile as discussed below :

1. *Humpage's speed reduction gear.* The Humpage's speed reduction gear was originally designed as a substitute for back gearing of a lathe, but its use is now considerably extended to all kinds of workshop machines and also in electrical machinery. In Humpage's speed reduction gear, as shown in Fig. 13.20, the driving shaft X and the driven shaft Y are co-axial. The driving shaft carries a bevel gear A and driven shaft carries a bevel gear E. The bevel gear B meshes with gear A (also known as pinion) and a fixed gear C. The gear E meshes with gear D which is compound with gear B.

This compound gear *B-D* is mounted on the arm or spindle *F* which is rigidly connected with a hollow sleeve *G*. The sleeve revolves freely loose on the axes of the driving and driven shafts.

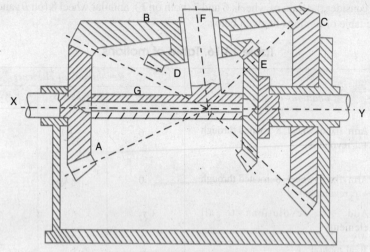

Fig. 13.20. Humpage's speed reduction gear.

2. Differential gear of an automobile. The differential gear used in the rear drive of an automobile is shown in Fig. 13.21. Its function is

(*a*) to transmit motion from the engine shaft to the rear driving wheels, and

(*b*) to rotate the rear wheels at different speeds while the automobile is taking a turn.

As long as the automobile is running on a straight path, the rear wheels are driven directly by the engine and speed of both the wheels is same. But when the automobile is taking a turn, the outer wheel will run faster than the [*] inner wheel because at that time the outer rear wheel has to cover more distance than the inner rear wheel. This is achieved by epicyclic gear train with bevel gears as shown in Fig. 13.21.

The bevel gear *A* (known as pinion) is keyed to the propeller shaft driven from the engine shaft through universal coupling. This gear *A* drives the gear *B* (known as crown gear) which rotates freely on the axle *P*. Two equal gears *C* and *D* are mounted on two separate parts *P* and *Q* of the rear axles respectively. These gears, in turn, mesh with equal pinions *E* and *F* which can rotate freely on the spindle provided on the arm attached to gear *B*.

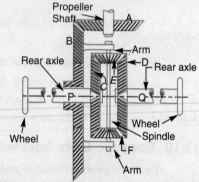

Fig. 13.21. Differential gear of an automobile.

When the automobile runs on a straight path, the gears *C* and *D* must rotate together. These gears are rotated through the spindle on the gear *B*. The gears *E* and *F* do not rotate on the spindle. But when the automobile is taking a turn, the inner rear wheel should have lesser speed than the outer rear wheel and due to relative speed of the inner and outer gears *D* and *C*, the gears *E* and *F* start rotating about the spindle axis and at the same time revolve about the axle axis.

Due to this epicyclic effect, the speed of the inner rear wheel decreases by a certain amount and the speed of the outer rear wheel increases, by the same amount. This may be well understood by drawing the table of motions as follows :

---

[*] This difficulty does not arise with the front wheels as they are greatly used for steering purposes and are mounted on separate axles and can run freely at different speeds.

Table 13.17. Table of motions.

Step No.	Conditions of motion	Revolutions of elements			
		Gear B	Gear C	Gear E	Gear D
1.	Gear B fixed-Gear C rotated through + 1 revolution (*i.e.* 1 revolution anticlockwise)	0	+ 1	$+\dfrac{T_C}{T_E}$	$-\dfrac{T_C}{T_E} \times \dfrac{T_E}{T_D} = -1$ $(\because T_C = T_D)$
2.	Gear B fixed-Gear C rotated through + x revolutions	0	+ x	$+x \times \dfrac{T_C}{T_E}$	$-x$
3.	Add + y revolutions to all elements	+ y	+ y	+ y	+ y
4.	Total motion	+ y	x + y	$y + x \times \dfrac{T_C}{T_E}$	$y - x$

From the table, we see that when the gear B, which derives motion from the engine shaft, rotates at y revolutions, then the speed of inner gear D (or the rear axle Q) is less than y by x revolutions and the speed of the outer gear C (or the rear axle P) is greater than y by x revolutions. In other words, the two parts of the rear axle and thus the two wheels rotate at two different speeds. We also see from the table that the speed of gear B is the mean of speeds of the gears C and D.

Example 13.16. *Two bevel gears A and B (having 40 teeth and 30 teeth) are rigidly mounted on two co-axial shafts X and Y. A bevel gear C (having 50 teeth) meshes with A and B and rotates freely on one end of an arm. At the other end of the arm is welded a sleeve and the sleeve is riding freely loose on the axes of the shafts X and Y. Sketch the arrangement.*

If the shaft X rotates at 100 r.p.m. clockwise and arm rotates at 100 r.p.m. anitclockwise, find the speed of shaft Y.

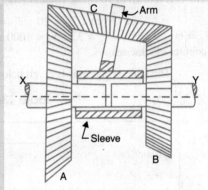

Fig. 13.22

Solution. Given : $T_A = 40$; $T_B = 30$; $T_C = 50$; $N_X = N_A = 100$ r.p.m. (clockwise) ; Speed of arm = 100 r.p.m. (anticlockwise)

The arangement is shown in Fig. 13.22.

The table of motions is drawn as below :

Table 13.18. Table of motions.

Step No.	Conditions of motion	Revolutions of elements			
		Arm	Gear A	Gear C	Gear B
1.	Arm B fixed, gear A rotated through + 1 revolution (*i.e.* 1 revolution anticlockwise)	0	+ 1	$\pm\dfrac{{}^*T_A}{T_C}$	$-\dfrac{T_A}{T_C} \times \dfrac{T_C}{T_B} = -\dfrac{T_A}{T_B}$
2.	Arm B fixed, gear A rotated through + x revolutions	0	+ x	$\pm x \times \dfrac{T_A}{T_C}$	$-x \times \dfrac{T_A}{T_B}$
3.	Add + y revolutions to all elements	+ y	+ y	+ y	+ y
4.	Total motion	+ y	x + y	$y \pm x \times \dfrac{T_A}{T_C}$	$y - x \times \dfrac{T_A}{T_B}$

---

* The $\pm$ sign is given to the motion of the wheel C because it is in a different plane. So we cannot indicate the direction of its motion specifically, *i.e.* either clockwise or anticlockwise.

Since the speed of the arm is 100 r.p.m. anticlockwise, therefore from the fourth row of the table,

$$y = +100$$

Also, the speed of the driving shaft X or gear A is 100 r.p.m. clockwise.

∴ $\quad\quad\quad x + y = -100 \quad$ or $\quad x = -y - 100 = -100 - 100 = -200$

∴ Speed of the driven shaft *i.e.* shaft Y,

$$N_Y = \text{Speed of gear } B = y - x \times \frac{T_A}{T_B} = 100 - \left(-200 \times \frac{40}{30}\right)$$

$$= +366.7 \text{ r.p.m.} = 366.7 \text{ r.p.m. (anticlockwise) } \textbf{Ans.}$$

Example 13.17. *In a gear train, as shown in Fig. 13.23, gear B is connected to the input shaft and gear F is connected to the output shaft. The arm A carrying the compound wheels D and E, turns freely on the output shaft. If the input speed is 1000 r.p.m. counter- clockwise when seen from the right, determine the speed of the output shaft under the following conditions :*

1. When gear C is fixed, and 2. when gear C is rotated at 10 r.p.m. counter clockwise.

Solution. Given : $T_B = 20$; $T_C = 80$; $T_D = 60$; $T_E = 30$; $T_F = 32$; $N_B = 1000$ r.p.m. (counter-clockwise)

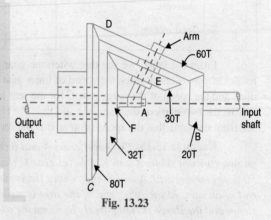

Fig. 13.23

The table of motions is given below :

Table 13.19. Table of motions.

Step No.	Conditions of motion	Revolutions of elements				
		Arm A	Gear B (or input shaft)	Compound wheel D-E	Gear C	Gear F (or output shaft)
1.	Arm fixed, gear *B* rotated through + 1 revolution (*i.e.* 1 revolution anticlockwise)	0	+ 1	$+\dfrac{T_B}{T_D}$	$-\dfrac{T_B}{T_D} \times \dfrac{T_D}{T_C}$ $= -\dfrac{T_B}{T_C}$	$-\dfrac{T_B}{T_D} \times \dfrac{T_E}{T_F}$
2.	Arm fixed, gear *B* rotated through + *x* revolutions	0	+ *x*	$+x \times \dfrac{T_B}{T_D}$	$-x \times \dfrac{T_B}{T_C}$	$-x \times \dfrac{T_B}{T_D} \times \dfrac{T_E}{T_F}$
3.	Add + *y* revolutions to all elements	+ *y*	+ *y*	+ *y*	+ *y*	+ *y*
4.	Total motion	+ *y*	*x* + *y*	$y + x \times \dfrac{T_B}{T_D}$	$y - x \times \dfrac{T_B}{T_C}$	$y - x \times \dfrac{T_B}{T_D} \times \dfrac{T_E}{T_F}$

1. *Speed of the output shaft when gear C is fixed*

Since the gear *C* is fixed, therefore from the fourth row of the table,

$$y - x \times \frac{T_B}{T_C} = 0 \qquad \text{or} \qquad y - x \times \frac{20}{80} = 0$$

∴ $\qquad\qquad\qquad y - 0.25\, x = 0$ ...(*i*)

We know that the input speed (or the speed of gear *B*) is 1000 r.p.m. counter clockwise, therefore from the fourth row of the table,

$$x + y = + 1000 \qquad\qquad ...(ii)$$

From equations (*i*) and (*ii*), $x = + 800$,   and $y = + 200$

∴ Speed of output shaft = Speed of gear $F = y - x \times \dfrac{T_B}{T_D} \times \dfrac{T_E}{T_F}$

$$= 200 - 800 \times \frac{20}{80} \times \frac{30}{32} = 200 - 187.5 = 12.5 \text{ r.p.m.}$$

$$= 12.5 \text{ r.p.m. (counter clockwise) } \mathbf{Ans.}$$

2. *Speed of the output shaft when gear C is rotated at 10 r.p.m. counter clockwise*

Since the gear *C* is rotated at 10 r.p.m. counter clockwise, therefore from the fourth row of the table,

$$y - x \times \frac{T_B}{T_C} = +10 \qquad \text{or} \qquad y - x \times \frac{20}{80} = 10$$

∴ $\qquad\qquad\qquad y - 0.25\, x = 10$ ...(*iii*)

From equations (*ii*) and (*iii*),

$$x = 792, \quad \text{and} \quad y = 208$$

∴ Speed of output shaft

$$= \text{Speed of gear } F = y - x \times \frac{T_B}{T_D} \times \frac{T_E}{T_F} = 208 - 792 \times \frac{20}{80} \times \frac{30}{32}$$

$$= 208 - 185.6 = 22.4 \text{ r.p.m.} = 22.4 \text{ r.p.m. (counter clockwise) } \mathbf{Ans.}$$

Example 13.18. *Fig. 13.24 shows a differential gear used in a motor car. The pinion A on the propeller shaft has 12 teeth and gears with the crown gear B which has 60 teeth. The shafts P and Q form the rear axles to which the road wheels are attached. If the propeller shaft rotates at 1000 r.p.m. and the road wheel attached to axle Q has a speed of 210 r.p.m. while taking a turn, find the speed of road wheel attached to axle P.*

Solution. Given : $T_A = 12$; $T_B = 60$; $N_A = 1000$ r.p.m. ; $N_Q = N_D = 210$ r.p.m.

Since the propeller shaft or the pinion *A* rotates at 1000 r.p.m., therefore speed of crown gear *B*,

$$N_B = N_A \times \frac{T_A}{T_B} = 1000 \times \frac{12}{60}$$

$$= 200 \text{ r.p.m.}$$

The table of motions is given below :

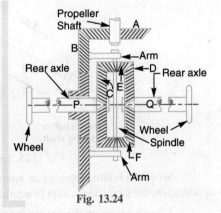

Fig. 13.24

Table 13.20. Table of motions.

Step No.	Conditions of motion	Revolutions of elements			
		Gear B	Gear C	Gear E	Gear D
1.	Gear B fixed-Gear C rotated through + 1 revolution (i.e. 1 revolution anticlockwise)	0	+ 1	$+\dfrac{T_C}{T_E}$	$-\dfrac{T_C}{T_E} \times \dfrac{T_E}{T_D} = -1$ $(\because T_C = T_D)$
2.	Gear B fixed-Gear C rotated through + x revolutions	0	+ x	$+x \times \dfrac{T_C}{T_E}$	– x
3.	Add + y revolutions to all elements	+ y	+ y	+ y	+ y
4.	Total motion	+ y	x + y	$y + x \times \dfrac{T_C}{T_E}$	y – x

Since the speed of gear B is 200 r.p.m., therefore from the fourth row of the table,

$$y = 200 \qquad \qquad ...(i)$$

Also, the speed of road wheel attached to axle Q or the speed of gear D is 210 r.p.m., therefore from the fourth row of the table,

$$y - x = 210 \qquad \text{or} \qquad x = y - 210 = 200 - 210 = -10$$

∴ Speed of road wheel attached to axle P

$$= \text{Speed of gear } C = x + y$$
$$= -10 + 200 = 190 \text{ r.p.m. } \textbf{Ans.}$$

13.11. Torques in Epicyclic Gear Trains

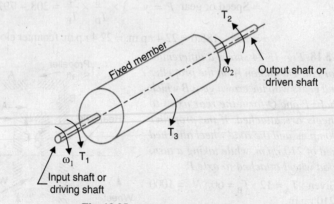

Fig. 13.25. Torques in epicyclic gear trains.

When the rotating parts of an epicyclic gear train, as shown in Fig. 13.25, have no angular acceleration, the gear train is kept in equilibrium by the three externally applied torques, *viz.*

1. Input torque on the driving member (T_1),

2. Output torque or resisting or load torque on the driven member (T_2),

3. Holding or braking or fixing torque on the fixed member (T_3).

The net torque applied to the gear train must be zero. In other words,

$$T_1 + T_2 + T_3 = 0 \qquad \qquad ...(i)$$

$$\therefore \qquad F_1.r_1 + F_2.r_2 + F_3.r_3 = 0 \qquad \qquad ...(ii)$$

where F_1, F_2 and F_3 are the corresponding externally applied forces at radii r_1, r_2 and r_3.

Further, if ω_1, ω_2 and ω_3 are the angular speeds of the driving, driven and fixed members respectively, and the friction be neglected, then the net kinetic energy dissipated by the gear train must be zero, *i.e.*

$$T_1.\omega_1 + T_2.\omega_2 + T_3.\omega_3 = 0 \qquad \qquad ...(iii)$$

But, for a fixed member, $\omega_3 = 0$

$$\therefore \qquad T_1.\omega_1 + T_2.\omega_2 = 0 \qquad \qquad ...(iv)$$

Notes : 1. From equations (*i*) and (*iv*), the holding or braking torque T_3 may be obtained as follows :

$$T_2 = -T_1 \times \frac{\omega_1}{\omega_2} \qquad \qquad ...[\text{From equation } (iv)]$$

and

$$T_3 = -(T_1 + T_2) \qquad \qquad ...[\text{From equation } (i)]$$

$$= T_1 \left(\frac{\omega_1}{\omega_2} - 1 \right) = T_1 \left(\frac{N_1}{N_2} - 1 \right)$$

2. When input shaft (or driving shaft) and output shaft (or driven shaft) rotate in the same direction, then the input and output torques will be in opposite directions. Similarly, when the input and output shafts rotate in opposite directions, then the input and output torques will be in the same direction.

Example 13.19. *Fig. 13.26 shows an epicyclic gear train. Pinion A has 15 teeth and is rigidly fixed to the motor shaft. The wheel B has 20 teeth and gears with A and also with the annular fixed wheel E. Pinion C has 15 teeth and is integral with B (B, C being a compound gear wheel). Gear C meshes with annular wheel D, which is keyed to the machine shaft. The arm rotates about the same shaft on which A is fixed and carries the compound wheel B, C. If the motor runs at 1000 r.p.m., find the speed of the machine shaft. Find the torque exerted on the machine shaft, if the motor develops a torque of 100 N-m.*

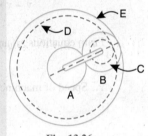

Fig. 13.26

Solution. Given : $T_A = 15$; $T_B = 20$; $T_C = 15$; $N_A = 1000$ r.p.m.; Torque developed by motor (or pinion *A*) = 100 N-m

First of all, let us find the number of teeth on wheels *D* and *E*. Let T_D and T_E be the number of teeth on wheels *D* and *E* respectively. Let d_A, d_B, d_C, d_D and d_E be the pitch circle diameters of wheels *A, B, C, D* and *E* respectively. From the geometry of the figure,

$$d_E = d_A + 2\, d_B \quad \text{and} \quad d_D = d_E - (d_B - d_C)$$

Since the number of teeth are proportional to their pitch circle diameters, therefore,

$$T_E = T_A + 2\, T_B = 15 + 2 \times 20 = 55$$

and

$$T_D = T_E - (T_B - T_C) = 55 - (20 - 15) = 50$$

Speed of the machine shaft

The table of motions is given below :

Table 13.21. Table of motions.

Step No.	Conditions of motion	Revolutions of elements				
		Arm	Pinion A	Compound wheel B-C	Wheel D	Wheel E
1.	Arm fixed-pinion A rotated through + 1 revolution (anticlockwise)	0	+ 1	$-\dfrac{T_A}{T_B}$	$-\dfrac{T_A}{T_B} \times \dfrac{T_C}{T_D}$	$-\dfrac{T_A}{T_B} \times \dfrac{T_B}{T_E} = -\dfrac{T_A}{T_E}$
2.	Arm fixed-pinion A rotated through + x revolutions	0	+ x	$-x \times \dfrac{T_A}{T_B}$	$-x \times \dfrac{T_A}{T_B} \times \dfrac{T_C}{T_D}$	$-x \times \dfrac{T_A}{T_E}$
3.	Add + y revolutions to all elements	+ y	+ y	+ y	+ y	+ y
4.	Total motion	+ y	x + y	$y - x \times \dfrac{T_A}{T_B}$	$y - x \times \dfrac{T_A}{T_B} \times \dfrac{T_C}{T_D}$	$y - x \times \dfrac{T_A}{T_E}$

We know that the speed of the motor or the speed of the pinion A is 1000 r.p.m. Therefore

$$x + y = 1000 \qquad\qquad ...(i)$$

Also, the annular wheel E is fixed, therefore

$$y - x \times \frac{T_A}{T_E} = 0 \quad \text{or} \quad y = x \times \frac{T_A}{T_E} = x \times \frac{15}{55} = 0.273\, x \qquad ...(ii)$$

From equations (i) and (ii),

$$x = 786 \quad \text{and} \quad y = 214$$

∴ Speed of machine shaft = Speed of wheel D,

$$N_D = y - x \times \frac{T_A}{T_B} \times \frac{T_C}{T_D} = 214 - 786 \times \frac{15}{20} \times \frac{15}{50} = +37.15 \text{ r.p.m.}$$

$$= 37.15 \text{ r.p.m. (anticlockwise) } \textbf{Ans.}$$

Torque exerted on the machine shaft

We know that

Torque developed by motor × Angular speed of motor

$$= \text{Torque exerted on machine shaft}$$
$$\times \text{ Angular speed of machine shaft}$$

or $\qquad 100 \times \omega_A = \text{Torque exerted on machine shaft} \times \omega_D$

∴ Torque exerted on machine shaft

$$= 100 \times \frac{\omega_A}{\omega_D} = 100 \times \frac{N_A}{N_D} = 100 \times \frac{1000}{37.15} = 2692 \text{ N-m } \textbf{Ans.}$$

Example 13.20. *An epicyclic gear train consists of a sun wheel S, a stationary internal gear E and three identical planet wheels P carried on a star-shaped planet carrier C. The size of different toothed wheels are such that the planet carrier C rotates at 1/5th of the speed of the sunwheel S. The minimum number of teeth on any wheel is 16. The driving torque on the sun wheel is 100 N-m. Determine : 1. number of teeth on different wheels of the train, and 2. torque necessary to keep the internal gear stationary.*

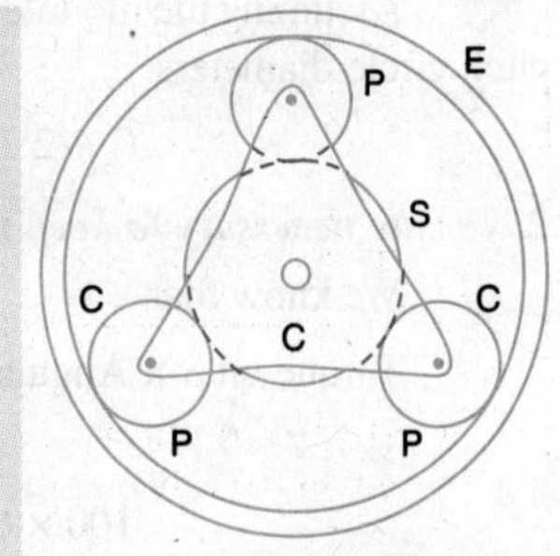

Fig. 13.27

Solution. Given : $N_C = \dfrac{N_S}{5}$

1. *Number of teeth on different wheels*

The arrangement of the epicyclic gear train is shown in Fig. 13.27. Let T_S and T_E be the number of teeth on the sun wheel S and the internal gear E respectively. The table of motions is given below :

Table 13.22. Table of motions.

Step No.	Conditions of motion	Revolutions of elements			
		Planet carrier C	Sun wheel S	Planet wheel P	Internal gear E
1.	Planet carrier C fixed, sunwheel S rotates through $+1$ revolution (*i.e.* 1 rev. anticlockwise)	0	$+1$	$-\dfrac{T_S}{T_P}$	$-\dfrac{T_S}{T_P} \times \dfrac{T_P}{T_E} = -\dfrac{T_S}{T_E}$
2.	Planet carrier C fixed, sunwheel S rotates through $+x$ revolutions	0	$+x$	$-x \times \dfrac{T_S}{T_P}$	$-x \times \dfrac{T_S}{T_E}$
3.	Add $+y$ revolutions to all elements	$+y$	$+y$	$+y$	$+y$
4.	Total motion	$+y$	$x+y$	$y - x \times \dfrac{T_S}{T_P}$	$y - x \times \dfrac{T_S}{T_E}$

We know that when the sunwheel S makes 5 revolutions, the planet carrier C makes 1 revolution. Therefore from the fourth row of the table,

$$y = 1, \quad \text{and} \quad x + y = 5 \quad \text{or} \quad x = 5 - y = 5 - 1 = 4$$

Since the gear E is stationary, therefore from the fourth row of the table,

$$y - x \times \frac{T_S}{T_E} = 0 \quad \text{or} \quad 1 - 4 \times \frac{T_S}{T_E} = 0 \quad \text{or} \quad \frac{T_S}{T_E} = \frac{1}{4}$$

$\therefore \qquad T_E = 4 T_S$

Since the minimum number of teeth on any wheel is 16, therefore let us take the number of teeth on sunwheel, $T_S = 16$

$\therefore \qquad T_E = 4\,T_S = 64$ **Ans.**

Let d_S, d_P and d_E be the pitch circle diameters of wheels S, P and E respectively. Now from the geometry of Fig. 13.27,

$$d_S + 2\,d_P = d_E$$

Assuming the module of all the gears to be same, the number of teeth are proportional to their pitch circle diameters.

$$T_S + 2\,T_P = T_E \quad \text{or} \quad 16 + 2\,T_P = 64 \quad \text{or} \quad T_P = 24 \text{ Ans.}$$

2. Torque necessary to keep the internal gear stationary

We know that

Torque on $S \times$ Angular speed of S

$$= \text{Torque on } C \times \text{Angular speed of } C$$

$$100 \times \omega_S = \text{Torque on } C \times \omega_C$$

$$\therefore \qquad \text{Torque on } C = 100 \times \frac{\omega_S}{\omega_C} = 100 \times \frac{N_S}{N_C} = 100 \times 5 = 500 \text{ N-m}$$

$\therefore$ Torque necessary to keep the internal gear stationary

$$= 500 - 100 = 400 \text{ N-m Ans.}$$

Example 13.21. *In the epicyclic gear train, as shown in Fig. 13.28, the driving gear A rotating in clockwise direction has 14 teeth and the fixed annular gear C has 100 teeth. The ratio of teeth in gears E and D is 98 : 41. If 1.85 kW is supplied to the gear A rotating at 1200 r.p.m., find : 1. the speed and direction of rotation of gear E, and 2. the fixing torque required at C, assuming 100 per cent efficiency throughout and that all teeth have the same pitch.*

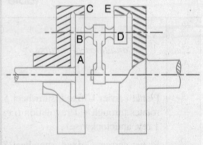

Fig. 13.28

Solution. Given : $T_A = 14$; $T_C = 100$; $T_E / T_D = 98 / 41$; $P_A = 1.85$ kW $= 1850$ W ; $N_A = 1200$ r.p.m.

Let d_A, d_B and d_C be the pitch circle diameters of gears A, B and C respectively. From Fig. 13.28,

$$d_A + 2\,d_B = d_C$$

Gears are extensively used in trains for power transmission.

Since teeth of all gears have the same pitch and the number of teeth are proportional to their pitch circle diameters, therefore

$$T_A + 2T_B = T_C \qquad \text{or} \qquad T_B = \frac{T_C - T_A}{2} = \frac{100 - 14}{2} = 43$$

The table of motions is now drawn as below :

Table 13.23. Table of motions.

Step No.	Conditions of motion	Arm	Gear A	Compound gear B-D	Gear C	Gear E
					Revolutions of elements	
1.	Arm fixed-Gear A rotated through – 1 revolution (*i.e.* 1 revolution clockwise)	0	– 1	$+\dfrac{T_A}{T_B}$	$+\dfrac{T_A}{T_B} \times \dfrac{T_B}{T_C}$ $= +\dfrac{T_A}{T_C}$	$+\dfrac{T_A}{T_B} \times \dfrac{T_D}{T_E}$
2.	Arm fixed-Gear A rotated through – x revolutions	0	– x	$+ x \times \dfrac{T_A}{T_B}$	$+ x \times \dfrac{T_A}{T_C}$	$+ x \times \dfrac{T_A}{T_B} \times \dfrac{T_D}{T_E}$
3.	Add – y revolutions to all elements	– y	– y	– y	– y	– y
4.	Total motion	– y	– y – x	$-y + x \times \dfrac{T_A}{T_B}$	$-y + x \times \dfrac{T_A}{T_C}$	$-y + x \times \dfrac{T_A}{T_B} \times \dfrac{T_D}{T_E}$

Since the annular gear *C* is fixed, therefore from the fourth row of the table,

$$- y + x \times \frac{T_A}{T_C} = 0 \qquad \text{or} \qquad - y + x \times \frac{14}{100} = 0$$

$$\therefore \qquad - y + 0.14\, x = 0 \qquad\qquad\qquad ...(i)$$

Also, the gear *A* is rotating at 1200 r.p.m., therefore

$$- x - y = 1200 \qquad\qquad\qquad ...(ii)$$

From equations (*i*) and (*ii*), $x = -1052.6$, and $y = -147.4$

1. Speed and direction of rotation of gear E

From the fourth row of the table, speed of gear *E*,

$$N_E = - y + x \times \frac{T_A}{T_B} \times \frac{T_D}{T_E} = 147.4 - 1052.6 \times \frac{14}{43} \times \frac{41}{98}$$

$$= 147.4 - 143.4 = 4 \text{ r.p.m.}$$

$$= 4 \text{ r.p.m. (anticlockwise) } \textbf{Ans.}$$

2. Fixing torque required at C

We know that torque on $A = \dfrac{P_A \times 60}{2\pi N_A} = \dfrac{1850 \times 60}{2\pi \times 1200} = 14.7$ N-m

Since the efficiency is 100 per cent throughout, therefore the power available at E (P_E) will be equal to power supplied at A (P_A).

∴ Torque on E

$$= \frac{P_A \times 60}{2\pi \times N_E} = \frac{1850 \times 60}{2\pi \times 4} = 4416 \text{ N-m}$$

∴ Fixing torque required at C

$$= 4416 - 14.7 = 4401.3 \text{ N-m } \textbf{Ans.}$$

Example 13.22. *An over drive for a vehicle consists of an epicyclic gear train, as shown in Fig. 13.29, with compound planets B-C. B has 15 teeth and meshes with an annulus A which has 60 teeth. C has 20 teeth and meshes with the sunwheel D which is fixed. The annulus is keyed to the propeller shaft Y which rotates at 740 rad /s. The spider which carries the pins upon which the planets revolve, is driven directly from main gear box by shaft X, this shaft being relatively free to rotate with respect to wheel D. Find the speed of shaft X, when all the teeth have the same module.*

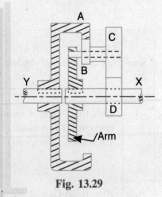

Fig. 13.29

When the engine develops 130 kW, what is the holding torque on the wheel D ? Assume 100 per cent efficiency throughout.

Solution. Given : $T_B = 15$; $T_A = 60$; $T_C = 20$; $\omega_Y = \omega_A = 740 \text{ rad /s}$; $P = 130 \text{ kW} = 130 \times 10^3 \text{ W}$

First of all, let us find the number of teeth on the sunwheel D (T_D). Let d_A, d_B, d_C and d_D be the pitch circle diameters of wheels A, B, C and D respectively. From Fig. 13.29,

$$\frac{d_D}{2} + \frac{d_C}{2} + \frac{d_B}{2} = \frac{d_A}{2} \quad \text{or} \quad d_D + d_C + d_B = d_A$$

Since the module is same for all teeth and the number of teeth are proportional to their pitch circle diameters, therefore

$$T_D + T_C + T_B = T_A \quad \text{or} \quad T_D = T_A - (T_C + T_B) = 60 - (20 + 15) = 25$$

The table of motions is given below :

Table 13.24. Table of motions.

Step No.	Conditions of motion	Revolutions of elements			
		Arm (or shaft X)	Wheel D	Compound wheel C-B	Wheel A (or shaft Y)
1.	Arm fixed-wheel D rotated through + 1 revolution (anticlockwise)	0	+ 1	$-\dfrac{T_D}{T_C}$	$-\dfrac{T_D}{T_C} \times \dfrac{T_B}{T_A}$
2.	Arm fixed-wheel D rotated through + x revolutions	0	+ x	$-x \times \dfrac{T_D}{T_C}$	$-x \times \dfrac{T_D}{T_C} \times \dfrac{T_B}{T_A}$
3.	Add + y revolutions to all elements	+ y	+ y	+ y	+ y
4.	Total motion	+ y	$x + y$	$y - x \times \dfrac{T_D}{T_C}$	$y - x \times \dfrac{T_D}{T_C} \times \dfrac{T_B}{T_A}$

Since the shaft Y or wheel A rotates at 740 rad/s, therefore

$$y - x \times \frac{T_D}{T_C} \times \frac{T_B}{T_A} = 740 \quad \text{or} \quad y - x \times \frac{25}{20} \times \frac{15}{60} = 740$$

$$y - 0.3125 \, x = 740 \qquad \qquad \qquad \text{...(i)}$$

Also the wheel D is fixed, therefore

$$x + y = 0 \quad \text{or} \quad y = -x \qquad \qquad ...(ii)$$

From equations (i) and (ii),

$$x = -563.8 \quad \text{and} \quad y = 563.8$$

Speed of shaft X

Since the shaft X will make the same number of revolutions as the arm, therefore

Speed of shaft X, ω_X = Speed of arm = y = 563.8 rad/s **Ans.**

Holding torque on wheel D

We know that torque on $A = P/\omega_A = 130 \times 10^3 / 740 = 175.7$ N-m

and Torque on $X = P/\omega_X = 130 \times 10^3/563.8 = 230.6$ N-m

∴ Holding torque on wheel D

$$= 230.6 - 175.7 = 54.9 \text{ N-m } \textbf{Ans.}$$

Example 13.23. *Fig. 13.30 shows some details of a compound epicyclic gear drive where I is the driving or input shaft and O is the driven or output shaft which carries two arms A and B rigidly fixed to it. The arms carry planet wheels which mesh with annular wheels P and Q and the sunwheels X and Y. The sun wheel X is a part of Q. Wheels Y and Z are fixed to the shaft I. Z engages with a planet wheel carried on Q and this planet wheel engages the fixed annular wheel R. The numbers of teeth on the wheels are :*

P = 114, Q = 120, R = 120, X = 36, Y = 24 and Z = 30.

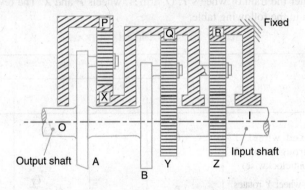

Fig. 13.30.

The driving shaft I makes 1500 r.p.m.clockwise looking from our right and the input at I is 7.5 kW.

1. Find the speed and direction of rotation of the driven shaft O and the wheel P.

2. If the mechanical efficiency of the drive is 80%, find the torque tending to rotate the fixed wheel R.

Solution. Given : $T_P = 144$; $T_Q = 120$; $T_R = 120$; $T_X = 36$; $T_Y = 24$; $T_Z = 30$; $N_I = 1500$ r.p.m. (clockwise) ; $P = 7.5$ kW = 7500 W ; $\eta = 80\% = 0.8$

First of all, consider the train of wheels Z, R and Q (arm). The revolutions of various wheels are shown in the following table.

Table 13.25. Table of motions.

Step No.	Conditions of motion	Q (Arm)	Z (also I)	R (Fixed)
		\[colspan Revolutions of elements\]		
1.	Arm fixed-wheel Z rotates through + 1 revolution (anticlockwise)	0	+ 1	$-\dfrac{T_Z}{T_R}$
2.	Arm fixed-wheel Z rotates through + x revolutions	0	+ x	$-x \times \dfrac{T_Z}{T_R}$
3.	Add + y revolutions to all elements	+ y	+ y	+ y
4.	Total motion	+ y	x + y	$y - x \times \dfrac{T_Z}{T_R}$

Since the driving shaft I as well as wheel Z rotates at 1500 r.p.m. clockwise, therefore

$$x + y = -1500 \qquad \ldots(i)$$

Also, the wheel R is fixed. Therefore

$$y - x \times \frac{T_Z}{T_R} = 0 \quad \text{or} \quad y = x \times \frac{T_Z}{T_R} = x \times \frac{30}{120} = 0.25\,x \qquad \ldots(ii)$$

From equations (i) and (ii),

$$x = -1200, \quad \text{and} \quad y = -300$$

Now consider the train of wheels Y, Q, arm A, wheels P and X. The revolutions of various elements are shown in the following table.

Table 13.26. Table of motions.

Step No.	Conditions of motion	Arm A, B and Shaft O	Wheel Y	Compound wheel Q-X	Wheel P
		\[colspan Revolutions of elements\]			
1.	Arm A fixed-wheel Y rotates through + 1 revolution (anticlockwise)	0	+ 1	$-\dfrac{T_Y}{T_Q}$	$+\dfrac{T_Y}{T_Q} \times \dfrac{T_X}{T_P}$
2.	Arm A fixed-wheel Y rotates through + x_1 revolutions	0	+ x_1	$-x_1 \times \dfrac{T_Y}{T_Q}$	$+ x_1 \times \dfrac{T_Y}{T_Q} \times \dfrac{T_X}{T_P}$
3.	Add + y_1 revolutions to all elements	+ y_1	+ y_1	+ y_1	+ y_1
4.	Total motion	+ y_1	$x_1 + y_1$	$y_1 - x_1 \times \dfrac{T_Y}{T_Q}$	$y_1 + x_1 \times \dfrac{T_Y}{T_Q} \times \dfrac{T_X}{T_P}$

Since the speed of compound wheel Q-X is same as that of Q, therefore

$$y_1 - x_1 \times \frac{T_Y}{T_Q} = y = -300$$

or

$$y_1 - x_1 \times \frac{24}{120} = -300$$

$$\therefore \qquad\qquad y_1 = 0.2\,x_1 - 300 \qquad\qquad\qquad\qquad\text{...(iii)}$$

Also   Speed of wheel Y = Speed of wheel Z or shaft I

$$\therefore \qquad\qquad x_1 + y_1 = x + y = -1500 \qquad\qquad\qquad\text{...(iv)}$$

$$x_1 + 0.2\,x_1 - 300 = -1500 \qquad\qquad\text{...[From equation (iii)]}$$

$$1.2\,x_1 = -1500 + 300 = -1200$$

or $\qquad\qquad\qquad x_1 = -1200/1.2 = -1000$

and $\qquad\qquad\qquad y_1 = -1500 - x_1 = -1500 + 1000 = -500$

1. Speed and direction of the driven shaft O and the wheel P

Speed of the driven shaft O,

$$N_O = y_1 = -500 = 500 \text{ r.p.m. clockwise } \textbf{Ans.}$$

and   Speed of the wheel P, $N_P = y_1 + x_1 \times \dfrac{T_Y}{T_Q} \times \dfrac{T_X}{T_P} = -500 - 1000 \times \dfrac{24}{120} \times \dfrac{36}{144}$

$$= -550 = 550 \text{ r.p.m. clockwise } \textbf{Ans.}$$

2. Torque tending to rotate the fixed wheel R

We know that the torque on shaft I or input torque

$$T_1 = \frac{P \times 60}{2\pi \times N_1} = \frac{7500 \times 60}{2\pi \times 1500} = 47.74 \text{ N-m}$$

and torque on shaft O or output torque,

$$T_2 = \frac{\eta \times P \times 60}{2\pi \times N_O} = \frac{0.8 \times 7500 \times 60}{2\pi \times 500} = 114.58 \text{ N-m}$$

Since the input and output shafts rotate in the same direction (*i.e.* clockwise), therefore input and output torques will be in opposite direction.

$\therefore$ Torque tending to rotate the fixed wheel R

$$= T_2 - T_1 = 114.58 - 47.74 = 66.84 \text{ N-m } \textbf{Ans.}$$

Example 13.24. *An epicyclic bevel gear train (known as Humpage's reduction gear) is shown in Fig. 13.31. It consists of a fixed wheel C, the driving shaft X and the driven shaft Y. The compound wheel B-D can revolve on a spindle F which can turn freely about the axis X and Y.*

Show that (i) if the ratio of tooth numbers T_B / T_D is greater than T_C / T_E, the wheel E will rotate in the same direction as wheel A, and (ii) if the ratio T_B / T_D is less than T_C / T_E, the direction of E is reversed.

If the numbers of teeth on wheels A, B, C, D and E are 34, 120, 150, 38 and 50 respectively and 7.5 kW is put into the shaft X at 500 r.p.m., what is the output torque of the shaft Y, and what are the forces (tangential to the pitch cones) at the contact points between wheels D and E and between wheels B and C, if the module of all wheels is 3.5 mm ?

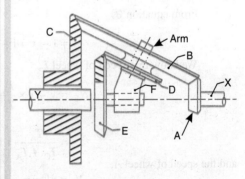

Fig. 13.31

Solution. Given : $T_A = 34$; $T_B = 120$; $T_C = 150$; $T_D = 38$; $T_E = 50$; $P_X = 7.5 \text{ kW} = 7500 \text{ W}$; $N_X = 500$ r.p.m. ; $m = 3.5$ mm

The table of motions is given below :

Table 13.27. Table of motions.

Step No.	Conditions of motion	Revolutions of elements				
		Spindle F	Wheel A (or shaft X)	Compound wheel B-D	Wheel C	Wheel E (or shaft Y)
1.	Spindle fixed, wheel A is rotated through $+1$ revolution	0	$+1$	$+\dfrac{T_A}{T_B}$	$-\dfrac{T_A}{T_B}\times\dfrac{T_B}{T_C}$ $=-\dfrac{T_A}{T_C}$	$-\dfrac{T_A}{T_B}\times\dfrac{T_D}{T_E}$
2.	Spindle fixed, wheel A is rotated through $+x$ revolutions	0	$+x$	$+x\times\dfrac{T_A}{T_B}$	$-x\times\dfrac{T_A}{T_C}$	$-x\times\dfrac{T_A}{T_B}\times\dfrac{T_D}{T_E}$
3.	Add $+y$ revolutions to all elements	$+y$	$+y$	$+y$	$+y$	$+y$
4.	Total motion	$+y$	$x+y$	$y+x\times\dfrac{T_A}{T_B}$	$y-x\times\dfrac{T_A}{T_C}$	$y-x\times\dfrac{T_A}{T_B}\times\dfrac{T_D}{T_E}$

Let us assume that the driving shaft X rotates through 1 revolution anticlockwise, therefore the wheel A will also rotate through 1 revolution anticlockwise.

$$\therefore \qquad x+y=+1 \quad \text{or} \quad y=1-x \qquad\qquad\qquad ...(i)$$

We also know that the wheel C is fixed, therefore

$$y-x\times\frac{T_A}{T_C}=0 \quad \text{or} \quad (1-x)-x\times\frac{T_A}{T_C}=0 \qquad ...\text{[From equation } (i)\text{]}$$

$$1-x\left(1+\frac{T_A}{T_C}\right)=0 \quad \text{or} \quad x\left(\frac{T_C+T_A}{T_C}\right)=1$$

and

$$x=\frac{T_C}{T_C+T_A} \qquad\qquad\qquad\qquad ...(ii)$$

From equation (i),

$$y=1-x=1-\frac{T_C}{T_C+T_A}=\frac{T_A}{T_C+T_A} \qquad\qquad ...(iii)$$

We know that speed of wheel E,

$$N_E=y-x\times\frac{T_A}{T_B}\times\frac{T_D}{T_E}=\frac{T_A}{T_C+T_A}-\frac{T_C}{T_C+T_A}\times\frac{T_A}{T_B}\times\frac{T_D}{T_E}$$

$$=\frac{T_A}{T_C+T_A}\left(1-\frac{T_C}{T_B}\times\frac{T_D}{T_E}\right) \qquad\qquad ...(iv)$$

and the speed of wheel A,

$$N_A=x+y=+1 \text{ revolution}$$

(i) If $\dfrac{T_B}{T_D}>\dfrac{T_C}{T_E}$ or $T_B\times T_E>T_C\times T_D$, then the equation (iv) will be positive. Therefore the wheel E will rotate in the same direction as wheel A. **Ans.**

(ii) If $\dfrac{T_B}{T_D} < \dfrac{T_C}{T_E}$ or $T_B \times T_E < T_C \times T_D$, then the equation (iv) will be negative. Therefore the wheel E will rotate in the opposite direction as wheel A. **Ans.**

Output torque of shaft Y

We know that the speed of the driving shaft X (or wheel A) or input speed is 500 r.p.m., therefore from the fourth row of the table,

$$x + y = 500 \quad \text{or} \quad y = 500 - x \qquad \qquad ...(v)$$

Since the wheel C is fixed, therefore

$$y - x \times \frac{T_A}{T_C} = 0 \quad \text{or} \quad (500 - x) - x \times \frac{34}{150} = 0 \qquad ...\text{[From equation (v)]}$$

$$\therefore \qquad 500 - x - 0.227\,x = 0 \quad \text{or} \quad x = 500/1.227 = 407.5 \text{ r.p.m.}$$

and
$$y = 500 - x = 500 - 407.5 = 92.5 \text{ r.p.m.}$$

Since the speed of the driven or output shaft Y (*i.e.* N_Y) is equal to the speed of wheel E (*i.e.* N_E), therefore

$$N_Y = N_E = y - x \times \frac{T_A}{T_B} \times \frac{T_D}{T_E} = 92.5 - 407.5 \times \frac{34}{120} \times \frac{38}{50}$$

$$= 92.5 - 87.75 = 4.75 \text{ r.p.m.}$$

Assuming 100 per cent efficiency of the gear train, input power P_X is equal to output power (P_Y), *i.e.*

$$P_Y = P_X = 7.5 \text{ kW} = 7500 \text{ W}$$

$\therefore$ Output torque of shaft Y,

$$= \frac{P_Y \times 60}{2\pi\,N_Y} = \frac{7500 \times 60}{2\pi \times 4.75} = 15\,076 \text{ N-m} = 15.076 \text{ kN-m} \quad \textbf{Ans.}$$

Tangential force between wheels D and E

We know that the pitch circle radius of wheel E,

$$r_E = \frac{m \times T_E}{2} = \frac{3.5 \times 50}{2} = 87.5 \text{ mm} = 0.0875 \text{ m}$$

$\therefore$ Tangential force between wheels D and E,

$$= \frac{\text{Torque on wheel } E}{\text{Pitch circle radius of wheel } E} = \frac{15.076}{0.0875} = 172.3 \text{ kN} \quad \textbf{Ans.}$$

$$...(\because \text{ Torque on wheel } E = \text{Torque on shaft } Y)$$

Tangential force between wheels B and C

We know that the input torque on shaft X or on wheel A

$$= \frac{P_X \times 60}{2\pi\,N_X} = \frac{7500 \times 60}{2\pi \times 500} = 143 \text{ N-m}$$

$\therefore$ Fixing torque on the fixed wheel C

$$= \text{Torque on wheel } E - \text{Torque on wheel } A$$

$$= 15\,076 - 143 = 14\,933 \text{ N-m} = 14.933 \text{ kN-m}$$

Pitch circle radius of wheel C,

$$r_C = \frac{m \times T_C}{2} = \frac{3.5 \times 150}{2} = 262.5 \text{ mm} = 0.2625 \text{ m}$$

Tangential force between wheels B and C

$$= \frac{\text{Fixing torque on wheel } C}{r_C} = \frac{14.933}{0.2625} = 57 \text{ kN Ans.}$$

EXERCISES

1. A compound train consists of six gears. The number of teeth on the gears are as follows :

Gear	:	A	B	C	D	E	F
No. of teeth	:	60	40	50	25	30	24

   The gears B and C are on one shaft while the gears D and E are on another shaft. The gear A drives gear B, gear C drives gear D and gear E drives gear F. If the gear A transmits 1.5 kW at 100 r.p.m. and the gear train has an efficiency of 80 per cent, find the torque on gear F. **[Ans. 30.55 N-m]**

2. Two parallel shafts are to be connected by spur gearing. The approximate distance between the shafts is 600 mm. If one shaft runs at 120 r.p.m. and the other at 360 r.p.m., find the number of teeth on each wheel, if the module is 8 mm. Also determine the exact distance apart of the shafts.
   [Ans. 114, 38 ; 608 mm]

3. In a reverted gear train, as shown in Fig. 13.32, two shafts A and B are in the same straight line and are geared together through an intermediate parallel shaft C. The gears connecting the shafts A and C have a module of 2 mm and those connecting the shafts C and B have a module of 4.5 mm. The speed of shaft A is to be about but greater than 12 times the speed of shaft B, and the ratio at each reduction is same. Find suitable number of teeth for gears. The number of teeth of each gear is to be a minimum but not less than 16. Also find the exact velocity ratio and the distance of shaft C from A and B.
   [Ans. 36, 126, 16, 56 ; 12.25 ; 162 mm]

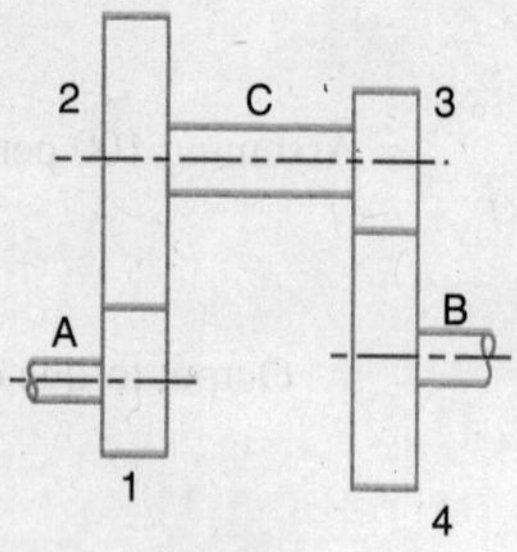

   Fig. 13.32

4. In an epicyclic gear train, as shown in Fig.13.33, the number of teeth on wheels A, B and C are 48, 24 and 50 respectively. If the arm rotates at 400 r.p.m., clockwise, find : 1. Speed of wheel C when A is fixed, and 2. Speed of wheel A when C is fixed.
   [Ans. 16 r.p.m. (clockwise) ; 16.67 (anticlockwise)]

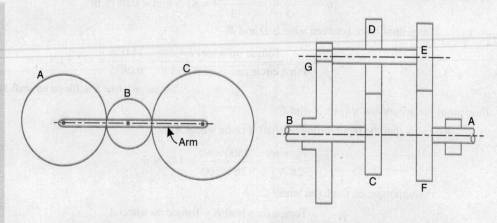

Fig. 13.33   Fig. 13.34

5. In an epicyclic gear train, as shown in Fig. 13.34, the wheel *C* is keyed to the shaft *B* and wheel *F* is keyed to shaft *A*. The wheels *D* and *E* rotate together on a pin fixed to the arm *G*. The number of teeth on wheels *C*, *D*, *E* and *F* are 35, 65, 32 and 68 respectively.

If the shaft *A* rotates at 60 r.p.m. and the shaft *B* rotates at 28 r.p.m. in the opposite direction, find the speed and direction of rotation of arm *G*.   [Ans. 90 r.p.m., in the same direction as shaft *A*]

6. An epicyclic gear train, as shown in Fig. 13.35, is composed of a fixed annular wheel *A* having 150 teeth. The wheel *A* is meshing with wheel *B* which drives wheel *D* through an idle wheel *C*, *D* being concentric with *A*. The wheels *B* and *C* are carried on an arm which revolves clockwise at 100 r.p.m. about the axis of *A* and *D*. If the wheels *B* and *D* have 25 teeth and 40 teeth respectively, find the number of teeth on *C* and the speed and sense of rotation of *C*.   [Ans. 30 ; 600 r.p.m. clockwise]

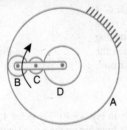

Fig. 13.35

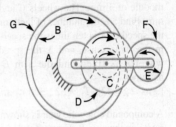

Fig. 13.36

7. Fig. 13.36, shows an epicyclic gear train with the following details :

A has 40 teeth external (fixed gear) ; *B* has 80 teeth internal ; *C - D* is a compound wheel having 20 and 50 teeth (external) respectively, *E-F* is a compound wheel having 20 and 40 teeth (external) respectively, and *G* has 90 teeth (external).

The arm runs at 100 r.p.m. in clockwise direction. Determine the speeds for gears *C*, *E*, and *B*.
[Ans. 300 r.p.m. clockwise ; 400 r.p.m. anticlockwise ; 150 r.p.m. clockwise]

8. An epicyclic gear train, as shown in Fig. 13.37, has a sun wheel *S* of 30 teeth and two planet wheels *P-P* of 50 teeth. The planet wheels mesh with the internal teeth of a fixed annulus *A*. The driving shaft carrying the sunwheel, transmits 4 kW at 300 r.p.m. The driven shaft is connected to an arm which carries the planet wheels. Determine the speed of the driven shaft and the torque transmitted, if the overall efficiency is 95%.   [Ans. 56.3 r.p.m. ; 644.5 N-m]

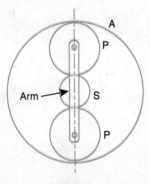

Fig. 13.37

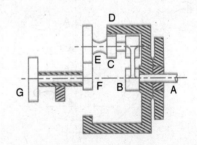

Fig. 13.38

9. An epicyclic reduction gear, as shown in Fig. 13.38, has a shaft *A* fixed to arm *B*. The arm *B* has a pin fixed to its outer end and two gears *C* and *E* which are rigidly fixed, revolve on this pin. Gear *C* meshes with annular wheel *D* and gear *E* with pinion *F*. *G* is the driver pulley and *D* is kept stationary.

The number of teeth are : *D* = 80 ; *C* = 10 ; *E* = 24 and *F* = 18.

If the pulley *G* runs at 200 r.p.m. ; find the speed of shaft *A*.

[Ans. 17.14 r.p.m. in the same direction as that of *G*]

10. A reverted epicyclic gear train for a hoist block is shown in Fig. 13.39. The arm E is keyed to the same shaft as the load drum and the wheel A is keyed to a second shaft which carries a chain wheel, the chain being operated by hand. The two shafts have common axis but can rotate independently. The wheels B and C are compound and rotate together on a pin carried at the end of arm E. The wheel D has internal teeth and is fixed to the outer casing of the block so that it does not rotate.

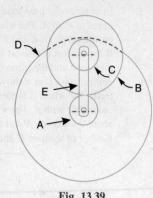

Fig. 13.39

The wheels A and B have 16 and 36 teeth respectively with a module of 3 mm. The wheels C and D have a module of 4 mm. Find : 1. the number of teeth on wheels C and D when the speed of A is ten times the speed of arm E, both rotating in the same sense, and 2. the speed of wheel D when the wheel A is fixed and the arm E rotates at 450 r.p.m. anticlockwise.

[Ans. $T_C = 13$; $T_D = 52$; 500 r.p.m. anticlockwise]

11. A compound epicyclic gear is shown diagrammatically in Fig. 13.40. The gears A, D and E are free to rotate on the axis P. The compound gear B and C rotate together on the axis Q at the end of arm F. All the gears have equal pitch. The number of external teeth on the gears A, B and C are 18, 45 and 21 respectively. The gears D and E are annular gears. The gear A rotates at 100 r.p.m. in the anticlockwise direction and the gear D rotates at 450 r.p.m. clockwise. Find the speed and direction of the arm and the gear E. [Ans. 400 r.p.m. clockwise ; 483.3 r.p.m. clockwise]

12. In an epicyclic gear train of the 'sun and planet type' as shown in Fig. 13.41, the pitch circle diameter of the internally toothed ring D is to be 216 mm and the module 4 mm. When the ring D is stationary, the spider A, which carries three planet wheels C of equal size, is to make one revolution in the same sense as the sun wheel B for every five revolutions of the driving spindle carrying the sunwheel B. Determine suitable number of teeth for all the wheels and the exact diameter of pitch circle of the ring.

[Ans. $T_B = 14$, $T_C = 21$, $T_D = 56$; 224 mm]

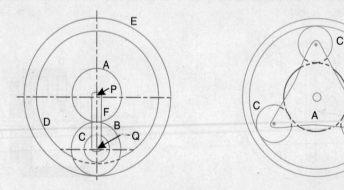

Fig. 13.40   **Fig. 13.41**

13. An epicyclic train is shown in Fig. 13.42. Internal gear A is keyed to the driving shaft and has 30 teeth. Compound wheel C and D of 20 and 22 teeth respectively are free to rotate on the pin fixed to the arm P which is rigidly connected to the driven shaft. Internal gear B which has 32 teeth is fixed. If the driving shaft runs at 60 r.p.m. clockwise, determine the speed of the driven shaft. What is the direction of rotation of driven shaft with reference to driving shaft? [Ans. 1980 r.p.m. clockwise]

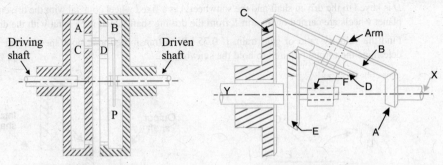

Fig. 13.42   Fig. 13.43

14.   A shaft *Y* is driven by a co-axial shaft *X* by means of an epicyclic gear train, as shown in Fig. 13.43.
       The wheel *A* is keyed to *X* and *E* to *Y*. The wheels *B* and *D* are compound and carried on an arm *F*
       which can turn freely on the common axes of *X* and *Y*. The wheel *C* is fixed. If the numbers of teeth
       on *A*, *B*, *C*, *D* and *E* are respectively 20, 64, 80, 30 and 50 and the shaft *X* makes 600 r.p.m.,
       determine the speed in r.p.m. and sense of rotation of the shaft *Y*.

                                                      [Ans. 30 r.p.m. in the same sense as shaft X]

15.   An epicyclic bevel gear train, as shown in Fig. 13.44, has fixed gear *B* meshing with pinion *C*. The
       gear *E* on the driven shaft meshes with the pinion *D*. The pinions *C* and *D* are keyed to a shaft,
       which revolves in bearings on the arm *A*. The arm *A* is keyed to the driving shaft. The number of
       teeth are : $T_B = 75$, $T_C = 20$, $T_D = 18$, and $T_E = 70$. Find the speed of the driven shaft, if 1. the driving
       shaft makes 1000 r.p.m., and 2. the gear *B* turns in the same sense as the driving shaft at 400
       r.p.m., the driving shaft still making 1000 r.p.m.

                                              [Ans. 421.4 r.p.m. in the same direction as driving shaft]

16.   The epicyclic gear train is shown in Fig. 13.45. The wheel *D* is held stationary by the shaft *A* and the
       arm *B* is rotated at 200 r.p.m. The wheels *E* (20 teeth) and *F* (40 teeth) are fixed together and rotate
       freely on the pin carried by the arm. The wheel *G* (30 teeth) is rigidly attached to the shaft *C*. Find the
       speed of shaft *C* stating the direction of rotation to that of *B*.

       If the gearing transmits 7.5 kW, what will be the torque required to hold the shaft *A* stationary, neglect-
       ing all friction losses?

                     [Ans. 466.7 r.p.m. in opposite direction of B; 511.5 N-m in opposite direction of B]

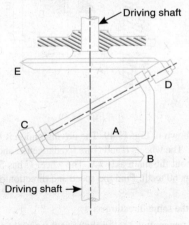

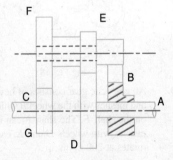

Fig. 13.44   Fig. 13.45

17.   An epicyclic gear train, as shown in Fig. 13.46, consists of two sunwheels *A* and *D* with 28 and 24
       teeth respectively, engaged with a compound planet wheels *B* and *C* with 22 and 26 teeth. The sunwheel

D is keyed to the driven shaft and the sunwheel *A* is a fixed wheel co-axial with the driven shaft. The planet wheels are carried on an arm *E* from the driving shaft which is co-axial with the driven shaft.

Find the velocity ratio of gear train. If 0.75 kW is transmitted and input speed being 100 r.p.m., determine the torque required to hold the sunwheel *A*. **[Ans. 2.64 ; 260.6 N-m]**

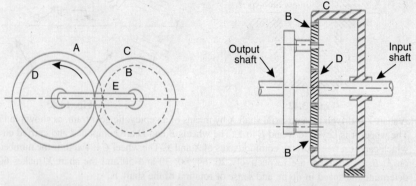

Fig. 13.46   Fig. 13.47

18. In the epicyclic reduction gear, as shown in Fig. 13.47, the sunwheel *D* has 20 teeth and is keyed to the input shaft. Two planet wheels *B*, each having 50 teeth, gear with wheel *D* and are carried by an arm *A* fixed to the output shaft. The wheels *B* also mesh with an internal gear *C* which is fixed. The input shaft rotates at 2100 r.p.m. Determine the speed of the output shaft and the torque required to fix *C* when the gears are transmitting 30 kW.

[Ans. 300 r.p.m. in the same sense as the input shaft ; 818.8 N-m]

19. An epicyclic gear train for an electric motor is shown in Fig. 13.48. The wheel *S* has 15 teeth and is fixed to the motor shaft rotating at 1450 r.p.m. The planet *P* has 45 teeth, gears with fixed annulus *A* and rotates on a spindle carried by an arm which is fixed to the output shaft. The planet *P* also gears with the sun wheel *S*. Find the speed of the output shaft. If the motor is transmitting 1.5 kW, find the torque required to fix the annulus *A*. **[Ans. 181.3 r.p.m. ; 69.14 N-m]**

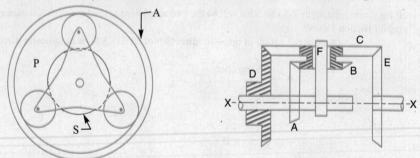

Fig. 13.48   Fig. 13.49

20. An epicyclic gear consists of bevel wheels as shown in Fig. 13.49. The driving pinion *A* has 20 teeth and meshes with the wheel *B* which has 25 teeth. The wheels *B* and *C* are fixed together and turn freely on the shaft *F*. The shaft *F* can rotate freely about the main axis *XX*. The wheel *C* has 50 teeth and meshes with wheels *D* and *E*, each of which has 60 teeth. Find the speed and direction of *E* when *A* rotates at 200 r.p.m., if

1. *D* is fixed, and **2.** *D* rotates at 100 r.p.m., in the same direction as *A*.

In both the cases, find the ratio of the torques transmitted by the shafts of the wheels *A* and *E*, the friction being neglected.

[Ans. 800 r.p.m. in the opposite direction of *A* ; 300 r.p.m. in the opposite

direction of *A* ; 4 ; 1.5]

DO YOU KNOW ?

1. What do you understand by 'gear train'? Discuss the various types of gear trains.
2. Explain briefly the differences between simple, compound, and epicyclic gear trains. What are the special advantages of epicyclic gear trains ?
3. Explain the procedure adopted for designing the spur wheels.
4. How the velocity ratio of epicyclic gear train is obtained by tabular method?
5. Explain with a neat sketch the 'sun and planet wheel'.
6. What are the various types of the torques in an epicyclic gear train ?

OBJECTIVE TYPE QUESTIONS

1. In a simple gear train, if the number of idle gears is odd, then the motion of driven gear will
   (a) be same as that of driving gear
   (b) be opposite as that of driving gear
   (c) depend upon the number of teeth on the driving gear
   (d) none of the above
2. The train value of a gear train is
   (a) equal to velocity ratio of a gear train   (b) reciprocal of velocity ratio of a gear train
   (c) always greater than unity   (d) always less than unity
3. When the axes of first and last gear are co-axial, then gear train is known as
   (a) simple gear train   (b) compound gear train
   (c) reverted gear train   (d) epicyclic gear train
4. In a clock mechanism, the gear train used to connect minute hand to hour hand, is
   (a) epicyclic gear train   (b) reverted gear train
   (c) compound gear train   (d) simple gear train
5. In a gear train, when the axes of the shafts, over which the gears are mounted, move relative to a fixed axis, is called
   (a) simple gear train   (b) compound gear train
   (c) reverted gear train   (d) epicyclic gear train
6. A differential gear in an automobile is a
   (a) simple gear train   (b) epicyclic gear train
   (c) compound gear train   (d) none of these
7. A differential gear in automobilies is used to
   (a) reduce speed   (b) assist in changing speed
   (c) provide jerk-free movement of vehicle   (d) help in turning

ANSWERS

1. (a)	2. (b)	3. (c)	4. (b)	5. (d)
6. (b)	7. (d)			

14

Gyroscopic Couple and Precessional Motion

Features

1. Introduction.
2. Precessional Angular Motion.
3. Gyroscopic Couple.
4. Effect of Gyroscopic Couple on an Aeroplane.
5. Terms Used in a Naval Ship.
6. Effect of Gyroscopic Couple on a Naval Ship during Steering.
7. Effect of Gyroscopic Couple on a Naval Ship during Pitching.
8. Effect of Gyroscopic Couple on a Navalship during Rolling.
9. Stability of a Four Wheel drive Moving in a Curved Path.
10. Stability of a Two Wheel Vehicle Taking a Turn.
11. Effect of Gyroscopic Couple on a Disc Fixed Rigidly at a Certain Angle to a Rotating Shaft.

14.1. Introduction

We have already discussed that,

1. When a body moves along a curved path with a uniform linear velocity, a force in the direction of centripetal acceleration (known as centripetal force) has to be applied externally over the body, so that it moves along the required curved path. This external force applied is known as *active force.*

2. When a body, itself, is moving with uniform linear velocity along a circular path, it is subjected to the centrifugal force * radially outwards. This centrifugal force is called *reactive force.* The action of the reactive or centrifugal force is to tilt or move the body along radially outward direction.

Note : Whenever the effect of any force or couple over a moving or rotating body is to be considered, it should be with respect to the reactive force or couple and not with respect to active force or couple.

---

* Centrifugal force is equal in magnitude to centripetal force but opposite in direction.

480

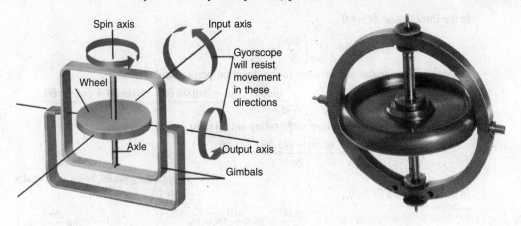

Gyroscopic inertia prevents a spinning top from falling sideways.

14.2. Precessional Angular Motion

We have already discussed that the angular acceleration is the rate of change of angular velocity with respect to time. It is a vector quantity and may be represented by drawing a vector diagram with the help of right hand screw rule (see chapter 2, Art. 2.13).

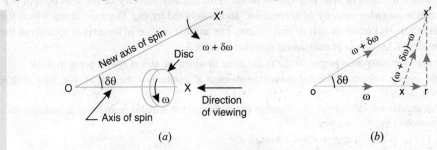

Fig. 14.1. Precessional angular motion.

Consider a disc, as shown in Fig. 14.1 (*a*), revolving or spinning about the axis *OX* (known as **axis of spin**) in anticlockwise when seen from the front, with an angular velocity ω in a plane at right angles to the paper.

After a short interval of time δt, let the disc be spinning about the new axis of spin *OX'* (at an angle $\delta\theta$) with an angular velocity $(\omega + \delta\omega)$. Using the right hand screw rule, initial angular velocity of the disc (ω) is represented by vector *ox*; and the final angular velocity of the disc ($\omega + \delta\omega$) is represented by vector *ox'* as shown in Fig. 14.1 (*b*). The vector *xx'* represents the change of angular velocity in time δt *i.e.* the angular acceleration of the disc. This may be resolved into two components, one parallel to *ox* and the other perpendicular to *ox*.

Component of angular acceleration in the direction of *ox*,

$$\alpha_t = \frac{xr}{\delta t} = \frac{or - ox}{\delta t} = \frac{ox' \cos \delta\theta - ox}{\delta t}$$

$$= \frac{(\omega + \delta\omega) \cos \delta\theta - \omega}{\delta t} = \frac{\omega\cos\delta\theta + \delta\omega \cos\delta\theta - \omega}{\delta t}$$

Since $\delta\theta$ is very small, therefore substituting $\cos \delta\theta = 1$, we have

$$\alpha_t = \frac{\omega + \delta\omega - \omega}{\delta t} = \frac{\delta\omega}{\delta t}$$

In the limit, when $\delta t \to 0$,

$$\alpha_t = \underset{\delta t \to 0}{\text{Lt}} \left(\frac{\delta \omega}{\delta t} \right) = \frac{d\omega}{dt}$$

Component of angular acceleration in the direction perpendicular to ox,

$$\alpha_c = \frac{rx'}{\delta t} = \frac{ox' \sin \delta\theta}{\delta t} = \frac{(\omega + \delta\omega) \sin \delta\theta}{\delta t} = \frac{\omega \sin \delta\theta + \delta\omega . \sin \delta\theta}{\delta t}$$

Since $\delta\theta$ is very small, therefore substituting $\sin \delta\theta = \delta\theta$, we have

$$\alpha_c = \frac{\omega . \delta\theta + \delta\omega . \delta\theta}{\delta t} = \frac{\omega . \delta\theta}{\delta t}$$

...(Neglecting $\delta\omega . \delta\theta$, being very small)

In the limit when $\delta t \to 0$,.

$$\alpha_c = \underset{\delta t \to 0}{\text{Lt}} \frac{\omega . \delta\theta}{\delta t} = \omega \times \frac{d\theta}{dt} = \omega . \omega_P \qquad ...\left(\text{Substituting } \frac{d\theta}{dt} = \omega_P \right)$$

∴ Total angular acceleration of the disc

$$= \text{vector } xx' = \text{vector sum of } \alpha_t \text{ and } \alpha_c$$

$$= \frac{d\omega}{dt} + \omega \times \frac{d\theta}{dt} = \frac{d\omega}{dt} + \omega . \omega_P$$

where $d\theta/dt$ is the angular velocity of the axis of spin about a certain axis, which is perpendicular to the plane in which the axis of spin is going to rotate. This angular velocity of the axis of spin (*i.e.* $d\theta/dt$) is known as **angular velocity of precession** and is denoted by ω_P. The axis, about which the axis of spin is to turn, is known as **axis of precession**. The angular motion of the axis of spin about the axis of precession is known as **precessional angular motion**.

Notes: 1. The axis of precession is perpendicular to the plane in which the axis of spin is going to rotate.

2. If the angular velocity of the disc remains constant at all positions of the axis of spin, then $d\theta/dt$ is zero; and thus α_c is zero.

3. If the angular velocity of the disc changes the direction, but remains constant in magnitude, then angular acceleration of the disc is given by

$$\alpha_c = \omega . d\theta/dt = \omega . \omega_P$$

The angular acceleration α_c is known as **gyroscopic acceleration**.

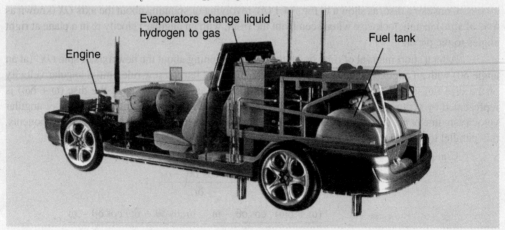

Engine   Evaporators change liquid hydrogen to gas   Fuel tank

This experimental car burns hydrogen fuel in an ordinary piston engine. Its exhaust gases cause no pollution, because they contain only water vapour.

Note : This picture is given as additional information.

14.3. Gyroscopic Couple

Consider a disc spinning with an angular velocity ω rad/s about the axis of spin *OX*, in anticlockwise direction when seen from the front, as shown in Fig. 14.2 (*a*). Since the plane in which the disc is rotating is parallel to the plane *YOZ*, therefore it is called *plane of spinning*. The plane *XOZ* is a horizontal plane and the axis of spin rotates in a plane parallel to the horizontal plane about an axis *OY*. In other words, the axis of spin is said to be rotating or processing about an axis *OY*. In other words, the axis of spin is said to be rotating or processing about an axis *OY* (which is perpendicular to both the axes *OX* and *OZ*) at an angular velocity ω_p rad/s. This horizontal plane *XOZ* is called *plane of precession* and *OY* is the *axis of precession*.

Let I = Mass moment of inertia of the disc about *OX*, and

ω = Angular velocity of the disc.

∴ Angular momentum of the disc

$$= I.\omega$$

Since the angular momentum is a vector quantity, therefore it may be represented by the vector $\vec{ox}$, as shown in Fig. 14.2 (*b*). The axis of spin *OX* is also rotating anticlockwise when seen from the top about the axis *OY*. Let the axis *OX* is turned in the plane *XOZ* through a small angle $\delta\theta$ radians to the position *OX'*, in time δt seconds. Assuming the angular velocity ω to be constant, the angular momentum will now be represented by vector *ox'*.

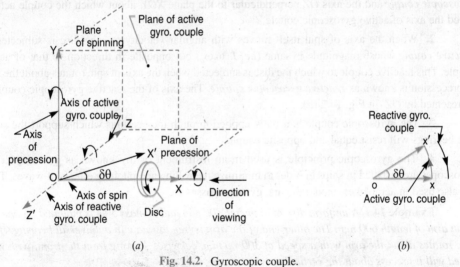

Fig. 14.2. Gyroscopic couple.

∴ Change in angular momentum

$$= \vec{ox'} - \vec{ox} = \vec{xx'} = \vec{ox}.\delta\theta \qquad \text{...(in the direction of } \vec{xx'})$$
$$= I.\,\omega.\delta\theta$$

and rate of change of angular momentum

$$= I.\omega \times \frac{\delta\theta}{dt}$$

Since the rate of change of angular momentum will result by the application of a couple to the disc, therefore the couple applied to the disc causing precession,

$$C = \underset{\delta t \to 0}{\text{Lt}}\ I.\omega \times \frac{\delta\theta}{\delta t} = I.\omega \times \frac{d\theta}{dt} = I.\omega.\omega_p \qquad \ldots\left(\because \frac{d\theta}{dt} = \omega_p\right)$$

where ω_p = Angular velocity of precession of the axis of spin or the speed of rotation of the axis of spin about the axis of precession OY.

In S.I. units, the units of C is N-m when I is in kg-m^2.

It may be noted that

1. The couple $I.\omega.\omega_p$, in the direction of the vector xx' (representing the change in angular momentum) is the *active gyroscopic couple*, which has to be applied over the disc when the axis of spin is made to rotate with angular velocity ω_p about the axis of precession. The vector xx' lies in the plane XOZ or the horizontal plane. In case of a very small displacement $\delta\theta$, the vector xx' will be perpendicular to the vertical plane XOY. Therefore the couple causing this change in the angular momentum will lie in the plane XOY. The vector xx', as shown in Fig. 14.2 (*b*), represents an

Above picture shows an aircraft propeller. These rotors play role in gyroscopic couple.

anticlockwise couple in the plane XOY. Therefore, the plane XOY is called the *plane of active gyroscopic couple* and the axis OZ perpendicular to the plane XOY, about which the couple acts, is called the axis of active gyroscopic couple.

2. When the axis of spin itself moves with angular velocity ω_p, the disc is subjected to *reactive couple* whose magnitude is same (*i.e.* $I.\omega.\omega_p$) but opposite in direction to that of active couple. This reactive couple to which the disc is subjected when the axis of spin rotates about the axis of precession is known as *reactive gyroscopic couple*. The axis of the reactive gyroscopic couple is represented by OZ' in Fig. 14.2 (*a*).

3. The gyroscopic couple is usually applied through the bearings which support the shaft. The bearings will resist equal and opposite couple.

4. The gyroscopic principle is used in an instrument or toy known as *gyroscope*. The gyroscopes are installed in ships in order to minimize the rolling and pitching effects of waves. They are also used in aeroplanes, monorail cars, gyrocompasses etc.

Example 14.1. *A uniform disc of diameter 300 mm and of mass 5 kg is mounted on one end of an arm of length 600 mm. The other end of the arm is free to rotate in a universal bearing. If the disc rotates about the arm with a speed of 300 r.p.m. clockwise, looking from the front, with what speed will it precess about the vertical axis?*

Solution. Given: d = 300 mm or r = 150 mm = 0.15 m ; m = 5 kg ; l = 600 mm = 0.6 m ; N = 300 r.p.m. or ω = $2\pi \times 300/60$ = 31.42 rad/s

We know that the mass moment of inertia of the disc, about an axis through its centre of gravity and perpendicular to the plane of disc,

$$I = m.r^2/2 = 5(0.15)^2/2 = 0.056 \text{ kg-m}^2$$

and couple due to mass of disc,

$$C = m.g.l = 5 \times 9.81 \times 0.6 = 29.43 \text{ N-m}$$

Let ω_p = Speed of precession.

We know that couple (C),

$$29.43 = I.\omega.\omega_p = 0.056 \times 31.42 \times \omega_p = 1.76 \, \omega_p$$

$\therefore$ ω_p = 29.43/1.76 = 16.7 rad/s **Ans.**

Example 14.2. *A uniform disc of 150 mm diameter has a mass of 5 kg. It is mounted centrally in bearings which maintain its axle in a horizontal plane. The disc spins about its axle with a constant speed of 1000 r.p.m. while the axle precesses uniformly about the vertical at 60 r.p.m. The directions of rotation are as shown in Fig. 14.3. If the distance between the bearings is 100 mm, find the resultant reaction at each bearing due to the mass and gyroscopic effects.*

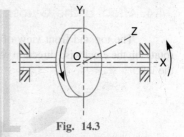

Fig. 14.3

Solution. Given: $d = 150$ mm or $r = 75$ mm $= 0.075$ m ; $m = 5$ kg ; $N = 1000$ r.p.m. or $\omega = 2\pi \times 1000/60 = 104.7$ rad/s (anticlockwise); $N_P = 60$ r.p.m. or $\omega_p = 2\pi \times 60/60 = 6.284$ rad/s (anticlockwise); $x = 100$ mm $= 0.1$ m

We know that mass moment of inertia of the disc, about an axis through its centre of gravity and perpendicular to the plane of disc,

$$I = m.r^2/2 = 5 \,(0.075)^2/2 = 0.014 \text{ kg m}^2$$

∴ Gyroscopic couple acting on the disc,

$$C = I. \omega. \omega_p = 0.014 \times 104.7 \times 6.284 = 9.2 \text{ N-m}$$

The direction of the reactive gyroscopic couple is shown in Fig.14.4 (*b*). Let *F* be the force at each bearing due to the gyroscopic couple.

$$\therefore \quad F = C/x = 9.2/0.1 = 92 \text{ N}$$

The force *F* will act in opposite directions at the bearings as shown in Fig. 14.4 (*a*). Now let R_A and R_B be the reaction at the bearing *A* and *B* respectively due to the weight of the disc. Since the disc is mounted centrally in bearings, therefore,

$$R_A = R_B = 5/2 = 2.5 \text{ kg} = 2.5 \times 9.81 = 24.5 \text{ N}$$

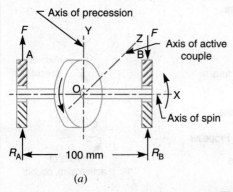

(*a*)

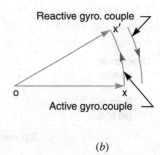

(*b*)

Fig. 14.4

Resultant reaction at each bearing

Let R_{A1} and R_{B1} = Resultant reaction at the bearings *A* and *B* respectively.

Since the reactive gyroscopic couple acts in clockwise direction when seen from the front, therefore its effect is to increase the reaction on the left hand side bearing (*i.e. A*) and to decrease the reaction on the right hand side bearing (*i.e. B*).

∴ $\qquad R_{A1} = F + R_A = 92 + 24.5 = 116.5 \text{ N}$ (upwards) **Ans.**

and $\qquad R_{B1} = F - R_B = 92 - 24.5 = 67.5 \text{ N}$ (downwards) **Ans.**

14.4. Effect of the Gyroscopic Couple on an Aeroplane

The top and front view of an aeroplane are shown in Fig 14.5 (a). Let engine or propeller rotates in the clockwise direction when seen from the rear or tail end and the aeroplane takes a turn to the left.

Let

ω = Angular velocity of the engine in rad/s,

m = Mass of the engine and the propeller in kg,

k = Its radius of gyration in metres,

I = Mass moment of inertia of the engine and the propeller in kg-m^2

$= m.k^2$,

v = Linear velocity of the aeroplane in m/s,

R = Radius of curvature in metres, and

ω_p = Angular velocity of precession $= \dfrac{v}{R}$ rad/s

∴ Gyroscopic couple acting on the aeroplane,

$$C = I.\omega.\omega_p$$

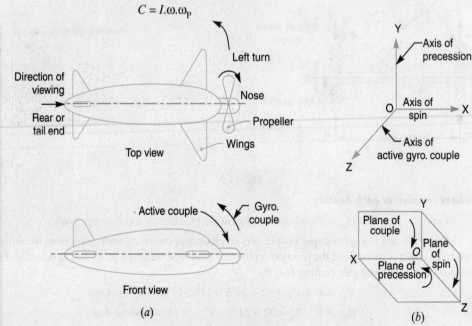

Fig. 14.5. Aeroplane taking a left turn.

Before taking the left turn, the angular momentum vector is represented by *ox*. When it takes left turn, the active gyroscopic couple will change the direction of the angular momentum vector from *ox* to *ox'* as shown in Fig. 14.6 (*a*). The vector *xx'*, in the limit, represents the change of angular momentum or the active gyroscopic couple and is perpendicular to *ox*. Thus the plane of active gyroscopic couple *XOY* will be perpendicular to *xx'* , *i.e.* vertical in this case, as shown in Fig 14.5 (*b*). By applying right hand screw rule to vector *xx'*, we find that the direction of active gyroscopic couple is clockwise as shown in the front view of Fig. 14.5 (*a*). In other words, for left hand turning, the active gyroscopic couple on the aeroplane in the axis *OZ* will be clockwise as shown in Fig. 14.5 (*b*).The reactive gyroscopic couple (equal in magnitude of active gyroscopic couple) will act in the opposite direction (*i.e.* in the anticlockwise direction) and the effect of this couple is, therefore, to **raise the nose** and **dip the tail** of the aeroplane.

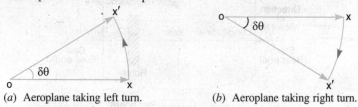

(*a*) Aeroplane taking left turn.   (*b*) Aeroplane taking right turn.

Fig. 14.6. Effect of gyroscopic couple on an aeroplane.

Notes : 1. When the aeroplane takes a **right turn** under similar conditions as discussed above, the effect of the reactive gyroscopic couple will be to **dip the nose** and **raise the tail** of the aeroplane.

2. When the engine or propeller rotates in **anticlockwise direction** when viewed from the rear or tail end and the aeroplane takes a **left turn**, then the effect of reactive gyroscopic couple will be to **dip the nose** and **raise the tail** of the aeroplane.

3. When the aeroplane takes a **right turn** under similar conditions as mentioned in note 2 above, the effect of reactive gyroscopic couple will be to **raise the nose** and **dip the tail** of the aeroplane.

4. When the engine or propeller rotates in **clockwise direction** when viewed from the front and the aeroplane takes a left turn, then the effect of reactive gyroscopic couple will be to **raise the tail** and **dip the nose** of the aeroplane.

5. When the aeroplane takes a **right turn** under similar conditions as mentioned in note 4-above, the effect of reactive gyroscopic couple will be to **raise the nose** and **dip the tail** of the aeroplane.

Example 14.3. *An aeroplane makes a complete half circle of 50 metres radius, towards left, when flying at 200 km per hr. The rotary engine and the propeller of the plane has a mass of 400 kg and a radius of gyration of 0.3 m. The engine rotates at 2400 r.p.m. clockwise when viewed from the rear. Find the gyroscopic couple on the aircraft and state its effect on it.*

Solution. Given : $R = 50$ m ; $v = 200$ km/hr $= 55.6$ m/s ; $m = 400$ kg ; $k = 0.3$ m ; $N = 2400$ r.p.m. or $\omega = 2\pi \times 2400/60 = 251$ rad/s

We know that mass moment of inertia of the engine and the propeller,

$$I = m.k^2 = 400(0.3)^2 = 36 \text{ kg-m}^2$$

and angular velocity of precession,

$$\omega_p = v/R = 55.6/50 = 1.11 \text{ rad/s}$$

We know that gyroscopic couple acting on the aircraft,

$$C = I. \omega. \omega_p = 36 \times 251.4 \times 1.11 = 100\ 46 \text{ N-m}$$

$$= 10.046 \text{ kN-m Ans.}$$

We have discussed in Art. 14.4 that when the aeroplane turns towards left, the effect of the gyroscopic couple is to lift the nose upwards and tail downwards. **Ans.**

14.5. Terms Used in a Naval Ship

The top and front views of a naval ship are shown in Fig 14.7. The fore end of the ship is called *bow* and the rear end is known as *stern* or *aft*. The left hand and right hand sides of the ship, when viewed from the stern are called *port* and *star-board* respectively. We shall now discuss the effect of gyroscopic couple on the naval ship in the following three cases:

1. Steering, 2. Pitching, and 3. Rolling.

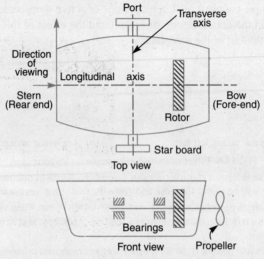

Fig. 14.7. Terms used in a naval ship.

14.6. Effect of Gyroscopic Couple on a Naval Ship during Steering

Steering is the turning of a complete ship in a curve towards left or right, while it moves forward. Consider the ship taking a left turn, and rotor rotates in the clockwise direction when viewed from the stern, as shown in Fig. 14.8. The effect of gyroscopic couple on a naval ship during steering taking left or right turn may be obtained in the similar way as for an aeroplane as discussed in Art.14.4.

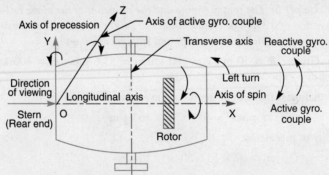

Fig. 14.8. Naval ship taking a left turn.

When the rotor of the ship rotates in the clockwise direction when viewed from the stern, it will have its angular momentum vector in the direction *ox* as shown in Fig. 14.9 (*a*). As the ship steers to the left, the active gyroscopic couple will change the angular momentum vector from *ox* to *ox'*. The vector *xx'* now represents the active gyroscopic couple and is perpendicular to *ox*. Thus the plane of active gyroscopic couple is perpendicular to *xx'* and its direction in the axis *OZ* for left hand turn is clockwise as shown in Fig. 14.8. The reactive gyroscopic couple of the same magnitude will act in the opposite direction (*i.e.* in anticlockwise direction). The *effect of this reactive gyroscopic couple is to raise the bow and lower the stern.*

Notes: 1. When the ship steers to the right under similar conditions as discussed above, the effect of the reactive gyroscopic couple, as shown in Fig. 14.9 (*b*), will be to **raise the stern** and **lower the bow.**

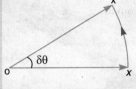

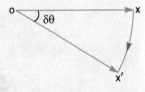

(*a*) Streeing to the left

(*b*) Streeing to the right

Fig. 14.9. Effect of gyroscopic couple on a naval ship during steering.

2. When the rotor rotates in the anticlockwise direction, when viewed from the stern and the ship is steering to the left, then the effect of reactive gyroscopic couple will be to **lower the bow** and **raise the stern.**

3. When the ship is steering to the right under similar conditions as discussed in note 2 above, then the effect of reactive gyroscopic couple will be to **raise the bow** and **lower the stern.**

4. When the rotor rotates in the clockwise direction when viewed from the bow or fore end and the ship is steering to the left, then the effect of reactive gyroscopic couple will be to **raise the stern** and **lower the bow.**

5. When the ship is steering to the right under similar conditions as discussed in note 4 above, then the effect of reactive gyroscopic couple will be to **raise the bow** and **lower the stern.**

6. The effect of the reactive gyroscopic couple on a boat propelled by a turbine taking left or right turn is similar as discussed above.

14.7. Effect of Gyroscopic Couple on a Naval Ship during Pitching

Pitching is the movement of a complete ship up and down in a vertical plane about transverse axis, as shown in Fig. 14.10 (*a*). In this case, the transverse axis is the axis of precession. The pitching of the ship is assumed to take place with simple harmonic motion *i.e.* the motion of the axis of spin about transverse axis is simple harmonic.

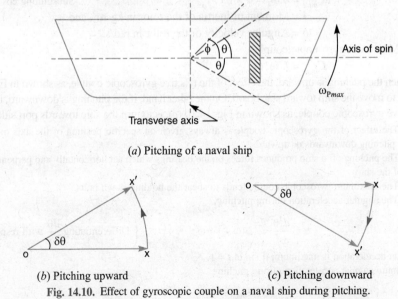

(*a*) Pitching of a naval ship

(*b*) Pitching upward

(*c*) Pitching downward

Fig. 14.10. Effect of gyroscopic couple on a naval ship during pitching.

Gryroscopic couple plays its role during ship's turning and pitching.

∴ Angular displacement of the axis of spin from mean position after time t seconds,

$$\theta = \phi \sin \omega_1 . t$$

where
ϕ = Amplitude of swing *i.e.* maximum angle turned from the mean position in radians, and

ω_1 = Angular velocity of S.H.M.

$$= \frac{2\pi}{\text{Time period of S.H.M. in seconds}} = \frac{2\pi}{t_p} \text{ rad/s}$$

Angular velocity of precession,

$$\omega_P = \frac{d\theta}{dt} = \frac{d}{dt}(\phi \sin \omega_1 . t) = \phi \omega_1 \cos \omega_1 t$$

The angular velocity of precession will be maximum, if $\cos \omega_1 . t = 1$.

∴ Maximum angular velocity of precession,

$$\omega_{Pmax} = \phi . \omega_1 = \phi \times 2\pi / t_p \qquad ...(\text{Substituting } \cos \omega_1 . t = 1)$$

Let
I = Moment of inertia of the rotor in kg-m², and

ω = Angular velocity of the rotor in rad/s.

∴ Maximum gyroscopic couple,

$$C_{max} = I. \omega. \omega_{Pmax}$$

When the pitching is upward, the effect of the reactive gyroscopic couple, as shown in Fig. 14.10 (*b*), will try to move the ship toward star-board. On the other hand, if the pitching is downward, the effect of the reactive gyroscopic couple, as shown in Fig. 14.10 (*c*), is to turn the ship towards port side.

Notes : 1. The effect of the gyroscopic couple is always given on specific position of the axis of spin *i.e.* whether it is pitching downwards or upwards.

2. The pitching of a ship produces forces on the bearings which act horizontally and perpendicular to the motion of the ship.

3. The maximum gyroscopic couple tends to shear the holding-down bolts.

4. The angular acceleration during pitching,

$$\alpha = \frac{d^2\theta}{dt^2} = -\phi(\omega_1)^2 \sin \omega_1 t \qquad ...\left(\text{Differentiating } \frac{d\theta}{dt} \text{ with respect to } t\right)$$

The angular acceleration is maximum, if $\sin \omega_1 t = 1$.

∴ Maximum angular acceleration during pitching,

$$\alpha_{max} = (\omega_1)^2$$

14.8. Effect of Gyroscopic Couple on a Naval Ship during Rolling

We know that, for the effect of gyroscopic couple to occur, the axis of precession should always be perpendicular to the axis of spin. If, however, the axis of precession becomes parallel to the axis of spin, there will be no effect of the gyroscopic couple acting on the body of the ship.

In case of rolling of a ship, the axis of precession (*i.e.* longitudinal axis) is always parallel to the axis of spin for all positions. Hence, there is no effect of the gyroscopic couple acting on the body of a ship.

Example 14.4. *The turbine rotor of a ship has a mass of 8 tonnes and a radius of gyration 0.6 m. It rotates at 1800 r.p.m. clockwise, when looking from the stern. Determine the gyroscopic couple, if the ship travels at 100 km/h and steer to the left in a curve of 75 m radius.*

Solution. Given: $m = 8$ t $= 8000$ kg ; $k = 0.6$ m ; $N = 1800$ r.p.m. or $\omega = 2\pi \times 1800/60$ $= 188.5$ rad/s ; $v = 100$ km/h $= 27.8$ m/s ; $R = 75$ m

We know that mass moment of inertia of the rotor,

$$I = m.k^2 = 8000\,(0.6)^2 = 2880 \text{ kg-m}^2$$

and angular velocity of precession,

$$\omega_p = v/R = 27.8/75 = 0.37 \text{ rad/s}$$

We know that gyroscopic couple,

$$C = I.\omega.\omega_p = 2880 \times 188.5 \times 0.37 = 200\ 866 \text{ N-m}$$

$$= 200.866 \text{ kN-m} \quad \text{Ans.}$$

We have discussed in Art. 14.6, that when the rotor rotates in clockwise direction when looking from the stern and the ship steers to the left, the effect of the reactive gyroscopic couple is to raise the bow and lower the stern.

Example 14.5. *The heavy turbine rotor of a sea vessel rotates at 1500 r.p.m. clockwise looking from the stern, its mass being 750 kg. The vessel pitches with an angular velocity of 1 rad/s. Determine the gyroscopic couple transmitted to the hull when bow is rising, if the radius of gyration for the rotor is 250 mm. Also show in what direction the couple acts on the hull?*

Solution. Given: $N = 1500$ r.p.m. or $\omega = 2\pi \times 1500/60 = 157.1$ rad/s; $m = 750$ kg; $\omega_p = 1$ rad/s; $k = 250$ mm $= 0.25$ m

We know that mass moment of inertia of the rotor,

$$I = m.k^2 = 750\,(0.25)^2 = 46.875 \text{ kg-m}^2$$

∴ Gyroscopic couple transmitted to the hull (*i.e.* body of the sea vessel),

Ship's propeller shown as a separate part. A ship's propeller is located at backside (stern) of the ship below the water surface.

$$C = I.\omega.\omega_p = 46.875 \times 157.1 \times 1 = 7364 \text{ N-m} = 7.364 \text{ kN-m}$$

We have discussed in Art. 14.7, that when the bow is rising *i.e.* when the pitching is upward, the reactive gyroscopic couple acts in the clockwise direction which moves the sea vessel towards star-board.

Example 14.6. *The turbine rotor of a ship has a mass of 3500 kg. It has a radius of gyration of 0.45 m and a speed of 3000 r.p.m. clockwise when looking from stern. Determine the gyroscopic couple and its effect upon the ship:*

1. when the ship is steering to the left on a curve of 100 m radius at a speed of 36 km/h.

2. when the ship is pitching in a simple harmonic motion, the bow falling with its maximum velocity. The period of pitching is 40 seconds and the total angular displacement between the two extreme positions of pitching is 12 degrees.

Solution. Given : $m = 3500$ kg ; $k = 0.45$ m; $N = 3000$ r.p.m. or $\omega = 2\pi \times 3000/60 = 314.2$ rad/s

1. When the ship is steering to the left

Given: $R = 100$ m ; $v = 36$ km/h $= 10$ m/s

We know that mass moment of inertia of the rotor,

$$I = m.k^2 = 3500\,(0.45)^2 = 708.75 \text{ kg-m}^2$$

and angular velocity of precession,

$$\omega_p = v/R = 10/100 = 0.1 \text{ rad/s}$$

∴ Gyroscopic couple,

$$C = I.\omega.\omega_p = 708.75 \times 314.2 \times 0.1 = 22\,270 \text{ N-m}$$

$$= 22.27 \text{ kN-m } \textbf{Ans.}$$

We have discussed in Art. 14.6, that when the rotor rotates clockwise when looking from the stern and the ship takes a left turn, the effect of the reactive gyroscopic couple is to raise the bow and lower the stern. **Ans.**

2. When the ship is pitching with the bow falling

Given: $t_p = 40$ s

Since the total angular displacement between the two extreme positions of pitching is 12° (*i.e.* $2\phi = 12°$), therefore amplitude of swing,

$$\phi = 12 / 2 = 6° = 6 \times \pi/180 = 0.105 \text{ rad}$$

and angular velocity of the simple harmonic motion,

$$\omega_1 = 2\pi / t_p = 2\pi / 40 = 0.157 \text{ rad/s}$$

We know that maximum angular velocity of precession,

$$\omega_p = \phi.\omega_1 = 0.105 \times 0.157 = 0.0165 \text{ rad/s}$$

∴ Gyroscopic couple,

$$C = I.\omega.\omega_p = 708.75 \times 314.2 \times 0.0165 = 3675 \text{ N-m}$$

$$= 3.675 \text{ kN-m } \textbf{Ans.}$$

We have discussed in Art. 14.7, that when the bow is falling (*i.e.* when the pitching is downward), the effect of the reactive gyroscopic couple is to move the ship towards port side. **Ans.**

Example 14.7. *The mass of the turbine rotor of a ship is 20 tonnes and has a radius of gyration of 0.60 m. Its speed is 2000 r.p.m. The ship pitches 6° above and 6° below the horizontal position. A complete oscillation takes 30 seconds and the motion is simple harmonic. Determine the following:*

1. Maximum gyroscopic couple, 2. Maximum angular acceleration of the ship during pitching, and 3. The direction in which the bow will tend to turn when rising, if the rotation of the rotor is clockwise when looking from the left.

Solution. Given : $m = 20$ t = 20 000 kg ; $k = 0.6$ m ; $N = 2000$ r.p.m. or $\omega = 2\pi \times 2000/60 = 209.5$ rad/s; $\phi = 6° = 6 \times \pi/180 = 0.105$ rad ; $t_p = 30$ s

1. *Maximum gyroscopic couple*

We know that mass moment of inertia of the rotor,

$$I = m.k^2 = 20\ 000\ (0.6)^2 = 7200 \text{ kg-m}^2$$

and angular velocity of the simple harmonic motion,

$$\omega_1 = 2\pi / t_p = 2\pi/30 = 0.21 \text{ rad/s}$$

∴ Maximum angular velocity of precession,

$$\omega_{Pmax} = \phi.\omega_1 = 0.105 \times 0.21 = 0.022 \text{ rad/s}$$

We know that maximum gyroscopic couple,

$$C_{max} = I.\omega.\omega_{Pmax} = 7200 \times 209.5 \times 0.022 = 33\ 185 \text{ N-m}$$
$$= 33.185 \text{ kN-m } \textbf{Ans.}$$

2. *Maximum angular acceleration during pitching*

We know that maximum angular acceleration during pitching

$$= \phi(\omega_1)^2 = 0.105\ (0.21)^2 = 0.0046 \text{ rad/s}^2 \textbf{ Ans.}$$

3. *Direction in which the bow will tend to turn when rising*

We have discussed in Art. 14.7, that when the rotation of the rotor is clockwise when looking from the left (*i.e.* rear end or stern) and when the bow is rising (*i.e.* pitching is upward), then the reactive gyroscopic couple acts in the clockwise direction which tends to turn the bow towards right (*i.e.* towards star-board). **Ans.**

Example 14.8. *A ship propelled by a turbine rotor which has a mass of 5 tonnes and a speed of 2100 r.p.m. The rotor has a radius of gyration of 0.5 m and rotates in a clockwise direction when viewed from the stern. Find the gyroscopic effects in the following conditions:*

1. The ship sails at a speed of 30 km/h and steers to the left in a curve having 60 m radius.

2. The ship pitches 6 degree above and 6 degree below the horizontal position. The bow is descending with its maximum velocity. The motion due to pitching is simple harmonic and the periodic time is 20 seconds.

3. The ship rolls and at a certain instant it has an angular velocity of 0.03 rad/s clockwise when viewed from stern.

Determine also the maximum angular acceleration during pitching. Explain how the direction of motion due to gyroscopic effect is determined in each case.

Solution. Given : $m = 5$ t = 5000 kg ; $N = 2100$ r.p.m. or $\omega = 2\pi \times 2100/60 = 220$ rad/s ; $k = 0.5$ m

1. *When the ship steers to the left*

Given: $v = 30$ km / h = 8.33 m / s ; $R = 60$ m

We know that angular velocity of precession,

$$\omega_p = v/R = 8.33/60 = 0.14 \text{ rad/s}$$

and mass moment of inertia of the rotor,

$$I = m.k^2 = 5000(0.5)^2 = 1250 \text{ kg-m}^2$$

∴ Gyroscopic couple,

$$C = I.\omega.\omega_p = 1250 \times 220 \times 0.14 = 38\,500 \text{ N-m} = 38.5 \text{ kN-m}$$

We have discussed in Art. 14.6, that when the rotor rotates in a clockwise direction when viewed from the stern and the ship steers to the left, the effect of reactive gyroscopic couple is to raise the bow and lower the stern. **Ans.**

2. *When the ship pitches with the bow descending*

Given: $\phi = 6° = 6 \times \pi/180 = 0.105$ rad/s ; $t_p = 20$ s

We know that angular velocity of simple harmonic motion,

$$\omega_1 = 2\pi / t_p = 2\pi / 20 = 0.3142 \text{ rad/s}$$

and maximum angular velocity of precession,

$$\omega_{Pmax} = \phi.\omega_1 = 0.105 \times 0.3142 = 0.033 \text{ rad/s}$$

∴ Maximum gyroscopic couple,

$$C_{max} = I.\omega.\omega_{Pmax} = 1250 \times 220 \times 0.033 = 9075 \text{ N-m}$$

Since the ship is pitching with the bow descending, therefore the effect of this maximum gyroscopic couple is to turn the ship towards port side. **Ans.**

3. *When the ship rolls*

Since the ship rolls at an angular velocity of 0.03 rad / s, therefore angular velocity of precession when the ship rolls,

$$\omega_p = 0.03 \text{ rad /s}$$

∴ Gyroscopic couple,

$$C = I.\omega.\omega_p = 1250 \times 220 \times 0.03 = 8250 \text{ N-m}$$

In case of rolling of a ship, the axis of precession is always parallel to the axis of spin for all positions, therefore there is no effect of gyroscopic couple. **Ans.**

Maximum angular acceleration during pitching

We know that maximum angular acceleration during pitching.

$$\alpha_{max} = \phi\,(\omega_1)^2 = 0.105\,(0.3142)^2 = 0.01 \text{ rad/s}^2 \text{ Ans.}$$

Example 14.9. *The turbine rotor of a ship has a mass of 2000 kg and rotates at a speed of 3000 r.p.m. clockwise when looking from a stern. The radius of gyration of the rotor is 0.5 m.*

Determine the gyroscopic couple and its effects upon the ship when the ship is steering to the right in a curve of 100 m radius at a speed of 16.1 knots (1 knot = 1855 m/h).

Calculate also the torque and its effects when the ship is pitching in simple harmonic motion, the bow falling with its maximum velocity. The period of pitching is 50 seconds and the total angular displacement between the two extreme positions of pitching is 12°. Find the maximum acceleration during pitching motion.

Solution. Given : $m = 2000$ kg ; $N = 3000$ r.p.m. or $\omega = 2\pi \times 3000/60 = 314.2$ rad/s ; $k = 0.5$ m ; $R = 100$ m ; $v = 16.1$ knots $= 16.1 \times 1855 / 3600 = 8.3$ m/s

Gyroscopic couple

We know that mass moment of inertia of the rotor,

$$I = m.k^2 = 2000\,(0.5)^2 = 500 \text{ kg-m}^2$$

and angular velocity of precession,

$$\omega_p = v/R = 8.3/100 = 0.083 \text{ rad /s}$$

∴ Gyroscopic couple,
$$C = I.\omega.\omega_p = 500 \times 314.2 \times 0.083 = 13\ 040 \text{ N-m} = 13.04 \text{ kN-m}$$

We have discussed in Art. 14.6, that when the rotor rotates clockwise when looking from a stern and the ship steers to the right, the effect of the reactive gyroscopic couple is to raise the stern and lower the bow. **Ans.**

Torque during pitching

Given : $t_p = 50$ s ; $2\phi = 12°$ or $\phi = 6° \times \pi/180 = 0.105$ rad

We know that angular velocity of simple harmonic motion,
$$\omega_1 = 2\pi /t_p = 2\pi /50 = 0.1257 \text{ rad/s}$$

and maximum angular velocity of precession,
$$\omega_{Pmax} = \phi.\omega_1 = 0.105 \times 0.1257 = 0.0132 \text{ rad/s}$$

∴ Torque or maximum gyroscopic couple during pitching,
$$C_{max} = I.\omega.\omega_{P\ max} = 500 \times 314.2 \times 0.0132 = 2074 \text{ N-m Ans.}$$

We have discussed in Art. 14.7, that when the pitching is downwards, the effect of the reactive gyroscopic couple is to turn the ship towards port side.

Maximum acceleration during pitching

We know that maximum acceleration during pitching
$$\alpha_{max} = \phi\ (\omega_1)^2 = 0.105\ (0.1257)^2 = 0.00166 \text{ rad/s}^2 \text{ Ans.}$$

14.9. Stability of a Four Wheel Drive Moving in a Curved Path

Consider the four wheels A, B, C and D of an automobile locomotive taking a turn towards left as shown in Fig. 14.11. The wheels A and C are inner wheels, whereas B and D are outer wheels. The centre of gravity (*C.G.*) of the vehicle lies vertically above the road surface.

Let m = Mass of the vehicle in kg,

W = Weight of the vehicle in newtons = $m.g$,

r_W = Radius of the wheels in metres,

R = Radius of curvature in metres ($R > r_W$),

h = Distance of centre of gravity, vertically above the road surface in metres,

x = Width of track in metres,

I_W = Mass moment of inertia of one of the wheels in kg-m^2,

ω_W = Angular velocity of the wheels or velocity of spin in rad/s,

I_E = Mass moment of inertia of the rotating parts of the engine in kg-m^2,

ω_E = Angular velocity of the rotating parts of the engine in rad/s,

G = Gear ratio = ω_E /ω_W,

v = Linear velocity of the vehicle in m/s = $\omega_W.r_W$

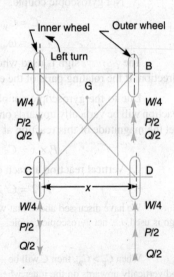

Fig. 14.11. Four wheel drive moving in a curved path.

A little consideration will show, that the weight of the vehicle (W) will be equally distributed over the four wheels which will act downwards. The reaction between each wheel and the road surface of the same magnitude will act upwards. Therefore

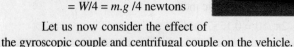

Road reaction over each wheel
= $W/4 = m.g /4$ newtons

Let us now consider the effect of the gyroscopic couple and centrifugal couple on the vehicle.

1. Effect of the gyroscopic couple

Since the vehicle takes a turn towards left due to the precession and other rotating parts, therefore a gyroscopic couple will act.

We know that velocity of precession,

$$\omega_P = v/R$$

∴ Gyroscopic couple due to 4 wheels,

$$C_W = 4\, I_W.\omega_W.\omega_P$$

and gyroscopic couple due to the rotating parts of the engine,

$$C_E = I_E.\omega_E.\omega_P = I_E.G.\omega_W.\omega_P \qquad \qquad ...(\because G = \omega_E/\omega_W)$$

∴ Net gyroscopic couple,

$$C = C_W \pm C_E = 4\, I_W.\omega_W.\omega_P \pm I_E.G.\omega_W.\omega_P$$
$$= \omega_W.\omega_P\,(4\, I_W \pm G.I_E)$$

The *positive* sign is used when the wheels and rotating parts of the engine rotate in the same direction. If the rotating parts of the engine revolves in opposite direction, then *negative* sign is used.

Due to the gyroscopic couple, vertical reaction on the road surface will be produced. The reaction will be vertically upwards on the outer wheels and vertically downwards on the inner wheels. Let the magnitude of this reaction at the two outer or inner wheels be P newtons. Then

$$P \times x = C \quad \text{or} \quad P = C/x$$

∴ Vertical reaction at each of the outer or inner wheels,

$$P\, /2 = C/\, 2x$$

Note: We have discussed above that when rotating parts of the engine rotate in opposite directions, then –ve sign is used, *i.e.* net gyroscopic couple,

$$C = C_W - C_E$$

When $C_E > C_W$, then C will be –ve. Thus the reaction will be vertically downwards on the outer wheels and vertically upwards on the inner wheels.

2. Effect of the centrifugal couple

Since the vehicle moves along a curved path, therefore centrifugal force will act outwardly at the centre of gravity of the vehicle. The effect of this centrifugal force is also to overturn the vehicle. We know that centrifugal force,

$$F_C = \frac{m \times v^2}{R}$$

∴ The couple tending to overturn the vehicle or overturning couple,

$$C_O = F_C \times h = \frac{m.v^2}{R} \times h$$

This overturning couple is balanced by vertical reactions, which are vertically upwards on the outer wheels and vertically downwards on the inner wheels. Let the magnitude of this reaction at the two outer or inner wheels be Q. Then

$$Q \times x = C_O \quad \text{or} \quad Q = \frac{C_O}{x} = \frac{m.v^2.h}{R.x}$$

∴ Vertical reaction at each of the outer or inner wheels,

$$\frac{Q}{2} = \frac{m.v^2.h}{2R.x}$$

∴ Total vertical reaction at each of the outer wheel,

$$P_O = \frac{W}{4} + \frac{P}{2} + \frac{Q}{2}$$

and total vertical reaction at each of the inner wheel,

$$P_I = \frac{W}{4} - \frac{P}{2} - \frac{Q}{2}$$

A little consideration will show that when the vehicle is running at high speeds, P_I may be zero or even negative. This will cause the inner wheels to leave the ground thus tending to overturn the automobile. In order to have the contact between the inner wheels and the ground, the sum of $P/2$ and $Q/2$ must be less than $W/4$.

Example 14.10. *A four-wheeled trolley car of mass 2500 kg runs on rails, which are 1.5 m apart and travels around a curve of 30 m radius at 24 km / h. The rails are at the same level. Each wheel of the trolley is 0.75 m in diameter and each of the two axles is driven by a motor running in a direction opposite to that of the wheels at a speed of five times the speed of rotation of the wheels. The moment of inertia of each axle with gear and wheels is 18 kg-m². Each motor with shaft and gear pinion has a moment of inertia of 12 kg-m². The centre of gravity of the car is 0.9 m above the rail level. Determine the vertical force exerted by each wheel on the rails taking into consideration the centrifugal and gyroscopic effects. State the centrifugal and gyroscopic effects on the trolley.*

Solution. Given : $m = 2500$ kg ; $x = 1.5$ m ; $R = 30$ m ; $v = 24$ km/h $= 6.67$ m/s ; $d_W = 0.75$ m or $r_W = 0.375$ m ; $G = \omega_E/\omega_W = 5$; $I_W = 18$ kg-m² ; $I_E = 12$ kg-m² ; $h = 0.9$ m

The weight of the trolley ($W = m.g$) will be equally distributed over the four wheels, which will act downwards. The reaction between the wheels and the road surface of the same magnitude will act upwards.

∴ Road reaction over each wheel $= W/4 = m.g/4 = 2500 \times 9.81/4 = 6131.25$ N

We know that angular velocity of the wheels,

$$\omega_W = v/r_W = 6.67/0.375 = 17.8 \text{ rad/s}$$

and angular velocity of precession, $\omega_p = v/R = 6.67/30 = 0.22$ rad/s

∴ Gyroscopic couple due to one pair of wheels and axle,

$$C_W = 2\,I_W . \omega_W . \omega_p = 2 \times 18 \times 17.8 \times 0.22 = 141 \text{ N-m}$$

and gyroscopic couple due to the rotating parts of the motor and gears,

$$C_E = 2\,I_E . \omega_E . \omega_p = 2\,I_E . G . \omega_W . \omega_p \qquad \dots (\because \omega_E = G.\, \omega_W)$$
$$= 2 \times 12 \times 5 \times 17.8 \times 0.22 = 470 \text{ N-m}$$

∴ Net gyroscopic couple, $\qquad C = C_W - C_E = 141 - 470 = -329$ N-m

... (–ve sign is used due to opposite direction of motor)

Due to this net gyroscopic couple, the vertical reaction on the rails will be produced. Since C_E is greater than C_W, therefore the reaction will be vertically downwards on the outer wheels and vertically upwards on the inner wheels. Let the magnitude of this reaction at each of the outer or inner wheel be $P/2$ newton.

∴ $\qquad P/2 = C/2x = 329 / 2 \times 1.5 = 109.7$ N

We know that centrifugal force, $\qquad F_C = m.v^2/R = 2500\,(6.67)^2/30 = 3707$ N

∴ Overturning couple, $\qquad C_O = F_C \times h = 3707 \times 0.9 = 3336.3$ N-m

This overturning couple is balanced by the vertical reactions which are vertically upwards on the outer wheels and vertically downwards on the inner wheels. Let the magnitude of this reaction at each of the outer or inner wheels be $Q/2$ newton.

∴ $\qquad Q/2 = C_O/2x = 3336.3 / 2 \times 1.5 = 1112.1$ N

We know that vertical force exerted on each outer wheel,

$$P_O = \frac{W}{4} - \frac{P}{2} + \frac{Q}{2} = 6131.25 - 109.7 + 1112.1 = 7142.65 \text{ N Ans.}$$

and vertical force exerted on each inner wheel,

$$P_I = \frac{W}{4} + \frac{P}{2} - \frac{Q}{2} = 6131.25 + 109.7 - 1112.1 = 5128.85 \text{ N Ans.}$$

Example 14.11. *A rear engine automobile is travelling along a track of 100 metres mean radius. Each of the four road wheels has a moment of inertia of 2.5 kg-m² and an effective diameter of 0.6 m. The rotating parts of the engine have a moment of inertia of 1.2 kg-m². The engine axis is parallel to the rear axle and the crankshaft rotates in the same sense as the road wheels. The ratio of engine speed to back axle speed is 3 : 1. The automobile has a mass of 1600 kg and has its centre of gravity 0.5 m above road level. The width of the track of the vehicle is 1.5 m.*

Determine the limiting speed of the vehicle around the curve for all four wheels to maintain contact with the road surface. Assume that the road surface is not cambered and centre of gravity of the automobile lies centrally with respect to the four wheels.

Solution. Given : $R = 100$ m ; $I_W = 2.5$ kg-m² ; $d_W = 0.6$ m or $r_W = 0.3$ m ; $I_E = 1.2$ kg-m²; $G = \omega_E/\omega_W = 3$; $m = 1600$ kg ; $h = 0.5$ m ; $x = 1.5$ m

The weight of the vehicle $(m.g)$ will be equally distributed over the four wheels which will act downwards. The reaction between the wheel and the road surface of the same magnitude will act upwards.

∴ Road reaction over each wheel

$$= W/4 = m.g / 4 = 1600 \times 9.81/4 = 3924 \text{ N}$$

Let v = Limiting speed of the vehicle in m/s.

We know that angular velocity of the wheels,

$$\omega_W = \frac{v}{r_W} = \frac{v}{0.3} = 3.33\ v\ \text{rad/s}$$

and angular velocity of precession,

$$\omega_P = \frac{v}{R} = \frac{v}{100} = 0.01\ v\ \text{rad/s}$$

∴ Gyroscopic couple due to 4 wheels,

$$C_W = 4\ I_W.\omega_W.\omega_P = 4 \times 2.5 \times \frac{v}{0.3} \times \frac{v}{100} = 0.33\ v^2\ \text{N-m}$$

and gyroscopic couple due to rotating parts of the engine,

$$C_E = I_E.\omega_E.\omega_P = I_E.G.\omega_W.\omega_P$$
$$= 1.2 \times 3 \times 3.33v \times 0.01v = 0.12\ v^2\ \text{N-m}$$

∴ Total gyroscopic couple,

$$C = C_W + C_E = 0.33\ v^2 + 0.12\ v^2 = 0.45\ v^2\ \text{N-m}$$

Due to this gyroscopic couple, the vertical reaction on the rails will be produced. The reaction will be vertically upwards on the outer wheels and vertically downwards on the inner wheels. Let the magnitude of this reaction at each of the outer or inner wheel be $P/2$ newtons.

∴ $$P/2 = C/2x = 0.45v^2/2 \times 1.5 = 0.15\ v^2\ \text{N}$$

We know that centrifugal force,

$$F_C = m.v^2/R = 1600 \times v^2/100 = 16\ v^2\ \text{N}$$

∴ Overturning couple acting in the outward direction,

$$C_O = F_C \times h = 16\ v^2 \times 0.5 = 8\ v^2\ \text{N-m}$$

This overturning couple is balanced by vertical reactions which are vertically upwards on the outer wheels and vertically downwards on the inner wheels. Let the magnitude of this reaction at each of the outer or inner wheels be $Q/2$ newtons.

∴ $$Q/2 = C_O/2x = 8\ v^2/2 \times 1.5 = 2.67\ v^2\ \text{N}$$

We know that total vertical reaction at each of the outer wheels,

$$P_O = \frac{W}{4} + \frac{P}{2} + \frac{Q}{2} \qquad \text{...(i)}$$

and total vertical reaction at each of the inner wheels,

$$P_I = \frac{W}{4} - \frac{P}{2} - \frac{Q}{2} = \frac{W}{4} - \left(\frac{P}{2} + \frac{Q}{2}\right) \qquad \text{...(ii)}$$

From equation (i), we see that there will always be contact between the outer wheels and the road surface because $W/4$, $P/2$ and $Q/2$ are vertically upwards. In order to have contact between the inner wheels and road surface, the reactions should also be vertically upwards, which is only possible if

$$\frac{P}{2} + \frac{Q}{2} \le \frac{W}{4}$$

i.e. $0.15 v^2 + 2.67 v^2 \le 3924$ or $2.82 v^2 \le 3924$

∴ $v^2 \le 3924/2.82 = 1391.5$

or $v \le 37.3$ m/s $= 37.3 \times 3600 / 1000 = 134.28$ km/h **Ans.**

Example 14.12. *A four wheeled motor car of mass 2000 kg has a wheel base 2.5 m, track width 1.5 m and height of centre of gravity 500 mm above the ground level and lies at 1 metre from the front axle. Each wheel has an effective diameter of 0.8 m and a moment of inertia of 0.8 kg-m². The drive shaft, engine flywheel and transmission are rotating at 4 times the speed of road wheel, in a clockwise direction when viewed from the front, and is equivalent to a mass of 75 kg having a radius of gyration of 100 mm. If the car is taking a right turn of 60 m radius at 60 km/h, find the load on each wheel.*

Solution. Given : $m = 2000$ kg : $b = 2.5$ m ; $x = 1.5$ m ; $h = 500$ mm $= 0.5$ m ; $L = 1$ m ; $d_W = 0.8$ m or $r_W = 0.4$ m ; $I_W = 0.8$ kg-m² ; $G = \omega_E / \omega_W = 4$; $m_E = 75$ kg ; $k_E = 100$ mm $= 0.1$ m ; $R = 60$ m ; $v = 60$ km/h $= 16.67$ m/s

Since the centre of gravity of the car lies at 1 m from the front axle and the weight of the car ($W = m.g$) lies at the centre of gravity, therefore weight on the front wheels and rear wheels will be different.

Let W_1 = Weight on the front wheels, and

         W_2 = Weight on the rear wheels.

Taking moment about the front wheels,

     $W_2 \times 2.5 = W \times 1 = m.g \times 1 = 2000 \times 9.81 \times 1 = 19\ 620$

∴ $W_2 = 19\ 620 / 2.5 = 7848$ N

We know that weight of the car or on the four wheels,

     $W = W_1 + W_2 = m.g = 2000 \times 9.81 = 19\ 620$ N

or $W_1 = W - W_2 = 19\ 620 - 7848 = 11\ 772$ N

∴ Weight on each of the front wheels

     $= W_1 / 2 = 11\ 772 / 2 = 5886$ N

and weight on each of the rear wheels

     $= W_2 / 2 = 7848 / 2 = 3924$ N

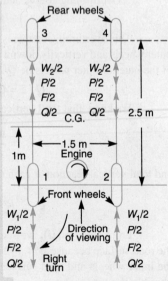

Since the weight of the car over the four wheels will act downwards, therefore the reaction between each wheel and the road surface of the same magnitude will act upwards as shown in Fig. 14.12.

Let us now consider the effect of gyroscopic couple due to four wheels and rotating parts of the engine.

We know angular velocity of wheels,

     $\omega_W = v/r_W = 16.67 / 0.4 = 41.675$ rad /s

and angular velocity of precession,

     $\omega_p = v/R = 16.67 / 60 = 0.278$ rad /s

Fig. 14.12

∴ Gyroscopic couple due to four wheels,

$$C_W = 4\,I_W.\omega_W.\omega_P$$
$$= 4 \times 0.8 \times 41.675 \times 0.278 = 37.1 \text{ N-m}$$

This gyroscopic couple tends to lift the front wheels and to press the rear wheels. In other words, the reaction will be vertically downward on the inner wheels (*i.e.* wheels 1 and 3) and vertically upward on the outer wheels (*i.e.* wheels 2 and 4) as shown in Fig. 14.12. Let $P/2$ newtons be the magnitude of this reaction at each of the inner or outer wheel.

∴ $\qquad P/2 = C_W/2x = 37.1/2 \times 1.5 = 12.37 \text{ N}$

We know that mass moment of inertia of rotating parts of the engine,

$$I_E = m_E\,(k_E)^2 = 75\,(0.1)^2 = 0.75 \text{ kg-m}^2 \qquad\qquad ...(\because I = m.k^2)$$

∴ Gyroscopic couple due to rotating parts of the engine,

$$C_E = I_E.\omega_E.\omega_P = m_E\,(k_E)^2\,G.\,\omega_W.\omega_P$$
$$= 75\,(0.1)^2\,4 \times 41.675 \times 0.278 = 34.7 \text{ N-m}$$

This gyroscopic couple tends to lift the front wheels and to press the outer wheels. In other words, the reaction will be vertically downwards on the front wheels and vertically upwards on the rear wheels as shown in Fig. 14.12. Let $F/2$ newtons be the magnitude of this reaction on each of the front and rear wheels.

∴ $\qquad F/2 = C_E/2b = 34.7/2 \times 2.5 = 6.94 \text{ N}$

Now let us consider the effect of centrifugal couple acting on the car. We know that centrifugal force,

$$F_C = m.v^2/R = 2000\,(16.67)^2/60 = 9263 \text{ N}$$

∴ Centrifugal couple tending to overturn the car or over turning couple,

$$C_O = F_C \times h = 9263 \times 0.5 = 4631.5 \text{ N-m}$$

This overturning couple tends to reduce the pressure on the inner wheels and to increase on the outer wheels. In other words, the reactions are vertically downward on the inner wheels and vertically upwards on the outer wheels. Let $Q/2$ be the magnitude of this reaction on each of the inner and outer wheels.

∴ $\qquad Q/2 = C_O/2x = 4631.5/2 \times 1.5 = 1543.83 \text{ N}$

From Fig. 14.12, we see that

Load on the front wheel 1

$$= \frac{W_1}{2} - \frac{P}{2} - \frac{F}{2} - \frac{Q}{2} = 5886 - 12.37 - 6.94 - 1543.83 = 4322.86 \text{ N Ans.}$$

Load on the front wheel 2

$$= \frac{W_1}{2} + \frac{P}{2} - \frac{F}{2} + \frac{Q}{2} = 5886 + 12.37 - 6.94 + 1543.83 = 7435.26 \text{ N Ans.}$$

Load on the rear wheel 3

$$= \frac{W_2}{2} - \frac{P}{2} + \frac{F}{2} - \frac{Q}{2} = 3924 - 12.37 + 6.94 - 1543.83 = 2374.74 \text{ N Ans.}$$

Load on the rear wheel 4

$$= \frac{W_2}{2} + \frac{P}{2} + \frac{F}{2} + \frac{Q}{2} = 3924 + 12.37 + 6.94 + 1543.83 = 5487.14 \text{ N Ans.}$$

Example 14.13. *A four-wheeled trolley car of total mass 2000 kg running on rails of 1.6 m gauge, rounds a curve of 30 m radius at 54 km/h. The track is banked at 8°. The wheels have an external diameter of 0.7 m and each pair with axle has a mass of 200 kg. The radius of gyration for each pair is 0.3 m. The height of centre of gravity of the car above the wheel base is 1 m. Determine, allowing for centrifugal force and gyroscopic couple actions, the pressure on each rail.*

Solution. Given : $m = 2000$ kg ; $x = 1.6$ m ; $R = 30$ m ; $v = 54$ km / h $= 15$ m / s ; $\theta = 8°$; $d_W = 0.7$ m or $r_W = 0.35$ m ; $m_1 = 200$ kg ; $k = 0.3$ m ; $h = 1$ m

First of all, let us find the reactions R_A and R_B at the wheels A and B respectively. The various forces acting on the trolley car are shown in Fig. 14.13.

Resolving the forces perpendicular to the track,

$$R_A + R_B = W \cos \theta + F_C \sin \theta = m.g \cos \theta + \frac{m.v^2}{R} \sin \theta$$

$$= 2000 \times 9.81 \cos 8° + \frac{2000 \,(15)^2}{30} \times \sin 8°$$

$$= 19\,620 \times 0.9903 + 15\,000 \times 0.1392 = 21\,518 \text{ N}$$

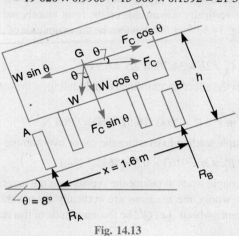

Fig. 14.13

Now taking moments about B,

$$R_A \times x = (W \cos \theta + F_C \sin \theta) \frac{x}{2} + W \sin \theta \times h - F_C \cos \theta \times h$$

$$\therefore \quad R_A = \left(m.g \cos \theta + \frac{m.v^2}{R} \sin \theta \right) \frac{1}{2} + \left(m.g \sin \theta - \frac{m.v^2}{R} \cos \theta \right) \frac{h}{x}$$

$$= \left(2000 \times 9.81 \cos 8° + \frac{2000 \,(15)^2}{30} \sin 8° \right) \frac{1}{2}$$

$$+ \left(2000 \times 9.81 \sin 8° - \frac{2000 \,(15)^2}{30} \cos 8° \right) \frac{1}{1.6}$$

$$= (19\,620 \times 0.9903 + 15\,000 \times 0.1392) \frac{1}{2}$$

$$+ (19\,620 \times 0.1392 - 15\,000 \times 0.9903) \frac{1}{1.6}$$

$$= (19\ 430 + 2088)\ \frac{1}{2} + (2731 - 14\ 855)\ \frac{1}{1.6}$$

$$= 10\ 759 - 7577 = 3182\ N$$

$$\therefore \qquad R_B = (R_A + R_B) - R_A = 21\ 518 - 3182 = 18\ 336\ N$$

We know that angular velocity of wheels,

$$\omega_W = \frac{v}{r_W} = \frac{15}{0.35} = 42.86\ \text{rad}/s$$

and angular velocity of precession,

$$\omega_P = \frac{v}{R} = \frac{15}{30} = 0.5\ \text{rad}/s$$

∴ Gyroscopic couple,

$$C = {}^* I\ \omega_W \cos \theta \times \omega_P = m_1.k^2.\omega_W \cos \theta.\omega_P \qquad ...(\because I = m_1.k^2)$$

$$= 200\ (0.3)^2\ 42.86 \cos 8° \times 0.5 = 382\ N\text{-}m$$

Due to this gyroscopic couple, the car will tend to overturn about the outer wheels. Let *P* be the force at each pair of wheels or each rail due to the gyroscopic couple,

$$\therefore \qquad P = C / x = 382 / 1.6 = 238.75\ N$$

We know that pressure (or total reaction) on the inner rail,

$$P_I = R_A - P = 3182 - 238.75 = 2943.25\ N\ \textbf{Ans.}$$

and pressure on the outer rail,

$$P_O = R_B + P = 18\ 336 + 238.75 = 18\ 574.75\ N\ \textbf{Ans.}$$

Example 14.14. *A pair of locomotive driving wheels with the axle, have a moment of inertia of 180 kg-m². The diameter of the wheel treads is 1.8 m and the distance between wheel centres is 1.5 m. When the locomotive is travelling on a level track at 95 km/h, defective ballasting causes one wheel to fall 6 mm and to rise again in a total time of 0.1 s. If the displacement of the wheel takes place with simple harmonic motion, find : 1. The gyroscopic couple set up, and 2. The reaction between the wheel and rail due to this couple.*

Solution. Given : $I = 180$ kg-m² ; $D = 1.8$ m or $R = 0.9$ m ; $x = 1.5$ m ; $v = 95$ km / h $= 26.4$ m /s

1. *Gyroscopic couple set up*

We know that angular velocity of the locomotive,

$$\omega = v/R = 26.4/\ 0.9 = 29.3\ \text{rad}/s$$

Since the defective ballasting causes one wheel to fall 6 mm and to rise again in a total time (*t*) of 0.1 s, therefore

$$\text{Amplitude, } A = \frac{1}{2}\ \text{Fall} = \frac{1}{2}\ \text{Rise} = \frac{1}{2} \times 6 = 3\ \text{mm}$$

and maximum velocity while falling,

$$v_{max} = \frac{2\pi}{t} \times A = \frac{2\pi}{0.1} \times 3 = 188.5\ \text{mm}/s = 0.1885\ \text{m}/s$$

∴ Maximum angular velocity of tilt of the axle or angular velocity of precession,

$$\omega_{P\ max} = \frac{v_{max}}{x} = \frac{0.1885}{1.5} = 0.126\ \text{rad}/s$$

---

* Angular momentum about axle = $I.\omega_W$

∴ Angular momentum about horizontal = $I.\omega_W \cos \theta$

We know that gyroscopic couple set up,

$$C = I.\omega.\omega_{P\,max} = 180 \times 29.3 \times 0.126 = 664.5 \text{ N-m Ans.}$$

The gyroscopic couple will act in a horizontal plane and this couple will tend to produce *swerve* *i.e.* it tends to turn the locomotive aside.

2. *Reaction between the wheel and rail due to the gyroscopic couple*

We know that the reaction between the wheel and rail due to the gyroscopic couple is

$$P = C / x = 664.5 / 1.5 = 443 \text{ N Ans.}$$

14.10. Stability of a Two Wheel Vehicle Taking a Turn

Consider a two wheel vehicle (say a scooter or motor cycle) taking a right turn as shown in Fig. 14.14 (*a*).

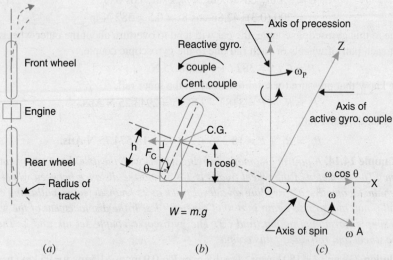

Fig. 14.14. Stability of a two wheel vehicle taking a turn.

Let m = Mass of the vehicle and its rider in kg,

W = Weight of the vehicle and its rider in newtons = $m.g$,

h = Height of the centre of gravity of the vehicle and rider,

r_W = Radius of the wheels,

R = Radius of track or curvature,

I_W = Mass moment of inertia of each wheel,

I_E = Mass moment of inertia of the rotating parts of the engine,

ω_W = Angular velocity of the wheels,

ω_E = Angular velocity of the engine,

G = Gear ratio = ω_E / ω_W,

Motorcycle taking a turn.

v = Linear velocity of the vehicle = $\omega_W \times r_W$,

θ = Angle of heel. It is inclination of the vehicle to the vertical for equilibrium.

Let us now consider the effect of the gyroscopic couple and centrifugal couple on the vehicle, as discussed below.

1. Effect of gyroscopic couple

We know that $\quad v = \omega_W \times r_W \quad$ or $\quad \omega_W = v / r_W$

and

$$\omega_E = G.\omega_W = G \times \frac{v}{r_W}$$

$\therefore$ Total $\quad (I \times \omega) = 2\,I_W \times \omega_W \pm I_E \times \omega_E$

$$= 2\,I_W \times \frac{v}{r_W} \pm I_E \times G \times \frac{v}{r_W} = \frac{v}{r_W}\,(2\,I_W \pm G.I_E)$$

and velocity of precession, $\omega_P = v / R$

A little consideration will show that when the wheels move over the curved path, the vehicle is always inclined at an angle θ with the vertical plane as shown in Fig. 14.14 (*b*). This angle is known as *angle of heel*. In other words, the axis of spin is inclined to the horizontal at an angle θ, as shown in Fig. 14.14 (*c*). Thus the angular momentum vector $I\omega$ due to spin is represented by *OA* inclined to *OX* at an angle θ. But the precession axis is vertical. Therefore the spin vector is resolved along *OX*.

$\therefore$ Gyroscopic couple,

$$C_1 = I.\omega \cos\theta \times \omega_P = \frac{v}{r_W}\,(2\,I_W \pm G.I_E)\cos\theta \times \frac{v}{R}$$

$$= \frac{v^2}{R.r_W}\,(2\,I_W \pm G.I_E)\cos\theta$$

Notes : (*a*) When the engine is rotating in the same direction as that of wheels, then the *positive* sign is used in the above expression and if the engine rotates in opposite direction, then *negative* sign is used.

(*b*) The gyroscopic couple will act over the vehicle outwards *i.e.* in the anticlockwise direction when seen from the front of the vehicle. The tendency of this couple is to overturn the vehicle in outward direction.

An aircraft of 1920's model.

2. *Effect of centrifugal couple*

We know that centrifugal force,

$$F_C = \frac{m.v^2}{R}$$

This force acts horizontally through the centre of gravity (*C.G.*) along the outward direction.

∴ Centrifugal couple,

$$C_2 = F_C \times h \cos \theta = \left(\frac{m.v^2}{R} \right) h \cos \theta$$

Since the centrifugal couple has a tendency to overturn the vehicle, therefore

Total overturning couple,

$$C_O = \text{Gyroscopic couple} + \text{Centrifugal couple}$$

$$= \frac{v^2}{R.r_W} (2 I_W + G.I_E) \cos \theta + \frac{m.v^2}{R} \times h \cos \theta$$

$$= \frac{v^2}{R} \left[\frac{2 I_W + G.I_E}{r_W} + m.h \right] \cos \theta$$

We know that balancing couple $= m.g.h \sin \theta$

The balancing couple acts in clockwise direction when seen from the front of the vehicle. Therefore for stability, the overturning couple must be equal to the balancing couple, *i.e.*

$$\frac{v^2}{R} \left(\frac{2 I_W + G.I_E}{r_W} + m.h \right) \cos \theta = m.g.h \sin \theta$$

From this expression, the value of the angle of heel (θ) may be determined, so that the vehicle does not skid.

Example 14.15. *Find the angle of inclination with respect to the vertical of a two wheeler negotiating a turn. Given : combined mass of the vehicle with its rider 250 kg ; moment of inertia of the engine flywheel 0.3 kg-m² ; moment of inertia of each road wheel 1 kg-m² ; speed of engine flywheel 5 times that of road wheels and in the same direction ; height of centre of gravity of rider with vehicle 0.6 m ; two wheeler speed 90 km/h ; wheel radius 300 mm ; radius of turn 50 m.*

Solution. Given : $m = 250$ kg ; $I_E = 0.3$ kg-m² ; $I_W = 1$ kg-m² ; $\omega_E = 5 \omega_W$ or $G = \dfrac{\omega_E}{\omega_W} = 5$; $h = 0.6$ m ; $v = 90$ km/h $= 25$ m/s ; $r_W = 300$ mm $= 0.3$ m ; $R = 50$ m

Let $\qquad$ θ = Angle of inclination with respect to the vertical of a two wheeler.

We know that gyroscopic couple,

$$C_1 = \frac{v^2}{R \times r_W} (2 I_W + G.I_E) \cos \theta = \frac{(25)^2}{50 \times 0.3} (2 \times 1 + 5 \times 0.3) \cos \theta$$

$$= 146 \cos \theta \text{ N-m}$$

and centrifugal couple, $\qquad C_2 = \dfrac{m.v^2}{R} \times h \cos \theta = \dfrac{250 \,(25)^2}{50} \times 0.6 \cos \theta = 1875 \cos \theta$ N-m

∴ Total overturning couple,

$$= C_1 + C_2 = 146 \cos \theta + 1875 \cos \theta = 2021 \cos \theta \text{ N-m}$$

We know that balancing couple

$$= m.g.h \sin \theta = 250 \times 9.81 \times 0.6 \sin \theta = 1471.5 \sin \theta \text{ N-m}$$

Since the overturning couple must be equal to the balancing couple for equilibrium condition, therefore

$$2021 \cos \theta = 1471.5 \sin \theta$$

∴ $\tan \theta = \sin \theta / \cos \theta = 2021 / 1471.5 = 1.3734$ or $\theta = 53.94°$ **Ans.**

Example 14.16. *A gyrowheel D of mass 0.5 kg, with a radius of gyration of 20 mm, is mounted in a pivoted frame C as shown in Fig. 14.15. The axis AB of the pivots passes through the centre of rotation O of the wheel, but the centre of gravity G of the frame C is 10 mm below O. The frame has a mass of 0.30 kg and the speed of rotation of the wheel is 3000 r.p.m. in the anticlockwise direction as shown.*

The entire unit is mounted on a vehicle so that the axis AB is parallel to the direction of motion of the vehicle. If the vehicle travels at 15 m/s in a curve of 50 metres radius, find the inclination of the gyrowheel from the vertical, when

1. The vehicle moves in the direction of the arrow 'X' taking a left hand turn along the curve, and

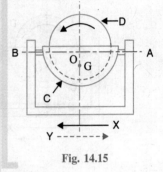

Fig. 14.15

2. The vehicle reverse at the same speed in the direction of arrow 'Y' along the same path.

Solution. Given : $m_1 = 0.5$ kg ; $k = 20$ mm $= 0.02$ m ; $OG = h = 10$ mm $= 0.01$ m ; $m_2 = 0.3$ kg ; $N = 3000$ r.p.m. or $\omega = 2 \pi \times 3000 / 60 = 314.2$ rad/s ; $v = 15$ m/s ; $R = 50$ m

We know that mass moment of inertia of the gyrowheel,

$$I = m_1.k^2 = 0.5 \, (0.02)^2 = 0.0002 \text{ kg-m}^2$$

and angular velocity of precession,

$$\omega_p = v/R = 15 / 50 = 0.3 \text{ rad /s}$$

Let θ = Angle of inclination of gyrowheel from the vertical.

1. *When the vehicle moves in the direction of arrow X taking a left turn along the curve*

We know that gyroscopic couple about O,

$$C_1 = I \, \omega.\omega_p \cos \theta = 0.0002 \times 314.2 \times 0.3 \cos \theta \text{ N-m}$$

$$= 0.019 \cos \theta \text{ N-m (anticlockwise)}$$

and centrifugal couple about O,

$$C_2 = \frac{m_2.v^2}{R} \times h \cos \theta = \frac{0.3 \, (15)^2}{50} \times 0.01 \cos \theta \text{ N-m}$$

$$= 0.0135 \cos \theta \text{ N-m (anticlockwise)}$$

∴ Total overturning couple

$$= C_1 - C_2 = 0.019 \cos \theta - 0.0135 \cos \theta$$

... (– ve sign due to opposite direction)

$$= 0.0055 \cos \theta \text{ N-m (anticlockwise)}$$

We know that balancing couple due to weight ($W_2 = m_2.g$) of the frame about O,

$$= m_2.g.h \sin \theta = 0.3 \times 9.81 \times 0.01 \sin \theta \text{ N-m}$$

$$= 0.029 \sin \theta \text{ N-m (clockwise)}$$

Since the overturning couple must be equal to the balancing couple for equilibrium condition, therefore

$$0.0055 \cos \theta = 0.029 \sin \theta$$

or

$$\tan \theta = \sin \theta / \cos \theta = 0.0055 / 0.029 = 0.1896$$

∴

$$\theta = 10.74° \text{ Ans.}$$

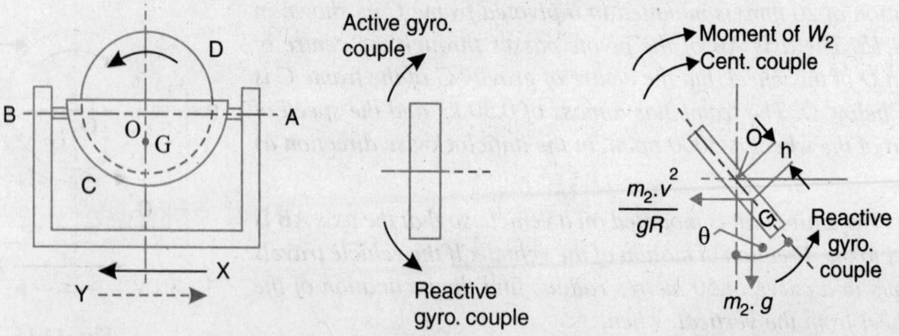

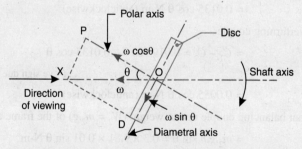

Fig. 14.16

2. When the vehicle reverses at the same speed in the direction of arrow Y along the same path

When the vehicle reverses at the same speed in the direction of arrow Y, then the gyroscopic and centrifugal couples (C_1 and C_2) will be in clockwise direction about O and the balancing couple due to weight ($W_2 = m_2.g$) of the frame about O will be in anticlockwise direction.

∴ Total overturning couple

$$= C_1 + C_2 = 0.019 \cos \theta + 0.0135 \cos \theta = 0.0325 \cos \theta \text{ N-m}$$

Equating the total overturning couple to the balancing couple, we have

$$0.0325 \cos \theta = 0.029 \sin \theta$$

or

$$\tan \theta = \sin \theta / \cos \theta = 0.0325 / 0.029 = 1.1207$$

∴

$$\theta = 48.26° \text{ Ans.}$$

14.11. Effect of Gyroscopic Couple on a Disc Fixed Rigidly at a Certain Angle to a Rotating Shaft

Consider a disc fixed rigidly to a rotating shaft such that the polar axis of the disc makes an angle θ with the shaft axis, as shown in Fig. 14.17. Let the shaft rotates with an angular velocity ω rad/s in the clockwise direction when viewed from the front. A little consideration will show that the disc will also rotate about OX with the same angular velocity ω rad/s. Let OP be the polar axis and OD the diametral axis of the disc.

Fig. 14.17. Effect of gyroscopic couple on a disc fixed rigidly at a certain angle to a rotating shaft.

∴ Angular velocity of the disc about the polar axis *OP* or the angular velocity of spin

$$= \omega \cos \theta \qquad \text{... (Component of } \omega \text{ in the direction of } OP)$$

Since the shaft rotates, therefore the point *P* will move in a plane perpendicular to the plane of paper. In other words, precession is produced about *OD*.

∴ Angular velocity of the disc about the diametral axis *OD* or the angular velocity of precession

$$= \omega \sin \theta$$

If I_P is the mass moment of inertia of the disc about the polar axis *OP*, then gyroscopic couple acting on the disc,

$$C_P = I_P.\omega \cos \theta.\omega \sin \theta = \frac{1}{2} \times I_P.\omega^2 \sin 2\theta$$

$$\text{... (} \because 2 \sin \theta \cos \theta = \sin 2\theta)$$

The effect of this gyroscopic couple is to turn the disc in the anticlockwise when viewed from the top, about an axis through *O* in the plane of paper.

Now consider the movement of point *D* about the polar axis *OP*. In this case, *OD* is axis of spin and *OP* is the axis of precession.

∴ Angular velocity of disc about *OD* or angular velocity of spin

$$= \omega \sin \theta$$

and angular velocity of *D* about *OP* or angular velocity of precession

$$= \omega \cos \theta$$

If I_D is the mass moment of inertia of the disc about the diametral axis *OD*, then gyroscopic couple acting on the disc,

$$C_D = I_D.\omega \sin \theta.\omega \cos \theta = \frac{1}{2} \times I_D.\omega^2 \sin 2\theta$$

The effect of this couple will be opposite to that of C_P.

∴ Resultant gyroscopic couple acting on the disc,

$$C = C_P - C_D = \frac{1}{2} \times \omega^2 \sin 2\theta \, (I_P - I_D)$$

This resultant gyroscopic couple will act in the anticlockwise direction as seen from the top. In other words, the shaft tends to turn in the plane of paper in anticlockwise direction as seen from the top, as a result the horizontal force is exerted on the shaft bearings.

Notes: 1. The mass moment of inertia of the disc about polar axis *OP*,

$$I_P = m.r^2/2$$

and mass moment of inertia of the disc about diametral axis *OD*,

$$I_D = m\left(\frac{l^2}{12} + \frac{r^2}{4}\right)$$

where
$$m = \text{Mass of disc,}$$
$$r = \text{Radius of disc, and}$$
$$l = \text{Width of disc.}$$

2. If the disc is thin, *l* may be neglected. In such a case

$$I_D = m.r^2/4$$

∴
$$C = \frac{1}{2} \times \omega^2 \sin 2\theta \left(\frac{m.r^2}{2} - \frac{m.r^2}{4}\right) = \frac{m}{8} \times \omega^2.r^2 \sin 2\theta$$

Example 14.17. *A shaft carries a uniform thin disc of 0.6 m diameter and mass 30 kg. The disc is out of truth and makes an angle of 1° with a plane at right angles to the axis of the shaft. Find the gyroscopic couple acting on the bearing when the shaft rotates at 1200 r.p.m.*

Solution. Given : $d = 0.6$ m or $r = 0.3$ m , $m = 30$ kg ; $\theta = 1°$; $N = 1200$ r.p.m. or $\omega = 2\pi \times 1200/60 = 125.7$ rad /s

We know that gyroscopic couple acting on the bearings,

$$C = \frac{m}{8} \times \omega^2 . r^2 \sin 2\theta = \frac{30}{8} (125.7)^2 (0.3)^2 \sin 2° = 186 \text{ N-m } \textbf{Ans.}$$

EXERCISES

1. A flywheel of mass 10 kg and radius of gyration 200 mm is spinning about its axis, which is horizontal and is suspended at a point distant 150 mm from the plane of rotation of the flywheel. Determine the angular velocity of precession of the flywheel. The spin speed of flywheel is 900 r.p.m.

    [**Ans. 0.39 rad/s**]

2. A horizontal axle *AB*, 1 m long, is pivoted at the mid point *C*. It carries a weight of 20 N at *A* and a wheel weighing 50 N at *B*. The wheel is made to spin at a speed of 600 r.p.m in a clockwise direction looking from its front. Assuming that the weight of the flywheel is uniformly distributed around the rim whose mean diameter is 0.6 m, calculate the angular velocity of precession of the system around the vertical axis through *C*.

    [**Ans. 0.52 rad/s**]

3. An aeroplane runs at 600 km / h. The rotor of the engine weighs 4000 N with radius of gyration of 1 metre. The speed of rotor is 3000 r.p.m. in anticlockwise direction when seen from rear side of the aeroplane.

    If the plane takes a loop upwards in a curve of 100 metres radius, find : 1. gyroscopic couple developed; and 2. effect of reaction gyroscopic couple developed on the body of aeroplane.

    [**Ans. 213.5 kN-m**]

4. An aeroplane makes a complete half circle of 50 metres radius, towards left, when flying at 200 km per hour. The rotary engine and the propeller of the plane has a mass of 400 kg with a radius of gyration of 300 mm. The engine runs at 2400 r.p.m. clockwise, when viewed from the rear. Find the gyroscopic couple on the aircraft and state its effect on it. What will be the effect, if the aeroplane turns to its right instead of to the left ?

    [**Ans. 10 kN-m**]

5. Each paddle wheel of a steamer have a mass of 1600 kg and a radius of gyration of 1.2 m. The steamer turns to port in a circle of 160 m radius at 24 km / h, the speed of the paddles being 90 r.p.m. Find the magnitude and effect of the gyroscopic couple acting on the steamer. [**Ans. 905.6 N-m**]

6. The rotor of the turbine of a yacht makes 1200 r.p.m. clockwise when viewed from stern. The rotor has a mass of 750 kg and its radius of gyration is 250 mm. Find the maximum gyroscopic couple transmitted to the hull (body of the yacht) when yacht pitches with maximum angular velocity of 1 rad /s. What is the effect of this couple ? [**Ans. 5892 N-m**]

7. The rotor of a turbine installed in a boat with its axis along the longitudinal axis of the boat makes 1500 r.p.m. clockwise when viewed from the stern. The rotor has a mass of 750 kg and a radius of gyration of 300 mm. If at an instant, the boat pitches in the longitudinal vertical plane so that the bow rises from the horizontal plane with an angular velocity of 1 rad /s, determine the torque acting on the boat and the direction in which it tends to turn the boat at the instant. [**Ans. 10.6 kN-m**]

8. The mass of a turbine rotor of a ship is 8 tonnes and has a radius of gyration 0.6 m. It rotates at 1800 r.p.m. clockwise when looking from the stern. Determine the gyroscopic effects in the following cases:

    1. If the ship travelling at 100 km / h strees to the left in a curve of 75 m radius, 2. If the ship is pitching and the bow is descending with maximum velocity. The pitching is simple harmonic, the periodic time being 20 seconds and the total angular movement between the extreme positions is 10°, and 3. If the ship is rolling and at a certain instant has an angular velocity of 0.03 rad/s clockwise when looking from stern.

In each case, explain clearly how you determine the direction in which the ship tends to move as a result of the gyroscopic action. [Ans. 201 kN-m ; 14.87 kN-m ; 16.3 kN-m]

9. The turbine rotor of a ship has a mass of 20 tonnes and a radius of gyration of 0.75 m. Its speed is 2000 r.p.m. The ship pitches 6° above and below the horizontal position. One complete oscillation takes 18 seconds and the motion is simple harmonic. Calculate :

1. the maximum couple tending to shear the holding down bolts of the turbine, 2. the maximum angular acceleration of the ship during pitching, and 3. the direction in which the bow will tend to turn while rising, if the rotation of the rotor is clockwise when looking from rear.

[Ans. **86.26 kN-m ; 0.0128 rad /s², towards star-board**]

10. A motor car takes a bend of 30 m radius at a speed of 60 km / hr. Determine the magnitudes of gyroscopic and centrifugal couples acting on the vehicle and state the effect that each of these has on the road reactions to the road wheels. Assume that :

Each road wheel has a moment of inertia of 3 kg-m² and an effective road radius of 0.4 m.

The rotating parts of the engine and transmission are equivalent to a flywheel of mass 75 kg with a radius of gyration of 100 mm. The engine turns in a clockwise direction when viewed from the front.

The back-axle ratio is 4 : 1, the drive through the gear box being direct. The gyroscopic effects of the half shafts at the back axle are to be ignored.

The car has a mass of 1200 kg and its centre of gravity is 0.6 m above the road wheel.

The turn is in a right hand direction.

If the turn has been in a left hand direction, all other details being unaltered, which answers, if any, need modification. [Ans. 347.5 N-m : 6670 N-m]

11. A rail car has a total mass of 4 tonnes. There are two axles, each of which together with its wheels and gearing has a total moment of inertia of 30 kg-m². The centre distance between the two wheels on an axle is 1.5 metres and each wheel is of 375 mm radius. Each axle is driven by a motor, the speed ratio between the two being 1 : 3. Each motor with its gear has a moment of inertia of 15 kg-m² and runs in a direction opposite to that of its axle. The centre of gravity of the car is 1.05 m above the rails.

Determine the limiting speed for this car, when it rounding a curve of 240 metres radius such that no wheel leaves the rail. Consider the centrifugal and gyroscopic effects completely. Assume that no cant is provided for outer rail. [Ans. 144 km / h]

12. A racing car weighs 20 kN. It has a wheel base of 2 m, track width 1 m and height of C.G. 300 mm above the ground level and lies midway between the front and rear axle. The engine flywheel rotates at 3000 r.p.m. clockwise when viewed from the front. The moment of inertia of the flywheel is 4 kg-m² and moment of inertia of each wheel is 3 kg-m². Find the reactions between the wheels and the ground when the car takes a curve of 15 m radius towards right at 30 km / h, taking into consideration the gyroscopic and the centrifugal effects. Each wheel radius is 400 mm.

[Ans. **Front inner wheel = 3341.7 N ; Front outer wheel = 6309.5 N ;**
Rear inner wheel = 3690.5 N ; Rear outer wheel = 6658.3 N]

13. A four wheel trolley car of total mass 2000 kg running on rails of 1 m gauge, rounds a curve of 25 m radius at 40 km / h. The track is banked at 10°. The wheels have an external diameter of 0.6 m and each pair of an axle has a mass of 200 kg. The radius of gyration for each pair is 250 mm. The height of C.G. of the car above the wheel base is 0.95 m. Allowing for centrifugal force and gyroscopic couple action, determine the pressure on each rail. [Ans. 4328 N ; 16 704 N]

14. A 2.2 tonne racing car has a wheel base of 2.4 m and a track of 1.4 m from the rear axle. The equivalent mass of engine parts is 140 kg with radius of gyration of 150 mm. The back axle ratio is 5. The engine shaft and flywheel rotate clockwise when viewed from the front. Each wheel has a diameter of 0.8 m and a moment of inertia of 0.7 kg-m². Determine the load distribution on the wheels when the car is rounding a curve of 100 m radius at a speed of 72 km / h to the left.

15. A disc has a mass of 30 kg and a radius of gyration about its axis of symmetry 125 mm while its radius of gyration about a diameter of the disc at right angles to the axis of symmetry is 75 mm. The disc is pressed on to the shaft but due to incorrect boring, the angle between the axis of symmetry and the actual axis of rotation is 0.25°, though both these axes pass through the centre of gravity of the disc. Assuming that the shaft is rigid and is carried between bearings 200 mm apart, determine the bearing forces due to the misalignment at a speed of 5000 r.p.m. [Ans. 1810 N]

16. A wheel of a locomotive, travelling on a level track at 90 km / h, falls in a spot hole 10 mm deep and rises again in a total time of 0.8 seconds. The displacement of the wheel takes place with simple harmonic motion. The wheel has a diameter of 3 m and the distance between the wheel centres is 1.75 m. The wheel pair with axle has a moment of inertia of 500 kg-m². Determine the magnitude and the effect of gyrocouple produced in this case. [Ans. 186.6 N-m]

17. Each road wheel of a motor cycle has a mass moment of inertia of 1.5 kg-m². The rotating parts of the engine of the motor cycle have a mass moment of inertia of 0.25 kg-m². The speed of the engine is 5 times the speed of the wheels and is in the same sense. The mass of the motor cycle with its rider is 250 kg and its centre of gravity is 0.6 m above the ground level.

Find the angle of heel if the cycle is travelling at 50 km / h and is taking a turn of 30 m radius. The wheel diameter is 0.6 m. [Ans. 35.7°]

18. A racing motor cyclist travels at 140 km/h round a curve of 120 m radius measured horizontally. The cycle and rider have mass of 150 kg and their centre of gravity lies at 0.7 m above the ground level when the motor cycle is vertical. Each wheel is 0.6 m in diameter and has moment of inertia about its axis of rotation 1.5 kg-m². The engine has rotating parts whose moment of inertia about their axis of rotation is 0.25 kg-m² and it rotates at five times the wheel speed in the same direction. Find : 1. the correct angle of banking of the track so that there is no tendency to side slip, and 2. the correct angle of inclination of the cycle and rider to the vertical. [Ans. 52.12°; 55.57°]

[**Hint.** In calculating the angle of banking of the track, neglect the effect of gyroscopic couple]

DO YOU KNOW ?

1. Write a short note on gyroscope.

2. What do you understand by gyroscopic couple ? Derive a formula for its magnitude.

3. Explain the application of gyroscopic principles to aircrafts.

4. Describe the gyroscopic effect on sea going vessels.

5. Explain the effect of the gyroscopic couple on the reaction of the four wheels of a vehicle negotiating a curve.

6. Discuss the effect of the gyroscopic couple on a two wheeled vehicle when taking a turn.

7. What will be the effect of the gyroscopic couple on a disc fixed at a certain angle to a rotating shaft ?

OBJECTIVE TYPE QUESTIONS

1. A disc is spinning with an angular velocity ω rad/s about the axis of spin. The couple applied to the disc causing precession will be

   (a) $\frac{1}{2} I.\omega^2$ (b) $I.\omega^2$ (c) $\frac{1}{2} I.\omega.\omega_P$ (d) $I.\omega.\omega_P$

   where I = Mass moment of inertia of the disc, and

              ω_P = Angular velocity of precession of the axis of spin.

2. A disc spinning on its axis at 20 rad/s will undergo precession when a torque 100 N-m is applied about an axis normal to it at an angular speed, if mass moment of inertia of the disc is the 1 kg-m²

   (a) 2 rad/s   (b) 5 rad/s   (c) 10 rad/s   (d) 20 rad/s

3. The engine of an aeroplane rotates in clockwise direction when seen from the tail end and the aeroplane takes a turn to the left. The effect of the gyroscopic couple on the aeroplane will be

   (a) to raise the nose and dip the tail   (b) to dip the nose and raise the tail

   (c) to raise the nose and tail   (d) to dip the nose and tail

4. The air screw of an aeroplane is rotating clockwise when looking from the front. If it makes a left turn, the gyroscopic effect will

    (*a*) tend to depress the nose and raise the tail

    (*b*) tend to raise the nose and depress the tail

    (*c*) tilt the aeroplane

    (*d*) none of the above

5. The rotor of a ship rotates in clockwise direction when viewed from the stern and the ship takes a left turn. The effect of the gyroscopic couple acting on it will be

    (*a*) to raise the bow and stern   (*b*) to lower the bow and stern

    (*c*) to raise the bow and lower the stern   (*d*) to lower the bow and raise the stern

6. When the pitching of a ship is upward, the effect of gyroscopic couple acting on it will be

    (*a*) to move the ship towards port side   (*b*) to move the ship towards star-board

    (*c*) to raise the bow and lower the stern   (*d*) to raise the stern and lower the bow

7. In an automobile, if the vehicle makes a left turn, the gyroscopic torque

    (*a*) increases the forces on the outer wheels   (*b*) decreases the forces on the outer wheels

    (*c*) does not affect the forces on the outer wheels

    (*d*) none of the above

8. A motor car moving at a certain speed takes a left turn in a curved path. If the engine rotates in the same direction as that of wheels, then due to the centrifugal forces

    (*a*) the reaction on the inner wheels increases and on the outer wheels decreases

    (*b*) the reaction on the outer wheels increases and on the inner wheels decreases

    (*c*) the reaction on the front wheels increases and on the rear wheels decreases

    (*d*) the reaction on the rear wheels increases and on the front wheels decreases

ANSWERS

1. (*d*)	**2.** (*b*)	**3.** (*a*)	**4.** (*b*)
5. (*c*)	**6.** (*b*)	**7.** (*a*)	**8.** (*b*)

15

Inertia Forces in Reciprocating Parts

15.1. Introduction

The inertia force is an imaginary force, which when acts upon a rigid body, brings it in an equilibrium position. It is numerically equal to the accelerating force in magnitude, but *opposite* in direction. Mathematically,

Inertia force = – Accelerating force = $– m.a$

where
m = Mass of the body, and

a = Linear acceleration of the centre of gravity of the body.

Similarly, the inertia torque is an imaginary torque, which when applied upon the rigid body, brings it in equilibrium position. It is equal to the accelerating couple in magnitude but *opposite* in direction.

15.2. Resultant Effect of a System of Forces Acting on a Rigid Body

Consider a rigid body acted upon by a system of forces. These forces may be reduced to a single resultant force

F whose line of action is at a distance *h* from the centre of gravity *G*. Now let us assume two equal and opposite forces (of magnitude *F*) acting through *G*, and parallel to the resultant force, without influencing the effect of the resultant force *F*, as shown in Fig. 15.1.

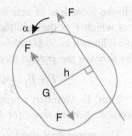

A little consideration will show that the body is now subjected to a couple (equal to *F* × *h*) and a force, equal and parallel to the resultant force *F* passing through *G*. The force *F* through *G* causes linear acceleration of the c.g. and the moment of the couple (*F* × *h*) causes angular acceleration of the body about an axis passing through *G* and perpendicular to the point in which the couple acts.

Fig. 15.1. Resultant effect of a system of forces acting on a rigid body.

Let   α = Angular acceleration of the rigid body due to couple,

   h = Perpendicular distance between the force and centre of gravity of the body,

   m = Mass of the body,

   k = Least radius of gyration about an axis through *G*, and

   I = Moment of inertia of the body about an axis passing through its centre of gravity and perpendicular to the point in which the couple acts
      = $m.k^2$

We know that

   Force, F = Mass × Acceleration = $m.a$ ...(*i*)

and $F.h = m.k^2.\alpha = I.\alpha$ ...($\because I = m.k^2$) ...(*ii*)

From equations (*i*) and (*ii*), we can find the values of *a* and α, if the values of *F*, *m*, *k*, and *h* are known.

15.3. D-Alembert's Principle

Consider a rigid body acted upon by a system of forces. The system may be reduced to a single resultant force acting on the body whose magnitude is given by the product of the mass of the body and the linear acceleration of the centre of mass of the body. According to Newton's second law of motion,

The above picture shows the reciprocating parts of a 19th century oil engine.

$$F = m.a$$ ...(*i*)

where   *F* = Resultant force acting on the body,

   m = Mass of the body, and

   a = Linear acceleration of the centre of mass of the body.

The equation (*i*) may also be written as:

$$F - m.a = 0$$ ...(*ii*)

A little consideration will show, that if the quantity – *m.a* be treated as a force, equal, opposite and with the same line of action as the resultant force F, and include this force with the system of forces of which F is the resultant, then the complete system of forces will be in equilibrium. This principle is known as *D-Alembert's principle*. The equal and opposite force $-m.a$ is known as *reversed effective force* or the *inertia force* (briefly written as F_I). The equation (*ii*) may be written as

$$F + F_I = 0 \qquad\qquad ...(iii)$$

Thus, D-Alembert's principle states that *the resultant force acting on a body together with the reversed effective force (or inertia force), are in equilibrium.*

This principle is used to reduce a dynamic problem into an equivalent static problem.

15.4. Velocity and Acceleration of the Reciprocating Parts in Engines

The velocity and acceleration of the reciprocating parts of the steam engine or internal combustion engine (briefly called as I.C. engine) may be determined by graphical method or analytical method. The velocity and acceleration, by graphical method, may be determined by one of the following constructions:

1. Klien's construction, **2.** Ritterhaus's construction, and **3.** Bennett's construction.

We shall now discuss these constructions, in detail, in the following pages.

15.5. Klien's Construction

Let OC be the crank and PC the connecting rod of a reciprocating steam engine, as shown in Fig. 15.2 (*a*). Let the crank makes an angle θ with the line of stroke PO and rotates with uniform angular velocity ω rad/s in a clockwise direction. The Klien's velocity and acceleration diagrams are drawn as discussed below:

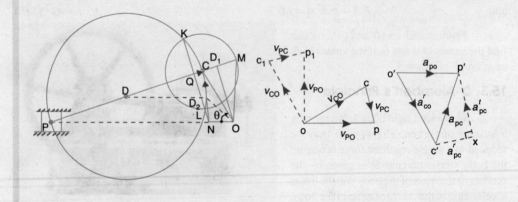

(*a*) Klien's acceleration diagram.   (*b*) Velocity diagram.   (*c*) Acceleration diagram.

Fig. 15.2. Klien's construction.

Klien's velocity diagram

First of all, draw OM perpendicular to OP; such that it intersects the line PC produced at M. The triangle OCM is known as *Klien's velocity diagram*. In this triangle OCM,

OM may be regarded as a line perpendicular to PO,

CM may be regarded as a line parallel to PC, and   ...(∵ It is the same line.)

CO may be regarded as a line parallel to CO.

We have already discussed that the velocity diagram for given configuration is a triangle *ocp* as shown in Fig. 15.2 (*b*). If this triangle is revolved through 90°, it will be a triangle $oc_1 p_1$, in which oc_1 represents v_{CO} (*i.e.* velocity of *C* with respect to *O* or velocity of crank pin *C*) and is paralel to *OC*,

op_1 represents v_{PO} (*i.e.* velocity of *P* with respect to *O* or velocity of cross-head or piston *P*) and is perpendicular to *OP*, and

$c_1 p_1$ represents v_{PC} (*i.e.* velocity of *P* with respect to *C*) and is parallel to *CP*.

A little consideration will show, that the triangles $oc_1 p_1$ and *OCM* are similar. Therefore,

$$\frac{oc_1}{OC} = \frac{op_1}{OM} = \frac{c_1 p_1}{CM} = \omega \text{ (a constant)}$$

or

$$\frac{v_{CO}}{OC} = \frac{v_{PO}}{OM} = \frac{v_{PC}}{CM} = \omega$$

∴

$$v_{CO} = \omega \times OC \; ; v_{PO} = \omega \times OM, \text{ and } v_{PC} = \omega \times CM$$

Thus, we see that by drawing the Klien's velocity diagram, the velocities of various points may be obtained without drawing a separate velocity diagram.

Klien's acceleration diagram

The Klien's acceleration diagram is drawn as discussed below:

1. First of all, draw a circle with *C* as centre and *CM* as radius.

2. Draw another circle with *PC* as diameter. Let this circle intersect the previous circle at *K* and *L*.

3. Join *KL* and produce it to intersect *PO* at *N*. Let *KL* intersect *PC* at *Q*. This forms the quadrilateral *CQNO*, which is known as *Klien's acceleration diagram.*

We have already discussed that the acceleration diagram for the given configuration is as shown in Fig. 15. 2 (*c*). We know that

(*i*) *o'c'* represents a_{CO}^r (*i.e.* radial component of the acceleration of crank pin *C* with respect to *O*) and is parallel to *CO*;

(*ii*) *c'x* represents a_{PC}^r (*i.e.* radial component of the acceleration of crosshead or piston *P* with respect to crank pin *C*) and is parallel to *CP* or *CQ*;

(*iii*) *xp'* represents a_{PC}^t (*i.e.* tangential component of the acceleration of *P* with respect to *C*) and is parallel to *QN* (because *QN* is perpendicular to *CQ*); and

(*iv*) *o'p'* represents a_{PO} (*i.e.* acceleration of *P* with respect to *O* or the acceleration of piston *P*) and is parallel to *PO* or *NO*.

A little consideration will show that the quadrilateral *o'c'x p'* [Fig. 15.2 (*c*)] is similar to quadrilateral *CQNO* [Fig. 15.2 (*a*)]. Therefore,

$$\frac{o'c'}{OC} = \frac{c'x}{CQ} = \frac{xp'}{QN} = \frac{o'p'}{NO} = \omega^2 \text{ (a constant)}$$

or

$$\frac{a^r_{CO}}{OC} = \frac{a^r_{PC}}{CQ} = \frac{a^t_{PC}}{QN} = \frac{a_{PO}}{NO} = \omega^2$$

∴

$$a^r_{CO} = \omega^2 \times OC; \; a^r_{PC} = \omega^2 \times CQ$$

$$a^t_{PC} = \omega^2 \times QN; \text{ and } a_{PO} = \omega^2 \times NO$$

Thus we see that by drawing the Klien's acceleration diagram, the acceleration of various points may be obtained without drawing the separate acceleration diagram.

Notes: 1. The acceleration of piston P with respect to crank pin C (*i.e.* a_{PC}) may be obtained from:

$$\frac{c'p'}{CN} = \omega^2 \quad \text{or} \quad \frac{a_{PC}}{CN} = \omega^2$$

∴

$$a_{PC} = \omega^2 \times CN$$

2. To find the velocity of any point D on the connecting rod PC, divide CM at D_1 in the same ratio as D divides CP. In other words,

$$\frac{CD_1}{CM} = \frac{CD}{CP}$$

∴ Velocity of D, $v_D = \omega \times OD_1$

3. To find the acceleration of any point D on the connecting rod PC, draw a line from a point D parallel to PO which intersects CN at D_2.

∴ Acceleration of D, $a_D = \omega^2 \times OD_2$

4. If the crank position is such that the point N lies on the right of O instead of to the left as shown in Fig. 15.2 (*a*), then the acceleration of the piston is negative. In other words, the piston is under going retardation.

5. The acceleration of the piston P is zero and its velocity is maximum, when N coincides with O. There is no simple graphical method of finding the corresponding crank position, but it can be shown that for N and O to coincide, the angle between the crank and the connecting rod must be slightly less than 90°. For most practical purposes, it is assumed that the acceleration of piston P is zero, when the crank OC and connecting rod PC are at right angles to each other.

15.6. Ritterhaus's Construction

Let OC be the crank and PC the connecting rod of a reiprocating steam engine, as shown in Fig. 15.3. Let the crank makes an angle θ with the line of stroke PO and rotates with uniform angular velocity ω rad/s in a clockwise direction. The Ritterhaus's velocity and acceleration diagrams are drawn as discussed below:

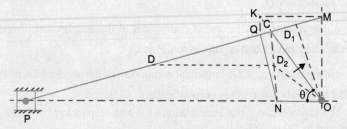

Fig. 15.3. Ritterhaus's construction.

Ritterhaus's velocity diagram

Draw OM perpendicular to the line of stroke PO, such that it intersects the line PC produced at M. The triangle OCM is known as *Ritterhaus's velocity diagram*. It is similar to Klien's velocity diagram.

∴ Velocity of *C* with respect to *O* or the velocity of crank pin *C*,

$$v_{CO} = v_C = \omega \times OC$$

Velocity of *P* with respect to *O* or the velocity of crosshead or piston *P*,

$$v_{PO} = v_P = \omega \times OM$$

and velocity of *P* with respect to *C*, $v_{PC} = \omega \times CM$

Ritterhaus's acceleration diagram

The Ritterhaus's acceleration diagram is drawn as discussed below:

1. From point *M*, draw *MK* parallel to the line of stroke *PO*, to interect *OC* produced at *K*.

2. Draw *KQ* parallel to *MO*. From *Q* draw *QN* perpendicular to *PC*.

3. The quadrilateral *CQNO* is known as ***Ritterhaus's acceleration diagram***. This is similar to Klien's acceleration diagram.

∴ Radial component of the acceleration of *C* with respect to *O* or the acceleration of crank pin *C*,

$$a^r_{CO} = a_C = \omega^2 \times OC$$

Radial component of the acceleration of the crosshead or piston *P* with respect to crank pin *C*,

$$a^r_{PC} = \omega^2 \times CQ$$

Tangential component of the acceleration of *P* with respect to *C*,

$$a^t_{PC} = \omega^2 \times QN$$

and acceleration of *P* with respect to *O* or the acceleration of piston *P*,

$$a_{PO} = a_P = \omega^2 \times NO$$

Notes : 1. The acceleration of piston *P* with respect to crank pin *C* is given by

$$a_{PC} = \omega^2 \times CN$$

2. To find the velocity of any point *D* on the connecting rod *PC*, divide *CM* at D_1 in the same ratio as *D* divides *CP*. In other words,

$$\frac{CD_1}{CM} = \frac{CD}{CP}$$

∴ Velocity of *D* $v_D = \omega \times OD_1$

3. To find the acceleration of any point *D* on the connecting rod *PC*, draw DD_2 parallel to the line of stroke *PO*, which intersects *CN* at D_2. The acceleration of *D* is given by

$$a_D = \omega^2 \times OD_2$$

15.7. Bennett's Construction

Let *OC* be the crank and *PC* the connecting rod of reciprocating steam engine, as shown in Fig. 15.4. Let the crank makes an angle θ with the line of stroke *PO* and rotates with uniform angular velocity ω rad/s in the clockwise direction. The Bennett's velocity and acceleration diagrams are drawn as discussed below:

Bennett's velocity diagram

When the crank *OC* is at right angle to the line of stroke, it occupies the postition OC_1 and the crosshead *P* moves to the position P_1, as shown in Fig. 15.4. Now, produce *PC* to intersect OC_1 at *M*. The triangle *OCM* is known as ***Bennett's velocity diagram***. It is similar to Klien's velocity diagram.

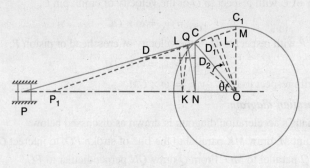

Fig. 15.4. Bennett's construction.

∴ Velocity of C with respect to O or the velocity of crank pin C,

$$v_{CO} = v_C = \omega \times OC$$

Velocity of P with respect to O or the velocity of crosshead or piston P,

$$v_{PO} = v_P = \omega \times OM$$

and velocity of P with respect to C, $\quad v_{PC} = \omega \times CM$.

Bennett's acceleration diagram

The Bennett's acceleration diagram is drawn as discussed below:

1. From O, draw OL_1 perpendicular to P_1C_1 (*i.e.* position of connecting rod PC when crank is at right angle). Mark the position of point L on the connecting rod PC such that $CL = C_1L_1$.

2. From L, draw LK perpendicular to PC and from point K draw KQ perpendicular to the line of stroke PO. From point C, draw CN perpendicular to the line of stroke PO. Join NQ. A little consideration will show that NQ is perpendicular to PC.

3. The quadrilateral $CQNO$ is known as *Bennett's acceleration diagram*. It is similar to Klien's acceleration diagram.

∴ Radial component of the acceleration of C with respect to O or the acceleration of the crank pin C,

$$a^r_{CO} = a_C = \omega^2 \times OC$$

Radial component of the acceleration of the crosshead or piston P with respect to crank pin C,

$$a^r_{PC} = \omega^2 \times CQ$$

Tangential component of the acceleration of P with respect to C,

$$a^t_{PC} = \omega^2 \times QN$$

and acceleration of P with respect to O or the acceleration of piston P,

$$a_{PO} = a_P = \omega^2 \times NO$$

Notes : 1. The acceleration of piston P with respect to crank pin C is given by

$$a_{PC} = \omega^2 \times CN$$

2. The velocity and acceleration of any point D on the connecting rod PC may be obtained in the similar way, as discussed in the previous articles, *i.e.*

Velocity of D, $v_D = \omega \times OD_1$

and $\quad$ Acceleration of D, $a_D = \omega^2 \times OD_2$

Example 15.1. *The crank and connecting rod of a reciprocating engine are 200 mm and 700 mm respectively. The crank is rotating in clockwise direction at 120 rad/s. Find with the help of Klein's construction: 1. Velocity and acceleration of the piston, 2. Velocity and acceleration of the mid point of the connecting rod, and 3. Angular velocity and angular acceleration of the connecting rod, at the instant when the crank is at 30° to I.D.C. (inner dead centre).*

Solution. Given: $OC = 200$ mm $= 0.2$ m ; $PC = 700$ mm $= 0.7$ m ; $\omega = 120$ rad/s

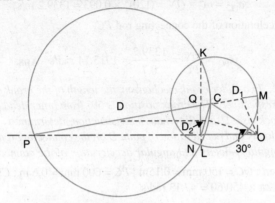

Fig. 15.5

The Klein's velocity diagram *OCM* and Klein's acceleration diagram *CQNO* as shown in Fig. 15.5 is drawn to some suitable scale, in the similar way as discussed in Art. 15.5. By measurement, we find that

$OM = 127$ mm $= 0.127$ m ; $CM = 173$ mm $= 0.173$ m ; $QN = 93$ mm $= 0.093$ m ; $NO = 200$ mm $= 0.2$ m

1. Velocity and acceleration of the piston

We know that the velocity of the piston *P*,

$$v_P = \omega \times OM = 120 \times 0.127 = 15.24 \text{ m/s } \textbf{Ans.}$$

and acceleration of the piston *P*,

$$a_P = \omega^2 \times NO = (120)^2 \times 0.2 = 2880 \text{ m/s}^2 \textbf{ Ans.}$$

2. Velocity and acceleration of the mid-point of the connecting rod

In order to find the velocity of the mid-point *D* of the connecting rod, divide *CM* at D_1 in the same ratio as *D* divides *CP*. Since *D* is the mid-point of *CP*, therefore D_1 is the mid-point of *CM*, *i.e.* $CD_1 = D_1M$. Join OD_1. By measurement,

$$OD_1 = 140 \text{ mm} = 0.14 \text{ m}$$

∴   Velocity of *D*, $v_D = \omega \times OD_1 = 120 \times 0.14 = 16.8$ m/s **Ans.**

In order to find the acceleration of the mid-point of the connecting rod, draw a line DD_2 parallel to the line of stroke *PO* which intersects *CN* at D_2. By measurement,

$$OD_2 = 193 \text{ mm} = 0.193 \text{ m}$$

∴ Acceleration of *D*,

$$a_D = \omega^2 \times OD_2 = (120)^2 \times 0.193 = 2779.2 \text{ m/s}^2 \textbf{ Ans.}$$

3. Angular velocity and angular acceleration of the connecting rod

We know that the velocity of the connecting rod *PC* (*i.e.* velocity of *P* with respect to *C*),

$$v_{PC} = \omega \times CM = 120 \times 0.173 = 20.76 \text{ m/s}$$

∴ Angular velocity of the connecting rod PC,

$$\omega_{PC} = \frac{v_{PC}}{PC} = \frac{20.76}{0.7} = 29.66 \text{ rad/s} \textbf{ Ans.}$$

We know that the tangential component of the acceleration of P with respect to C,

$$a_{PC}^t = \omega^2 \times QN = (120)^2 \times 0.093 = 1339.2 \text{ m/s}^2$$

∴ Angular acceleration of the connecting rod PC,

$$\alpha_{PC} = \frac{a_{PC}^t}{PC} = \frac{1339.2}{0.7} = 1913.14 \text{ rad/s}^2 \textbf{ Ans.}$$

Example 15.2. *In a slider crank mechanism, the length of the crank and connecting rod are 150 mm and 600 mm respectively. The crank position is 60° from inner dead centre. The crank shaft speed is 450 r.p.m. clockwise. Using Ritterhaus's construction, determine 1. Velocity and acceleration of the slider, 2. Velocity and acceleration of point D on the connecting rod which is 150 mm from crank pin C, and 3. angular velocity and angular acceleration of the connecting rod.*

Solution. Given : $OC = 150$ mm $= 0.15$ m ; $PC = 600$ mm $= 0.6$ m ; $CD = 150$ mm $= 0.15$ m ; $N = 450$ r.p.m. or $\omega = 2\pi \times 450/60 = 47.13$ rad/s

The Ritterhaus's velocity diagram OCM and acceleration diagram $CQNO$, as shown in Fig. 15.6, is drawn to some suitable scale in the similar way as discussed in Art. 15.6. By measurement, we find that

$OM = 145$ mm $= 0.145$ m ; $CM = 78$ mm $= 0.078$ m ; $QN = 130$ mm $= 0.13$ m ; and $NO = 56$ mm $= 0.056$ m

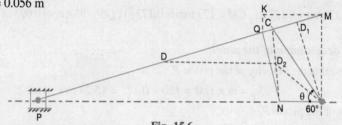

Fig. 15.6

1. Velocity and acceleration of the slider

We know that the velocity of the slider P,

$$v_P = \omega \times OM = 47.13 \times 0.145 = 6.834 \text{ m/s} \textbf{ Ans.}$$

and acceleration of the slider P,

$$a_P = \omega^2 \times NO = (47.13)^2 \times 0.056 = 124.4 \text{ m/s}^2 \textbf{ Ans.}$$

2. Velocity and acceleration of point D on the connecting rod

In order to find the velocity of point D on the connecting rod, divide CM at D_1 in the same ratio as D divides CP. In other words,

$$\frac{CD_1}{CM} = \frac{CD}{CP} \quad \text{or} \quad CD_1 = \frac{CD}{CP} \times CM = \frac{150}{600} \times 78 = 19.5 \text{ mm}$$

Join OD_1. By measurement, $OD_1 = 145$ mm $= 0.145$ m

∴ Velocity of point D,

$$v_D = \omega \times OD_1 = 47.13 \times 0.145 = 6.834 \text{ m/s} \textbf{ Ans.}$$

In order to find the acceleration of point D on the connecting rod, draw DD_2 parallel to the line of stroke PO. Join OD_2. By measurement, we find that $OD_2 = 120$ mm $= 0.12$ m.

∴ Acceleration of point D,

$$a_D = \omega^2 \times OD_2 = (47.13)^2 \times 0.12 = 266.55 \text{ m/s}^2 \text{ Ans.}$$

3. *Angular velocity and angular acceleration of the connecting rod*

We know that the velocity of the connecting rod PC (or the velocity of point P with respect to C),

$$v_{PC} = \omega \times CM = 47.13 \times 0.078 = 3.676 \text{ m/s}$$

∴ Angular velocity of the connecting rod,

$$\omega_{PC} = \frac{v_{PC}}{PC} = \frac{3.676}{0.6} = 6.127 \text{ rad/s Ans.}$$

We know that the tangential component of the acceleration of P with respect to C,

$$a_{PC}^t = \omega^2 \times QN = (47.13)^2 \times 0.13 = 288.76 \text{ m/s}^2$$

∴ Angular acceleration of the connecting rod PC,

$$\alpha_{PC} = \frac{a_{PC}^t}{PC} = \frac{288.76}{0.6} = 481.27 \text{ rad/s}^2 \text{ Ans.}$$

15.8. Approximate Analytical Method for Velocity and Acceleration of the Piston

Consider the motion of a crank and connecting rod of a reciprocating steam engine as shown in Fig. 15.7. Let OC be the crank and PC the connecting rod. Let the crank rotates with angular velocity of ω rad/s and the crank turns through an angle θ from the inner dead centre (briefly written as I.D.C). Let x be the displacement of a reciprocating body P from I.D.C. after time t seconds, during which the crank has turned through an angle θ.

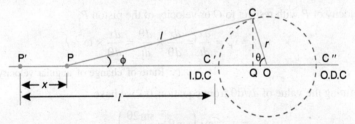

Fig. 15.7. Motion of a crank and connecting rod of a reciprocating steam engine.

Let

l = Length of connecting rod between the centres,

r = Radius of crank or crank pin circle,

ϕ = Inclination of connecting rod to the line of stroke PO, and

n = Ratio of length of connecting rod to the radius of crank = l/r.

Velocity of the piston

From the geometry of Fig. 15.7,

$$x = P'P = OP' - OP = (P'C' + C'O) - (PQ + QO)$$

$$= (l + r) - (l \cos \phi + r \cos \theta) \qquad \cdots \left(\begin{array}{l} \because \quad PQ = l \cos \phi, \\ \text{and } QO = r \cos \theta \end{array} \right)$$

$$= r\,(1 - \cos\theta) + l\,(1 - \cos\phi) = r\left[(1 - \cos\theta) + \frac{l}{r}(1 - \cos\phi)\right]$$

$$= r\,[(1 - \cos\theta) + n\,(1 - \cos\phi)] \qquad \qquad ...(i)$$

From triangles CPQ and CQO,

$$CQ = l\sin\phi = r\sin\theta \quad \text{or} \quad l/r = \sin\theta/\sin\phi$$

$$\therefore \qquad \qquad n = \sin\theta/\sin\phi \quad \text{or} \quad \sin\phi = \sin\theta/n \qquad \qquad ...(ii)$$

We know that, $\qquad \cos\phi = \left(1 - \sin^2\phi\right)^{\frac{1}{2}} = \left(1 - \dfrac{\sin^2\theta}{n^2}\right)^{\frac{1}{2}}$

Expanding the above expression by binomial theorem, we get

$$\cos\phi = 1 - \frac{1}{2} \times \frac{\sin^2\theta}{n^2} + ... \qquad \qquad ...\text{(Neglecting higher terms)}$$

or $\qquad \qquad 1 - \cos\phi = \dfrac{\sin^2\theta}{2n^2} \qquad \qquad ...(iii)$

Substituting the value of $(1 - \cos\phi)$ in equation (i), we have

$$x = r\left[(1 - \cos\theta) + n \times \frac{\sin^2\theta}{2n^2}\right] = r\left[(1 - \cos\theta) + \frac{\sin^2\theta}{2n}\right] \qquad ..(iv)$$

Differentiating equation (iv) with respect to θ,

$$\frac{dx}{d\theta} = r\left[\sin\theta + \frac{1}{2n} \times 2\sin\theta.\cos\theta\right] = r\left(\sin\theta + \frac{\sin 2\theta}{2n}\right) \qquad ...(v)$$

$$(\because 2\sin\theta.\cos\theta = \sin 2\theta)$$

$\therefore$ Velocity of P with respect to O or velocity of the piston P,

$$v_{PO} = v_P = \frac{dx}{dt} = \frac{dx}{d\theta} \times \frac{d\theta}{dt} = \frac{dx}{d\theta} \times \omega$$

$$...(\because \text{Ratio of change of angular velocity} = d\theta/dt = \omega)$$

Substituting the value of $dx/d\theta$ from equation (v), we have

$$v_{PO} = v_P = \omega r\left(\sin\theta + \frac{\sin 2\theta}{2n}\right) \qquad \qquad ...(vi)$$

Note: We know that by Klien's construction,

$$v_P = \omega \times OM$$

Comparing this equation with equation (vi), we find that

$$OM = r\left(\sin\theta + \frac{\sin 2\theta}{2n}\right)$$

Acceleration of the piston

Since the acceleration is the rate of change of velocity, therefore acceleration of the piston P,

$$a_P = \frac{dv_P}{dt} = \frac{dv_P}{d\theta} \times \frac{d\theta}{dt} = \frac{dv_P}{d\theta} \times \omega$$

Differentiating equation (*vi*) with respect to θ,

$$\frac{dv_P}{d\theta} = \omega.r \left[\cos\theta + \frac{\cos 2\theta \times 2}{2n} \right] = \omega.r \left[\cos\theta + \frac{\cos 2\theta}{n} \right]$$

Substituting the value of $\dfrac{dv_P}{d\theta}$ in the above equation, we have

$$a_P = \omega.r \left[\cos\theta + \frac{\cos 2\theta}{n} \right] \times \omega = \omega^2.r \left[\cos\theta + \frac{\cos 2\theta}{n} \right] \qquad ...(vii)$$

Notes : 1. When crank is at the inner dead centre (I.D.C.), then θ = 0°.

$$\therefore \qquad a_P = \omega^2.r \left[\cos 0° + \frac{\cos 0°}{n} \right] = \omega^2.r \left(1 + \frac{1}{n} \right)$$

2. When the crank is at the outer dead centre (O.D.C.), then θ = 180°.

$$\therefore \qquad a_P = \omega^2.r \left[\cos 180° + \frac{\cos 2 \times 180°}{n} \right] = \omega^2.r \left(-1 + \frac{1}{n} \right)$$

As the direction of motion is reversed at the outer dead centre, therefore changing the sign of the above expression,

$$a_P = \omega^2.r \left[1 - \frac{1}{n} \right]$$

Above picture shows a diesel engine. Steam engine, petrol engine and diesel engine, all have reciprocating parts such as piston, piston rod, etc.

15.9. Angular Velocity and Acceleration of the Connecting Rod

Consider the motion of a connecting rod and a crank as shown in Fig. 15.7. From the geometry of the figure, we find that

$$CQ = l \sin\phi = r \sin\theta$$

$$\therefore \qquad \sin\phi = \frac{r}{l} \times \sin\theta = \frac{\sin\theta}{n} \qquad \qquad \dots\left(\because n = \frac{l}{r}\right)$$

Differentiating both sides with respect to time t,

$$\cos\phi \times \frac{d\phi}{dt} = \frac{\cos\theta}{n} \times \frac{d\theta}{dt} = \frac{\cos\theta}{n} \times \omega \qquad \qquad \dots\left(\because \frac{d\theta}{dt} = \omega\right)$$

Since the angular velocity of the connecting rod PC is same as the angular velocity of point P with respect to C and is equal to $d\phi/dt$, therefore angular velocity of the connecting rod,

$$\omega_{PC} = \frac{d\phi}{dt} = \frac{\cos\theta}{n} \times \frac{\omega}{\cos\phi} = \frac{\omega}{n} \times \frac{\cos\theta}{\cos\phi}$$

We know that, $\cos\phi = \left(1 - \sin^2\phi\right)^{\frac{1}{2}} = \left(1 - \frac{\sin^2\theta}{n^2}\right)^{\frac{1}{2}} \qquad \dots\left(\because \sin\phi = \frac{\sin\theta}{n}\right)$

$$\therefore \qquad \omega_{PC} = \frac{\omega}{n} \times \frac{\cos\theta}{\left(1 - \frac{\sin^2\theta}{n^2}\right)^{\frac{1}{2}}} = \frac{\omega}{n} \times \frac{\cos\theta}{\frac{1}{n}(n^2 - \sin^2\theta)^{1/2}}$$

$$= \frac{\omega\cos\theta}{(n^2 - \sin^2\theta)^{1/2}} \qquad \qquad \dots(i)$$

Angular acceleration of the connecting rod PC,

$$\alpha_{PC} = \text{Angular acceleration of } P \text{ with respect to } C = \frac{d\,(\omega_{PC})}{dt}$$

We know that

$$\frac{d\,(\omega_{PC})}{dt} = \frac{d\,(\omega_{PC})}{d\theta} \times \frac{d\theta}{dt} = \frac{d\,(\omega_{PC})}{d\theta} \times \omega \qquad \qquad \dots(ii)$$

$$\dots(\because d\theta/dt = \omega)$$

Now differentiating equation (i), we get

$$\frac{d\,(\omega_{PC})}{d\theta} = \frac{d}{d\theta}\left[\frac{\omega\cos\theta}{(n^2 - \sin^2\theta)^{1/2}}\right]$$

$$= \omega\left[\frac{(n^2 - \sin^2\theta)^{1/2}(-\sin\theta)] - [(\cos\theta) \times \frac{1}{2}(n^2 - \sin^2\theta)^{-1/2} \times -2\sin\theta\cos\theta}{n^2 - \sin^2\theta}\right]$$

$$= \omega\left[\frac{(n^2 - \sin^2\theta)^{1/2}(-\sin\theta) + (n^2 - \sin^2\theta)^{-1/2}\sin\theta\cos^2\theta}{n^2 - \sin^2\theta}\right]$$

$$= -\omega\sin\theta\left[\frac{(n^2 - \sin^2\theta)^{1/2} - (n^2 - \sin^2\theta)^{-1/2}\cos^2\theta}{n^2 - \sin^2\theta}\right]$$

$$= -\omega\sin\theta\left[\frac{(n^2 - \sin^2\theta) - \cos^2\theta}{(n^2 - \sin^2\theta)^{3/2}}\right] \qquad \dots\text{[Dividing and multiplying by } (n^2 - \sin^2\theta)^{1/2}]$$

$$= \frac{-\omega \sin \theta}{(n^2 - \sin^2 \theta)^{3/2}} \left[n^2 - (\sin^2 \theta + \cos^2 \theta) \right] = \frac{-\omega \sin \theta \, (n^2 - 1)}{(n^2 - \sin^2 \theta)^{3/2}}$$

$$...(\because \sin^2 \theta + \cos^2 \theta = 1)$$

$$\therefore \quad \alpha_{PC} = \frac{d(\omega_{PC})}{d\theta} \times \omega = \frac{-\omega^2 \sin \theta \, (n^2 - 1)}{(n^2 - \sin^2 \theta)^{3/2}} \qquad ...[\text{From equation } (ii)] \qquad ...(iii)$$

The negative sign shows that the sense of the acceleration of the connecting rod is such that it tends to reduce the angle φ.

Notes: 1. Since $\sin^2 \theta$ is small as compared to n^2, therefore it may be neglected. Thus, equations (i) and (iii) are reduced to

$$\omega_{PC} = \frac{\omega \cos \theta}{n}, \quad \text{and} \quad \alpha_{PC} = \frac{-\omega^2 \sin \theta \, (n^2 - 1)}{n^3}$$

2. Also in equation (iii), unity is small as compared to n^2, hence the term unity may be neglected.

$$\therefore \qquad \alpha_{PC} = \frac{-\omega^2 \sin \theta}{n}$$

Example 15.3. *If the crank and the connecting rod are 300 mm and 1 m long respectively and the crank rotates at a constant speed of 200 r.p.m., determine:1. The crank angle at which the maximum velocity occurs, and 2. Maximum velocity of the piston.*

Solution. Given : $r = 300$ mm $= 0.3$ m ; $l = 1$ m ; $N = 200$ r.p.m. or $\omega = 2\pi \times 200/60 = 20.95$ rad/s

1. *Crank angle at which the maximum velocity occurs*

Let $\qquad\qquad\qquad \theta =$ Crank angle from the inner dead centre at which the maximum velocity occurs.

We know that ratio of length of connecting rod to crank radius,

$$n = l/r = 1/0.3 = 3.33$$

and velocity of the piston,

$$v_P = \omega.r \left(\sin \theta + \frac{\sin 2\theta}{2n} \right) \qquad\qquad ...(i)$$

For maximum velocity of the piston,

$$\frac{dv_P}{d\theta} = 0 \quad i.e. \quad \omega.r \left(\cos \theta + \frac{2 \cos 2\theta}{2n} \right) = 0$$

or $\qquad n \cos \theta + 2 \cos^2 \theta - 1 = 0 \qquad\qquad ...(\because \cos 2\theta = 2 \cos^2 \theta - 1)$

$$2 \cos^2 \theta + 3.33 \cos \theta - 1 = 0$$

$$\therefore \qquad \cos \theta = \frac{-3.33 \pm \sqrt{(3.33)^2 + 4 \times 2 \times 1}}{2 \times 2} = 0.26 \qquad\qquad ...(\text{Taking} + \text{ve sign})$$

or $\qquad\qquad \theta = 75°$ **Ans.**

2. *Maximum velocity of the piston*

Substituting the value of $\theta = 75°$ in equation (i), maximum velocity of the piston,

$$v_{P(max)} = \omega.r \left[\sin 75° + \frac{\sin 150°}{2n} \right] = 20.95 \times 0.3 \left[0.966 + \frac{0.5}{3.33} \right] \text{ m/s}$$

$$= 6.54 \text{ m/s} \quad \textbf{Ans.}$$

Example 15.4. *The crank and connecting rod of a steam engine are 0.3 m and 1.5 m in length. The crank rotates at 180 r.p.m. clockwise. Determine the velocity and acceleration of the piston when the crank is at 40 degrees from the inner dead centre position. Also determine the position of the crank for zero acceleration of the piston.*

Solution. Given : $r = 0.3$; $l = 1.5$ m ; $N = 180$ r.p.m. or $\omega = 2\pi \times 180/60 = 18.85$ rad/s; $\theta = 40°$

Velocity of the piston

We know that ratio of lengths of the connecting rod and crank,

$$n = l/r = 1.5/0.3 = 5$$

∴ Velocity of the piston,

$$v_P = \omega.r\left(\sin\theta + \frac{\sin 2\theta}{2n}\right) = 18.85 \times 0.3\left(\sin 40° + \frac{\sin 80°}{2 \times 5}\right)\text{m/s}$$

$$= 4.19 \text{ m/s Ans.}$$

Acceleration of the piston

We know that acceleration of piston,

$$a_P = \omega^2.r\left(\cos\theta + \frac{\cos 2\theta}{n}\right) = (18.85)^2 \times 0.3\left(\cos 40° + \frac{\cos 80°}{5}\right)\text{m/s}^2$$

$$= 85.35 \text{ m/s}^2 \text{ Ans.}$$

Position of the crank for zero acceleration of the piston

Let θ_1 = Position of the crank from the inner dead centre for zero acceleration of the piston.

We know that acceleration of piston,

$$a_P = \omega^2.r\left(\cos\theta_1 + \frac{\cos 2\theta_1}{n}\right)$$

or

$$0 = \frac{\omega^2.r}{n}(n\cos\theta_1 + \cos 2\theta_1) \qquad\qquad ...(\because a_P = 0)$$

∴ $n\cos\theta_1 + \cos 2\theta_1 = 0$

$5\cos\theta_1 + 2\cos^2\theta_1 - 1 = 0$ or $2\cos^2\theta_1 + 5\cos\theta_1 - 1 = 0$

∴

$$\cos\theta_1 = \frac{-5 \pm \sqrt{5^2 + 4 \times 1 \times 2}}{2 \times 2} = 0.1862 \qquad ...(\text{Taking} + \text{ve sign})$$

or $\theta_1 = 79.27°$ or $280.73°$ **Ans.**

Example 15.5. *In a slider crank mechanism, the length of the crank and connecting rod are 150 mm and 600 mm respectively. The crank position is 60° from inner dead centre. The crank shaft speed is 450 r.p.m. (clockwise). Using analytical method, determine: 1. Velocity and acceleration of the slider, and 2. Angular velocity and angular acceleration of the connecting rod.*

Solution. Given : $r = 150$ mm $= 0.15$ m ; $l = 600$ mm $= 0.6$ m ; $\theta = 60°$; $N = 450$ r.p.m or $\omega = 2\pi \times 450/60 = 47.13$ rad/s

1. Velocity and acceleration of the slider

We know that ratio of the length of connecting rod and crank,

$$n = l/r = 0.6/0.15 = 4$$

∴ Velocity of the slider,

$$v_P = \omega.r\left(\sin\theta + \frac{\sin 2\theta}{2n}\right) = 47.13 \times 0.15\left(\sin 60° + \frac{\sin 120°}{2 \times 4}\right) \text{m/s}$$

$$= 6.9 \text{ m/s Ans.}$$

and acceleration of the slider,

$$a_P = \omega^2.r\left(\cos\theta + \frac{\cos 2\theta}{n}\right) = (47.13)^2 \times 0.15\left(\cos 60° + \frac{\cos 120°}{4}\right)\text{m/s}^2$$

$$= 124.94 \text{ m/s}^2 \text{ Ans.}$$

2. *Angular velocity and angular acceleration of the connecting rod*

We know that angular velocity of the connecting rod,

$$\omega_{PC} = \frac{\omega \cos\theta}{n} = \frac{47.13 \times \cos 60°}{4} = 5.9 \text{ rad/s Ans.}$$

and angular acceleration of the connecting rod,

$$\alpha_{PC} = \frac{\omega^2 \sin\theta}{n} = \frac{(47.13)^2 \times \sin 60°}{4} = 481 \text{ rad/s}^2 \text{ Ans.}$$

15.10. Forces on the Reciprocating Parts of an Engine, Neglecting the Weight of the Connecting Rod

The various forces acting on the reciprocating parts of a horizontal engine are shown in Fig. 15.8. The expressions for these forces, neglecting the weight of the connecting rod, may be derived as discussed below :

1. *Piston effort*. It is the net force acting on the piston or crosshead pin, along the line of stroke. It is denoted by F_P in Fig. 15.8.

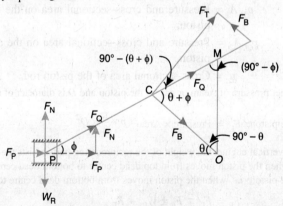

Fig. 15.8. Forces on the reciprocating parts of an engine.

Let m_R = Mass of the reciprocating parts, *e.g.* piston, crosshead pin or gudgeon pin etc., in kg, and

W_R = Weight of the reciprocating parts in newtons = $m_R.g$

We know that acceleration of the reciprocating parts,

$$a_R = a_P = \omega^2.r\left(\cos\theta + \frac{\cos 2\theta}{n}\right)$$

∴ *Accelerating force or inertia force of the reciprocating parts,

$$F_I = m_R \cdot a_R = m_R \cdot \omega^2 \cdot r \left(\cos \theta + \frac{\cos 2\theta}{n} \right)$$

It may be noted that in a horizontal engine, the reciprocating parts are accelerated from rest, during the first half of the stroke (*i.e.* when the piston moves from inner dead centre to outer dead centre). It is, then, retarded during the latter half of the stroke (*i.e.* when the piston moves from outer dead centre to inner dead centre). The inertia force due to the acceleration of the reciprocating parts, opposes the force on the piston due to the difference of pressures in the cylinder on the two sides of the piston. On the other

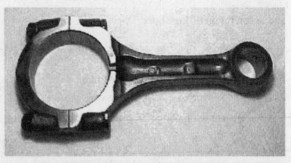

Connecting rod of a petrol engine.

hand, the inertia force due to retardation of the reciprocating parts, helps the force on the piston. Therefore,

Piston effort, $\quad F_P$ = Net load on the piston ∓ Inertia force

$\qquad = F_L \mp F_I \qquad\qquad$ ...(Neglecting frictional resistance)

$\qquad = F_L \mp F_I - R_F \qquad$ ...(Considering frictional resistance)

where $\qquad\qquad R_F$ = Frictional resistance.

The –ve sign is used when the piston is accelerated, and +ve sign is used when the piston is retarded.

In a double acting reciprocating steam engine, net load on the piston,

$$F_L = p_1 A_1 - p_2 A_2 = p_1 A_1 - p_2 (A_1 - a)$$

where $\qquad p_1, A_1$ = Pressure and cross-sectional area on the back end side of the piston,

$\qquad p_2, A_2$ = Pressure and cross-sectional area on the crank end side of the piston,

$\qquad a$ = Cross-sectional area of the piston rod.

Notes : 1. If 'p' is the net pressure of steam or gas on the piston and D is diameter of the piston, then

Net load on the piston, $\quad F_L$ = Pressure × Area = $p \times \dfrac{\pi}{4} \times D^2$

2. In case of a vertical engine, the weight of the reciprocating parts assists the piston effort during the downward stroke (*i.e.* when the piston moves from top dead centre to bottom dead centre) and opposes during the upward stroke of the piston (*i.e.* when the piston moves from bottom dead centre to top dead centre).

∴ Piston effort, $\qquad F_P = F_L \mp F_I \pm W_R - R_F$

2. *Force acting along the connecting rod.* It is denoted by F_Q in Fig. 15.8. From the geometry of the figure, we find that

$$F_Q = \frac{F_P}{\cos \phi}$$

---

* The acceleration of the reciprocating parts by Klien's construction is,

$\qquad\qquad a_p = \omega^2 \times NO$

∴ $\qquad\qquad F_I = m_R \cdot \omega^2 \times NO$

We know that $\quad \cos \phi = \sqrt{1 - \dfrac{\sin^2 \theta}{n^2}}$

$\therefore \qquad\qquad F_Q = \dfrac{F_P}{\sqrt{1 - \dfrac{\sin^2 \theta}{n^2}}}$

3. *Thrust on the sides of the cylinder walls or normal reaction on the guide bars.* It is denoted by F_N in Fig. 15.8. From the figure, we find that

$$F_N = F_Q \sin \phi = \dfrac{F_P}{\cos \phi} \times \sin \phi = F_P \tan \phi \qquad ...\left[\because F_Q = \dfrac{F_P}{\cos \phi} \right]$$

4. *Crank-pin effort and thrust on crank shaft bearings.* The force acting on the connecting rod F_Q may be resolved into two components, one perpendicular to the crank and the other along the crank. The component of F_Q perpendicular to the crank is known as ***crank-pin effort*** and it is *denoted by* F_T in Fig. 15.8. The component of F_Q along the crank produces a thrust on the crank shaft bearings and it is denoted by F_B in Fig. 15.8.

Resolving F_Q perpendicular to the crank,

$$F_T = F_Q \sin (\theta + \phi) = \dfrac{F_P}{\cos \phi} \times \sin (\theta + \phi)$$

and resolving F_Q along the crank,

$$F_B = F_Q \cos (\theta + \phi) = \dfrac{F_P}{\cos \phi} \times \cos (\theta + \phi)$$

5. *Crank effort* or *turning moment or torque on the crank shaft.* The product of the crank-pin effort (F_T) and the crank pin radius (r) is known as ***crank effort*** or ***turning moment*** or ***torque on the crank shaft***. Mathematically,

Crank effort, $\qquad T = F_T \times r = \dfrac{F_P \sin (\theta + \phi)}{\cos \phi} \times r$

$$= \dfrac{F_P (\sin \theta \cos \phi + \cos \theta \sin \phi)}{\cos \phi} \times r$$

$$= F_P \left(\sin \theta + \cos \theta \times \dfrac{\sin \phi}{\cos \phi} \right) \times r$$

$$= F_P (\sin \theta + \cos \theta \tan \phi) \times r \qquad\qquad ...(i)$$

We know that $l \sin \phi = r \sin \theta$

$$\sin \phi = \dfrac{r}{l} \sin \theta = \dfrac{\sin \theta}{n} \qquad\qquad ...\left(\because n = \dfrac{l}{r} \right)$$

and $\qquad \cos \phi = \sqrt{1 - \sin^2 \phi} = \sqrt{1 - \dfrac{\sin^2 \theta}{n^2}} = \dfrac{1}{n} \sqrt{n^2 - \sin^2 \theta}$

$\therefore \qquad \tan \phi = \dfrac{\sin \phi}{\cos \phi} = \dfrac{\sin \theta}{n} \times \dfrac{n}{\sqrt{n^2 - \sin^2 \theta}} = \dfrac{\sin \theta}{\sqrt{n^2 - \sin^2 \theta}}$

Substituting the value of tan ϕ in equation (i), we have crank effort,

$$T = F_P \left(\sin \theta + \frac{\cos \theta \sin \theta}{\sqrt{n^2 - \sin^2 \theta}} \right) \times r$$

$$= F_P \times r \left(\sin \theta + \frac{\sin 2\theta}{2\sqrt{n^2 - \sin^2 \theta}} \right) \qquad \text{...}(ii)$$

$$\text{...}(\because \; 2 \cos \theta \sin \theta = \sin 2\theta)$$

Note: Since $\sin^2 \theta$ is very small as compared to n^2 therefore neglecting $\sin^2 \theta$, we have,

Crank effort, $\qquad T = F_P \times r \left(\sin \theta + \frac{\sin 2\theta}{2n} \right) = F_P \times OM$

We have seen in Art. 15.8, that

$$OM = r \left(\sin \theta + \frac{\sin 2\theta}{2n} \right)$$

Therefore, it is convenient to find OM instead of solving the large expression.

Example 15.6. *Find the inertia force for the following data of an I.C. engine.*

Bore = 175 mm, stroke = 200 mm, engine speed = 500 r.p.m., length of connecting rod = 400 mm, crank angle = 60° from T.D.C and mass of reciprocating parts = 180 kg.

Solution. Given : *D =175 mm ; L = 200 mm = 0.2 m or $r = L / 2 = 0.1$ m ; N = 500 r.p.m. or $\omega = 2\pi \times 500/60$ =52.4 rad/s ; l = 400 mm = 0.4 m ; m_R = 180 kg

The inertia force may be calculated by graphical method or analytical method as discussed below:

1. *Graphical method*

First of all, draw the Klien's acceleration diagram $OCQN$ to some suitable scale as shown in Fig. 15.9. By measurement,

$$ON = 38 \text{ mm} = 0.038 \text{ m}$$

$\therefore$ Acceleration of the reciprocating parts,

$$a_R = \omega^2 \times ON$$
$$= (52.4)^2 \times 0.038 = 104.34 \text{ m/s}$$

We know that inertia force,

$$F_I = m_R \times a_R = 180 \times 104.34 \text{ N}$$
$$= 18\,780 \text{ N} = 18.78 \text{ kN Ans.}$$

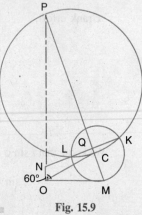

Fig. 15.9

2. *Analytical method*

We know that ratio of lengths of connecting rod and crank,

$$n = l / r = 0.4 / 0.1 = 4$$

$\therefore$ Inertia force, $\qquad F_I = m_R .\omega^2 .r \left(\cos \theta + \frac{\cos 2\theta}{n} \right)$

$$= 180 \times (52.4)^2 \times 0.1 \left(\cos 60° + \frac{\cos 120°}{4} \right) = 18\,530 \text{ N}$$

$$= 18.53 \text{ kN Ans.}$$

---

* Superfluous data.

Example 15.7. *The crank-pin circle radius of a horizontal engine is 300 mm. The mass of the reciprocating parts is 250 kg. When the crank has travelled 60° from I.D.C., the difference between the driving and the back pressures is 0.35 N/mm². The connecting rod length between centres is 1.2 m and the cylinder bore is 0.5 m. If the engine runs at 250 r.p.m. and if the effect of piston rod diameter is neglected, calculate : 1. pressure on slide bars, 2. thrust in the connecting rod, 3. tangential force on the crank-pin, and 4. turning moment on the crank shaft.*

Solution. Given : $r = 300$ mm $= 0.3$ m ; $m_R = 250$ kg; $\theta = 60°$; $p_1 - p_2 = 0.35$ N/mm²; $l = 1.2$ m ; $D = 0.5$ m $= 500$ mm ; $N = 250$ r.p.m. or $\omega = 2\pi \times 250/60 = 26.2$ rad/s

First of all, let us find out the piston effort (F_P).

We know that net load on the piston,

$$F_L = (p_1 - p_2)\frac{\pi}{4} \times D^2 = 0.35 \times \frac{\pi}{4}(500)^2 = 68\,730 \text{ N}$$

...($\because$ Force = Pressure × Area)

Ratio of length of connecting rod and crank,

$$n = l / r = 1.2 / 0.3 = 4$$

and accelerating or inertia force on reciprocating parts,

$$F_I = m_R \cdot \omega^2 r\left(\cos.\theta + \frac{\cos 2\theta}{n}\right)$$

$$= 250\,(26.2)^2\,0.3\left(\cos 60° + \frac{\cos 120°}{4}\right) = 19\,306 \text{ N}$$

$\therefore$ Piston effort, $F_P = F_L - F_I = 68\,730 - 19\,306 = 49\,424$ N $= 49.424$ kN

1. Pressure on slide bars

Let ϕ = Angle of inclination of the connecting rod to the line of stroke.

We know that, $\sin \phi = \dfrac{\sin \theta}{n} = \dfrac{\sin 60°}{4} = \dfrac{0.866}{4} = 0.2165$

$\therefore$ $\phi = 12.5°$

We know that pressure on the slide bars,

$$F_N = F_P \tan \phi = 49.424 \times \tan 12.5° = 10.96 \text{ kN}   \textbf{Ans.}$$

2. Thrust in the connecting rod

We know that thrust in the connecting rod,

$$F_Q = \frac{F_P}{\cos \phi} = \frac{49.424}{\cos 12.5°} = 50.62 \text{ kN Ans.}$$

3. Tangential force on the crank-pin

We know that tangential force on the crank pin,

$$F_T = F_Q \sin(\theta + \phi) = 50.62 \sin(60° + 12.5°) = 48.28 \text{ kN Ans.}$$

4. Turning moment on the crank shaft

We know that turning moment on the crank shaft,

$$T = F_T \times r = 48.28 \times 0.3 = 14.484 \text{ kN-m Ans.}$$

Example 15.8. *A vertical double acting steam engine has a cylinder 300 mm diameter and 450 mm stroke and runs at 200 r.p.m. The reciprocating parts has a mass of 225 kg and the piston rod is 50 mm diameter. The connecting rod is 1.2 m long. When the crank has turned through 125° from the top dead centre, the steam pressure above the piston is 30 kN/m² and below the piston is 1.5 kN/m². Calculate the effective turning moment on the crank shaft.*

Solution. Given : $D = 300$ mm $= 0.3$ m ; $L = 450$ mm or $r = L/2 = 225$ mm $= 0.225$ m ; $N = 200$ r.p.m. or $\omega = 2\pi \times 200/60 = 20.95$ rad/s ; $m_R = 225$ kg ; $d = 50$ mm $= 0.05$ m ; $l = 1.2$ m ; $\theta = 125°$; $p_1 = 30$ kN/m² $= 30 \times 10^3$ N/m² ; $p_2 = 1.5$ kN/m² $= 1.5 \times 10^3$ N/m²

We know that area of the piston,

$$A_1 = \frac{\pi}{4} \times D^2 = \frac{\pi}{4} \times (0.3)^2 = 0.0707 \text{ m}^2$$

and area of the piston rod, $\quad a = \frac{\pi}{4} \times d^2 = \frac{\pi}{4} \times (0.05)^2 = 0.001\,96 \text{ m}^2$

∴ Force on the piston due to steam pressure,

$$\begin{aligned}
F_L &= p_1.A_1 - p_2(A_1 - a) \\
&= 30 \times 10^3 \times 0.0707 - 1.5 \times 10^3 (0.0707 - 0.001\,96)\,\text{N} \\
&= 2121 - 103 = 2018 \text{ N}
\end{aligned}$$

Ratio of lengths of connecting rod and crank,

$$n = l\,/\,r = 1.2\,/\,0.225 = 5.33$$

and inertia force on the reciprocating parts,

$$\begin{aligned}
F_I &= m_R.\omega^2.r\left(\cos\theta + \frac{\cos 2\theta}{n}\right) \\
&= 225\,(20.95)^2 \times 0.225\left(\cos 125° + \frac{\cos 250°}{5.33}\right) = -\,14\,172 \text{ N}
\end{aligned}$$

We know that for a vertical engine, net force on the piston or piston effort,

$$\begin{aligned}
F_P &= F_L - F_I + m_R.g \\
&= 2018 - (-\,14\,172) + 225 \times 9.81 = 18\,397 \text{ N}
\end{aligned}$$

Let $\qquad\qquad \phi =$ Angle of inclination of the connecting rod to the line of stroke.

We know that, $\quad \sin\phi = \dfrac{\sin\theta}{n} = \dfrac{\sin 125°}{5.33} = \dfrac{0.8191}{5.33} = 0.1537$

∴ $\qquad\qquad \phi = 8.84°$

We know that effective turning moment on the crank shaft,

$$T = \frac{F_P \times \sin(\theta + \phi)}{\cos\phi} \times r = \frac{18397 \sin(125° + 8.84°)}{\cos 8.84°} \times 0.225 \text{ N-m}$$

$$= 3021.6 \text{ N-m Ans.}$$

Example 15.9. *The crank and connecting rod of a petrol engine, running at 1800 r.p.m. are 50 mm and 200 mm respectively. The diameter of the piston is 80 mm and the mass of the reciprocating parts is 1 kg. At a point during the power stroke, the pressure on the piston is 0.7 N/mm², when it has moved 10 mm from the inner dead centre. Determine : 1. Net load on the gudgeon pin, 2. Thrust in the connecting rod, 3. Reaction between the piston and cylinder, and 4. The engine speed at which the above values become zero.*

Solution. Given : $N = 1800$ r.p.m. or $\omega = 2\pi \times 1800/60 = 188.52$ rad/s ; $r = 50$ mm $= 0.05$ m; $l = 200$ mm ; $D = 80$ mm ; $m_R = 1$ kg ; $p = 0.7$ N/mm² ; $x = 10$ mm

1. *Net load on the gudgeon pin*

We know that load on the piston,

$$F_L = \frac{\pi}{4} D^2 \times p = \frac{\pi}{4} \times (80)^2 \times 0.7 = 3520 \text{ N}$$

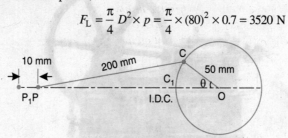

Fig. 15.10

When the piston has moved 10 mm from the inner dead centre, *i.e.* when $P_1P = 10$ mm, the crank rotates from OC_1 to OC through an angle θ as shown in Fig. 15.10.

By measurement, we find that *$\theta = 33°$.

We know that ratio of lengths of connecting rod and crank,

$$n = l/r = 200/50 = 4$$

and inertia force on the reciprocating parts,

$$F_I = m_R . a_R = m_R . \omega^2 . r \left(\cos \theta + \frac{\cos 2\theta}{n} \right)$$

$$= 1 \times (188.52)^2 \times 0.05 \left(\cos 33° + \frac{\cos 66°}{4} \right) = 1671 \text{ N}$$

We know that net load on the gudgeon pin,

$$F_P = F_L - F_I = 3520 - 1671 = 1849 \text{ N Ans.}$$

2. *Thrust in the connecting rod*

Let ϕ = Angle of inclination of the connecting rod to the line of stroke.

We know that, $\sin \phi = \dfrac{\sin \theta}{n} = \dfrac{\sin 33°}{4} = \dfrac{0.5446}{4} = 0.1361$

∴ $\phi = 7.82°$

---

* The angle θ may also be obtained as follows:

We know that $x = r \left[(1 - \cos \theta) + \dfrac{\sin^2 \theta}{2n} \right] = r \left[(1 - \cos \theta) + \dfrac{1 - \cos^2 \theta}{2n} \right]$

$$10 = 50 \left[(1 - \cos \theta) + \frac{1 - \cos^2 \theta}{2 \times 4} \right] = \frac{50}{8} \left[(8 - 8 \cos \theta + 1 - \cos^2 \theta) \right]$$

$$= 50 - 50 \cos \theta + 6.25 - 6.25 \cos^2 \theta$$

or $6.25 \cos^2 \theta + 50 \cos \theta - 56.25 = 0$

Solving this quadratic equation, we get $\theta = 33.14°$

Twin-cylinder aeroplane engine.

We know that thrust in the connecting rod,

$$F_Q = \frac{F_P}{\cos \phi} = \frac{1849}{\cos 7.82°} = 1866.3 \text{ N} \textbf{ Ans.}$$

3. Reaction between the piston and cylinder

We know that reaction between the piston and cylinder,

$$F_N = F_P \tan \phi = 1849 \tan 7.82° = 254 \text{ N} \textbf{ Ans.}$$

4. Engine speed at which the above values will become zero

A little consideration will show that the above values will become zero, if the inertia force on the reciprocating parts (F_I) is equal to the load on the piston (F_L). Let ω_1 be the speed in rad/s, at which $F_I = F_L$.

$$\therefore \quad m_R \ (\omega_1)^2 \ r \left(\cos \theta + \frac{\cos 2\theta}{n} \right) = \frac{\pi}{4} \ D^2 \times p$$

$$1 \ (\omega_1)^2 \times 0.05 \left(\cos 33° + \frac{\cos 66°}{4} \right) = \frac{\pi}{4} \times (80)^2 \times 0.7 \quad \text{or} \quad 0.0 \ 47 \ (\omega_1)^2 = 3520$$

$$\therefore \quad\quad\quad\quad (\omega_1)^2 = 3520 \ / \ 0.047 = 74 \ 894 \text{ or } \omega_1 = 273.6 \text{ rad/s}$$

$\therefore$ Corresponding speed in r.p.m.,

$$N_1 = 273.6 \times 60 \ / \ 2\pi = 2612 \text{ r.p.m.} \textbf{ Ans.}$$

Example 15.10. *During a trial on steam engine, it is found that the acceleration of the piston is 36 m/s² when the crank has moved 30° from the inner dead centre position. The net effective steam pressure on the piston is 0.5 N/mm² and the frictional resistance is equivalent to a force of 600 N. The diameter of the piston is 300 mm and the mass of the reciprocating parts is 180 kg. If the length of the crank is 300 mm and the ratio of the connecting rod length to the crank length is 4.5, find: 1. Reaction on the guide bars, 2. Thrust on the crank shaft bearings, and 3. Turning moment on the crank shaft.*

Solution. Given : $a_P = 36$ m/s² ; $\theta = 30°$; $p = 0.5$ N/mm² ; $R_F = 600$ N; $D = 300$ mm ; $m_R = 180$ kg ; $r = 300$ mm $= 0.3$ m ; $n = l / r = 4.5$

1. Reaction on the guide bars

First of all, let us find the piston effort (F_P). We know that load on the piston,

$$F_L = p \times \frac{\pi}{4} \times D^2 = 0.5 \times \frac{\pi}{4} \times (300)^2 = 35 350 \text{ N}$$

and inertia force due to reciprocating parts,

$$F_I = m_R \times a_P = 180 \times 36 = 6480 \text{ N}$$

∴ Piston effort, $F_P = F_L - F_I - R_F = 35\ 350 - 6480 - 600 = 28\ 270 \text{ N} = 28.27 \text{ kN}$

Let ϕ = Angle of inclination of the connecting rod to the line of stroke.

We know that $\sin \phi = \sin \theta / n = \sin 30°/4.5 = 0.1111$

∴ $\phi = 6.38°$

We know that reaction on the guide bars,

$$F_N = F_P \tan \phi = 28.27 \tan 6.38° = 3.16 \text{ kN Ans.}$$

2. *Thrust on the crank shaft bearing*

We know that thrust on the crank shaft bearings,

$$F_B = \frac{F_P \cos(\theta + \phi)}{\cos \phi} = \frac{28.27 \cos(30° + 6.38°)}{\cos 6.38°} = 22.9 \text{ kN Ans.}$$

3. *Turning moment on the crank shaft*

We know that turning moment on the crank shaft,

$$T = \frac{F_P \sin(\theta + \phi)}{\cos \phi} \times r = \frac{28.27 \sin(30° + 6.38°)}{\cos 6.38°} \times 0.3 \text{ kN-m}$$

$$= 5.06 \text{ kN-m}$$

Example 15.11. *A vertical petrol engine 100 mm diameter and 120 mm stroke has a connecting rod 250 mm long. The mass of the piston is 1.1 kg. The speed is 2000 r.p.m. On the expansion stroke with a crank 20° from top dead centre, the gas pressure is 700 kN/m². Determine:*

1. Net force on the piston, 2. Resultant load on the gudgeon pin, 3. Thrust on the cylinder walls, and 4. Speed above which, other things remaining same, the gudgeon pin load would be reversed in direction.

Solution. Given: $D = 100 \text{ mm} = 0.1 \text{ m}$; $L = 120 \text{ mm} = 0.12 \text{ m}$ or $r = L/2 = 0.06 \text{ m}$; $l = 250 \text{ mm} = 0.25 \text{ m}$; $m_R = 1.1 \text{ kg}$; $N = 2000 \text{ r.p.m.}$ or $\omega = 2\pi \times 2000/60 = 209.5 \text{ rad/s}$; $\theta = 20°$; $p = 700 \text{ kN/m}^2$

1. *Net force on the piston*

The configuration diagram of a vertical engine is shown in Fig. 15.11.

We know that force due to gas pressure,

$$F_L = p \times \frac{\pi}{4} \times D^2 = 700 \times \frac{\pi}{4} \times (0.1)^2 = 5.5 \text{ kN}$$

$$= 5500 \text{ N}$$

and ratio of lengths of the connecting rod and crank,

$$n = l/r = 0.25/0.06 = 4.17$$

∴ Inertia force on the piston,

$$F_I = m_R . \omega^2 . r \left(\cos \theta + \frac{\cos 2\theta}{n} \right)$$

$$= 1.1 \times (209.5)^2 \times 0.06 \times \left(\cos 20° + \frac{\cos 40°}{4.17} \right)$$

$$= 3254 \text{ N}$$

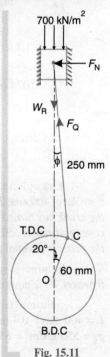

Fig. 15.11

We know that for a vertical engine, net force on the piston,

$$F_P = F_L - F_I + W_R = F_L - F_I + m_R \cdot g$$
$$= 5500 - 3254 + 1.1 \times 9.81 = 2256.8 \text{ N Ans.}$$

2. Resultant load on the gudgeon pin

Let ϕ = Angle of inclination of the connecting rod to the line of stroke.

We know that,

$$\sin \phi = \sin \theta / n = \sin 20° / 4.17 = 0.082$$

$\therefore$ $\phi = 4.7°$

We know that resultant load on the gudgeon pin,

$$F_Q = \frac{F_P}{\cos \phi} = \frac{2256.8}{\cos 4.7°} = 2265 \text{ N Ans.}$$

3. Thrust on the cylinder walls

We know that thrust on the cylinder walls,

$$F_N = F_P \tan \phi = 2256.8 \times \tan 4.7° = 185.5 \text{ N Ans.}$$

4. Speed, above which, the gudgeon pin load would be reversed in direction

Let N_1 = Required speed, in r.p.m.

The gudgeon pin load *i.e.* F_Q will be reversed in direction, if F_Q becomes negative. This is only possible when F_P is negative. Therefore, for F_P to be negative, F_I must be greater than $(F_L + W_R)$,

i.e. $$m_R (\omega_1)^2 r \left(\cos \theta + \frac{\cos 2\theta}{n} \right) > 5500 + 1.1 \times 9.81$$

$$1.1 \times (\omega_1)^2 \times 0.06 \left(\cos 20° + \frac{\cos 40°}{4.17} \right) > 5510.8$$

$$0.074 (\omega_1)^2 > 5510.8 \quad \text{or} \quad (\omega_1)^2 > 5510.8/0.074 \text{ or } 74\,470$$

or $$\omega_1 > 273 \text{ rad/s}$$

$\therefore$ Corresponding speed in r.p.m.,

$$N_1 > 273 \times 60 / 2\pi \quad \text{or} \quad 2606 \text{ r.p.m. Ans.}$$

Example 15. 12. *A horizontal steam engine running at 120 r.p.m. has a bore of 250 mm and a stroke of 400 mm. The connecting rod is 0.6 m and mass of the reciprocating parts is 60 kg. When the crank has turned through an angle of 45° from the inner dead centre, the steam pressure on the cover end side is 550 kN/m² and that on the crank end side is 70 kN/m². Considering the diameter of the piston rod equal to 50 mm, determine:*

1. turning moment on the crank shaft, 2. thrust on the bearings, and 3. acceleration of the flywheel, if the power of the engine is 20 kW, mass of the flywheel 60 kg and radius of gyration 0.6 m.

Solution. Given : $N = 120$ r.p.m. or $\omega = 2\pi \times 120/60 = 12.57$ rad/s ; $D = 250$ mm $= 0.25$ m ; $L = 400$ mm $= 0.4$ m or $r = L/2 = 0.2$ m ; $l = 0.6$ m ; $m_R = 60$ kg ; $\theta = 45°$; $d = 50$ mm $= 0.05$ m ; $p_1 = 550$ kN/m² $= 550 \times 10^3$ N/m² ; $p_2 = 70$ kN/m² $= 70 \times 10^3$ N/m²

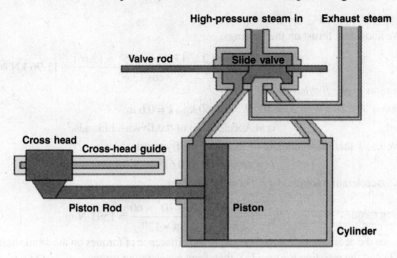

High-pressure steam in **Exhaust steam**

Valve rod   **Slide valve**

Cross head
Cross-head guide

Piston Rod   **Piston**

Cylinder

1. *Turning moment on the crankshaft*

First of all, let us find the net load on the piston (F_P).

We know that area of the piston on the cover end side,

$$A_1 = \frac{\pi}{4} \times D^2 = \frac{\pi}{4} \times (0.25)^2 = 0.049 \text{ m}^2$$

and area of piston rod, $\qquad a = \frac{\pi}{4} \times d^2 = \frac{\pi}{4} \times (0.05)^2 = 0.00196 \text{ m}^2$

∴ Net load on the piston,

$$F_L = p_1.A_1 - p_2.\, A_2 = p_1.A_1 - p_2\,(A_1 - a)$$
$$= 550 \times 10^3 \times 0.049 - 70 \times 10^3\,(0.049 - 0.001\,96) = 23657 \text{ N}$$

We know that ratio of lengths of the connecting rod and crank,

$$n = l/r = 0.6/0.2 = 3$$

and inertia force on the reciprocating parts,

$$F_I = m_R.\omega^2.r\left(\cos\theta + \frac{\cos 2\theta}{n}\right)$$

$$= 60 \times (12.57)^2 \times 0.2\left(\cos 45° + \frac{\cos 90°}{3}\right) = 1340 \text{ N}$$

∴ Net force on the piston or piston effort,

$$F_P = F_L - F_I = 23657 - 1340 = 22\,317 \text{ N} = 22.317 \text{ kN}$$

Let $\qquad\qquad \phi$ = Angle of inclination of the connecting rod to the line of stroke.

We know that, $\quad \sin\phi = \sin\theta/n = \sin 45°/3 = 0.2357$

∴ $\qquad\qquad\qquad \phi = 13.6°$

We know that turning moment on the crankshaft,

$$T = \frac{F_P \sin(\theta + \phi)}{\cos\phi} \times r = \frac{22.317 \times \sin(45° + 13.6°)}{\cos 13.6°} \times 0.2 \text{ kN-m}$$

$$= 3.92 \text{ kN-m} = 3920 \text{ N-m} \quad \textbf{Ans.}$$

2. Thrust on the bearings

We know that thrust on the bearings,

$$F_B = \frac{F_P \cos (\theta + \phi)}{\cos \phi} = \frac{22.317 \times \cos (45° + 13.6°)}{\cos 13.6°} = 11.96 \text{ kN Ans.}$$

3. Acceleration of the flywheel

Given: $P = 20 \text{ kW} = 20 \times 10^3 \text{ W}$; $m = 60 \text{ kg}$; $k = 0.6 \text{ m}$

Let $\qquad\qquad\qquad \alpha$ = Acceleration of the flywheel in rad/s².

We know that mass moment of inertia of the flywheel,

$$I = m.k^2 = 60 \times (0.6)^2 = 21.6 \text{ kg-m}^2$$

∴ Accelerating torque, $T_A = I.\alpha = 21.6 \, \alpha$ N-m $\qquad\qquad\qquad$ ...(i)

and resisting torque, $\qquad T_R = \dfrac{P \times 60}{2\pi N} = \dfrac{20 \times 10^3 \times 60}{2\pi \times 120} = 1591 \text{ N-m} \qquad \left(\because P = \dfrac{2\pi NT}{60} \right)$

Since the accelerating torque is equal to the difference of torques on the crankshaft or turning moment (T) and the resisting torque (T_R), therefore, accelerating torque,

$$T_A = T - T_R = 3920 - 1591 = 2329 \text{ N-m} \qquad\qquad ...(ii)$$

From equation (i) and (ii),

$$\alpha = 2329/21.6 = 107.8 \text{ rad/s}^2 \quad \textbf{Ans.}$$

Example 15.13. *A vertical, single cylinder, single acting diesel engine has a cylinder diameter 300 mm, stroke length 500 mm, and connecting rod length 4.5 times the crank length. The engine runs at 180 r.p.m. The mass of the reciprocating parts is 280 kg. The compression ratio is 14 and the pressure remains constant during the injection of the oil for 1/10th of the stroke. If the compression and expansion follows the law $p.V^{1.35}$ = constant, find: 1. Crank-pin effort, 2. Thrust on the bearings, and 3. Turning moment on the crank shaft, when the crank displacement is 45° from the inner dead centre position during expansion stroke.*

The suction pressure may be taken as 0.1 N/mm².

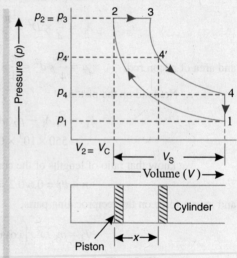

Fig. 15.12

Solution. Given : D = 300 mm = 0.3 m ; L = 500 mm = 0.5 m or r = 0.25 m ; l = 4.5 r or $n = l/r$ = 4.5; N = 180 r.p.m. or $\omega = 2\pi \times 180/60 = 18.85$ rad/s ; m_R = 280 kg ; $\dfrac{V_1}{V_2} = 14$; $\theta = 45°$; $p_1 = 0.1$ N/mm²

The pressure-volume (*i.e.* p-V) diagram for a *diesel engine is shown in Fig 15.12, in which

1-2 represents the compression, 2-3 represents the injection of fuel, 3-4 represents the expansion, and 4-1 represents the exhaust.

Let p_1, p_2, p_3, and p_4 = Pressures corresponding to points 1, 2, 3 and 4 respectively, and

V_1, V_2, V_3, and $\quad V_4$ = Volumes corresponding to points 1, 2, 3 and 4 respectively.

---

* In a diesel engine, the compression and expansion are isentropic *i.e.* according to the law $p.V^l$ = constant. The injection of fuel takes place at constant pressure and the exhaust is at constant volume.

Since the compression follows the law $p.V^{1.35} =$ constant, therefore

$$p_1 (V_1)^{1.35} = p_2 (V_2)^{1.35}$$

or

$$p_2 = p_1 \left(\frac{V_1}{V_2}\right)^{1.35} = 0.1 \times (14)^{1.35} = 3.526 \text{ N/mm}^2$$

We know that swept volume,

$$V_S = \frac{\pi}{4} \times D^2 \times L = \frac{\pi}{4} \times (0.3)^2 \times 0.5 = 0.035 \text{ m}^3$$

and   compression ratio, $= \frac{V_1}{V_2} = \frac{V_C + V_S}{V_C} = 1 + \frac{V_S}{V_C}$ ...($\because V_2 = V_C$)

$\therefore$ $14 = 1 + \dfrac{0.035}{V_C}$ or $V_C = \dfrac{0.035}{14 - 1} = 0.0027 \text{ m}^3$

Since the injection of fuel takes place at constant pressure (*i.e.* $p_2 = p_3$) and continues up to 1/10th of the stroke, therefore volume at the end of the injection of fuel,

$$V_3 = V_C + \frac{1}{10} \times V_S = 0.0027 + \frac{0.035}{10} = 0.0062 \text{ m}^3$$

When the crank displacement is 45° (*i.e.* when $\theta = 45°$) from the inner dead centre during expansion stroke, the corresponding displacement of the piston (marked by point 4' on the *p-V* diagram) is given by

$$x = r\left[(1 - \cos \theta) + \frac{\sin^2 \theta}{2n}\right] = r\left[(1 - \cos 45°) + \frac{\sin^2 45°}{2 \times 4.5}\right]$$

$$= 0.25\left[(1 - 0.707) + \frac{0.5}{9}\right] = 0.087 \text{ m}$$

$\therefore$ $V_4' = V_C + \dfrac{\pi}{4} \times D^2 \times x = 0.0027 + \dfrac{\pi}{4} \times (0.3)^2 \times 0.087 = 0.0088 \text{ m}^2$

Since the expansion follows the law $p.V^{1.35} =$ constant, therefore,

$$p_3 (V_3)^{1.35} = p_{4'} (V_{4'})^{1.35}$$

$\therefore$ $p_{4'} = p_3 \left(\dfrac{V_3}{V_{4'}}\right)^{1.35} = 3.526\left(\dfrac{0.0062}{0.0088}\right)^{1.35} = 2.2 \text{ N/mm}^2$

Difference of pressures on two sides of the piston,

$$p = p_{4'} - p_1 = 2.2 - 0.1 = 2.1 \text{ N/mm}^2 = 2.1 \times 10^6 \text{ N/m}^2$$

$\therefore$ Net load on the piston,

$$F_L = p \times \frac{\pi}{4} \times D^2 = 2.1 \times 10^6 \times \frac{\pi}{4} \times (0.3)^2 = 148\,460 \text{ N}$$

Inertia force on the reciprocating parts,

$$F_I = m_R.\omega^2.r\left(\cos \theta + \frac{\cos 2\theta}{n}\right)$$

$$= 280 \times (18.85)^2 \times 0.25\left(\cos 45° + \frac{\cos 90°}{4.5}\right) = 17585 \text{ N}$$

We know that net force on the piston or piston effort,

$$F_P = F_L - F_I + W_R = F_L - F_I + m_R \cdot g$$
$$= 148\,460 - 17\,585 + 280 \times 9.81 = 133\,622 \text{ N}$$

1. Crank-pin effort

Let ϕ = Angle of inclination of the connecting rod to the line of stroke.

We know that, $\sin \phi = \sin \theta / n = \sin 45° / 4.5 = 0.1571$

∴ $\phi = 9.04°$

We know that crank-pin effort,

$$F_T = \frac{F_P \sin (\theta + \phi)}{\cos \phi} = \frac{133\,622 \times \sin (45° + 9.04°)}{\cos 9.04°} = 109\,522 \text{ N}$$
$$= 109.522 \text{ kN} \textbf{ Ans.}$$

2. Thrust on the bearings

We know that thrust on the bearings,

$$F_B = \frac{F_P \cdot \cos (\theta + \phi)}{\cos \phi} = \frac{133\,622 \times \cos (45° + 9.04°)}{\cos 9.04°} = 79\,456 \text{ N}$$
$$= 79.956 \text{ kN} \textbf{ Ans.}$$

3. Turning moment on the crankshaft

We know that the turning moment on the crankshaft,

$$T = F_T \times r = 109.522 \times 0.25 = 27.38 \text{ kN-m} \textbf{ Ans.}$$

Example 15.14. *A vertical double acting steam engine has cylinder diameter 240 mm, length of stroke 360 mm and length of connecting rod 0.6 m. The crank rotates at 300 r.p.m. and the mass of the reciprocating parts is 160 kg. The steam is admitted at a pressure of 8 bar gauge and cut-off takes place at 1/3rd of the stroke. The expansion of steam is hyperbolic. The exhaust of steam takes place at a pressure of – 0.75 bar gauge. The frictional resistance is equivalent to a force of 500 N. Determine the turning moment on the crankshaft, when the piston is 75° from the top dead centre. Neglect the effect of clearance and assume the atmospheric presssure as 1.03 bar.*

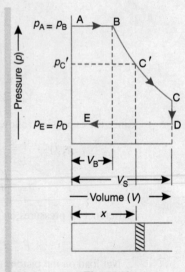

Fig. 15.13

Solution. Given : $D = 240$ mm $= 0.24$ m ; $L = 360$ mm $= 0.36$ m or $r = L/2 = 0.18$ m ; $l = 0.6$ m ; $N = 300$ r.p.m. or $\omega = 2\pi \times 300/60 = 31.42$ rad/s; $m_R = 160$ kg ; $p_A = 8 + 1.03 = 9.03$ bar $= 903 \times 10^3$ N/m^2 ; $p_E = -0.75 + 1.03 = 0.28$ bar $= 28 \times 10^3$ N/m^2 ; $F_R = 500$ N ; $\theta = 75°$

First of all, let us find the piston effort (F_P).

The pressure-volume (p-V) diagram for a steam engine, neglecting clearance, is shown in Fig. 15.13, in which AB represents the admission of steam, BC the expansion and DE the exhaust of steam. The steam is cut-off at point B.

We know that the stroke volume,

$$V_S = \frac{\pi}{4} \times D^2 \times L = \frac{\pi}{4} \times (0.24)^2 \times 0.36 = 0.0163 \text{ m}^3$$

Since the admission of steam is cut-off at 1/3rd of the stroke, therefore volume of steam at cut-off,

$$V_B = V_S / 3 = 0.0163/3 = 0.005\ 43\ m^3$$

We know that ratio of the lengths of the connecting rod and crank,

$$n = l/r = 0.6/0.18 = 3.33$$

When the crank position is 75° from the top dead centre (*i.e.* when θ = 75°), the displacement of the piston (marked by point *C'* on the expansion curve *BC*) is given by

$$x = r\left[(1 - \cos\theta) + \frac{\sin^2\theta}{2n}\right] = 0.18\left[1 - \cos 75° + \frac{\sin^2 75°}{2 \times 3.33}\right]$$

$$= 0.1586\ m$$

∴ $$V_C' = V_S \times \frac{x}{L} = 0.0163 \times \frac{0.1586}{0.36} = 0.0072\ m^3$$

Since the expansion is hyperbolic (*i.e.* according to the law pV = constant), therefore

$$p_B . V_B = p_C' . V_C'$$

or $$p_C' = \frac{p_B \times V_B}{V_C'} = \frac{903 \times 10^3 \times 0.005\,43}{0.0072} = 681 \times 10^3\ N/m^2$$

∴ Difference of pressures on the two sides of the piston,

$$p = p_C' - p_E = 681 \times 10^3 - 28 \times 10^3 = 653 \times 10^3\ N/m^2$$

We know that net load on the piston,

$$F_L = \frac{\pi}{4} \times D^2 \times p = \frac{\pi}{4} \times (0.24)^2 \times 653 \times 10^3 = 29545\ N$$

and inertia force on the reciprocating parts,

$$F_I = m_R . \omega^2 . r\left(\cos\theta + \frac{\cos 2\theta}{n}\right)$$

$$= 160 \times (31.42)^2 \times 0.18\left(\cos 75° + \frac{\cos 150°}{3.33}\right) = -36\ N$$

∴ Piston effort, $$F_P = F_L - F_I + W_R - F_R$$

$$= 29545 - (-36) + 160 \times 9.81 - 500 = 30651\ N$$

Turning moment on the crankshaft

Let ϕ = Angle of inclination of the connecting rod to the line of stroke.

We know that $$\sin\phi = \sin\theta/n = \sin 75°/3.33 = 0.29$$

∴ $$\phi = 16.86°$$

We know that turning moment on the crankshaft

$$T = \frac{F_P \sin(\theta + \phi)}{\cos\phi} \times r = \frac{30651 \sin(75° + 16.86°)}{\cos 16.86°} \times 0.18\ N\text{-}m$$

$$= 5762\ N\text{-}m\ \textbf{Ans.}$$

15.11. Equivalent Dynamical System

In order to determine the motion of a rigid body, under the action of external forces, it is usually convenient to replace the rigid body by two masses placed at a fixed distance apart, in such a way that,

1. the sum of their masses is equal to the total mass of the body ;
2. the centre of gravity of the two masses coincides with that of the body ; and
3. the sum of mass moment of inertia of the masses about their centre of gravity is equal to the mass moment of inertia of the body.

When these three conditions are satisfied, then it is said to be an *equivalent dynamical system*. Consider a rigid body, having its centre of gravity at G, as shown in Fig. 15.14.

Let m = Mass of the body,

k_G = Radius of gyration about its centre of gravity G,

m_1 and m_2 = Two masses which form a dynamical equivalent system,

l_1 = Distance of mass m_1 from G,

l_2 = Distance of mass m_2 from G, and

L = Total distance between the masses m_1 and m_2.

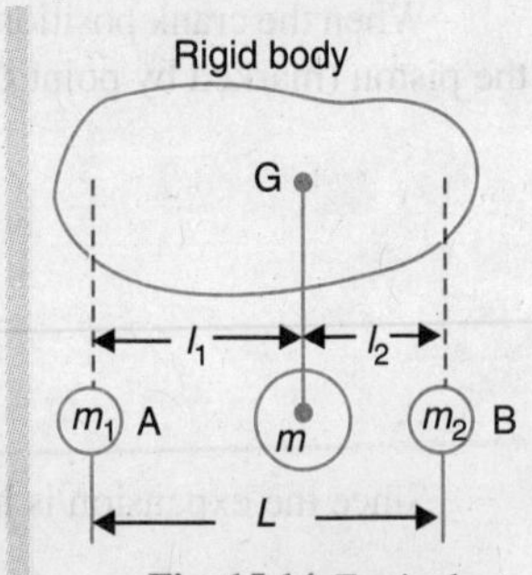

Fig. 15.14. Equivalent dynamical system.

Thus, for the two masses to be dynamically equivalent,

$$m_1 + m_2 = m \qquad \ldots(i)$$

$$m_1 l_1 = m_2 l_2 \qquad \ldots(ii)$$

and

$$m_1 (l_1)^2 + m_2 (l_2)^2 = m (k_G)^2 \qquad \ldots(iii)$$

From equations (*i*) and (*ii*),

$$m_1 = \frac{l_2 . m}{l_1 + l_2} \qquad \ldots(iv)$$

and

$$m_2 = \frac{l_1 . m}{l_1 + l_2} \qquad \ldots(v)$$

Substituting the value of m_1 and m_2 in equation (*iii*), we have

$$\frac{l_2 . m}{l_1 + l_2}(l_1)^2 + \frac{l_1 . m}{l_1 + l_2}(l_2)^2 = m(k_G)^2 \quad \text{or} \quad \frac{l_1 l_2 (l_1 + l_2)}{l_1 + l_2} = (k_G)^2$$

$$\therefore \qquad l_1 . l_2 = (k_G)^2 \qquad \ldots(vi)$$

This equation gives the essential condition of placing the two masses, so that the system becomes dynamical equivalent. The distance of one of the masses (*i.e.* either l_1 or l_2) is arbitrary chosen and the other distance is obtained from equation (*vi*).

Note : When the radius of gyration k_G is not known, then the position of the second mass may be obtained by considering the body as a compound pendulum. We have already discussed, that the length of the simple pendulum which gives the same frequency as the rigid body (*i.e.* compound pendulum) is

$$L = \frac{(k_G)^2 + h^2}{h} = \frac{(k_G)^2 + (l_1)^2}{l_1} \qquad \text{..(Replacing } h \text{ by } l_1)$$

We also know that $\quad l_1 l_2 = (k_G)^2$

$$\therefore \qquad L = \frac{l_1 l_2 + (l_1)^2}{l_1} = l_2 + l_1$$

This means that the second mass is situated at the *centre of oscillation* or *percussion* of the body, which is at a distance of $l_2 = (k_G)^2/l_1$.

15.12. Determination of Equivalent Dynamical System of Two Masses by Graphical Method

Consider a body of mass m, acting at G as shown in Fig. 15.15. This mass m, may be replaced by two masses m_1 and m_2 so that the system becomes dynamical equivalent. The position of mass m_1 may be fixed arbitrarily at A. Now draw perpendicular CG at G, equal in length of the radius of gyration of the body, k_G. Then join AC and draw CB perpendicular to AC intersecting AG produced in B. The point B now fixes the position of the second mass m_2.

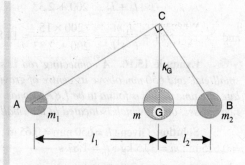

Fig. 15.15. Determination of equivalent dynamical system by graphical method.

A little consideration will show that the triangles ACG and BCG are similar. Therefore,

$$\frac{k_G}{l_1} = \frac{l_2}{k_G} \quad \text{or} \quad (k_G)^2 = l_1.l_2$$

...(Same as before)

Example 15.15. *The connecting rod of a gasoline engine is 300 mm long between its centres. It has a mass of 15 kg and mass moment of inertia of 7000 kg-mm². Its centre of gravity is at 200 mm from its small end centre. Determine the dynamical equivalent two-mass system of the connecting rod if one of the masses is located at the small end centre.*

Solution. Given : $l = 300$ mm ; $m = 15$ kg; $I = 7000$ kg-mm² ; $l_1 = 200$ mm

The connecting rod is shown in Fig. 15.16.

Let k_G = Radius of gyration of the connecting rod about an axis passing through its centre of gravity G.

We know that mass moment of inertia (I),

$$7000 = m\,(k_G)^2 = 15\,(k_G)^2$$

$\therefore$ $(k_G)^2 = 7000/15 = 466.7$ mm² or $k_G = 21.6$ mm

It is given that one of the masses is located at the small end centre. Let the other mass is placed at a distance l_2 from the centre of gravity G, as shown in Fig. 15.17.

We know that for a dynamical equivalent system,

$$l_1.l_2 = (k_G)^2$$

$\therefore$ $l_2 = \dfrac{(k_G)^2}{l_1} = \dfrac{466.7}{200} = 2.33$ mm

Let m_1 = Mass placed at the small end centre, and

m_2 = Mass placed at a distance l_2 from the centre of gravity G.

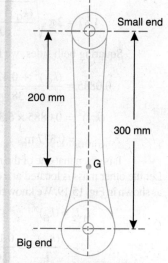

Fig. 15.16

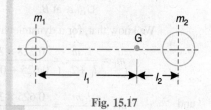

Fig. 15.17

We know that

$$m_1 = \frac{l_2.m}{l_1 + l_2} = \frac{2.33 \times 15}{200 + 2.33} = 0.17 \text{ kg Ans.}$$

and

$$m_2 = \frac{l_1.m}{l_1 + l_2} = \frac{200 \times 15}{200 + 2.33} = 14.83 \text{ kg Ans.}$$

Example 15.16. *A connecting rod is suspended from a point 25 mm above the centre of small end, and 650 mm above its centre of gravity, its mass being 37.5 kg. When permitted to oscillate, the time period is found to be 1.87 seconds. Find the dynamical equivalent system constituted of two masses, one of which is located at the small end centre.*

Solution. Given : $h = 650$ mm $= 0.65$ m ; $l_1 = 650 - 25 = 625$ mm $= 0.625$ m ; $m = 37.5$ kg ; $t_p = 1.87$ s

First of all, let us find the radius of gyration (k_G) of the connecting rod (considering it as a compound pendulum), about an axis passing through its centre of gravity, G.

We know that for a compound pendulum, time period of oscillation (t_p),

$$1.87 = 2\pi \sqrt{\frac{(k_G)^2 + h^2}{g.h}} \quad \text{or} \quad \frac{1.87}{2\pi} = \sqrt{\frac{(k_G)^2 + (0.65)^2}{9.81 \times 0.65}}$$

Squaring both sides, we have

$$0.0885 = \frac{(k_G)^2 + 0.4225}{6.38}$$

$$(k_G)^2 = 0.0885 \times 6.38 - 0.4225 = 0.1425 \text{ m}^2$$

$$\therefore \quad k_G = 0.377 \text{ m}$$

It is given that one of the masses is located at the small end centre. Let the other mass is located at a distance l_2 from the centre of gravity G, as shown in Fig. 15.19. We know that, for a dynamically equivalent system,

$$l_1.l_2 = (k_G)^2$$

$$\therefore \quad l_2 = \frac{(k_G)^2}{l_1} = \frac{0.1425}{0.625} = 0.228 \text{ m}$$

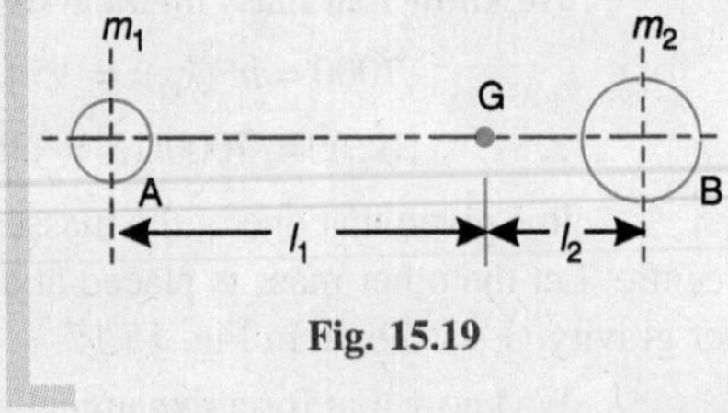

Let m_1 = Mass placed at the small end centre A, and

m_2 = Mass placed at a distance l_2 from G, *i.e.* at B.

We know that, for a dynamically equivalent system,

$$m_1 = \frac{l_2.m}{l_1 + l_2} = \frac{0.228 \times 37.5}{0.625 + 0.228} = 10 \text{ kg Ans.}$$

and

$$m_2 = \frac{l_1.m}{l_1 + l_2} = \frac{0.625 \times 37.5}{0.625 + 0.228} = 27.5 \text{ kg Ans.}$$

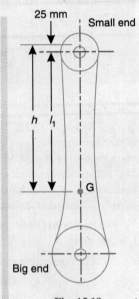

Fig. 15.18

Fig. 15.19

Example 15.17. *The following data relate to a connecting rod of a reciprocating engine:*

Mass = 55 kg; Distance between bearing centres = 850 mm; Diameter of small end bearing = 75 mm; Diameter of big end bearing = 100 mm; Time of oscillation when the connecting rod is suspended from small end = 1.83 s; Time of oscillation when the connecting rod is suspended from big end = 1.68 s.

Determine: 1. the radius of gyration of the rod about an axis passing through the centre of gravity and perpendicular to the plane of oscillation; 2. the moment of inertia of the rod about the same axis; and 3. the dynamically equivalent system for the connecting rod, constituted of two masses, one of which is situated at the small end centre.

Solution. Given : $m = 55$ kg ; $l = 850$ mm $= 0.85$ m ; $d_1 = 75$ mm $= 0.075$ m ; $d_2 = 100$ mm $= 0.1$ m ; $t_{p1} = 1.83$ s ; $t_{p2} = 1.68$ s

First of all, let us find the lengths of the equivalent simple pendulum when suspended

(*a*) from the top of small end bearing; and

(*b*) from the top of big end bearing.

Let L_1 = Length of equivalent simple pendulum when suspended from the top of small end bearing,

L_2 = Length of equivalent simple pendulum when suspended from the top of big end bearing,

h_1 = Distance of centre of gravity, G, from the top of small end bearing, and

h_2 = Distance of centre of gravity, G, from the top of big end bearing.

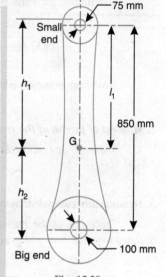

Fig. 15.20

We know that for a simple pendulum

$$t_{p1} = 2\pi \sqrt{\frac{L_1}{g}} \quad \text{or} \quad \left(\frac{t_{p1}}{2\pi}\right)^2 = \frac{L_1}{g} \qquad \text{...(Squaring both sides)}$$

$$\therefore \quad L_1 = g\left(\frac{t_{p1}}{2\pi}\right)^2 = 9.81\left(\frac{1.83}{2\pi}\right)^2 = 0.832 \text{ m}$$

Similarly, $\quad L_2 = g\left(\frac{t_{p2}}{2\pi}\right)^2 = 9.81\left(\frac{1.68}{2\pi}\right)^2 = 0.7 \text{ m}$

1. Radius of gyration of the rod about an axis passing through the centre of gravity and perpendicular to the plane of oscillation

Let k_G = Required radius of gyration of the rod.

We know that the length of equivalent simple pendulum,

$$L = \frac{(k_G)^2 + h^2}{h} \quad \text{or} \quad (k_G)^2 = L.h - h^2 = h(L - h)$$

$\therefore$ When the rod is suspended from the top of small end bearing,

$$(k_G)^2 = h_1(L_1 - h_1) \qquad \text{...(i)}$$

and when the rod is suspended from the top of big end bearing,

$$(k_G)^2 = h_2 (L_2 - h_2) \qquad \qquad ...(ii)$$

Also, from the geometry of the Fig. 15.20,

$$h_1 + h_2 = \frac{d_1}{2} + l + \frac{d_2}{2} = \frac{0.075}{2} + 0.85 + \frac{0.1}{2} = 0.9375 \text{ m}$$

$$\therefore \qquad h_2 = 0.9375 - h_1 \qquad \qquad ...(iii)$$

From equations (i) and (ii),

$$h_1 (L_1 - h_1) = h_2 (L_2 - h_2)$$

Substituting the value of h_2 from equation (iii),

$$h_1 (0.832 - h_1) = (0.9375 - h_1) \left[0.7 - (0.9375 - h_1) \right]$$

$$0.832\, h_1 - (h_1)^2 = -0.223 + 1.175\, h_1 - (h_1)^2$$

$$0.343\, h_1 = 0.233 \text{ or } h_1 = 0.223 / 0.343 = 0.65 \text{ m}$$

Now from equation (i),

$$(k_G)^2 = 0.65\,(0.832 - 0.65) = 0.1183 \text{ or } k_G = 0.343 \text{ m Ans.}$$

2. Moment of inertia of the rod

We know that moment of inertia of the rod,

$$I = m\,(k_G)^2 = 55 \times 0.1183 = 6.51 \text{ kg-m}^2 \text{Ans.}$$

3. Dynamically equivalent system for the rod

Since one of the masses (m_1) is situated at the centre of small end bearing, therefore its distance from the centre of gravity, G, is

$$l_1 = h_1 - 0.075 / 2 = 0.65 - 0.0375 = 0.6125 \text{ m}$$

Let $\qquad\qquad m_2 =$ Magnitude of the second mass, and

$\qquad\qquad l_2 =$ Distance of the second mass from the centre of gravity, G, towards big end bearing.

For a dynamically equivalent system,

$$l_1.l_2 = (k_G)^2 \text{ or } l_2 = \frac{(k_G)^2}{l_1} = \frac{0.1183}{0.6125} = 0.193 \text{ m}$$

We know that $\quad m_1 = \dfrac{l_2.m}{l_1 + l_2} = \dfrac{0.193 \times 55}{0.6125 + 0.193} = 13.18 \text{ kg Ans.}$

and $\qquad\qquad m_2 = \dfrac{l_1.m}{l_1 + l_2} = \dfrac{0.6125 \times 55}{0.6125 + 0.193} = 41.82 \text{ kg Ans.}$

15.13. Correction Couple to be Applied to Make Two Mass System Dynamically Equivalent

In Art. 15.11, we have discussed the conditions for equivalent dynamical system of two bodies. A little consideration will show that when two masses are placed arbitrarily*, then the condi-

---

* When considering the inertia forces on the connecting rod in a mechanism, we replace the rod by two masses arbitrarily. This is discussed in Art. 15.14.

tions (*i*) and (*ii*) as given in Art. 15.11 will only be satisfied. But the condition (*iii*) is not possible to satisfy. This means that the mass moment of inertia of these two masses placed arbitrarily, will differ than that of mass moment of inertia of the rigid body.

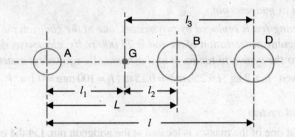

Fig. 15.21. Correction couple to be applied to make the two-mass system dynamically equivalent.

Consider two masses, one at *A* and the other at *D* be placed arbitrarily, as shown in Fig. 15.21.

Let $\qquad l_3$ = Distance of mass placed at *D* from *G*,

$\qquad I_1$ = New mass moment of inertia of the two masses;

$\qquad k_1$ = New radius of gyration;

$\qquad \alpha$ = Angular acceleration of the body;

$\qquad I$ = Mass moment of inertia of a dynamically equivalent system;

$\qquad k_G$ = Radius of gyration of a dynamically equivalent system.

We know that the torque required to accelerate the body,

$$T = I.\alpha = m\,(k_G)^2\,\alpha \qquad \qquad ...(i)$$

Similarly, the torque required to accelerate the two-mass system placed arbitrarily,

$$T_1 = I_1.\alpha = m\,(k_1)^2\,\alpha \qquad \qquad ...(ii)$$

∴ Difference between the torques required to accelerate the two-mass system and the torque required to accelerate the rigid body,

$$T' = T_1 - T = m\,(k_1)^2\,\alpha - m\,(k_G)^2\,\alpha = m\,[(k_1)^2 - (k_G)^2]\,\alpha \qquad \qquad ...(iv)$$

The difference of the torques T' is known as ***correction couple***. This couple must be applied, when the masses are placed arbitrarily to make the system dynamical equivalent. This, of course, will satisfy the condition (*iii*) of Art. 15.11.

Note: We know that $\qquad (k_G)^2 = l_1.l_2, \quad$ and $\quad (k_1)^2 = l_1.l_3$

∴ Correction couple, $\qquad T' = m\,(l_1.l_3 - l_1.l_2)\,\alpha = m.l_1\,(l_3 - l_2)\,\alpha$

But $\qquad\qquad\qquad\qquad l_3 - l_2 = l - L$

∴ $\qquad\qquad\qquad\qquad T' = m.l_1\,(l - L)\,\alpha$

where $\qquad\qquad\qquad l$ = Distance between the two arbitrarily masses, and

$\qquad\qquad\qquad\qquad L$ = Distance between the two masses for a true dynamically equivalent system. It is the equivalent length of a simple pendulum when a body is suspended from an axis which passes through the position of mass *m*, and perpendicular to the plane of rotation of the two mass system.

$$= \frac{(k_G)^2 + (l_1)^2}{l_1}$$

Example 15.18. *A connecting rod of an I.C. engine has a mass of 2 kg and the distance between the centre of gudgeon pin and centre of crank pin is 250 mm. The C.G. falls at a point 100 mm from the gudgeon pin along the line of centres. The radius of gyration about an axis through the C.G. perpendicular to the plane of rotation is 110 mm. Find the equivalent dynamical system if only one of the masses is located at gudgeon pin.*

If the connecting rod is replaced by two masses, one at the gudgeon pin and the other at the crank pin and the angular acceleration of the rod is 23 000 rad/s² clockwise, determine the correction couple applied to the system to reduce it to a dynamically equivalent system.

Solution. Given : $m = 2$ kg ; $l = 250$ mm $= 0.25$ m ; $l_1 = 100$ mm $= 0.1$ m ; $k_G = 110$ mm $= 0.11$ m ; $\alpha = 23\ 000$ rad/s²

Equivalent dynamical system

It is given that one of the masses is located at the gudgeon pin. Let the other mass be located at a distance l_2 from the centre of gravity. We know that for an equivalent dynamical system.

$$l_1.l_2 = (k_G)^2 \quad \text{or} \quad l_2 = \frac{(k_G)^2}{l_1} = \frac{(0.11)^2}{0.1} = 0.121 \text{ m}$$

Let m_1 = Mass placed at the gudgeon pin, and

m_2 = Mass placed at a distance l_2 from C.G.

We know that $m_1 = \dfrac{l_2.m}{l_1 + l_2} = \dfrac{0.121 \times 2}{0.1 + 0.121} = 1.1$ kg **Ans.**

and $m_2 = \dfrac{l_1.m}{l_1 + l_2} = \dfrac{0.1 \times 2}{0.1 + 0.121} = 0.9$ kg **Ans.**

Correction couple

Since the connecting rod is replaced by two masses located at the two centres (*i.e.* one at the gudgeon pin and the other at the crank pin), therefore,

$$l = 0.1 \text{ m}, \quad \text{and} \quad l_3 = l - l_1 = 0.25 - 0.1 = 0.15 \text{ m}$$

Let k_1 = New radius of gyration.

We know that $(k_1)^2 = l_1.l_3 = 0.1 \times 0.15 = 0.015 \text{ m}^2$

∴ Correction couple,

$$T' = m(k_1^2 - k_G^2)\ \alpha = 2\left[0.015 - (0.11)^2\right] 23\ 000 = 133.4 \text{ N-m } \textbf{Ans.}$$

Note : Since T' is positive, therefore, the direction of correction couple is same as that of angular acceleration *i.e.* clockwise.

15.14. Inertia Forces in a Reciprocating Engine, Considering the Weight of Connecting Rod

In a reciprocating engine, let OC be the crank and PC, the connecting rod whose centre of gravity lies at G. The inertia forces in a reciprocating engine may be obtained graphically as discussed below:

1. First of all, draw the acceleration diagram $OCQN$ by Klien's construction. We know that the acceleration of the piston P with respect to O,

$$a_{PO} = a_P = \omega^2 \times NO,$$

acting in the direction from N to O. Therefore, the inertia force F_I of the reciprocating parts will act in the opposite direction as shown in Fig. 15.22.

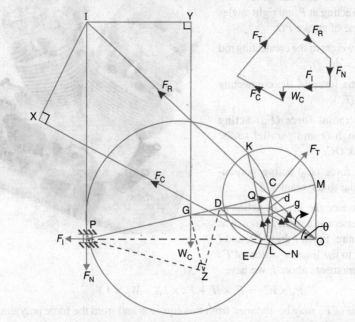

Fig. 15.22. Inertia forces in reciprocating engine, considering the weight of connecting rod.

2. Replace the connecting rod by dynamically equivalent system of two masses as discussed in Art. 15.12. Let one of the masses be arbitrarily placed at P. To obtain the position of the other mass, draw GZ perpendicular to CP such that $GZ = k$, the radius of gyration of the connecting rod. Join PZ and from Z draw perpendicular to DZ which intersects CP at D. Now, D is the position of the second mass.

Note: The position of the second mass may also be obtained from the equation,
$$GP \times GD = k^2$$

3. Locate the points G and D on NC which is the acceleration image of the connecting rod. This is done by drawing parallel lines from G and D to the line of stroke PO. Let these parallel lines intersect NC at g and d respectively. Join gO and dO. Therefore, acceleration of G with respect to O, in the direction from g to O,
$$a_{GO} = a_G = \omega^2 \times gO$$
and acceleration of D with respect to O, in the direction from d to O,
$$a_{DO} = a_D = \omega^2 \times dO$$

4. From D, draw DE parallel to dO which intersects the line of stroke PO at E. Since the accelerating forces on the masses at P and D intersect at E, therefore their resultant must also pass through E. But their resultant is equal to the accelerang force on the rod, so that the line of action of the accelerating force on the rod, is given by a line drawn through E and parallel to gO, in the direction from g to O. The inertia force of the connecting rod F_C therefore acts through E and in the opposite direction as shown in Fig. 15.22. The inertia force of the connecting rod is given by
$$F_C = m_C \times \omega^2 \times gO \qquad \qquad \ldots(i)$$
where m_C = Mass of the connecting rod.

A little consideration will show that the forces acting on the connecting rod are :

(a)   Inertia force of the reciprocating parts (F_I) acting along the line of stroke PO,

(b) The side thrust between the crosshead and the guide bars (F_N) acting at P and right angles to line of stroke PO,

(c) The weight of the connecting rod ($W_C = m_C \cdot g$),

(d) Inertia force of the connecting rod (F_C),

(e) The radial force (F_R) acting through O and parallel to the crank OC,

(f) The force (F_T) acting perpendicular to the crank OC.

Radial engines of a motor cycle.

Now, produce the lines of action of F_R and F_N to intersect at a point I, known as instantaneous centre. From I draw $I\,X$ and $I\,Y$, perpendicular to the lines of action of F_C and W_C. Taking moments about I, we have

$$F_T \times IC = F_I \times IP + F_C \times IX + W_C \times IY \qquad ...(ii)$$

The value of F_T may be obtained from this equation and from the force polygon as shown in Fig. 15.22, the forces F_N and F_R may be calculated. We know that, torque exerted on the crankshaft to overcome the inertia of the moving parts $= F_T \times OC$

Note : When the mass of the reciprocating parts is neglected, then F_I is zero.

15.15. Analytical Method for Inertia Torque

The effect of the inertia of the connecting rod on the crankshaft torque may be obtained as discussed in the following steps:

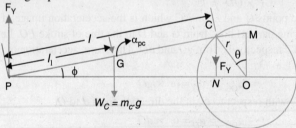

Fig. 15.23. Analytical method for inertia torque.

1. The mass of the connecting rod (m_C) is divided into two masses. One of the mass is placed at the crosshead pin P and the other at the crankpin C as shown in Fig. 15.23, so that the centre of gravity of these two masses coincides with the centre of gravity of the rod G.

2. Since the inertia force due to the mass at C acts radially outwards along the crank OC, therefore the mass at C has no effect on the crankshaft torque.

3. The inertia force of the mass at P may be obtained as follows:

Let m_C = Mass of the connecting rod,

l = Length of the connecting rod,

l_1 = Length of the centre of gravity of the connecting rod from P.

∴ Mass of the connecting rod at P,

$$= \frac{l - l_1}{l} \times m_C$$

The mass of the reciprocating parts (m_R) is also acting at P. Therefore,

Total equivalent mass of the reciprocating parts acting at P

$$= m_R + \frac{l - l_1}{l} \times m_C$$

∴ Total inertia force of the equivalent mass acting at P,

$$F_I = \left(m_R + \frac{l - l_1}{l} \times m_C \right) a_R \qquad \ldots(i)$$

where a_R = Acceleration of the reciprocating parts

$$= \omega^2 . r \left(\cos\theta + \frac{\cos 2\theta}{n} \right)$$

∴ $$F_I = \left[m_R + \frac{l - l_1}{l} \times m_C \right] \omega^2 . r \left(\cos\theta + \frac{\cos 2\theta}{n} \right)$$

and corresponding torque exerted on the crank shaft,

$$T_I = F_I \times OM = F_I . r \left(\sin\theta + \frac{\sin 2\theta}{2\sqrt{n^2 - \sin^2\theta}} \right) \qquad \ldots(ii)$$

Note : Usually the value of OM is measured by drawing the perpendicular from O on PO which intersects PC produced at M.

4. In deriving the equation (ii) of the torque exerted on the crankshaft, it is assumed that one of the two masses is placed at C and the other at P. This assumption does not satisfy the condition for kinetically equivalent system of a rigid bar. Hence to compensate for it, a correcting torque is necessary whose value is given by

$$T' = m_C \left[(k_1)^2 - (k_G)^2 \right] \alpha_{PC} = m_C . l_1 (l - L) \alpha_{PC}$$

where L = Equivalent length of a simple pendulum when swung about an axis through P

$$= \frac{(k_G)^2 + (l_1)^2}{l_1}$$

α_{PC} = Angular acceleration of the connecting rod PC.

$$= \frac{-\omega^2 \sin\theta}{n} \qquad \ldots\text{(From Art. 15.9)}$$

The correcting torque T' may be applied to the system by two equal and opposite forces F_Y acting through P and C. Therefore,

$$F_Y \times PN = T' \quad \text{or} \quad F_Y = T'/PN$$

and corresponding torque on the crankshaft,

$$T_C = F_Y \times NO = \frac{T'}{PN} \times NO \qquad \ldots(iii)$$

We know that, $NO = OC \cos\theta = r \cos\theta$

and $PN = PC \cos\phi = l \cos\phi$

$$\therefore \qquad \frac{NO}{PN} = \frac{r \cos \theta}{l \cos \phi} = \frac{\cos \theta}{n \cos \phi} \qquad \qquad ...\left(\because n = \frac{l}{r} \right)$$

$$= \frac{\cos \theta}{n \sqrt{1 - \dfrac{\sin^2 \theta}{n^2}}} = \frac{\cos \theta}{\sqrt{n^2 - \sin^2 \theta}} \qquad ...\left(\because \cos \phi = \sqrt{1 - \dfrac{\sin^2 \theta}{n^2}} \right)$$

Since $\sin^2\theta$ is very small as compared to n^2, therefore neglecting $\sin^2\theta$, we have

$$\frac{NO}{PN} = \frac{\cos \theta}{n}$$

Substituting this value in equation (*iii*), we have

$$T_C = T' \times \frac{\cos \theta}{n} = m_C \times l_1 \, (l - L) \, \alpha_{PC} \times \frac{\cos \theta}{n}$$

$$= - m_C \times l_1 \, (l - L) \, \frac{\omega^2 \sin \theta}{n} \times \frac{\cos \theta}{n} \qquad ...\left(\because \alpha_{PC} = \frac{-\omega^2 \sin \theta}{n} \right)$$

$$= - m_C \times l_1 \, (l - L) \, \frac{\omega^2 \sin 2\theta}{2 \, n^2} \qquad ...(\because 2 \sin \theta \cos \theta = \sin 2\theta)$$

5. The equivalent mass of the rod acting at C,

$$m_2 = m_C \times \frac{l_1}{l}$$

$\therefore$ Torque exerted on the crank shaft due to mass m_2,

$$T_W = - m_2 \times g \times NO = - m_C \times g \times \frac{l_1}{l} \times NO = - m_C \times g \times \frac{l_1}{l} \times r \cos \theta$$

$$...(\because NO = r \cos \theta)$$

$$= - m_C \times g \times \frac{l_1}{n} \times \cos \theta \qquad \qquad ...(\because l / r = n)$$

6. The total torque exerted on the crankshaft due to the inertia of the moving parts is the algebraic sum of T_I, T_C and T_W.

Example 15.19. *The crank and connecting rod lengths of an engine are 125 mm and 500 mm respectively. The mass of the connecting rod is 60 kg and its centre of gravity is 275 mm from the crosshead pin centre, the radius of gyration about centre of gravity being 150 mm.*

If the engine speed is 600 r.p.m. for a crank position of 45° from the inner dead centre, determine, using Klien's or any other construction 1. the acceleration of the piston; 2. the magnitude, position and direction of inertia force due to the mass of the connecting rod.

Solution. Given : $r = OC = 125$ mm ; $l = PC = 500$ mm; $m_C = 60$ kg ; $PG = 275$ mm ; $k_G = 150$ mm ; $N = 600$ r.p.m. or $\omega = 2\pi \times 600/60 = 62.84$ rad/s ; $\theta = 45°$

1. *Acceleration of the piston*

Let $\qquad\qquad a_P$ = Acceleration of the piston.

First of all, draw the configuration diagram OCP, as shown in Fig. 15.24, to some suitable scale, such that

$$OC = r = 125 \text{ mm} ; PC = l = 500 \text{ mm} ; \text{ and } \theta = 45°.$$

Now, draw the Klien's acceleration diagram *OCQN,* as shown in Fig. 15.24, in the same manner as already discussed. By measurement,

$$NO = 90 \text{ mm} = 0.09 \text{ m}$$

∴ Acceleration of the piston,

$$a_P = \omega^2 \times NO = (62.84)^2 \times 0.09 = 355.4 \text{ m/s} \textbf{ Ans.}$$

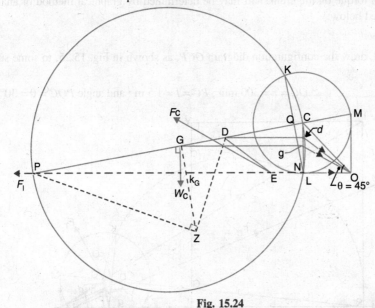

Fig. 15.24

2. The magnitude, position and direction of inertia force due to the mass of the connecting rod

The magnitude, postition and direction of the inertia force may be obtained as follows:

(*i*) Replace the connecting rod by dynamical equivalent system of two masses, assuming that one of the masses is placed at *P* and the other mass at *D*. The position of the point *D* is obtained as discussed in Art. 15.12.

(*ii*) Locate the points *G* and *D* on *NC* which is the acceleration image of the connecting rod. Let these points are *g* and *d* on *NC*. Join *gO* and *dO*. By measurement,

$$gO = 103 \text{ mm} = 0.103 \text{ m}$$

∴ Acceleration of *G*, $a_G = \omega^2 \times gO$, acting in the direction from *g* to *O*.

(*iii*) From point *D*, draw *DE* parallel to *dO*. Now *E* is the point through which the inertia force of the connecting rod passes. The magnitude of the inertia force of the connecting rod is given by

$$F_C = m_C \times \omega^2 \times gO = 60 \times (62.84)^2 \times 0.103 = 24\,400 \text{ N} = 24.4 \text{ kN Ans.}$$

(*iv*) From point *E*, draw a line parallel to *gO*, which shows the position of the inertia force of the connecting rod and acts in the opposite direction of *gO*.

Example 15.20. *The following data refer to a steam engine:*

Diameter of piston = 240 mm; stroke = 600 mm ; length of connecting rod = 1.5 m ; mass of reciprocating parts = 300 kg; mass of connecting rod = 250 kg; speed = 125 r.p.m ; centre of gravity of connecting rod from crank pin = 500 mm ; radius of gyration of the connecting rod about an axis through the centre of gravity = 650 mm.

Determine the magnitude and direction of the torque exerted on the crankshaft when the crank has turned through 30° from inner dead centre.

Solution. Given : $D = 240$ mm $= 0.24$ m ; $L = 600$ mm or $r = L/2 = 300$ mm $= 0.3$ m ; $l = 1.5$ m ; $m_R = 300$ kg ; $m_C = 250$ kg ; $N = 125$ r.p.m. or $\omega = 2\pi \times 125/60 = 13.1$ rad/s ; $GC = 500$ mm $= 0.5$ m ; $k_G = 650$ mm $= 0.65$ m ; $\theta = 30°$

The inertia torque on the crankshaft may be determined by graphical method or analytical method as discussed below:

1. *Graphical method*

First of all, draw the configuration diagram *OCP*, as shown in Fig. 15.25, to some suitable scale, such that

$$OC = r = 300 \text{ mm} ; PC = l = 1.5 \text{ m} ; \text{ and angle } POC = \theta = 30°.$$

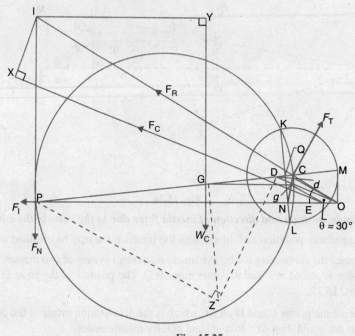

Fig. 15.25

Now draw the Klien's acceleration diagram *OCQN*, as shown in Fig. 15.25, and complete the figure in the similar manner as discussed in Art. 15.14.

By measurement; $NO = 0.28$ m ; $gO = 0.28$ m ; $IP = 1.03$ m ; $IX = 0.38$ m ; $IY = 0.98$ m, and $IC = 1.7$ m.

We know that inertia force of reciprocating parts,

$$F_I = m_R \times \omega^2 \times NO = 300 \times (13.1)^2 \times 0.28 = 14\ 415 \text{ N}$$

and inertia force of connecting rod,

$$F_C = m_C \times \omega^2 \times gO = 250 \times (13.1)^2 \times 0.28 = 12\ 013 \text{ N}$$

Let F_T = Force acting perpendicular to the crank *OC*.

Taking moments about point *I*,

$$F_T \times IC = F_I \times IP + W_C \times IY + F_C \times IX$$

$$F_T \times 1.7 = 14\ 415 \times 1.03 + 250 \times 9.81 \times 0.98 + 12013 \times 0.38 = 21\ 816$$

$$\therefore \qquad F_T = 21.816/1.7 = 12\ 833 \text{ N} \qquad\qquad ...(\because W_C = m_C.g)$$

We know that torque exerted on the crankshaft

$$= F_T \times r = 12\ 833 \times 0.3 = 3850 \text{ N-m } \textbf{Ans.}$$

2. *Analytical method*

We know that the distance of centre of gravity (G) of the connecting rod from P, i.e.,

$$l_1 = l - GC = 1.5 - 0.5 = 1 \text{ m}$$

$\therefore$ Inertia force due to total mass of the reciprocating parts at P,

$$F_I = \left(m_R + \frac{l - l_1}{l} \times m_C \right) \omega^2 . r \left(\cos\theta + \frac{\cos 2\theta}{n} \right)$$

$$= \left(300 + \frac{1.5 - 1}{1.5} \times 250 \right) \times (13.1)^2 \times .0.3 \left(\cos 30° + \frac{\cos 60°}{5} \right) = 19\ 064 \text{ N}$$

$$...\left[\because n = \frac{l}{r} = \frac{1.5}{0.3} = 5 \right]$$

$\therefore$ Corresponding torque due to F_I,

$$T_I = F_I \times OM = F_I . r \left(\sin\theta + \frac{\sin 2\theta}{2\sqrt{n^2 - \sin^2\theta}} \right)$$

$$= 19\ 064 \times 0.3 \left(\sin 30° + \frac{\sin 60°}{2\sqrt{5^2 - \sin^2 30°}} \right)$$

$$= 5719.2 \times 0.587 = 3357 \text{ N-m (anticlockwise)}$$

Equivalent length of a simple pendulum when swung about an axis through P,

$$L = \frac{(k_G)^2 + (l_1)^2}{l_1} = \frac{(0.65)^2 + 1^2}{1} = 1.42 \text{ m}$$

$\therefore$ Correcting torque,

$$T_C = m_C . l_1 (l - L) \left[\frac{\omega^2 \sin 2\theta}{2n^2} \right]$$

$$= 250 \times 1 (1.5 - 1.42) \left[\frac{(13.1)^2 \sin 60°}{2 \times 5^2} \right] = 59.5 \text{ N-m (anticlockwise)}$$

Torque due to the weight of the connecting rod at C,

$$T_W = W_C \times \frac{l_1}{n} \times \cos\theta = m_C \times g \times \frac{l_1}{n} \times \cos\theta$$

$$= 250 \times 9.81 \times \frac{1}{5} \times \cos 30° = 424.8 \text{ N-m (anticlockwise)}$$

$\therefore$ Total torque exerted on the crankshaft,

$$= T_I + T_C + T_W$$

$$= 3357 + 59.5 + 424.8 = 3841.3 \text{ N-m (anticlockwise) } \textbf{Ans.}$$

Note: The slight difference in results arrived at by the above two methods is mainly due to error in measurement in graphical method.

Example 15.21. *A vertical engine running at 1200 r.p.m. with a stroke of 110 mm, has a connecting rod 250 mm between centres and mass 1.25 kg. The mass centre of the connecting rod is 75 mm from the big end centre and when suspended as a pendulum from the gudgeon pin axis makes 21 complete oscillations in 20 seconds.*

1. Calculate the radius of gyration of the connecting rod about an axis through its mass centre.

2. When the crank is at 40° from the top dead centre and the piston is moving downwards, find analytically, the acceleration of the piston and the angular acceleration of the connecting rod. Hence find the inertia torque exerted on the crankshaft. To make the two-mass system to be dynamically equivalent to the connecting rod, necessary correction torque has to be applied and since the engine is vertical, gravity effects are to be considered.

Solution. Given : $N = 1200$ r.p.m. or $\omega = 2\pi \times 1200/60 = 125.7$ rad/s ; $L = 110$ mm or $r = L/2 = 55$ mm $= 0.055$ m ; $l = PC = 250$ mm $= 0.25$ m ; $m_C = 1.25$ kg ; $CG = 75$ mm $= 0.075$ m ; $\theta = 40°$

The configuration diagram of the engine is shown in Fig. 15.26.

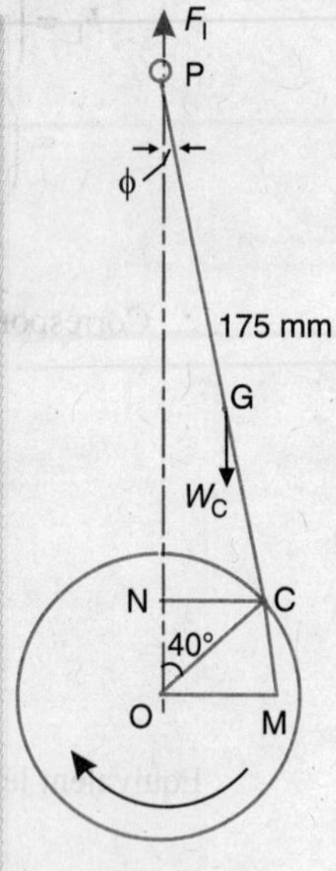

1. Radius of gyration of the connecting rod about an axis through its mass centre

Let $\quad k_G$ = Radius of gyration of the connecting rod about an axis through its mass centre,

$\quad l_1$ = Distance of the centre of gravity from the point of suspension = PG

$\quad = 250 - 75 = 175$ mm $= 0.175$ m

Since the connecting rod makes 21 complete oscillations in 20 seconds, therefore frequency of oscillation,

$$n = \frac{21}{20} = 1.05 \text{ Hz}$$

We know that for a compound pendulum, frequency of oscillation,

$$n = \frac{1}{2\pi} \sqrt{\frac{g.l_1}{(k_G)^2 + (l_1)^2}} \quad \text{or} \quad n^2 = \frac{1}{4\pi^2} \times \frac{g.l_1}{(k_G)^2 + (l_1)^2}$$

...(Squaring both sides)

Fig. 15.26

and $\quad (k_G)^2 = \frac{g.l_1}{4\pi^2 n^2} - (l_1)^2 = \frac{9.81 \times 0.175}{4\pi^2 \times (1.05)^2} - (0.175)^2 = 0.0088 \text{ m}^2$

∴ $\quad k_G = 0.094$ m $= 94$ mm **Ans.**

2. Acceleration of the piston

We know that acceleration of the piston,

$$a_P = \omega^2.r \left(\cos \theta + \frac{\cos 2\theta}{n} \right) = (125.7)^2 \, 0.055 \left(\cos 40° + \frac{\cos 80°}{0.25/0.055} \right)$$

$$= 698.7 \text{ m/s}^2 \text{ Ans.} \qquad \qquad ...(\because n = l/r)$$

Angular acceleration of the connecting rod

We know that mass of the connecting rod at P,

$$\alpha_{PC} = \frac{-\omega^2 \sin \theta}{n} = \frac{-(125.7)^2 \sin 40°}{0.25/0.055} = -2234.4 \text{ rad/s}^2 \text{ Ans.}$$

Inertia torque exerted on the crankshaft

We know that mass of the connecting rod at P,

$$m_1 = \frac{l - l_1}{l} \times m_C = \frac{0.25 - 0.175}{0.25} \times 1.25 = 0.375 \text{ kg}$$

∴ Vertical inertia force,

$$F_I = m_1 . a_P = 0.375 \times 698.7 = 262 \text{ N}$$

and corresponding torque due to F_I,

$$T_I = -F_I \times OM = -262 \times 0.0425 = -11.135 \text{ N-m}$$

$$= 11.135 \text{ N-m (anticlockwise)} \qquad \text{...(By measurement, } OM = 0.0425 \text{ m)}$$

We know that the equivalent length of a simple pendulum when swung about an axis passing through P,

$$L = \frac{(k_G)^2 + (l_1)^2}{l_1} = \frac{(0.094)^2 + (0.175)^2}{0.175} = 0.225 \text{ m}$$

∴ Correction couple,

$$T' = -m_C . l_1 (l - L) \, \alpha_{PC} = -1.25 \times 0.175 (0.25 - 0.225) \, 2234.4 = -12.22 \text{ N-m}$$

Corresponding torque on the crankshaft,

$$T_C = \frac{T' \cos \theta}{n} = \frac{-12.22 \times \cos 40°}{0.25/0.055} = -2.06 \text{ N-m} = 2.06 \text{ N-m (anticlockwise)}$$

Torque due to the mass at P,

$$T_P = m_1 \times g \times OM = 0.375 \times 9.81 \times 0.0425 = 0.156 \text{ N-m (clockwise)}$$

Equivalent mass of the connecting rod at C,

$$m_2 = m_C \times \frac{l_1}{l} = 1.25 \times \frac{0.175}{0.25} = 0.875 \text{ kg}$$

Torque due to mass at C,

$$T_W = m_2 \times g \times NC = 0.875 \times 9.81 \times 0.035 = 0.3 \text{ N-m (clockwise)}$$

$$\text{...(By measurement, } NC = 0.035 \text{ m)}$$

∴ Inertia torque exerted on the crankshaft

$$= T_I + T_C - T_P - T_W$$

$$= 11.135 + 2.06 - 0.156 - 0.3 = 12.739 \text{ N-m (anticlockwise)} \textbf{Ans.}$$

Example 15.22. *The connecting rod of an internal combustion engine is 225 mm long and has a mass 1.6 kg. The mass of the piston and gudgeon pin is 2.4 kg and the stroke is 150 mm. The cylinder bore is 112.5 mm. The centre of gravity of the connecting rod is 150 mm from the small end. Its radius of gyration about the centre of gravity for oscillations in the plane of swing of the connecting rod is 87.5 mm. Determine the magnitude and direction of the resultant force on the crank pin when the crank is at 40° and the piston is moving away from inner dead centre under an effective gas presure of 1.8 MN/m². The engine speed is 1200 r.p.m.*

Solution. Given : $l = PC = 225$ mm $= 0.225$ m; $m_C = 1.6$ kg; $m_R = 2.4$ kg; $L = 150$ mm or $r = L/2 = 75$ mm $= 0.075$ m ; $D = 112.5$ mm $= 0.1125$ m ; $PG = 150$ mm ; $k_G = 87.5$ mm $= 0.0875$ m ; $\theta = 40°$; $p = 1.8$ MN/m² $= 1.8 \times 10^6$ N/m² ; $N = 1200$ r.p.m. or $\omega = 2\pi \times 1200/60 = 125.7$ rad/s

First of all, draw the configuration diagram *OCP*, as shown in Fig. 15.27 to some suitable scale, such that $OC = r = 75$ mm ; $PC = l = 225$ mm ; and $\theta = 40°$.

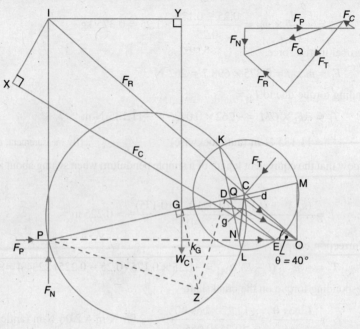

Fig. 15.27

Now, draw the Klien's acceleration diagram *OCQN*. Complete the diagram in the same manner as discussed earlier. By measurement,

$NO = 0.0625$ m ; $gO = 0.0685$ m ; $IC = 0.29$ m ; $IP = 0.24$ m ; $IY = 0.148$ m ; and $IX = 0.08$ m

We know that force due to gas pressure,

$$F_L = \frac{\pi}{4} \times D^2 \times p = \frac{\pi}{4} \times (0.1125)^2 \times 1.8 \times 10^6 = 17\ 895 \text{ N}$$

Inertia force due to mass of the reciprocating parts,

$$F_I = m_R \times \omega^2 \times NO = 2.4\,(125.7)^2 \times 0.0625 = 2370 \text{ N}$$

∴ Net force on the piston,

$$F_P = F_L - F_I = 17\ 895 - 2370 = 15\ 525 \text{ N}$$

Inertia force due to mass of the connecting rod,

$$F_C = m_C \times \omega^2 \times gO = 1.6 \times (125.7)^2 \times 0.0685 = 1732 \text{ N}$$

Let F_T = Force acting perpendicular to the crank *OC*.

Now, taking moments about point *I*,

$$F_P \times IP = W_C \times IY + F_C \times IX + F_T \times IC$$
$$15\ 525 \times 0.24 = 1.6 \times 9.81 \times 0.148 + 1732 \times 0.08 + F_T \times 0.29$$

∴ $\qquad\qquad F_T = 12\ 362 \text{ N}$ ...(∵ $W_C = m_C.g$)

Let us now find the values of F_N and F_R in magnitude and direction. Draw the force polygon as shown in Fig. 15.25.

By measurement, F_N = 3550 N; and F_R = 7550 N

The magnitude and direction of the resultant force on the crank pin is given by F_Q, which is the resultant of F_R and F_T.

By measurement, F_Q = 13 750 N **Ans.**

EXERCISES

1. The crank and connecting rod of a reciprocating engine are 150 mm and 600 mm respectively. The crank makes an angle of 60° with the inner dead centre and revolves at a uniform speed of 300 r.p.m. Find, by Klein's or Ritterhaus's construction, 1. Velocity and acceleration of the piston, 2. Velocity and acceleration of the mid-point D of the connecting rod, and 3. Angular velocity and angular acceleration of the connecting rod. [Ans. 4.6 m/s, 61.7 m/s² ; 4.6 m/s, 93.8 m/s² ; 4.17 rad/s, 214 rad/s²]

2. In a slider crank mechanism, the length of the crank and connecting rod are 100 mm and 400 mm respectively. The crank rotates uniformly at 600 r.p.m. clockwise. When the crank has turned through 45° from the inner dead centre, find, by analytical method : 1. Velocity and acceleration of the slider, 2. Angular velocity and angular acceleration of the connecting rod. Check your result by Klein's or Bennett's construction. [Ans. 5.2 m/s; 279 m/s²; 11 rad/s; 698 rad/s²]

3. A petrol engine has a stroke of 120 mm and connecting rod is 3 times the crank length. The crank rotates at 1500 r.p.m. in clockwise direction. Determine: 1. Velocity and acceleration of the piston, and 2. Angular velocity and angular acceleration of the connecting rod, when the piston had travelled one-fourth of its stroke from I.D.C. [Ans. 8.24 m/s, 1047 m/s²; 37 rad/s, 5816 rad/s²]

4. The stroke of a steam engine is 600 mm and the length of connecting rod is 1.5 m. The crank rotates at 180 r.p.m. Determine: 1. velocity and acceleration of the piston when crank has travelled through an angle of 40° from inner dead centre, and 2. the position of the crank for zero acceleration of the piston. [Ans. 4.2 m/s, 85.4 m/s²; 79.3° from I.D.C]

5. The following data refer to a steam engine :

   Diameter of piston = 240 mm; stroke = 600 mm; length of connecting rod = 1.5 m; mass of reciprocating parts = 300 kg; speed = 125 r.p.m.

   Determine the magnitude and direction of the inertia force on the crankshaft when the crank has turned through 30° from inner dead centre. [Ans. 14.92 kN]

6. A vertical petrol engine 150 mm diameter and 200 mm stroke has a connecting rod 350 mm long. The mass of the piston is 1.6 kg and the engine speed is 1800 r.p.m. On the expansion stroke with crank angle 30° from top dead centre, the gas pressure is 750 kN/m². Determine the net thrust on the piston. [Ans. 7535 N]

7. A horizontal steam engine running at 240 r.p.m. has a bore of 300 mm and stroke 600 mm. The connecting rod is 1.05 m long and the mass of reciprocating parts is 60 kg. When the crank is 60° past its inner dead centre, the steam pressure on the cover side of the piston is 1.125 N/mm² while that on the crank side is 0.125 N/mm². Neglecting the area of the piston rod, determine : 1. the force in the piston rod ; and 2. the turning moment on the crankshaft. [Ans. 66.6 kN ; 19.86 kN-m]

8. A steam engine 200 mm bore and 300 mm stroke has a connecting rod 625 mm long. The mass of the reciprocating parts is 15 kg and the speed is 250 r.p.m. When the crank is at 30° to the inner dead centre and moving outwards, the difference in steam pressures is 840 kN/m². If the crank pin radius is 30 mm, determine: 1. the force on the crankshaft bearing; and 2. the torque acting on the frame. [Ans. 20.04 kN ; 2253 N-m]

9. A vertical single cylinder engine has a cylinder diameter of 250 mm and a stroke of 450 mm. The reciprocating parts have a mass of 180 kg. The connecting rod is 4 times the crank radius and the speed is 360 r.p.m. When the crank has turned through an angle of 45° from top dead centre, the net pressure on the piston is 1.05 MN/m². Calculate the effective turning moment on the crankshaft for this position. [Ans. 2368 N-m]

10. A horizontal, double acting steam engine has a stroke of 300 mm and runs at 240 r.p.m. The cylinder diameter is 200 mm, connecting rod is 750 mm long and the mass of the reciprocating parts is 70 kg. The steam is admitted at 600 kN/m^2 for one-third of the stroke, after which expansion takes place according to the hyperbolic law $p.V$ = constant. The exhaust pressure is 20 kN/m^2. Neglecting the effect of clearance and the diameter of the piston rod, find : 1. Thrust in the connecting rod, and 2. Effective turning moment on the crankshaft when the crank has turned through 120° from inner dead centre. **[Ans. 11.506 kN; 1322 N-m]**

11. A horizontal steam engine running at 150 r.p.m. has a bore of 200 mm and a stroke of 400 mm. The connecting rod is 1 m long and the reciprocating parts has a mass of 60 kg. When the crank has turned through an angle of 30° from inner dead centre, steam pressure on the cover side is 0.6 N/mm^2 while on the crankside is 0.1 N/mm^2. Neglecting the area of the piston rod, determine: 1. turning moment on the crankshaft, 2. acceleration of the flywheel, if the mean resistance torque is 600 N-m and the moment of inertia is 2.8 kg-m^2. **[Ans. 1508 N-m; 324.3 rad/s^2]**

12. The ratio of the connecting rod length to crank length for a vertical petrol engine is 4:1. The bore / stroke is 80/100 mm and mass of the reciprocating parts is 1 kg. The gas pressure on the piston is 0.7N/mm^2 when it has moved 10 mm from T.D.C. on its power stroke. Determine the net load on the gudgeon pin. The engine runs at 1800 r.p.m. At what engine speed will this load be zero? **[Ans. 1862.8 N; 2616 r.p.m.]**

13. A petrol engine 90 mm in diameter and 120 mm stroke has a connecting rod of 240 mm length. The piston has a mass of 1 kg and the speed is 1800 r.p.m. On the explosion stroke with the crank at 30° from top dead centre, the gas pressure is 0.5 N/mm^2. Find :

    1. the resultant load on the gudgeon pin, 2. the thrust on the cylinder walls, and 3. the speed, above which other things remaining same, the gudgeon pin load would be reserved in direction.

    Also calculate the crank effort at the given position of the crank.

    [Ans. 1078 N; 136 N ; 2212 r.p.m.; 39.4 N-m]

14. A single cylinder vertical engine has a bore of 300 mm, storke 360 mm and a connecting rod of length 720 mm. The mass of the reciprocating parts is 130 kg. When the piston is at quarter stroke from top dead centre and is moving downwards, the net pressure on it is 0.6 MPa. If the speed of the engine is 250 r.p.m., calculate the turning moment on the crankshaft at the instant corresponding to the position stated above. **[Ans. 6295 N-m]**

15. A horizontal, single cylinder, single acting, otto cycle gas engine has a bore of 300 mm and a stroke of 500 mm. The engine runs at 180 r.p.m. The ratio of compression is 5.5. The maximum explosion pressure is 3.2 N/mm^2 gauge and expansion follows the law $p.V^{1.3}$ = constant. If the mass of the piston is 150 kg and the connecting rod is 1.25 m long. Calculate the turning moment on the crankshaft when the crank has turned through 60° from the inner dead centre. The atmospheric pressure is 0.1 N/mm^2. **[Ans. 15.6 kN-m]**

16. A vertical single cylinder, diesel engine running at 300 r.p.m. has a cylinder diameter 250 mm and stroke 400 mm. The mass of the reciprocating parts is 200 kg. The length of the connecting rod is 0.8 m. The ratio of compression is 14 and the pressure remains constant during injection of oil for 1/10th of stroke. If the index of the law of expansion and compression is 1.35, find the torque on the crankshaft when it makes an angle of 60° with the top dead centre during the expansion stroke. The suction pressure may be taken as 0.1 N/mm^2. **[Ans. 7034 N-m]**

17. A gas engine is coupled to a compressor, the two cylinders being horizontally opposed with the pistons connected to a common crank pin. The stroke of each piston is 500 mm and the ratio of the length of the connecting rod to the length of crank is 5. The cylinder diameters are 200 mm and 250 mm and the masses of reciprocating parts are 130 kg and 150 kg respectively. When the crank has moved through 60° from inner dead centre on the firing stroke, the pressure of gas on the engine cylinder is 1 N/mm^2 gauge and the pressure in the compressor cylinder is 0.1 N/mm^2 gauge. If the crank moves with 200 r.p.m. and the flywheel of radius of gyration 1 m has a mass of 1350 kg, determine the angular acceleration of the flywheel. **[Ans. 2.4 rad/s^2]**

18. The length of a connecting rod of an engine is 500 mm measured between the centres and its mass is 18 kg. The centre of gravity is 125 mm from the crank pin centre and the crank radius is 100 mm.

Determine the dynamically equivalent system keeping one mass at the small end. The frequency of oscillation of the rod, when suspended from the centre of the small end is 43 vibrations per minute.

[Ans. 4.14 kg; 13.86 kg]

19. A small connecting rod 220 mm long between centres has a mass of 2 kg and a moment of inertia of 0.02 kg-m² about its centre of gravity. The centre of gravity is located at a distance of 150 mm from the small end centre. Determine the dynamically equivalent two mass system when one mass is located at the small end centre.

If the connecting rod is replaced by two masses located at the two centres, find the correction couple that must be applied for complete dynamical equivalence of the system when the angular acceleration of the connecting rod is 20 000 rad/s² anticlockwise.

[Ans. 0.617 kg; 1.383 kg; 20 N-m (anticlockwise)]

20. The connecting rod of a horizontal reciprocating engine is 400 mm and length of the stroke is 200 mm. The mass of the reciprocating parts is 125 kg and that the connecting rod is 100 kg. The radius of gyration of the connecting rod about an axis through the centre of gravity is 120 mm and the distance of centre of gravity of the connecting rod from big end centre is 160 mm. The engine runs at 750 r.p.m. Determine the torque exerted on the crankshaft when the crank has turned 30° from the inner dead centre.

[Ans. 7078 N-m]

21. If the crank has turned through 135° from the inner dead centre in the above question, find the torque on the crankshaft.

[Ans. 5235 N-m]

DO YOU KNOW ?

1. Define 'inertia force' and 'inertia torque'.

2. Draw and explain Klien's construction for determining the velocity and acceleration of the piston in a slider crank mechanism.

3. Explain Ritterhaus's and Bennett's constructions for determining the acceleration of the piston of a reciprocating engine.

4. How are velocity and acceleration of the slider of a single slider crank chain determined analytically?

5. Derive an expression for the inertia force due to reciprocating mass in reciprocating engine, neglecting the mass of the connecting rod.

6. What is the difference between piston effort, crank effort and crank-pin effort?

7. Discuss the method of finding the crank effort in a reciprocating single acting, single cylinder petrol engine.

8. The inertia of the connecting rod can be replaced by two masses concentrated at two points and connected rigidly together. How to determine the two masses so that it is dynamically equivalent to the connecting rod ? Show this.

9. Given acceleration image of a link. Explain how dynamical equivalent system can be used to determine the direction of inertia force on it.

10. Describe the graphical and analytical method of finding the inertia torque on the crankshaft of a horizontal reciprocating engine.

11. Derive an expression for the correction torque to be applied to a crankshaft if the connecting rod of a reciprocating engine is replaced by two lumped masses at the piston pin and the crank pin respectively.

OBJECTIVE TYPE QUESTIONS

1. When the crank is at the inner dead centre, in a horizontal reciprocating steam engine, then the velocity of the piston will be

   (a) zero   (b) minimum   (c) maximum

2. The acceleration of the piston in a reciprocating steam engine is given by

(a) $\omega.r\left(\sin\theta + \dfrac{\sin 2\theta}{n}\right)$

(b) $\omega.r\left(\cos\theta + \dfrac{\cos 2\theta}{n}\right)$

(c) $\omega^2.r\left(\sin\theta + \dfrac{\sin 2\theta}{n}\right)$

(d) $\omega^2.r\left(\cos\theta + \dfrac{\cos 2\theta}{n}\right)$

where ω = Angular velocity of the crank,

r = Radius of the crank,

θ = Angle turned by the crank from inner dead centre, and

n = Ratio of length of connecting rod to crank radius.

3. A rigid body, under the action of external forces, can be replaced by two masses placed at a fixed distance apart. The two masses form an equivalent dynamical system, if

(a) the sum of two masses is equal to the total mass of the body

(b) the centre of gravity of the two masses coincides with that of the body

(c) the sum of mass moment of inertia of the masses about their centre of gravity is equal to the mass moment of inertia of the body

(d) all of the above

4. The essential condition of placing the two masses, so that the system becomes dynamically equivalent is

(a) $l_1.l_2 = k_G^2$ (b) $l_1.l_2 = k_G$ (c) $l_1 = k_G$ (d) $l_2 = k_G$

where l_1 and l_2 = Distance of two masses from the centre of gravity of the body, and

k_G = Radius of gyration of the body.

5. In an engine, the work done by inertia forces in a cycle is

(a) positive   (b) zero   (c) negative   (d) none of these

ANSWERS

1. (a)   2. (d)   3. (d)   4. (a)   5. (a)

16

Turning Moment Diagrams and Flywheel

16.1. Introduction

The turning moment diagram (also known as *crank-effort diagram*) is the graphical representation of the turning moment or crank-effort for various positions of the crank. It is plotted on cartesian co-ordinates, in which the turning moment is taken as the ordinate and crank angle as abscissa.

16.2. Turning Moment Diagram for a Single Cylinder Double Acting Steam Engine

A turning moment diagram for a single cylinder double acting steam engine is shown in Fig. 16.1. The vertical ordinate represents the turning moment and the horizontal ordinate represents the crank angle.

We have discussed in Chapter 15 (Art. 15.10.) that the turning moment on the crankshaft,

$$T = F_P \times r \left(\sin \theta + \frac{\sin 2\theta}{2\sqrt{n^2 - \sin^2 \theta}} \right)$$

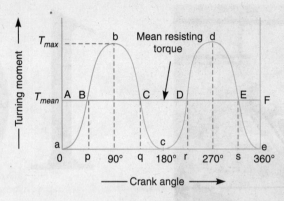

Fig. 16.1. Turning moment diagram for a single cylinder, double acting steam engine.

where

F_P = Piston effort,

r = Radius of crank,

n = Ratio of the connecting rod length and radius of crank, and

θ = Angle turned by the crank from inner dead centre.

From the above expression, we see that the turning moment (T) is zero, when the crank angle (θ) is zero. It is maximum when the crank angle is 90° and it is again zero when crank angle is 180°.

This is shown by the curve *abc* in Fig. 16.1 and it represents the turning moment diagram for outstroke. The curve *cde* is the turning moment diagram for instroke and is somewhat similar to the curve *abc*.

Since the work done is the product of the turning moment and the angle turned, therefore the area of the turning moment diagram represents the work done per revolution. In actual practice, the engine is assumed to work against the mean resisting torque, as shown by a horizontal line *AF*. The height of the ordinate *a A* represents the mean height of the turning moment diagram. Since it is assumed that the work done by the turning moment per revolution is equal to the work done against the mean resisting torque, therefore the area of the rectangle *aAFe* is proportional to the work done against the mean resisting torque.

For flywheel, have a look at your tailor's manual sewing machine.

Notes: 1. When the turning moment is positive (*i.e.* when the engine torque is more than the mean resisting torque) as shown between points *B* and *C* (or *D* and *E*) in Fig. 16.1, the crankshaft accelerates and the work is done by the steam.

2. When the turning moment is negative (*i.e.* when the engine torque is less than the mean resisting torque) as shown between points C and D in Fig. 16.1, the crankshaft retards and the work is done on the steam.

3. If T = Torque on the crankshaft at any instant, and

T_{mean} = Mean resisting torque.

Then accelerating torque on the rotating parts of the engine

$$= T - T_{mean}$$

4. If $(T - T_{mean})$ is positive, the flywheel accelerates and if $(T - T_{mean})$ is negative, then the flywheel retards.

16.3. Turning Moment Diagram for a Four Stroke Cycle Internal Combustion Engine

A turning moment diagram for a four stroke cycle internal combustion engine is shown in Fig. 16.2. We know that in a four stroke cycle internal combustion engine, there is one working stroke after the crank has turned through two revolutions, *i.e.* 720° (or 4 π radians).

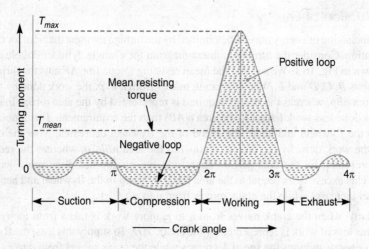

Fig. 16.2. Turning moment diagram for a four stroke cycle internal combustion engine.

Since the pressure inside the engine cylinder is less than the atmospheric pressure during the suction stroke, therefore a negative loop is formed as shown in Fig. 16.2. During the compression stroke, the work is done on the gases, therefore a higher negative loop is obtained. During the expansion or working stroke, the fuel burns and the gases expand, therefore a large positive loop is obtained. In this stroke, the work is done by the gases. During exhaust stroke, the work is done on the gases, therefore a negative loop is formed. It may be noted that the effect of the inertia forces on the piston is taken into account in Fig. 16.2.

16.4. Turning Moment Diagram for a Multi-cylinder Engine

A separate turning moment diagram for a compound steam engine having three cylinders and the resultant turning moment diagram is shown in Fig. 16.3. The resultant turning moment diagram is the sum of the turning moment diagrams for the three cylinders. It may be noted that the first cylinder is the high pressure cylinder, second cylinder is the intermediate cylinder and the third cylinder is the low pressure cylinder. The cranks, in case of three cylinders, are usually placed at 120° to each other.

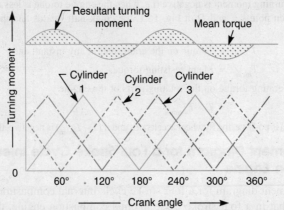

Fig. 16.3. Turning moment diagram for a multi-cylinder engine.

16.5. Fluctuation of Energy

The fluctuation of energy may be determined by the turning moment diagram for one complete cycle of operation. Consider the turning moment diagram for a single cylinder double acting steam engine as shown in Fig. 16.1. We see that the mean resisting torque line AF cuts the turning moment diagram at points B, C, D and E. When the crank moves from a to p, the work done by the engine is equal to the area aBp, whereas the energy required is represented by the area $aABp$. In other words, the engine has done less work (equal to the area $a\,AB$) than the requirement. This amount of energy is taken from the flywheel and hence the speed of the flywheel decreases. Now the crank moves from p to q, the work done by the engine is equal to the area $pBbCq$, whereas the requirement of energy is represented by the area $pBCq$. Therefore, the engine has done more work than the requirement. This excess work (equal to the area BbC) is stored in the flywheel and hence the speed of the flywheel increases while the crank moves from p to q.

Similarly, when the crank moves from q to r, more work is taken from the engine than is developed. This loss of work is represented by the area $C\,c\,D$. To supply this loss, the flywheel gives up some of its energy and thus the speed decreases while the crank moves from q to r. As the crank moves from r to s, excess energy is again developed given by the area $D\,d\,E$ and the speed again increases. As the piston moves from s to e, again there is a loss of work and the speed decreases. The variations of energy above and below the mean resisting torque line are called *fluctuations of energy*. The areas BbC, CcD, DdE, etc. represent fluctuations of energy.

A little consideration will show that the engine has a maximum speed either at q or at s. This is due to the fact that the flywheel absorbs energy while the crank moves from p to q and from r to s. On the other hand, the engine has a minimum speed either at p or at r. The reason is that the flywheel gives out some of its energy when the crank moves from a to p and q to r. The difference between the maximum and the minimum energies is known as *maximum fluctuation of energy*.

16.6. Determination of Maximum Fluctuation of Energy

A turning moment diagram for a multi-cylinder engine is shown by a wavy curve in Fig. 16.4. The horizontal line AG represents the mean torque line. Let a_1, a_3, a_5 be the areas above the mean torque line and a_2, a_4 and a_6 be the areas below the mean torque line. These areas represent some quantity of energy which is either added or subtracted from the energy of the moving parts of the engine.

Let the energy in the flywheel at $A = E$, then from Fig. 16.4, we have

Energy at $B = E + a_1$

Energy at $C = E + a_1 - a_2$

Energy at $D = E + a_1 - a_2 + a_3$

Energy at $E = E + a_1 - a_2 + a_3 - a_4$

Energy at $F = E + a_1 - a_2 + a_3 - a_4 + a_5$

Energy at $G = E + a_1 - a_2 + a_3 - a_4 + a_5 - a_6$

$\qquad$ = Energy at A (*i.e.* cycle repeats after G)

Let us now suppose that the greatest of these energies is at B and least at E. Therefore,

Maximum energy in flywheel

$$= E + a_1$$

A flywheel stores energy when the supply is in excess and releases energy when energy is in deficit.

Minimum energy in the flywheel

$$= E + a_1 - a_2 + a_3 - a_4$$

∴ Maximum fluctuation of energy,

$$\Delta E = \text{Maximum energy} - \text{Minimum energy}$$

$$= (E + a_1) - (E + a_1 - a_2 + a_3 - a_4) = a_2 - a_3 + a_4$$

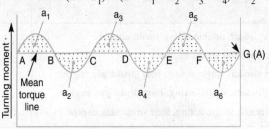

Fig. 16.4. Determination of maximum fluctuation of energy.

16.7. Coefficient of Fluctuation of Energy

It may be defined as the **ratio of the maximum fluctuation of energy to the work done per cycle.** Mathematically, coefficient of fluctuation of energy,

$$C_E = \frac{\text{Maximum fluctuation of energy}}{\text{Work done per cycle}}$$

The work done per cycle (in N-m or joules) may be obtained by using the following two relations :

1. Work done per cycle $= T_{mean} \times \theta$

where $\qquad T_{mean}$ = Mean torque, and

$\qquad\qquad \theta$ = Angle turned (in radians), in one revolution.

$\qquad\qquad = 2\pi$, in case of steam engine and two stroke internal combustion engines

$\qquad\qquad = 4\pi$, in case of four stroke internal combustion engines.

The mean torque (T_{mean}) in N-m may be obtained by using the following relation :

$$T_{mean} = \frac{P \times 60}{2\pi N} = \frac{P}{\omega}$$

where

P = Power transmitted in watts,

N = Speed in r.p.m., and

ω = Angular speed in rad/s = $2\pi N/60$

2. The work done per cycle may also be obtained by using the following relation :

$$\text{Work done per cycle} = \frac{P \times 60}{n}$$

where

n = Number of working strokes per minute,

= N, in case of steam engines and two stroke internal combustion engines,

= $N/2$, in case of four stroke internal combustion engines.

The following table shows the values of coefficient of fluctuation of energy for steam engines and internal combustion engines.

Table 16.1. Coefficient of fluctuation of energy (C_E) for steam and internal combustion engines.

S.No.	Type of engine	Coefficient of fluctuation of energy (C_E)
1.	Single cylinder, double acting steam engine	0.21
2.	Cross-compound steam engine	0.096
3.	Single cylinder, single acting, four stroke gas engine	1.93
4.	Four cylinders, single acting, four stroke gas engine	0.066
5.	Six cylinders, single acting, four stroke gas engine	0.031

16.8. Flywheel

A flywheel used in machines serves as a reservoir, which stores energy during the period when the supply of energy is more than the requirement, and releases it during the period when the requirement of energy is more than the supply.

In case of steam engines, internal combustion engines, reciprocating compressors and pumps, the energy is developed during one stroke and the engine is to run for the whole cycle on the energy produced during this one stroke. For example, in internal combustion engines, the energy is developed only during expansion or power stroke which is much more than the engine load and no energy is being developed during suction, compression and exhaust strokes in case of four stroke engines and during compression in case of two stroke engines. The excess energy developed during power stroke is absorbed by the flywheel and releases it to the crankshaft during other strokes in which no energy is developed, thus rotating the crankshaft at a uniform speed. A little consideration will show that when the flywheel absorbs energy, its speed increases and when it releases energy, the speed decreases. Hence a flywheel does not maintain a constant speed, it simply reduces the fluctuation of speed. In other words, *a flywheel controls the speed variations caused by the fluctuation of the engine turning moment during each cycle of operation.*

In machines where the operation is intermittent like *punching machines, shearing machines, rivetting machines, crushers, etc., the flywheel stores energy from the power source during the greater portion of the operating cycle and gives it up during a small period of the cycle. Thus, the energy from the power source to the machines is supplied practically at a constant rate throughout the operation.

Note: The function of a **governor in an engine is entirely different from that of a flywheel. It regulates the mean speed of an engine when there are variations in the load, *e.g.*, when the load on the engine increases, it becomes necessary to increase the supply of working fluid. On the other hand, when the load decreases, less working fluid is required. The governor automatically controls the supply of working fluid to the engine with the varying load condition and keeps the mean speed of the engine within certain limits.

As discussed above, the flywheel does not maintain a constant speed, it simply reduces the fluctuation of speed. It does not control the speed variations caused by the varying load.

16.9. Coefficient of Fluctuation of Speed

The difference between the maximum and minimum speeds during a cycle is called the *maximum fluctuation of speed*. The ratio of the maximum fluctuation of speed to the mean speed is called the *coefficient of fluctuation of speed*.

Let N_1 and N_2 = Maximum and minimum speeds in r.p.m. during the cycle, and

$$N = \text{Mean speed in r.p.m.} = \frac{N_1 + N_2}{2}$$

∴ Coefficient of fluctuation of speed,

$$C_S = \frac{N_1 - N_2}{N} = \frac{2(N_1 - N_2)}{N_1 + N_2}$$

$$= \frac{\omega_1 - \omega_2}{\omega} = \frac{2(\omega_1 - \omega_2)}{\omega_1 + \omega_2} \qquad \text{...(In terms of angular speeds)}$$

$$= \frac{v_1 - v_2}{v} = \frac{2(v_1 - v_2)}{v_1 + v_2} \qquad \text{...(In terms of linear speeds)}$$

The coefficient of fluctuation of speed is a limiting factor in the design of flywheel. It varies depending upon the nature of service to which the flywheel is employed.

Note. The reciprocal of the coefficient of fluctuation of speed is known as *coefficient of steadiness* and is denoted by *m*.

$$\therefore \quad m = \frac{1}{C_S} = \frac{N}{N_1 - N_2}$$

16.10. Energy Stored in a Flywheel

A flywheel is shown in Fig. 16.5. We have discussed in Art. 16.5 that when a flywheel absorbs energy, its speed increases and when it gives up energy, its speed decreases.

Let m = Mass of the flywheel in kg,

k = Radius of gyration of the flywheel in metres,

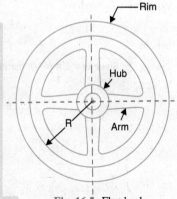

Fig. 16.5. Flywheel.

I = Mass moment of inertia of the flywheel about its axis of rotation in kg-m² = $m.k^2$,

N_1 and N_2 = Maximum and minimum speeds during the cycle in r.p.m.,

ω_1 and ω_2 = Maximum and minimum angular speeds during the cycle in rad/s,

N = Mean speed during the cycle in r.p.m. = $\dfrac{N_1 + N_2}{2}$,

ω = Mean angular speed during the cycle in rad/s = $\dfrac{\omega_1 + \omega_2}{2}$,

C_S = Coefficient of fluctuation of speed, = $\dfrac{N_1 - N_2}{N}$ or $\dfrac{\omega_1 - \omega_2}{\omega}$

We know that the mean kinetic energy of the flywheel,

$$E = \frac{1}{2} \times I.\omega^2 = \frac{1}{2} \times m.k^2.\omega^2 \qquad \text{(in N-m or joules)}$$

As the speed of the flywheel changes from ω_1 to ω_2, the maximum fluctuation of energy,

$$\Delta E = \text{Maximum K.E.} - \text{Minimum K.E.}$$

$$= \frac{1}{2} \times I \left(\omega_1\right)^2 - \frac{1}{2} \times I \left(\omega_2\right)^2 = \frac{1}{2} \times I \left[\left(\omega_1\right)^2 - \left(\omega_2\right)^2 \right]$$

$$= \frac{1}{2} \times I \left(\omega_1 + \omega_2\right)\left(\omega_1 - \omega_2\right) = I.\omega\left(\omega_1 - \omega_2\right) \qquad \ldots(i)$$

$$\ldots\left(\because \omega = \frac{\omega_1 + \omega_2}{2} \right)$$

$$= I.\omega^2 \left(\frac{\omega_1 - \omega_2}{\omega} \right) \qquad \ldots \text{(Multiplying and dividing by } \omega)$$

$$= I.\omega^2.C_S = m.k^2.\omega^2.C_S \qquad \ldots (\because I = m.k^2) \quad \ldots(ii)$$

$$= 2.E.C_S \text{ (in N–m or joules)} \qquad \ldots\left(\because E = \frac{1}{2} \times I.\omega^2 \right) \ldots (iii)$$

The radius of gyration (k) may be taken equal to the mean radius of the rim (R), because the thickness of rim is very small as compared to the diameter of rim. Therefore, substituting $k = R$, in equation (ii), we have

$$\Delta E = m.R^2.\omega^2.C_S = m.v^2.C_S$$

where

v = Mean linear velocity (i.e. at the mean radius) in m/s = $\omega.R$

Notes. 1. Since $\omega = 2\pi N/60$, therefore equation (i) may be written as

$$\Delta E = I \times \frac{2\pi N}{60} \left(\frac{2\pi N_1}{60} - \frac{2\pi N_2}{60} \right) = \frac{4\pi^2}{3600} \times I \times N \left(N_1 - N_2 \right)$$

$$= \frac{\pi^2}{900} \times m.k^2.N\left(N_1 - N_2 \right)$$

$$= \frac{\pi^2}{900} \times m.k^2.N^2.C_S \qquad \ldots\left(\because C_s = \frac{N_1 - N_2}{N} \right)$$

2. In the above expressions, only the mass moment of inertia of the flywheel rim (I) is considered and the mass moment of inertia of the hub and arms is neglected. This is due to the fact that the major portion of the mass of the flywheel is in the rim and a small portion is in the hub and arms. Also the hub and arms are nearer to the axis of rotation, therefore the mass moment of inertia of the hub and arms is small.

Example 16.1. *The mass of flywheel of an engine is 6.5 tonnes and the radius of gyration is 1.8 metres. It is found from the turning moment diagram that the fluctuation of energy is 56 kN-m. If the mean speed of the engine is 120 r.p.m., find the maximum and minimum speeds.*

Solution. Given : $m = 6.5$ t $= 6500$ kg ; $k = 1.8$ m ; $\Delta E = 56$ kN-m $= 56 \times 10^3$ N-m ; $N = 120$ r.p.m.

Let N_1 and N_2 = Maximum and minimum speeds respectively.

We know that fluctuation of energy (ΔE),

$$56 \times 10^3 = \frac{\pi^2}{900} \times m.k^2 . N (N_1 - N_2) = \frac{\pi^2}{900} \times 6500 \, (1.8)^2 \, 120 \, (N_1 - N_2)$$

$$= 27\,715 \, (N_1 - N_2)$$

$\therefore$ $\qquad N_1 - N_2 = 56 \times 10^3 / 27\,715 = 2$ r.p.m. ...(*i*)

We also know that mean speed (N),

$$120 = \frac{N_1 + N_2}{2} \text{ or } N_1 + N_2 = 120 \times 2 = 240 \text{ r.p.m.} \qquad ...(ii)$$

From equations (*i*) and (*ii*),

$\qquad N_1 = 121$ r.p.m., and $N_2 = 119$ r.p.m. **Ans.**

Example 16.2. *The flywheel of a steam engine has a radius of gyration of 1 m and mass 2500 kg. The starting torque of the steam engine is 1500 N-m and may be assumed constant. Determine: 1. the angular acceleration of the flywheel, and 2. the kinetic energy of the flywheel after 10 seconds from the start.*

Solution. Given : $k = 1$ m ; $m = 2500$ kg ; $T = 1500$ N-m

1. *Angular acceleration of the flywheel*

Let $\qquad \alpha$ = Angular acceleration of the flywheel.

We know that mass moment of inertia of the flywheel,

$$I = m.k^2 = 2500 \times 1^2 = 2500 \text{ kg-m}^2$$

$\therefore$ Starting torque of the engine (T),

$$1500 = I.\alpha = 2500 \times \alpha \quad \text{or} \quad \alpha = 1500 / 2500 = 0.6 \text{ rad /s}^2 \text{ **Ans.**}$$

2. *Kinetic energy of the flywheel*

First of all, let us find out the angular speed of the flywheel after 10 seconds from the start (*i.e.* from rest), assuming uniform acceleration.

Let $\qquad \omega_1$ = Angular speed at rest = 0

$\qquad \omega_2$ = Angular speed after 10 seconds, and

$\qquad t$ = Time in seconds.

We know that $\qquad \omega_2 = \omega_1 + \alpha \, t = 0 + 0.6 \times 10 = 6$ rad /s

∴ Kinetic energy of the flywheel

$$= \frac{1}{2} \times I \left(\omega_2 \right)^2 = \frac{1}{2} \times 2500 \times 6^2 = 45\,000 \text{ N-m} = 45 \text{ kN-m } \textbf{Ans.}$$

Example 16.3. *A horizontal cross compound steam engine develops 300 kW at 90 r.p.m. The coefficient of fluctuation of energy as found from the turning moment diagram is to be 0.1 and the fluctuation of speed is to be kept within ± 0.5% of the mean speed. Find the weight of the flywheel required, if the radius of gyration is 2 metres.*

Solution. Given : $P = 300$ kW $= 300 \times 10^3$ W; $N = 90$ r.p.m.; $C_E = 0.1$; $k = 2$ m

We know that the mean angular speed,

$$\omega = 2 \pi N / 60 = 2 \pi \times 90/60 = 9.426 \text{ rad/s}$$

Let ω_1 and ω_2 = Maximum and minimum speeds respectively.

Since the fluctuation of speed is ± 0.5% of mean speed, therefore total fluctuation of speed,

$$\omega_1 - \omega_2 = 1\% \ \omega = 0.01 \ \omega$$

and coefficient of fluctuation of speed,

$$C_S = \frac{\omega_1 - \omega_2}{\omega} = 0.01$$

We know that work done per cycle

$$= P \times 60 / N = 300 \times 10^3 \times 60 / 90 = 200 \times 10^3 \text{ N-m}$$

∴ Maximum fluctuation of energy,

$$\Delta E = \text{Work done per cycle} \times C_E = 200 \times 10^3 \times 0.1 = 20 \times 10^3 \text{ N-m}$$

Let m = Mass of the flywheel.

We know that maximum fluctuation of energy (ΔE),

$$20 \times 10^3 = m.k^2.\omega^2.C_S = m \times 2^2 \times (9.426)^2 \times 0.01 = 3.554 \ m$$

∴ $\quad m = 20 \times 10^3/3.554 = 5630 \text{ kg} \quad \textbf{Ans.}$

Example 16.4. *The turning moment diagram for a petrol engine is drawn to the following scales : Turning moment, 1 mm = 5 N-m ; crank angle, 1 mm = 1°. The turning moment diagram repeats itself at every half revolution of the engine and the areas above and below the mean turning moment line taken in order are 295, 685, 40, 340, 960, 270 mm². The rotating parts are equivalent to a mass of 36 kg at a radius of gyration of 150 mm. Determine the coefficient of fluctuation of speed when the engine runs at 1800 r.p.m.*

Solution. Given : $m = 36$ kg ; $k = 150$ mm $= 0.15$ m ; $N = 1800$ r.p.m. or $\omega = 2 \pi \times 1800/60 = 188.52$ rad /s

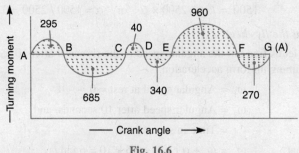

Fig. 16.6

The turning moment diagram is shown in Fig. 16.6.

Since the turning moment scale is 1 mm = 5 N-m and crank angle scale is 1 mm = 1° = π/180 rad, therefore,

1 mm² on turning moment diagram

$$= 5 \times \frac{\pi}{180} = \frac{\pi}{36} \text{ N-m}$$

Let the total energy at $A = E$, then referring to Fig. 16.6,

Energy at $B = E + 295$

... (**Maximum energy**)

Energy at $C = E + 295 - 685 = E - 390$

Energy at $D = E - 390 + 40 = E - 350$

Energy at $E = E - 350 - 340 = E - 690$ ...(**Minimum energy**)

Energy at $F = E - 690 + 960 = E + 270$

Energy at $G = E + 270 - 270 = E = $ Energy at A

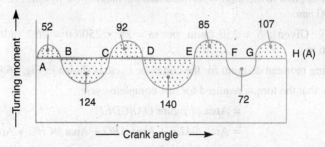
Flywheel of an electric motor.

We know that maximum fluctuation of energy,

$$\Delta E = \text{Maximum energy} - \text{Minimum energy}$$

$$= (E + 295) - (E - 690) = 985 \text{ mm}^2$$

$$= 985 \times \frac{\pi}{36} = 86 \text{ N-m} = 86 \text{ J}$$

Let C_S = Coefficient of fluctuation of speed.

We know that maximum fluctuation of energy (ΔE),

$$86 = m.k^2 \omega^2 . C_S = 36 \times (0.15)^2 \times (188.52)^2 C_S = 28\,787\, C_S$$

∴ $C_S = 86 / 28\,787 = 0.003$ or 0.3% **Ans.**

Example 16.5. *The turning moment diagram for a multicylinder engine has been drawn to a scale 1 mm = 600 N-m vertically and 1 mm = 3° horizontally. The intercepted areas between the output torque curve and the mean resistance line, taken in order from one end, are as follows :*

+ 52, – 124, + 92, – 140, + 85, – 72 and + 107 mm², when the engine is running at a speed of 600 r.p.m. If the total fluctuation of speed is not to exceed ± 1.5% of the mean, find the necessary mass of the flywheel of radius 0.5 m.

Solution. Given : $N = 600$ r.p.m. or $\omega = 2\pi \times 600 / 60 = 62.84$ rad / s ; $R = 0.5$ m

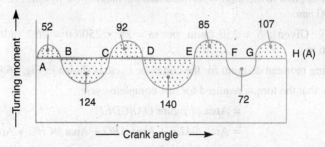

Fig. 16.7

Since the total fluctuation of speed is not to exceed ± 1.5% of the mean speed, therefore

$$\omega_1 - \omega_2 = 3\% \,\omega = 0.03 \,\omega$$

and coefficient of fluctuation of speed,

$$C_s = \frac{\omega_1 - \omega_2}{\omega} = 0.03$$

The turning moment diagram is shown in Fig. 16.7.

Since the turning moment scale is 1 mm = 600 N-m and crank angle scale is 1 mm = 3° = 3° × π/180 = π / 60 rad, therefore

1 mm² on turning moment diagram

$$= 600 \times \pi/60 = 31.42 \text{ N-m}$$

Let the total energy at A = E, then referring to Fig. 16.7,

Energy at B = E + 52   ...(Maximum energy)

Energy at C = E + 52 – 124 = E – 72

Energy at D = E – 72 + 92 = E + 20

Energy at E = E + 20 – 140 = E – 120   ...(Minimum energy)

Energy at F = E – 120 + 85 = E – 35

Energy at G = E – 35 – 72 = E – 107

Energy at H = E – 107 + 107 = E = Energy at A

We know that maximum fluctuation of energy,

$$\Delta E = \text{Maximum energy} - \text{Minimum energy}$$

$$= (E + 52) - (E - 120) = 172 = 172 \times 31.42 = 5404 \text{ N-m}$$

Let   m = Mass of the flywheel in kg.

We know that maximum fluctuation of energy (Δ E),

$$5404 = m.R^2.\omega^2.C_S = m \times (0.5)^2 \times (62.84)^2 \times 0.03 = 29.6 \ m$$

∴   m = 5404 / 29.6 = 183 kg   **Ans.**

Example 16.6. *A shaft fitted with a flywheel rotates at 250 r.p.m. and drives a machine. The torque of machine varies in a cyclic manner over a period of 3 revolutions. The torque rises from 750 N-m to 3000 N-m uniformly during 1/2 revolution and remains constant for the following revolution. It then falls uniformly to 750 N-m during the next 1/2 revolution and remains constant for one revolution, the cycle being repeated thereafter.*

Determine the power required to drive the machine and percentage fluctuation in speed, if the driving torque applied to the shaft is constant and the mass of the flywheel is 500 kg with radius of gyration of 600 mm.

Solution. Given : N = 250 r.p.m. or ω = 2π × 250/60 = 26.2 rad/s ; m = 500 kg ; k = 600 mm = 0.6 m

The turning moment diagram for the complete cycle is shown in Fig. 16.8.

We know that the torque required for one complete cycle

$$= \text{Area of figure } OABCDEF$$

$$= \text{Area } OAEF + \text{Area } ABG + \text{Area } BCHG + \text{Area } CDH$$

$$= OF \times OA + \frac{1}{2} \times AG \times BG + GH \times CH + \frac{1}{2} \times HD \times CH$$

$$= 6\pi \times 750 + \frac{1}{2} \times \pi(3000 - 750) + 2\pi(3000 - 750)$$
$$+ \frac{1}{2} \times \pi(3000 - 750)$$
$$= 11\,250\,\pi\ \text{N-m} \qquad \qquad \qquad ...(i)$$

If T_{mean} is the mean torque in N-m, then torque required for one complete cycle

$$= T_{mean} \times 6\,\pi\ \text{N-m} \qquad \qquad \qquad ...(ii)$$

From equations (*i*) and (*ii*),

$$T_{mean} = 11\,250\,\pi\,/\,6\,\pi = 1875\ \text{N-m}$$

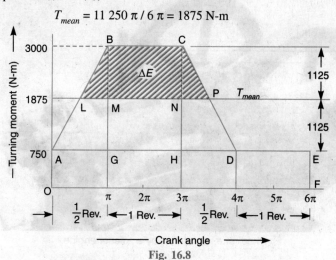

Fig. 16.8

Power required to drive the machine

We know that power required to drive the machine,

$$P = T_{mean} \times \omega = 1875 \times 26.2 = 49\,125\ \text{W} = 49.125\ \text{kW}\ \textbf{Ans.}$$

Coefficient of fluctuation of speed

Let C_S = Coefficient of fluctuation of speed.

First of all, let us find the values of *LM* and *NP*. From similar triangles *ABG* and *BLM*,

$$\frac{LM}{AG} = \frac{BM}{BG} \quad \text{or} \quad \frac{LM}{\pi} = \frac{3000 - 1875}{3000 - 750} = 0.5 \quad \text{or} \quad LM = 0.5\,\pi$$

Now, from similar triangles *CHD* and *CNP*,

$$\frac{NP}{HD} = \frac{CN}{CH} \quad \text{or} \quad \frac{NP}{\pi} = \frac{3000 - 1875}{3000 - 750} = 0.5 \quad \text{or} \quad NP = 0.5\,\pi$$

From Fig. 16.8, we find that

$$BM = CN = 3000 - 1875 = 1125\ \text{N-m}$$

Since the area above the mean torque line represents the maximum fluctuation of energy, therefore, maximum fluctuation of energy,

$$\Delta E = \text{Area } LBCP = \text{Area } LBM + \text{Area } MBCN + \text{Area } PNC$$

$$= \frac{1}{2} \times LM \times BM + MN \times BM + \frac{1}{2} \times NP \times CN$$

$$= \frac{1}{2} \times 0.5\pi \times 1125 + 2\pi \times 1125 + \frac{1}{2} \times 0.5\pi \times 1125$$

$$= 8837 \text{ N-m}$$

We know that maximum fluctuation of energy (ΔE),

$$8837 = m.k^2.\omega^2.C_S = 500 \times (0.6)^2 \times (26.2)^2 \times C_S = 123\,559\,C_S$$

$$C_S = \frac{8837}{123\,559} = 0.071 \text{ Ans.}$$

Flywheel of a pump run by a diesel engine.

Example 16.7. *During forward stroke of the piston of the double acting steam engine, the turning moment has the maximum value of 2000 N-m when the crank makes an angle of 80° with the inner dead centre. During the backward stroke, the maximum turning moment is 1500 N-m when the crank makes an angle of 80° with the outer dead centre. The turning moment diagram for the engine may be assumed for simplicity to be represented by two triangles.*

If the crank makes 100 r.p.m. and the radius of gyration of the flywheel is 1.75 m, find the coefficient of fluctuation of energy and the mass of the flywheel to keep the speed within ± 0.75% of the mean speed. Also determine the crank angle at which the speed has its minimum and maximum values.

Solution. Given : $N = 100$ r.p.m. or $\omega = 2\pi \times 100/60 = 10.47$ rad /s; $k = 1.75$ m

Since the fluctuation of speed is ± 0.75% of mean speed, therefore total fluctuation of speed,

$$\omega_1 - \omega_2 = 1.5\% \, \omega$$

and coefficient of fluctuation of speed,

$$C_S = \frac{\omega_1 - \omega_2}{\omega} = 1.5\% = 0.015$$

Coefficient of fluctuation of energy

The turning moment diagram for the engine during forward and backward strokes is shown in Fig. 16.9. The point O represents the inner dead centre (I.D.C.) and point G represents the outer dead centre (O.D.C). We know that maximum turning moment when crank makes an angle of 80° (or $80 \times \pi / 180 = 4\pi/9$ rad) with I.D.C.,

$$\therefore \qquad AB = 2000 \text{ N-m}$$

and maximum turning moment when crank makes an angle of 80° with outer dead centre (O.D.C.) or $180° + 80° = 260° = 260 \times \pi / 180 = 13 \pi / 9$ rad with I.D.C.,

$$LM = 1500 \text{ N-m}$$

Let $T_{mean} = EB = QM = $ Mean resisting torque.

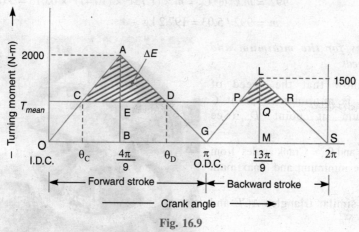

Fig. 16.9

We know that work done per cycle

$$= \text{Area of triangle } OAG + \text{Area of triangle } GLS$$

$$= \frac{1}{2} \times OG \times AB + \frac{1}{2} \times GS \times LM$$

$$= \frac{1}{2} \times \pi \times 2000 + \frac{1}{2} \times \pi \times 1500 = 1750\,\pi \text{ N-m} \qquad ...(i)$$

We also know that work done per cycle

$$= T_{mean} \times 2\,\pi \text{ N-m} \qquad ...(ii)$$

From equations (*i*) and (*ii*),

$$T_{mean} = 1750\,\pi\,/\,2\,\pi = 875 \text{ N-m}$$

From similar triangles *ACD* and *AOG*,

$$\frac{CD}{AE} = \frac{OG}{AB}$$

or

$$CD = \frac{OG}{AB} \times AE = \frac{OG}{AB}(AB - EB) = \frac{\pi}{2000}(2000 - 875) = 1.764 \text{ rad}$$

∴ Maximum fluctuation of energy,

$$\Delta E = \text{Area of triangle } ACD = \frac{1}{2} \times CD \times AE$$

$$= \frac{1}{2} \times CD\,(AB - EB) = \frac{1}{2} \times 1.764\,(2000 - 875) = 992 \text{ N-m}$$

We know that coefficient of fluctuation of energy,

$$C_E = \frac{\text{Max.fluctuation of energy}}{\text{Work done per cycle}} = \frac{992}{1750\pi} = 0.18 \text{ or } 18\% \text{ **Ans.**}$$

Mass of the flywheel

Let m = Mass of the flywheel.

We know that maximum fluctuation of energy (ΔE),

$$992 = m.k^2.\omega^2.C_S = m \times (1.75)^2 \times (10.47)^2 \times 0.015 = 5.03\ m$$

$\therefore$ $m = 992\ /\ 5.03 = 197.2$ kg **Ans.**

Crank angles for the minimum and maximum speeds

We know that the speed of the flywheel is minimum at point C and maximum at point D (See Art. 16.5).

Let θ_C and θ_D = Crank angles from I.D.C., for the minimum and maximum speeds.

From similar triangles ACE and AOB,

Flywheel of small steam engine.

$$\frac{CE}{OB} = \frac{AE}{AB}$$

or

$$CE = \frac{AE}{AB} \times OB = \frac{AB - EB}{AB} \times OB = \frac{2000 - 875}{2000} \times \frac{4\pi}{9} = \frac{\pi}{4}\ \text{rad}$$

$\therefore$ $\theta_C = \dfrac{4\pi}{9} - \dfrac{\pi}{4} = \dfrac{7\pi}{36}\ \text{rad} = \dfrac{7\pi}{36} \times \dfrac{180}{\pi} = 35°$ **Ans.**

Again from similar triangles AED and ABG,

$$\frac{ED}{BG} = \frac{AE}{AB}$$

or

$$ED = \frac{AE}{AB} \times BG = \frac{AB - EB}{AB}(OG - OB)$$

$$= \frac{2000 - 875}{2000}\left(\pi - \frac{4\pi}{9}\right) = \frac{2.8\pi}{9}\ \text{rad}$$

$\therefore$ $\theta_D = \dfrac{4\pi}{9} + \dfrac{2.8\pi}{9} = \dfrac{6.8\pi}{9}\ \text{rad} = \dfrac{6.8\pi}{9} \times \dfrac{180}{\pi} = 136°$ **Ans.**

Example 16.8. *A three cylinder single acting engine has its cranks set equally at 120° and it runs at 600 r.p.m. The torque-crank angle diagram for each cycle is a triangle for the power stroke with a maximum torque of 90 N-m at 60° from dead centre of corresponding crank. The torque on the return stroke is sensibly zero. Determine : 1. power developed. 2. coefficient of fluctuation of speed, if the mass of the flywheel is 12 kg and has a radius of gyration of 80 mm, 3. coefficient of fluctuation of energy, and 4. maximum angular acceleration of the flywheel.*

Solution. Given : $N = 600$ r.p.m. or $\omega = 2\pi \times 600/60 = 62.84$ rad /s; $T_{max} = 90$ N-m; $m = 12$ kg; $k = 80$ mm $= 0.08$ m

The torque-crank angle diagram for the individual cylinders is shown in Fig. 16.10 (*a*), and the resultant torque-crank angle diagram for the three cylinders is shown in Fig. 16.10 (*b*).

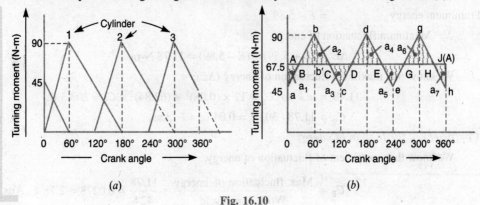

(*a*)   (*b*)

Fig. 16.10

1. *Power developed*

We know that work done/cycle

$$= \text{Area of three triangles} = 3 \times \frac{1}{2} \times \pi \times 90 = 424 \text{ N-m}$$

and mean torque, $\qquad T_{mean} = \dfrac{\text{Work done / cycle}}{\text{Crank angle / cycle}} = \dfrac{424}{2\pi} = 67.5 \text{ N-m}$

∴ Power developed $= T_{mean} \times \omega = 67.5 \times 62.84 = 4240 \text{ W} = 4.24 \text{ kW}$ **Ans.**

2. *Coefficient of fluctuation of speed*

Let $\qquad\qquad C_S = $ Coefficient of fluctuation of speed.

First of all, let us find the maximum fluctuation of energy (ΔE).

From Fig. 16.10 (*b*), we find that

$$a_1 = \text{Area of triangle } AaB = \frac{1}{2} \times AB \times Aa$$

$$= \frac{1}{2} \times \frac{\pi}{6} \times (67.5 - 45) = 5.89 \text{ N-m} = a_7 \quad ...(\because AB = 30° = \pi / 6 \text{ rad})$$

$$a_2 = \text{Area of triangle } BbC = \frac{1}{2} \times BC \times bb'$$

$$= \frac{1}{2} \times \frac{\pi}{3} (90 - 67.5) = 11.78 \text{ N-m} \qquad ...(\because BC = 60° = \pi/3 \text{ rad})$$

$$= a_3 = a_4 = a_5 = a_6$$

Now, let the total energy at $A = E$, then referring to Fig. 16.10 (*b*),

Energy at $B = E - 5.89$

Energy at $C = E - 5.89 + 11.78 = E + 5.89$

Energy at $D = E + 5.89 - 11.78 = E - 5.89$

Energy at $E = E - 5.89 + 11.78 = E + 5.89$

Energy at $G = E + 5.89 - 11.78 = E - 5.89$

Energy at $H = E - 5.89 + 11.78 = E + 5.89$

Energy at $J = E + 5.89 - 5.89 = E = \text{Energy at } A$

From above we see that maximum energy

$$= E + 5.89$$

and minimum energy $\qquad = E - 5.89$

∴ * Maximum fluctuation of energy,

$$\Delta E = (E + 5.89) - (E - 5.89) = 11.78 \text{ N-m}$$

We know that maximum fluctuation of energy (ΔE),

$$11.78 = m.k^2.\omega^2.C_S = 12 \times (0.08)^2 \times (62.84)^2 \times C_S = 303.3 \ C_S$$

∴ $\qquad C_S = 11.78 / 303.3 = 0.04 \text{ or } 4\% \ \textbf{Ans.}$

3. *Coefficient of fluctuation of energy*

We know that coefficient of fluctuation of energy,

$$C_E = \frac{\text{Max. fluctuation of energy}}{\text{Work done/cycle}} = \frac{11.78}{424} = 0.0278 = 2.78\% \ \textbf{Ans.}$$

4. *Maximum angular acceleration of the flywheel*

Let $\qquad \alpha$ = Maximum angular acceleration of the flywheel.

We know that,

$$T_{max} - T_{mean} = I.\alpha = m.k^2.\alpha$$

$$90 - 67.5 = 12 \times (0.08)^2 \times \alpha = 0.077 \ \alpha$$

∴ $\qquad \alpha = \frac{90 - 67.5}{0.077} = 292 \text{ rad} / \text{s}^2 \ \textbf{Ans.}$

Example 16.9. *A single cylinder, single acting, four stroke gas engine develops 20 kW at 300 r.p.m. The work done by the gases during the expansion stroke is three times the work done on the gases during the compression stroke, the work done during the suction and exhaust strokes being negligible. If the total fluctuation of speed is not to exceed ± 2 per cent of the mean speed and the turning moment diagram during compression and expansion is assumed to be triangular in shape, find the moment of inertia of the flywheel.*

Solution. Given : $P = 20 \text{ kW} = 20 \times 10^3 \text{ W}$; $N = 300$ r.p.m. or $\omega = 2\pi \times 300/60 = 31.42$ rad/s

Since the total fluctuation of speed ($\omega_1 - \omega_2$) is not to exceed ± 2 per cent of the mean speed (ω), therefore

$$\omega_1 - \omega_2 = 4\% \ \omega$$

and coefficient of fluctuation of speed,

$$C_S = \frac{\omega_1 - \omega_2}{\omega} = 4\% = 0.04$$

The turning moment-crank angle diagram for a four stroke engine is shown in Fig. 16.11. It is assumed to be triangular during compression and expansion strokes, neglecting the suction and exhaust strokes.

---

* Since the area above the mean torque line represents the maximum fluctuation of energy, therefore maximum fluctuation of energy,

$$\Delta E = \text{Area } Bbc = \text{Area } DdE = \text{Area } Ggh$$

$$= \frac{1}{2} \times \frac{\pi}{3} (90 - 67.5) = 11.78 \text{ N-m}$$

We know that for a four stroke engine, number of working strokes per cycle,

$$n = N/2 = 300 / 2 = 150$$

$\therefore$ Work done/cycle $= P \times 60/n = 20 \times 10^3 \times 60/150 = 8000$ N-m ...(*i*)

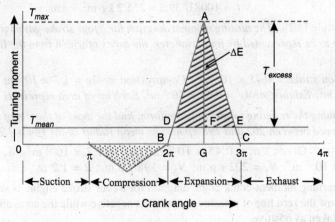

Fig. 16.11

Since the work done during suction and exhaust strokes is negligible, therefore net work done per cycle (during compression and expansion strokes)

$$= W_E - W_C = W_E - \frac{W_E}{3} = \frac{2}{3} W_E \qquad ... (\because W_E = 3W_C) \; ...(ii)$$

Equating equations (*i*) and (*ii*), work done during expansion stroke,

$$W_E = 8000 \times 3/2 = 12\,000 \text{ N-m}$$

We know that work done during expansion stroke (W_E),

$$12\,000 = \text{Area of triangle } ABC = \frac{1}{2} \times BC \times AG = \frac{1}{2} \times \pi \times AG$$

$\therefore \qquad AG = T_{max} = 12\,000 \times 2/\pi = 7638$ N-m

and mean turning moment,

$$^* T_{mean} = FG = \frac{\text{Work done/cycle}}{\text{Crank angle/cycle}} = \frac{8000}{4\pi} = 637 \text{ N-m}$$

$\therefore$ Excess turning moment,

$$T_{excess} = AF = AG - FG = 7638 - 637 = 7001 \text{ N-m}$$

Now, from similar triangles ADE and ABC,

$$\frac{DE}{BC} = \frac{AF}{AG} \quad \text{or} \quad DE = \frac{AF}{AG} \times BC = \frac{7001}{7638} \times \pi = 2.88 \,\text{rad}$$

Since the area above the mean turning moment line represents the maximum fluctuation of energy, therefore maximum fluctuation of energy,

$$\Delta E = \text{Area of } \Delta ADE = \frac{1}{2} \times DE \times AF = \frac{1}{2} \times 2.88 \times 7001 = 10081 \text{ N-m}$$

---

* The mean turning moment (T_{mean}) may also be obtained by using the following relation :

$$P = T_{mean} \times \omega \text{ or } T_{mean} = P/\omega = 20 \times 10^3/31.42 = 637 \text{ N-m}$$

Let I = Moment of inertia of the flywheel in kg-m^2.

We know that maximum fluctuation of energy (ΔE),

$$10\,081 = I.\omega^2.C_S = I \times (31.42)^2 \times 0.04 = 39.5\,I$$

$$\therefore \qquad I = 10081/\,39.5 = 255.2 \text{ kg-m}^2 \quad \textbf{Ans.}$$

Example 16.10. *The turning moment diagram for a four stroke gas engine may be assumed for simplicity to be represented by four triangles, the areas of which from the line of zero pressure are as follows :*

Suction stroke = 0.45 × 10^{-3} m^2; Compression stroke = 1.7 × 10^{-3} m^2; Expansion stroke = 6.8 × 10^{-3} m^2; Exhaust stroke = 0.65 × 10^{-3} m^2. Each m^2 of area represents 3 MN-m of energy.

Assuming the resisting torque to be uniform, find the mass of the rim of a flywheel required to keep the speed between 202 and 198 r.p.m. The mean radius of the rim is 1.2 m.

Solution. Given : $a_1 = 0.45 \times 10^{-3}$ m^2 ; $a_2 = 1.7 \times 10^{-3}$ m^2 ; $a_3 = 6.8 \times 10^{-3}$ m^2; $a_4 = 0.65 \times 10^{-3}$ m^2; $N_1 = 202$ r.p.m; $N_2 = 198$ r.p.m.; $R = 1.2$ m

The turning moment-crank angle diagram for a four stroke engine is shown in Fig. 16.12. The areas below the zero line of pressure are taken as negative while the areas above the zero line of pressure are taken as positive.

$$\therefore \qquad \text{Net area} = a_3 - (a_1 + a_2 + a_4)$$

$$= 6.8 \times 10^{-3} - (0.45 \times 10^{-3} + 1.7 \times 10^{-3} + 0.65 \times 10^{-3}) = 4 \times 10^{-3} \text{ m}^2$$

Since the energy scale is 1 m^2 = 3 MN-m = 3 × 10^6 N-m, therefore,

Net work done per cycle = $4 \times 10^{-3} \times 3 \times 10^6 = 12 \times 10^3$ N-m $\qquad$ ...(i)

We also know that work done per cycle,

$$= T_{mean} \times 4\pi \text{ N-m} \qquad \qquad ...(ii)$$

From equations (i) and (ii),

$$T_{mean} = FG = 12 \times 10^3/4\pi = 955 \text{ N-m}$$

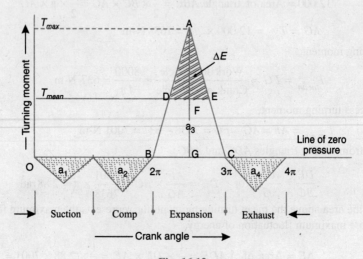

Fig. 16.12

Work done during expansion stroke

$$= a_3 \times \text{Energy scale} = 6.8 \times 10^{-3} \times 3 \times 10^6 = 20.4 \times 10^3 \text{ N-m} \quad ...(iii)$$

Also, work done during expansion stroke

$$= \text{Area of triangle } ABC$$

$$= \frac{1}{2} \times BC \times AG = \frac{1}{2} \times \pi \times AG = 1.571 \times AG \qquad \dots (iv)$$

From equations (iii) and (iv),

$$AG = 20.4 \times 10^3/1.571 = 12\,985 \text{ N-m}$$

∴ Excess torque,

$$T_{excess} = AF = AG - FG = 12\,985 - 955 = 12\,030 \text{ N-m}$$

Now from similar triangles ADE and ABC,

$$\frac{DE}{BC} = \frac{AF}{AG} \quad \text{or} \quad DE = \frac{AF}{AG} \times BC = \frac{12\,030}{12\,985} \times \pi = 2.9 \text{ rad}$$

We know that the maximum fluctuation of energy,

$$\Delta E = \text{Area of } \Delta ADE = \frac{1}{2} \times DE \times AF = \frac{1}{2} \times 2.9 \times 12030 \text{ N-m}$$

$$= 17\,444 \text{ N-m}$$

Mass of the rim of a flywheel

Let $\qquad m$ = Mass of the rim of a flywheel in kg, and

$\qquad N$ = Mean speed of the flywheel

$$= \frac{N_1 + N_2}{2} = \frac{202 + 198}{2} = 200 \text{ r.p.m.}$$

We know that the maximum fluctuation of energy (ΔE),

$$17\,444 = \frac{\pi^2}{900} \times m.R^2.N\,(N_1 - N_2) = \frac{\pi^2}{900} \times m\,(1.2)^2\,200 \times (202 - 198)$$

$$= 12.63 \, m$$

∴ $\qquad m = 17\,444\,/12.36 = 1381 \text{ kg} \quad \textbf{Ans.}$

Example 16.11. *The turning moment curve for an engine is represented by the equation,* $T = (20\,000 + 9500 \sin 2\theta - 5700 \cos 2\theta)$ *N-m, where* θ *is the angle moved by the crank from inner dead centre. If the resisting torque is constant, find:*

1. Power developed by the engine ; 2. Moment of inertia of flywheel in kg-m², if the total fluctuation of speed is not to exceed 1% of mean speed which is 180 r.p.m; and 3. Angular acceleration of the flywheel when the crank has turned through 45° from inner dead centre.

Solution. Given : $T = (20\,000 + 9500 \sin 2\theta - 5700 \cos 2\theta)$ N-m ; $N = 180$ r.p.m. or $\omega = 2\pi \times 180/60 = 18.85$ rad/s

Since the total fluctuation of speed ($\omega_1 - \omega_2$) is 1% of mean speed (ω), therefore coefficient of fluctuation of speed,

$$C_S = \frac{\omega_1 - \omega_2}{\omega} = 1\% = 0.01$$

1. *Power developed by the engine*

We know that work done per revolution

$$= \int_0^{2\pi} T\,d\theta = \int_0^{2\pi} (20\,000 + 9500 \sin 2\theta - 5700 \cos 2\theta)\,d\theta$$

$$= \left[20\,000\theta - \frac{9500\cos 2\theta}{2} - \frac{5700\sin 2\theta}{2} \right]_0^{2\pi}$$

$$= 20\,000 \times 2\pi = 40\,000\,\pi \text{ N-m}$$

and mean resisting torque of the engine,

$$T_{mean} = \frac{\text{Work done per revolution}}{2\pi} = \frac{40\,000\,\pi}{2\pi} = 20\,000 \text{ N-m}$$

We know that power developed by the engine

$$= T_{mean} \cdot \omega = 20\,000 \times 18.85 = 377\,000 \text{ W} = 377 \text{ kW } \textbf{Ans.}$$

2. *Moment of inertia of the flywheel*

Let I = Moment of inertia of the flywheel in kg-m^2.

The turning moment diagram for one stroke (*i.e.* half revolution of the crankshaft) is shown in Fig. 16.13. Since at points B and D, the torque exerted on the crankshaft is equal to the mean resisting torque on the flywheel, therefore,

$$T = T_{mean}$$

$$20\,000 + 9500\sin 2\theta - 5700\cos 2\theta = 20\,000$$

or $$9500\sin 2\theta = 5700\cos 2\theta$$

$$\tan 2\theta = \sin 2\theta / \cos 2\theta = 5700/9500 = 0.6$$

∴ $$2\theta = 31° \text{ or } \theta = 15.5°$$

∴ $$\theta_B = 15.5° \text{ and } \theta_D = 90° + 15.5° = 105.5°$$

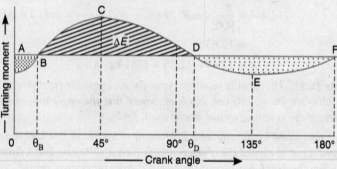

Fig. 16.13

Maximum fluctuation of energy,

$$\Delta E = \int_{\theta_B}^{\theta_D} \left(T - T_{mean} \right) d\theta$$

$$= \int_{15.5°}^{105.5°} \left(20\,000 + 9500\sin 2\theta - 5700\cos 2\theta - 20\,000 \right) d\theta$$

$$= \left[-\frac{9500\cos 2\theta}{2} - \frac{5700\sin 2\theta}{2} \right]_{15.5°}^{105.5°} = 11\,078 \text{ N-m}$$

We know that maximum fluctuation of energy (ΔE),

$$11\ 078 = I.\omega^2.C_S = I \times (18.85)^2 \times 0.01 = 3.55\ I$$

$$\therefore \quad I = 11078/3.55 = 3121 \text{ kg-m}^2 \text{ Ans.}$$

3. *Angular acceleration of the flywheel*

Let α = Angular acceleration of the flywheel, and

θ = Angle turned by the crank from inner dead centre = 45° ... (Given)

The angular acceleration in the flywheel is produced by the excess torque over the mean torque. We know that excess torque at any instant,

$$
\begin{aligned}
T_{excess} &= T - T_{mean} \\
&= 20000 + 9500 \sin 2\theta - 5700 \cos 2\theta \\
&\qquad - 20000 \\
&= 9500 \sin 2\theta - 5700 \cos 2\theta
\end{aligned}
$$

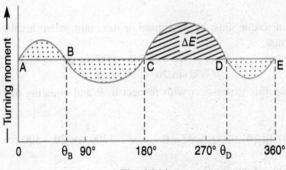

Nowadays steam turbines like this can be produced entirely by computer-controlled machine tools, directly from the engineer's computer.

Note : This picture is given as additional information.

$\therefore$ Excess torque at 45°

$$= 9500 \sin 90° - 5700 \cos 90° = 9500 \text{ N-m} \qquad \ldots (i)$$

We also know that excess torque

$$= I.\alpha = 3121 \times \alpha \qquad \ldots (ii)$$

From equations (*i*) and (*ii*),

$$\alpha = 9500/3121 = 3.044 \text{ rad /s}^2 \text{ Ans.}$$

Example 16.12. *A certain machine requires a torque of (5000 + 500 sin θ) N-m to drive it, where θ is the angle of rotation of shaft measured from certain datum. The machine is directly coupled to an engine which produces a torque of (5000 + 600 sin 2θ) N-m. The flywheel and the other rotating parts attached to the engine has a mass of 500 kg at a radius of gyration of 0.4 m. If the mean speed is 150 r.p.m., find : 1. the fluctuation of energy, 2. the total percentage fluctuation of speed, and 3. the maximum and minimum angular acceleration of the flywheel and the corresponding shaft position.*

Solution. Given : T_1 = (5000 + 500 sin θ) N-m ; T_2 = (5000 + 600 sin 2θ) N-m ; m = 500 kg; k = 0.4 m ; N = 150 r.p.m. or $\omega = 2\pi \times 150/60 = 15.71$ rad/s

Fig. 16.14

1. *Fluctuation of energy*

We know that change in torque

$$= T_2 - T_1 = (5000 + 600 \sin 2\theta) - (5000 + 500 \sin \theta)$$
$$= 600 \sin 2\theta - 500 \sin \theta$$

This change is zero when

$$600 \sin 2\theta = 500 \sin \theta \quad \text{or} \quad 1.2 \sin 2\theta = \sin \theta$$

$$1.2 \times 2 \sin \theta \cos \theta = \sin \theta \quad \text{or} \quad 2.4 \sin \theta \cos \theta = \sin \theta \quad \dots (\because \sin 2\theta = 2 \sin \theta \cos \theta)$$

∴ Either $\sin \theta = 0 \quad \text{or} \quad \cos \theta = 1/2.4 = 0.4167$

when $\sin \theta = 0, \theta = 0°, 180° \text{ and } 360°$

i.e. $\theta_A = 0°, \theta_C = 180° \text{ and } \theta_E = 360°$

when $\cos \theta = 0.4167, \theta = 65.4° \text{ and } 294.6°$

i.e. $\theta_B = 65.4° \text{ and } \theta_D = 294.6°$

The turning moment diagram is shown in Fig. 16.14. The maximum fluctuation of energy lies between C and D (*i.e.* between 180° and 294.6°), as shown shaded in Fig. 16.14.

∴ Maximum fluctuation of energy,

$$\Delta E = \int_{180°}^{294.6°} \left(T_2 - T_1 \right) d\theta$$

$$= \int_{180°}^{294.6°} \left[(5000 + 600 \sin 2\theta) - (5000 + 500 \sin \theta) \right] d\theta$$

$$= \left[-\frac{600 \cos 2\theta}{2} + 500 \cos \theta \right]_{180°}^{294.6°} = 1204 \text{ N-m } \textbf{Ans.}$$

2. *Total percentage fluctuation of speed*

Let C_S = Total percentage fluctuation of speed.

We know that maximum fluctuation of energy (ΔE),

$$1204 = m.k^2.\omega^2.C_S = 500 \times (0.4)^2 \times (15.71)^2 \times C_S = 19\,744\ C_S$$

∴ $C_S = 1204 / 19\,744 = 0.061 \quad \text{or} \quad 6.1\% \textbf{ Ans.}$

3. *Maximum and minimum angular acceleration of the flywheel and the corresponding shaft positions*

The change in torque must be maximum or minimum when acceleration is maximum or minimum. We know that

Change in torque, $T = T_2 - T_1 = (5000 + 600 \sin 2\theta) - (5000 + 500 \sin \theta)$
$$= 600 \sin 2\theta - 500 \sin \theta \qquad \dots(i)$$

Differentiating this expression with respect to θ and equating to zero for maximum or minimum values.

∴ $\dfrac{d}{d\theta}(600 \sin 2\theta - 500 \sin \theta) = 0 \quad \text{or} \quad 1200 \cos 2\theta - 500 \cos \theta = 0$

or $12 \cos 2\theta - 5 \cos \theta = 0$

$$12 (2 \cos^2 \theta - 1) - 5 \cos \theta = 0 \qquad \dots (\because \cos 2\theta = 2 \cos^2 \theta - 1)$$

$$24 \cos^2 \theta - 5 \cos \theta - 12 = 0$$

$$\therefore \qquad \cos \theta = \frac{5 \pm \sqrt{25 + 4 \times 12 \times 24}}{2 \times 24} = \frac{5 \pm 34.3}{48}$$

$$= 0.8187 \quad \text{or} \quad - 0.6104$$

$$\therefore \qquad \theta = 35° \quad \text{or} \quad 127.6° \text{ Ans.}$$

Substituting $\theta = 35°$ in equation (*i*), we have maximum torque,

$$T_{max} = 600 \sin 70° - 500 \sin 35° = 277 \text{ N-m}$$

Substituting $\theta = 127.6°$ in equation (*i*), we have minimum torque,

$$T_{min} = 600 \sin 255.2° - 500 \sin 127.6° = -976 \text{ N-m}$$

We know that maximum acceleration,

$$\alpha_{max} = \frac{T_{max}}{I} = \frac{277}{500 \times (0.4)^2} = 3.46 \text{ rad/s}^2 \quad \textbf{Ans.} \qquad \dots (\because I = m.k^2)$$

and minimum acceleration (or maximum retardation),

$$\alpha_{min} = \frac{T_{min}}{I} = \frac{976}{500 \times (0.4)^2} = 12.2 \text{ rad/s}^2 \quad \textbf{Ans.}$$

Example 16.13. *The equation of the turning moment curve of a three crank engine is (5000 + 1500 sin 3 θ) N-m, where θ is the crank angle in radians. The moment of inertia of the flywheel is 1000 kg-m² and the mean speed is 300 r.p.m. Calculate : 1. power of the engine, and 2. the maximum fluctuation of the speed of the flywheel in percentage when (i) the resisting torque is constant, and (ii) the resisting torque is (5000 + 600 sin θ) N-m.*

Solution. Given : $T = (5000 + 1500 \sin 3\theta)$ N-m ; $I = 1000$ kg-m² ; $N = 300$ r.p.m. or $\omega = 2\pi \times 300/60 = 31.42$ rad/s

1. *Power of the engine*

We know that work done per revolution

$$= \int_0^{2\pi} (5000 + 1500 \sin 3\theta) d\theta = \left[5000\theta - \frac{1500 \cos 3\theta}{3} \right]_0^{2\pi}$$

$$= 10\,000\,\pi \text{ N-m}$$

$\therefore$ Mean resisting torque,

$$T_{mean} = \frac{\text{Work done/rev}}{2\pi} = \frac{10000\pi}{2\pi} = 5000 \text{ N-m}$$

We know that power of the engine,

$$P = T_{mean} \cdot \omega = 5000 \times 31.42 = 157\,100 \text{ W} = 157.1 \text{ kW} \textbf{ Ans.}$$

2. *Maximum fluctuation of the speed of the flywheel*

Let C_S = Maximum or total fluctuation of speed of the flywheel.

(i) When resisting torque is constant

The turning moment diagram is shown in Fig. 16.15. Since the resisting torque is constant, therefore the torque exerted on the shaft is equal to the mean resisting torque on the flywheel.

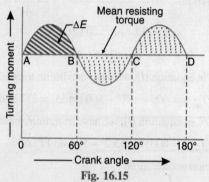

Fig. 16.15

$\therefore$ $\qquad T = T_{mean}$

$$5000 + 1500 \sin 3\theta = 5000$$

$$1500 \sin 3\theta = 0 \quad \text{or} \quad \sin 3\theta = 0$$

$\therefore$ $\qquad 3\theta = 0° \quad \text{or} \quad 180°$

$$\theta = 0° \quad \text{or} \quad 60°$$

$\therefore$ Maximum fluctuation of energy,

$$\Delta E = \int_{0}^{60°} (T - T_{mean})\, d\theta = \int_{0}^{60°} (5000 + 1500 \sin 3\theta - 5000)\, d\theta$$

$$= \int_{0}^{60°} 1500 \sin 3\theta\, d\theta = \left[-\frac{1500 \cos 3\theta}{3} \right]_{0}^{60°} = 1000 \text{ N-m}$$

We know that maximum fluctuation of energy (ΔE),

$$1000 = I.\omega^2.C_S = 1000 \times (31.42)^2 \times C_S = 987\,216\ C_S$$

$\therefore$ $\qquad C_S = 1000 / 987\,216 = 0.001 \text{ or } 0.1\% \textbf{ Ans.}$

(ii) When resisting torque is (5000 + 600 sin θ) N-m

The turning moment diagram is shown in Fig. 16.16. Since at points B and C, the torque exerted on the shaft is equal to the mean resisting torque on the flywheel, therefore

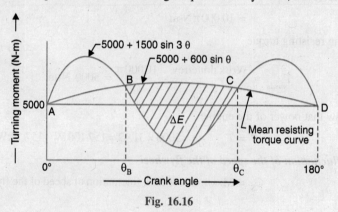

Fig. 16.16

$5000 + 1500 \sin 3\theta = 5000 + 600 \sin \theta$ or $2.5 \sin 3\theta = \sin \theta$

$2.5 (3 \sin \theta - 4 \sin^3 \theta) = \sin \theta$ ...($\because \sin 3\theta = 3 \sin \theta - 4 \sin^3 \theta$)

$3 - 4 \sin^2\theta = 0.4$ ...(Dividing by 2.5 sin θ)

$$\sin^2 \theta = \frac{3 - 0.4}{4} = 0.65 \quad \text{or} \quad \sin \theta = 0.8062$$

$\therefore \qquad \theta = 53.7° \quad \text{or} \quad 126.3° \quad i.e. \quad \theta_B = 53.7°, \text{ and } \theta_C = 126.3°$

∴ Maximum fluctuation of energy,

$$*\Delta E = \int_{53.7°}^{126.3°} \left[(5000 + 1500 \sin 3\theta) - (5000 + 600 \sin \theta) \right] d\theta$$

$$= \int_{53.7°}^{126.3°} (1500 \sin 3\theta - 600 \sin \theta) d\theta = \left[-\frac{1500 \cos 3\theta}{3} + 600 \cos \theta \right]_{53.7°}^{126.3°}$$

$$= -1656 \text{ N-m}$$

We know that maximum fluctuation of energy (ΔE),

$$1656 = I.\omega^2.C_S = 1000 \times (31.42)^2 \times C_S = 987\,216\, C_S$$

$\therefore \qquad C_S = 1656 / 987\,216 = 0.00\,168 \quad \text{or} \quad 0.168\% \text{ **Ans.**}$

16.11. Dimensions of the Flywheel Rim

Consider a rim of the flywheel as shown in Fig. 16.17.

Let D = Mean diameter of rim in metres,

R = Mean radius of rim in metres,

A = Cross-sectional area of rim in m^2,

ρ = Density of rim material in kg/m^3,

N = Speed of the flywheel in r.p.m.,

ω = Angular velocity of the flywheel in rad/s,

v = Linear velocity at the mean radius in m/s
$= \omega.R = \pi D.N/60$, and

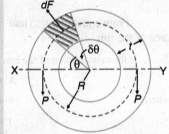

Fig. 16.17. Rim of a flywheel.

σ = Tensile stress or hoop stress in N/m^2 due to the centrifugal force.

Consider a small element of the rim as shown shaded in Fig. 16.17. Let it subtends an angle $\delta\theta$ at the centre of the flywheel.

Volume of the small element

$$= A \times R.\delta\theta$$

∴ Mass of the small element

$$dm = \text{Density} \times \text{volume} = \rho.A.R.\delta\theta$$

and centrifugal force on the element, acting radially outwards,

$$dF = dm.\omega^2.R = \rho.A.R^2.\omega^2.\delta\theta$$

---

* Since the fluctuation of energy is negative, therefore it is shown below the mean resisting torque curve, in Fig. 16.16.

Vertical component of dF

$$= dF.\sin\theta = \rho.A.R^2.\omega^2.\delta\theta.\sin\theta$$

∴ Total vertical upward force tending to burst the rim across the diameter XY.

$$= \rho.A.R^2.\omega^2 \int_0^\pi \sin\theta.d\theta = \rho.A.R^2.\omega^2 \left[-\cos\theta \right]_0^\pi$$

$$= 2\rho.A.R^2.\omega^2 \qquad \qquad \dots (i)$$

This vertical upward force will produce tensile stress or hoop stress (also called centrifugal stress or circumferential stress), and it is resisted by $2P$, such that

$$2P = 2\,\sigma.A \qquad \qquad \dots (ii)$$

Equating equations (i) and (ii),

$$2.\rho.A.R^2.\omega^2 = 2\sigma.A$$

or

$$\sigma = \rho.R^2.\omega^2 = \rho.v^2 \qquad \qquad \dots(\because v = \omega.R)$$

∴

$$v = \sqrt{\frac{\sigma}{\rho}} \qquad \qquad \dots(iii)$$

We know that mass of the rim,

$$m = \text{Volume} \times \text{density} = \pi\,D.A.\rho$$

∴

$$A = \frac{m}{\pi.D.\rho} \qquad \qquad \dots(iv)$$

From equations (iii) and (iv), we may find the value of the mean radius and cross-sectional area of the rim.

Note: If the cross-section of the rim is a rectangular, then

$$A = b \times t$$

where

$$b = \text{Width of the rim, and}$$

$$t = \text{Thickness of the rim.}$$

Example 16.14. *The turning moment diagram for a multi-cylinder engine has been drawn to a scale of 1 mm to 500 N-m torque and 1 mm to 6° of crank displacement. The intercepted areas between output torque curve and mean resistance line taken in order from one end, in sq. mm are*

– 30, + 410, – 280, + 320, – 330, + 250, – 360, + 280, – 260 sq. mm, when the engine is running at 800 r.p.m.

The engine has a stroke of 300 mm and the fluctuation of speed is not to exceed ± 2% of the mean speed. Determine a suitable diameter and cross-section of the flywheel rim for a limiting value of the safe centrifugal stress of 7 MPa. The material density may be assumed as 7200 kg/m³. The width of the rim is to be 5 times the thickness.

Solution. Given : $N = 800$ r.p.m. or $\omega = 2\pi \times 800 / 60 = 83.8$ rad/s; *Stroke = 300 mm ; $\sigma = 7$ MPa $= 7 \times 10^6$ N/m² ; $\rho = 7200$ kg/m³

Since the fluctuation of speed is ± 2% of mean speed, therefore total fluctuation of speed,

$$\omega_1 - \omega_2 = 4\% \ \omega = 0.04\ \omega$$

---

* Superfluous data.

and coefficient of fluctuation of speed,

$$C_S = \frac{\omega_1 - \omega_2}{\omega} = 0.04$$

Diameter of the flywheel rim

Let D = Diameter of the flywheel rim in metres, and

v = Peripheral velocity of the flywheel rim in m/s.

We know that centrifugal stress (σ),

$$7 \times 10^6 = \rho.v^2 = 7200\ v^2 \quad \text{or} \quad v^2 = 7 \times 10^6 / 7200 = 972.2$$

$\therefore$ $v = 31.2$ m/s

We know that $v = \pi\ D.N/60$

$\therefore$ $D = v \times 60 / \pi\ N = 31.2 \times 60/\pi \times 800 = 0.745$ m **Ans.**

Cross-section of the flywheel rim

Let t = Thickness of the flywheel rim in metres, and

b = Width of the flywheel rim in metres = $5\ t$ ...(Given)

$\therefore$ Cross-sectional area of flywheel rim,

$$A = b.t = 5\ t \times t = 5\ t^2$$

First of all, let us find the mass (m) of the flywheel rim. The turning moment diagram is shown in Fig 16.18.

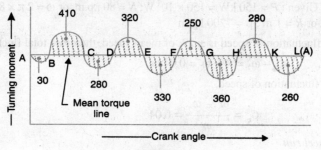

Fig. 16.18

Since the turning moment scale is 1 mm = 500 N-m and crank angle scale is 1 mm = 6° = $\pi /30$ rad, therefore

1 mm² on the turning moment diagram

$$= 500 \times \pi / 30 = 52.37\ \text{N-m}$$

Let the energy at $A = E$, then referring to Fig. 16.18,

Energy at $B = E - 30$ ...(Minimum energy)

Energy at $C = E - 30 + 410 = E + 380$

Energy at $D = E + 380 - 280 = E + 100$

Energy at $E = E + 100 + 320 = E + 420$ ...(Maximum energy)

Energy at $F = E + 420 - 330 = E + 90$

Energy at $G = E + 90 + 250 = E + 340$

Energy at $H = E + 340 - 360 = E - 20$

Energy at $K = E - 20 + 280 = E + 260$

Energy at $L = E + 260 - 260 = E =$ Energy at A

We know that maximum fluctuation of energy,

$$\Delta E = \text{Maximum energy} - \text{Minimum energy}$$

$$= (E + 420) - (E - 30) = 450 \text{ mm}^2$$

$$= 450 \times 52.37 = 23\,566 \text{ N-m}$$

We also know that maximum fluctuation of energy (ΔE),

$$23\,566 = m.v^2.C_S = m \times (31.2)^2 \times 0.04 = 39\,m$$

$\therefore$ $\qquad m = 23566 / 39 = 604 \text{ kg}$

We know that mass of the flywheel rim (m),

$$604 = \text{Volume} \times \text{density} = \pi\,D.A.\rho$$

$$= \pi \times 0.745 \times 5t^2 \times 7200 = 84\,268\,t^2$$

$\therefore$ $\qquad t^2 = 604 / 84\,268 = 0.007\,17 \text{ m}^2 \text{ or } t = 0.085 \text{ m} = 85 \text{ mm Ans.}$

and $\qquad b = 5t = 5 \times 85 = 425 \text{ mm Ans.}$

Example 16.15. *A single cylinder double acting steam engine develops 150 kW at a mean speed of 80 r.p.m. The coefficient of fluctuation of energy is 0.1 and the fluctuation of speed is ± 2% of mean speed. If the mean diameter of the flywheel rim is 2 metre and the hub and spokes provide 5% of the rotational inertia of the flywheel, find the mass and cross-sectional area of the flywheel rim. Assume the density of the flywheel material (which is cast iron) as 7200 kg/m³.*

Solution. Given : $P = 150 \text{ kW} = 150 \times 10^3 \text{ W}$; $N = 80$ r.p.m. or $\omega = 2\,\pi \times 80\,/60 = 8.4$ rad/s; $C_E = 0.1$; $D = 2$ m or $R = 1$ m ; $\rho = 7200$ kg/m³

Since the fluctuation of speed is ± 2% of mean speed, therefore total fluctuation of speed,

$$\omega_1 - \omega_2 = 4\%\ \omega = 0.04\ \omega$$

and coefficient of fluctuation of speed,

$$C_S = \frac{\omega_1 - \omega_2}{\omega} = 0.04$$

Mass of the flywheel rim

Let $\qquad m = $ Mass of the flywheel rim in kg, and

$\qquad I = $ Mass moment of inertia of the flywheel in kg-m².

We know that work done per cycle

$$= P \times 60/N = 150 \times 10^3 \times 60 / 80 = 112.5 \times 10^3 \text{ N-m}$$

and maximum fluctuation of energy,

$$\Delta E = \text{Work done /cycle} \times C_E = 112.5 \times 10^3 \times 0.1 = 11\,250 \text{ N-m}$$

We also know that maximum fluctuation of energy (ΔE),

$$11\,250 = I.\omega^2.C_S = I \times (8.4)^2 \times 0.04 = 2.8224\,I$$

$\therefore$ $\qquad I = 11\,250 / 2.8224 = 3986 \text{ kg-m}^2$

Since the hub and spokes provide 5% of the rotational inertia of the flywheel, therefore, mass moment of inertia of the flywheel rim (I_{rim}) will be 95% of the flywheel, *i.e.*

$$I_{rim} = 0.95\,I = 0.95 \times 3986 = 3787 \text{ kg-m}^2$$

and

$$I_{rim} = m.k^2 \quad \text{or} \quad {}^*m = \frac{I_{rim}}{k^2} = \frac{3787}{1^2} = 3787 \text{ kg} \text{ Ans.} \qquad \dots (\because k = R)$$

Cross-sectional area of the flywheel rim

Let $\qquad A$ = Cross-sectional area of flywheel rim in m^2.

We know that the mass of the flywheel (m),

$$3787 = 2\pi R \times A \times \rho = 2\pi \times 1 \times A \times 7200 = 45\,245\,A$$

$\therefore \qquad\qquad A = 3787/45\,245 = 0.084 \text{ m}^2 \text{ Ans.}$

Example 16.16. *A multi-cylinder engine is to run at a speed of 600 r.p.m. On drawing the turning moment diagram to a scale of 1 mm = 250 N-m and 1 mm = 3°, the areas above and below the mean torque line in mm² are : + 160, – 172, + 168, – 191, + 197, – 162*

The speed is to be kept within ± 1% of the mean speed of the engine. Calculate the necessary moment of inertia of the flywheel. Determine the suitable dimensions of a rectangular flywheel rim if the breadth is twice its thickness. The density of the cast iron is 7250 kg/m³ and its hoop stress is 6 MPa. Assume that the rim contributes 92% of the flywheel effect.

Solution. Given : N = 600 r.p.m. or $\omega = 2\pi \times 600/60 = 62.84$ rad /s; ρ = 7250 kg/m³; σ = 6 MPa = 6×10^6 N/m²

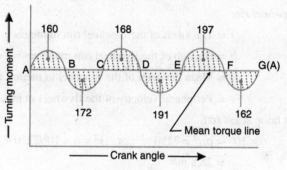

Fig. 16.19

Since the fluctuation of speed is ± 1% of mean speed, therefore, total fluctuation of speed,

$$\omega_1 - \omega_2 = 2\% \, \omega = 0.02 \, \omega$$

and coefficient of fluctuation of speed,

$$C_S = \frac{\omega_1 - \omega_2}{\omega} = 0.02$$

Moment of inertia of the flywheel

Let $\qquad I$ = Moment of inertia of the flywheel in kg-m².

The turning moment diagram is shown in Fig. 16.19. The turning moment scale is 1 mm = 250 N-m and crank angle scale is 1 mm = 3° = π /60 rad, therefore,

1 mm² of turning moment diagram

$$= 250 \times \pi /60 = 13.1 \text{ N-m}$$

---

* The mass of the flywheel rim (m) may also be obtained by using the following relation:

$$\Delta E_{rim} = 0.95 \, (\Delta E) = 0.95 \times 11\,250 = 10\,687.5 \text{ N-m}$$

and $\qquad \Delta E_{rim} = m.k^2.\omega^2.C_S = m\,(1)^2 \times (8.4)^2 \times 0.04 = 2.8224 \, m$

$\therefore \qquad m = (\Delta E)_{rim} / 2.8224 = 10\,687.5 / 2.8224 = 3787 \text{ kg}$

Let the total energy at $A = E$. Therefore from Fig. 16.19, we find that

Energy at $B = E + 160$

Energy at $C = E + 160 - 172 = E - 12$

Energy at $D = E - 12 + 168 = E + 156$

Energy at $E = E + 156 - 191 = E - 35$ ... (**Minimum energy**)

Energy at $F = E - 35 + 197 = E + 162$ ... (**Maximum energy**)

Energy at $G = E + 162 - 162 = E =$ Energy at A

We know that maximum fluctuation of energy,

$$\Delta E = \text{Maximum energy} - \text{Minimum energy}$$
$$= (E + 162) - (E - 35) = 197 \text{ mm}^2$$
$$= 197 \times 13.1 = 2581 \text{ N-m}$$

We also know that maximum fluctuation of energy (ΔE),

$$2581 = I.\omega^2.C_S = I \times (62.84)^2 \times 0.02 = 79 \, I$$

∴ $\qquad I = 2581/79 = 32.7 \text{ kg-m}^2$ **Ans.**

Dimensions of the flywheel rim

Let $\qquad t$ = Thickness of the flywheel rim in metres,

$\qquad b$ = Breadth of the flywheel rim in metres = $2\,t$ ... (Given)

$\qquad D$ = Mean diameter of the flywheel in metres, and

$\qquad v$ = Peripheral velocity of the flywheel in m/s.

We know that hoop stress (σ),

$$6 \times 10^6 = \rho.v^2 = 7250 \, v^2 \quad \text{or} \quad v^2 = 6 \times 10^6/7250 = 827.6$$

∴ $\qquad v = 28.8 \text{ m/s}$

We know that $\qquad v = \pi DN/60, \quad \text{or} \quad D = v \times 60 \,/\, \pi N = 28.8 \times 60/\pi \times 600 = 0.92 \text{ m}$

Now, let us find the mass (m) of the flywheel rim. Since the rim contributes 92% of the flywheel effect, therefore maximum fluctuation of energy of rim,

$$\Delta E_{rim} = 0.92 \times \Delta E = 0.92 \times 2581 = 2375 \text{ N-m}$$

We know that maximum fluctuation of energy of rim (ΔE_{rim}),

$$2375 = m.v^2.C_S = m \times (28.8)^2 \times 0.02 = 16.6 \, m$$

∴ $\qquad m = 2375/16.6 = 143 \text{ kg}$

Also $\qquad m$ = Volume × density = $\pi D.A.\rho = \pi D.b.t.\rho$

∴ $\qquad 143 = \pi \times 0.92 \times 2\,t \times t \times 7250 = 41\,914 \, t^2$

$$t^2 = 143 \,/\, 41\,914 = 0.0034 \text{ m}^2$$

or $\qquad t = 0.0584 \text{ m} = 58.4 \text{ mm}$ **Ans.**

and $\qquad b = 2\,t = 116.8 \text{ mm}$ **Ans.**

Example 16.17. *The turning moment diagram of a four stroke engine may be assumed for the sake of simplicity to be represented by four triangles in each stroke. The areas of these triangles are as follows:*

Suction stroke = 5×10^{-5} m^2; Compression stroke = 21×10^{-5} m^2; Expansion stroke = 85×10^{-5} m^2; Exhaust stroke = 8×10^{-5} m^2.

All the areas excepting expanssion stroke are negative. Each m^2 of area represents 14 MN-m of work.

Assuming the resisting torque to be constant, determine the moment of inertia of the flywheel to keep the speed between 98 r.p.m. and 102 r.p.m. Also find the size of a rim-type flywheel based on the minimum material criterion, given that density of flywheel material is 8150 kg/m^3 ; the allowable tensile stress of the flywheel material is 7.5 MPa. The rim cross-section is rectangular, one side being four times the length of the other.

Solution. Given: $a_1 = 5 \times 10^{-5}$ m^2; $a_2 = 21 \times 10^{-5}$ m^2; $a_3 = 85 \times 10^{-5}$ m^2; $a_4 = 8 \times 10^{-5}$ m^2; $N_2 = 98$ r.p.m.; $N_1 = 102$ r.p.m.; $\rho = 8150$ kg/m^3; $\sigma = 7.5$ MPa $= 7.5 \times 10^6$ N/m^2

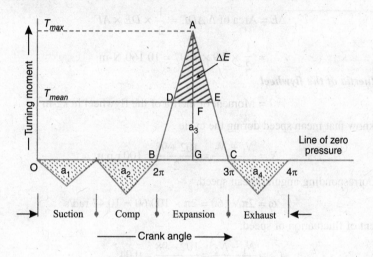

Fig. 16.20

The turning moment-crank angle diagram for a four stroke engine is shown in Fig. 16.20. The areas below the zero line of pressure are taken as negative while the areas above the zero line of pressure are taken as positive.

$\therefore$ Net area $= a_3 - (a_1 + a_2 + a_4)$

$\qquad = 85 \times 10^5 - (5 \times 10^5 + 21 \times 10^{-5} + 8 \times 10^{-5}) = 51 \times 10^{-5}$ m^2

Since $1 m^2 = 14$ MN-m $= 14 \times 10^6$ N-m of work, therefore

Net work done per cycle

$\qquad = 51 \times 10^{-5} \times 14 \times 10^6 = 7140$ N-m $\qquad \qquad ...(i)$

We also know that work done per cycle

$\qquad = T_{mean} \times 4\pi$ N-m $\qquad \qquad ...(ii)$

From equations (i) and (ii),

$\qquad T_{mean} = FG = 7140 / 4\pi = 568$ N-m

Work done during expansion stroke

$\qquad = a_3 \times$ Work scale $= 85 \times 10^{-5} \times 14 \times 10^6 = 11\,900$ N-m $\qquad ...(iii)$

Also, work done during expansion stroke

$$= \frac{1}{2} \times BC \times AG = = \frac{1}{2} \times \pi \times AG = 1.571 \, AG \qquad \text{...}(iv)$$

From equations (iii) and (iv),

$$AG = 11\,900/1.571 = 7575 \text{ N-m}$$

∴ Excess torque $= AF = AG - FG = 7575 - 568 = 7007$ N-m

Now from similar triangles ADE and ABC,

$$\frac{DE}{BC} = \frac{AF}{AG} \qquad \text{or} \qquad DE = \frac{AF}{AG} \times BC = \frac{7007}{7575} \times \pi = 2.9 \text{ rad}$$

We know that maximum fluctuation of energy,

$$\Delta E = \text{Area of } \Delta ADE = \frac{1}{2} \times DE \times AF$$

$$= \frac{1}{2} \times 2.9 \times 7007 = 10\,160 \text{ N-m}$$

Moment of Inertia of the flywheel

Let $I = $ Moment of inertia of the flywheel in kg-m^2.

We know that mean speed during the cycle

$$N = \frac{N_1 + N_2}{2} = \frac{102 + 98}{2} = 100 \text{ r.p.m.}$$

∴ Corresponding angular mean speed,

$$\omega = 2\pi N / 60 = 2\pi \times 100/60 = 10.47 \text{ rad/s}$$

and coefficient of fluctuation of speed,

$$C_S = \frac{N_1 - N_2}{N} = \frac{102 - 98}{100} = 0.04$$

We know that maximum fluctuation of energy (ΔE),

$$10\,160 = I.\omega^2.C_S = I\,(10.47)^2 \times 0.04 = 4.385 \, I$$

∴ $I = 10160 / 4.385 = 2317 \text{ kg-m}^2$ **Ans.**

Size of flywheel

Let $t = $ Thickness of the flywheel rim in metres,

$b = $ Width of the flywheel rim in metres $= 4\,t$ ...(Given)

$D = $ Mean diameter of the flywheel in metres, and

$v = $ Peripheral velocity of the flywheel in m/s.

We know that hoop stress (σ),

$$7.5 \times 10^6 = \rho \, . \, v^2 = 8150 \, v^2$$

∴ $$v^2 = \frac{7.5 \times 10^6}{8150} = 920 \text{ or } v = 30.3 \text{ m/s}$$

and $$v = \pi DN/60 \text{ or } D = v \times 60/\pi N = 30.3 \times 60/\pi \times 100 = 5.786 \text{ m}$$

Now let us find the mass (m) of the flywheel rim. We know that maximum fluctuation of energy (ΔE),

$$10\ 160 = m.v^2\ C_S = m \times (30.3)^2 \times 0.04 = 36.72\ m$$

$$\therefore \qquad m = 10\ 160/36.72 = 276.7\ \text{kg}$$

Also

$$m = \text{Volume} \times \text{density} = \pi D \times A \times \rho = \pi D \times b \times t \times \rho$$

$$276.7 = \pi \times 5.786 \times 4t \times t \times 8150 = 592\ 655\ t^2$$

$$\therefore \qquad t^2 = 276.7/592\ 655 = 4.67 \times 10^{-4}\ \text{or}\ t = 0.0216\ \text{m} = 21.6\ \text{mm}\ \textbf{Ans.}$$

and

$$b = 4t = 4 \times 21.6 = 86.4\ \text{mm}\ \textbf{Ans.}$$

Example 16.18. *An otto cycle engine develops 50 kW at 150 r.p.m. with 75 explosions per minute. The change of speed from the commencement to the end of power stroke must not exceed 0.5% of mean on either side. Find the mean diameter of the flywheel and a suitable rim cross-section having width four times the depth so that the hoop stress does not exceed 4 MPa. Assume that the flywheel stores 16/15 times the energy stored by the rim and the work done during power stroke is 1.40 times the work done during the cycle. Density of rim material is 7200 kg/m³.*

Solution. Given : $P = 50\ \text{kW} = 50 \times 10^3\ \text{W}$; $N = 150$ r.p.m. or $\omega = 2\ \pi \times 150/60 = 15.71$ rad/s; $n = 75$; $\sigma = 4\ \text{MPa} = 4 \times 10^6\ \text{N/m}^2$; $\rho = 7200\ \text{kg/m}^3$

First of all, let us find the mean torque (T_{mean}) transmitted by the engine or flywheel. We know that the power transmitted (P),

$$50 \times 10^3 = T_{mean} \times \omega = T_{mean} \times 15.71$$

$$\therefore \qquad T_{mean} = 50 \times 10^3/15.71 = 3182.7\ \text{N-m}$$

Since the explosions per minute are equal to $N/2$, therefore, the engine is a four stroke cycle engine. The turning moment diagram of a four stroke engine is shown in Fig. 16.21.

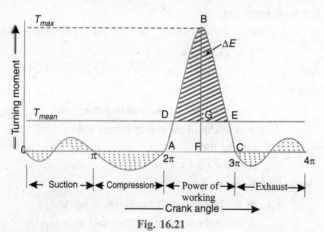

Fig. 16.21

We know that *work done per cycle

$$= T_{mean} \times \theta = 3182.7 \times 4\pi = 40\ 000\ \text{N-m}$$

---

* The work done per cycle for a four stroke engine is also given by

$$\text{Work done per cycle} = \frac{P \times 60}{\text{Number of explosions/min}} = \frac{P \times 60}{n} = \frac{50 \times 10^3 \times 60}{75} = 40000\ \text{N-m}$$

∴ Workdone during power or working stroke

$$= 1.4 \times \text{work done per cycle} \qquad \text{....(Given)}$$
$$= 1.4 \times 40\,000 = 56\,000 \text{ N-m} \qquad ...(i)$$

The workdone during power stroke is shown by a triangle ABC in Fig. 16.20, in which base $AC = \pi$ radians and height $BF = T_{max}$.

∴ Work done during working stroke

$$= \frac{1}{2} \times \pi \times T_{max} = 1.571\, T_{max} \qquad ...(ii)$$

From equations (i) and (ii), we have

$$T_{max} = 56\,000/1.571 = 35\,646 \text{ N-m}$$

We know that the excess torque,

$$T_{excess} = BG = BF - FG = T_{max} - T_{mean} = 35\,646 - 3182.7 = 32\,463.3 \text{ N-m}$$

Now, from similar triangles BDE and ABC,

$$\frac{DE}{AC} = \frac{BG}{BF} \quad \text{or} \quad DE = \frac{BG}{BF} \times AC = \frac{32\,463.3}{35\,646} \times \pi = 0.9107\,\pi$$

We know that maximum fluctuation of energy,

$$\Delta E = \text{Area of triangle } BDE = \frac{1}{2} \times DE \times BG$$

$$= \frac{1}{2} \times 0.9107\,\pi \times 32\,463.3 = 46\,445 \text{ N-m}$$

Mean diameter of the flywheel

Let $\qquad\qquad D$ = Mean diameter of the flywheel in metres, and

$\qquad\qquad v$ = Peripheral velocity of the flywheel in m/s.

We know that hoop stress (σ),

$$4 \times 10^6 = \rho.v^2 = 7200\, v^2 \quad \text{or} \quad v^2 = 4 \times 10^6/7200 = 556$$

∴ $\qquad\qquad v = 23.58 \text{ m/s}$

We know that $\qquad v = \pi\, DN/60 \quad \text{or} \quad D = v \times 60/N = 23.58 \times 60/\pi \times 150 = 3 \text{ m } \textbf{Ans.}$

Cross-sectional dimensions of the rim

Let $\qquad\qquad t$ = Thickness of the rim in metres, and

$\qquad\qquad b$ = Width of the rim in metres = $4\, t$ $\qquad\qquad$ ...(Given)

∴ Cross-sectional area of the rim,

$$A = b \times t = 4\, t \times t = 4\, t^2$$

First of all, let us find the mass of the flywheel rim.

Let $\qquad\qquad m$ = Mass of the flywheel rim in kg, and

$\qquad\qquad E$ = Total energy of the flywheel in N-m.

Since the fluctuation of speed is 0.5% of the mean speed on either side, therefore total fluctuation of speed,

$$N_2 - N_1 = 1\% \text{ of mean speed} = 0.01\, N$$

and coefficient of fluctuation of speed,

$$C_s = \frac{N_1 - N_2}{N} = 0.01$$

We know that the maximum fluctuation of energy (ΔE),

$$46\,445 = E \times 2C_S = E \times 2 \times 0.01 = 0.02\,E$$

$$\therefore \quad E = 46\,445/0.02 = 2322 \times 10^3 \text{ N-m}$$

Since the energy stored by the flywheel is $\dfrac{16}{15}$ times the energy stored by the rim, therefore, the energy of the rim,

$$E_{rim} = \frac{15}{16}E = \frac{15}{16} \times 232 \times 10^3 = 2177 \times 10^3 \text{ N-m}$$

We know that energy of the rim (E_{rim}),

$$2177 \times 10^3 = \frac{1}{2} \times m \times v^2 = m\,(23.58)^2 = 278\,m$$

$$\therefore \quad m = 2177 \times 10^3/278 = 7831 \text{ kg}$$

We also know that mass of the flywheel rim (m),

$$7831 = \pi D \times A \times \rho = \pi \times 3 \times 4t^2 \times 7200 = 271\,469t^2$$

$$\therefore \quad t^2 = 7831/271\,469 = 0.0288 \text{ or } t = 0.17\,\text{m} = 170\,\text{mm Ans.}$$

and $\qquad\qquad b = 4\,t = 4 \times 170 = 680 \text{ mm Ans.}$

16.12. Flywheel in Punching Press

We have discussed in Art. 16.8 that the function of a flywheel in an engine is to reduce the fluctuations of speed, when the load on the crankshaft is constant and the input torque varies during the cycle. The flywheel can also be used to perform the same function when the torque is constant and the load varies during the cycle. Such an application is found in punching press or in a rivetting machine. A punching press is shown diagrammatically in Fig. 16.22. The crank is driven by a motor which supplies constant torque and the punch is at the position of the slider in a slider-crank mechanism. From Fig. 16.22, we see that the load acts only during the rotation of the crank from $\theta = \theta_1$ to $\theta = \theta_2$, when the actual punching takes place and the load is zero for the rest of the cycle. Unless a flywheel is used, the speed of the crankshaft will increase too much during the rotation of crank from $\theta = \theta_2$ to $\theta = 2\pi$ or $\theta = 0$ and again from $\theta = 0$ to $\theta = \theta_1$, because there is no load while input energy continues to be supplied. On the other hand, the drop in speed of the crankshaft is very large during the rotation of crank from

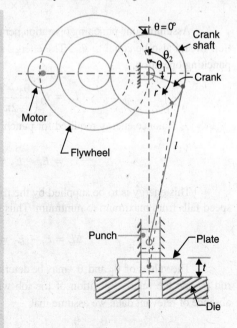

Fig. 16.22. Operation of flywheel in a punching press.

$\theta = \theta_1$ to $\theta = \theta_2$ due to much more load than the energy supplied. Thus the flywheel has to absorb excess energy available at one stage and has to make up the deficient energy at the other stage to keep the fluctuations of speed within permissible limits. This is done by choosing the suitable moment of inertia of the flywheel.

Let E_1 be the energy required for punching a hole. This energy is determined by the size of the hole punched, the thickness of the material and the physical properties of the material.

Let d_1 = Diameter of the hole punched,

t_1 = Thickness of the plate, and

τ_u = Ultimate shear stress for the plate material.

Punching press and flywheel.

∴ Maximum shear force required for punching,

$$F_S = \text{Area sheared} \times \text{Ultimate shear stress} = \pi\, d_1 .t_1\, \tau_u$$

It is assumed that as the hole is punched, the shear force decreases uniformly from maximum value to zero.

∴ Work done or energy required for punching a hole,

$$E_1 = \frac{1}{2} \times F_S \times t$$

Assuming one punching operation per revolution, the energy supplied to the shaft per revolution should also be equal to E_1. The energy supplied by the motor to the crankshaft during actual punching operation,

$$E_2 = E_1 \left(\frac{\theta_2 - \theta_1}{2\pi} \right)$$

∴ Balance energy required for punching

$$= E_1 - E_2 = E_1 - E_1 \left(\frac{\theta_2 - \theta_1}{2\pi} \right) = E_1 \left(1 - \frac{\theta_2 - \theta_1}{2\pi} \right)$$

This energy is to be supplied by the flywheel by the decrease in its kinetic energy when its speed falls from maximum to minimum. Thus maximum fluctuation of energy,

$$\Delta E = E_1 - E_2 = E_1 \left(1 - \frac{\theta_2 - \theta_1}{2\pi} \right)$$

The values of θ_1 and θ_2 may be determined only if the crank radius (r), length of connecting rod (l) and the relative position of the job with respect to the crankshaft axis are known. In the absence of relevant data, we assume that

$$\frac{\theta_2 - \theta_1}{2\pi} = \frac{t}{2s} = \frac{t}{4r}$$

where $\quad\quad\quad\quad\quad\quad\quad t$ = Thickness of the material to be punched,

$\quad\quad\quad\quad\quad\quad\quad\quad\quad s$ = Stroke of the punch = $2 \times$ Crank radius = $2\,r$.

By using the suitable relation for the maximum fluctuation of energy (ΔE) as discussed in the previous articles, we can find the mass and size of the flywheel.

Example 16.19. *A punching press is driven by a constant torque electric motor. The press is provided with a flywheel that rotates at maximum speed of 225 r.p.m. The radius of gyration of the flywheel is 0.5 m. The press punches 720 holes per hour; each punching operation takes 2 second and requires 15 kN-m of energy. Find the power of the motor and the minimum mass of the flywheel if speed of the same is not to fall below 200 r. p. m.*

Solution. Given N_1 = 225 r.p.m ; k = 0.5 m ; Hole punched = 720 per hr; E_1 = 15 kN-m = 15×10^3 N-m ; N_2 = 200 r.p.m.

Power of the motor

We know that the total energy required per second

$\quad\quad\quad\quad\quad\quad\quad$ = Energy required / hole × No. of holes / s

$\quad\quad\quad\quad\quad\quad\quad$ = $15 \times 10^3 \times 720/3600 = 3000$ N-m/s

$\therefore$ Power of the motor = 3000 W = 3 kW **Ans.** $\quad\quad\quad\quad\quad\quad$ ($\because$ 1 N-m/s = 1 W)

Minimum mass of the flywheel

Let $\quad\quad\quad\quad\quad m$ = Minimum mass of the flywheel.

Since each punching operation takes 2 seconds, therefore energy supplied by the motor in 2 seconds,

$$E_2 = 3000 \times 2 = 6000 \text{ N-m}$$

$\therefore$ Energy to be supplied by the flywheel during punching or maximum fluctuation of energy,

$$\Delta E = E_1 - E_2 = 15 \times 10^3 - 6000 = 9000 \text{ N-m}$$

Mean speed of the flywheel,

$$N = \frac{N_1 + N_2}{2} = \frac{225 + 200}{2} = 212.5 \text{ r.p.m}$$

We know that maximum fluctuation of energy (ΔE),

$$9000 = \frac{\pi^2}{900} \times m.k^2.N\,(N_1 - N_2)$$

$$= \frac{\pi^2}{900} \times m \times (0.5)^2 \times 212.5 \times (225 - 200) = 14.565\,m$$

$\therefore \quad\quad\quad\quad\quad m$ = 9000/14.565 = 618 kg **Ans.**

Example 16.20. *A machine punching 38 mm holes in 32 mm thick plate requires 7 N-m of energy per sq. mm of sheared area, and punches one hole in every 10 seconds. Calculate the power of the motor required. The mean speed of the flywheel is 25 metres per second. The punch has a stroke of 100 mm.*

Find the mass of the flywheel required, if the total fluctuation of speed is not to exceed 3% of the mean speed. Assume that the motor supplies energy to the machine at uniform rate.

Solution. Given : d = 38 mm ; t = 32 mm ; E_1 = 7 N-m/mm^2 of sheared area ; v = 25 m/s ; s = 100 mm ; $v_1 - v_2$ = 3% v = 0.03 v

Power of the motor required

We know that sheared area,

$$A = \pi d . t = \pi \times 38 \times 32 = 3820 \text{ mm}^2$$

Since the energy required to punch a hole is 7 N-m/mm² of sheared area, therefore total energy required per hole,

$$E_1 = 7 \times 3820 = 26\ 740 \text{ N-m}$$

Also the time required to punch a hole is 10 second, therefore energy required for punching work per second

$$= 26\ 740/10 = 2674 \text{ N-m/s}$$

∴ Power of the motor required

$$= 2674 \text{ W} = 2.674 \text{ kW Ans.}$$

Mass of the flywheel required

Let m = Mass of the flywheel in kg.

Since the stroke of the punch is 100 mm and it punches one hole in every 10 seconds, therefore the time required to punch a hole in a 32 mm thick plate

$$= \frac{10}{2 \times 100} \times 32 = 1.6 \text{ s}$$

∴ Energy supplied by the motor in 1.6 seconds,

$$E_2 = 2674 \times 1.6 = 4278 \text{ N-m}$$

Energy to be supplied by the flywheel during punching or the maximum fluctuation of energy,

$$\Delta E = E_1 - E_2 = 26\ 740 - 4278 = 22\ 462 \text{ N-m}$$

Coefficient of fluctuation of speed,

$$C_S = \frac{v_1 - v_2}{v} = 0.03$$

We know that maximum fluctuation of energy (ΔE),

$$22\ 462 = m.v^2 . C_S = m \times (25)^2 \times 0.03 = 18.75\ m$$

∴ $$m = 22\ 462 / 18.75 = 1198 \text{ kg Ans.}$$

Note : The value of maximum fluctuation of energy (ΔE) may also be determined as discussed in Art. 16.12. We know that energy required for one punch,

$$E_1 = 26\ 740 \text{ N-m}$$

and $$\Delta E = \left(1 - \frac{\theta_2 - \theta_1}{2\pi} \right) = E_1 \left(1 - \frac{t}{2s} \right) \qquad \dots \left(\because \frac{\theta_2 - \theta_1}{2\pi} = \frac{t}{2s} \right)$$

$$= 26\ 740 \left[1 - \frac{32}{2 \times 100} \right] = 22\ 462 \text{ N-m}$$

Example 16.21. *A riveting machine is driven by a constant torque 3 kW motor. The moving parts including the flywheel are equivalent to 150 kg at 0.6 m radius. One riveting operation takes 1 second and absorbs 10 000 N-m of energy. The speed of the flywheel is 300 r.p.m. before riveting. Find the speed immediately after riveting. How many rivets can be closed per minute?*

Solution. Given : $P = 3$ kW ; $m = 150$ kg ; $k = 0.6$ m ; $N_1 = 300$ r.p.m. or $\omega_1 = 2\pi \times 300/60 = 31.42$ rad/s

Speed of the flywheel immediately after riveting

Let ω_2 = Angular speed of the flywheel immediately after riveting.

We know that energy supplied by the motor,

$$E_2 = 3\,\text{kW} = 3000\,\text{W} = 3000\,\text{N-m/s} \qquad (\because 1\,\text{W} = 1\,\text{N-m/s})$$

But energy absorbed during one riveting operation which takes 1 second,

$$E_1 = 10\,000\,\text{N-m}$$

∴ Energy to be supplied by the flywheel for each riveting operation per second or the maximum fluctuation of energy,

$$\Delta E = E_1 - E_2 = 10\,000 - 3000 = 7000\,\text{N-m}$$

We know that maximum fluctuation of energy (ΔE),

$$7000 = \frac{1}{2} \times m.k^2\left[(\omega_1)^2 - (\omega_2)^2\right] = \frac{1}{2} \times 150 \times (0.6)^2 \times \left[(31.42)^2 - (\omega_2)^2\right]$$

$$= 27\left[987.2 - (\omega_2)^2\right]$$

∴ $(\omega_2)^2 = 987.2 - 7000/27 = 728$ or $\omega_2 = 26.98\,\text{rad/s}$

Corresponding speed in r.p.m.,

$$N_2 = 26.98 \times 60 / 2\,\pi = 257.6\,\text{r.p.m. \textbf{Ans.}}$$

Number of rivets that can be closed per minute

Since the energy absorbed by each riveting operation which takes 1 second is 10 000 N-m, therefore, number of rivets that can be closed per minute,

$$= \frac{E_2}{E_1} \times 60 = \frac{3000}{10\,000} \times 60 = 18 \text{ rivets \textbf{Ans.}}$$

Example 16.22. *A punching press is required to punch 40 mm diameter holes in a plate of 15 mm thickness at the rate of 30 holes per minute. It requires 6 N-m of energy per mm² of sheared area. If the punching takes 1/10 of a second and the r.p.m. of the flywheel varies from 160 to 140, determine the mass of the flywheel having radius of gyration of 1 metre.*

Solution. Given: $d = 40$ mm; $t = 15$ mm; No. of holes = 30 per min.; Energy required = 6 N-m/mm²; Time = 1/10 s = 0.1 s; $N_1 = 160$ r.p.m.; $N_2 = 140$ r.p.m.; $k = 1$m

We know that sheared area per hole

$$= \pi\,d.t = \pi \times 40 \times 15 = 1885\,\text{mm}^2$$

∴ Energy required to punch a hole,

$$E_1 = 6 \times 1885 = 11\,310\,\text{N-m}$$

and energy required for punching work per second

$$= \text{Energy required per hole} \times \text{No. of holes per second}$$

$$= 11\,310 \times 30/60 = 5655\,\text{N-m/s}$$

Since the punching takes 1/10 of a second, therefore, energy supplied by the motor in 1/10 second,

$$E_2 = 5655 \times 1/10 = 565.5\,\text{N-m}$$

∴ Energy to be supplied by the flywheel during punching a hole or maximum fluctuation of energy of the flywheel,

$$\Delta E = E_1 - E_2 = 11\,310 - 565.5 = 10\,744.5\,\text{N-m}$$

Mean speed of the flywheel,

$$N = \frac{N_1 + N_2}{2} = \frac{160 + 140}{2} = 150 \text{ r.p.m.}$$

We know that maximum fluctuation of energy (ΔE),

$$10\,744.5 = \frac{\pi^2}{900} \times m.k^2\,N\,(N_1 - N_2)$$

$$= 0.011 \times m \times 1^2 \times 150\,(160 - 140) = 33\,m$$

∴ $m = 10744.5 / 33 = 327 \text{ kg } \textbf{Ans.}$

Example 16.23. *A punching machine makes 25 working strokes per minute and is capable of punching 25 mm diameter holes in 18 mm thick steel plates having an ultimate shear strength 300 MPa. The punching operation takes place during 1/10th of a revolution of the crankshaft.*

Estimate the power needed for the driving motor, assuming a mechanical efficiency of 95 percent. Determine suitable dimensions for the rim cross-section of the flywheel, having width equal to twice thickness. The flywheel is to revolve at 9 times the speed of the crankshaft. The permissible coefficient of fluctuation of speed is 0.1.

The flywheel is to be made of cast iron having a working stress (tensile) of 6 MPa and density of 7250 kg/m³. The diameter of the flywheel must not exceed 1.4 m owing to space restrictions. The hub and the spokes may be assumed to provide 5% of the rotational inertia of the wheel.

Solution. Given : $n = 25$; $d_1 = 25$ mm $= 0.025$ m; $t_1 = 18$ mm $= 0.018$ m ; $\tau_u = 300$ MPa $= 300 \times 10^6$ N/m² ; $\eta_m = 95\% = 0.95$; $C_S = 0.1$; $\sigma = 6$ MPa $= 6 \times 10^6$ N/m²; $\rho = 7250$ kg/m³; $D = 1.4$ m or $R = 0.7$ m

Power needed for the driving motor

We know that the area of plate sheared ,

$$A_S = \pi d_1 \times t_1 = \pi \times 0.025 \times 0.018 = 1414 \times 10^{-6} \text{ m}^2$$

∴ Maximum shearing force required for punching,

$$F_S = A_S \times \tau_u = 1414 \times 10^{-6} \times 300 \times 10^6 = 424\,200\,\text{N}$$

and energy required per stroke

$$= \text{Average shear force} \times \text{Thickness of plate}$$

$$= \frac{1}{2} \times F_S \times t_1 = \frac{1}{2} \times 424\,200 \times 0.018 = 3817.8 \text{ N-m}$$

∴ Energy required per min

$$= \text{Energy/stroke} \times \text{No. of working strokes/min}$$

$$= 3817.8 \times 25 = 95\,450 \text{ N-m}$$

We know that the power needed for the driving motor

$$= \frac{\text{Energy required per min}}{60 \times \eta_m} = \frac{95\,450}{60 \times 0.95} = 1675 \text{ W} = 1.675 \text{ kW } \textbf{Ans.}$$

Dimensions for the rim cross-section

Let t = Thickness of rim in metres, and

b = Width of rim in metres = $2t$ ... (Given)

∴ Cross-sectional area of rim,

$$A = b \times t = 2t \times t = 2t^2$$

Since the punching operation takes place (*i.e.* energy is consumed) during 1/10th of a revolution of the crankshaft, therefore during 9/10th of the revolution of a crankshaft, the energy is stored in the flywheel.

∴ Maximum fluctuation of energy,

$$\Delta E = \frac{9}{10} \times \text{Energy/stroke} = \frac{9}{10} \times 3817.8 = 3436 \, \text{N-m}$$

Let m = Mass of the flywheel in kg.

Since the hub and the spokes provide 5% of the rotational inertia of the wheel, therefore the maximum fluctuation of energy provided by the flywheel by the rim will be 95%.

∴ Maximum fluctuation of energy provided by the rim,

$$\Delta E_{rim} = 0.95 \times \Delta E = 0.95 \times 3436 = 3264 \, \text{N-m}$$

Since the flywheel is to revolve at 9 times the speed of the crankshaft and there are 25 working strokes per minute, therefore, mean speed of the flywheel,

$$N = 9 \times 25 = 225 \, \text{r.p.m.}$$

and mean angular speed,

$$\omega = 2\pi \times 225/60 = 23.56 \, \text{rad/s}$$

We know that maximum fluctuation of energy $\left(\Delta E_{rim}\right)$,

$$3264 = m.R^2.\omega^2.C_S = m \times (0.7)^2 \times (23.56)^2 \times 0.1 = 27.2m$$

∴ $m = 3264/27.2 = 120 \, \text{kg}$

We also know that mass of the flywheel (m),

$$120 = \pi D \times A \times \rho = \pi \times 1.4 \times 2t^2 \times 7250 = 63\,782\,t^2$$

∴ $t^2 = 120/63\,782 = 0.001\,88$ or $t = 0.044 \, \text{m} = 44 \, \text{mm}$ **Ans.**

and $b = 2t = 2 \times 44 = 88 \, \text{mm}$ **Ans.**

EXERCISES

1. An engine flywheel has a mass of 6.5 tonnes and the radius of gyration is 2 m. If the maximum and minimum speeds are 120 r. p. m. and 118 r. p. m. respectively, find maximum fluctuation of energy.   [Ans. 67. 875 kN-m]

2. A vertical double acting steam engine develops 75 kW at 250 r.p.m. The maximum fluctuation of energy is 30 per cent of the work done per stroke. The maximum and minimum speeds are not to vary more than 1 per cent on either side of the mean speed. Find the mass of the flywheel required, if the radius of gyration is 0.6 m.   [Ans. 547 kg]

3. In a turning moment diagram, the areas above and below the mean torque line taken in order are 4400, 1150, 1300 and 4550 mm² respectively. The scales of the turning moment diagram are:

   Turning moment, 1 mm = 100 N-m ; Crank angle, 1 mm = 1°

   Find the mass of the flywheel required to keep the speed between 297 and 303 r.p.m., if the radius of gyration is 0.525 m.   [Ans. 417 kg]

4. The turning moment diagram for a multicylinder engine has been drawn to a scale of 1 mm = 4500 N-m vertically and 1 mm = 2.4° horizontally. The intercepted areas between output torque curve and mean resistance line taken in order from one end are 342, 23, 245, 303, 115, 232, 227, 164 mm², when the engine is running at 150 r.p.m. If the mass of the flywheel is 1000 kg and the total fluctuation of speed does not exceed 3% of the mean speed, find the minimum value of the radius of gyration.   [Ans. 1.034 m]

5. An engine has three single-acting cylinders whose cranks are spaced at 120° to each other. The turning moment diagram for each cylinder consists of a triangle having the following values:

Angle	0°	60°	180°	180° – 360°
Torque (N-m)	0	200	0	0

Find the mean torque and the moment of inertia of the flywheel to keep the speed within 180 ± 3 r.p.m.
[Ans. 150 N-m; 1.22 kg-m²]

6. The turning moment diagram for a four stroke gas engine may be assumed for simplicity to be represented by four triangles, the areas of which from the line of zero pressure are as follows:

Expansion stroke = 3550 mm²; exhaust stroke = 500 mm²; suction stroke = 350 mm²; and compression stroke = 1400 mm². Each mm² represents 3 N-m.

Assuming the resisting moment to be uniform, find the mass of the rim of a flywheel required to keep the mean speed 200 r.p.m. within ± 2%. The mean radius of the rim may be taken as 0.75 m. Also determine the crank positions for the maximum and minimum speeds.
[Ans. 983 kg; 4° and 176° from I. D. C]

7. A single cylinder, single acting, four stroke cycle gas engine develops 20 kW at 250 r.p.m. The work done by the gases during the expansion stroke is 3 times the work done on the gases during the compression stroke. The work done on the suction and exhaust strokes may be neglected. If the flywheel has a mass of 1.5 tonnes and has a radius of gyration of 0.6m, find the cyclic fluctuation of energy and the coefficient of fluctuation of speed.

[Ans. 12.1 kN-m; 3.26%]

8. The torque exerted on the crank shaft of a two stroke engine is given by the equation:

$$T(N\text{-}m) = 14\,500 + 2300 \sin 2\theta - 1900 \cos 2\theta$$

where θ is the crank angle displacement from the inner dead centre. Assuming the resisting torque to be constant, determine: 1. The power of the engine when the speed is 150 r.p.m. ; 2. The moment of inertia of the flywheel if the speed variation is not to exceed ± 0.5% of the mean speed; and 3. The angular acceleration of the flywheel when the crank has turned through 30° from the inner dead centre. · [Ans. 228 kW; 1208 kg-m²; 0.86 rad/s²]

9. A certain machine requires a torque of $(2000 + 300 \sin \theta)$ N-m to drive it, where θ is the angle of rotation of its shaft measured from some datum. The machine is directly coupled to an electric motor developing uniform torque. The mean speed of the machine is 200 r.p.m.

Find: 1. the power of the driving electric motor, and 2. the moment of inertia of the flywheel required to be used if the fluctuation of speed is limited to ±2% .
[Ans. 41.9 kW; 34.17 kg-m²]

10. The equation of the turning moment diagram for the three crank engine is given by:

$$T (N\text{-}m) = 25\,000 - 7500 \sin 3\theta$$

where θ radians is the crank angle from inner dead centre. The moment of inertia of the flywheel is 400 kg-m² and the mean engine speed is 300 r.p.m. Calculate the power of the engine and the total percentage fluctuation of speed of the flywheel, if 1. The resisting torque is constant, and 2. The resisting torque is $(25\,000 + 3600 \sin \theta)$ N-m.
[Ans. 785 kW; 1.27%; 2.28%]

11. A single cylinder double acting steam engine delivers 185 kW at 100 r.p.m. The maximum fluctuation of energy per revolution is 15 per cent of the energy developed per revolution. The speed variation is limited to 1 per cent either way from the mean. The mean diameter of the rim is 2.4 m. Find the mass and cross-sectional dimensions of the flywheel rim when width of rim is twice the thickness. The density of flywheel material is 7200 kg/m³.

[Ans. 5270 kg; 440 mm; 220 mm]

12. A steam engine runs at 150 r.p.m. Its turning moment diagram gave the following area measurements in mm^2 taken in order above and below the mean torque line:

500, – 250, 270, – 390, 190, – 340, 270, – 250

The scale for the turning moment is 1 mm = 500 N-m, and for crank angle is 1mm = 5°.

The fluctuation of speed is not to exceed ± 1.5% of the mean, determine the cross-section of the rim of the flywheel assumed rectangular with axial dimension equal to 1.5 times the radial dimension. The hoop stress is limited to 3 MPa and the density of the material of the flywheel is 7500 kg/m^3.

[**Ans. 222 mm; 148 mm**]

13. The turning moment diagram for the engine is drawn to the following scales:

Turning moment, 1 mm = 1000 N-m and crank angle, 1 mm = 6°.

The areas above and below the mean turning moment line taken in order are : 530, 330, 380, 470, 180, 360, 350 and 280 mm^2.

The mean speed of the engine is 150 r.p.m. and the total fluctuation of speed must not exceed 3.5% of mean speed. Determine the diameter and mass of the flywheel rim, assuming that the total energy of the flywheel to be 15/14 that of rim. The peripheral velocity of the flywheel is 15 m/s. Find also the suitable cross-scetional area of the rim of the flywheel. Take density of the material of the rim as 7200 kg/m^3.

[**Ans. 1.91 m; 8063 kg; 0.1866 m^2**]

14. A single cylinder internal combustion engine working on the four stroke cycle develops 75 kW at 360 r.p.m. The fluctuation of energy can be assumed to be 0.9 times the energy developed per cycle. If the fluctuation of speed is not to exceed 1 per cent and the maximum centrifugal stress in the flywheel is to be 5.5 MPa, estimate the mean diameter and the cross-sectional area of the rim. The material of the rim has a density of 7.2 Mg/m^3.

[**Ans. 1.47 m; 0.088 m^2**]

15. A cast iron flywheel used for a four stroke I.C. engine is developing 187.5 kW at 250 r.p.m. The hoop stress developed in the flywheel is 5.2 MPa. The total fluctuation of speed is to be limited to 3% of the mean speed. If the work done during the power stroke is 1/3 times more than the average workdone during the whole cycle, find:

1. mean diameter of the flywheel, 2. mass of the flywheel and 3. cross-sectional dimensions of the rim when the width is twice the thickness. The density of cast iron may be taken as 7220 kg/m$^3.$

[**Ans 2.05m; 4561 kg; 440 mm, 220 mm**]

16. A certain machine tool does work intermittently. The machine is fitted with a flywheel of mass 200 kg and radius of gyration of 0.4 m. It runs at a speed of 400 r.p.m. between the operations. The machine is driven continuously by a motor and each operation takes 8 seconds. When the machine is doing its work, the speed drops from 400 to 250 r.p.m. Find 1. minimum power of the motor, when there are 5 operations performed per minute, and 2. energy expanded in performing each operation.

[**Ans. 4.278 kW; 51.33 kN-m**]

17. A constant torque 4 kW motor drives a riveting machine. A flywheel of mass 130 kg and radius of gyration 0.5 m is fitted to the riveting machine. Each riveting operation takes 1 second and requires 9000 N-m of energy. If the speed of the flywheel is 420 r.p.m. before riveting, find: 1. the fall in speed of the flywheel after riveting; and 2. the number of rivets fitted per hour.

[**Ans. 385.15 r.p.m.; 1600**]

18. A machine has to carry out punching operation at the rate of 10 holes per minute. It does 6 kN-m of work per mm^2 of the sheared area in cutting 25 mm diameter holes in 20 mm thick plates. A flywheel is fitted to the machine shaft which is driven by a constant torque. The fluctuation of speed is between 180 and 200 r.p.m. The actual punching takes 1.5 seconds. The frictional losses are equivalent to 1/6 of the work done during punching. Find: 1. Power required to drive the punching machine, and 2. Mass of the flywheel, if the radius of gyration of the wheel is 0.5 m. [**Ans. 1.588 W; 686 kg**]

19. The crankshaft of a punching machine runs at a speed of 300 r.p.m. During punching of 10 mm diameter holes in mild steel sheets, the torque required by the machine increases uniformly from 1000 N-m to 4000 N-m while the shaft turns through 40°, remains constant for the next 100°, decreases uniformly to 1000 N-m for the next 40° and remains constant for the next 180°. This cycle is repeated during each revolution. The power is supplied by a constant torque motor and the fluctuation of speed is to be limited to ± 3% of the mean speed. Find the power of the motor and the moment of inertia of the flywheel fitted to the machine.

[Ans. 68 kW; 67.22 kg-m²]

20. A punching press pierces 35 holes per minute in a plate using 10 kN-m of energy per hole during each revolution. Each piercing takes 40 per cent of the time needed to make one revolution. A cast iron flywheel used with the punching machine is driven by a constant torque electric motor. The flywheel rotates at a mean speed of 210 r.p.m. and the fluctuation of speed is not to exceed ±1 per cent of the mean speed. Find : 1. power of the electric motor, 2. mass of the flywheel, and 3. cross-sectional dimensions of the rim when the width is twice its thickness. Take hoop stress for cast iron = 4 MPa and density of cast iron = 7200 kg/m³.

[Ans. 5.83 kW; 537 kg; 148 mm, 74 mm]

DO YOU KNOW ?

1. Draw the turning moment diagram of a single cylinder double acting steam engine.

2. Explain precisely the uses of turning moment diagram of reciprocating engines.

3. Explain the turning moment diagram of a four stroke cycle internal combustion engine.

4. Discuss the turning moment diagram of a multicylinder engine.

5. Explain the terms 'fluctuation of energy' and 'fluctuation of speed' as applied to flywheels.

6. Define the terms 'coefficient of fluctuation of energy' and 'coefficient of fluctuation of speed', in the case of flywheels.

7. What is the function of a flywheel? How does it differ from that of a governor?

8. Prove that the maximum fluctuation of energy,

$$\Delta E = E \times 2C_S$$

where E = Mean kinetic energy of the flywheel, and

               C_S = Coefficient of fluctuation of speed.

OBJECTIVE TYPE QUESTIONS

1. The maximum fluctuation of energy is the
   (a) sum of maximum and minimum energies
   (b) difference between the maximum and minimum energies
   (c) ratio of the maximum energy and minimum energy
   (d) ratio of the mean resisting torque to the work done per cycle

2. In a turning moment diagram, the variations of energy above and below the mean resisting torque line is called
   (a) fluctuation of energy
   (b) maximum fluctuation of energy
   (c) coefficient of fluctuation of energy
   (d) none of the above

3. The ratio of the maximum fluctuation of speed to the mean speed is called
   - (a) fluctuation of speed
   - (b) maximum fluctuation of speed
   - (c) coefficient of fluctuation of speed
   - (d) none of these

4. The ratio of the maximum fluctuation of energy to the, ... is called coefficient of fluctuation of energy.
   - (a) minimum fluctuation of energy
   - (b) work done per cycle

5. The maximum fluctuation of energy in a flywheel is equal to
   - (a) $I.\omega(\omega_1 - \omega_2)$
   - (b) $I.\omega^2.C_S$
   - (c) $2E.C_S$
   - (d) all of these·

   where

   I = Mass moment of inertia of the flywheel,

   E = Mean kinetic energy of the flywheel,

   C_S = Coefficient of fluctuation of speed, and

   ω = Mean angular speed = $\dfrac{\omega_1 + \omega_2}{2}$.

ANSWERS

1. (b)	2. (a)	3. (c)	4. (b)	5. (d)

17

Steam Engine Valves and Reversing Gears

Features

17.1. Introduction

The valves are used to control the steam which drives the piston of a reciprocating steam engine. The valves have to perform the four distinct operations on the steam used on one side (*i.e.* cover end) of the piston, as shown by the indicator diagram (also known as pressure-volume diagram) in Fig. 17.1. These operations are as follows:

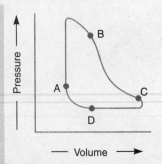

Fig. 17.1. Indicator diagram of a reciprocating steam engine.

1. Admission or opening of inlet valve for admission of steam to the cylinder. The point *A* represents the point for admission of steam just before the end of return stroke and it is continued up to the point *B*.

2. *Cut-off* or closing of inlet valve in order to stop the admission of steam prior to expansion. The point *B* represents the cut-off point of steam. The curve *BC* represents the expansion of steam in the engine cylinder.

3. *Release* or opening of exhaust valve to allow the expanded steam to escape from the cylinder to the atmosphere or to the condenser or to a larger cylinder. The point *C* represents the opening of the valve for releasing the steam. The exhaust continues during the return stroke upto point *D*.

4. *Compression* or closing of exhaust valve for stopping the release of steam from the cylinder prior to compression. The point *D* represents the closing of exhaust valve. The steam which remains in the cylinder is compressed from *D* to *A* and acts as a cushion for the reciprocating parts.

The same operations, as discussed above, are performed on steam in the same order on the other side (or crank end) of the piston for each cycle or each revolution of the crank shaft. In other words, for a double acting piston, there are eight valve operations per cycle. All these eight operations may be performed

    (*i*) by a single slide valve such as *D*-slide valve,

    (*ii*) by two piston valves, one for either end of cylinder, and

    (*iii*) by two pairs of valves (one pair for each end of the cylinder), such as corliss valves or drop valves. One valve at each end of the cylinder performs the operations of admission and cut-off while the other valve performs the operations of release and compression.

The engine performance depends upon the setting of the valves. In order to set a valve at a correct position, a valve diagram is necessary.

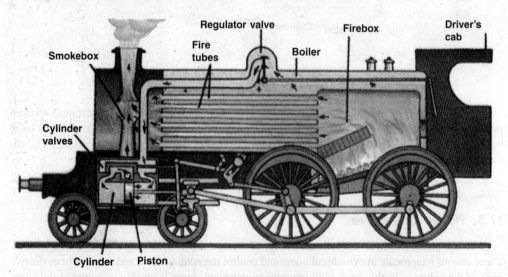

Sectional view of a steam engine.

17.2. D-slide Valve

The simplest type of the slide valve, called the *D*-slide valve, is most commonly used to control the admission, cut-off, release and compression of steam in the cylinder of reciprocating steam engine. The usual arrangement of the *D*-slide valve, valve chest and cylinder for a double acting steam engine is shown in Fig. 17.2 (*a*).

The steam from the boiler is admitted to the steam chest through a steam pipe. The recess R in the valve is always open to the exhaust port which, in turn, is open either to atmosphere or to the condenser. The ports P_1 and P_2 serve to admit steam into the cylinder or to pass out the steam from the cylinder. The valve is driven from an eccentric keyed to the crankshaft. It reciprocates across the ports and opens them alternately to admit high pressure steam from the steam chest and to exhaust the used steam, through recess R to exhaust port.

The D-slide valve in its mid position relative to the ports is shown in Fig. 17.2 (*a*). In this position, the outer edge of the valve overlaps the steam port by an amount s. This distance s (*i.e.* lapping on the outside of steam port) is called the *steam lap or outside lap*. The inner edge of the valve, also, overlaps the steam port by an amount e. This distance e (*i.e.* overlapping on the inside) is called the *exhaust lap or inside lap*.

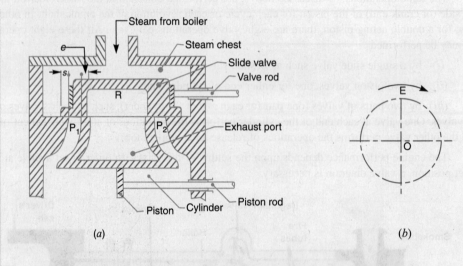

Fig. 17.2. *D*-slide valve.

The displacement of the valve may be assumed to take place with simple harmonic motion, since the *obliquity of the eccentric rod is very small. Thus the eccentric centre line OE will be at right angles to the line of stroke when the valve is in its mid-position. This is shown in Fig. 17.2 (*b*) for clockwise rotation of the crank.

Note: Since the steam is admitted from outside the steam chest, therefore the D-slide valve is also known as *Outside admission valve*.

17.3. Piston Slide Valve

The piston slide valve, as shown in Fig. 17.3 (*a*), consists of two rigidly connected pistons. These pistons reciprocate in cylindrical liners and control the admission to, and exhaust from the two ends of the cylinder. In this case, high pressure superheated steam is usually admitted to the space between the two pistons through O and exhaust takes place from the ends of the valve chest through E. This type of valve is mostly used for locomotives and high pressure cylinders of marine engines. The piston slide valve has the following advantages over the D-slide valve :

---

* Since the length of the eccentric rod varies from 15 to 20 times the eccentricity (also known as throw of the eccentric), therefore the effect of its obliquity is very small. The **eccentricity** or the **throw of eccentric** is defined as the distance between the centre of crank shaft O and the centre of eccentric E. Thus the distance OE is the eccentricity.

1. Since there is no unbalanced steam thrust between the valve and its seat as the pressure on the two sides is same, therefore the power absorbed in operating the piston valve is less than the *D*-slide valve.

2. The wear of the piston valve is less than the wear of the *D*-slide valve.

3. Since the valve spindle packing is subjected to the relatively low pressure and temperature of the exhaust steam, therefore the danger of leakage is less.

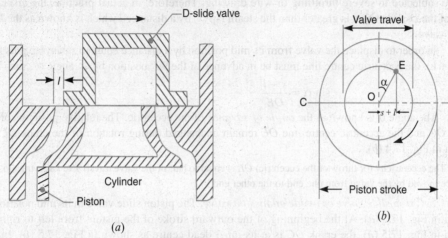

Fig. 17.3. Piston slide valve.

The position of the steam lap (*s*) and exhaust lap (*e*) for the piston valve in its mid position is shown in Fig. 17.3 (*a*). The eccentric position for the clockwise rotation of the crank is shown in Fig. 17.3(*b*).

Note: Since the steam enters from the inside of the two pistons, therefore the piston valve is also known as *inside admission valve*.

17.4. Relative Positions of Crank and Eccentric Centre Lines

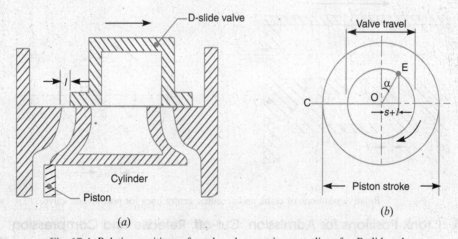

Fig. 17.4. Relative positions of crank and eccentric centre lines for *D*-slide valve.

We have discussed the *D*-slide valve (also known as outside admission valve) and piston slide valve (also known as inside admission valve) in Art. 17.2 and Art. 17.3 respectively. Now we shall discuss the relative positions of the crank and the eccentric centre lines for these slide valves.

1. *D-slide or outside admission valve*. The *D*-slide valve in its mid position is shown in Fig. 17.2 (*a*). At the beginning of the stroke of the piston from left to right as shown in Fig. 17.4 (*a*), the crank *OC* is at its inner dead centre position as shown in Fig. 17.4 (*b*). A little consideration will show that the steam will only be admitted to the cylinder if the *D*-slide valve moves from its mid position towards the right atleast by a distance equal to the steam lap (*s*). It may be noted that if only this minimum required distance is moved by the valve, then the steam admitted to the cylinder will be subjected to severe throttling or wire drawing. Therefore, in actual practice, the displacement of the *D*-slide valve is greater than the steam lap (*s*) by a distance *l* which is known as the *lead* of the valve.

In order to displace the valve from its mid position by a distance equal to steam lap plus lead (*i.e.* *s* + *l*), the eccentric centre line must be in advance of the 90° position by an angle α, such that

$$\sin \alpha = \frac{s + l}{OE}$$

The angle α is known as the *angle of advance* of the eccentric. The relative positions of the crank *OC* and the eccentric centre line *OE* remain unchanged during rotation of the crank *OC*, as shown in Fig. 17.4 (*b*).

Note : The eccentricity (or throw of the eccentric) *OE* is equal to half of the valve travel. The valve travel is the distance moved by the valve from one end to the other end.

2. *Piston slide valve or inside admission valve*. The piston slide valve in its mid position is shown in Fig. 17.3 (*a*). At the beginning of the outward stroke of the piston, from left to right as shown in Fig. 17.5 (*a*), the crank *OC* is at its inner dead centre as shown in Fig. 17.5 (*b*). In the similar way as discussed for *D*-slide valve, the valve should be displaced from its mean position by a distance equal to the steam lap plus lead (*i.e.* *s* + *l*) of the valve. The relative positions of the crank *OC* and the eccentric centre line *OE* are as shown in Fig. 17.5 (*b*). In this case, the angle of advance is (180° + α), and

$$\sin \alpha = \frac{s + l}{OE}$$

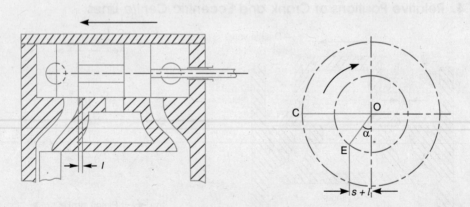

Fig. 17.5. Relative positions of crank and eccentric centre lines for piston slide valve.

17.5. Crank Positions for Admission, Cut-off, Release and Compression

In the previous article, we have discussed the relative positions of the crank and eccentric centre lines for both the *D*-slide valve and piston slide valve. Here we will discuss only the *D*-slide valve to mark the positions of crank for admission, cut-off, release and compression. The same principle may be applied to obtain the positions of crank for piston slide valve.

1. *Crank position for admission*. At admission for the cover end of the cylinder, the outer edge of the D-slide valve coincides with the outer edge of the port P_1. The valve moves from its mid position towards right, as shown by arrow A in Fig. 17.6 (a), by an amount equal to steam lap s. At the same time, the piston moves towards left as shown by thick lines in Fig. 17.6 (a). The corresponding position of the crank is OC_1 and the eccentric centre line is shown by OE_1 in Fig. 17.6 (b), such that

$$\angle C_1\, OE_1 = 90° + \alpha$$

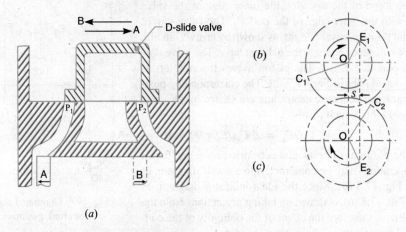

(*a*)

Fig. 17.6. Crank positions for admission and cut-off.

2. *Crank position for cut-off*. A little consideration will show that the cut-off will occur on the cover end of the cylinder when the outer edge of the D-slide valve coincides with the outer edge of the port P_1 while the valve moves towards left as shown by arrow B. The piston now occupies the position as shown by dotted lines in Fig. 17.6 (a). The corresponding position of the crank is OC_2 and the eccentric centre line is shown by OE_2 in Fig. 17.6 (c), such that

$$\angle C_2OE_2 = \angle C_1OE_1 = 90° + \alpha$$

3. *Crank position for release*. At release for the cover end of the cylinder, the inner edge of the D-slide valve coincides with the inner edge of the port P_1. The valve moves from its mid position towards left, as shown by arrow C in Fig. 17.7 (a), by a distance equal to the exhaust lap e. Thus the

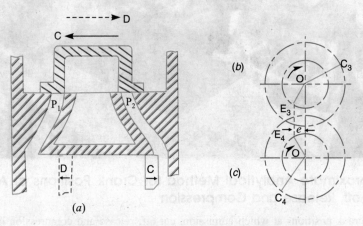

(*a*)

Fig. 17.7. Crank positions for release and compression.

valve opens the port to exhaust. At the same time, the piston moves towards right as shown by thick lines in Fig. 17.7 (*a*). The corresponding positions of crank and eccentric centre line are shown by OC_3 and OE_3 in Fig. 17.7 (*b*), such that

$$\angle C_3 OE_3 = 90° + \alpha$$

4. *Crank position for compression*. At compression, for the cover end of the cylinder, the inner edge of the valve coincides with the inner edge of the port P_1. The valve moves from its mid position towards right, as shown by arrow D in Fig. 17.7 (*a*), by a distance equal to the exhaust lap *e*. The valve now closes the port to exhaust. The piston moves towards left as shown by dotted lines in Fig. 17.7 (*a*). The corresponding positions of crank and eccentric centre line are shown by OC_4 and OE_4 in Fig. 17.7 (*c*), such that

$$\angle C_4 OE_4 = \angle C_3 OE_3 = 90° + \alpha$$

The positions of crank and eccentric centre line for all the four operations may be combined into a single diagram, as shown in Fig. 17.8 (*a*). Since the ideal indicator diagram, as shown in Fig. 17.8 (*b*), is drawn by taking projections from the crank positions, therefore the effect of the obliquity of the connecting rod is neglected.

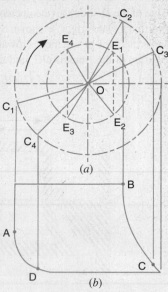

Fig. 17.8. Combined diagram of crank positions.

17.6. Approximate Analytical Method for Crank Positions at Admission, Cut-off, Release and Compression

The crank positions at which admission, cut-off, release and compression occur may be obtained directly by analytical method as discussed below :

Let x = Displacement of the valve from its mid-position,

θ = Crank angle,

r = Eccentricity or throw of eccentric = $\dfrac{1}{2}$ × Travel of valve,

α = Angle of advance of eccentric.

Since the displacement of the valve may be assumed to take place with simple harmonic motion, therefore

$$x = r \sin (\theta + \alpha) \qquad \ldots (i)$$

But at admission and cut-off,

$$x = \text{Steam lap, } s$$

$\therefore$

$$s = r \sin (\theta + \alpha) \qquad \ldots\text{[From equation } (i)]$$

or

$$\theta + \alpha = \sin^{-1}\left(\frac{s}{r}\right), \text{ and } \theta = \sin^{-1}\left(\frac{s}{r}\right) - \alpha \qquad \ldots (ii)$$

The two values of θ which satisfy the equation (ii) give the crank positions for admission and cut-off.

Similarly, at release and compression, x = exhaust lap (e) and is negative as measured from the origin O.

$\therefore$

$$- e = r \sin (\theta + \alpha) \qquad \ldots \text{[From equation } (i)]$$

or

$$\theta + \alpha = \sin^{-1}\left(\frac{-e}{r}\right), \text{ and } \theta = \sin^{-1}\left(\frac{-e}{r}\right) - \alpha \qquad \ldots (iii)$$

The two values of θ which satisfy the equation (iii) give the crank positions for release and compression.

Example 17.1. *The D-slide valve taking steam on its outside edges has a total travel of 150 mm. The steam and exhaust laps for the cover end of the cylinder are 45 mm and 20 mm respectively. If the lead for the cover end is 6 mm, calculate the angle of advance and determine the main crank angles at admission, cut-off, release and compression respectively for the cover end. Assume the motion of the valve as simple harmonic.*

Solution. Given : $2\,r = 2\,OE = 150$ mm or $r = OE = 75$ mm ; $s = 45$ mm ; $e = 20$ mm ; $l = 6$ mm

Angle of advance

Let α = Angle of advance.

We know that

$$\sin \alpha = \frac{s + l}{OE} = \frac{45 + 6}{75} = 0.68$$

or $\alpha = 42.8°$ **Ans.**

Crank angles at admission, cut-off, release and compression

Let

$\theta_1, \theta_2, \theta_3$ and θ_4 = Crank angles at admission, cut-off, release and compression respectively.

Prototype of an industrial steam engine.

We know that for admission and cut-off,

$$\theta + \alpha = \sin^{-1}\left(\frac{s}{r}\right) = \sin^{-1}\left(\frac{45}{75}\right) = \sin^{-1}(0.6) = 36.87° \text{ or } 143.13°$$

$$\therefore \qquad \theta_1 = 36.87° - \alpha = 36.87° - 42.8° = -5.93° \textbf{ Ans.}$$

and $\qquad \theta_2 = 143.13° - \alpha = 143.13° - 42.8° = 100.33° \textbf{ Ans.}$

We know that for release and compression,

$$\theta + \alpha = \sin^{-1}\left(\frac{-e}{r}\right) = \sin^{-1}\left(\frac{-20}{75}\right) = \sin^{-1}(-0.2667)$$

$$= 195.47° \text{ or } 344.53°$$

$$\therefore \qquad \theta_3 = 195.47° - \alpha = 195.47° - 42.8° = 152.67° \textbf{ Ans.}$$

and $\qquad \theta_4 = 344.53° - \alpha = 344.53° - 42.8° = 301.73° \textbf{ Ans.}$

17.7. Valve Diagram

The crank positions for admission, cut-off, release and compression may be easily determined by graphical constructions known as *valve diagrams*. There are various methods of drawing the valve diagrams but the following three are important from the subject point of view :

1. Zeuner valve diagram. 2. Reuleaux valve diagram, and 3. Bilgram valve diagram.

We shall discuss these valve diagrams, in detail as follows.

17.8. Zeuner Valve Diagram

The Zeuner's valve diagram, as shown in Fig. 17.9, is drawn as discussed in the following steps :

1. First of all, draw *AB* equal to the travel of the valve to some suitable scale. This diameter *AB* also represents the stroke of the piston to a different scale.

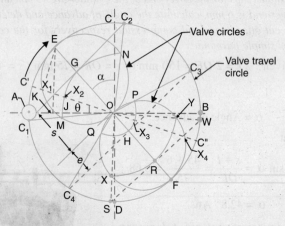

Fig. 17.9. Zeuner valve diagram.

2. Draw a circle on the diameter *AB* such that *OA = OB* = eccentricity or throw of the eccentric. The circle *ACBD* is known as the *valve travel circle*, where diameter *CD* is perpendicular to *AB*.

3. Draw *EOF* making an angle α, the angle of advance of the eccentric, with *CD*. It may be noted that the angle α is measured from *CD* in the direction opposite to the rotation of the crank and eccentric as marked by an arrow in Fig. 17.9.

4. In case the angle of advance (α) is not given, then mark *OJ* = steam lap (*s*), and *JK* = lead (*l*) of the valve. Draw *KE* perpendicular to *AB* which intersects the valve travel circle at *E*. The angle *EOC* is now the angle of advance.

5. Draw circles on *OE* and *OF* as diameters. These circles are called *valve circles*.

6. With *O* as centre, draw an arc of radius *OG* equal to steam lap (*s*) cutting the valve circle at *M* and *N*. Join *OM* and *ON* and produce them to cut the valve travel circle at C_1 and C_2 respectively. Now OC_1 and OC_2 represent the positions of crank at admission and cut-off respectively.

Note : The circle with centre *A* and radius equal to lead (*l*) will touch the line $C_1 C_2$.

7. Again with *O* as centre, draw an arc of radius *OH* equal to exhaust lap (*e*) cutting the valve circle at *P* and *Q*. Join *OP* and *OQ* and produce them to cut the valve travel circle at C_3 and C_4 respectively. Now OC_3 and OC_4 represent the position of crank at release and compression respectively.

8. For any position of the crank such as *OC'*, as shown in Fig. 17.9, the distance OX_1 represents the displacement of the valve from its mid position and the distance $X_1 X_2$ (the point X_1 is on the valve circle and the point X_2 is on the arc *JGN*) gives the opening of the port to steam. The distance $X_3 X_4$ (point X_3 is on the arc *QHP* and point X_4 is on the valve circle) obtained by producing the crank *OC'*, gives the opening of the port to exhaust for the crank position *OC'*. The proof of the diagram is as follows :

Join EX_1. Now angle $EX_1O = 90°$.

$$\therefore \quad \angle OEX_1 + \angle X_1OE = 90° = \angle AOC = \theta + \angle X_1OE + \alpha$$

or $$\angle OEX_1 = \theta + \alpha$$

Now from triangle OEX_1,

$$OX_1 = OE \sin (\theta + \alpha)$$

or $$x = r \sin (\theta + \alpha)$$

where x = Displacement of the valve from its mid position, and

r = Eccentricity or throw of eccentric.

Now $$OX_1 = OX_2 + X_1 X_2$$

∴ Opening of port to steam when the valve has moved a distance *x* from its mid-position,

$$X_1 X_2 = OX_1 - OX_2 = r \sin (\theta + \alpha) - s \qquad ...(\because OX_2 = \text{Steam lap, } s)$$

9. Mark *HR* = width of the steam port. Now with *O* as centre, draw an arc through *R* intersecting the valve circle at *X* and *Y*. The lines *OS* and *OW* through *X* and *Y* respectively determines the angle *WOS* through which the crank turns while the steam port is full open to exhaust. The maximum opening of port to exhaust is *HF*. A similar construction on the other valve circle will determine the angle through which the crank turns while the steam port is not full open to steam. Fig. 17.9 shows that the steam port is not full open to steam and the maximum opening of the port to steam is *GE*.

Note : The valve diagram, as shown in Fig. 17.9, is for the steam on the cover end side of the piston or for one-half of the *D*-slide valve. In order to draw the valve diagram for the crank end side of the piston (or the other half of the valve), the same valve circles are used but the two circles and the lines associated with them change places. For the sake of clearness, the valve diagrams for the two ends of the piston is drawn separately.

17.9. Reuleaux's Valve Diagram

The Reuleaux's valve diagram is very simple to draw as compared to the Zeuner's valve diagram. Therefore it is widely used for most problems on slide valves. The Reuleaux's valve diagram, as shown in Fig. 17.10, is drawn as discussed in the following steps :

1. First of all, draw *AB* equal to the travel of the valve to some suitable scale. This diameter *AB* also represents the stroke of the piston to a different scale.

2. Draw a circle on the diameter *AB* such that *OA* = *OB* = eccentricity or throw of the eccentric. This circle $ACBD$ is known as valve travel circle where diameter CD is perpendicular to AB.

3. Draw EOF making an angle α, the angle of advance of eccentric, with CD. It may be noted that the angle α is measured from CD in the direction opposite to the rotation of crank and eccentric as marked by an arrow in Fig. 17.10.

4. Draw GOH perpendicular to EOF. Now draw chords $C_1 C_2$ and $C_3 C_4$ parallel to GH and at distances equal to steam lap (s) and exhaust lap (e) from GH respectively.

5. Now OC_1, OC_2, OC_3 and OC_4 represent the positions of crank at admission, cutt-off, release and compression respectively.

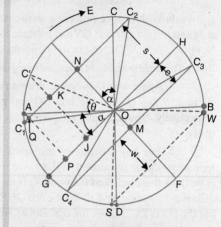

Fig. 17.10. Reuleaux's valve diagram.

The proof of the diagram is as follows :

Let OC' be any crank position making an angle θ with the inner dead centre, as shown in Fig.17.10. Draw $C'J$ perpendicular to GH. From right angled triangle $OC'J$,

$$C'J = C'O \sin C'OJ = r \sin (\theta + \alpha) \qquad \text{...}(i)$$

where $\qquad\qquad r = C'O = $ Eccentricity or throw of eccentric.

But the displacement of the valve from its mid-position corresponding to crank angle θ is given by

$$x = r \sin (\theta + \alpha) \qquad \text{...}(ii)$$

From equations (i) and (ii),

$$C'J = x$$

It, therefore, follows that the length of the perpendicular from C' to the diameter GH is equal to the displacement of the valve from mid-position when the crank is in the position OC'.

We see from Fig. 17.10, that when the crank is in position OC_1 or OC_2, the length of the perpendicular from C_1 or C_2 on GH is equal to the steam lap (s). Therefore OC_1 and OC_2 must represent the crank positions at admission and cut-off respectively. Similarly, when the crank is in position OC_3 and OC_4, the length of perpendicular from C_3 or C_4 on GH is equal to the exhaust lap (e). Therefore OC_3 and OC_4 must represent the crank positions at release and compression respectively.

Opening of the port to steam

We see from Fig. 17.10, that when the crank is in position OC', the displacement of the valve $C'J$, from its mid-position, exceeds the steam lap (s) by a distance $C'K$. The distance $C'K$ represents the amount of port opening to steam. Therefore when the crank is in position OA (i.e. at the inner dead centre), the perpendicular distance from A to GH, i.e. AP represents the displacement of the valve from its mid-position. The distance AP exceeds the steam lap (s) by a distance AQ which is equal to the lead of valve and represents the amount of port opening to steam.

The maximum possible opening of the port to steam is equal to NE i.e. ($r–s$) where r is the throw of the eccentric or half travel of the valve and s is the steam lap. Similarly, the maximum possible opening of the port to exhaust is equal to MF i.e. ($r–e$) where e is the exhaust lap. The difference ($r–e$) may exceed the width of the actual port through which the steam is admitted to and exhausted from the cylinder. In that case, the port will remain fully open for a certain period of crank rotation. In order to find the duration of this period, draw a chord *SW* parallel to C_3C_4 at a distance equal to the width of the steam port (w). The port will remain fully open to exhaust when the crank rotates from the positon *OW* to *OS*.

17.10. Bilgram Valve Diagram

The Bilgram valve diagram, as shown in Fig. 17.11, is drawn as discussed in the following steps :

1. First of all, draw *AB* equal to the travel of the valve to some suitable scale. This diameter *AB* also represents the stroke of the piston to a different scale.

A 1930's Steam locomotive.

2. Draw a circle on the diameter *AB* such that *OA = OB* = eccentricity or throw of the eccentric. This circle is known as valve travel circle.

3. Draw diameter *GOH* making an angle α, the angle of advance, with *AB*. The angle α is measured from *AB* in the direction opposite to the rotation of crank and eccentric as marked by an arrow in Fig. 17.11.

4. Draw two circles with centres *G* and *H* and radii equal to steam lap (s) and exhaust lap (e) respectively as shown in Fig. 17.11.

5. The lines OC_1 and OC_2 are tangential to the steam lap circles and they represent the crank positions for admission and cut-off respectively. Similarly OC_3 and OC_4 are tangential to the exhaust lap circles and represent the crank positions for release and compression.

The proof of the diagram is as follows :

Let *OC'* be any crank position making an angle θ with the inner dead centre, as shown in Fig. 17.11. Draw perpendiculars *GE* on *OC'* and *HF* on *OC'* produced.

Since the triangles *OGE* and *OHF* are similar, therefore

$$GE = HF = OG \sin (\theta + \alpha) = r \sin (\theta + \alpha) \qquad ...(i)$$

where $\qquad r = OG$ = Eccentricity or throw of eccentric.

But the displacement of the valve from its mid-position corresponding to crank angle θ, is given by

$$x = r \sin (\theta + \alpha) \qquad ...(ii)$$

From equations (*i*) and (*ii*),

$$GE = x$$

It, therefore, follows that the length of the perpendicular from G (or H) on OC' (or OC' produced) is equal to the displacement of the valve from mid-position when the crank is in the position OC'.

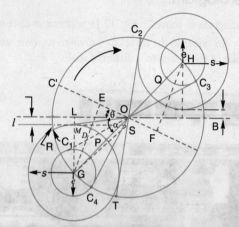

Fig. 17.11. Bilgram valve diagram.

We see from Fig. 17.11, that the length of the perpendiculars from G and H on OC_1 and OC_2 respectively are equal to steam lap (s). Therefore OC_1 and OC_2 must represent the crank positions at admission and cut-off respectively, Similarly, the length of perpendiculars from H and G on OC_3 and OC_4 respectively are equal to exhaust lap (e). Therefore OC_3 and OC_4 must represent the crank positions at release and compression respectively.

Opening of the port to steam

We see from Fig. 17.11, that when the crank is in position OC', the displacement of the valve GE, from its mid-position, exceeds the steam lap (s) by a distance DE. The distance DE represents the amount of port opening to steam. Therefore, when the crank is in position OA (*i.e.* at the inner dead centre), the perpendicular distance from G to OA (*i.e.* GL) represents the displacement of the valve from its mid-position. The distance GL exceeds the steam lap (s) by a distance ML which is equal to lead of the valve and represents the amount of port opening to steam.

The maximum opening of the port to steam is equal to OP or $(r - s)$ where r is the throw of eccentric or half travel of the valve and s is the steam lap. Similarly the maximum opening of the port to exhaust is OQ or $(r - e)$ where e is the exhaust lap.

Notes : 1. The point G lies on the intersection of the bisectors of angles C_1OT and RST.

2. The Bilgram valve diagram is usually used to determine throw of the eccentric, valve travel, angle of advance of the eccentric, steam and exhaust laps when the crank positions at cut-off and release, lead of valve and width of steam port are known.

Example 17.2. *The following particulars refer to a D-slide valve :*

Total valve travel = 150 mm ; Steam lap = 45 mm ; Exhaust lap = 20 mm ; Lead = 6 mm.

Draw the Zeuner's valve diagram for the cover end and determine the angle of advance of the eccentric, main crank angles at admission, cut-off, release and compression, opening of port to steam for 30° of crank rotation and maximum opening of port to steam. If the width of the port is 40 mm, determine the angle through which the crank turns so that the exhaust valve is full open.

Solution. Given : $AB = 150$ mm ; $s = 45$ mm ; $e = 20$ mm ; $l = 6$ mm

Angle of advance of eccentric and main crank angles at admission, cut-off, release and compression

The Zeuner's valve diagram for the cover end is drawn as discussed in the following steps :

1. First of all draw AB = 150 mm, to some suitable scale, to represent the total valve travel. Draw a circle on this diameter AB such that $OA = OB$ = throw of the eccentric. This circle is known as valve travel circle. Draw COD perpendicular to AB.

2. Mark OJ = steam lap = 45 mm, and JK = lead = 6 mm. Through K, draw a perpendicular on AB which intersects the valve travel circle at E. Join OE. Now angle COE represents the angle of advance of the eccentric (α) in a direction opposite to the direction of rotation of crank and eccentric (shown clockwise in Fig. 17.12). By measurement, we find that

$$\alpha = \angle COE = 42.5° \text{ Ans.}$$

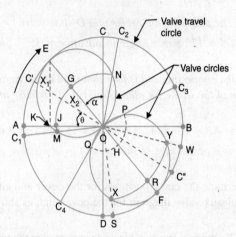

Fig. 17.12

3. Draw a circle on OE as diameter. This circle is known as valve circle. Now with O as centre, draw an arc of radius equal to steam lap (*i.e.* 45 mm) which intersects the valve circle at M and N. Join OM and ON and produce them to intersect the valve travel circle at C_1 and C_2 respectively. The lines OC_1 and OC_2 represent the crank positions at admission and cut-off respectively. By measurement, we find that

Crank angle at admission from inner dead centre A

$$= \angle AOC_1 = -6° \text{ Ans.}$$

and crank angle at cut-off from inner dead centre A

$$= \angle AOC_2 = 101° \text{ Ans.}$$

4. Now draw the diameter EOF. On OF draw a valve circle as shown in Fig. 17.12. With O as centre, draw an arc of radius equal to exhaust lap (*i.e.* 20 mm) which intersects the valve circle at P and Q. Join OP and OQ and produce them to intersect the valve travel circle at C_3 and C_4 respectively. Now OC_3 and OC_4 represent the crank positions at release and compression respectively. By measurement, we find that

Crank angle at release from inner dead centre A

$$= \angle AOC_3 = 153° \text{ Ans.}$$

and crank angle at compression from inner dead centre A

$$= \angle AOC_4 = 302° \text{ Ans.}$$

Opening of port to steam for 30° of crank rotation and maximum opening of port to steam

Let OC' be the crank at $\theta = 30°$ from the inner dead centre, as shown in Fig. 17.12. The crank

OC' intersects the valve circle at X_1 and arc MGN at X_2. Now $X_1 X_2$ represents the opening of port to steam for 30° of crank rotation. By measurement, we find that

$$X_1 X_2 = 27 \text{ mm Ans.}$$

and maximum opening of port to steam,

$$GE = 30 \text{ mm Ans.}$$

Angle through which the crank turns so that the exhaust valve is full open

Mark HR = width of port = 40 mm as shown in Fig. 17.12. Now with O as centre, draw an arc passing through R which intersects the valve circle at X and Y. The angle XOY represents the crank angle at which the exhaust valve is full open. By measurement, we find that

$$\angle XOY = 72° \text{ Ans.}$$

Example 17.3. *The following data refer to a D-slide valve :*

Total valve travel = 120 mm ; Angle of advance = 35° ; Steam lap = 25 mm ; Exhuast lap = 8 mm.

If the length of the connecting rod is four times the crank radius, determine the positions of the piston as percentage of the stroke for admission, cut-off, release and compression for both ends of the piston.

Solution. Given : $AB = 120$ mm ; $\alpha = 35°$, $s = 25$ mm ; $e = 8$ mm

Positions of the piston as a percentage of the stroke for admission, cut-off, release and compression for cover end of the piston.

First of all, determine the crank positions for the cover end either by Zeuner's or Reuleaux valve diagram. The Reuleaux valve diagram for the cover end, as shown in Fig. 17.13, is drawn as follows :

1. Draw $AB = 120$ mm to some suitable scale to represent the total valve travel. This diameter AB also represents the stroke of the piston. Draw a circle on diameter AB such that $OA = OB$ = Throw of the eccentric or radius of crank.

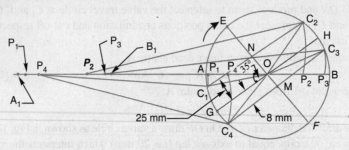

Fig. 17.13

2. Draw a line GOH making an angle of 35°, the angle of advance, in a direction opposite to the rotation of crank which is clockwise as shown in Fig. 17.13.

3. Draw EOF perpendicular to GOH and mark ON = steam lap = 25 mm and OM = exhaust lap = 8 mm. Through N and M draw lines parallel to GOH which intersect the valve travel circle at C_1, C_2, C_3 and C_4. Now OC_1, OC_2, OC_3 and OC_4 represent the crank positions at admission, cut-off release and compression respectively.

At inner dead centre A and outer dead centre B, the connecting rod is in line with the crank. Since the connecting rod is 4 times the crank radius OA, therefore mark $AA_1 = BB_1 = 4 \times OA = 4 \times 60$ = 240 mm. Now $A_1 B_1 = AB = 120$ mm and represents the stroke of the piston. With C_1, C_2, C_3, C_4 as centres and radius equal to length of connecting rod *i.e.* 240 mm, mark the corresponding positions of piston as shown by points P_1, P_2, P_3 and P_4 in Fig. 17.13. By measurement, the piston position as percentage of stroke is given by :

At admission $= \dfrac{B_1P_1}{B_1A_1} \times 100$ of return stroke $= \dfrac{119}{120} \times 100 = 99.17\%$ **Ans.**

At cut-off $= \dfrac{A_1P_2}{A_1B_1} \times 100$ of forward stroke $= \dfrac{96}{120} \times 100 = 80\%$ **Ans.**

At release $= \dfrac{A_1P_3}{A_1B_1} \times 100$ of forward stroke $= \dfrac{116}{120} \times 100 = 96.67\%$ **Ans.**

At compression $= \dfrac{B_1P_4}{B_1A_1} \times 100$ of return stroke $= \dfrac{100}{120} \times 100 = 83.33\%$ **Ans.**

Note : The points p_1, p_2, p_3 and p_4 on AB are the corresponding points of P_1, P_2, P_3 and P_4 respectively. These points may be obtained by drawing the arcs through C_1, C_2, C_3 and C_4 with their centres at P_1, P_2, P_3 and P_4 and radius equal to the length of connecting rod. Now the piston positions as percentage of stroke is given by :

At admission $= \dfrac{Bp_1}{BA} \times 100$ of return stroke ; At cut-off $= \dfrac{Ap_2}{AB} \times 100$ of forward stroke

At release $= \dfrac{Ap_3}{AB} \times 100$ of forward stroke ; At compression $= \dfrac{Bp_4}{BA} \times 100$ of return stroke

Positions of the piston as a percentage of the stroke for admission, cut-off, release and compression for crank end of the piston.

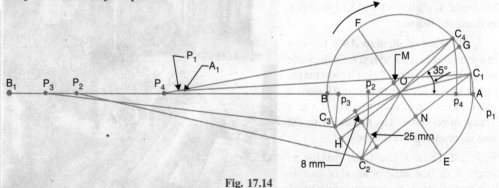

Fig. 17.14

The valve diagram for the crank end is drawn by rotating the valve diagram for the cover end through 180° in the direction of rotation of the crank, as shown in Fig. 17.14. By measurement, the piston positions as percentrage of stroke is given by :

At admission $= \dfrac{B_1P_1}{B_1A_1} \times 100$ of forward stroke $= \dfrac{Bp_1}{BA} \times 100$ of forward stroke

$= \dfrac{119}{120} \times 100 = 99.17\%$ **Ans.**

At cut-off $= \dfrac{A_1 P_2}{A_1 B_1} \times 100$ of return stroke $= \dfrac{Ap_2}{AB} \times 100$ of return stroke

$$= \dfrac{85}{120} \times 100 = 70.83\% \textbf{ Ans.}$$

At release $= \dfrac{A_1 P_3}{A_1 B_1} \times 100$ of return stroke $= \dfrac{Ap_3}{AB} \times 100$ of return stroke

$$= \dfrac{112}{120} \times 100 = 93.33\% \textbf{ Ans.}$$

At compression $= \dfrac{B_1 P_4}{B_1 A_1} \times 100$ of forward stroke $= \dfrac{Bp_4}{BA} \times 100$ of forward stroke

$$= \dfrac{106}{120} \times 100 = 88.33\% \textbf{ Ans.}$$

Example 17.4. *A slide valve has a travel of 125 mm. The angle of advance of the eccentric is 35°. The cut-off and release takes place at 75 per cent and 95 per cent of the stroke at each end of the cylinder. If the connecting rod is 4 times the crank length, find steam lap, exhaust lap and lead for each end of the valve.*

Solution. Given : $AB = 125$ mm ; $\alpha = 35°$

Piston position at cut-off for both ends (*i.e.* cover and crank end)

$$= 75\% \text{ of stroke}$$

Piston position at release for both ends

$$= 95\% \text{ of stroke}$$

Steam lap, exhaust lap and lead for the cover end

The Reuleaux's diagram for the cover end, as shown in Fig. 17.15, is drawn as discussed below :

1. First of all, draw $AB = 125$ mm to some suitable scale, to represent the valve travel. This diameter AB also represents the piston stroke. On this diameter AB draw a valve travel circle such that $OA = OB =$ Throw of eccentric. The radius OA or OB also represents the crank radius.

2. Draw a line GOH making an angle of 35°, the angle of advance, in a direction opposite to the rotation of the crank which is clockwise as shown in Fig. 17.15.

3. At inner dead centre A and outer dead centre B, the connecting rod is in line with the crank. Since the connecting rod is 4 times the crank radius, therefore mark AA_1 $= 4 \times OA = 4 \times 125/2 = 250$ mm. Now $A_1 B_1 = AB = 125$ mm and represents the stroke of the piston.

Broaching machine. Broaching is a process of machining through holes of any cross sectional shape, straight and helical slots, external surfaces of various shapes, external and internal toothed gears, splines, keyways and rifling.

Note : This picture is given as additional information.

4. Since the cut-off takes place at 75 percent of the stroke, therefore

$$\frac{A_1P_2}{A_1B_1} = \frac{Ap_2}{AB} = 0.75$$

∴ $A_1P_2 = A\,p_2 = 0.75 \times A_1B_1 = 0.75 \times 125 = 94$ mm

...(∵ $A_1B_1 = AB = 125$ mm)

With P_2 as centre and radius equal to $P_2\,p_2$ (*i.e.* length of connecting rod), draw an arc through p_2 which intersects the valve travel circle at C_2. This point C_2 represents the crank-pin position at cut-off.

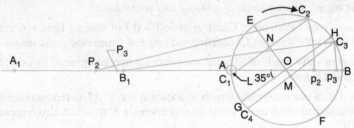

Fig. 17.15

5. From C_2 draw C_2C_1 parallel to *GH* which intersects a line *EOF* (perpendicular to *GOH*) at *N*. The point C_1 represents the crank-pin position at admission and *ON* is the steam lap. By measurement,

Steam lap $= ON = 32$ mm   **Ans.**

6. Since the release takes place at 95 % of the stroke, therefore

$$\frac{A_1P_3}{A_1B_1} = \frac{Ap_3}{AB} = 0.95$$

∴ $A_1P_3 = Ap_3 = 0.95 \times A_1B_1 = 0.95 \times 125 = 118.8$ mm

With P_3 as centre and radius equal to $P_3\,p_3$ (*i.e.* length of connecting rod), draw an arc through p_3 which intersects the valve travel circle at C_3. This point C_3 represents the crank-pin position at release.

7. From C_3 draw C_3C_4 parallel to *GH* which intersects a line *EOF* at *M*. The point C_4 represents the crank-pin position at compression and *OM* is the exhaust lap. By measurement,

Exhaust lap $= OM = 8$ mm **Ans.**

8. In order to find the lead, draw a circle with centre *A* such that C_1C_2 is tangential to this circle (or draw *AL* perpendicular to C_1C_2). The perpendicular *AL* represents the lead of the valve. By measurement,

Lead $= AL = 6$ mm **Ans.**

Steam lap, exhaust lap and lead for the crank end

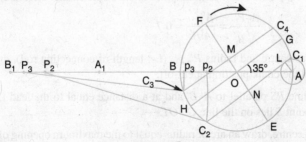

Fig. 17.16

The Reuleaux's valve diagram for the crank end, as shown in Fig. 17.16, is drawn by rotating the valve diagram for the cover end, through 180°. By measurement,

$$\text{Steam lap} = ON = 20 \text{ mm Ans.}$$

$$\text{Exhaust lap} = OM = 12 \text{ mm Ans.}$$

and

$$\text{Lead} = AL = 16 \text{ mm Ans.}$$

Example 17.5. *The following data refer to a D-slide valve for the cover end :*

Position of the crank at cut off = 0.7 of stroke ; Lead = 6 mm ; Maximum opening of port to steam = 45 mm ; connecting rod length = 4 times crank length.

Find the travel of valve, angle of advance and steam lap.

Solution. Given : Position of Crank at cut-off = 0.7 of stroke ; Lead = 6 mm ; Maximum opening of port to steam = 45 mm ; Connecting rod length = 4 times the crank length.

The travel of valve, angle of advance and steam lap may be obtained by using Bilgram valve diagram as discussed below :

1. Draw $A'B'$ of any convenient length, as shown in Fig. 17.17, to represent the assumed valve travel. Draw the assumed valve travel circle on this diameter $A' B'$ which also represents the piston stroke (assumed).

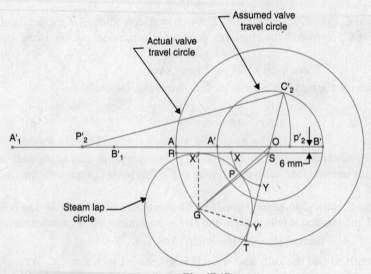

Fig. 17.17

2. Since the length of connecting rod is 4 times the crank OA', therefore mark $A'A'_1, = B' B'_1 = 4 \times OA'$. Now $A'_1 B'_1$ represents the piston stroke.

3. The cut-off for the cover end takes place at 0.7 of the stroke, therefore mark

$$\frac{A'_1 P'_2}{A'_1 B'_1} = \frac{A' p'_2}{A' B'} = 0.7$$

4. Now P'_2 as centre and radius $P'_2 p'_2$ (*i.e.* length of connecting rod), draw an arc $p'_2 C'_2$. Now OC'_2 represents the crank position at cut-off.

5. Draw a line RS parallel to $A' B'$ and at a distance equal to the lead *i.e.* 6 mm, to some suitable scale. The point S lies on the line $C'_2 OT$.

6. With O as centre, draw an arc of radius equal to the maximum opening of port to steam (*i.e.* 45 mm) which intersects RS at X and OT at Y.

7. Draw the bisector of angle *RST*. The point *G* on this bisector is obtained by hit and trial such that the circle with centre *G* touches the maximum opening arc at *P*, the lines *RS* and *ST*. The point *G* is a point on the actual valve travel circle and represents the centre for steam lap circle.

By measurement, we find that

$$\text{Travel of valve } = 2\,AO = 2\,GO = 216 \text{ mm Ans.}$$

$$\text{Angle of advance } = \angle AOG = 40° \text{ Ans.}$$

$$\text{Steam lap } = GP = 63 \text{ mm Ans.}$$

Example 17.6. *In a steam engine, the D-slide valve has a cut-off at 70 per cent of the stroke at each end of the cylinder. The steam lap and the lead for the cover end are 20 mm and 6 mm respectively. If the length of the connecting rod is 4 times the crank length, find : valve travel, and angle of advance of the eccentric. Determine also the steam lap and lead of the crank end.*

Solution. Given : Position of piston at cut-off on both sides of the cylinder = 70% of stroke ; Steam lap = 20 mm ; Lead = 6 mm ; Connecting rod length = 4 × crank length.

Valve travel and angle of advance of the eccentric

Since we have to find the valve travel, therefore the Bilgram valve diagram is used. The position of the crank OC'_2 for cut-off at 70 per cent of stroke is obtained in the similar manner as discussed in the previous example. The Bilgram valve diagram is now completed as follows :

1. Draw *RS* parallel to *A' B'* and at a distance equal to the lead *i.e.* 6 mm, to some suitable scale as shown in Fig. 17.18. The point *S* lies on the line $C'_2\,OT$.

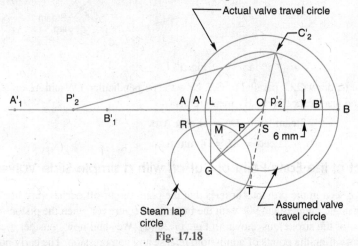

Fig. 17.18

2. Draw the bisector of the angle *RST*. Obtain the *point *G* on this bisector, by hit and trial, such that a circle with centre *G* and radius equal to the steam lap *i.e.* 20 mm touches the lines *RS* and *ST*.

3. Now with *O* as centre and radius equal to *OG* draw the actual valve travel circle.

By measurement, we find that

$$\text{Valve travel } = AB = 76 \text{ mm Ans.}$$

and angle of advance of the eccentric $= \angle AOG = 42° \text{ Ans.}$

---

* The point *G* may also be obtained by drawing a perpendicular from *A'O* such that *LG* = steam lap + lead = 20 + 6 = 26 mm.

Steam lap and lead for the crank end

Since the valve travel and angle of advance of the eccentric is known, therefore the steam lap and lead for the crank end may be easily found by using Reuleaux valve diagram as discussed below:

1. Draw $AB = 76$ mm to some suitable scale, as shown in Fig. 17.19, to represent the valve travel. This diameter AB also represents the piston stroke and $OA = OB =$ Throw of eccentric or radius of crank.

2. Since cut-off for the crank end takes place at 70 per cent of the stroke, therefore mark

$$\frac{Ap_2}{AB} = 0.7 \text{ or } Ap_2 = 0.7 \times AB = 0.7 \times 76 = 53.2 \text{ mm}$$

3. Now with centre P_2 and radius equal to $P_2 p_2$ (*i.e.* length of connecting rod), draw an arc $p_2 C_2$. Now OC_2 represents the position of crank at cut-off for crank end.

4. Draw GOH at an angle of 42°, the advance of the eccentric, with AB in the direction opposite to the rotation of crank which is shown clockwise in Fig. 17.19.

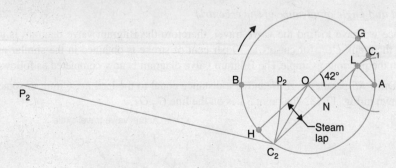

Fig. 17.19

5. From C_2 draw $C_2 C_1$ parallel to GH. Now the perpendicular, ON and AL on $C_2 C_1$ represent the steam lap and lead respectively. By measurement

$$\text{Steam lap} = ON = 11 \text{ mm Ans.}$$

$$\text{Lead} = AL = 14 \text{ mm Ans.}$$

17.11. Effect of the Early Point of Cut-off with a simple Slide Valve

We have seen in the previous articles that the point of cut-off occurs very late *i.e.* when the crank makes an angle greater than 90° with the inner dead centre (or when the piston moves greater than 50 per cent of the stroke), as shown in Fig. 17.20 (*a*). We shall now consider the effect of the early point of cut-off on the points of admission, release and compression. The early point of cut-off (considering the crank at 90°) may be obtained by the following three methods :

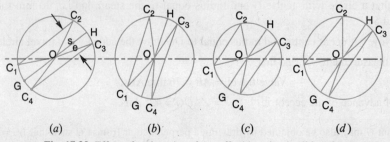

Fig. 17.20. Effect of early point of cut-off with a simple slide valve.

First Method

The simplest method of obtaining the earlier cut-off is by increasing the angle of advance of the eccentric while the throw of the eccentric, steam lap and exhaust lap are kept constant. We see from Fig. 17.20 (*b*), that by increasing the angle of advance for the earlier cut-off will also make admission, release and compression earlier than as shown in Fig. 17.20 (*a*). This will, obviously reduce the length of effective stroke of the piston.

Second Method

Fig. 17.20 (*c*) shows that the earlier cut-off may also be obtained by increasing the angle of advance of the eccentric but reducing the throw of the eccentric (or the valve travel) in order to retain the same timing for admission as in the normal diagram shown in Fig. 17.20 (*a*). The steam lap and exhaust lap are constant. We see from Fig. 17.20 (*c*) that the release and compression occur earlier but not so early as in Fig. 17.20 (*b*). The objection to this method is that the maximum opening of the port to steam and exhaust is reduced due to the shortening of valve travel. This will cause withdrawing or throttling of steam.

Blades of the helicopter propeller push the air downwards and the resultant reaction gives helicopter the necessary lifting power.

Note : This picture is given as additional information.

Third Method

Another method for obtaining the earlier cut-off is to increase the steam lap and the angle of advance of the eccentric, as shown in Fig. 17.20 (*d*), but keeping constant the travel and lead of the valve [*i.e.* same as in Fig. 17.20 (*a*)]. The advantage of this method is that there will be a normal timing of the admission and a smaller reduction in the maximum opening of the port to steam. But the necessity of increasing the steam lap of the valve makes it unsuitable from practical point of view.

17.12. Meyer's Expansion Valve

We have seen in the previous article that in order to obtain earlier cut-off, other operations such as admission, release and compression also take place earlier which is undesirable. The Meyer's expansion valve not only enables the cut-off to take place early in the stroke with normal timing for admission, release and compression, but it also enables the cut-off to be varied while the engine is running. There are two valves known as *main valve* and *expansion valve* which are driven by separate eccentric from the main crankshaft as shown in Fig. 17.21.

The main valve, is similar to the ordinary slide valve, except that it is provided with extensions and the steam passes from the steam chest through the ports P_1 or P_2. The admission of steam to the main valve is controlled by the expansion valve which slides on the back of the main valve. The expansion valve consists of two blocks or plates E_1 and E_2 mounted on a spindle. It may be noted that in order to admit steam into the cylinder, not only the ports P_1 or P_2 in the main valve are in communication with the main ports P'_1 or P'_2 but at the same time these must be uncovered by the expansion plates E_1 or E_2 as the case may be.

In order to obtain variable cut-off according to the requirement, the position of the plates E_1 and E_2 is varied by means of a spindle having right and left hand threads. The spindle extends to the engine room so that the operator can vary the position of E_1 and E_2 while the engine is running . Thus the variable cut-off is achieved by the expansion valve without the change of lead, maximum opening to steam or points of admission, release and compression.

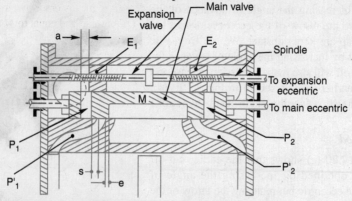

Fig. 17.21. Meyer's expansion valve.

Fig. 17.21 shows that both the valves are in mid-position. A little consideration will show that steam lap (s) and exhaust lap (e) for the main valve are positive whereas the steam lap (a) for the expansion valve is negative (*i.e.* the port P_1 instead of being covered by the expansion valve in mid-position, is open to steam by a distance a). The points of admission, release, compression and the least point of cut-off may be obtained in the usual manner by the Reuleaux or Bilgram valve diagrams.

17.13. Virtual or Equivalent Eccentric for the Meyer's Expansion Valve

In order to obtain the setting of the expansion valve for the predetermined cut-off or *vice-versa,* the Reuleaux or Bilgram valve diagram is drawn from the *virtual* or *equivalent eccentric*. It is defined as an eccentric having such a length and angle of advance that will cause cut-off to take place at the same position, as is caused by the combined effect of main eccentric and expansion eccentric.

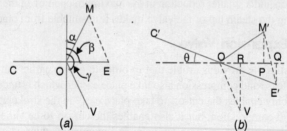

Fig. 17.22. Virtual or equivalent eccentric for the Meyer's expansion valve.

In the Meyer's expansion valve, the main valve is driven by an eccentric having an angle of advance of 25° to 30° and the expansion valve is driven by an eccentric having an angle of advance 80° to 90°. If the engine has to be reversible, the angle of advance must be 90° so that the cut-off takes place at the same fraction of the stroke for the same setting of the expansion valve whatever may be the direction of rotation of the crank. Fig. 17.22 (*a*) shows the relative positions of the crank OC, main eccentric OM, and expansion eccentric OE, when the crank is at the inner dead centre. The angle of advance of the main eccentric OM is denoted by α and the angle of advance of the expansion eccentric OE is taken as $\beta = 90°$. When the crank OC has turned through an angle θ from the inner dead centre, the corresponding positions of the main eccentric and the expansion eccentric are shown in Fig. 17.22 (*b*). The displacement of the main valve from its mid-position is represented by OP, the projection of OM' on the line of stroke. Similarly the displacement of expansion valve from its mid-position is represented by OQ, the projection of OE' on the line of stroke. In both the cases, the obliquity of the eccentric rod is neglected. The difference between OQ and OP (*i.e. PQ*) is the displacement of the expansion valve relative to the main valve, in this case towards the right. The displacement PQ may also be obtained by drawing a line OV parallel and equal to $M'E'$ and then OR, the projection of OV on the line of stroke, will be equal to PQ. Thus we see that for the given positions of the main eccentric OM' and expansion eccentric OE', the displacement PQ is equal to the displacement given by a single eccentric OV. This eccentric OV is termed as *virual* or *equivalent eccentric*. Since the throw and the angle of advance are referred with respect to inner dead centre , the virtual or equivalent eccentric may be obtained by drawing OV parallel and equal to ME in Fig. 17.22 (*a*). Now γ is the angle of advance and OV is the throw for the virtual or equivalent eccentric. The cut-off will take place for the crank position in which R lies at a distance 'a' to the left of O. This position is most easily found by applying the Reuleaux valve diagram to the virtual or equivalent eccentric OV.

Fig. 17.23 (*a*) shows the Reuleaux valve diagram for the main eccentric OM in order to determine the crank positions for admission, release, compression and for the latest possible cut-off.

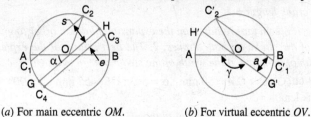

(*a*) For main eccentric OM.   (*b*) For virtual eccentric OV.

Fig. 17.23. Reuleaux valve diagram.

The Reuleaux valve diagram for the virtual eccentric OV as shown in Fig. 17.23 (*b*) is drawn as follows :

    1. First of all, draw a circle on diameter $AB = 2\,OV$.

    2. Draw $G'H'$ making an angle α with AB in the direction opposite to the rotation of crank.

    3. Draw $C'_1 C'_2$ parallel to $G'H'$ and at a distance equal to the steam lap (*a*) for the expansion valve.

    4. Now OC'_2 represents the crank position at which the cut-off takes place. An increase or decrease of the steam lap (*a*) gives respectively a later or earlier cut-off. The steam lap (*a*) is altered by means of a right and a left hand threaded spindle.

17.14. Minimum Width and Best Setting of the Expansion Plate for Meyer's Expansion Valve

The minimum width and best setting of the expansion plate E_1 or E_2 for the Meyer's expansion valve may be obtained as discussed below :

1. Minimum *width of the expansion plate E_1 or E_2*

Let OV = Throw of the virtual eccentric,

             a = Steam lap of the expansion valve, and

            p = Width of the port P_1 or P_2 in the main valve as shown in Fig. 17.21.

Since the maximum displacement, from the mid-position, of the expansion valve relative to the main valve is equal to the throw of the virtual eccentric OV, therefore

            Maximum overlap of the expansion valve and the port

$$= OV - a$$

    ∴ Minimum width of the expansion plate E_1 or E_2 (Fig. 17.21) required to prevent steam from being re-admitted past the inner edge of the plate

$$= OV - a + p$$

2. Best setting of the expansion plate E_1 or E_2

Due to the obliquity of the connecting rod, the steam lap (a) for the two expansion plates, for the same point of cut-off, must be different.

Let a_1 = Steam lap for the expansion plate E_1 on the cover side, and

a_2 = Steam lap for the expansion plate E_2 on the crank side.

Generally, the difference between the two steam laps, *i.e.* ($a_1 - a_2$) is different with the change of point of cut-off. In actual practice, when the expansion plates are assembled on the valve spindle, they may be given different laps. But the difference ($a_1 - a_2$) once fixed will remain constant for all values of the steam lap. Therefore for the best results, it is necessary to use such a value of ($a_1 - a_2$) which gives as nearly as possible equal cut-off on both strokes over the full range of cut-off required.

Example 17.7. *The following particulars refer to a Meyer's expansion valve :*

Throw of main eccentric = 50 mm ; angle of advance of main eccentric = 30° ; Throw of expansion eccentric = 55 mm ; Angle of advance of expansion eccentric = 90° ; Ratio of connecting rod length to crank length = 5.

Find : 1. Steam laps required on the expansion plates in order to give cut-off at 0.2, 0.3, 0.4, 0.5, and 0.6 of the stroke on both strokes, 2. The best setting of the expansion plates, and 3. The minimum width of the plate, if the width of the steam port in main valve is 28 mm.

Solution. Given : OM = 50 mm ; α = 30° ; OE = 55 mm ; β = 90° ; Ratio of connecting rod length to crank length = 5

1. Steam lap required on the expansion plates

First of all, determine the throw and angle of advance of the virtual eccentric OV as shown in Fig. 17.24. By measurement, throw of virtual eccentric,

$$OV = 53 \text{ mm}$$

and angle of advance, γ = 143°

Now draw the Reuleaux valve diagram, as shown in Fig. 17.25, for the virtual eccentric OV as discussed below :

1. Draw a cirlce on the diameter AB, such that

$$AB = 2 \times OV = 2 \times 53 = 106 \text{ mm}$$

Fig. 17.24

2. Draw $C'_1 \, OC'_2$ making an angle γ = 143° with AB, where γ is the angle of advance for the virtual eccentric.

3. Since the length of connecting rod is 5 times the crank length, therefore draw $AA_1 = BB_1 = 5 \times OA$. The distance $A_1B_1 = AB$ represents the stroke length.

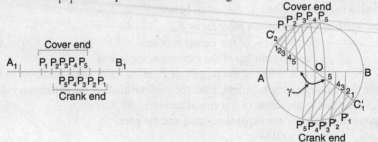

Fig. 17.25

4. Mark the points P_1, P_2, P_3, P_4 and P_5 corresponding to 0.2, 0.3, 0.4, 0.5 and 0.6 of the stroke respectively for the cover end and crank end as shown in Fig. 17.25.

5. Now with centres P_1, P_2, P_3, P_4 and P_5 and radius equal to 5 times OA, obtain the crank-pin positions P'_1, P'_2, P'_3, P'_4, and P'_5 corresponding to 0.2, 0.3, 0.4, 0.5 and 0.6 of the stroke at which cut-off is required to take place for both the ends.

6. The perpendicular distances for P'_1, P'_2 ..... etc. on $C'_1\, OC'_2$ for both the ends represent the steam lap (a) for the virtual eccentric. By measurement, the required values of the steam lap (a) are tabulated below :

Cut off	0.2	0.3	0.4	0.5	0.6
Steam lap (cover end) in mm	12	24	32	39	46 **Ans.**
Steam lap (crank end) in mm	19	30	39	46	50 **Ans.**
Difference in mm	7	6	7	7	4

2. *Best setting of the expansion plates*

From the above table, we see that if the steam lap on the end is kept 7mm more than the steam lap on the cover end, then the cut off will occur at approximately the same fraction of the stroke for both ends of the cylinder.

Therefore, for best results, the expansion plates may be set with steam lap at the crank end 7mm greater than that at cover end. **Ans.**

3. *Minimum width of expansion plate*

From the above table, we see that the minimum steam lap on the cover end is 12 mm and on the crank end is 19 mm. Since the width of the steam port in the main valves is 28 mm (*i.e.* $p = 28$ mm), therefore

Minimum width of the expansion plate on the cover end

$$= OV - a + p = 53 - 12 + 28 = 69 \text{ mm } \textbf{Ans.} \quad ...\text{(Substituting } a = 12 \text{ mm)}$$

and minimum width of the expansion plate on the crank end

$$= OV - a + p = 53 - 19 + 28 = 62 \text{ mm } \textbf{Ans.} \quad ...\text{(Substituting, } a = 19 \text{ mm)}$$

17.15. Reversing Gears

The primary function of the reversing gear is to reverse the direction of motion of the crankshaft in steam engines. It also enables to vary the power developed by the engine by altering the point of cut-off while the engine is running. Following two types of the reversing gears are generally used :

1. Link motions, and **2.** Radial valve gears.

In *link motions,* two eccentrics are keyed to the crankshaft, one for forward motion and the other for backward motion. A suitable link mechanism is introduced between the eccentrics and the valve rod so that the valve may receive its motion either wholly from one of the two eccentrics or partly from one and partly from the other. The examples of link motions are Stephenson link motion, Gooch link motion and Allan link motion. The Stephenson link motion is most widely used.

In *radial valve gears*, a single eccentric or its equivalent is used which serves the same object as two separate eccentrics of link motions. The examples of radial valve gears are Hackworth gear and Walschaert gear.

Notes : 1. In order to determine the approximate piston position at which admission, cut-off, release and compression takes place for a given setting of the gear, a simplified graphical method may be used. The method consists in finding the throw and angle of advance of a single eccentric (known as virtual or equivalent eccentric) which gives approximately the same motion as obtained from a reversing gear. The method of finding the throw and angle of advance differs for the two types of the reversing gears and is discussed in the following pages.

2. After determining the equivalent eccentric, the Reuleaux or Bilgram valve diagram is drawn to determine the piston positions at which admission, cut-off, release and compression take place for a given setting of the gear.

17.16. Principle of Link Motions–Virtual Eccentric for a Valve With an Offset Line of Stroke

Let OC be the crank making an angle θ with the inner dead centre as shown in Fig. 17.26. The corresponding position of one of the eccentrics is represented by OE making an angle $(\theta + \alpha)$ with the vertical, where α is the angle of advance. As the crank OC revolves, the end A of the eccentric rod EA reciprocates along the line PA (*i.e.* in the direction of the path of the valve rod connected to the valve). The line of stroke of the valve is off-set by OP. It is required to find the throw and angle of advance of an eccentric with axis at P, which will give to A the same motion as it receives from the actual eccentric OE.

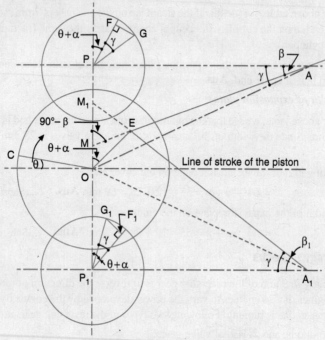

Fig. 17.26. Principle of link motions.

A little consideration will show that when the line AE is produced to cut the vertical line OP at M, then the triangle OEM represents the velocity triangle for the mechanism OEA, with all its sides perpendicular to those of a usual velocity triangle.

Let
ω = Angular speed of crank or eccentric in rad/s,
v_A = Velocity of the point A,
v_E = Velocity of the point E, and
β = Angle of inclination of AE with AP.

We know that

$$\frac{v_A}{v_E} = \frac{OM}{OE} = \frac{\sin \angle OEM}{\sin \angle OME} \qquad \dots\left(\because \text{ In any triangle, } \frac{a}{\sin A} = \frac{b}{\sin B}\right)$$

$$= \frac{\sin [180° - (\theta + \alpha) - (90° + \beta)]}{\sin (90° + \beta)} = \frac{\cos (\theta + \alpha + \beta)}{\cos \beta}$$

$$\therefore \quad v_A = v_E \times \frac{\cos (\theta + \alpha + \beta)}{\cos \beta} = \omega \times \frac{OE}{\cos \beta} \times \cos (\theta + \alpha + \beta) \ ...(\because v_E = \omega.\ OE)$$

Thus the velocity of A of the eccentric EA is same as can be obtained from a virtual eccentric with centre P having throw equal to (OE/ cos β) and the angle of advance (α + β). Since the position of eccentric OE changes with the rotation of crank , therefore the inclination of the eccentric EA with the horizontal (*i.e.* angle β) also changes. This change of angle β is very small because the eccentric rod length EA is 10 to 20 times the throw of eccentric OE. If γ is taken as the mean inclination of the eccentric rod EA, then the throw of virtual eccentric will be OE/ cos γ with an angle of advance (α + γ). Such an arrangement of the eccentric rod is called *open rod arrangement.*

If the eccentric rod EA instead of lying above the line of stroke of the piston (*i.e.* open rod arrangement), it is in crossed position by crossing the line of stroke (*i.e.* crossed-rod arrangement) as shown by EA_1 in Fig. 17.26, then the velocity triangle for the mechanism OEA_1 will be triangle OEM_1. In this case

$$\frac{v_{A1}}{v_E} = \frac{OM_1}{OE} = \frac{\sin \angle OEM_1}{\sin \angle OME}$$

$$= \frac{\sin [180° - (\theta + \alpha) - (90° - \beta_1)]}{\sin (90° - \beta_1)} = \frac{\cos (\theta + \alpha - \beta_1)}{\cos \beta_1}$$

$$\therefore \quad v_{A1} = v_E \times \frac{\cos (\theta + \alpha - \beta_1)}{\cos \beta_1} = \omega \times \frac{OE}{\cos \beta_1} \times \cos (\theta + \alpha - \beta_1)$$

$$= \omega \times \frac{OE}{\cos \gamma} \times \cos (\theta + \alpha - \gamma) \qquad ...(\text{Taking mean } \beta_1 = \gamma)$$

From the above expression, we see that for the crossed rod arrangement, the throw for the virtual eccentric with centre P_1 is same *i.e.* OE/ cos γ but the angle of advance is (α – γ).

The throw and angle of advance of the virtual eccentric may be determined by the simple graphical construction as discussed below :

1. For A, draw PF parallel and equal to OE. From F draw FG perpendicular to PF. The angle FPG is equal to γ. Now PG is the virtual eccentric.

2. Similarly for A_1, P_1G_1 is the virtual eccentric.

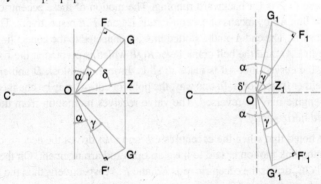

(*a*) For open rod arrangement   (*b*) For crossed rod arrangement.

Fig. 17.27. Determination of virtual eccentrics.

We have already discussed that in link motions, there are two eccentrics. These two eccentrics are connected to their respective eccentric rods. The ends of these eccentric rods are connected to a slotted link in which a die block slides. The die block is connected to the valve through a valve rod. The resultant graphical construction for the open rod and crossed rod arrangements is shown in Fig. 17.27 (*a*) and (*b*) respectively. The determination of virtual eccentrics OG and OG' for the two eccentrics of the open rod arrangement is shown in Fig. 17.27 (*a*) whereas the determination of virtual eccentrics OG_1 and OG'_1 for the eccentrics of the crossed rod arrangement is shown in Fig. 17.27 (*b*). The straight lines GG' in Fig. 17.27 (*a*) and $G_1G'_1$ in Fig. 17.27 (*b*) are divided at Z and Z' respectively in the same ratio in which the die block, for a given setting of the link motion, divides the slotted link in which it slides. Now OZ is the throw of the virtual eccentric and δ is the angle of advance for the open rod arrangement. Similarly OZ_1 is the throw of the virtual eccentric and δ' is the angle of advance for the crossed rod arrangement.

17.17. Stephenson Link Motion

The Stephenson link motion, as shown in Fig. 17.28, is the most commonly used reversing gear in steam engines. It is simple in construction and gives a good steam distribution. Fig. 17.28 shows the arrangement of the gear in mid-position, where OC is the crank and OE and OE_1 are the two eccentrics fixed on the driving shaft or axle in case of a locomotive. The eccentric OE is for

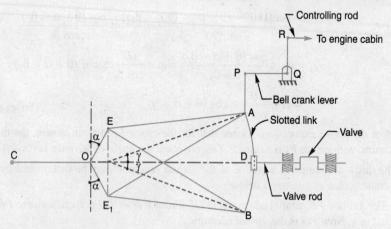

Fig. 17.28. Stephenson link motion.

forward running and OE_1 is for backward running. The motion of these eccentrics is transmitted to the *curved slotted link AB by means of eccentric rods EA and E_1B respectively. The link AB can also slide on the die block D. The end A on the slotted link is connected to the controlling rod in the engine cabin through the link AP and the bell crank lever RQP which is pivoted at the fixed fulcrum Q. By moving the lever, the curved link AB is made to slide through the block D and enables the latter to derive its motion either from B or A. In this way, the point of cut-off may be changed and the direction of motion of the engine may be reversed. The valve receives its motion from the block D and the valve rod is guided horizontally.

It may be noted that when the eccentrics OE and OE_1 drives the eccentric rods EA and E_1B respectively, then the link motion is said to have an open rod arrangement. On the other hand, if the eccentrics OE and OE_1 drives the eccentric rods EB and E_1A respectively, then the link motion is said to have crossed rod arrangement. This arrangement gives different steam distribution.

---

* The radius of curvature of the link AB with either open or crossed rod arrangement is generally equal to the length of the eccentric rod EA or E_1B.

The link motion is said to be in *full forward gear position,* when the curved link is lowered so that *A* and *D* coincides. In this position, the valve receives its motion entirely from the eccentric *OE.* When the curved link is raised so that *B* and *D* coincide, it is said to be in *full backward gear position.* In this position, the valve recieves its motion entirely from the eccentric OE_1. Similarly, when *D* lies in the middle of *AB*, the link motion is said to be in *mid-gear position.* In this position (or for any other position of *D* between *AB*), the valve recieves its motion partly from the eccentric *OE* and partly from the eccentric OE_1.

17.18. Virtual or Equivalent Eccentric for Stephenson Link Motion

The Stephenson link motion in an intermediate position is shown in Fig. 17.29. Let us now find out the equivalent eccentric for the intermediate positions of the die block *D*. If we assume that ends *A* and *B* of the curved link *AB* move along a straight path parallel to the line of stroke of the valve, the equivalent eccentric for the ends *A* and *B* and for the die block *D* may be determined in the similar manner as discussed in Art 17.16. Fig. 17.30 (*a*) and (*b*) has been reproduced for the two positions (*i.e.* when *D* is in mid-position and in intermediate position) of the open rod arrangement. In Fig. 17.30 (*a*), *OH* is the equivalent eccentric for the mid-gear whereas in Fig. 17.30 (*b*), *OZ* is the equivalent eccentric for any other position. If the construction is repeated for different positions of the die block *D*, various points similar to *Z* may be obtained. Now a curve is drawn through the various positions of *Z*. A close approximation to this curve may be obtained by drawing a circular arc through the points *E*, *H* and E_1 as shown in Fig. 17.30 (*a*). Now the equivalent eccentric for the gear position, as shown in Fig. 17.29, may be determined by dividing the *arc EHE_1 at *Z* in the same ratio as *D* divides *AB*.

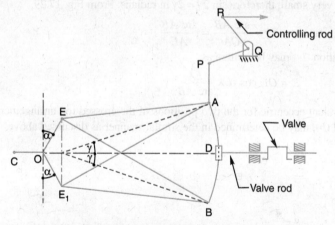

Fig. 17.29. Stephenon link motion in an intermediate position.

Let *R* be the radius of the arc of the circle representing the locus of the points similar to *Z* as shown in Fig. 17.30 (*a*).

∴
$$R^2 = (OJ)^2 + (EJ)^2 = (OH - HJ)^2 + (EJ)^2 = (R - HJ)^2 + (EJ)^2$$
$$= R^2 + (HJ)^2 - 2R \times HJ + (EJ)^2$$

or
$$R = \frac{(HJ)^2 + (EJ)^2}{2\,HJ} \qquad \qquad ...(i)$$

Now
$$EJ = OE \cos \alpha \qquad \qquad ...(ii)$$

---

* A very close result can be obtained by dividing *GH* at *Z* in the same ratio as *D* divides *AB*.

and
$$HJ = GD = EG \cos \alpha = (OE \tan \gamma) \cos \alpha \qquad \text{...(iii)}$$

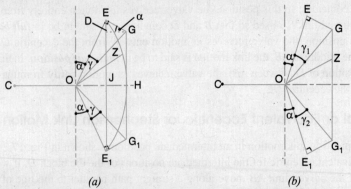

(a)   *(b)*

Fig. 17.30. Equivalent eccentric for the two positions of the open rod arrangement.

Substuting the values of EJ and HJ from equations *(ii)* and *(iii)* in equation *(i)*,

$$R = \frac{(OE \tan \gamma)^2 \cos^2 \alpha + (OE \cos \alpha)^2}{2 (OE \tan \gamma) \cos \alpha}$$

$$= \frac{OE \cos \alpha \, (1 + \tan^2 \gamma)}{2 \tan \gamma} = \frac{OE \cos \alpha \times \sec^2 \gamma}{2 \tan \gamma} \qquad \text{...(} \because 1 + \tan^2\gamma = \sec^2\gamma \text{)}$$

$$= \frac{OE \cos \alpha}{2 \sin \gamma \cos \gamma} = \frac{OE \cos \alpha}{\sin 2\gamma} \qquad \text{...(iv)}$$

where γ = Mean inclination of the eccentric rod to the line of stroke of the valve.

Since γ is very small, therefore $\sin 2\gamma = 2\gamma$ in radians. From Fig. 17.29,

$$\sin 2\gamma = 2\gamma = \frac{\text{arc } AB}{OA} = \frac{\text{arc } AB}{AE}$$

Now equation *(iv)* may be written as

$$R = OE \cos \alpha \times \frac{EA}{\text{arc } AB} \qquad \text{...(v)}$$

The equivalent eccentric for the two positions of the crossed rod arrangement, as shown in Fig. 17.31 *(a)* and *(b)*, may be determined in the similar manner as discussed above.

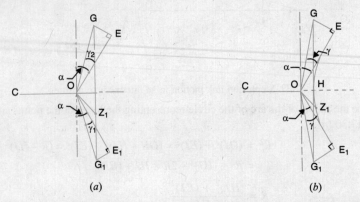

(a)   *(b)*

Fig. 17.31. Equivalent eccentric for the two positions of the crossed rod arrangement.

After finding the equivalent eccentric for a given setting of the gear, the corresponding Reuleaux of Bilgram diagram is drawn to determine the crank positions at admission, cut-off, release and compression.

Note: Comparing Fig. 17.30 (*a*) for open rod arrangement and Fig. 17.31 (*a*) for crossed rod arrangement, we see that the projection of the virtual eccentric on the line of stroke for any given setting of the gear when it moves from full gear to mid gear position,

1. increases in case of open rod arrangement, and

2. decreases in case of crossed rod arrangement.

This projection is equal to steam lap plus lead. The steam lap being constant, it follows that during *linking up* the gear (*i.e.* when the gear moves from full gear position to mid-gear position), the lead increases in open rod arrangement, while it decreases in crossed rod arrangement.

Example 17.8. *A stephenson link motion with open rods has a throw of each eccentric 75 mm and an angle of advance 18°. The length of the curved slotted link is 400 mm and its radius of curvature is equal to the length of the eccentric rod which is 1.15 m. Determine the throw and angle of advance of the equivalent eccentric when 1. the gear is in the mid-position and 2. the gear is in the middle of full-gear and mid-gear.*

Solution. Given $OE = 75$ mm ; $\alpha = 18°$; Arc $AB = 400$ mm; $EA = 1.15$ m $= 1150$ mm

1. Throw and angle of advance of the equivalent eccentric when the gear is in mid-position

Let R = Radius of the arc or the locus of points similar to Z, as shown in Fig. 17.30 (*a*).

We know that

$$R = OE \cos \alpha \times \frac{EA}{\text{arc } AB}$$

$$= 75 \times \cos 18° \times \frac{1150}{400} = 205 \text{ mm}$$

Now draw OE and OE_1 equal to 75 mm and at an angle of 18° to vertical YY_1 as shown in Fig. 17.32. The point P on the line of stroke is found by drawing an arc either from E or E_1 such that $EP = E_1P = R = 205$ mm. With P as centre and radius 205 mm draw an arc EHE_1. Now OH represents the equivalent eccentric and angle YOH is its angle of advance when the gear is in mid-position. By measurement, throw of equivalent eccentric,

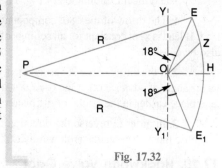

$$OH = 38 \text{ mm Ans.}$$

and   angle of advance $= \angle YOH = 90°$ Ans.

Fig. 17.32

2. Throw and angle of advance of the equivalent eccentric when the gear is in the middle of the full-gear and mid-gear

In Fig. 17.32, the point E represents the full-gear position and H the mid-gear position. When the gear is in the middle of the full-gear and mid-gear positions, *i.e.* in the middle of E and H, divide the arc EH such that $EZ = ZH$. Now OZ represents the equivalent eccentric and angle YOZ is its angle of advance. By measurement, throw of equivalent eccentric,

$$OZ = 50 \text{ mm Ans.}$$

and   angle of advance $= \angle YOH = 45°$ Ans.

17.19. Radial Valve Gears

We have already discussed that in radial valve gears, only one eccentric or its equivalent is used. The principle on which the radial valve gears operate is discussed below :

Let OC be the crank and OE the eccentric for a D-slide valve as shown in Fig. 17.33 (a). OX and OY are the projections of OE along OC and perpendicular to OC respectively. When the crank turns through an angle θ from the inner dead centre, the distance moved by the valve from its mid-position is given by OM which is the projection of the eccentric OE on the line of stroke, as shown in Fig. 17.33 (b). OX and OY are the projections of the eccentric OE along the crank OC and perpendicular to OC. OP and OL are the projections of OX and OY on the line of stroke. From Fig. 17.33 (b),

$$OM = OL + LM = OL + {}^*OP$$

From the above expression, it follows that a motion given to the valve by the eccentric OE (*i.e.* displacement OM) may be obtained by combining the displacements OL and OP obtained from two separate eccentrics OY and OX. The eccentric OY is 90° out of phase with the engine crank OC and is known as **90° component eccentric.** The eccentric OX is 180° out of phase with the engine crank OC and is known as **180° component eccentric.**

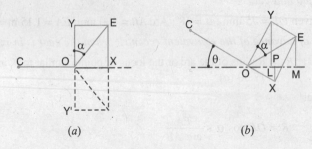

(a) (b)

Fig. 17.33. Radial valve gear.

The critical examination of Fig. 17.33 shows that

1. The throw of the 180° component eccentric (*i.e.* OX) is equal to the sum of steam lap and lead. If lead is kept constant for all settings of the gear, the throw of the 180° component eccentric will also be constant.

2. If the throw of the 90° component eccentric (*i.e.* OY) is reduced, the eccentric OE will have larger angle of advance α ($\because$ $\tan \alpha = OX/OY$). The increase of angle of advance will cause cut-off to take place earlier in the stroke of the piston.

3. In order to reverse the direction of rotation of the crank, the direction of 90° component eccentric must be reversed as shown by OY' in Fig. 17.33 (a).

17.20. Hackworth Valve Gear

This is the earliest of the radial valve gears in which the eccentric OE is placed directly opposite to the main crank OC, as shown in Fig. 17.34. The eccentric centre E is coupled to a sliding or die block D which reciprocates along the slotted bar GH which is pivoted to the frame at F. The slotted bar GH is inclined to OF which is perpendicular to the line of stroke. The inclination of GH (*i.e.* angle β) is fixed for a given setting of the gear and is a maximum for the full gear positions. In order to reverse the direction of rotation of the engine, the slotted bar GH is tilted into the dotted position as shown in Fig. 17.34. In mid-gear position, the slotted bar occupies the vertical position OZ so that the motion of die block D is then perpendicular to the line of stroke of the engine. For constant lead of the valve for all settings, the length of eccentric rod ED must be such that D and F coincide, when the crank is in either dead centre positions. The valve is driven by a connecting link AB from a point A on the eccentric rod ED.

---

* $LM = OP$, being the projection of two equal and parallel lines OX' and EY respectively.

The throw of the virtual or equivalent eccentric and its angle of advance may be determined as follows :

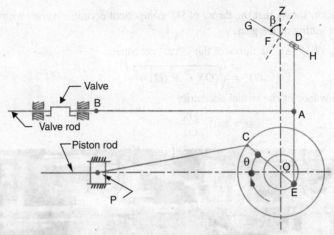

Fig. 17.34. Hackworth valve gear.

The virtual eccentric *OV* is assumed to be equivalent to two eccentrics, *i.e.* 180° component eccentric *OX* and 90° component eccentric *OY*, as shown in Fig. 17.35 (*a*). First of all, let us find the values of *OX* and *OY*. During the motion of crank *OC* from one dead centre to another dead centre, the point *E* on the eccentric as well as link *DAE* moves through a distance equal to 2 *OE* along the line of stroke, while the distance moved perpendicular to the line of stroke is zero because *D* occupies the position *F* at both the dead centres. Now the displacement of the valve during the motion of crank from one dead centre to another will be *AA'* or 2 *OX*. This may be clearly understood from Fig. 17.35 (*b*).

$$\therefore \qquad \frac{2OX}{2OE} = \frac{DA}{DE} \quad \text{or} \quad OX = \frac{DA}{DE} \times OE \qquad \qquad ...(i)$$

This equation shows that the throw of 180° component eccentric is independent of the setting of the gear. This throw (*i.e. OX*) is equal to steam lap plus lead.

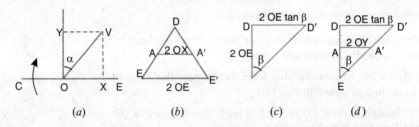

Fig. 17.35. Determination of throw and angle of advance of the virtual or equivalent eccentric.

Now considering the motion of the crank *OC* from one vertical position to another vertical position. The point *E* on the eccentric as well as the link *DAE* moves through a vertical distance equal to 2 *OE*, while the horizontal distance moved by the point *E* is zero. Since the slotted bar *GH* is inclined at an angle β, therefore from Fig. 17.35 (*c*),

Horizontal distance moved by $D = DD' = 2OE \tan β$

Now the displacement of the valve during the motion of crank from one vertical position to another will be 2 *OY*. Therefore from Fig. 17.35 (*d*),

$$\frac{2\,OY}{2\,OE\tan\beta} = \frac{EA}{ED} \quad \text{or} \quad OY = \frac{EA}{ED}\times OE\tan\beta \qquad \qquad ...(ii)$$

This equation shows that the throw of 90° component eccentric varies with the angle β *i.e.* with the particular setting of the gear.

From Fig. 17.35 (*a*), the throw of the virtual eccentric,

$$OV = \sqrt{(OX)^2 + (OY)^2} \qquad \qquad ...(iii)$$

and the angle of advance of the virtual eccentric,

$$\alpha = \tan^{-1}\frac{OX}{OY} \qquad \qquad ...(iv)$$

Inside view of a factory.

Note : This picture is given as additional information.

The equivalent eccentric for a given setting of the gear may be determined graphically as discussed below :

1. Draw OE, to some suitable scale, to represent the throw of the actual eccentric as shown in Fig. 17.36.

2. Through E, draw ED inclined at angle β to OE so that OD represents $OE\tan\beta$ to scale. The angle β is drawn upwards when slotted bar GH (Fig. 17.34) is in full line position and it is drawn downwards when GH is tilted to the dotted position, as shown in Fig. 17.36.

3. Divide OE at X in the same proportion as A divides ED in Fig. 17.34. Through X draw a line perpendicualr to OE to meet ED at V. Now OV is the equivalent eccentric for the motion of the valve.

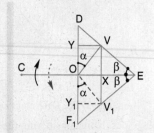

Fig. 17.36

Example 17.9. *In a Hackworth radial valve gear, as shown in Fig. 17.37, the dimensions of various link are as follows :*

OC = 225 mm; CP = 800 mm; DE = 625 mm and AE = 300 mm

If the lead is constant at 3 mm, the steam lap is 18 mm and the angle β is 20°, find the length of eccentric OE, the distance OF, the effective valve travel and the effective angle of advance.

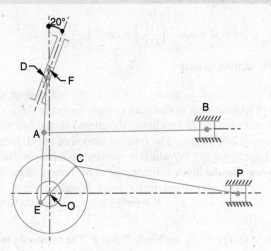

Fig. 17.37

Solution. Given : $l = 3$ mm ; $s = 18$ mm ; $β = 20°$

Length of eccentric OE

We know that in case of a Hackworth radial valve gear, the virtual eccentric OV may be assumed to be equivalent to two eccentrics, *i.e.* 180° component eccentric and 90° component eccentric as shown in Fig. 17.38. The throw of the 180° component eccentric is given by

$$OX = \frac{DA}{DE} \times OE = \frac{DE - AE}{DE} \times OE = \frac{625 - 300}{625} \times OE$$

$$= 0.52 \, OE \qquad \qquad ...(i)$$

Also $\qquad OX = s + l = 18 + 3 = 21$ mm $\qquad ...(ii)$

From equations (*i*) and (*ii*),

$$OE = 21/0.52 = 40.4 \text{ mm}$$

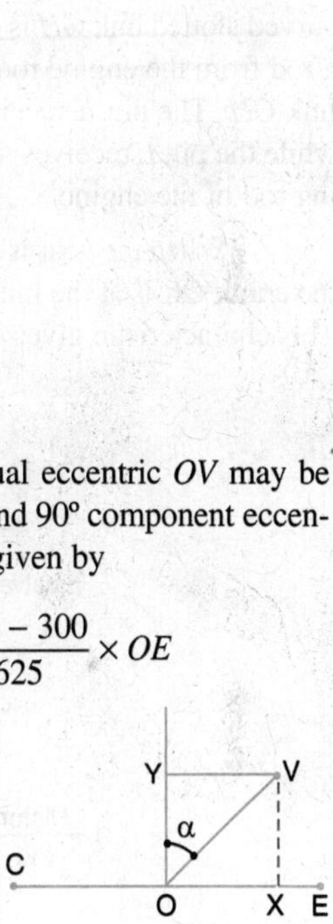

Distance OF

Fig. 17.38

When the eccentric OE is along the line of stroke, the point D coincides with F and the angle $FOE = 90°$.

$$\therefore \qquad (OF)^2 + (OE)^2 = (DE)^2$$

or $\qquad OF = \sqrt{(DE)^2 - (OE)^2} = \sqrt{(625)^2 - (40.4)^2} = 623.7 \text{ mm Ans.}$

Effective valve travel

We know that the 90° component eccentric,

$$OY = \frac{EA}{ED} \times OE \, \tan β = \frac{300}{625} \times 40.4 \, \tan 20° = 7.06 \text{ mm}$$

$\therefore$ Throw of the virtual eccentric,

$$OV = \sqrt{(OX)^2 + (OY)^2} = \sqrt{(21)^2 + (7.06)^2} = 22.15 \text{ mm}$$

and effective valve travel $\qquad = 2 \times OV = 2 \times 22.15 = 44.3 \text{ mm Ans.}$

Effective angle of advance

We know that effective angle of advance,

$$\alpha = \tan^{-1}\left(\frac{OX}{OY}\right) = \tan^{-1}\left(\frac{21}{7.06}\right) = \tan^{-1} 2.9745 = 71.4° \text{ Ans.}$$

17.21. Walschaert's Valve Gear

The Walschaert's valve gear, as shown in Fig. 17.39, is the most extensively used of all reversing gears on modern locomotives. In this gear, a single eccentric OE is used and is set at 90° to the main crank OC. The eccentric rod EG oscillates the curved slotted link GH about the fulcrum F which is fixed to the frame of the engine. The relative motion of the sliding or die block D in the curved slotted link GH is due to the link PQ which is operated by means of a bell crank lever SRQ and a rod from the engine room. The die block D is capable of movement along the whole length of the link GH. The pin K receives its motion from the die block D and ultimately from the eccentric OE, while the pin L receives its motion from a point B on the main crosshead A, where AC is the connecting rod of the engine.

When the gear is in mid-position, the block D is at F. The radius of link GH is such that when the crank OC is at the inner dead centre position and the gear is reversed, the point K remains at rest. This characteristic gives constant lead during all conditions of running.

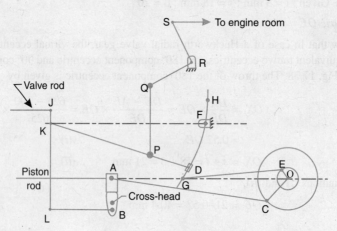

Fig. 17.39. Walschaert's valve gear.

Neglecting obliquities of all the rods, the throw of the virtual eccentric and its angle of advance may be determined in the similar manner as discussed in the previous article. The virtual eccentric OV is assumed to be equivalent to two eccentrics *i.e.* 180° component eccentric OX and 90° component eccentric OY, as shown in Fig. 17.40 (*a*).

First of all, let us find the values of OX and OY. Considering the motion of crank OC from one dead centre to another dead centre, the crosshead A and hence the point L on the link JKL moves through a distance equal to 2 OC. During this motion of the crank, the point G on the slotted link and hence the point K on the link JKL occupy the same position as at start. In other words, the distance moved by K is zero. Now the displacement of the valve during the motion of crank from one dead centre to another dead centre will be JJ' or 2 OX.

From Fig. 17.40 (*b*),

$$\frac{2\,OX}{2\,OC} = \frac{JK}{KL} \quad \text{or} \quad OX = \frac{JK}{KL} \times OC \qquad \qquad ...(i)$$

Thus OX is constant for all positions of the block D on the link GH and the lead remains unchanged during all conditions of running. In case the point J lies on the same side of K as L, the motion of J and L will be in phase. In this position, OX is termed as $0°$ *component eccentric.*

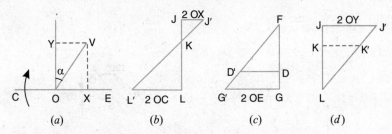

Fig. 17.40. Determination of throw and angle of advance of the virtual eccentric.

Now considering the motion of the eccentric OE from one dead centre position to another dead centre, the crank pin C moves from one vertical position to another, thus not traversing any horizontal distance. During this motion of the eccentric, the distance moved by the crosshead A and thus the point L on the link JKL will be zero. At the same time, the point E on the eccentric OE and the point G on the curved slotted link GH moves through a distance $2 OE$. Since the curved slotted link GH is hinged at F, therefore the die block D moves through a distance DD' which is given by

$$\frac{DD'}{2OE} = \frac{FD}{FG} \quad \text{or} \quad DD' = \frac{FD}{FG} \times 2OE \qquad \text{...[From Fig. 17.40 (c)]}$$

Since point K lies on the link DK, therefore point K will move through the same distance as that of D, *i.e.*

$$KK' = DD' = \frac{FD}{FG} \times 2OE$$

Now the displacement of the valve during the motion of the crank from one vertical position to another will be JJ' or $2 OY$. From Fig. 17.40 (d),

$$\frac{JJ'}{KK'} = \frac{JL}{KL} \quad \text{or} \quad \frac{2OY \times FG}{FD \times 2OE} = \frac{JL}{KL}$$

$$\therefore \qquad OY = \frac{JL}{KL} \times \frac{FD}{FG} \times OE \qquad \text{...(ii)}$$

The position of D on the curved slotted link GH may be varied by operating the bell crank lever from the rod in the engine room in order to suit load conditions or to effect the reversal of direction or rotation.

From Fig. 17.40 (a), the throw of the virtual eccentric,

$$OV = \sqrt{(OX)^2 + (OY)^2} \qquad \text{...(iii)}$$

and the angle of advance of the virtual eccentric,

$$\alpha = \tan^{-1} \frac{OX}{OY} \qquad \text{...(iv)}$$

Example 17.10. *In a Walschaert valve gear, as shown in Fig. 17.39, the engine crank is 300 mm long. The least cut-off in the head end of the cylinder is at 120°. At this, the maximum opening to steam is 45 mm and the lead is 6 mm. If the length of the eccentric is 115 mm, find the ratios $\dfrac{JL}{KL}$ and $\dfrac{FG}{FD}$ of the gear. Neglect the obliquities of all the rods.*

Solution. Given : $OC = 300$ mm ; crank angle at cut-off $= 120°$; Maximum opening to steam $= 45$ mm ; $l = 6$ mm ; $OE = 115$ mm

First of all, draw the Bilgram valve diagram as discussed below :

1. Draw OC_2, the position of crank at cut-off, at $120°$ to the line of stroke OV as shown in Fig. 17.41.

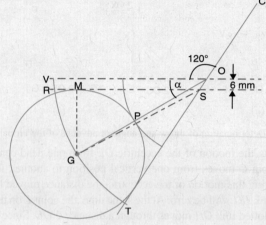

Fig. 17.41

2. Draw a line parallel to OV and at a distance equal to the lead (6 mm) which intersects C_2O produced at S.

3. With centre O, draw an arc with radius $OP = 45$ mm, the maximum opening of steam.

4. Draw the bisector of the angle RST. On this bisector, obtain a point G such that a circle drawn with centre G touches the lines SR, ST and the point P. Join OG.

By measurement, we find that throw of the virtual eccentric,

$$OV = OG = 81.5 \text{ mm}$$

and angle of advance of the virtual eccentric

$$\alpha = 32°$$

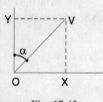

Fig. 17.42

The virtual eccentric OV is assumed to be equivalent to two eccentrics, *i.e.* $180°$ component eccentric OX and $90°$ component eccentric OY, as shown in Fig. 17.42.

∴ $180°$ component eccentric

$$= OX = VY = OV \sin \alpha = 81.5 \sin 32° = 43.2 \text{ mm}$$

and $90°$ component eccentric,

$$OY = OV \cos 32° = 81.5 \times 0.848 = 69.1 \text{ mm}$$

We know that $OX = \dfrac{JK}{KL} \times OC$ ...(Refer Fig. 17.39)

∴ $\dfrac{JK}{KL} = \dfrac{OX}{OC} = \dfrac{43.2}{300} = 0.144$

Now $\dfrac{JL}{KL} = \dfrac{KL + JK}{KL} = 1 + \dfrac{JK}{KL} = 1 + 0.144 = 1.144$ **Ans.**

Again we know that

$$OY = \dfrac{JL}{KL} \times \dfrac{FD}{FG} \times OE$$

∴ $\dfrac{FG}{FD} = \dfrac{JL}{KL} \times \dfrac{OE}{OY} = 1.144 \times \dfrac{115}{69.1} = 1.9$ **Ans.**

EXERCISES

1. A *D*-slide valve has a travel of 100 mm, angle of advance 30° and the exhaust lap at both ends of the valve is 12 mm. The cut-off takes place at 85% of the stroke on the cover end of the cylinder. Determine the lead and the point of release for this stroke.

   If the lead is same for both the ends, find the point of cut-off on the crank end and the steam lap. The length of the connecting rod is 4 times the crank length.

   [**Ans. 7.2 mm; 98% of stroke, 78% of stroke, 18 mm**]

2. The travel of a slide valve is 100 mm and the lead at the crank end is 6 mm. If the length of connecting rod is 4.5 times the crank length, find the angle of advance, steam lap and exhaust lap to give cut-off and release at 65% and 95% of the stroke respectively. [**Ans. 38°, 24 mm, 12 mm**]

3. The following data refer to a *D*-slide valve :

   Valve travel = 150 mm; Lead at cover end = 6 mm ; Connecting rod length = 5 times crank length; Cut-off at both ends of the piston = 0.7 stroke

   Determine the angle of advance of the eccentric and maximum opening of port to steam and steam lap for the cover end. Find also the steam lap and lead for the crank end of the valve.

   [**Ans. 40°, 35 mm; 40 mm; 26 mm; 22 mm**]

4. A simple slide valve with outside admission provides a lead of 3 mm, a maximum port opening of 18 mm and a cut-off at 62% at the out-stroke (*i.e.* at the crank end). The ratio of the connecting rod length to the crank radius is 3.7. Find the valve travel, steam lap and the angle of advance. If the exhaust lap is 12.5 mm, find the percentage of stroke at which release and compression will occur.

   [**Ans. 78 mm, 20 mm, 37°; 92.5% of forward stroke, 88% of return stroke**]

5. A steam engine fitted with a *D*-slide valve gives a cut-off at 65% of the stroke and release at 90% of the stroke for both ends of the cylinder. The width of the ports is 25 mm, maximum opening of port to steam is 18 mm and the valve lead at the cover end is 6 mm. If the length of the connecting rod is 5 times the crank length, find the total valve travel and the angle of advance of the eccentric. Determine also the valve lead at the crank end and the steam and exhaust laps for both ends of the cylinder.

   [**Ans. 88 mm, 45.5; *l* (crank end) = 14 mm, *s* (cover end) = 25 mm, (crank end) = 17.5 mm, *e* (cover end) = 6.5 mm, *e* (crank end) = 10.8 mm**]

6. The following particulars refer to a Meyer's expansion valve :

   Angle of advance of main eccentric = 35°; Travel of main valve = 150 mm; Angle of advance of expansion eccentric = 90°; Throw of expansion eccentric = 75 mm ; Ratio of connecting rod length to crank length = 4.

   Find the steam laps required at the two ends of the expansion valve in order to give cut-off at 0.2, 0.4 and 0.6 of the stroke on both strokes. Determine also the best setting of the expansion plates.

   [**Ans. 24 mm, 48 mm, 64 mm for cover end; 38 mm, 60 mm, 68 mm for crank end**]

7. The dimensions of a Hackworth valve gear, as shown in Fig. 17.34 (Page 645) are as follows :

   OC = 300 mm; *CP* = 700 mm; *OE* = 145 mm; *ED* = 800 mm and *EA* = 550 mm.

   The die block *D* coincides with *F* when the crank is at dead centres. Find the throw and the angle of advance of the equivalent eccentric when the inclination of the slotted link is 30° with the vertical.

   [**Ans. 73.3 mm; 38.2°**]

8. The Walschaert radial valve gear of a locomotive engine in which the slide valve has inside admission, is shown in Fig. 17.43. The main crank *OC* is 250 mm and the crank *OE* is 75 mm.

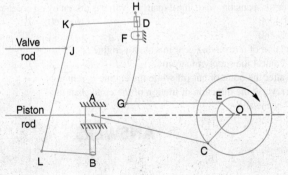

Fig. 17.43

If $DE = 0.6\ FG$ and $JK = 0.15\ JL$, find the travel of the valve. When the cut off is to take place at 60% of the stroke of the piston, find steam lap and lead of the valve. The motion of points K and L may each be assumed simple harmonic along a horizontal straight line.

[Ans. 100 mm, 32.5 mm, 0.75 mm]

DO YOU KNOW ?

1. State the function of a valve in a steam engine. Name the types of valves commonly used to control the various operations in a steam engine.

2. Describe the action of a D-slide valve and piston slide valve. Discuss the advantages of a piston slide valve over D-slide valve.

3. Define steam lap, exhaust lap and angle of advance for a simple slide valve with 1. out-side steam admission, and 2. inside steam admission.

4. Explain how the ponts of admission, cut-off, release and compression are determined for a D-slide valve using any one of the following constructions :
   1. Zeuner valve diagram. 2. Reuleaux valve diagram, and 3. Bilgram valve diagram.

5. Discuss with the help of diagrams, the disadvantages of earlier cut-off with a simple slide valve.

6. Explain with the help of a neat sketch, the function of a Meyer's expansion valve in a steam engine.

7. What do you understand by virtual or equivalent eccentric? How it is obtained for the Meyer's expansion valve?

8. Why the reversing gears are used in steam engines? State the commonly used types of reversing gears and how they differ from one another?

9. Describe, with the help of a line diagram, the working of a Stephenson link motion. How the virtual eccentric and its angle of advance for any setting of this link motion is determined?

10. Discuss the principle underlying the use of a radial valve gear.

11. Explain, with the help of a line diagram, the working of a Hackworth valve gear. Discuss the method to determine the virtual eccentric and its angle of advance for this gear.

12. Describe, with the help of a line diagram, the working of a Walschaert's valve gear. How will you determine the virtual eccentric and its angle of advance for this gear?

OBJECTIVE TYPE QUESTIONS

1. In a steam engine, the distance by which the outer edge of the D-slide valve overlaps the steam port is called
   (a) lead
   (b) steam lap
   (c) exhaust lap
   (d) none of these

2. The D-slide valve is also known as
   (a) inside admission valve
   (b) outside admission valve
   (c) piston slide valve
   (d) none of these

3. In Meyer's expansion valve, main valve is driven by an eccentric having an angle of advance
   (a) $10° – 15°$
   (b) $15° – 25°$
   (c) $25° – 30°$
   (d) $30° – 40°$

4. In Meyer's expansion valve, the expansion valve is driven by an eccentric having an angle of advance
   (a) $50° – 60°$
   (b) $60° – 70°$
   (c) $70° – 80°$
   (d) $80° – 90°$

5. The function of a reversing gear in a steam engine is
   (a) to control the supply of steam
   (b) to alter the point of cut-off while the engine is running
   (c) to reverse the direction of motion of the crankshaft
   (d) all of the above

ANSWERS

| 1. (b) | 2. (b) | 3. (c) | 4. (d) | 5. (b),(c) |

18

Governors

18.1. Introduction

The function of a governor is to regulate the mean speed of an engine, when there are variations in the load *e.g.* when the load on an engine increases, its speed decreases, therefore it becomes necessary to increase the supply of working fluid. On the other hand, when the load on the engine decreases, its speed increases and thus less working fluid is required. The governor automatically controls the supply of working fluid to the engine with the varying load conditions and keeps the mean speed within certain limits.

A little consideration will show, that when the load increases, the configuration of the governor changes and a valve is moved to increase the supply of the working fluid ; *conversely*, when the load decreases, the engine speed increases and the governor decreases the supply of working fluid.

Note : We have discussed in Chapter 16 (Art. 16.8) that the function of a flywheel in an engine is entirely different from that of a governor. It controls the speed variation caused by the fluctuations of the engine turning moment during each cycle of operation. It does not control the speed variations caused by a varying load. The varying demand for power is met by the governor regulating the supply of working fluid.

18.2. Types of Governors

The governors may, broadly, be classified as

1. Centrifugal governors, and 2. Inertia governors.

The centrifugal governors, may further be classified as follows :

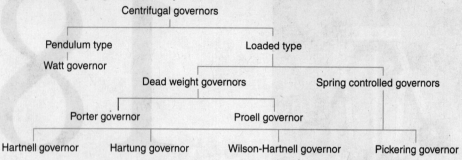

18.3. Centrifugal Governors

The centrifugal governors are based on the balancing of centrifugal force on the rotating balls by an equal and opposite radial force, known as the *controlling force**.It consists of two balls of equal mass, which are attached to the arms as shown in Fig. 18.1. These balls are known as *governor balls* or *fly balls*. The balls revolve with a spindle, which is driven by the engine through bevel gears. The upper ends of the arms are pivoted to the spindle, so that the balls may rise up or fall down as they revolve about the vertical axis. The arms are connected by the links to a sleeve, which is keyed to the spindle. This sleeve revolves with the spindle ; but can slide up and down. The balls and the sleeve rises when the spindle speed increases, and falls when the speed decreases. In order to limit the travel of the sleeve in upward and downward directions, two stops S, S are provided on the spindle. The sleeve is connected by a bell crank lever to a throttle valve. The supply of the working fluid decreases when the sleeve rises and increases when it falls.

When the load on the engine increases, the engine and the governor speed decreases. This results in the decrease of centrifugal force on the balls. Hence the balls move inwards and the sleeve moves downwards. The downward movement of the sleeve operates a throttle valve at the other end of the bell crank lever to increase the supply of working fluid and thus the engine speed is increased. In this case, the extra power output is provided to balance the increased load. When the load on the engine decreases, the engine and the governor speed increases, which results in the increase of centrifugal force on the balls. Thus the balls move outwards and the sleeve rises upwards. This upward movement of the sleeve reduces the supply of the working fluid and hence the speed is decreased. In this case, the power output is reduced.

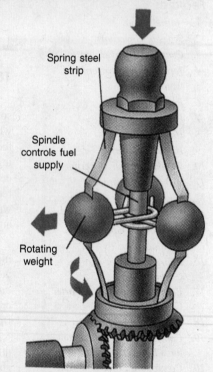

Spring steel strip

Spindle controls fuel supply

Rotating weight

A governor controls engine speed. As it rotates, the weights swing outwards, pulling down a spindle that reduces the fuel supply at high speed.

---

* The controlling force is provided either by the action of gravity as in Watt governor or by a spring as in case of Hartnell governor.

Note : When the balls rotate at uniform speed, controlling force is equal to the centrifugal force and they balance each other.

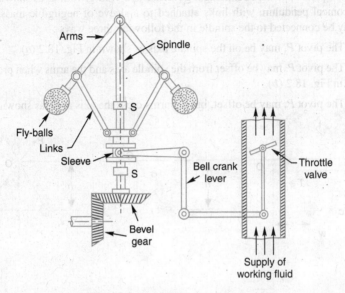

Fig. 18.1. Centrifugal governor.

18.4. Terms Used in Governors

The following terms used in governors are important from the subject point of view ;

1. *Height of a governor.* It is the vertical distance from the centre of the ball to a point where the axes of the arms (or arms produced) intersect on the spindle axis. It is usually denoted by *h*.

2. *Equilibrium speed.* It is the speed at which the governor balls, arms etc., are in complete equilibrium and the sleeve does not tend to move upwards or downwards.

3. *Mean equilibrium speed.* It is the speed at the mean position of the balls or the sleeve.

4. *Maximum and minimum equilibrium speeds.* The speeds at the maximum and minimum radius of rotation of the balls, without tending to move either way are known as maximum and minimum equilibrium speeds respectively.

Note : There can be many equilibrium speeds between the mean and the maximum and the mean and the minimum equilibrium speeds.

5. *Sleeve lift.* It is the vertical distance which the sleeve travels due to change in equilibrium speed.

Centrifugal governor

18.5. Watt Governor

The simplest form of a centrifugal governor is a Watt governor, as shown in Fig. 18.2. It is basically a conical pendulum with links attached to a sleeve of negligible mass. The arms of the governor may be connected to the spindle in the following three ways :

1. The pivot P, may be on the spindle axis as shown in Fig. 18.2 (a).

2. The pivot P, may be offset from the spindle axis and the arms when produced intersect at O, as shown in Fig. 18.2 (b).

3. The pivot P, may be offset, but the arms cross the axis at O, as shown in Fig. 18.2 (c).

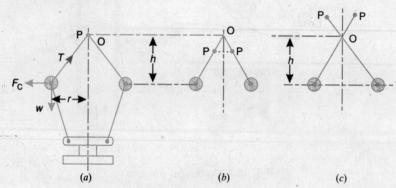

Fig. 18.2. Watt governor.

Let
m = Mass of the ball in kg,

w = Weight of the ball in newtons = $m.g$,

T = Tension in the arm in newtons,

ω = Angular velocity of the arm and ball about the spindle axis in rad/s,

r = Radius of the path of rotation of the ball *i.e.* horizontal distance from the centre of the ball to the spindle axis in metres,

F_C = Centrifugal force acting on the ball in newtons = $m.\omega^2.r$, and

h = Height of the governor in metres.

It is assumed that the weight of the arms, links and the sleeve are negligible as compared to the weight of the balls. Now, the ball is in equilibrium under the action of

1. the centrifugal force (F_C) acting on the ball, 2. the tension (T) in the arm, and 3. the weight (w) of the ball.

Taking moments about point O, we have

$$F_C \times h = w \times r = m.g.r$$

or
$$m.\omega^2.r.h = m.g.r \quad \text{or} \quad h = g/\omega^2 \qquad \ldots (i)$$

When g is expressed in m/s^2 and ω in rad/s, then h is in metres. If N is the speed in r.p.m., then

$$\omega = 2\pi N/60$$

∴
$$h = \frac{9.81}{(2\pi N/60)^2} = \frac{895}{N^2} \text{ metres} \qquad \ldots (\because g = 9.81 \text{ m/s}^2) \ldots (ii)$$

Note : We see from the above expression that the height of a governor h, is inversely proportional to N^2. Therefore at high speeds, the value of h is small. At such speeds, the change in the value of h corresponding to a small change in speed is insufficient to enable a governor of this type to operate the mechanism to give the necessary change in the fuel supply. This governor may only work satisfactorily at relatively low speeds *i.e.* from 60 to 80 r.p.m.

Example 18.1. *Calculate the vertical height of a Watt governor when it rotates at 60 r.p.m. Also find the change in vertical height when its speed increases to 61 r.p.m.*

Solution. Given : $N_1 = 60$ r.p.m. ; $N_2 = 61$ r.p.m.

Initial height

We know that initial height,

$$h_1 = \frac{895}{(N_1)^2} = \frac{895}{(60)^2} = 0.248 \text{ m}$$

Change in vertical height

We know that final height,

$$h_2 = \frac{895}{(N_2)^2} = \frac{895}{(61)^2} = 0.24 \text{ m}$$

∴   Change in vertical height

$$= h_1 - h_2 = 0.248 - 0.24 = 0.008 \text{ m} = 8 \text{ mm Ans.}$$

18.6. Porter Governor

The Porter governor is a modification of a Watt's governor, with central load attached to the sleeve as shown in Fig. 18.3 (*a*). The load moves up and down the central spindle. This additional downward force increases the speed of revolution required to enable the balls to rise to any pre-determined level.

Consider the forces acting on one-half of the governor as shown in Fig. 18.3 (*b*).

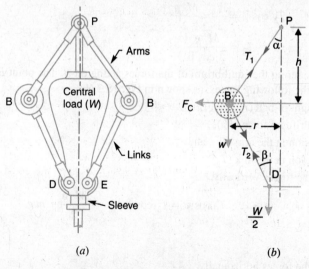

(*a*)   (*b*)

Fig. 18.3. Porter governor.

Let m = Mass of each ball in kg,

w = Weight of each ball in newtons = $m.g$,

M = Mass of the central load in kg,

W = Weight of the central load in newtons = $M.g$,

r = Radius of rotation in metres,

h = Height of governor in metres ,

N = Speed of the balls in r.p.m .,

ω = Angular speed of the balls in rad/s
$= 2\pi N/60$ rad/s,

F_C = Centrifugal force acting on the ball
in newtons $= m.\omega^2.r$,

T_1 = Force in the arm in newtons,

T_2 = Force in the link in newtons,

α = Angle of inclination of the arm (or
upper link) to the vertical, and

β = Angle of inclination of the link

(or lower link) to the vertical.

Though there are several ways of determining the relation between the height of the governor (h) and the angular speed of the balls (ω), yet the following two methods are important from the subject point of view :

1. Method of resolution of forces ; and
2. Instantaneous centre method.

A big hydel generator. Governors are used to control the supply of working fluid (water in hydel generators).

Note : This picture is given as additional information.

1. *Method of resolution of forces*

Considering the equilibrium of the forces acting at D, we have

$$T_2 \cos \beta = \frac{W}{2} = \frac{M.g}{2}$$

or
$$T_2 = \frac{M.g}{2 \cos \beta} \qquad \ldots (i)$$

Again, considering the equilibrium of the forces acting on B. The point B is in equilibrium under the action of the following forces, as shown in Fig. 18.3 (b).

(i) The weight of ball ($w = m.g$),

(ii) The centrifugal force (F_C),

(iii) The tension in the arm (T_1), and

(iv) The tension in the link (T_2).

Resolving the forces vertically,

$$T_1 \cos \alpha = T_2 \cos \beta + w = \frac{M.g}{2} + m.g \qquad \ldots (ii)$$

$$\ldots \left(\because T_2 \cos \beta = \frac{M.g}{2} \right)$$

Resolving the forces horizontally,

$$T_1 \sin \alpha + T_2 \sin \beta = F_C$$

$$T_1 \sin \alpha + \frac{M.g}{2 \cos \beta} \times \sin \beta = F_C \qquad \ldots \left(\because T_2 = \frac{M.g}{2 \cos \beta} \right)$$

$$T_1 \sin \alpha + \frac{M.g}{2} \times \tan \beta = F_C$$

∴
$$T_1 \sin \alpha = F_C - \frac{M.g}{2} \times \tan \beta \qquad \ldots (iii)$$

Dividing equation (*iii*) by equation (*ii*),

$$\frac{T_1 \sin \alpha}{T_1 \cos \alpha} = \frac{F_C - \dfrac{M.g}{2} \times \tan \beta}{\dfrac{M.g}{2} + m.g}$$

or

$$\left(\frac{M.g}{2} + m.g\right) \tan \alpha = F_C - \frac{M.g}{2} \times \tan \beta$$

$$\frac{M.g}{2} + m.g = \frac{F_C}{\tan \alpha} - \frac{M.g}{2} \times \frac{\tan \beta}{\tan \alpha}$$

Substituting $\dfrac{\tan \beta}{\tan \alpha} = q$, and $\tan \alpha = \dfrac{r}{h}$, we have

$$\frac{M.g}{2} + m.g = m.\omega^2.r \times \frac{h}{r} - \frac{M.g}{2} \times q \qquad \dots (\because F_C = m.\omega^2.r)$$

or

$$m.\omega^2.h = m.g + \frac{M.g}{2}(1 + q)$$

$\therefore$

$$h = \left[m.g + \frac{M.g}{2}(1 + q)\right]\frac{1}{m.\omega^2} = \frac{m + \dfrac{M}{2}(1 + q)}{m} \times \frac{g}{\omega^2} \qquad \dots (iv)$$

or

$$\omega^2 = \left[m.g + \frac{Mg}{2}(1 + q)\right]\frac{1}{m.h} = \frac{m + \dfrac{M}{2}(1 + q)}{m} \times \frac{g}{h}$$

or

$$\left(\frac{2\pi N}{60}\right)^2 = \frac{m + \dfrac{M}{2}(1 + q)}{m} \times \frac{g}{h}$$

$\therefore$

$$N^2 = \frac{m + \dfrac{M}{2}(1 + q)}{m} \times \frac{g}{h}\left(\frac{60}{2\pi}\right)^2 = \frac{m + \dfrac{M}{2}(1 + q)}{m} \times \frac{895}{h} \qquad \dots (v)$$

$$\dots \text{(Taking } g = 9.81 \text{ m/s}^2)$$

Notes : 1. When the length of arms are equal to the length of links and the points *P* and *D* lie on the same vertical line, then

$$\tan \alpha = \tan \beta \qquad \text{or} \qquad q = \tan \alpha / \tan \beta = 1$$

Therefore, the equation (*v*) becomes

$$N^2 = \frac{(m + M)}{m} \times \frac{895}{h} \qquad \dots (vi)$$

2. When the loaded sleeve moves up and down the spindle, the frictional force acts on it in a direction opposite to that of the motion of sleeve.

If *F* = Frictional force acting on the sleeve in newtons, then the equations (*v*) and (*vi*) may be written as

$$N^2 = \frac{m.g + \left(\dfrac{M.g \pm F}{2}\right)(1 + q)}{m.g} \times \frac{895}{h} \qquad \dots (vii)$$

$$= \frac{m.g + (M.g \pm F)}{m.g} \times \frac{895}{h} \qquad \dots \text{(When } q = 1) \dots (viii)$$

The + sign is used when the sleeve moves upwards or the governor speed increases and negative sign is used when the sleeve moves downwards or the governor speed decreases.

3. On comparing the equation (*vi*) with equation (*ii*) of Watt's governor (Art. 18.5), we find that the mass of the central load (*M*) increases the height of governor in the ratio $\dfrac{m+M}{m}$.

2. Instantaneous centre method

In this method, equilibrium of the forces acting on the link *BD* are considered. The instantaneous centre *I* lies at the point of intersection of *PB* produced and a line through *D* perpendicular to the spindle axis, as shown in Fig. 18.4. Taking moments about the point *I*,

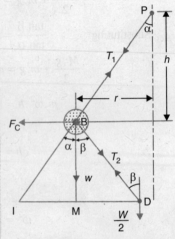

$$F_C \times BM = w \times IM + \frac{W}{2} \times ID$$

$$= m.g \times IM + \frac{M.g}{2} \times ID$$

$$\therefore \quad F_C = m.g \times \frac{IM}{BM} + \frac{M.g}{2} \times \frac{ID}{BM}$$

$$= m.g \times \frac{IM}{BM} + \frac{M.g}{2}\left(\frac{IM + MD}{BM}\right)$$

$$= m.g \times \frac{IM}{BM} + \frac{M.g}{2}\left(\frac{IM}{BM} + \frac{MD}{BM}\right)$$

Fig. 18.4. Instantaneous centre method.

$$= m.g \tan \alpha + \frac{M.g}{2}(\tan \alpha + \tan \beta)$$

$$\dots\left(\because \frac{IM}{BM} = \tan \alpha, \text{ and } \frac{MD}{BM} = \tan \beta\right)$$

Dividing throughout by tan α,

$$\frac{F_C}{\tan \alpha} = m.g + \frac{M.g}{2}\left(1 + \frac{\tan \beta}{\tan \alpha}\right) = m.g + \frac{M.g}{2}(1+q) \qquad \dots\left(\because q = \frac{\tan \beta}{\tan \alpha}\right)$$

We know that $F_C = m.\omega^2.r$, and $\tan \alpha = \dfrac{r}{h}$

$$\therefore \quad m.\omega^2.r \times \frac{h}{r} = m.g + \frac{M.g}{2}(1+q)$$

or

$$h = \frac{m.g + \dfrac{M.g}{2}(1+q)}{m} \times \frac{1}{\omega^2} = \frac{m + \dfrac{M}{2}(1+q)}{m} \times \frac{g}{\omega^2}$$

$$\dots \text{(Same as before)}$$

When $\tan \alpha = \tan \beta$ or $q = 1$, then

$$h = \frac{m + M}{m} \times \frac{g}{\omega^2}$$

Example 18.2. *A Porter governor has equal arms each 250 mm long and pivoted on the axis of rotation. Each ball has a mass of 5 kg and the mass of the central load on the sleeve is 15 kg. The radius of rotation of the ball is 150 mm when the governor begins to lift and 200 mm when the governor is at maximum speed. Find the minimum and maximum speeds and range of speed of the governor.*

Solution. Given : $BP = BD = 250$ mm $= 0.25$ m ; $m = 5$ kg ; $M = 15$ kg ; $r_1 = 150$ mm $= 0.15$m; $r_2 = 200$ mm $= 0.2$ m

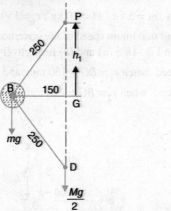
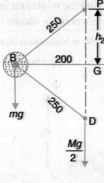

(*a*) Minimum position. (*b*) Maximum position.

Fig. 18.5

The minimum and maximum positions of the governor are shown in Fig. 18.5 (*a*) and (*b*) respectively.

Minimum speed when $r_1 = BG = 0.15$ m

Let $N_1 = $ Minimum speed.

From Fig. 18.5 (*a*), we find that height of the governor,

$$h_1 = PG = \sqrt{(PB)^2 - (BG)^2} = \sqrt{(0.25)^2 - (0.15)^2} = 0.2 \text{ m}$$

We know that

$$(N_1)^2 = \frac{m + M}{m} \times \frac{895}{h_1} = \frac{5 + 15}{5} \times \frac{895}{0.2} = 17\,900$$

∴ $N_1 = 133.8$ r.p.m. **Ans.**

Maximum speed when $r_2 = BG = 0.2$ m

Let $N_2 = $ Maximum speed.

From Fig. 18.5 (*b*), we find that height of the governor,

$$h_2 = PG = \sqrt{(PB)^2 - (BG)^2} = \sqrt{(0.25)^2 - (0.2)^2} = 0.15 \text{ m}$$

We know that

$$(N_2)^2 = \frac{m+M}{m} \times \frac{895}{h_2} = \frac{5+15}{5} \times \frac{895}{0.15} = 23\,867$$

∴ $N_2 = 154.5$ r.p.m. **Ans.**

Range of speed

We know that range of speed

$$= N_2 - N_1 = 154.4 - 133.8 = 20.7 \text{ r.p.m.} \textbf{ Ans.}$$

Example 18.3. *The arms of a Porter governor are each 250 mm long and pivoted on the governor axis. The mass of each ball is 5 kg and the mass of the central sleeve is 30 kg. The radius of rotation of the balls is 150 mm when the sleeve begins to rise and reaches a value of 200 mm for maximum speed. Determine the speed range of the governor. If the friction at the sleeve is equivalent of 20 N of load at the sleeve, determine how the speed range is modified.*

Solution. Given : $BP = BD = 250$ mm ; $m = 5$ kg ; $M = 30$ kg ; $r_1 = 150$ mm ; $r_2 = 200$ mm

First of all, let us find the minimum and maximum speed of the governor. The minimum and maximum position of the governor is shown in Fig. 18.6 (*a*) and (*b*) respectively.

Let $\quad N_1 =$ Minimum speed when $r_1 = BG = 150$ mm, and

$\quad\quad N_2 =$ Maximum speed when $r_2 = BG = 200$ mm.

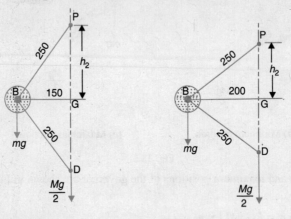

(*a*) Minimum position.   (*b*) Maximum position.

Fig. 18.6

Speed range of the governor

From Fig. 18.6 (*a*), we find that height of the governor,

$$h_1 = PG = \sqrt{(PB)^2 - (BG)^2} = \sqrt{(250)^2 - (150)^2} = 200 \text{ mm} = 0.2 \text{ m}$$

We know that

$$(N_1)^2 = \frac{m + M}{m} \times \frac{895}{h_1} = \frac{5 + 30}{5} \times \frac{895}{0.2} = 31\,325$$

$\therefore \quad\quad N_1 = 177 \text{ r.p.m.}$

From Fig. 18.6 (*b*), we find that height of the governor,

$$h_2 = PG = \sqrt{(PB)^2 - (BG)^2} = \sqrt{(250)^2 - (200)^2} = 150 \text{ mm} = 0.15 \text{ m}$$

We know that

$$(N_2)^2 = \frac{m + M}{m} \times \frac{895}{h_2} = \frac{5 + 30}{5} \times \frac{895}{0.15} = 41\,767$$

$\therefore \quad\quad N_2 = 204.4 \text{ r.p.m.}$

We know that speed range of the governor

$$= N_2 - N_1 = 204.4 - 177 = 27.4 \text{ r.p.m. } \textbf{Ans.}$$

Speed range when friction at the sleeve is equivalent of 20 N of load (i.e. when F = 20 N)

We know that when the sleeve moves downwards, the frictional force (F) acts upwards and the minimum speed is given by

$$(N_1)^2 = \frac{m.g + (M.g - F)}{m.g} \times \frac{895}{h_1}$$

$$= \frac{5 \times 9.81 + (30 \times 9.81 - 20)}{5 \times 9.81} \times \frac{895}{0.2} = 29500$$

$$\therefore \qquad\qquad N_1 = 172 \text{ r.p.m.}$$

We also know that when the sleeve moves upwards, the frictional force (F) acts downwards and the maximum speed is given by

$$(N_2)^2 = \frac{m.g + (M.g + F)}{m.g} \times \frac{895}{h_2}$$

$$= \frac{5 \times 9.81 + (30 \times 9.81 + 20)}{5 \times 9.81} \times \frac{895}{0.15} = 44200$$

$$\therefore \qquad\qquad N_2 = 210 \text{ r.p.m.}$$

We know that speed range of the governor

$$= N_2 - N_1 = 210 - 172 = 38 \text{ r.p.m. } \textbf{Ans.}$$

Example 18.4. *In an engine governor of the Porter type, the upper and lower arms are 200 mm and 250 mm respectively and pivoted on the axis of rotation. The mass of the central load is 15 kg, the mass of each ball is 2 kg and friction of the sleeve together with the resistance of the operating gear is equal to a load of 24 N at the sleeve. If the limiting inclinations of the upper arms to the vertical are 30° and 40°, find, taking friction into account, range of speed of the governor.*

Solution . Given : $BP = 200$ mm $= 0.2$ m ; $BD = 250$ mm $= 0.25$ m ; $M = 15$ kg ; $m = 2$ kg ; $F = 24$ N ; $\alpha_1 = 30°$; $\alpha_2 = 40°$

First of all, let us find the minimum and maximum speed of the governor.

The minimum and maximum position of the governor is shown Fig. 18.7 (*a*) and (*b*) respectively.

Let $\qquad\qquad N_1 = $ Minimum speed, and

$\qquad\qquad\qquad N_2 = $ Maximum speed.

From Fig. 18.7 (*a*), we find that minimum radius of rotation,

$$r_1 = BG = BP \sin 30° = 0.2 \times 0.5 = 0.1 \text{ m}$$

Height of the governor,

$$h_1 = PG = BP \cos 30° = 0.2 \times 0.866 = 0.1732 \text{ m}$$

and
$$DG = \sqrt{(BD)^2 - (BG)^2} = \sqrt{(0.25)^2 - (0.1)^2} = 0.23\,\text{m}$$

∴ $\tan \beta_1 = BG/DG = 0.1/0.23 = 0.4348$

and $\tan \alpha_1 = \tan 30° = 0.5774$

∴ $q_1 = \dfrac{\tan \beta_1}{\tan \alpha_1} = \dfrac{0.4348}{0.5774} = 0.753$

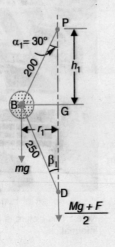 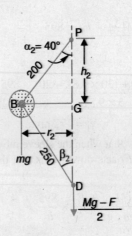

All dimensions in mm.

(a) Minimum position.   (b) Maximum position.

Fig. 18.7

We know that when the sleeve moves downwards, the frictional force (F) acts upwards and the minimum speed is given by

$$(N_1)^2 = \dfrac{m.g + \left(\dfrac{M.g - F}{2}\right)(1 + q_1)}{m.g} \times \dfrac{895}{h_1}$$

$$= \dfrac{2 \times 9.81 + \left(\dfrac{15 \times 9.81 - 24}{2}\right)(1 + 0.753)}{2 \times 9.81} \times \dfrac{895}{0.1732} = 33596$$

∴ $N_1 = 183.3$ r.p.m.

Now from Fig. 18.7 (b), we find that maximum radius of rotation,

$$r_2 = BG = BP \sin 40° = 0.2 \times 0.643 = 0.1268 \text{ m}$$

Height of the governor,

$$h_2 = PG = BP \cos 40° = 0.2 \times 0.766 = 0.1532 \text{ m}$$

and $$DG = \sqrt{(BD)^2 - (BG)^2} = \sqrt{(0.25)^2 - (0.1268)^2} = 0.2154 \text{ m}$$

∴ $\tan \beta_2 = BG/DG = 0.1268 / 0.2154 = 0.59$

and $\tan \alpha_2 = \tan 40° = 0.839$

∴ $q_2 = \dfrac{\tan \beta_2}{\tan \alpha_2} = \dfrac{0.59}{0.839} = 0.703$

We know that when the sleeve moves upwards, the frictional force (F) acts downwards and the maximum speed is given by

$$(N_2)^2 = \frac{m.g + \left(\dfrac{M.g + F}{2}\right)(1 + q_2)}{m.g} \times \frac{895}{h_2}$$

$$= \frac{2 \times 9.81 + \left(\dfrac{15 \times 9.81 + 24}{2}\right)(1 + 0.703)}{2 \times 9.81} \times \frac{895}{0.1532} = 49\,236$$

∴ $N_2 = 222$ r.p.m.

We know that range of speed

$$= N_2 - N_1 = 222 - 183.3 = 38.7 \text{ r.p.m. Ans.}$$

Example 18.5. *A Porter governor has all four arms 250 mm long. The upper arms are attached on the axis of rotation and the lower arms are attached to the sleeve at a distance of 30 mm from the axis. The mass of each ball is 5 kg and the sleeve has a mass of 50 kg. The extreme radii of rotation are 150 mm and 200 mm. Determine the range of speed of the governor.*

Solution. Given : $BP = BD = 250$ mm ; $DH = 30$ mm ; $m = 5$ kg ; $M = 50$ kg ; $r_1 = 150$ mm ; $r_2 = 200$ mm

First of all, let us find the minimum and maximum speed of the governor. The minimum and maximum position of the governor is shown in Fig. 18.8 (*a*) and (*b*) respectively.

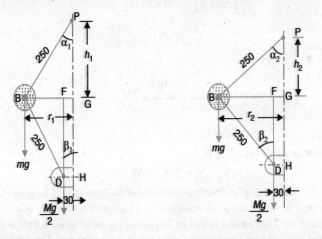

(*a*) Minimum position.   (*b*) Maximum position.

Fig. 18.8

Let $N_1 =$ Minimum speed when $r_1 = BG = 150$ mm ; and

               $N_2 =$ Maximum speed when $r_2 = BG = 200$ mm.

From Fig. 18.8 (*a*), we find that height of the governor,

$$h_1 = PG = \sqrt{(BP)^2 - (BG)^2} = \sqrt{(250)^2 - (150)^2} = 200 \text{ mm} = 0.2 \text{ m}$$

$$BF = BG - FG = 150 - 30 = 120 \text{ mm} \qquad \ldots (\because FG = DH)$$

and
$$DF = \sqrt{(DB)^2 - (BF)^2} = \sqrt{(250)^2 - (120)^2} = 219 \text{ mm}$$

$$\therefore \quad \tan \alpha_1 = BG/PG = 150 / 200 = 0.75$$

and
$$\tan \beta_1 = BF/DF = 120/219 = 0.548$$

$$\therefore \quad q_1 = \frac{\tan \beta_1}{\tan \alpha_1} = \frac{0.548}{0.75} = 0.731$$

We know that
$$(N_1)^2 = \frac{m + \dfrac{M}{2}(1 + q_1)}{m} \times \frac{895}{h_1} = \frac{5 + \dfrac{50}{2}(1 + 0.731)}{5} \times \frac{895}{0.2} = 43\,206$$

$$\therefore \quad N_1 = 208 \text{ r.p.m.}$$

From Fig. 18.8(b), we find that height of the governor,

$$h_2 = PG = \sqrt{(BP)^2 - (BG)^2} = \sqrt{(250)^2 - (200)^2} = 150 \text{ mm} = 0.15 \text{ m}$$

$$BF = BG - FG = 200 - 30 = 170 \text{ mm}$$

and
$$DF = \sqrt{(DB)^2 - (BF)^2} = \sqrt{(250)^2 - (170)^2} = 183 \text{ mm}$$

$$\therefore \quad \tan \alpha_2 = BG/PG = 200/150 = 1.333$$

and
$$\tan \beta_2 = BF/DF = 170/183 = 0.93$$

$$\therefore \quad q_2 = \frac{\tan \beta_2}{\tan \alpha_2} = \frac{0.93}{1.333} = 0.7$$

We know that

$$(N_2)^2 = \frac{m + \dfrac{M}{2}(1 + q_2)}{m} \times \frac{895}{h_2} = \frac{5 + \dfrac{50}{2}(1 + 0.7)}{5} \times \frac{895}{0.15} = 56\,683$$

$$\therefore \quad N_2 = 238 \text{ r.p.m.}$$

We know that range of speed

$$= N_2 - N_1 = 238 - 208 = 30 \text{ r.p.m. } \textbf{Ans.}$$

Example 18.6. *The arms of a Porter governor are 300 mm long. The upper arms are pivoted on the axis of rotation. The lower arms are attached to a sleeve at a distance of 40 mm from the axis of rotation. The mass of the load on the sleeve is 70 kg and the mass of each ball is 10 kg. Determine the equilibrium speed when the radius of rotation of the balls is 200 mm. If the friction is equivalent to a load of 20 N at the sleeve, what will be the range of speed for this position ?*

Solution. Given : $BP = BD = 300$ mm ; $DH = 40$ mm ; $M = 70$ kg ; $m = 10$ kg ; $r = BG = 200$ mm

Equilibrium speed when the radius of rotation r = BG = 200 mm

Let
$$N = \text{Equilibrium speed.}$$

The equilibrium position of the governor is shown in Fig. 18.9. From the figure, we find that height of the governor,

$$h = PG = \sqrt{(BP)^2 - (BG)^2} = \sqrt{(300)^2 - (200)^2} = 224 \text{ mm}$$

$$= 0.224 \text{ m}$$

$\therefore \qquad BF = BG - FG = 200 - 40 = 160 \text{ mm}$

$$\ldots (\because FG = DH)$$

and $\qquad DF = \sqrt{(DB)^2 - (BF)^2} = \sqrt{(300)^2 - (160)^2} = 254 \text{ mm}$

$\therefore \tan \alpha = BG/PG = 200 / 224 = 0.893$

and $\quad \tan \beta = BF/DF = 160 / 254 = 0.63$

$\therefore \qquad q = \dfrac{\tan \beta}{\tan \alpha} = \dfrac{0.63}{0.893} = 0.705$

We know that

$$N_2 = \dfrac{m + \dfrac{M}{2}(1 + q)}{m} \times \dfrac{895}{h}$$

$$= \dfrac{10 + \dfrac{70}{2}(1 + 0.705)}{10} \times \dfrac{895}{0.224} = 27\,840$$

$\therefore \quad N = 167 \text{ r.p.m. } \textbf{Ans.}$

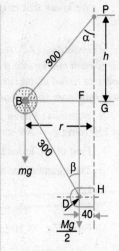

All dimensions in mm.
Fig. 18.9

Range of speed when friction is equivalent to load of 20 N at the sleeve (i.e. when F = 20 N)

Let $\quad N_1 = $ Minimum equilibrium speed, and

$\qquad N_2 = $ Maximum equilibrium speed.

We know that when the sleeve moves downwards, the frictional force (F) acts upwards and the minimum equilibrium speed is given by

$$(N_1)^2 = \dfrac{m.g + \left(\dfrac{M.g - F}{2}\right)(1 + q)}{m.g} \times \dfrac{895}{h}$$

$$= \dfrac{10 \times 9.81 + \left(\dfrac{70 \times 9.81 - 20}{2}\right)(1 + 0.705)}{10 \times 9.81} \times \dfrac{895}{0.224} = 27\,144$$

$\therefore \quad N_1 = 164.8 \text{ r.p.m.}$

An 18th century governor.

We also know that when the sleeve moves upwards, the frictional force (F) acts downwards and the maximum equilibrium speed is given by

$$(N_2)^2 = \dfrac{m.g + \left(\dfrac{M.g + F}{2}\right)(1 + q)}{m.g} \times \dfrac{895}{h}$$

$$= \dfrac{10 \times 9.81 + \left(\dfrac{70 \times 9.81 + 20}{2}\right)(1 + 0.705)}{10 \times 9.81} \times \dfrac{895}{0.224} = 28\,533$$

$\therefore \quad N_2 = 169 \text{ r.p.m.}$

We know that range of speed

$$= N_2 - N_1 = 169 - 164.8 = 4.2 \text{ r.p.m. Ans.}$$

Example 18.7. *A loaded Porter governor has four links each 250 mm long, two revolving masses each of 3 kg and a central dead weight of mass 20 kg. All the links are attached to respective sleeves at radial distances of 40 mm from the axis of rotation. The masses revolve at a radius of 150 mm at minimum speed and at a radius of 200 mm at maximum speed. Determine the range of speed.*

Solution. Given : $BP = BD = 250$ mm ; $m = 3$ kg ; $M = 20$ kg ; $PQ = DH = 40$ mm ; $r_1 = 150$ mm ; $r_2 = 200$ mm

First of all, let us find the minimum and maximum speed of the governor.

The minimum and maximum position of the governor is shown in Fig. 18.10 (*a*) and (*b*) respectively.

Let
$$N_1 = \text{Minimum speed when } r_1 = BG = 150 \text{ mm, and}$$
$$N_2 = \text{Minimum speed when } r_2 = BG = 200 \text{ mm.}$$

From Fig. 18.10 (*a*), we find that

$$BF = BG - FG = 150 - 40 = 110 \text{ mm}$$

and
$$\sin \alpha_1 = BF / BP = 110 / 250 = 0.44 \qquad \text{or} \qquad \alpha_1 = 26.1°$$

∴ Height of the governor,

$$h_1 = OG = BG / \tan \alpha_1 = 150 / \tan 26.1° = 306 \text{ mm} = 0.306 \text{ m}$$

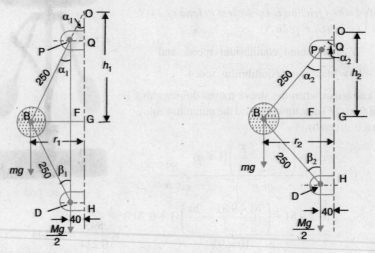

All dimensions in mm.

(*a*) Minimum position.   (*b*) Maximum position.

Fig. 18.10

Since all the links are attached to respective sleeves at equal distances (*i.e.* 40 mm) from the axis of rotation, therefore

$$\tan \alpha_1 = \tan \beta_1 \qquad \text{or} \qquad q = 1$$

We know that
$$(N_1)^2 = \frac{m + M}{m} \times \frac{895}{h_1} = \frac{3 + 20}{3} \times \frac{895}{0.306} = 22\,424$$

$$N_1 = 150 \text{ r.p.m.}$$

Now from Fig. 18.10 (*b*), we find that

$$BF = BG - FG = 200 - 40 = 160 \text{ mm}$$

and

$$\sin \alpha_2 = BF/BP = 160 / 250 = 0.64 \quad \text{or} \quad \alpha_2 = 39.8°$$

∴ Height of the governor,

$$h_2 = OG = BG / \tan \alpha_2 = 200 / \tan 39.8° = 240 \text{ mm} = 0.24 \text{ m}$$

In this case also,

$$\tan \alpha_2 = \tan \beta_2 \quad \text{or} \quad q = 1$$

We know that

$$(N_2)^2 = \frac{m + M}{m} \times \frac{895}{h_2} = \frac{3 + 20}{3} \times \frac{895}{0.24} = 28\,590$$

∴

$$N_2 = 169 \text{ r.p.m.}$$

We know that range of speed

$$= N_2 - N_1 = 169 - 150 = 19 \text{ r.p.m. Ans.}$$

Example 18.8. *All the arms of a Porter governor are 178 mm long and are hinged at a distance of 38 mm from the axis of rotation. The mass of each ball is 1.15 kg and mass of the sleeve is 20 kg. The governor sleeve begins to rise at 280 r.p.m. when the links are at an angle of 30° to the vertical. Assuming the friction force to be constant, determine the minimum and maximum speed of rotation when the inclination of the arms to the vertical is 45°.*

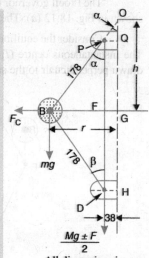

Solution. Given : $BP = BD = 178$ mm ; $PQ = DH = 38$ mm ; $m = 1.15$ kg ; $M = 20$ kg ; $N = 280$ r.p.m. ; $\alpha = \beta = 30°$

First of all, let us find the friction force (F). The equilibrium position of the governor when the links are at 30° to vertical, is shown in Fig. 18.11. From the figure, we find that radius of rotation,

$$r = BG = BF + FG = BP \times \sin \alpha + FG$$
$$= 178 \sin 30° + 38 = 127 \text{ mm}$$

and height of the governor,

$$h = BG / \tan \alpha$$
$$= 127 / \tan 30° = 220 \text{ mm} = 0.22 \text{ m}$$

We know that

$$N^2 = \frac{m.g + (Mg \pm F)}{m.g} \times \frac{895}{h}$$

$$\ldots (\because \tan \alpha = \tan \beta \text{ or } q = 1)$$

All dimensions in mm.

Fig. 18.11

$$(280)^2 = \frac{1.15 \times 9.81 + 20 \times 9.81 \pm F}{1.15 \times 9.81} \times \frac{895}{0.22}$$

or

$$\pm F = \frac{(280)^2 \times 1.15 \times 9.81 \times 0.22}{895} - 1.15 \times 9.81 - 20 \times 9.81$$

$$= 217.5 - 11.3 - 196.2 = 10 \text{ N}$$

We know that radius of rotation when inclination of the arms to the vertical is 45° (*i.e.* when $\alpha = \beta = 45°$),

$$r = BG = BF + FG = BP \times \sin \alpha + FG$$
$$= 178 \sin 45° + 38 = 164 \text{ mm}$$

and height of the governor,

$$h = BG / \tan \alpha = 164 / \tan 45° = 164 \text{ mm} = 0.164 \text{ m}$$

Let N_1 = Minimum speed of rotation, and

N_2 = Maximum speed of rotation.

We know that

$$(N_1)^2 = \frac{m.g + (M.g - F)}{m.g} \times \frac{895}{h}$$

$$= \frac{1.15 \times 9.81 + (20 \times 9.81 - 10)}{1.15 \times 9.81} \times \frac{895}{0.164} = 95\,382$$

∴ $N_1 = 309$ r.p.m. **Ans.**

and $$(N_2)^2 = \frac{m.g + (M.g + F)}{m.g} \times \frac{895}{h}$$

$$= \frac{1.15 \times 9.81 + (20 \times 9.81 + 10)}{1.15 \times 9.81} \times \frac{895}{0.164} = 105\,040$$

$N_2 = 324$ r.p.m. **Ans.**

18.7. Proell Governor

The Proell governor has the balls fixed at B and C to the extension of the links DF and EG, as shown in Fig. 18.12 (a). The arms FP and GQ are pivoted at P and Q respectively.

Consider the equilibrium of the forces on one-half of the governor as shown in Fig. 18.12 (b). The instantaneous centre (I) lies on the intersection of the line PF produced and the line from D drawn perpendicualr to the spindle axis. The perpendicular BM is drawn on ID.

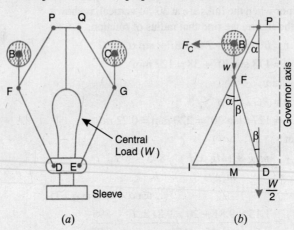

(a)   (b)

Fig. 18.12. Proell governor.

Taking moments about I, using the same notations as discussed in Art. 18.6 (Porter governor),

$$F_C \times BM = w \times IM + \frac{W}{2} \times ID = m.g \times IM + \frac{M.g}{2} \times ID \qquad \dots(i)$$

∴ $$F_C = m.g \times \frac{IM}{BM} + \frac{M.g}{2}\left(\frac{IM + MD}{BM}\right) \qquad \dots(\because ID = IM + MD)$$

Multiplying and dividing by *FM*, we have

$$F_C = \frac{FM}{BM}\left[m.g \times \frac{IM}{FM} + \frac{M.g}{2}\left(\frac{IM}{FM} + \frac{MD}{FM} \right) \right]$$

$$= \frac{FM}{BM}\left[m.g \times \tan\alpha + \frac{M.g}{2}(\tan\alpha + \tan\beta) \right]$$

$$= \frac{FM}{BM} \times \tan\alpha \left[m.g + \frac{M.g}{2}\left(1 + \frac{\tan\beta}{\tan\alpha} \right) \right]$$

We know that $F_C = m.\omega^2 r$; $\tan\alpha = \dfrac{r}{h}$ and $q = \dfrac{\tan\beta}{\tan\alpha}$

$$\therefore \qquad m.\omega^2.r = \frac{FM}{BM} \times \frac{r}{h}\left[m.g + \frac{M.g}{2}(1+q) \right]$$

and

$$\omega^2 = \frac{FM}{BM}\left[\frac{m + \dfrac{M}{2}(1+q)}{m} \right]\frac{g}{h} \qquad \qquad ...(ii)$$

Substituting $\omega = 2\pi N/60$, and $g = 9.81 \text{ m/s}^2$, we get

$$N^2 = \frac{FM}{BM}\left[\frac{m + \dfrac{M}{2}(1+q)}{m} \right]\frac{895}{h} \qquad \qquad ...(iii)$$

Notes : 1. The equation (*i*) may be applied to any given configuration of the governor.

2. Comparing equation (*iii*) with the equation (*v*) of the Porter governor (Art. 18.6), we see that the equilibrium speed reduces for the given values of *m*, *M* and *h*. Hence in order to have the same equilibrium speed for the given values of *m*, *M* and *h*, balls of smaller masses are used in the Proell governor than in the Porter governor.

3. When $\alpha = \beta$, then $q = 1$. Therefore equation (*iii*) may be written as

$$N^2 = \frac{FM}{BM}\left(\frac{m+M}{m} \right)\frac{895}{h} \qquad \qquad (h \text{ being in metres}) ...(iv)$$

Example 18.9. *A Proell governor has equal arms of length 300 mm. The upper and lower ends of the arms are pivoted on the axis of the governor. The extension arms of the lower links are each 80 mm long and parallel to the axis when the radii of rotation of the balls are 150 mm and 200 mm. The mass of each ball is 10 kg and the mass of the central load is 100 kg. Determine the range of speed of the governor.*

Solution. Given : $PF = DF = 300$ mm ; $BF = 80$ mm ; $r_1 = 150$ mm; $r_2 = 200$ mm ; $m = 10$ kg ; $M = 100$ kg ;

First of all, let us find the minimum and maximum speed of the governor. The minimum and maximum position of the governor is shown in Fig. 18.13.

Let $\qquad N_1 =$ Minimum speed when radius of rotation, $r_1 = FG = 150$ mm ; and

$\qquad N_2 =$ Maximum speed when radius of rotation , $r_2 = FG = 200$ mm.

From Fig. 18.13 (*a*), we find that height of the governor,

$$h_1 = PG = \sqrt{(PF)^2 - (FG)^2} = \sqrt{(300)^2 - (150)^2} = 260 \text{ mm} = 0.26 \text{ m}$$

and
$$FM = GD = PG = 260 \text{ mm} = 0.26 \text{ m}$$

∴
$$BM = BF + FM = 80 + 260 = 340 \text{ mm} = 0.34 \text{ m}$$

We know that
$$(N_1)^2 = \frac{FM}{BM}\left(\frac{m+M}{m}\right)\frac{895}{h_1} \qquad \ldots (\because \alpha = \beta \text{ or } q = 1)$$

$$= \frac{0.26}{0.34}\left(\frac{10+100}{10}\right)\frac{895}{0.26} = 28\,956 \quad \text{or} \quad N_1 = 170 \text{ r.p.m.}$$

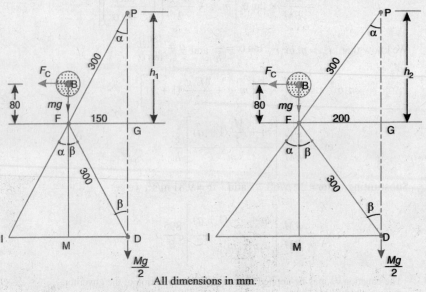

(a) Minimum position.   (a) Maximum position.

Fig. 18.13

Now from Fig. 18.13 (b), we find that height of the governor,

$$h_2 = PG = \sqrt{(PF)^2 - (FG)^2} = \sqrt{(300)^2 - (200)^2} = 224 \text{ mm} = 0.224 \text{ m}$$

and
$$FM = GD = PG = 224 \text{ mm} = 0.224 \text{ m}$$

∴
$$BM = BF + FM = 80 + 224 = 304 \text{ mm} = 0.304 \text{ m}$$

We know that
$$(N_2)^2 = \frac{FM}{BM}\left(\frac{m+M}{m}\right)\frac{895}{h_2} \qquad \ldots (\because \alpha = \beta \text{ or } q = 1)$$

$$= \frac{0.224}{0.304}\left(\frac{10+100}{10}\right)\frac{895}{0.224} = 32\,385 \quad \text{or} \quad N_2 = 180 \text{ r.p.m.}$$

We know that range of speed
$$= N_2 - N_1 = 180 - 170 = 10 \text{ r.p.m. Ans.}$$

Note : The example may also be solved as discussed below :

From Fig. 18.13 (a), we find that

$$\sin \alpha = \sin \beta = 150/300 = 0.5 \qquad \text{or} \qquad \alpha = \beta = 30°$$

and
$$MD = FG = 150 \text{ mm} = 0.15 \text{ m}$$

$$FM = FD \cos \beta = 300 \cos 30° = 260 \text{ mm} = 0.26 \text{ m}$$

$$IM = FM \tan \alpha = 0.26 \tan 30° = 0.15 \text{ m}$$

$$BM = BF + FM = 80 + 260 = 340 \text{ mm} = 0.34 \text{ m}$$

$$ID = IM + MD = 0.15 + 0.15 = 0.3 \text{ m}$$

We know that centrifugal force,

$$F_C = m\,(\omega_1)^2 \cdot r_1 = 10 \left(\frac{2\pi N_1}{60} \right)^2 0.15 = 0.0165\,(N_1)^2$$

Now taking moments about point I,

$$F_C \times BM = m.g \times IM + \frac{M.g}{2} \times ID$$

or $$0.0165\,(N_1)^2\,0.34 = 10 \times 9.81 \times 0.15 + \frac{100 \times 9.81}{2} \times 0.3$$

$$0.0056\,(N_1)^2 = 14.715 + 147.15 = 161.865$$

∴ $$(N_1)^2 = \frac{161.865}{0.0056} = 28\,904 \quad \text{or} \quad N_1 = 170 \text{ r.p.m.}$$

Similarly N_2 may be calculated.

An overview of a combined cycle power plant. Governors are used in power plants to control the flow of working fluids.

Note : This picture is given as additional information.

Example 18.10. *A governor of the Proell type has each arm 250 mm long. The pivots of the upper and lower arms are 25 mm from the axis. The central load acting on the sleeve has a mass of 25 kg and the each rotating ball has a mass of 3.2 kg. When the governor sleeve is in mid-position, the extension link of the lower arm is vertical and the radius of the path of rotation of the masses is 175 mm. The vertical height of the governor is 200 mm.*

If the governor speed is 160 r.p.m. when in mid-position, find : 1. length of the extension link; and 2. tension in the upper arm.

Solution. Given : $PF = DF = 250$ mm $= 0.25$ m ; $PQ = DH = KG = 25$ mm $= 0.025$ m ; $M = 25$ kg ; $m = 3.2$ kg ; $r = FG = 175$ mm $= 0.175$ m ; $h = QG = PK = 200$ mm $= 0.2$ m ; $N = 160$ r.p.m.

1. Length of the extension link

Let $\qquad BF$ = Length of the extension link.

The Proell governor in its mid-position is shown in Fig. 18.14.

From the figure, we find that

$$FM = GH = QG = 200 \text{ mm} = 0.2 \text{ m}$$

We know that

$$N^2 = \frac{FM}{BM}\left(\frac{m+M}{m}\right)\frac{895}{h}$$

$$\dots (\because \alpha = \beta \text{ or } q = 1)$$

$$(160)^2 = \frac{0.2}{BM}\left(\frac{3.2+25}{3.2}\right)\frac{895}{0.2} = \frac{7887}{BM}$$

$\therefore \qquad BM = 7887/(160)^2 = 0.308$ m

From Fig. 18.14,

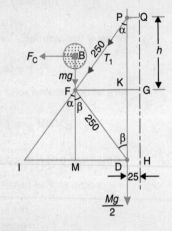

Fig. 18.14. All dimensions in mm.

$$BF = BM - FM = 0.308 - 0.2 = 0.108 \text{ m} = 108 \text{ mm} \quad \textbf{Ans.}$$

2. Tension in the upper arm

Let $\qquad T_1$ = Tension in the upper arm.

$$PK = \sqrt{(PF)^2 - (FK)^2} = \sqrt{(PF)^2 - (FG - KG)^2}$$

$$= \sqrt{(250)^2 - (175 - 25)^2} = 200 \text{ mm}$$

$$\cos \alpha = PK/PF = 200/250 = 0.8$$

and $\qquad T_1 \cos \alpha = mg + \frac{Mg}{2} = 3.2 \times 9.81 + \frac{25 \times 9.81}{2} = 154 \text{ N}$

$\therefore \qquad T_1 = \frac{154}{\cos \alpha} = \frac{154}{0.8} = 192.5 \text{ N} \quad \textbf{Ans.}$

Example 18.11. *The following particulars refer to a Proell governor with open arms :*

Length of all arms = 200 mm ; distance of pivot of arms from the axis of rotation = 40 mm ; length of extension of lower arms to which each ball is attached = 100 mm ; mass of each ball = 6 kg and mass of the central load = 150 kg. If the radius of rotation of the balls is 180 mm when the arms are inclined at an angle of 40° to the axis of rotation, find the equilibrium speed for the above configuration.

Solution. Given : $PF = DF = 200$ mm ; $PQ = DK = HG = 40$ mm ; $BF = 100$ mm ; $m = 6$ kg; $M = 150$ kg ; $r = JG = 180$ mm $= 0.18$ m ; $\alpha = \beta = 40°$

Let $\qquad N$ = Equilibrium speed.

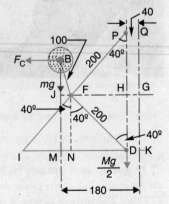

Fig. 18.15. All dimensions in mm.

From the equilibrium position of the governor, as shown in Fig. 18.15, we find that

$$PH = PF \times \cos 40°$$

$$= 200 \times 0.766 = 153.2 \, mm$$

$$= 0.1532 \, m$$

and

$$FH = PF \times \sin 40° = 200 \times 0.643 = 128.6 \, mm$$

∴

$$JF = JG - HG - FH = 180 - 40 - 128.6 = 11.4 \, mm$$

and

$$BJ = \sqrt{(BF)^2 - (JF)^2} = \sqrt{(100)^2 - (11.4)^2} = 99.4 \, mm$$

We know that $BM = BJ + JM = 99.4 + 153.2 = 252.6 \, mm$ ... ($\because JM = HD = PH$)

$$IM = IN - NM = FH - JF = 128.6 - 11.4 = 117.2 \, mm$$

                                              ... ($\because IN = ND = FH$)

and

$$ID = IN + ND = 2 \times IN = 2 \times FH = 2 \times 128.6 = 257.2 \, mm$$

Now taking moments about the instantaneous centre I,

$$F_C \times BM = m.g \times IM + \frac{M \cdot g}{2} \times ID$$

$$F_C \times 252.6 = 6 \times 9.81 \times 117.2 + \frac{150 \times 9.81}{2} \times 257.2 = 196 \ 125$$

∴

$$F_C = \frac{196 \ 125}{252.6} = 776.4 \, N$$

We know that centrifugal force (F_C),

$$776.4 = m.\omega^2 .r = 6 \left(\frac{2\pi N}{60} \right)^2 0.18 = 0.012 \, N^2$$

∴

$$N^2 = \frac{776.4}{0.012} = 64 \ 700 \quad \text{or} \quad N = 254 \text{ r.p.m. } \textbf{Ans.}$$

Example 18.12. *A Proell governor has all four arms of length 305 mm. The upper arms are pivoted on the axis of rotation and the lower arms are attached to a sleeve at a distance of 38 mm from the axis. The mass of each ball is 4.8 kg and are attached to the extension of the lower arms which are 102 mm long. The mass on the sleeve is 54 kg. The minimum and maximum radii of governor are 165 mm and 216 mm. Assuming that the extensions of the lower arms are parallel to the governor axis at the minimum radius, find the corresponding equilibrium speeds.*

Solution. Given : $PF = DF = 305$ mm ; $DH = 38$ mm ; $BF = 102$ mm ; $m = 4.8$ kg ; $M = 54$ kg

Equilibrium speed at the minimum radius of governor

The radius of the governor is the distance of the point of intersection of the upper and lower arms from the governor axis. When the extensions of the lower arms are parallel to the governor axis, then the radius of the governor (FG) is equal to the radius of rotation (r_1).

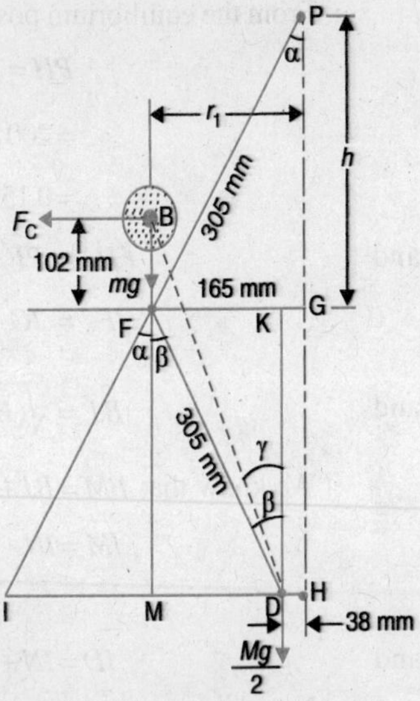

The governor configuration at the minimum radius (*i.e.* when $FG = 165$ mm) is shown in Fig. 18.16.

Let $\quad N_1 =$ Equilibrium speed at the minimum radius *i.e.* when $FG = r_1 = 165$ mm.

From Fig. 18.16, we find that

$$\sin \alpha = \frac{FG}{FP} = \frac{165}{305} = 0.541$$

$$\therefore \qquad \alpha = 32.75°$$

and $\qquad \tan \alpha = \tan 32.75° = 0.6432$

Also $\qquad \sin \beta = \frac{FK}{DF} = \frac{FG - KG}{DF}$

$$= \frac{165 - 38}{305} = 0.4164$$

$$\therefore \qquad \beta = 24.6°$$

and $\qquad \tan \beta = \tan 24.6° = 0.4578$

We know that

$$q = \frac{\tan \beta}{\tan \alpha} = \frac{0.4578}{0.6432} = 0.712$$

From Fig. 18.16, we find that height of the governor,

$$h = PG = \sqrt{(PF)^2 - (FG)^2} = \sqrt{(305)^2 - (165)^2} = 256.5 \text{ mm} = 0.2565 \text{ m}$$

$$MD = FK = FG - KG = 165 - 38 = 127 \text{ mm}$$

$$\therefore \qquad FM = \sqrt{(DF)^2 - (MD)^2} = \sqrt{(305)^2 - (127)^2} = 277 \text{ mm} = 0.277 \text{ m}$$

and $\qquad BM = BF + FM = 102 + 277 = 379 \text{ mm} = 0.379 \text{ m}$

We know that

$$(N_1)^2 = \frac{FM}{BM} \left[\frac{m + \dfrac{M}{2}(1+q)}{m} \right] \frac{895}{h}$$

$$= \frac{0.277}{0.379} \left[\frac{4.8 + \dfrac{54}{2}(1 + 0.712)}{4.8} \right] \frac{895}{0.2565} = 27\,109$$

$$\therefore \qquad N_1 = 165 \text{ r.p.m. Ans.}$$

Note : The valve of N_1 may also be obtained by drawing the governor configuration to some suitable scale and measuring the distances *BM*, *IM* and *ID*. Now taking moments about point *I*,

$$F_C \times BM = m.g \times IM + \frac{M.g}{2} \times ID,$$

where $\qquad F_C =$ Centrifugal force $= m(\omega_1)^2 r_1 = m \left(\dfrac{2\pi N_1}{60} \right)^2 r_1$

Equilibrium speed at the maximum radius of governor

Let $\qquad N_2 =$ Equilibrium speed at the maximum radius of governor, *i.e.* when $F_1 G_1$

$$= r_2 = 216 \text{ mm}.$$

Fig. 18.16

First of all, let us find the values of BD and γ in Fig. 18.16. We know that

$$BD = \sqrt{(BM)^2 + (MD)^2} = \sqrt{(379)^2 + (127)^2} = 400 \text{ mm}$$

and $\quad\quad\quad\quad \tan\gamma = MD/BM = 127/379 = 0.335 \quad\quad \text{or} \quad \gamma = 18.5°$

The governor configuration at the maximum radius of $F_1G_1 = 216$ mm is shown in Fig. 18.17. From the geometry of the figure,

$$\sin\alpha_1 = \frac{F_1G_1}{P_1F_1} = \frac{216}{305} = 0.7082$$

$\therefore \quad\quad\quad\quad\quad \alpha_1 = 45.1°$

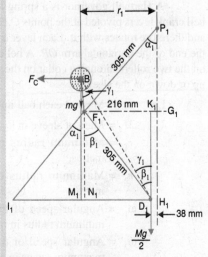

Fig. 18.17

$$\sin\beta_1 = \frac{F_1K_1}{F_1D_1} = \frac{F_1G_1 - K_1G_1}{F_1D_1}$$

$$= \frac{216 - 38}{305} = 0.5836$$

$\therefore \quad\quad\quad\quad\quad \beta_1 = 35.7°$

Since the extension is rigidly connected to the lower arm (*i.e.* DFB or $D_1F_1B_1$ is one continuous link) therefore B_1D_1 and angle $B_1D_1F_1$ do not change. In other words,

$$B_1D_1 = BD = 400 \text{ mm}$$

and $\quad\quad \gamma - \beta = \gamma_1 - \beta_1$ or $\gamma_1 = \gamma - \beta + \beta_1$

$$= 18.5° - 24.6° + 35.7° = 29.6°$$

$\therefore \quad$ Radius of rotation,

$$r_2 = M_1D_1 + D_1H_1 = B_1D_1 \times \sin\gamma_1 + 38 \text{ mm}$$

$$= 400 \sin 29.6° + 38 = 235.6 \text{ mm} = 0.2356 \text{ m}$$

From Fig. 18.17, we find that

$$B_1M_1 = B_1D_1 \times \cos\gamma_1 = 400 \times \cos 29.6° = 348 \text{ mm} = 0.348 \text{ m}$$

$$F_1N_1 = F_1D_1 \times \cos\beta_1 = 305 \times \cos 35.7° = 248 \text{ mm} = 0.248 \text{ m}$$

$$I_1N_1 = F_1N_1 \times \tan\alpha_1 = 0.248 \times \tan 45.1° = 0.249 \text{ m}$$

$$N_1D_1 = F_1D_1 \times \sin\beta_1 = 305 \times \sin 35.7 = 178 \text{ mm} = 0.178 \text{ m}$$

$\therefore \quad\quad I_1D_1 = I_1N_1 + N_1D_1 = 0.249 + 0.178 = 0.427 \text{ m}$

$$M_1D_1 = B_1D_1 \sin\gamma_1 = 400 \sin 29.6° = 198 \text{ mm} = 0.198 \text{ m}$$

$\therefore \quad\quad I_1M_1 = I_1D_1 - M_1D_1 = 0.427 - 0.198 = 0.229 \text{ m}$

We know that centrifugal force,

$$F_C = m(\omega_2)^2 r_2 = 4.8\left(\frac{2\pi N_2}{60}\right)^2 0.2356 = 0.0124\,(N_2)^2$$

Now taking moments about point I_1,

$$F_C \times B_1M_1 = m.g \times I_1M_1 + \frac{M.g}{2} \times I_1D_1$$

$$0.0124\,(N_2)^2 \times 0.348 = 4.8 \times 9.81 \times 0.229 + \frac{54 \times 9.81}{2} \times 0.427$$

$$0.0043\,(N_2)^2 = 10.873 + 113.1 = 123.883$$

$$\therefore \qquad (N_2)^2 = \frac{123.883}{0.0043} = 28\,810 \qquad \text{or} \qquad N_2 = 170\,\text{r.p.m.} \quad \textbf{Ans.}$$

Note : The value of N_2 may also be obtained by drawing the governor configuration to some suitable scale and measuring the distances B_1M_1, I_1M_1 and I_1D_1.

18.8. Hartnell Governor

A Hartnell governor is a spring loaded governor as shown in Fig. 18.18. It consists of two bell crank levers pivoted at the points O,O to the frame. The frame is attached to the governor spindle and therefore rotates with it. Each lever carries a ball at the end of the vertical arm OB and a roller at the end of the horizontal arm OR. A helical spring in compression provides equal downward forces on the two rollers through a collar on the sleeve. The spring force may be adjusted by screwing a nut up or down on the sleeve.

Let m = Mass of each ball in kg,

M = Mass of sleeve in kg,

r_1 = Minimum radius of rotation in metres,

r_2 = Maximum radius of rotation in metres,

ω_1 = Angular speed of the governor at minimum radius in rad/s,

ω_2 = Angular speed of the governor at maximum radius in rad/s,

S_1 = Spring force exerted on the sleeve at ω_1 in newtons,

S_2 = Spring force exerted on the sleeve at ω_2 in newtons,

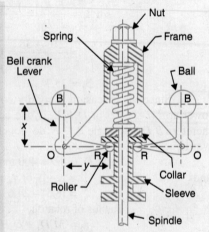

Fig. 18.18. Hartnell governor.

F_{C1} = Centrifugal force at ω_1 in newtons = $m\,(\omega_1)^2\,r_1$,

F_{C2} = Centrifugal force at ω_2 in newtons = $m\,(\omega_2)^2\,r_2$,

s = Stiffness of the spring or the force required to compress the spring by one mm,

x = Length of the vertical or ball arm of the lever in metres,

y = Length of the horizontal or sleeve arm of the lever in metres, and

r = Distance of fulcrum O from the governor axis or the radius of rotation when the governor is in mid-position, in metres.

Consider the forces acting at one bell crank lever. The minimum and maximum position is shown in Fig. 18.19. Let h be the compression of the spring when the radius of rotation changes from r_1 to r_2.

For the minimum position *i.e.* when the radius of rotation changes from r to r_1, as shown in Fig. 18.19 (*a*), the compression of the spring or the lift of sleeve h_1 is given by

$$\frac{h_1}{y} = \frac{a_1}{x} = \frac{r - r_1}{x} \qquad \qquad \ldots(i)$$

Similarly, for the maximum position *i.e.* when the radius of rotation changes from r to r_2, as shown in Fig. 18.19 (*b*), the compression of the spring or lift of sleeve h_2 is given by

$$\frac{h_2}{y} = \frac{a_2}{x} = \frac{r_2 - r}{x} \qquad \qquad \ldots(ii)$$

Adding equations (*i*) and (*ii*),

$$\frac{h_1 + h_2}{y} = \frac{r_2 - r_1}{x} \qquad \text{or} \qquad \frac{h}{y} = \frac{r_2 - r_1}{x} \qquad \qquad \dots (\because h = h_1 + h_2)$$

$$\therefore \qquad h = (r_2 - r_1)\frac{y}{x} \qquad \qquad \dots (iii)$$

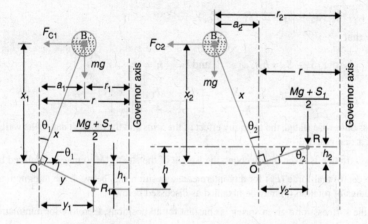

(*a*) Minimum position.   (*b*) Maximum position.

Fig. 18.19

Now for minimum position, taking moments about point *O*, we get

$$\frac{M.g + S_1}{2} \times y_1 = F_{C1} \times x_1 - m.g \times a_1$$

or
$$M.g + S_1 = \frac{2}{y_1}(F_{C1} \times x_1 - m.g \times a_1) \qquad \qquad \dots (iv)$$

Again for maximum position, taking moments about point *O*, we get

$$\frac{M.g + S_2}{2} \times y_2 = F_{C2} \times x_2 + m.g \times a_2$$

or
$$M.g + S_2 = \frac{2}{y_2}(F_{C2} \times x_2 + m.g \times a_2) \qquad \qquad \dots (v)$$

Subtracting equation (*iv*) from equation (*v*),

$$S_2 - S_1 = \frac{2}{y_2}(F_{C2} \times x_2 + m.g \times a_2) - \frac{2}{y_1}(F_{C1} \times x_1 - m.g \times a_1)$$

We know that

$$S_2 - S_1 = h.s, \qquad \text{and} \qquad h = (r_2 - r_1)\frac{y}{x}$$

$$\therefore \qquad s = \frac{S_2 - S_1}{h} = \left(\frac{S_2 - S_1}{r_2 - r_1}\right)\frac{x}{y}$$

Neglecting the obliquity effect of the arms (*i.e.* $x_1 = x_2 = x$, and $y_1 = y_2 = y$) and the moment due to weight of the balls (*i.e. m.g*), we have for minimum position,

$$\frac{M.g + S_1}{2} \times y = F_{C1} \times x \qquad \text{or} \qquad M.g + S_1 = 2F_{C1} \times \frac{x}{y} \qquad \qquad \dots (vi)$$

Similarly for maximum position,

$$\frac{M.g + S_2}{2} \times y = F_{C2} \times x \quad \text{or} \quad M.g + S_2 = 2F_{C2} \times \frac{x}{y} \qquad \ldots (vii)$$

Subtracting equation (vi) from equation (vii),

$$S_2 - S_1 = 2(F_{C2} - F_{C1})\frac{x}{y} \qquad \ldots (viii)$$

We know that

$$S_2 - S_1 = h.s, \qquad \text{and} \qquad h = (r_2 - r_1)\frac{y}{x}$$

$$\therefore \qquad s = \frac{S_2 - S_1}{h} = 2\left(\frac{F_{C2} - F_{C1}}{r_2 - r_1}\right)\left(\frac{x}{y}\right)^2 \qquad \ldots (ix)$$

Notes : 1. Unless otherwise stated, the obliquity effect of the arms and the moment due to the weight of the balls is neglected, in actual practice.

2. When friction is taken into account, the weight of the sleeve $(M.g)$ may be replaced by $(M.g \pm F)$.

3. The centrifugal force (F_C) for any intermediate position (*i.e.* between the minimum and maximum position) at a radius of rotation (r) may be obtained as discussed below :

Since the stiffness for a given spring is constant for all positions, therefore for minimum and intermediate position,

$$s = 2\left(\frac{F_C - F_{C1}}{r - r_1}\right)\left(\frac{x}{y}\right)^2 \qquad \ldots (x)$$

and for intermediate and maximum position,

$$s = 2\left(\frac{F_{C2} - F_C}{r_2 - r}\right)\left(\frac{x}{y}\right)^2 \qquad \ldots (xi)$$

$$\therefore \qquad \text{From equations } (ix), (x) \text{ and } (xi),$$

$$\frac{F_{C2} - F_{C1}}{r_2 - r_1} = \frac{F_C - F_{C1}}{r - r_1} = \frac{F_{C2} - F_C}{r_2 - r}$$

or

$$F_C = F_{C1} + (F_{C2} - F_{C1})\left(\frac{r - r_1}{r_2 - r_1}\right) = F_{C2} - (F_{C2} - F_{C1})\left(\frac{r_2 - r}{r_2 - r_1}\right)$$

Example 18.13. *A Hartnell governor having a central sleeve spring and two right-angled bell crank levers moves between 290 r.p.m. and 310 r.p.m. for a sleeve lift of 15 mm. The sleeve arms and the ball arms are 80 mm and 120 mm respectively. The levers are pivoted at 120 mm from the governor axis and mass of each ball is 2.5 kg. The ball arms are parallel to the governor axis at the lowest equilibrium speed. Determine : 1. loads on the spring at the lowest and the highest equilibrium speeds, and 2. stiffness of the spring.*

Solution. Given : $N_1 = 290$ r.p.m. or $\omega_1 = 2\pi \times 290/60 = 30.4$ rad/s ; $N_2 = 310$ r.p.m. or $\omega_2 = 2\pi \times 310/60 = 32.5$ rad/s ; $h = 15$ mm $= 0.015$ m ; $y = 80$ mm $= 0.08$ m ; $x = 120$ mm $= 0.12$ m ; $r = 120$ mm $= 0.12$ m ; $m = 2.5$ kg

1. *Loads on the spring at the lowest and highest equilibrium speeds*

Let $S_1 = $ Spring load at lowest equilibrium speed, and

$S_2 = $ Spring load at highest equilibrium speed.

Since the ball arms are parallel to governor axis at the lowest equilibrium speed (*i.e.* at $N_1 = 290$ r.p.m.), as shown in Fig. 18.20 (*a*), therefore

$$r = r_1 = 120 \text{ mm} = 0.12 \text{ m}$$

We know that centrifugal force at the minimum speed,

$$F_{C1} = m\,(\omega_1)^2\,r_1 = 2.5\,(30.4)^2\,0.12 = 277 \text{ N}$$

Now let us find the radius of rotation at the highest equilibrium speed, *i.e.* at $N_2 = 310$ r.p.m. The position of ball arm and sleeve arm at the highest equilibrium speed is shown in Fig. 18.20 (*b*).

Let $r_2 = $ Radius of rotation at $N_2 = 310$ r.p.m.

We know that $\qquad h = (r_2 - r_1)\,\dfrac{y}{x}$

or $\qquad r_2 = r_1 + h\left(\dfrac{x}{y}\right) = 0.12 + 0.015\left(\dfrac{0.12}{0.08}\right) = 0.1425 \text{ m}$

∴ Centrifugal force at the maximum speed,

$$F_{C2} = m\,(\omega_2)^2\,r_2 = 2.5 \times (32.5)^2 \times 0.1425 = 376 \text{ N}$$

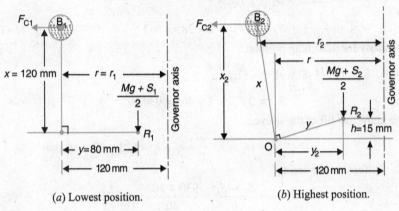

(*a*) Lowest position.   (*b*) Highest position.

Fig. 18.20

Neglecting the obliquity effect of arms and the moment due to the weight of the balls, we have for lowest position,

$$M.g + S_1 = 2F_{C1} \times \frac{x}{y} = 2 \times 277 \times \frac{0.12}{0.08} = 831 \text{ N}$$

∴ $\qquad S_1 = 831 \text{ N Ans.}$ $\qquad\qquad\qquad\qquad$ (∵ $M = 0$)

and for highest position,

$$M.g + S_2 = 2F_{C2} \times \frac{x}{y} = 2 \times 376 \times \frac{0.12}{0.08} = 1128 \text{ N}$$

∴ $\qquad S_2 = 1128 \text{ N Ans.}$ $\qquad\qquad\qquad\qquad$ (∵ $M = 0$)

2. Stiffness of the spring

We know that stiffness of the spring,

$$s = \frac{S_2 - S_1}{h} = \frac{1128 - 831}{15} = 19.8 \text{ N/mm Ans.}$$

Example 18.14. *In a spring loaded Hartnell type governor, the extreme radii of rotation of the balls are 80 mm and 120 mm. The ball arm and the sleeve arm of the bell crank lever are equal in length. The mass of each ball is 2 kg. If the speeds at the two extreme positions are 400 and 420 r.p.m., find : 1. the initial compression of the central spring, and 2. the spring constant.*

Solution. Given : $r_1 = 80$ mm $= 0.08$ m ; $r_2 = 120$ mm $= 0.12$ m ; $x = y$; $m = 2$ kg ; $N_1 = 400$ r.p.m. or $\omega_1 = 2\pi \times 400/60 = 41.9$ rad/s ; $N_2 = 420$ r.p.m. or $\omega_2 = 2\pi \times 420/60 = 44$ rad/s

Initial compression of the central spring

We know that the centrifugal force at the minimum speed,

$$F_{C1} = m\,(\omega_1)^2\, r_1 = 2\,(41.9)^2\; 0.08 = 281 \text{ N}$$

and centrifugal force at the maximum speed,

$$F_{C2} = m\,(\omega_2)^2\, r_2 = 2\,(44)^2\; 0.12 = 465 \text{ N}$$

Let　　　　　　　　　　S_1 = Spring force at the minimum speed, and

　　　　　　　　　　　S_2 = Spring force at the maximum speed.

We know that for minimum position,

$$M\,.g + S_1 = 2\,F_{C1} \times \frac{x}{y}$$

$\therefore$　　　　　　　　$S_1 = 2\,F_{C1} = 2 \times 281 = 562 \text{ N}$　　　　　　...($\because M = 0$ and $x = y$)

Similarly for maximum position,

$$M\,.g + S_2 = 2\,F_{C2} \times \frac{x}{y}$$

$\therefore$　　　　　　　　$S_2 = 2\,F_{C2} = 2 \times 465 = 930 \text{ N}$

We know that lift of the sleeve,

$$h = (r_2 - r_1)\,\frac{y}{x} = r_2 - r_1 = 120 - 80 = 40 \text{ mm}$$　　　　...($\because x = y$)

$\therefore$　Stiffness of the spring,

$$s = \frac{S_2 - S_1}{h} = \frac{930 - 562}{40} = 9.2 \text{ N/mm}$$

We know that initial compression of the central spring

$$= \frac{S_1}{s} = \frac{562}{9.2} = 61 \text{ mm} \quad \textbf{Ans.}$$

2. *Spring constant*

We have calculated above that the spring constant or stiffness of the spring,

$$s = 9.2 \text{ N/mm} \quad \textbf{Ans.}$$

Example 18.15. *A spring loaded governor of the Hartnell type has arms of equal length. The masses rotate in a circle of 130 mm diameter when the sleeve is in the mid position and the ball arms are vertical. The equilibrium speed for this position is 450 r.p.m., neglecting friction. The maximum sleeve movement is to be 25 mm and the maximum variation of speed taking in account the friction to be 5 per cent of the mid position speed. The mass of the sleeve is 4 kg and the friction may be considered equivalent to 30 N at the sleeve. The power of the governor must be sufficient to over-come the friction by one per cent change of speed either way at mid-position. Determine, neglecting obliquity effect of arms ; 1. The value of each rotating mass : 2. The spring stiffness in N/mm ; and 3. The initial compression of spring.*

Solution. Given : $x = y$; $d = 130$ mm or $r = 65$ mm $= 0.065$ m ; $N = 450$ r.p.m. or $\omega = 2\pi \times 450/60 = 47.13$ rad/s ; $h = 25$ mm $= 0.025$ m ; $M = 4$ kg ; $F = 30$ N

1. *Value of each rotating mass*

Let　　　　　　　　　　m = Value of each rotating mass in kg, and

　　　　　　　　　　　S = Spring force on the sleeve at mid position in newtons.

Since the change of speed at mid position to overcome friction is 1 per cent either way (*i.e.* ± 1%), therefore

Minimum speed at mid position,

$$\omega_1 = \omega - 0.01\omega = 0.99\omega = 0.99 \times 47.13 = 46.66 \text{ rad/s}$$

and maximum speed at mid-position,

$$\omega_2 = \omega + 0.01\omega = 1.01\omega = 1.01 \times 47.13 = 47.6 \text{ rad/s}$$

∴ Centrifugal force at the minimum speed,

$$F_{C1} = m\,(\omega_1)^2\,r = m\,(46.66)^2\,0.065 = 141.5\,m\,\text{N}$$

and centrifugal force at the maximum speed,

$$F_{C2} = m\,(\omega_2)^2\,r = m\,(47.6)^2\,0.065 = 147.3\,m\,\text{N}$$

We know that for minimum speed at mid-position,

$$S + (M.g - F) = 2\,F_{C1} \times \frac{x}{y}$$

or

$$S + (4 \times 9.81 - 30) = 2 \times 141.5\,m \times 1$$
$$\dots (\because\ x = y)$$

∴

$$S + 9.24 = 283\,m \quad \dots (i)$$

and for maximum speed at mid-position,

$$S + (M.g + F) = 2\,F_{C2} \times \frac{x}{y}$$

$$S + (4 \times 9.81 + 30) = 2 \times 147.3\,m \times 1$$
$$\dots (\because\ x = y)$$

∴

$$S + 69.24 = 294.6\,m$$
$$\dots (ii)$$

From equations (*i*) and (*ii*),

$$m = 5.2 \text{ kg Ans.}$$

A steam turbine used in thermal power stations.

Note : This picture is given as additional information.

2. Spring stiffness in N/mm

Let s = Spring stiffness in N/mm.

Since the maximum variation of speed, considering friction is ± 5% of the mid-position speed, therefore,

Minimum speed considering friction,

$$\omega_1' = \omega - 0.05\omega = 0.95\omega = 0.95 \times 47.13 = 44.8 \text{ rad/s}$$

and maximum speed considering friction,

$$\omega_2' = \omega + 0.05\omega = 1.05\omega = 1.05 \times 47.13 = 49.5 \text{ rad/s}$$

We know that minimum radius of rotation considering friction,

$$r_1 = r - h_1 \times \frac{x}{y} = 0.065 - \frac{0.025}{2} = 0.0525 \text{ m}$$

$$\dots \left(\because\ x = y, \text{ and } h_1 = \frac{h}{2} \right)$$

and maximum radius of rotation considering friction,

$$r_2 = r + h_2 \times \frac{x}{y} = 0.065 + \frac{0.025}{2} = 0.0775 \text{ m}$$

$$\dots \left(\because x = y, \text{ and } h_2 = \frac{h}{2} \right)$$

∴ Centrifugal force at the minimum speed considering friction,

$$F_{C1}' = m\,(\omega'_1)^2\,r_1 = 5.2\,(44.8)^2\,0.0525 = 548 \text{ N}$$

and centrifugal force at the maximum speed considering friction,

$$F_{C2}' = m\,(\omega_2')^2\,r_2 = 5.2\,(49.5)^2\,0.0775 = 987 \text{ N}$$

Let S_1 = Spring force at minimum speed considering friction, and

S_2 = Spring force at maximum speed considering friction.

We know that for minimum speed considering friction,

$$S_1 + (M.g - F) = 2\,F_{C1}' \times \frac{x}{y}$$

$$S_1 + (4 \times 9.81 - 30) = 2 \times 548 \times 1 \qquad \dots(\because x = y)$$

∴ $\qquad S_1 + 9.24 = 1096 \qquad$ or $\qquad S_1 = 1096 - 9.24 = 1086.76 \text{ N}$

and for maximum speed considering friction,

$$S_2 + (M.g + F) = 2\,F_{C2}' \times \frac{x}{y}$$

$$S_2 + (4 \times 9.81 + 30) = 2 \times 987 \times 1 \qquad \dots(\because x = y)$$

∴ $\qquad S_2 + 69.24 = 1974 \qquad$ or $\qquad S_2 = 1974 - 69.24 = 1904.76 \text{ N}$

We know that stiffness of the spring,

$$s = \frac{S_2 - S_1}{h} = \frac{1904.76 - 1086.76}{25} = 32.72 \text{ N/mm } \textbf{Ans.}$$

3. Initial compression of the spring

We know that initial compression of the spring

$$= \frac{S_1}{s} = \frac{1086.76}{32.72} = 33.2 \text{ mm } \textbf{Ans.}$$

Example 18.16. *In a spring loaded governor of the Hartnell type, the mass of each ball is 1kg, length of vertical arm of the bell crank lever is 100 mm and that of the horizontal arm is 50 mm. The distance of fulcrum of each bell crank lever is 80 mm from the axis of rotation of the governor. The extreme radii of rotation of the balls are 75 mm and 112.5 mm. The maximum equilibrium speed is 5 per cent greater than the minimum equilibrium speed which is 360 r.p.m. Find, neglecting obliquity of arms, initial compression of the spring and equilibrium speed corresponding to the radius of rotation of 100 mm.*

Solution. Given : $m = 1$ kg ; $x = 100$ mm $= 0.1$ m ; $y = 50$ mm $= 0.05$ m ; $r = 80$ mm $= 0.08$ m ; $r_1 = 75$ mm $= 0.075$ m ; $r_2 = 112.5$ mm $= 0.1125$ m ; $N_1 = 360$ r.p.m. or $\omega_1 = 2\pi \times 360/60 = 37.7$ rad/s

Since the maximum equilibrium speed is 5% greater than the minimum equilibrium speed (ω_1), therefore maximum equilibrium speed,

$$\omega_2 = 1.05 \times 37.7 = 39.6 \text{ rad/s}$$

We know that centrifugal force at the minimum equilibrium speed,

$$F_{C1} = m\,(\omega_1)^2\,r_1 = 1\,(37.7)^2\,0.075 = 106.6 \text{ N}$$

and centrifugal force at the maximum equilibrium speed,

$$F_{C2} = m(\omega_2)^2 r_2 = 1(39.6)^2 0.1125 = 176.4 \text{ N}$$

Initial compression of the spring

Let S_1 = Spring force corresponding to ω_1, and

S_2 = Spring force corresponding to ω_2.

Since the obliquity of arms is neglected, therefore for minimum equilibrium position,

$$M \cdot g + S_1 = 2 F_{C1} \times \frac{x}{y} = 2 \times 106.6 \times \frac{0.1}{0.05} = 426.4 \text{ N}$$

$$\therefore \qquad S_1 = 426.4 \text{ N} \qquad \qquad ...(\because M = 0)$$

and for maximum equilibrium position,

$$M \cdot g + S_2 = 2 F_{C2} \times \frac{x}{y} = 2 \times 176.4 \times \frac{0.1}{0.05} = 705.6 \text{ N}$$

$$\therefore \qquad S_2 = 705.6 \text{ N} \qquad \qquad ...(\because M = 0)$$

We know that lift of the sleeve,

$$h = (r_2 - r_1) \frac{y}{x} = (0.1125 - 0.075) \frac{0.05}{0.1} = 0.018\,75 \text{ m}$$

and stiffness of the spring $s = \dfrac{S_2 - S_1}{h} = \dfrac{705.6 - 426.4}{0.018\,75} = 14\,890 \text{ N/m} = 14.89 \text{ N/mm}$

∴ Initial compression of the spring

$$= \frac{S_1}{s} = \frac{426.4}{14.89} = 28.6 \text{ mm} \quad \textbf{Ans.}$$

Equilibrium speed corresponding to radius of rotation r = 100 mm = 0.1 m

Let N = Equilibrium speed in r.p.m.

Since the obliquity of the arms is neglected, therefore the centrifugal force at any instant,

$$F_C = F_{C1} + (F_{C2} - F_{C1})\left(\frac{r - r_1}{r_2 - r_1}\right)$$

$$= 106.6 + (176.4 - 106.6)\left(\frac{0.1 - 0.075}{0.1125 - 0.075}\right) = 153 \text{ N}$$

We know that centrifugal force (F_C),

$$153 = m \cdot \omega^2 \cdot r = 1\left(\frac{2\pi N}{60}\right)^2 0.1 = 0.0011\,N^2$$

$$\therefore \qquad N^2 = 153/0.0011 = 139\,090 \qquad \text{or} \qquad N = 373 \text{ r.p.m.} \quad \textbf{Ans.}$$

Example 18.17. *In a spring loaded governor of the Hartnell type, the mass of each ball is 5 kg and the lift of the sleeve is 50 mm. The speed at which the governor begins to float is 240 r.p.m., and at this speed the radius of the ball path is 110 mm. The mean working speed of the governor is 20 times the range of speed when friction is neglected. If the lengths of ball and roller arm of the bell crank lever are 120 mm and 100 mm respectively and if the distance between the centre of pivot of bell crank lever and axis of governor spindle is 140 mm, determine the initial compression of the spring taking into account the obliquity of arms.*

If friction is equivalent to a force of 30 N at the sleeve, find the total alteration in speed before the sleeve begins to move from mid-position.

Solution. Given : $m = 5$ kg ; $h = 50$ mm $= 0.05$ m ; $N_1 = 240$ r.p.m. or $\omega_1 = 2\pi \times 240/60 = 25.14$ rad/s ; $r_1 = 110$ mm $= 0.11$ m ; $x = 120$ mm $= 0.12$ m ; $y = 100$ mm $= 0.1$ m ; $r = 140$ mm $= 0.14$ m ; $F = 30$ N

Initial compression of the spring taking into account the obliquity of arms

First of all, let us find out the maximum speed of rotation (ω_2) in rad/s.

We know that mean working speed,

$$\omega = \frac{\omega_1 + \omega_2}{2}$$

and range of speed, neglecting friction

$$= \omega_2 - \omega_1$$

Since the mean working speed is 20 times the range of speed, therefore

$$\omega = 20 \, (\omega_2 - \omega_1)$$

or

$$\frac{\omega_1 + \omega_2}{2} = 20 \, (\omega_2 - \omega_1)$$

$$25.14 + \omega_2 = 40 \, (\omega_2 - 25.14) = 40 \, \omega_2 - 1005.6$$

∴

$$40 \, \omega_2 - \omega_2 = 25.14 + 1005.6 = 1030.74 \qquad \text{or} \qquad \omega_2 = 26.43 \text{ rad/s}$$

The minimum and maximum position of the governor balls is shown in Fig. 18.21 (a) and (b) respectively.

Let $r_2 =$ Maximum radius of rotation.

We know that lift of the sleeve,

$$h = (r_2 - r_1) \, \frac{y}{x}$$

or

$$r_2 = r_1 + h \times \frac{x}{y} = 0.11 + 0.05 \times \frac{0.12}{0.1} = 0.17 \text{ m}$$

We know that centrifugal force at the minimum speed,

$$F_{C1} = m \, (\omega_1)^2 \, r_1 = 5 \, (25.14)^2 \, 0.11 = 347.6 \text{ N}$$

and centrifugal force at the maximum speed,

$$F_{C2} = m \, (\omega_2)^2 \, r_2 = 5 \, (26.43)^2 \, 0.17 = 593.8 \text{ N}$$

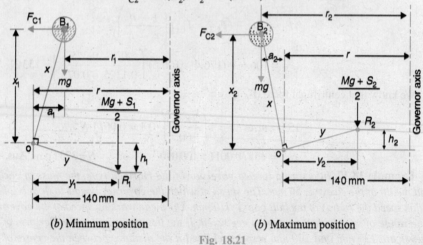

(b) Minimum position   (b) Maximum position

Fig. 18.21

Since the obliquity of arms is to be taken into account, therefore from the minimum position as shown in Fig. 18.21 (a),

$$a_1 = r - r_1 = 0.14 - 0.11 = 0.03 \text{ m}$$

$$x_1 = \sqrt{x^2 - (a_1)^2} = \sqrt{(0.12)^2 - (0.03)^2} = 0.1162 \text{ m}$$

and
$$y_1 = \sqrt{y^2 - (h_1)^2} = \sqrt{(0.1)^2 - (0.025)^2} = 0.0986 \text{ m}$$
$$\ldots (\because \ h_1 = h/2 = 0.025 \text{ m})$$

Similarly, for the maximum position, as shown in Fig. 18.21 (*b*),
$$a_2 = r_2 - r = 0.17 - 0.14 = 0.03 \text{ m}$$

∴
$$x_2 = x_1 = 0.1162 \text{ m} \qquad\qquad \ldots (\because \ a_2 = a_1)$$

and
$$y_2 = y_1 = 0.0986 \text{ m} \qquad\qquad \ldots (\because \ h_2 = h_1)$$

Now taking moments about point *O* for the minimum position as shown in Fig. 18.21 (*a*),

$$\frac{M.g + S_1}{2} \times y_1 = F_{C1} \times x_1 - m.g \times a_1$$

$$\frac{S_1}{2} \times 0.0968 = 347.6 \times 0.1162 - 5 \times 9.81 \times 0.03 = 38.9 \text{ N} \quad \ldots (\because \ M = 0)$$

∴
$$S_1 = 2 \times 38.9/0.0968 = 804 \text{ N}$$

Similarly, taking moments about point *O* for the maximum position as shown in Fig. 18.21 (*b*),

$$\frac{M.g + S_2}{2} \times y_2 = F_{C2} \times x_2 + m.g \times a_2$$

$$\frac{S_2}{2} \times 0.0968 = 593.8 \times 0.1162 + 5 \times 9.81 \times 0.03 = 70.47 \text{ N} \quad \ldots (\because \ M = 0)$$

∴
$$S_2 = 2 \times 70.47/0.0968 = 1456 \text{ N}$$

We know that stiffness of the spring

$$s = \frac{S_2 - S_1}{h} = \frac{1456 - 804}{50} = 13.04 \text{ N/mm}$$

∴ Initial compression of the spring

$$= \frac{S_1}{s} = \frac{804}{13.04} = 61.66 \text{ mm } \textbf{Ans.}$$

Total alternation in speed when friction is taken into account

We know that spring force for the mid-position,

$$S = S_1 + h_1.s = 804 + 25 \times 13.04 = 1130 \text{ N} \ \ldots (\because \ h_1 = h/2 = 25 \text{ mm})$$

and mean angular speed,
$$\omega = \frac{\omega_1 + \omega_2}{2} = \frac{25.14 + 26.43}{2} = 25.785 \text{ rad/s}$$

or
$$N = \omega \times 60/2\pi = 25.785 \times 60/2\pi = 246.2 \text{ r.p.m.}$$

∴ Speed when the sleeve begins to move downwards from the mid-position,

$$N' = N \sqrt{\frac{S - F}{S}} = 246.2 \sqrt{\frac{1130 - 30}{1130}} = 243 \text{ r.p.m.}$$

and speed when the sleeve begins to move upwards from the mid-position,

$$N'' = N \sqrt{\frac{S + F}{S}} = 246.2 \sqrt{\frac{1130 + 30}{1130}} = 249 \text{ r.p.m.}$$

∴ Alteration in speed $= N'' - N' = 249 - 243 = 6 \text{ r.p.m. } \textbf{Ans.}$

Example 18.18. *Fig. 18.22 shows diagrammatically a centrifugal governor. The masses 'm' are directly connected to one another by two parallel and identical close coiled springs, one on either side. In the position shown, with the mass arms parallel to the axis of rotation, the equilibrium speed is 900 r.p.m. Given ball circle radius = 70 mm ; length of ball arm = 85 mm and length of sleeve arm = 50 mm.*

1. When the speed is increased by 1% without any change of radius for the given position, an axial force of 30 N is required at the sleeve to maintain equilibrium. Determine the mass of each ball.

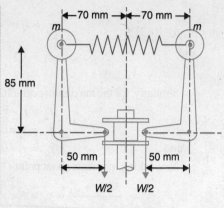

Fig. 18.22.

2. Find the stiffness and initial extension of each spring, if the rate of sleeve movement, when in mid position is 20 mm for 480 r.p.m. change of speed.

Solution. Given : N = 900 r.p.m. or $\omega = 2\pi \times 900/60 = 94.26$ rad/s ; r = 70 mm = 0.07 m; x = 85 mm = 0.085 m ; y = 50 mm = 0.05 m ; W = 30 N

1. Mass of each ball

Let m = Mass of each ball in kg.

We know that centrifugal force at the equilibrium speed,

$$F_C = m.\omega^2.r = m (94.26)^2 \, 0.07 = 622 \, m \text{N}$$

Since the speed is increased by 1% without any change of radius, therefore increased speed,

$$\omega_1 = \omega + 0.01 \, \omega = 1.01 \, \omega = 1.01 \times 94.26 = 95.2 \text{ rad/s}$$

and centrifugal force at the increased speed,

$$F_{C1} = m (\omega_1)^2 \, r = m (95.2)^2 \, 0.07 = 634.4 \, m \text{N}$$

Now taking moments about point O as shown in Fig. 18.23, we get

$$(F_{C1} - F_C) \, 0.085 = \frac{W}{2} \times 0.05$$

$$(634.4 \, m - 622 \, m) \, 0.085 = \frac{30}{2} \times 0.05 = 0.75$$

$$1.054 \, m = 0.75$$

or $$m = 0.75/1.054 = 0.7 \text{ kg Ans.}$$

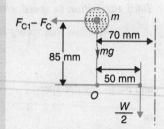

Fig. 18.23

2. Stiffness and initial extension of each spring

Let s = Stiffness of each spring.

We know that centrifugal force at the equilibrium speed, *i.e.* at 900 r.p.m.

$$F_C = 622 \, m = 622 \times 0.7 = 435.4 \text{ N}$$

Since the change of speed is 480 r.p.m., therefore increased speed,

$$N_2 = 900 + 480 = 1380 \text{ r.p.m.}$$

∴ Angular increased speed,

$$\omega_2 = 2\pi \times 1380/60 = 144.5 \text{ rad/s}$$

Also, it is given that for 480 r.p.m. change of speed, the rate of sleeve movement is 20 mm, *i.e.*

$$h = 20 \text{ mm} = 0.02 \text{ m}$$

Let r = Radius of rotation at 900 r.p.m. = 0.07 m ...(Given)

r_2 = Radius of rotation at 1380 r.p.m.

We know that for the radius of rotation to change from r to r_2, the increase in length of radius of rotation is

$$r_2 - r = h \times \frac{x}{y} = 0.02 \times \frac{0.085}{0.05} = 0.034 \text{ m}$$

∴ $$r_2 = r + 0.034 = 0.07 + 0.034 = 0.104 \text{ m}$$

and centrifugal force at the increased speed (ω_2),

$$F_{C2} = m (\omega_2)^2 r_2 = 0.7 (144.5)^2 \, 0.104 = 1520 \text{ N}$$

∴ Stiffness of each spring,

$$s = \frac{\text{Increase in force for one ball}}{\text{Increase in length for each spring}} = \frac{F_{C2} - F_C}{2 (r_2 - r)} = \frac{1520 - 435.4}{2 (0.104 - 0.07)}$$

$$= 15\,950 \text{ N/m} = 15.95 \text{ N/mm Ans.}$$

and initial extension of each spring

$$= \frac{F_C}{s} = \frac{435.4}{15.95} = 27.3 \text{ mm Ans.}$$

Example 18.19. *In a spring controlled governor of the type, as shown in Fig. 18.24, the mass of each ball is 1.5 kg and the mass of the sleeve is 8 kg. The two arms of the bell crank lever are at right angles and their lengths are OB = 100 mm and OA = 40 mm. The distance of the fulcrum O of each bell crank lever from the axis of rotation is 50 mm and minimum radius of rotation of the governor balls is also 50 mm. The corresponding equilibrium speed is 240 r.p.m. and the sleeve is required to lift 10 mm for an increase in speed of 5 per cent. Find the stiffness and initial compression of the spring.*

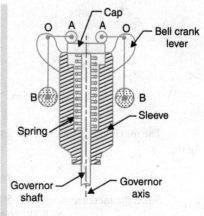

Fig. 18.24

Solution. Given : $m = 1.5$ kg ; $M = 8$ kg ; $OB = x$ = 100 mm = 0.1 m ; $OA = y = 40$ mm = 0.04 m ; $r = 50$ mm = 0.05 m; $r_1 = 50$ mm = 0.05 m ; $N_1 = 240$ r.p.m. or $\omega_1 = 2 \pi \times 240/60 = 25.14$ rad/s ; $h = 10$ mm = 0.01 m ; Increase in speed = 5%

Stiffness of the spring

The spring controlled governor of the type, as shown in Fig. 18.24, has the pivots for the bell crank lever on the moving sleeve. The spring is compressed between the sleeve and the cap which is fixed to the end of the governor shaft. The simplest way of analysing this type of governor is by taking moments about the instantaneous centre of all the forces which act on one of the bell crank levers.

The minimum position of the governor is shown in Fig. 18.25 (*a*).

We know that the centrifugal force acting on the ball at the minimum equilibrium speed,

$$F_{C1} = m (\omega_1)^2 r_1 = 1.5 (25.14)^2 \, 0.05 = 47.4 \text{ N}$$

Let S_1 = Spring force at the minimum equilibrium speed.

The instantaneous centre I for the bell crank lever coincides with the roller centre A. Taking moments about A,

$$F_{C1} \times x = \left(m.g + \frac{M.g + S_1}{2} \right) OA$$

$$47.4 \times 0.1 = \left(1.5 \times 9.81 + \frac{8 \times 9.81 + S_1}{2} \right) 0.04 = 0.6 + 1.57 + 0.02\, S_1$$

$$4.74 = 2.17 + 0.02\, S_1 \quad \text{or} \quad S_1 = \frac{4.74 - 2.17}{0.02} = 128.5 \text{ N}$$

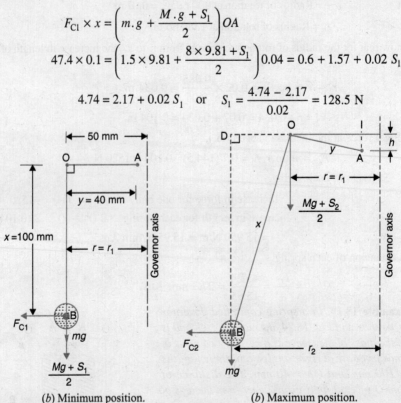

(b) Minimum position.   (b) Maximum position.

Fig. 18.25

The maximum position of the governor is shown in Fig. 18.25 (b). From the geometry of the figure,

$$\frac{r_2 - r_1}{x} = \frac{h}{y} \quad \text{or} \quad r_2 = r_1 + h \times \frac{x}{y} = 0.05 + 0.01 \times \frac{0.1}{0.04} = 0.075 \text{ m}$$

Since the increase in speed is 5%, therefore the maximum equilibrium speed of rotation,

$$N_2 = N_1 + 0.05\, N_1 = 1.05\, N_1 = 1.05 \times 240 = 252 \text{ r.p.m.}$$

or

$$\omega_2 = 2\pi \times 252/60 = 26.4 \text{ rad/s}$$

∴ Centrifugal force acting on the ball at the maximum equilibrium speed,

$$F_{C2} = m\, (\omega_2)^2\, r_2 = 1.5\, (26.4)^2\, 0.075 = 78.4 \text{ N}$$

Let S_2 = Spring force at the maximum equilibrium speed.

The instantaneous centre in this case lies at I as shown in Fig. 18.25 (b). From the geometry of the figure,

$$OI = \sqrt{(OA)^2 - (IA)^2} = \sqrt{y^2 - h^2} = \sqrt{(0.04)^2 - (0.01)^2} = 0.0387 \text{ m}$$

$$BD = \sqrt{(OB)^2 - (OD)^2} = \sqrt{x^2 - (r_2 - r_1)^2}$$

$$= \sqrt{(0.1)^2 - (0.075 - 0.05)^2} = 0.097 \text{ m}$$

$$ID = OI + OD = 0.0387 + (0.075 - 0.05) = 0.0637 \text{ m}$$

Now taking moments about I,

$$F_{C2} \times BD = m.g \times ID + \frac{M.g + S_2}{2} \times OI$$

$$78.4 \times 0.097 = 1.5 \times 9.81 \times 0.0637 + \left(\frac{8 \times 9.81 + S_2}{2}\right) 0.0387$$

$$7.6 = 0.937 + 1.52 + 0.02\ S_2 = 2.457 + 0.019\ S_2$$

∴

$$S_2 = \frac{7.6 - 2.457}{0.019} = 270.7 \text{ N}$$

We know that stiffness of the spring,

$$s = \frac{S_2 - S_1}{h} = \frac{270.7 - 128.5}{10} = 14.22 \text{ N/mm} \text{ Ans.}$$

Initial compression of the spring

We know that initial compression of the spring

$$= \frac{S_1}{s} = \frac{128.5}{14.22} = 9.04 \text{ mm} \text{ Ans.}$$

An overview of a thermal power station.

Note : This picture is given as additional information.

18.9. Hartung Governor

A spring controlled governor of the Hartung type is shown in Fig. 18.26 (*a*). In this type of governor, the vertical arms of the bell crank levers are fitted with spring balls which compress against the frame of the governor when the rollers at the horizontal arm press against the sleeve.

Let
S = Spring force,

F_C = Centrifugal force,

M = Mass on the sleeve, and

x and y = Lengths of the vertical and horizontal arm of the bell crank lever respectively.

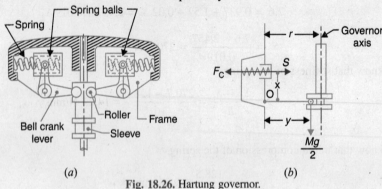

Fig. 18.26. Hartung governor.

Fig. 18.26 (*a*) and (*b*) show the governor in mid-position. Neglecting the effect of obliquity of the arms, taking moments about the fulcrum *O*,

$$F_C \times x = S \times x + \frac{M.g}{2} \times y$$

Example 18.20. *In a spring-controlled governor of the Hartung type, the length of the ball and sleeve arms are 80 mm and 120 mm respectively. The total travel of the sleeve is 25 mm. In the mid position, each spring is compressed by 50 mm and the radius of rotation of the mass centres is 140 mm. Each ball has a mass of 4 kg and the spring has a stiffness of 10 kN/m of compression. The equivalent mass of the governor gear at the sleeve is 16 kg. Neglecting the moment due to the revolving masses when the arms are inclined, determine the ratio of the range of speed to the mean speed of the governor. Find, also, the speed in the mid-position.*

Solution. Given : x = 80 mm = 0.08 mm ; y = 120 mm = 0.12 m ; h = 25 mm = 0.025 m ; r = 140 mm = 0.14 m ; m = 4 kg ; s = 10 kN/m = 10 × 10³ N/m ; M = 16 kg ; Initial compression = 50 mm = 0.05 m

Mean speed of the governor

First of all, let us find the mean speed of the governor *i.e.* the speed when the governor is in mid-position as shown in Fig. 18.27 (*a*).

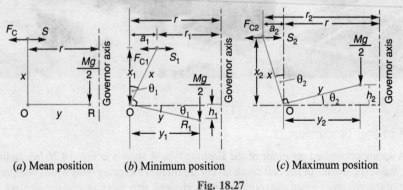

(*a*) Mean position   (*b*) Minimum position   (*c*) Maximum position

Fig. 18.27

Let ω = Mean angular speed in rad/s, and

N = Mean speed in r.p.m.

We know that the centrifugal force acting on the ball spring,

$$F_C = m.\omega^2.r = 4 \times \omega^2 \times 0.14 = 0.56 \, \omega^2 \, \text{N}$$

and Spring force, S = Stiffness × Initial compression = $10 \times 10^3 \times 0.05 = 500$ N

Now taking moments about point O, neglecting the moment due to the revolving masses, we have

$$F_C \times x = S \times x + \frac{M.g}{2} \times y$$

$$0.56 \, \omega^2 \times 0.08 = 500 \times 0.08 + \frac{16 \times 9.81}{2} \times 0.12 = 40 + 9.42 = 49.42$$

$\therefore$

$$\omega^2 = \frac{49.42}{0.56 \times 0.08} = 1103 \quad \text{or} \quad \omega = 33.2 \text{ rad/s}$$

and

$$N = \frac{33.23 \times 60}{2\pi} = 317 \text{ r.p.m. } \textbf{Ans.}$$

Ratio of range of speed to mean speed

Let ω_1 = Minimum angular speed in rad/s, at the minimum radius of rotation r_1,

ω_2 = Maximum angular speed in rad/s, at the maximum radius of rotation r_2,

N_1 and N_2 = Corresponding minimum and maximum speeds in r.p.m.

The minimum and maximum position is shown in Fig. 18.27 (*b*) and (*c*) respectively. First of all, let us find the minimum speed N_1.

From the geometry of the Fig. 18.27 (*b*),

$$\frac{r - r_1}{h_1} = \frac{x}{y} \quad \text{or} \quad r_1 = r - h_1 \times \frac{x}{y} = 0.14 - \frac{0.025}{2} \times \frac{0.08}{0.12} = 0.132 \text{ m}$$

$$\dots (\because h_1 = h/2)$$

We know that centrifugal force at the minimum position,

$$F_{C1} = m \, (\omega_1)^2 \, r_1 = 4 \, (\omega_1)^2 \, 0.132 = 0.528 \, (\omega_1)^2 \, \text{N}$$

and spring force at the minimum position,

$$S_1 = [\text{Initial compression} - (r - r_1)] \times \text{Stiffness}$$

$$= [0.05 - (0.14 - 0.132)] \, 10 \times 10^3 = 420 \text{ N}$$

Now taking moments about the fulcrum O, neglecting the obliquity of arms (*i.e.* taking $x_1 = x$ and $y_1 = y$),

$$F_{C1} \times x = S_1 \times x + \frac{M.g}{2} \times y$$

$$0.528 \, (\omega_1)^2 \, 0.08 = 420 \times 0.08 + \frac{16 \times 9.81}{2} \times 0.12 = 33.6 + 9.42 = 43.02$$

$\therefore$

$$(\omega_1)^2 = \frac{43.02}{0.528 \times 0.08} = 1019 \quad \text{or} \quad \omega_1 = 32 \text{ rad/s}$$

and

$$N_1 = \frac{32 \times 60}{2\pi} = 305.5 \text{ r.p.m.}$$

Now let us find the maximum speed N_2. From the geometry of the Fig. 18.27 (c),

$$\frac{r_2 - r}{h_2} = \frac{x}{y} \quad \text{or} \quad r_2 = r + h_2 \times \frac{x}{y} = 0.14 + \frac{0.025}{2} \times \frac{0.08}{0.12} = 0.148 \text{ m}$$

$$\ldots (\because\ h_2 = h/2)$$

We know that centrifugal force at the maximum position,

$$F_{C2} = m\ (\omega_2)^2\ r_2 = 4\ (\omega_2)^2\ 0.148 = 0.592\ (\omega_2)^2 \text{ N}$$

and spring force at the maximum position,

$$S_2 = [\text{Initial compression} + (r_2 - r)] \times \text{Stiffness}$$
$$= [0.05 + (0.148 - 0.14)] \times 10 \times 10^3 = 580 \text{ N}$$

Now taking moments about the fulcrum O, neglecting obliquity of arms (*i.e.* taking $x_2 = x$ and $y_2 = y$),

$$F_{C2} \times x = S_2 \times x + \frac{M \cdot g}{2} \times y$$

$$0.592\ (\omega_2)^2\ 0.08 = 580 \times 0.08 + \frac{16 \times 9.81}{2} \times 0.12 = 46.4 + 9.42 = 55.82$$

$$\therefore \qquad (\omega_2)^2 = \frac{55.82}{0.592 \times 0.08} = 1178 \quad \text{or} \quad \omega_2 = 34.32 \text{ rad/s}$$

and

$$N_2 = \frac{34.32 \times 60}{2\pi} = 327.7 \text{ r.p.m.}$$

We know that range of speed

$$= N_2 - N_1 = 327.7 - 305.5 = 22.2 \text{ r.p.m.}$$

$\therefore$ Ratio of range of speed to mean speed

$$= \frac{N_2 - N_1}{N} = \frac{22.2}{317} = 0.07 \quad \text{or} \quad 7\% \text{ Ans.}$$

18.10. Wilson-Hartnell Governor

A Wilson-Hartnell governor is a governor in which the balls are connected by a spring in tension as shown in Fig. 18.28. An auxiliary spring is attached to the sleeve mechanism through a lever by means of which the equilibrium speed for a given radius may be adjusted. The main spring may be considered of two equal parts each belonging to both the balls. The line diagram of a Wilson-Hartnell governor is shown in Fig. 18.29.

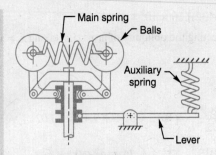

Wilson-Hartnell governor.

Fig. 18.28

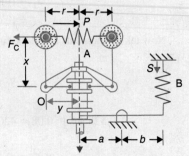

Line diagram of Wilson-Hartnell governor.

Fig. 18.29

Let $\qquad P$ = Tension in the main spring or ball spring A,

$\qquad S$ = Tension in the auxiliary spring B,

$\qquad m$ = Mass of each ball,

$\qquad M$ = Mass of sleeve,

$\qquad s_b$ = Stiffness of each ball spring,

$\qquad s_a$ = Stiffness of auxiliary spring,

$\qquad F_C$ = Centrifugal force of each ball, and

$\qquad r$ = Radius of rotation of balls,

Now total downward force on the sleeve

$$= M.g + S \times b/a$$

Taking moments about O and neglecting the effect of the pull of gravity on the ball,

$$(F_C - P)\, x = \frac{M.g + S \times b/a}{2} \times y$$

Let suffixes 1 and 2 be used to denote the values at minimum and maximum equilibrium speeds respectively.

$\therefore$ At minimum equilibrium speed,

$$(F_{C1} - P_1)\, x = \frac{M.g + S_1 \times b/a}{2} \times y \qquad \ldots (i)$$

and at maximum equilibrium speed,

$$(F_{C2} - P_2)\, x = \frac{M.g + S_2 \times b/a}{2} \times y \qquad \ldots (ii)$$

Subtracting equation (i) from equation (ii), we have

$$[(F_{C2} - F_{C1}) - (P_2 - P_1)]\, x = (S_2 - S_1)\, \frac{b}{a} \times \frac{y}{2} \qquad \ldots (iii)$$

When the radius increases from r_1 to r_2, the ball springs extend by the amount $2\,(r_2 - r_1)$ and the auxiliary spring extend by the amount $(r_2 - r_1)\,\dfrac{y}{x} \times \dfrac{b}{a}$

$\therefore \qquad P_2 - P_1 = 2\,s_b \times 2\,(r_2 - r_1) = 4\,s_b\,(r_2 - r_1)$

and $\qquad S_2 - S_1 = s_a\,(r_2 - r_1)\,\dfrac{y}{x} \times \dfrac{b}{a}$

Substituting the values of $(P_2 - P_1)$ and $(S_2 - S_1)$ in equation (iii),

$$[(F_{C2} - F_{C1}) - 4\,s_b\,(r_2 - r_1)]\, x = s_a\,(r_2 - r_1)\,\frac{y}{x} \times \frac{b}{a} \times \frac{b}{a} \times \frac{y}{2}$$

$$(F_{C2} - F_{C1}) - 4\,s_b\,(r_2 - r_1) = \frac{s_a}{2}\,(r_2 - r_1) \left(\frac{y}{x} \times \frac{b}{a}\right)^2$$

$$\therefore \quad 4\,s_b + \frac{s_a}{2}\left(\frac{y}{x} \times \frac{b}{a}\right)^2 = \frac{F_{C2} - F_{C1}}{r_2 - r_1}$$

Note : When the auxiliary spring is not used, then $s_a = 0$.

$$\therefore \qquad 4\,s_b = \frac{F_{C2} - F_{C1}}{r_2 - r_1} \qquad \text{or} \qquad s_b = \frac{F_{C2} - F_{C1}}{4\,(r_2 - r_1)}$$

Example 18.21. *The following particulars refer to a Wilson-Hartnell governor :*

Mass of each ball = 2 kg ; minimum radius = 125 mm ; maximum radius = 175 mm ; minimum speed = 240 r.p.m. ; maximum speed = 250 r.p.m. ; length of the ball arm of each bell crank lever = 150 mm; length of the sleeve arm of each bell crank lever = 100 mm ; combined stiffness of the two ball springs = 0.2 kN/m. Find the equivalent stiffness of the auxiliary spring referred to the sleeve.

Solution. Given : $m = 2$ kg ; $r_1 = 125$ mm $= 0.125$ m ; $r_2 = 175$ mm $= 0.175$ m ; $N_1 = 240$ r.p.m. or $\omega_1 = 2\,\pi \times 240/60 = 25.14$ rad/s ; $N_2 = 250$ r.p.m. or $\omega_2 = 2\,\pi = 250/60 = 26.2$ rad/s ; $x = 150$ mm $= 0.15$ m ; $y = 100$ mm $= 0.1$ m ; $s_b = 0.2$ kN/m $= 200$ N/m

Let $\quad\quad\quad\quad\quad\quad$ s = Equivalent stiffness of the auxiliary spring referred to the sleeve

$$= s_a \left(\frac{b}{a}\right)^2$$

We know that centrifugal force at the minimum speed,

$$F_{C1} = m\,(\omega_1)^2\,r_1 = 2\,(25.14)^2\,0.125 = 158 \text{ N}$$

and centrifugal force at the maximum speed,

$$F_{C2} = m\,(\omega_2)^2\,r_2 = 2\,(26.2)^2\,0.175 = 240 \text{ N}$$

We know that

$$4\,s_b + \frac{s_a}{2}\left(\frac{y}{x} \times \frac{b}{a}\right)^2 = \frac{F_{C2} - F_{C1}}{r_2 - r_1}$$

$$4 \times 200 + \frac{s_a}{2}\left(\frac{0.1}{0.15} \times \frac{b}{a}\right)^2 = \frac{240 - 158}{0.175 - 0.125} = 1640$$

$$800 + 0.22\,s_a\left(\frac{b}{a}\right)^2 = 1640 \quad\text{or}\quad 0.22\,s_a\left(\frac{b}{a}\right)^2 = 1640 - 800 = 840$$

$$\therefore \quad\quad s_a\left(\frac{b}{a}\right)^2 = 800/0.22 = 3818 \text{ N/m} = 3.818 \text{ kN/m } \text{Ans.}$$

Example 18.22. *A spring loaded governor is shown in Fig. 18.30. The two balls, each of mass 6 kg, are connected across by two springs . An auxiliary spring B provides an additional force at the sleeve through the medium of a lever which pivots about a fixed centre at its left hand end. In the mean position, the radius of the governor balls is 120 mm and the speed is 600 r.p.m. The tension in each spring is then 1 kN. Find the tension in the spring B for this position.*

When the sleeve moves up 15 mm, the speed is to be 630 r.p.m. Find the necessary stiffness of the spring B, if the stiffness of each spring A is 10 kN/m. Neglect the moment produced by the mass of the balls.

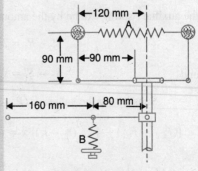

Fig. 18.30

Solution. Given : $m = 6$ kg ; $r = r_1 = 120$ mm $= 0.12$ m ; $N = N_1 = 600$ r.p.m. or $\omega_1 = 2\pi \times 600/60 = 62.84$ rad/s

Tension in spring B

Let $\quad\quad\quad\quad\quad\quad$ S_{B1} = Spring force or tension in spring B, and

$\quad\quad\quad\quad\quad\quad\quad\quad$ M.g = Total load at the sleeve.

We know that centrifugal force at the minimum speed,

$$F_{C1} = m \, (\omega_1)^2 \, r_1 = 6 \, (62.84)^2 \, 0.12 = 2843 \text{ N}$$

Since the tension in each spring A is 1 kN and there are two springs, therefore

Total spring force in spring A,

$$S_{A1} = 2 \times 1 = 2 \text{ kN} = 2000 \text{ N}$$

Taking moments about the pivot P (neglecting the moment produced by the mass of balls) in order to find the force Mg on the sleeve, in the mean position as shown in Fig. 18.31 (*a*),

$$F_{C1} \times 90 = S_{A1} \times 90 + \frac{M.g}{2} \times 90 \quad \text{or} \quad F_{C1} = S_{A1} + \frac{M.g}{2}$$

$\therefore$
$$M.g = 2 \, F_{C1} - 2 \, S_{A1} = 2 \times 2843 - 2 \times 2000 = 1686 \text{ N}$$

Now taking moments about point Q,

$$S_{B1} \times 160 = M.g \, (80 + 160) = 1686 \times 240 = 404 \, 640$$

$\therefore$
$$S_{B1} = 404 \, 640/160 = 2529 \text{ N} \quad \textbf{Ans.}$$

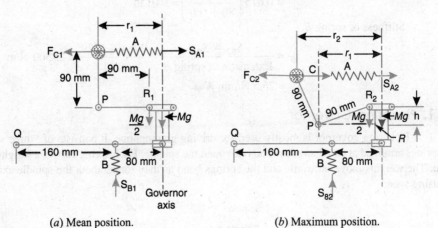

(*a*) Mean position.   (*b*) Maximum position.

Fig. 18.31

Stiffness of the spring B

Given : $h = 15$ mm $= 0.015$ m ; $N_2 = 630$ r.p.m. or $\omega_2 = 2 \, \pi \times 630/60 = 66$ rad/s; $s_A = 10$ kN/m $= 10 \times 10^3$ N/m

Let s_B = Stiffness of spring B.

The maximum position is shown in Fig. 18.31 (*b*).

First of all, let us find the maximum radius of rotation (r_2) when the sleeve moves up by 0.015 m. We know that

$$h = (r_2 - r_1) \, \frac{y}{x} \quad \text{or} \quad r_2 = r_1 + h \times \frac{x}{y} = 0.12 + 0.015 = 0.135 \text{ m}$$

$$\dots (\because x = y = 90 \text{ mm} = 0.09 \text{ m})$$

$\therefore$ Centrifugal force at the maximum speed,

$$F_{C2} = m \, (\omega_2)^2 \, r_2 = 6 \, (66)^2 \, 0.135 = 3528 \text{ N}$$

We know that extension of the spring A,

$$= 2 \, (r_2 - r_1) \times \text{No. of springs} = 2 \, (0.135 - 0.12) \, 2 = 0.06 \text{ m}$$

∴ Total spring force in spring A,

$$S_{A2} = S_{A1} + \text{Extension of springs} \times \text{Stiffness of springs} (s_A)$$
$$= 2000 + 0.06 \times 10 \times 10^3 = 2600 \text{ N}$$

Now taking moments about P, neglecting the obliquity of arms,

$$F_{C2} \times 90 = S_{A2} \times 90 + \frac{M \cdot g}{2} \times 90 \quad \text{or} \quad F_{C2} = S_{A2} + \frac{M \cdot g}{2}$$

∴ $$M.g = 2 F_{C2} - 2 S_{A2} = 2 \times 3528 - 2 \times 2600 = 1856 \text{ N}$$

Again taking moments about point Q (neglecting the moment produced by the mass of balls) in order to find the spring force (S_{B2}) when sleeve rises as shown in Fig. 18.31 (b),

$$S_{B2} \times 160 = M.g (80 + 160) = 1856 \times 240 = 445\,440$$

∴ $$S_{B2} = 445\,440 / 160 = 2784 \text{ N}$$

When the sleeve rises 0.015 m, the extension in spring B

$$= 0.015 \left(\frac{160}{80 + 160} \right) = 0.01 \text{ m}$$

∴ Stiffness of spring B,

$$s_B = \frac{S_{B2} - S_{B1}}{\text{Extension of spring } B} = \frac{2784 - 2529}{0.01} = 25\,500 \text{ N/m}$$
$$= 25.5 \text{ N/mm Ans.}$$

18.11. Pickering Governor

A Pickering governor is mostly used for driving gramophone. It consists of [*]three straight leaf springs arranged at equal angular intervals round the spindle. Each spring carries a weight at the centre. The weights move outwards and the springs bend as they rotate about the spindle axis with increasing speed.

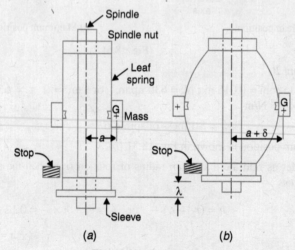

Fig. 18.32. Pickering governor.

In Fig. 18.32 (a), the governor is at rest. When the governor rotates, the springs together with the weights are deflected as shown in Fig. 18.32 (b). The upper end of the spring is attached by a

[*] Only two leaf springs are shown in Fig. 18.32.

screw to hexagonal nut fixed to the governor spindle. The lower end of the spring is attached to a sleeve which is free to slide on the spindle. The spindle runs in a bearing at each end and is driven through gearing by the motor. The sleeve can rise until it reaches a stop, whose position is adjustable.

Let m = Mass attached at the centre of the leaf spring,

a = Distance from the spindle axis to the centre of gravity of the mass, when the governor is at rest,

ω = Angular speed of the governor spindle,

δ = Deflection of the centre of the leaf spring at angular speed ω,

$a + \delta$ = Distance from the spindle axis to the centre of gravity of the mass, when the governor is rotating, and

λ = Lift of the sleeve corresponding to the deflection δ.

We know that the maximum deflection of a leaf spring with both ends fixed and carrying a load (W) at the centre is,

$$\delta = \frac{W.l^3}{192 \, EI} \qquad \ldots (i)$$

where l = Distance between the fixed ends of the spring,

E = Young's modulus of the material of the spring, and

I = Moment of inertia of its cross-section about the neutral axis = $\dfrac{b.t^3}{12}$

(where b and t are width and thickness of spring).

In case of a Pickering governor, the central load is the centrifugal force.

$\therefore$ $W = F_C = m.\omega^2 (a + \delta)$ $\qquad \ldots (ii)$

Substituting the value of W in equation (i), we have

$$\delta = \frac{m.\omega^2 (a + \delta) \, l^3}{192 \, E.I}$$

Note: The empirical relation between the lift of the sleeve and the deflection δ is, $\lambda = \dfrac{2.4 \, \delta^2}{l}$ approximately.

Example 18.23. *A gramophone is driven by a Pickering governor. The mass of each disc attached to the centre of a leaf spring is 20 g. The each spring is 5 mm wide and 0.125 mm thick. The effective length of each spring is 40 mm. The distance from the spindle axis to the centre of gravity of the mass when the governor is at rest, is 10 mm. Find the speed of the turntable when the sleeve has risen 0.8 mm and the ratio of the governor speed to the turntable speed is 10.5. Take E = 210 kN/mm².*

Solution. Given : $m = 20$ g = 0.02 kg ; $b = 5$ mm ; $t = 0.125$ mm ; $a = 10$ mm = 0.01 m ; $E = 210$ kN/mm² = 210×10^3 N/mm²

We know that moment of inertia of the spring about its neutral axis,

$$I = \frac{b.t^3}{12} = \frac{5 (0.125)^3}{12} = 0.8 \times 10^{-3} \text{ mm}^4$$

Since the effective length of each spring is 40 mm and lift of sleeve (λ) = 0.8 mm, therefore

Length of spring between fixed ends,

$l = 40 - 0.8 = 39.2$ mm

We know that the central deflection (λ),

$$0.8 = \frac{2.4 \, \delta^2}{l} = \frac{2.4 \, \delta^2}{39.2} = 0.06 \, \delta^2$$

$\therefore$ $\qquad$ $\delta^2 = 0.8/0.06 = 13.3$ $\quad$ or $\quad$ $\delta = 3.65$ mm

Let $\qquad$ N = Speed of the governor, and

$\qquad$ N_1 = Speed of the turntable.

$\therefore$ $\qquad$ $N/N_1 = 10.5$ $\hfill$ ...(Given)

We know that $\quad$ $\delta = \dfrac{m.\omega^2\,(a+\delta)\,l^3}{192\,E.I}$

$$3.65 = \frac{0.02\,\omega^2\,(10+3.65)\,(39.2)^3}{192 \times 210 \times 10^3 \times 0.8 \times 10^{-3}} = \frac{16\,445\,\omega^2}{32\,256} = 0.51\,\omega^2$$

$\therefore$ $\qquad$ $\omega^2 = \dfrac{3.65}{0.51} = 7.156$ $\quad$ or $\quad$ $\omega = 2.675$ rad/s

and $\qquad$ $N = \omega \times 60/2\pi = 2.675 \times 60/2\pi = 25.5$ r.p.m. **Ans.**

$\therefore$ $\qquad$ $N_1 = N/10.5 = 25.5/10.5 = 2.43$ r.p.m. **Ans.**

18.12. Sensitiveness of Governors

Consider two governors A and B running at the same speed. When this speed increases or decreases by a certain amount, the lift of the sleeve of governor A is greater than the lift of the sleeve of governor B. It is then said that the governor A is more sensitive than the governor B.

In general, the greater the lift of the sleeve corresponding to a given fractional change in speed, the greater is the sensitiveness of the governor. It may also be stated in another way that for a given lift of the sleeve, the sensitiveness of the governor increases as the speed range decreases. This definition of sensitiveness may be quite satisfactory when the governor is considered as an independent mechanism. But when the governor is fitted to an engine, the practical requirement is simply that the change of equilibrium speed from the full load to the no load position of the sleeve should be as small a fraction as possible of the mean equilibrium speed. The actual displacement of the sleeve is immaterial, provided that it is sufficient to change the energy supplied to the engine by the required amount. For this reason, the sensitiveness is defined as the *ratio of the difference between the maximum and minimum equilibrium speeds to the mean equilibrium speed.*

Let $\qquad$ N_1 = Minimum equilibrium speed,

$\qquad$ N_2 = Maximum equilibrium speed, and

$\qquad$ N = Mean equilibrium speed $= \dfrac{N_1 + N_2}{2}$.

$\therefore$ $\quad$ Sensitiveness of the governor

$$= \frac{N_2 - N_1}{N} = \frac{2(N_2 - N_1)}{N_1 + N_2}$$

$$= \frac{2(\omega_2 - \omega_1)}{\omega_1 + \omega_2} \hspace{2cm} \text{... (In terms of angular speeds)}$$

18.13. Stability of Governors

A governor is said to be *stable* when for every speed within the working range there is a definite configuration *i.e.* there is only one radius of rotation of the governor balls at which the governor is in equilibrium. For a stable governor, if the equilibrium speed increases, the radius of governor balls must also increase.

Note : A governor is said to be unstable, if the radius of rotation decreases as the speed increases.

18.14. Isochronous Governors

A governor is said to be *isochronous* when the equilibrium speed is constant (*i.e.* range of speed is zero) for all radii of rotation of the balls within the working range, neglecting friction. The isochronism is the stage of infinite sensitivity.

Let us consider the case of a Porter governor running at speeds N_1 and N_2 r.p.m. We have discussed in Art. 18.6 that

$$(N_1)^2 = \frac{m + \dfrac{M}{2}(1+q)}{m} \times \frac{895}{h_1} \qquad \ldots (i)$$

and

$$(N_2)^2 = \frac{m + \dfrac{M}{2}(1+q)}{m} \times \frac{895}{h_2} \qquad \ldots (ii)$$

For isochronism, range of speed should be zero *i.e.* $N_2 - N_1 = 0$ or $N_2 = N_1$. Therefore from equations (*i*) and (*ii*), $h_1 = h_2$, which is impossible in case of a Porter governor. Hence a *Porter governor cannot be isochronous.*

Now consider the case of a Hartnell governor running at speeds N_1 and N_2 r.p.m. We have discussed in Art. 18.8 that

$$M.g + S_1 = 2\, F_{C1} \times \frac{x}{y} = 2 \times m \left(\frac{2\pi N_1}{60}\right)^2 r_1 \times \frac{x}{y} \qquad \ldots (iii)$$

and

$$M.g + S_2 = 2\, F_{C2} \times \frac{x}{y} = 2 \times m \left(\frac{2\pi N_2}{60}\right)^2 r_2 \times \frac{x}{y} \qquad \ldots (iv)$$

For isochronism, $N_2 = N_1$. Therefore from equations (*iii*) and (*iv*),

$$\frac{M.g + S_1}{M.g + S_2} = \frac{r_1}{r_2}$$

Note : The isochronous governor is not of practical use because the sleeve will move to one of its extreme positions immediately the speed deviates from the isochronous speed.

18.15. Hunting

A governor is said to be *hunt* if the speed of the engine fluctuates continuously above and below the mean speed. This is caused by a too sensitive governor which changes the fuel supply by a large amount when a small change in the speed of rotation takes place. For example, when the load on the engine increases, the engine speed decreases and, if the governor is very sensitive, the governor sleeve immediately falls to its lowest position. This will result in the opening of the

A forklift is used to carry small loads from one place to the other inside a factory.

control valve wide which will supply the fuel to the engine in excess of its requirement so that the engine speed rapidly increases again and the governor sleeve rises to its highest position. Due to this movement of the sleeve, the control valve will cut off the fuel supply to the engine and thus the engine speed begins to fall once again. This cycle is repeated indefinitely.

Such a governor may admit either the maximum or the minimum amount of fuel. The effect of this will be to cause wide fluctuations in the engine speed or in other words, the engine will hunt.

18.16. Effort and Power of a Governor

The *effort of a governor* is the mean force exerted at the sleeve for a given percentage change of speed* (or lift of the sleeve). It may be noted that when the governor is running steadily, there is no force at the sleeve. But, when the speed changes, there is a resistance at the sleeve which opposes its motion. It is assumed that this resistance which is equal to the effort, varies uniformly from a maximum value to zero while the governor moves into its new position of equilibrium.

The *power of a governor* is the work done at the sleeve for a given percentage change of speed. It is the product of the mean value of the effort and the distance through which the sleeve moves. Mathematically,

$$\text{Power} = \text{Mean effort} \times \text{lift of sleeve}$$

18.17. Effort and Power of a Porter Governor

The effort and power of a Porter governor may be determined as discussed below.

Let N = Equilibrium speed corresponding to the configuration as shown in Fig. 18.33 (*a*), and

c = Percentage increase in speed.

∴ Increase in speed = $c.N$

and increased speed = $N + c.N = N(1 + c)$

The equilibrium position of the governor at the increased speed is shown in Fig. 18.33 (*b*).

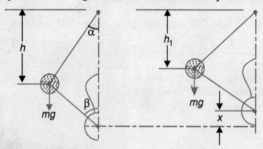

(*a*) Position at equilibrium speed.   (*a*) Position at increased speed.

Fig. 18.33

We have discussed in Art. 18.6 that when the speed is N r.p.m., the sleeve load is $M.g$. Assuming that the angles α and β are equal, so that $q = 1$, then the height of the governor,

$$h = \frac{m + M}{m} \times \frac{895}{N^2} \text{ (in metres)} \qquad \ldots (i)$$

When the increase of speed takes place, a downward force P will have to be exerted on the sleeve in order to prevent the sleeve from rising. If the speed increases to $(1 + c) N$ r.p.m. and the height of the governor remains the same, the load on the sleeve increases to $M_1.g$. Therefore

$$h = \frac{m + M_1}{m} \times \frac{895}{(1 + c)^2 N^2} \text{ (in metres)} \qquad \ldots (ii)$$

Equating equations (*i*) and (*ii*), we have

$$m + M = \frac{m + M_1}{(1 + c)^2} \quad \text{or} \quad M_1 = (m + M)(1 + c^2) - m$$

and

$$M_1 - M = (m + M)(1 + c)^2 - m - M = (m + M)[(1 + c)^2 - 1] \qquad \ldots (iii)$$

---

* In comparing different types of governors, it is convenient to take the change of speed as one per cent.

A little consideration will show that $(M_1 - M)g$ is the downward force which must be applied in order to prevent the sleeve from rising as the speed increases. It is the same force which acts on the governor sleeve immediately after the increase of speed has taken place and before the sleeve begins to move. When the sleeve takes the new position as shown in Fig. 18.33 (b), this force gradually diminishes to zero.

Let $\qquad$ P = Mean force exerted on the sleeve during the increase in speed or the effort of the governor.

$$\therefore \qquad P = \frac{(M_1 - M)\,g}{2} = \frac{(m + M)\,[(1 + c)^2 - 1]\,g}{2}$$

$$= \frac{(m + M)\,[1 + c^2 + 2c - 1]\,g}{2} = c\,(m + M)\,g \qquad \ldots (iv)$$

$$\ldots \text{(Neglecting } c^2 \text{, being very small)}$$

If F is the frictional force (in newtons) at the sleeve, then

$$P = c\,(m.g + M.g \pm F)$$

We have already discussed that the power of a governor is the product of the governor effort and the lift of the sleeve.

Let $\qquad$ x = Lift of the sleeve.

$\therefore \qquad$ Governor power = $P \times x$ $\qquad \ldots (v)$

If the height of the governor at speed N is h and at an increased speed $(1 + c)\,N$ is h_1, then

$$x = 2\,(h - h_1)$$

As there is no resultant force at the sleeve in the two equilibrium positions, therefore

$$h = \frac{m + M}{m} \times \frac{895}{N^2}, \qquad \text{and} \qquad h_1 = \frac{m + M}{m} \times \frac{895}{(1 + c)^2\,N^2},$$

$$\therefore \qquad \frac{h_1}{h} = \frac{1}{(1 + c)^2} \qquad \text{or} \qquad h_1 = \frac{h}{(1 + c)^2}$$

We know that $\qquad x = 2\,(h - h_1) = 2\left[h - \frac{h}{(1 + c)^2}\right] = 2\,h\left[1 - \frac{1}{(1 + c)^2}\right]$

$$= 2\,h\left[\frac{1 + c^2 + 2c - 1}{1 + c^2 + 2c}\right] = 2\,h\left(\frac{2c}{1 + 2c}\right) \qquad \ldots (vi)$$

$$\ldots \text{(Neglecting } c^2 \text{, being very small)}$$

Substituting the values of P and x in equation (v), we have

Governor power $\qquad = c\,(m + M)\,g \times 2\,h\left(\frac{2c}{1 + 2c}\right) = \frac{4c^2}{1 + 2c}\,(m + M)\,g.h \qquad \ldots (vii)$

Notes : 1. If α is not equal to β, *i.e.* $\tan \beta / \tan \alpha = q$, then the equations (i) and (ii) may be written as

$$h = \frac{m + \dfrac{M}{2}\,(1 + q)}{m} \times \frac{895}{N^2} \qquad \ldots (viii)$$

When speed increases to $(1 + c)\,N$ and height of the governor remains the same, then

$$h = \frac{m + \dfrac{M_1}{2}\,(1 + q)}{m} \times \frac{895}{(1 + c)^2\,N^2} \qquad \ldots (ix)$$

From equations (*viii*) and (*ix*), we have

$$m + \frac{M}{2}(1+q) = \frac{m + \frac{M_1}{2}(1+q)}{(1+c)^2}$$

or

$$\frac{M_1}{2}(1+q) = \left[m + \frac{M}{2}(1+q)\right](1+c)^2 - m$$

∴

$$\frac{M_1}{2} = \frac{m(1+c)^2}{1+q} + \frac{M}{2}(1+c)^2 - \frac{m}{1+q}$$

or

$$\frac{M_1}{2} - \frac{M}{2} = \frac{m(1+c)^2}{1+q} + \frac{M}{2}(1+c)^2 - \frac{m}{1+q} - \frac{M}{2}$$

$$= \frac{m}{1+q}[(1+c)^2 - 1] + \frac{M}{2}[(1+c)^2 - 1]$$

$$= \left[\frac{m}{1+q} + \frac{M}{2}\right][(1+c)^2 - 1]$$

∴ Governor effort, $P = \left(\dfrac{M_1 - M}{2}\right)g = \left[\dfrac{m}{1+q} + \dfrac{M}{2}\right][1 + c^2 + 2c - 1]\,g$

$$= \left(\frac{m}{1+q} + \frac{M}{2}\right)(2c)\,g = \left(\frac{2m}{1+q} + M\right)c.g \qquad \text{...(Neglecting } c^2)$$

The equation (*vi*) for the lift of the sleeve becomes,

$$x = (1+q)\,h\left(\frac{2c}{1+2c}\right)$$

∴ Governor power $= P \times x = \left(\dfrac{2m}{1+q} + M\right)c.g\,(1+q)\,h\left(\dfrac{2c}{1+2c}\right)$

$$= \frac{2c^2}{1+2c}[2m + M(1+q)]g.h = \frac{4c^2}{1+2c}\left[m + \frac{M}{2}(1+q)\right]g.h$$

2. The above method of determining the effort and power of a Porter governor may be followed for any other type of the governor.

Example 18.24. *A Porter governor has equal arms each 250 mm long and pivoted on the axis of rotation. Each ball has a mass of 5 kg and the mass of the central load on the sleeve is 25 kg. The radius of rotation of the ball is 150 mm when the governor begins to lift and 200 mm when the governor is at maximum speed. Find the range of speed, sleeve lift, governor effort and power of the governor in the following cases :*

1. When the friction at the sleeve is neglected, and

2. When the friction at the sleeve is equivalent to 10 N.

Solution. Given : $BP = BD = 250$ mm ; $m = 5$ kg ; $M = 25$ kg ; $r_1 = 150$ mm ; $r_2 = 200$ mm ; $F = 10$ N

1. When the friction at the sleeve is neglected

First of all, let us find the minimum and maximum speed of rotation. The minimum and maximum position of the governor is shown in Fig. 18.34 (*a*) and (*b*) respectively.

Let N_1 = Minimum speed, and

N_2 = Maximum speed.

From Fig. 18.34 (*a*),

$$h_1 = PG = \sqrt{(BP)^2 - (BG)^2} = \sqrt{(250)^2 - (150)^2} = 200 \text{ mm} = 0.2 \text{ m}$$

From Fig. 18.34 (*b*),

$$h_2 = PG = \sqrt{(BP)^2 - (BG)^2} = \sqrt{(250)^2 - (200)^2} = 150 \text{ mm} = 0.15 \text{ m}$$

We know that
$$(N_1)^2 = \frac{m+M}{m} \times \frac{895}{h_1} = \frac{5+25}{5} \times \frac{895}{0.2} = 26\ 850$$

∴
$$N_1 = 164 \text{ r.p.m.}$$

and
$$(N_2)^2 = \frac{m+M}{m} \times \frac{895}{h_2} = \frac{5+25}{5} \times \frac{895}{0.15} = 35\ 800$$

∵
$$N_2 = 189 \text{ r.p.m.}$$

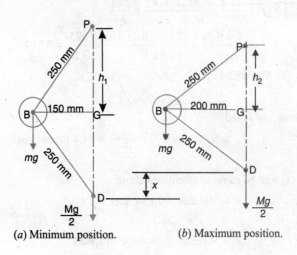

(*a*) Minimum position.   (*b*) Maximum position.

Fig. 18.34

Range of speed

We know that range of speed

$$= N_2 - N_1 = 189 - 164 = 25 \text{ r.p.m. } \textbf{Ans.}$$

Sleeve lift

We know that sleeve lift,

$$x = 2 (h_1 - h_2) = 2 (200 - 150) = 100 \text{ mm} = 0.1 \text{ m } \textbf{Ans.}$$

Governor effort

Let
$$c = \text{Percentage increase in speed.}$$

We know that increase in speed or range of speed,

$$c.N_1 = N_2 - N_1 = 25 \text{ r.p.m.}$$

∴
$$c = 25/N_1 = 25/164 = 0.152$$

We know that governor effort,

$$P = c (m + M) g = 0.152 (5 + 25) 9.81 = 44.7 \text{ N } \textbf{Ans.}$$

Power of the governor

We know that power of the governor

$$= P.x = 44.7 \times 0.1 = 4.47 \text{ N-m Ans.}$$

2. When the friction at the sleeve is taken into account

We know that $\quad (N_1)^2 = \dfrac{m.g + (M.g - F)}{m.g} \times \dfrac{895}{h_1}$

$$= \dfrac{5 \times 9.81 + (25 \times 9.81 - 10)}{5 \times 9.81} \times \dfrac{895}{0.2} = 25\,938$$

∴ $\quad N_1 = 161$ r.p.m.

and $\quad (N_2)^2 = \dfrac{m.g + (M.g + F)}{m.g} \times \dfrac{895}{h_2}$

$$= \dfrac{5 \times 9.81 + (25 \times 9.81 + 10)}{5 \times 9.81} \times \dfrac{895}{0.15} = 37\,016$$

∴ $\quad N_2 = 192.4$ r.p.m.

Range of speed

We know that range of speed

$$= N_2 - N_1 = 192.4 - 161 = 31.4 \text{ r.p.m. Ans.}$$

Sleeve lift

The sleeve lift (x) will be same as calculated above.

∴ Sleeve lift, $\qquad x = 100 \text{ mm} = 0.1 \text{ m Ans.}$

Governor effort

Let $\qquad c = $ Percentage increase in speed.

We know that increase in speed or range of speed,

$$c.N_1 = N_2 - N_1 = 31.4 \text{ r.p.m.}$$

∴ $\qquad c = 31.4/N_1 = 31.4/161 = 0.195$

We know that governor effort,

$$P = c (m.g + M.g + F) = 0.195 (5 \times 9.81 + 25 \times 9.81 + 10) \text{ N}$$

$$= 57.4 \text{ N Ans.}$$

Power of the governor

We know that power of the governor

$$= P.x = 57.4 \times 0.1 = 5.74 \text{ N-m Ans.}$$

Example 18.25. *The upper arms of a Porter governor has lengths 350 mm and are pivoted on the axis of rotation. The lower arms has lengths 300 mm and are attached to the sleeve at a distance of 40 mm from the axis. Each ball has a mass of 4 kg and mass on the sleeve is 45 kg. Determine the equilibrium speed for a radius of rotation of 200 mm and find also the effort and power of the governor for 1 per cent speed change.*

Solution. Given : $PB = 350$ mm $= 0.35$ m ; $BD = 300$ mm $= 0.3$ m ; $DE = 40$ mm $= 0.04$ m ; $m = 4$ kg ; $M = 45$ kg ; $r = BG = 200$ mm $= 0.2$ m ; $c = 1\% = 0.01$

Equilibrium speed

Let N = Equilibrium speed.

The equilibrium position of the governor is shown in Fig. 18.35. From the geometry of the figure,

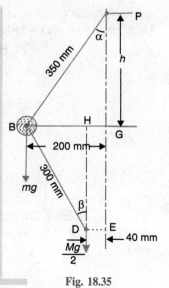

Fig. 18.35

$$h = PG = \sqrt{(PB)^2 - (BG)^2}$$

$$= \sqrt{(0.35)^2 - (0.2)^2} = 0.287 \text{ m}$$

$$\tan \alpha = \frac{BG}{PG} = \frac{0.2}{0.287} = 0.697$$

∴ $$BH = BG - HG = 0.2 - 0.04 = 0.16 \text{ m}$$

$$\dots (\because HG = DE)$$

and $$DH = \sqrt{(BD)^2 - (BH)^2}$$

$$= \sqrt{(0.3)^2 - (0.16)^2} = 0.254 \text{ m}$$

∴ $$\tan \beta = BH/DH = 0.16 / 0.254 = 0.63$$

and $$q = \frac{\tan \beta}{\tan \alpha} = \frac{0.63}{0.697} = 0.904$$

We know that

$$N^2 = \frac{m + \dfrac{M}{2}(1 + q)}{m} \times \frac{895}{h} = \frac{4 + \dfrac{45}{2}(1 + 0.904)}{4} \times \frac{895}{0.287} = 36\,517$$

∴ $$N = 191 \text{ r.p.m. } \textbf{Ans.}$$

Effort of the governor

We know that effort of the governor,

$$P = c\left(\frac{2m}{1 + q} + M\right) g = 0.01\left(\frac{2 \times 4}{1 + 0.904} + 45\right) 9.81 = 4.8 \text{ N } \textbf{Ans.}$$

Power of the governor

We know that power of the governor

$$= \frac{4c^2}{1 + 2c}\left[m + \frac{M}{2}(1 + q)\right] g.h$$

$$= \frac{4(0.01)^2}{1 + 2 \times 0.01}\left[4 + \frac{45}{2}(1 + 0.904)\right] 9.81 \times 0.287 = 0.052 \text{ N-m}$$

$$= 52 \text{ N-mm } \textbf{Ans.}$$

Example 18.26. *The radius of rotation of the balls of a Hartnell governor is 80 mm at the minimum speed of 300 r.p.m. Neglecting gravity effect, determine the speed after the sleeve has lifted by 60 mm. Also determine the initial compression of the spring, the governor effort and the power.*

The particulars of the governor are given below:

Length of ball arm = 150 mm ; length of sleeve arm = 100 mm ; mass of each ball = 4 kg ; and stiffness of the spring = 25 N/mm.

Solution. Given : $r_1 = 80$ mm $= 0.08$ m ; $N_1 = 300$ r.p.m. or $\omega_1 = 2\pi \times 300/60 = 31.42$ rad/s ; $h = 60$ mm $= 0.06$ m ; $x = 150$ mm $= 0.15$ m ; $y = 100$ mm $= 0.1$ m ; $m = 4$ kg ; $s = 25$ N/mm

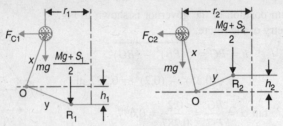

(a) Minimum position.   (b) Maximum position.

Fig. 18.36

The minimum and maximum position of the governor is shown in Fig. 18.36 (a) and (b) respectively. First of all, let us find the maximum radius of rotation (r_2). We know that lift of the sleeve,

$$h = (r_2 - r_1) \frac{y}{x}$$

or
$$r_2 = r_1 + h \times \frac{x}{y} = 0.08 + 0.06 \times \frac{0.15}{0.1} = 0.17 \text{ m} \qquad \dots (\because h = h_1 + h_2)$$

Maximum speed of rotation

Let $\qquad N_2$ = Maximum speed of rotation, and

$\qquad S_1$ and S_2 = Spring force at the minimum and maximum speed respectively, in newtons.

We know that centrifugal force at the minimum speed,

$$F_{C1} = m \, (\omega_1)^2 \, r_1 = 4 \, (31.42)^2 \, 0.08 = 316 \text{ N}$$

Now taking moments about the fulcrum O of the bell crank lever when in minimum position as shown in Fig. 18.36 (a). The gravity effect is neglected, *i.e.* the moment due to the weight of balls, sleeve and the bell crank lever arms is neglected.

$$\therefore \qquad F_{C1} \times x = \frac{M.g + S_1}{2} \times y \qquad \text{or} \qquad S_1 = 2 \, F_{C1} \times \frac{x}{y} = 2 \times 316 \times \frac{0.15}{0.1} = 948 \text{ N}$$

$$\dots (\because M = 0)$$

We know that $S_2 - S_1 = h.s$ or $S_2 = S_1 + h.s = 948 + 60 \times 25 = 2448$ N

We know that centrifugal force at the maximum speed,

$$F_{C2} = m \, (\omega_2)^2 \, r_2 = m \left(\frac{2\pi N_2}{60}\right)^2 r_2 = 4 \left(\frac{2\pi N_2}{60}\right)^2 0.17 = 0.007\,46 \, (N_2)^2$$

Now taking moments about the fulcrum O when in maximum position, as shown in Fig. 18.36 (b),

$$F_{C2} \times x = \frac{M.g + S_2}{2} \times y$$

$$0.007\,46 \, (N_2)^2 \, 0.15 = \frac{2448}{2} \times 0.1 \qquad \text{or} \qquad 0.001\,12 \, (N_2)^2 = 122.4 \qquad \dots (\because M = 0)$$

$$(N_2)^2 = \frac{122.4}{0.001\,12} = 109\,286 \qquad \text{or} \qquad N_2 = 331 \text{ r.p.m. Ans.}$$

Initial compression of the spring

We know that initial compression of the spring

$$= \frac{S_1}{s} = \frac{948}{25} = 37.92 \text{ mm} \textbf{ Ans.}$$

Governor effort

We know that the governor effort,

$$P = \frac{S_2 - S_1}{2} = \frac{2448 - 948}{2} = 750 \text{ N} \textbf{ Ans.}$$

Governor power

We know that the governor power

$$= P \times h = 750 \times 0.06 = 45 \text{ N-m} \textbf{ Ans.}$$

Example 18.27. *In a Hartnell governor, the lengths of ball and sleeve arms of a bell crank lever are 120 mm and 100 mm respectively. The distance of the fulcrum of the bell crank lever from the governor axis is 140 mm. Each governor ball has a mass of 4 kg. The governor runs at a mean speed of 300 r.p.m. with the ball arms vertical and sleeve arms horizontal. For an increase of speed of 4 per cent, the sleeve moves 10 mm upwards. Neglecting friction, find :*

1. the minimum equilibrium speed if the total sleeve movement is limited to 20 mm, 2. the spring stiffness, 3. the sensitiveness of the governor, and 4. the spring stiffness if the governor is to be isochronous at 300 r.p.m.

Solution. Given : $x = 120$ mm $= 0.12$ m ; $y = 100$ mm $= 0.1$ m ; $r = 140$ mm $= 0.14$ m ; $m = 4$ kg ; $N = 300$ r.p.m. or $\omega = 2\pi \times 300/60 = 31.42$ rad/s ; $h_1 = 10$ mm $= 0.01$ m ; $h = 20$ mm $= 0.02$ m

1. *Minimum equilibrium speed*

Let $\quad N_1$ = Minimum equilibrium speed,

$\quad r_1$ = Radius of rotation in the minimum position, *i.e.* when the sleeve moves downward, and

$\quad r_2$ = Radius of rotation in the maximum position, *i.e.* when the sleeve moves upward.

Since the increase in speed is 4%, therefore maximum speed,

$$N_2 = N + 0.04 N = 1.04 N = 1.04 \times 300 = 312 \text{ r.p.m.}$$

or $\quad \omega_2 = 2\pi \times 312 / 60 = 32.7$ rad/s

We know that lift of the sleeve for the maximum position,

$$h_2 = h - h_1 = 0.02 - 0.01 = 0.01 \text{ m}$$

Now for the minimum position,

$$\frac{h_1}{y} = \frac{r - r_1}{x} \quad \text{or} \quad r_1 = r - h_1 \times \frac{x}{y} = 0.14 - 0.01 \times \frac{0.12}{0.1} = 0.128 \text{ m}$$

Similarly for the maximum position,

$$\frac{h_2}{y} = \frac{r_2 - r}{x} \quad \text{or} \quad r_2 = r + h_2 \times \frac{x}{y} = 0.14 + 0.01 \times \frac{0.12}{0.1} = 0.152 \text{ m}$$

We know that centrifugal force in the mean position,

$$F_C = m.\omega^2.r = 4 (31.42)^2 \, 0.14 = 553 \text{ N}$$

Centrifugal force in the minimum position,

$$F_{C1} = m (\omega_1)^2 \, r_1 = 4 \left(\frac{2\pi N_1}{60} \right)^2 0.128 = 0.0056 (N_1)^2 \qquad \dots (i)$$

and centrifugal force in the maximum position,

$$F_{C2} = m.(\omega_2)^2\, r_2 = 4\,(32.7)^2\,0.152 = 650\ N$$

We know that centrifugal force at any instant,

$$F_C = F_{C1} + (F_{C2} - F_{C1})\left(\frac{r - r_1}{r_2 - r_1}\right)$$

$$553 = F_{C1} + (650 - F_{C1})\left(\frac{0.14 - 0.128}{0.152 - 0.128}\right) = 0.5\,F_{C1} + 325$$

$$\therefore \qquad F_{C1} = \frac{553 - 325}{0.5} = 456\ N \qquad\qquad ..(ii)$$

From equations (i) and (ii),

$$(N_1)^2 = \frac{456}{0.0056} = 81\,428 \qquad\text{or}\qquad N_1 = 285.4\ \text{r.p.m. Ans.}$$

2. Spring stiffness

Let S_1 and S_2 = Spring force at the minimum and maximum position.

Neglecting the effect of obliquity of arms, we have for the minimum position,

$$\frac{M.g + S_1}{2} \times y = F_{C1} \times x \quad\text{or}\quad S_1 = 2\,F_{C1} \times \frac{x}{y} = 2 \times 456 \times \frac{0.12}{0.1} = 1094.4\ N$$

$$\ldots (\because M = 0)$$

and for the maximum position,

$$\frac{M.g + S_2}{2} \times y = F_{C2} \times x \quad\text{or}\quad S_2 = 2\,F_{C2} \times \frac{x}{y} = 2 \times 650 \times \frac{0.12}{0.1} = 1560\ N$$

We know that spring stiffness,

$$s = \frac{S_2 - S_1}{h} = \frac{1560 - 1064.4}{20} = 23.28\ \text{N/mm Ans.}$$

3. Sensitiveness of the governor

We know that sensitiveness of the governor

$$= \frac{2\,(N_2 - N_1)}{N_1 + N_2} = \frac{2\,(312 - 285.4)}{285.4 + 312} = 0.089 \quad\text{or}\quad 8.9\%\ \text{Ans.}$$

4. Spring stiffness for the governor to be isochronous at 300 r.p.m.

The governor is isochronous, when $N = N_1 = N_2 = 300$ r.p.m. or $\omega = \omega_1 = \omega_2 = 31.42$ rad/s

$$\therefore \qquad F_{C1} = m.\omega^2.r_1 = 4\,(31.42)^2\,0.128 = 505.5\ N$$

and $\qquad F_{C2} = m.\omega^2.r_2 = 4\,(31.42)^2\,0.152 = 600\ N$

We know that $\quad S_1 = 2\,F_{C1} \times \dfrac{x}{y} = 2 \times 505.5 \times \dfrac{0.12}{0.1} = 1213\ N$

and $\qquad S_2 = 2\,F_{C2} \times \dfrac{x}{y} = 2 \times 600 \times \dfrac{0.12}{0.1} = 1440\ N$

$\therefore$ Spring stiffness, $s = \dfrac{S_2 - S_1}{h} = \dfrac{1440 - 1213}{20} = 11.35\ \text{N/mm Ans.}$

18.18. Controlling Force

We have seen earlier that when a body rotates in a circular path, there is an inward radial force or centripetal force acting on it. In case of a governor running at a steady speed, the inward force acting on the rotating balls is known as *controlling force*. It is equal and opposite to the centrifugal reaction.

∴ Controlling force, $F_C = m.\omega^2.r$

The controlling force is provided by the weight of the sleeve and balls as in Porter governor and by the spring and weight as in Hartnell governor (or spring controlled governor).

When the graph between the controlling force (F_C) as ordinate and radius of rotation of the balls (r) as abscissa is drawn, then the graph obtained is known as *controlling force diagram*. This diagram enables the stability and sensitiveness of the governor to be examined and also shows clearly the effect of friction.

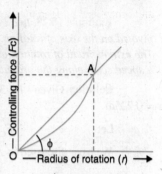

Fig. 18.37. Controlling force diagram.

18.19. Controlling Force Diagram for Porter Governor

The controlling force diagram for a Porter governor is a curve as shown in Fig. 18.37. We know that controlling force,

$$F_C = m.\omega^2 .r = m \left(\frac{2 \pi N}{60} \right)^2 r$$

or

$$N^2 = \frac{1}{m} \left(\frac{60}{2\pi} \right)^2 \left(\frac{F_C}{r} \right) = \frac{1}{m} \left(\frac{60}{2\pi} \right)^2 (\tan \phi) \qquad \ldots \left[\because \frac{F_C}{r} = \tan \phi \right]$$

∴

$$N = \frac{60}{2\pi} \left(\frac{\tan \phi}{m} \right)^{1/2} \qquad \ldots(i)$$

where ϕ is the angle between the axis of radius of rotation and a line joining a given point (say A) on the curve to the origin O.

Notes : 1. In case the governor satisfies the condition for stability, the angle ϕ must increase with radius of rotation of the governor balls. In other words, the equilibrium speed must increase with the increase of radius of rotation of the governor balls.

2. For the governor to be more sensitive, the change in the value of ϕ over the change of radius of rotation should be as small as possible.

3. For the isochronous governor, the controlling force curve is a straight line passing through the origin. The angle ϕ will be constant for all values of the radius of rotation of the governor. From equation (i)

$$\tan \phi = \frac{F_C}{r} = \frac{m.\omega^2 .r}{r} = m.\omega^2 = m \left(\frac{2\pi N}{60} \right)^2 = C.N^2$$

where

$$C = m \left(\frac{2\pi}{60} \right)^2 = \text{constant}$$

Using the above relation, the angle ϕ may be determined for different values of N and the lines are drawn from the origin* . These lines enable the equilibrium speed corresponding to a given radius of rotation to be determined. Alternatively, the same results may be obtained more simply by setting-off a speed scale along any arbitrarily chosen ordinate. The controlling force is calculated for one constant radius of rotation and for different arbitrarily chosen values of speed. The values thus obtained are set-off along the ordinate that corresponds to the chosen radius and marked with the appropriate speeds.

---

* See Example 18.28, Fig. 18.39.

Example 18.28. *In a Porter governor, the length of each arm is 300 mm and all the arms are pivoted on the axis of rotation. The mass of each ball is 7.5 kg and the mass of the sleeve is 45 kg. The extreme radii of rotation are 150 mm and 225 mm. Draw the controlling force curve and set-off a speed scale along the ordinate corresponding to a radius of 250 mm.*

Solution. Given : $l = 300$ mm $= 0.3$ m ; $m = 7.5$ kg ; $r_1 = 150$ mm $= 0.15$ m ; $r_2 = 225$ mm $= 0.225$ m

Let F_C = Controlling force.

We have discussed in Art 18.6 that

$$\left(\frac{M.g}{2} + m.g\right) \tan \alpha = F_C - \frac{M.g}{2} \times \tan \beta$$

∴

$$F_C = \left(\frac{M.g}{2} + m.g\right) \tan \alpha + \frac{M.g}{2} \times \tan \beta$$

$$= \left(\frac{M.g}{2} + m.g + \frac{M.g}{2} \times \frac{\tan \beta}{\tan \alpha}\right) \tan \alpha$$

Substituting $\dfrac{\tan \beta}{\tan \alpha} = q$, and $\tan \alpha = \dfrac{r}{h}$, we get

$$F_C = \left[\frac{M.g}{2}(1+q) + m.g\right]\frac{r}{h}$$

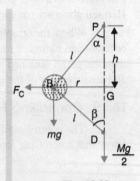

Fig. 18.38

Since $\alpha = \beta$ as shown in Fig. 18.38, therefore $q = 1$.

∴

$$F_C = (m.g + M.g)\frac{r}{h} = g\,(m + M) \times \frac{r}{\sqrt{l^2 - r^2}} \qquad \dots \left[\because h = \sqrt{l^2 - r^2}\right]$$

The following table shows the values of F_C for different values of r.

r (in metres)	0.025	0.05	0.075	0.1	0.125	0.15	0.175	0.2	0.225	0.25
$h = \sqrt{l^2 - r^2}$	0.2894	0.2958	0.2905	0.2828	0.2727	0.2598	0.2437	0.2236	0.1985	0.1658
F_C (in newtons)	44.5	87	133	182	236	297	370	461	584	776

These values are plotted to draw the controlling force curve as shown in Fig. 18.39. In order to set-off the speed scale along the ordinate through $r = 250$ mm $= 0.25$ m, we have

$$F_C = m.\omega^2.r = 7.5\left(\frac{2\pi N}{60}\right)^2 0.25 = 0.02\ N^2$$

The values of F_C for different values of N are given in the following table.

N (in r.p.m.)	100	125	150	160	170	180	190	200
F_C (in newtons)	200	312.5	450	512	578	648	722	800

The speed scale is now marked on the graph as shown in Fig. 18.39.

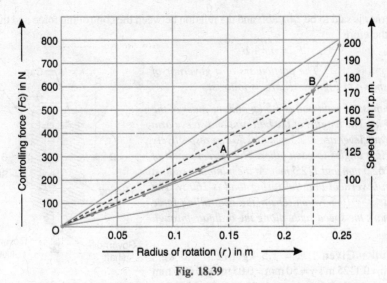

Fig. 18.39

The range of equilibrium speeds for the governor is obtained by drawing lines from the origin (shown dotted in Fig. 18.39) through the two points *A* (when *r* = 0.15 m) and *B* (when *r* = 0.225 m) on the controlling force curve.

From the graph, we see that these lines intersect the speed scale at approximately 160 r.p.m. and 180 r.p.m. **Ans.**

18.20. Controlling Force Diagram for Spring-controlled Governors

The controlling force diagram for the spring controlled governors is a straight line, as shown in Fig. 18.40. We know that controlling force,

$$F_C = m.\omega^2.r \quad \text{or} \quad F_C/r = m.\omega^2$$

The following points, for the stability of spring-controlled governors, may be noted :

1. For the governor to be stable, the controlling force (F_C) must increase as the radius of rotation (*r*) increases, *i.e.* F_C / r must increase as *r* increases. Hence the controlling force line *AB* when produced must intersect the controlling force axis below the origin, as shown in Fig. 18.40.

The relation between the controlling force (F_C) and the radius of rotation (*r*) for the *stability* of spring controlled governors is given by the following equation

$$F_C = a.r - b \qquad \text{... (i)}$$

where *a* and *b* are constants.

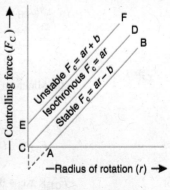

Fig. 18.40

2. The value of *b* in equation (*i*) may be made either zero or positive by increasing the initial tension of the spring. If *b* is zero, the controlling force line *CD* passes through the origin and the governor becomes *isochronous* because F_C/r will remain constant for all radii of rotation.

The relation between the controlling force and the radius of rotation, for an *isochronous governor* is, therefore,

$$F_C = a.r \qquad \text{... (ii)}$$

3. If *b* is greater than zero or positive, then F_C/r decreases as *r* increases, so that the equilibrium speed of the governor decreases with an increase of the radius of rotation of balls, which is impracticable.

Such a governor is said to be *unstable* and the relation between the controlling force and the radius of rotation is, therefore

$$F_C = a.r + b \qquad \qquad \dots (iii)$$

Example 18.29. *The particulars of a governor of the type as shown in Fig. 18.41, are as follows:*

The mass of each ball is 1.5 kg and the mass of the sleeve is 7.5 kg. The lengths of the ball arm and sleeve arm of the bell crank lever are 112.5 mm and 50 mm respectively and are at right angles to each other. The extreme radii of rotation are 62.5 mm and 112.5 mm. At the minimum radius, the ball arm is vertical and the spring load is 160 N. The spring stiffness is 10.5 N/mm. Draw the controlling force curve and mark the speed scale along the ordinate through 125 mm.

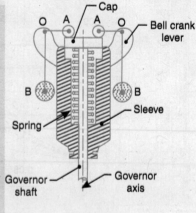

Fig. 18.41

Solution. Given : $m = 1.5$ kg ; $M = 7.5$ kg ; $x = 112.5$ mm $= 0.1125$ m ; $y = 50$ mm $= 0.05$ m ; $r_1 = 62.5$ mm $= 0.0625$ m ; $r_2 = 112.5$ mm $= 0.1125$ m ; $S_1 = 160$ N ; $s = 10.5$ N/mm $= 10\,500$ N/m

Let S_1 and S_2 be the spring loads at the minimum and maximum radius of rotation.

The minimum and maximum position of the balls is shown in Fig. 18.42 (*a*) and (*b*) respectively. Taking moments about the instantaneous centre *I*, for the maximum position as shown in Fig. 18.42 (*b*),

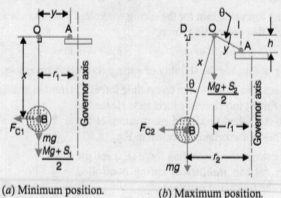

(*a*) Minimum position.   (*b*) Maximum position.

Fig. 18.42

$$F_{C2} \times BD = m.g \times ID + \frac{M.g + S_2}{2} \times IO$$

or

$$F_{C2} \times x \cos \theta = m.g \,(x \sin \theta + y \cos \theta) + \frac{M.g + S_2}{2} \times y \cos \theta$$

$$\therefore \qquad F_{C2} = m.g \left(\tan \theta + \frac{y}{x} \right) + \frac{M.g + S_2}{2} \times \frac{y}{x} \qquad \dots (i)$$

We know that

$$S_2 - S_1 = h.s = y \sin \theta \times s$$

$$\therefore \qquad S_2 = S_1 + y \sin \theta \times s = 160 + 0.05 \times \sin \theta \times 10\,500$$

$$= 160 + 525 \sin \theta \qquad \dots (ii)$$

Now the equation (*i*) may be written as

$$F_{C2} = 1.5 \times 9.81 \left(\tan \theta + \frac{0.05}{0.1125} \right) + \frac{7.5 \times 9.81 + 160 + 525 \sin \theta}{2} \times \frac{0.05}{0.1125}$$

$$= 14.7 \tan \theta + 116.5 \sin \theta + 58.5 \qquad \ldots (iii)$$

From the geometry of Fig. 18.42 (*b*), we find that

$$r_2 = r_1 + OD = r_1 + x \sin \theta = 0.0625 + 0.1125 \sin \theta \qquad \ldots (iv)$$

In order to determine the controlling force and the radius of rotation of the ball for different values of θ, the angle θ is treated as variable. From equations (*iii*) and (*iv*), the values of controlling force (F_C) and radius of rotation (r) for different values of θ are tabulated below :

$\theta°$	0	5	10	15	20	25	30
$\sin \theta$	0	0.0871	0.1736	0.2588	0.342	0.4226	0.5
$\tan \theta$	0	0.0875	0.1763	0.2679	0.364	0.4663	0.5773
F_C (N)	58.5	70	81.3	92.6	103.7	114.6	125.2
r (m)	0.0625	0.0723	0.082	0.092	0.101	0.11	0.1187

The graph between F_C and r is plotted as shown in Fig. 18.43. It may be seen that the controlling force curve is nearly a straight line.

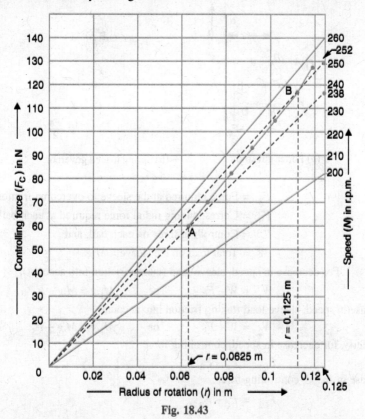

Fig. 18.43

In order to set off the speed scale along the ordinate through $r = 125$ mm $= 0.125$ m,

$$F_C = m.\omega^2.r = 1.5\left(\frac{2\pi N}{60}\right)^2 0.125 = 0.002\,06\ N^2$$

The corresponding values of F_C and N are given in the following table :

N (r.p.m.)	200	210	220	230	240	250	260
F_C (N)	82.4	90.8	99.7	109	118.6	128.7	139.2

The speed scale is now marked on the graph as shown in Fig. 18.43. The range of equilibrium speeds for the governor is obtained by drawing lines from the origin (shown dotted in Fig. 18.43) through the two points A (when $r = 0.0625$ m) and B (when $r = 0.1125$ m) on the controlling force curve.

From the graph we see that these lines intersect the speed scale at approximately 238 r.p.m. and 252 r.p.m.   **Ans.**

18.21. Coefficient of Insensitiveness

In the previous articles, we have assumed the governor to be frictionless. In actual practice, there is always friction in the joints and operating mechanism of the governor. Since the frictional force always acts in the opposite direction to that of motion, therefore, when the speed of rotation decreases, the friction prevents the downward movement of the sleeve and the radial inward movement of the balls. On the other hand, when the speed of rotation increases, the friction prevents the upward movement of the sleeve and radial outward movement of the balls.

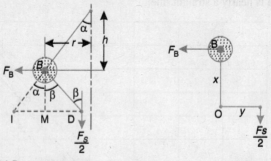

(a) Porter governor.   (b) Spring loaded governor.

Fig. 18.44

Let F_S = Force required at the sleeve to overcome friction,

F_B = Corresponding radial force required at each ball,

F_C = Controlling force on each ball, and

W = Total load on the sleeve = $M.g$.

∴   For decrease in speed, sleeve load (taking friction into account),

$$W_1 = W - F_S \qquad \text{or} \qquad M_1.g = M.g - F_S$$

and for increase in speed, sleeve load (taking friction into account),

$$W_2 = W + F_S \qquad \text{or} \qquad M_1.g = M.g + F_S$$

Similarly, for decrease in speed, controlling force,

$$F_{C1} = F_C - F_B$$

and for increase in speed, controlling force,

$$F_{C2} = F_C + F_B$$

Thus for a Porter governor, as shown Fig. 18.44 (*a*), the relation between F_S and F_B may be obtained by taking moments about the instantaneous centre *I*.

$$\therefore \qquad F_B \times BM = \frac{F_S}{2}(IM + MD)$$

or

$$F_B = \frac{F_S}{2}\left(\frac{IM + MD}{BM}\right) = \frac{F_S}{2}(\tan \alpha + \tan \beta) = \frac{F_S}{2}\left(1 + \frac{\tan \beta}{\tan \alpha}\right)\tan \alpha$$

$$= \frac{F_S}{2}(1 + q)\tan \alpha = \frac{F_S}{2}(1 + q)\frac{r}{h} \qquad \ldots (i)$$

$$\ldots \left(\because q = \frac{\tan \beta}{\tan \alpha}, \text{ and } \tan \alpha = \frac{r}{h}\right)$$

Similarly, for spring loaded governors as shown in Fig. 18.44 (*b*), taking moments about the fulcrum *O* of the bell crank lever,

$$F_B \times x = \frac{F_S}{2} \times y \qquad \text{or} \qquad F_B = F_S \times \frac{y}{2x} \qquad \ldots (ii)$$

Fig. 18.45 shows the effect of friction on the controlling force diagram. We see that for one value of the radius of rotation (*i.e. OA*), there are three values of controlling force as discussed below:

1. For speed decreasing, the controlling force reduces to F_{C1} (or *AD*) and the corresponding speed on the speed scale is *N'*.

2. For speed increasing, the controlling force increases to F_{C2} (or *AC*) and the corresponding speed on the speed scale is *N'*.

3. For friction neglected, the controlling force is F_C (or *AB*) and the corresponding speed on the speed scale is *N*.

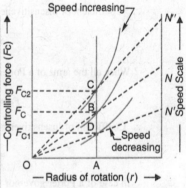

Fig. 18.45. Effect of friction on controlling force.

From above, it is concluded that when the radius of rotation is *OA*, the speed of rotation may vary within the limits *N'* and *N''* without causing any displacement (up or down) of the governor sleeve. The governor is said to be *insensitive* if the speed fluctuates over this range.

The ratio $\dfrac{N'' - N'}{N}$ is called the *coefficient of insensitiveness* of the governor.

Since the controlling force is proportional to the square of the speed at a given radius, therefore for a governor speed *N*,

$$F_C \propto N^2 \qquad \text{or} \qquad F_C = C.N^2 \qquad \ldots (iii)$$

Similarly, for speed *N'*,

$$F_{C1} = C (N')^2 \qquad \ldots (iv)$$

and for speed *N''*, $\qquad F_{C2} = C (N'')^2 \qquad \ldots (v)$

Subtracting equation (*iv*) from equation (*v*), we have

$$F_{C2} - F_{C1} = C [(N'')^2 - (N')^2]$$

or

$$(F_C + F_B) - (F_C - F_B) = C [(N'')^2 - (N')^2]$$

$$2F_B = C [(N'')^2 - (N')^2] \qquad \ldots (vi)$$

Dividing equation (*vi*) by equation (*iii*)

$$\frac{2F_B}{F_C} = \frac{(N'')^2 - (N')^2}{N^2} = \frac{(N'' + N')(N'' - N')}{N^2} = \frac{N'' + N'}{N} \times \frac{N'' - N'}{N}$$

Since $\dfrac{N'' + N'}{2}$ is approximately equal to N, therefore

$$\frac{2F_B}{F_C} = 2 \times \frac{N'' - N'}{N}$$

∴ Coefficient of insensitiveness

$$= \frac{N'' - N'}{N} = \frac{F_B}{F_C} \qquad \qquad \dots (vii)$$

Notes : 1 In case of a Porter governor, as shown in Fig. 18.44 (*a*), (*i.e.* when the lower arm is not attached on the governor axis),

$$F_B = \frac{F_S}{2}(1 + q)\frac{r}{h}$$

∴ Coefficient of insensitiveness

$$= \frac{N'' - N'}{N} = \frac{F_B}{F_C} = \frac{F_S}{2F_C}(1 + q)\frac{r}{h} \qquad \qquad \dots (viii)$$

2. When all the arms of a Porter governor are attached to the governor axis, then $q = 1$. In that case,

$$F_B = F_S \times \frac{r}{h}$$

∴ Coefficient of insensitiveness

$$= \frac{N'' - N'}{N} = \frac{F_B}{F_C} = \frac{F_S}{F_C} \times \frac{r}{h} \qquad \qquad \dots (ix)$$

3. In case of a Porter governor when all the arms are attached to the governor axis, the coefficient of insensitiveness may also be determined as discussed below :

Let h = Height of the governor at the mean speed N, when friction is neglected,

F = Frictional force on the sleeve,

N' and N'' = Minimum and maximum speed when friction is taken into account.

We have discussed above that the governor is insensitive when the sleeve does not move downwards when the speed falls to N' or upwards when the speed rises to N''. In other words, the height of the governor (h) remains the same for minimum and maximum speeds N' and N'' respectively. We know that

$$N^2 = \frac{m + M}{m} \times \frac{895}{h}$$

Similarly, $$(N')^2 = \frac{m.g + (M.g - F)}{m.g} \times \frac{895}{h}$$

and $$(N'')^2 = \frac{m.g + (M.g + F)}{m.g} \times \frac{895}{h}$$

Now $(N'')^2 - (N')^2 = (N'' + N')(N'' - N') = 2N(N'' - N')$ $\dots \left(\because N = \dfrac{N'' + N'}{2} \right)$

∴ $$N'' - N' = \frac{(N'')^2 - (N')^2}{2N}$$

and coefficient of insensitiveness

$$= \frac{N'' - N'}{N} = \frac{(N'')^2 - (N')^2}{2\,N^2} = \frac{\dfrac{m.g + (M.g + F)}{m.g} - \dfrac{m.g + (M.g - F)}{m.g}}{2\left(\dfrac{m + M}{m}\right)}$$

$$= \frac{1}{2}\left[\frac{2\,F}{(m+M)\,g}\right] = \frac{F}{(m+M)\,g} \qquad\qquad ...(x)$$

4. In case of a Porter governor, when the upper arms are pivoted to the governor axis and the lower arms are at a certain distance from the governor axis *i.e.* when α is not equal to β (Refer Art. 18.6), then it may be proved that

Coefficient of insensitiveness

$$\frac{N'' - N'}{N} = \frac{F\,(1+q)}{2\,m.g + M.g\,(1+q)}$$

5. In case of a Hartnell governor,

$$F_B = F_S \times \frac{y}{2x}$$

$\therefore$ Coefficient of insensitiveness $= \dfrac{N'' - N'}{N} = \dfrac{F_B}{F_C} = \dfrac{F_S}{F_C} \times \dfrac{y}{2x}$ ... (xi)

Example 18.30. *A Porter governor has equal arms 200 mm long pivoted on the axis of rotation. The mass of each ball is 3 kg and the mass on the sleeve is 15 kg. The ball path is 120 mm when the governor begins to lift and 160 mm at the maximum speed. Determine the range of speed.*

If the friction at the sleeve is equivalent to a force of 10 N, find the coefficient of insensitiveness.

Solution. Given : $BP = BD = 200$ mm $= 0.2$ m ; $m = 3$ kg ; $M = 15$ kg ; $r_1 = 120$ mm $= 0.12$ m ; $r_2 = 160$ mm $= 0.16$ m ; $F = 10$ N

Range of speed

First of all, let us find the minimum and maximum speed of rotation.

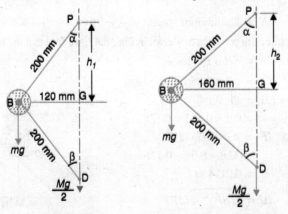

(*a*) Minimum position.   (*b*) Maximum position.

Fig. 18.46

The minimum and maximum position of the balls is shown in Fig 18.46 (*a*) and (*b*) respectively.

Let N_1 = Minimum speed, and

                  N_2 = Maximum speed.

From Fig. 18.46 (a), $\qquad h_1 = \sqrt{(BP)^2 - (BG)^2} = \sqrt{(0.2)^2 - (0.12)^2} = 0.16$ m

and from Fig. 18.46 (b), $\qquad h_2 = \sqrt{(BP)^2 - (BG)^2} = \sqrt{(0.2)^2 - (0.16)^2} = 0.12$ m

We know that $\qquad (N_1)^2 = \dfrac{m + M}{m} \times \dfrac{895}{h_1} = \dfrac{3 + 15}{3} \times \dfrac{895}{0.16} = 33\,563$

∴ $\qquad N_1 = 183.2$ r.p.m.

Similarly $\qquad (N_2)^2 = \dfrac{m + M}{m} \times \dfrac{895}{h_2} = \dfrac{3 + 15}{3} \times \dfrac{895}{0.12} = 44\,750$

∴ $\qquad N_2 = 211.5$ r.p.m.

We know that range of speed

$$= N_2 - N_1 = 211.5 - 183.2 = 28.3 \text{ r.p.m. } \textbf{Ans.}$$

Coefficient of insensitiveness

We know that coefficient of insensitiveness,

$$\frac{N'' - N'}{N} = \frac{F}{(m + M)\,g} = \frac{10}{(3 + 15)\,9.81} = 0.0566 = 5.66\% \text{ Ans.}$$

Example 18.31. *The following particulars refer to a Proell governor with open arms :*

Length of all arms = 200 mm, distance of pivot of arms from the axis of rotation = 40 mm, length of extension of lower arms to which the ball is attached = 100 mm, mass of each ball = 6 kg and mass of the central load = 150 kg. If the radius of rotation of the balls is 180 mm when the arms are inclined at 40° to the axis of rotation, find :

1. the equilibrium speed for the above configuration, 2. the coefficient of insensitiveness if the friction of the governor mechanism is equivalent to a force of 20 N at the sleeve, and 3. the range of speed between which the governor is inoperative.

Solution. Given : $PF = FD = 200$ mm $= 0.2$ m ; $DK = 40$ mm $= 0.04$ m ; $BF = 100$ mm $= 0.1$ m ; $m = 6$ kg ; $M = 150$ kg ; $r = JG = 180$ mm $= 0.18$ m ; $F = 20$ N

1. *Equilibrium speed*

Let $\qquad N$ = Equilibrium speed.

From the equilibrium position, as shown in Fig 18.47, we find that the height of the governor,

$$h = PH = PF \cos 40°$$
$$= 0.2 \times 0.766 = 0.1532 \text{ m}$$

and $\qquad FH = PF \sin 40°$
$$= 0.2 \times 0.643 = 0.1286 \text{ m}$$

∴ $\qquad JF = JG - HG - FH$
$$= 0.18 - 0.04 - 0.1286$$
$$= 0.0114 \text{ m}$$

and $\qquad BJ = \sqrt{(BF)^2 - (JF)^2}$
$$= \sqrt{(0.1)^2 - (0.0114)^2}$$
$$= 0.0993 \text{ m}$$

$$BM = BJ + JM$$
$$= 0.0993 + 0.1532 = 0.2525 \text{ m}$$

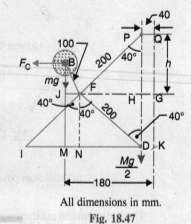

All dimensions in mm.

Fig. 18.47

$$\dots (\because JM = HD = PH)$$

$$IM = IN - MN = FH - JF = 0.1286 - 0.0114 = 0.1172 \text{ m}$$
$$ID = 2 \times IN = 2 \times FH = 2 \times 0.1286 = 0.2572 \text{ m}$$

We know that centrifugal force,

$$F_C = m.\omega^2.r = 6\left(\frac{2\pi N}{60}\right)^2 0.18 = 0.012 \ N^2$$

Now taking moments about I,

$$F_C \times BM = m.g \times IM + \frac{M.g}{2} \times ID$$

$$0.012 \ N^2 \times 0.2525 = 6 \times 9.81 \times 0.1172 + \frac{150 \times 9.81}{2} \times 0.2572$$

or $\qquad 0.003 \ 03 \ N^2 = 6.9 + 189.2 = 196.1$

∴ $\qquad N^2 = 196.1/0.003 \ 03 = 64 \ 720$ or $\quad N = 254.4$ r.p.m. **Ans.**

Coefficient of insensitiveness

Let $\qquad N'$ and $N'' = $ Minimum and maximum speed considering friction.

We know that centrifugal force at the minimum speed,

$$F_C' = m \ (\omega')^2 \ r = 6\left(\frac{2\pi N'}{60}\right)^2 0.18 = 0.012 \ (N')^2$$

and centrifugal force at the maximum speed,

$$F_C'' = m \ (\omega'')^2 \ r = 6\left(\frac{2\pi N''}{60}\right)^2 0.18 = 0.012 \ (N'')^2$$

Taking moments about I, when sleeve moves downwards,

$$F_C' \times BM = m.g \times IM + \frac{M.g - F}{2} \times ID$$

$$0.012(N')^2 0.2525 = 6 \times 9.81 \times 0.1172 + \frac{150 \times 9.81 - 20}{2} \times 0.2572$$

$$0.003 \ 03 \ (N')^2 = 6.9 + 186.7 = 193.6$$

∴ $\qquad (N')^2 = 193.6/0.003 \ 03 = 63 \ 894 \qquad$ or $\qquad N' = 252.8$ r.p.m.

Again taking moments about I, when the sleeve moves upwards,

$$F_C'' \times BM = m.g \times IM + \frac{M.g + F}{2} \times ID$$

$$0.012 \ (N'')^2 \ 0.2525 = 6 \times 9.81 \times 0.1172 + \frac{150 \times 9.81 + 20}{2} \times 0.2572$$

$$0.003 \ 03 \ (N'')^2 = 6.9 + 191.8 = 198.7$$

∴ $\qquad (N'')^2 = 198.7/0.003 \ 03 = 65 \ 578 \qquad$ or $\qquad N'' = 256$ r.p.m.

We know that coefficient of insensitiveness,

$$\frac{N'' - N'}{N} = \frac{256 - 252.8}{254.4} = 0.0126 \text{ or } 1.26\% \text{ **Ans.**}$$

3. Range of speed

We know that range of speed

$$= N'' - N' = 256 - 252.8 = 3.2 \text{ r.p.m. **Ans.**}$$

Example 18.32. *A spring controlled governor is shown in Fig. 18.48. The central spindle does not move axially. The mass of the sleeve is 20 kg and the frictional resistance to its movement is equivalent to 20 N. The balls attached to the right angled bell crank levers have mass 4 kg each. The stiffness of the spring is 40 N/mm compression. The radius of rotation of the balls is 125 mm when the sleeve is in its lowest position, and the ball arms are vertical and the spring exerts a force of 600 N. Determine :*

1. *the speed at which the sleeve will begin to rise from its lowest position,*

2. *the range of speed when the sleeve is 12.5 mm above its lowest position, and*

3. *the coefficient of insensitiveness at higher speed.*

Solution. Given : $M = 20$ kg ; $F = 20$ N ; $m = 4$ kg ; $s = 40$ N/mm ; $r_1 = 125$ mm $= 0.125$ m ; $S_1 = 600$ N

1. *Speed at which sleeve will begin to rise from its lowest position*

Let $\qquad N_1$ = Required speed.

The lowest position is shown in Fig. 18.49 (*a*).

We know that the centrifugal force at the lowest position,

$$F_{C1} = m\,(\omega_1)^2\,r_1 = 4\left(\frac{2\pi N_1}{60}\right)^2 0.125 = 0.0055\,(N_1)^2$$

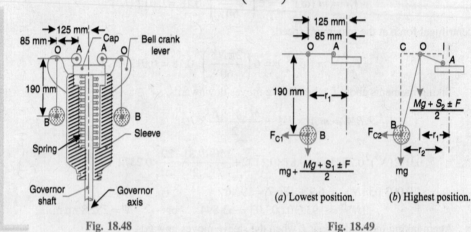

(*a*) Lowest position.   (*b*) Highest position.

Fig. 18.48   Fig. 18.49

Since the sleeve is about to rise, therefore frictional resistance is taken positive. Also the central spindle is stationary, therefore all the forces are transferred to both the pivots of the bell crank lever *i.e.* $\dfrac{M.g + S_1 + F}{2}$ at each pivot, as shown in Fig. 18.49 (*a*).

Since the pivot O moves vertically and the roller A moves horizontally, therefore A is the instantaneous centre of the bell crank lever.

Now taking moments about A,

$$F_{C1} \times OB = \left(m.g + \frac{M.g + S_1 + F}{2}\right) OA$$

$$0.0055\,(N_1)^2\,0.19 = \left(4 \times 9.81 + \frac{20 \times 9.81 + 600 + 20}{2}\right) 0.085$$

$$0.001\,05\,(N_1)^2 = 3.3 + 34.7 = 38 \qquad \text{or} \qquad (N_1)^2 = 38\,/\,0.001\,05 = 36\,190$$

∴ $\qquad\qquad\qquad N_1 = 190$ r.p.m. **Ans.**

2. *Range of speed*

The highest position is shown in Fig. 18.49 (*b*).

Let N_2 = Maximum speed,

h = Lift of the sleeve = 12.5 mm = 0.0125 m   . . . (Given)

r_2 = Maximum radius of rotation of the balls, and

S_2 = Maximum spring force.

We know that lift of the sleeve

$$h = (r_2 - r_1) \times \frac{y}{x} = (r_2 - r_1) \times \frac{OA}{OB} \qquad \text{... (Here } x = OB \text{, and } y = OA)$$

$\therefore \qquad r_2 = r_1 + h \times OB/OA = 0.125 + 0.0125 \times 0.19/0.085 = 0.153$ m

We know that centrifugal force at the highest position,

$$F_{C2} = m \, (\omega_2)^2 \, r_2 = 4 \left(\frac{2\pi N_2}{60} \right)^2 0.153 = 0.0067 \, (N_2)^2$$

and $\qquad S_2 - S_1 = h.s \qquad$ or $\qquad S_2 = S_1 + h.s = 600 + 12.5 \times 40 = 1100$ N

From Fig 18.49 (*b*), we find that

$$OI = \sqrt{(OA)^2 - (AI)^2} = \sqrt{(85)^2 - (12.5)^2} = 84 \text{ mm} = 0.084 \text{ m}$$

$$\ldots (\because AI = h)$$

$$BC = \sqrt{(OB)^2 - (OC)^2} = \sqrt{(190)^2 - (153 - 125)^2} = 188 \text{ mm} = 0.188 \text{ m}$$

$$\ldots (\because OC = r_2 - r_1)$$

and $\qquad IC = OI + OC = 84 + (153 - 125) = 112$ mm = 0.112 m

Now taking moments about the instantaneous centre *I*,

$$F_{C2} \times BC = m.g \times IC + \frac{M.g + S_2 \pm F}{2} \times OI$$

The ± sign denotes that at the highest position, the sleeve may either rise or fall. Therefore

$$0.0067 \, (N_2)^2 \, 0.188 = 4 \times 9.81 \times 0.112 + \left(\frac{20 \times 9.81 + 1100 \pm 20}{2} \right) 0.084$$

$0.001\,26 \, (N_2)^2 = 4.4 + 54.4 \pm 0.84 = 58.8 \pm 0.84$

Taking – ve sign, when the sleeve is about to fall,

$0.001\,26 \, (N_2)^2 = 58.8 - 0.84 = 57.96$

$(N_2)^2 = 57.96/0.001\,26 = 46\,000 \qquad$ or $\qquad N_2 = 214.5$ r.p.m.

Taking + ve sign, when the sleeve is about to lift,

$0.001\,26 \, (N_2')^2 = 58.8 + 0.84 = 59.64$

$(N_2')^2 = 59.64/0.001\,26 = 47\,333 \qquad$ or $\qquad N_2' = 217.5$ r.p.m.

$\therefore$ Range of speed at the maximum radius

$$= N_2' - N_2 = 217.5 - 214.5 = 3 \text{ r.p.m.} \textbf{Ans.}$$

3. Coefficient of insensitiveness at higher speed

We know that coefficient of insensitiveness

$$= \frac{2\,(N_2' - N_2)}{N_2' + N_2} = \frac{2\,(217.5 - 214.5)}{217.5 + 214.5} = 0.014 = 1.4\%\ \text{Ans.}$$

Example 18.33. *In a spring controlled governor, the curve of controlling force is a straight line. When balls are 400 mm apart, the controlling force is 1200 N and when 200 mm apart, the controlling force is 450 N. At what speed will the governor run when the balls are 250 mm apart? What initial tension on the spring would be required for isochronism and what would then be the speed ? The mass of each ball is 9 kg.*

Solution. Given : When balls are 400 mm apart, *i.e.* when the radius of rotation (r_2) is 200 mm, the controlling force,

$$F_{C2} = 1200\ \text{N}$$

When balls are 200 mm apart *i.e.* when the radius of rotation (r_1) is 100 mm, the controlling force,

$$F_{C1} = 450\ \text{N}$$

Mass of each ball, $m = 9\ \text{kg}$

Speed of the governor when the balls are 250 mm apart, i.e. when radius of rotation (r) is 125 mm

Let · N = Required speed.

We know that for the stability of the spring controlled governors, the controlling force (F_C) is expressed in the form

$$^{*}F_C = a.r - b \qquad\qquad \dots (i)$$

When $r = r_1 = 100\ \text{mm} = 0.1\ \text{m, then}$

$$450 = a \times 0.1 - b = 0.1\,a - b \qquad\qquad \dots(ii)$$

and when $r = r_2 = 200\ \text{mm} = 0.2\ \text{m, then}$

$$1200 = a \times 0.2 - b = 0.2\,a - b \qquad\qquad \dots (iii)$$

From equations (*ii*) and (*iii*), we find that

$$a = 7500, \qquad \text{and} \qquad b = 300$$

Now the equation (*i*) may be written as

$$F_C = 7500\,r - 300 \qquad\qquad \dots (iv)$$

Substituting $r = 125\ \text{mm} = 0.125\ \text{m, in equation } (iv)\text{, we get}$

$$F_C = 7500 \times 0.125 - 300 = 637.5\ \text{N}$$

We know that $F_C = m.\omega^2 . r = m\left(\dfrac{2\pi N}{60}\right)^{2} r$

$$637.5 = 9\left(\frac{2\pi N}{60}\right)^{2} 0.125 = 0.012\ 34\ N^2$$

∴ $N^2 = 637.5\,/\,0.012\ 34\ = 51\ 661 \quad \text{or} \qquad N = 227.3\ \text{r.p.m.}\ \ \textbf{Ans.}$

---

*   We find that $\dfrac{F_{C1}}{r_1} = \dfrac{450}{0.1} = 4500$ and $\dfrac{F_{C2}}{r_2} = \dfrac{1200}{0.2} = 6000.$

Since F_C/r increases as r increases, therefore for stability

$$F_C = a.r - b \qquad \text{(See Art. 18.20)}$$

Initial tension on the spring for isochronism

We have discussed in Art. 18.20 that for an isochronous governor, the controlling force line passes through the origin (*i.e.* $b = 0$). The value of b is made zero by increasing the initial tension of the spring to 300 N.

∴ Initial tension on the spring for isochronism = 300 N **Ans.**

Isochronous speed

Let N' = Isochronous speed, and

F_C' = Controlling force at the isochronous speed.

We know that for isochronism,

$$F_C' = a.r \quad \text{or} \quad m\,(\omega')^2\, r = a.r \quad \text{or} \quad m\,(\omega')^2 = a$$

∴ $$m\left(\frac{2\pi N'}{60}\right)^2 = a \quad \text{or} \quad 9 \times 0.011\,(N')^2 = 7500$$

$$(N)^2 = 7500 / 0.099 = 75\,758 \quad \text{or} \quad N' = 275 \text{ r.p.m. } \textbf{Ans.}$$

Example 18.34. *The controlling force (F_C) in newtons and the radius of rotation (r) in metres for a spring controlled governor is given by the expression*

$$F_C = 2800\,r - 76$$

The mass of the ball is 5 kg and the extreme radii of rotation of the balls are 100 mm and 175 mm. Find the maximum and minimum speeds of equilibrium. If the friction of the governor mechanism is equivalent to a force of 5 N at each ball, find the coefficient of insensitiveness of the governor at the extreme radii.

Solution. Given : $m = 5$ kg ; $r_1 = 100$ mm = 0.1 m ; $r_2 = 175$ mm = 0.175 m

Maximum and minimum speeds of equilibrium

Let N_2 and N_1 = Maximum and minimum speeds of equilibrium respectively.

The controlling force is given by the expression,

$$F_C = 2800\,r - 76$$

∴ Controlling force at the minimum radius of rotation (*i.e.* at $r_1 = 0.1$ m),

$$F_{C1} = 2800 \times 0.1 - 76 = 204 \text{ N}$$

and controlling force at the maximum radius of rotation (*i.e.* at $r_2 = 0.175$ m),

$$F_{C2} = 2800 \times 0.175 - 76 = 414 \text{ N}$$

We know that $$F_{C1} = m\,(\omega_1)^2\, r_1 = m\left(\frac{2\pi N_1}{60}\right)^2 r_1$$

or $$204 = 5\left(\frac{2\pi N_1}{60}\right)^2 0.1 = 0.0055\,(N_1)^2$$

∴ $$(N_1)^2 = 204 / 0.0055 = 37\,091 \quad \text{or} \quad N_1 = 192.6 \text{ r.p.m. } \textbf{Ans.}$$

Similarly $$F_{C2} = m\,(\omega_2)^2\, r_2 = m\left(\frac{2\pi N_2}{60}\right)^2 r_2$$

or $$414 = 5\left(\frac{2\pi N_2}{60}\right)^2 0.175 = 0.0096\,(N_2)^2$$

∴ $$(N_2)^2 = 414 / 0.0096 = 43\,125 \quad \text{or} \quad N_2 = 207.6 \text{ r.p.m. } \textbf{Ans.}$$

Coefficient of insensitiveness

Let N_1' and N_2' = Minimum and maximum speeds of the governor considering friction.

We know that frictional force at each ball

$$= 5 \text{ N} \qquad \qquad \text{...(Given)}$$

$$\therefore \qquad F_{C1} - F = m \, (\omega_1')^2 \, r_1 = m \left(\frac{2\pi N_1'}{60} \right)^2 r_1$$

$$204 - 5 = 5 \left(\frac{2\pi N_1'}{60} \right)^2 0.1 = 0.0055 \, (N_1')^2$$

$$\therefore \qquad (N_1')^2 = \frac{204 - 5}{0.0055} = 36 \; 182 \text{ or } N_1' = 190.2 \text{ r.p.m.}$$

Similarly $\qquad F_{C2} + F = m \, (\omega_2')^2 \, r_2 = m \left(\frac{2\pi N_2'}{60} \right)^2 r_2$

$$414 + 5 = 5 \left(\frac{2\pi N_2'}{60} \right)^2 0.175 = 0.0096 \, (N_2')^2$$

$$\therefore \qquad (N_2')^2 = \frac{414 + 5}{0.0096} = 43 \; 646 \text{ or } N_2' = 209 \text{ r.p.m.}$$

We know that coefficient of insensitiveness

$$= \frac{2 \, (N_2' - N_1')}{N_2' + N_1'} = \frac{2 \, (209 - 190.2)}{209 + 190.2} = 0.094 \text{ or } 9.4\% \text{ Ans.}$$

EXERCISES

1. The length of the upper arm of a Watt governor is 400 mm and its inclination to the vertical is 30°. Find the percentage increase in speed, if the balls rise by 20 mm. **[Ans. 3%]**

2. A Porter governor has two balls each of mass 3 kg and a central load of mass 15 kg. The arms are all 200 mm long, pivoted on the axis. If the maximum and minimum radii of rotation of the balls are 160 mm and 120 mm respectively, find the range of speed. **[Ans. 28.3 r.p.m.]**

3. In a Porter governor, the mass of the central load is 18 kg and the mass of each ball is 2 kg. The top arms are 250 mm while the bottom arms are each 300 mm long. The friction of the sleeve is 14 N. If the top arms make 45° with the axis of rotation in the equilibrium position, find the range of speed of the governor in that position. **[Ans. 15 r.p.m.]**

4. A loaded governor of the Porter type has equal arms and links each 250 mm long. The mass of each ball is 2 kg and the central mass is 12 kg. When the ball radius is 150 mm, the valve is fully open and when the radius is 185 mm, the valve is closed. Find the maximum speed and the range of speed. If the maximum speed is to be increased 20% by an addition of mass to the central load, find what additional mass is required. **[Ans. 193 r.p.m. ; 16 r.p.m.; 6.14 kg]**

5. The arms of a Porter governor are 300 mm long. The upper arms are pivoted on the axis of rotation and the lower arms are attached to the sleeve at a distance of 35 mm from the axis of rotation. The load on the sleeve is 54 kg and the mass of each ball is 7 kg. Determine the equilibrium speed when the

radius of the balls is 225 mm. What will be the range of speed for this position, if the frictional resistances to the motion of the sleeve are equivalent to a force of 30 N?

[Ans. 174.3 r.p.m. ; 8.5 r.p.m.]

6. In a Porter governor, the upper and lower arms are each 250 mm long and are pivoted on the axis of rotation. The mass of each rotating ball is 3 kg and the mass of the sleeve is 20 kg. The sleeve is in its lowest position when the arms are inclined at 30° to the governor axis. The lift of the sleeve is 36 mm. Find the force of friction at the sleeve, if the speed at the moment it rises from the lowest position is equal to the speed at the moment it falls from the highest position. Also, find the range of speed of the governor. [Ans. 9.8 N ; 16 r.p.m.]

7. A Porter governor has links 150 mm long and are attached to pivots at a radial distance of 30 mm from the vertical axis of the governor. The mass of each ball is 1.75 kg and the mass of the sleeve is 25 kg. The governor sleeve begins to rise at 300 r.p.m. when the links are at 30° to the vertical. Assuming the friction force to be constant, find the minimum and maximum speed of rotation when the inclination of the links is 45° to the vertical. [Ans. 284 r.p.m. ; 347 r.p.m.]

8. A Proell governor has all the four arms of length 250 mm. The upper and lower ends of the arms are pivoted on the axis of rotation of the governor. The extension arms of the lower links are each 100 mm long and parallel to the axis when the radius of the ball path is 150 mm. The mass of each ball is 4.5 kg and the mass of the central load is 36 kg. Determine the equilibrium speed of the governor.

[Ans. 164 r.p.m.]

9. A Proell governor has arms of 300 mm length. The upper arms are hinged on the axis of rotation, whereas the lower arms are pivoted at a distance of 35 mm from the axis of rotation. The extension of lower arms to which the balls are attached are 100 mm long. The mass of each ball is 8 kg and the mass on the sleeve is 60 kg. At the minimum radius of rotation of 200 mm, the extensions are parallel to the governor axis. Determine the equilibrium speed of the governor for the given configuration. What will be the equilibrium speed for the maximum radius of 250 mm?

[Ans. 144.5 r.p.m. ; 158.2 r.p.m.]

10. A spring controlled governor of the Hartnell type with a central spring under compression has balls each of mass 2 kg. The ball and sleeve arms of the bell crank levers are respectively 100 mm and 60 mm long and are at right angles. In the lowest position of the governor sleeve, the radius of rotation of the balls is 80 mm and the ball arms are parallel to the governor axis. Find the initial load on the spring in order that the sleeve may begin to lift at 300 r.p.m. If the stiffness of the spring is 30 kN/m, what is the equilibrium speed corresponding to a sleeve lift of 10 mm? [Ans. 527 N ; 342 r.p.m.]

11. In a governor of the Hartnell type, the mass of each ball is 1.5 kg and the lengths of the vertical and horizontal arms of the bell crank lever are 100 mm and 50 mm respectively. The fulcrum of the bell crank lever is at a distance of 90 mm from the axis of rotation. The maximum and minimum radii of rotation of balls are 120 mm and 80 mm and the corresponding equilibrium speeds are 325 and 300 r.p.m. Find the stiffness of the spring and the equilibrium speed when the radius of rotation is 100 mm.

[Ans. 18 kN/m, 315 r.p.m.]

12. A governor of the Hartnell type has equal balls of mass 3 kg, set initially at a radius of 200 mm. The arms of the bell crank lever are 110 mm vertically and 150 mm horizontally. Find : 1. the initial compressive force on the spring, if the speed for an initial ball radius of 200 mm is 240 r.p.m. ; and 2. the stiffness of the spring required to permit a sleeve movement of 4 mm on a fluctuation of 7.5 per cent in the engine speed. [Ans. 556 N ; 23.75 N/mm]

13. A spring controlled governor of the Hartnell type has the following data :

Mass of the ball = 1.8 kg ; Mass of the sleeve = 6 kg ; Ball and sleeve arms of the bell crank lever = 150 mm and 120 mm respectively. The equilibrium speed and radius of rotation for the lowest position of the sleeve are 400 r.p.m. and 150 mm respectively. The sleeve lift is 10 mm and the change in speed for full sleeve lift is 5%. During an overhaul, the spring was compressed 2 mm more than the correct compression for the initial setting. Determine the stiffness of the spring and the new equilibrium speed for the lowest position of the sleeve. [Ans. 28.96 N/mm ; 472 r.p.m.]

14. A spring controlled governor of the Hartnell type has two rotating balls of mass 1.35 kg each. The ball arm is 75 mm and the sleeve arm is 62.5 mm. In the mid position of the sleeve, the sleeve arm is horizontal and the balls rotate in a circle of 100 mm radius. The total sleeve movement is 30 mm.

    Due to maladjustment of the spring, it is found that the equilibrium speed at the topmost position of the sleeve is 420 r.p.m. and that corresponding to the lowest position is 435 r.p.m.

    Determine : 1. stiffness and initial compression of the spring, and 2. the required initial compression of the spring to give an equilibrium speed at the topmost position which is 12 r.p.m. more than at the lowest position. Neglect the moment due to mass of the balls.

    [Ans. 6.3 N/mm, 87.54 mm ; 53.5 mm]

15. A Hartnell governor has two rotating balls, of mass 2.7 kg each. The ball radius is 125 mm in the mean position when the ball arms are vertical and the speed is 150 r.p.m. with the sleeve rising. The length of the ball arms is 140 mm and the length of the sleeve arms 90 mm. The stiffness of the spring is 7 kN/m and the total sleeve movement is 12 mm from the mean position. Allowing for a constant friction force of 14 N acting at the sleeve, determine the speed range of the governor in the lowest and highest sleeve positions. Neglect the obliquity of the ball arms.   [Ans. 10.7 r.pm., 6.6 r.pm.]

16. The spring controlled governor of the Hartung type has two rotating masses each of 2.5 kg and the limits of their radius of rotation are 100 mm and 125 mm. The each mass is directly controlled by a spring attached to it and to the inner casing of the governor as shown in Fig 18.26 (a). The stiffness of the spring is 8 kN/m and the force on each spring, when the masses are in their mid-position, is 320 N. In addition, there is an equivalent constant inward radial force of 80 N acting on each revolving mass in order to allow for the dead weight of the mechanism. Neglecting friction, find the range of speed of the governor.   [Ans. 51 r.p.m.]

17. In a spring controlled governor of the Hartung type, the lengths of the horizontal and vertical arms of the bell crank levers are 100 mm and 80 mm respectively. The fulcrum of the bell crank lever is at a distance of 120 mm from the axis of the governor. The each revolving mass is 9 kg. The stiffness of the spring is 25 kN/m. If the length of each spring is 120 mm when the radius of rotation is 70 mm and the equilibrium speed is 360 r.p.m., find the free length of the spring. If the radius of rotation increases to 120 mm, what will be the corresponding percentage increase in speed ?

    [Ans 145.75 mm ; 10.83%]

    [Hint. Free length of the spring = Length of the spring + compression of the spring]

18. The following particulars refer to a Wilson-Hartnell governor :

    Mass of each ball = 4 kg ; minimum radius = 80 mm ; maximum radius = 90 mm ; minimum speed = 240 r.p.m.; maximum speed = 252 r.p.m.; length of the ball arm of each bell crank lever   = 80 mm ; length of sleeve arm of each bell crank lever = 60 mm ; combined stiffness of the two ball springs = 750 N/m.

    Find the required stiffness of the auxiliary spring, if the lever is pivoted at the mid-point.

    [Ans. 6.786 kN/m]

19. A spring loaded governor of the Wilson-Hartnell type is shown in Fig 18.50. Two balls each of mass 4 kg are connected across by two springs A. The stiffness of each spring is 750 N/m and a free length of 100 mm. The length of ball arm of each bell crank lever is 80 mm and that of sleeve arm is 60 mm. The lever is pivoted at its mid-point. The speed of the governor is 240 r.p.m. in its mean position and the radius of rotation of the ball is 80 mm. If the lift of the sleeve is 7.5 mm for an increase of speed of 5%, find the required stiffness of the auxiliary spring B.

    [Ans. 6.756 kN/m]

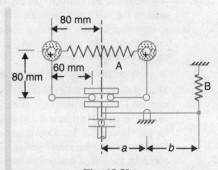

Fig. 18.50

20. A Porter governor has all four arms 200 mm long. The upper arms are pivoted on the axis of rotation and the lower arms are attached to a sleeve at a distance of 25 mm from the axis. Each ball has a mass of 2 kg and the mass of the load on the sleeve is 20 kg. If the radius of rotation of the balls at a speed of 250 r.p.m. is 100 mm, find the speed of the governor after the sleeve has lifted 50 mm. Also determine the effort and power of the governor. **[Ans. 275.6 r.p.m.; 22.4 N ; 1.12 N-m]**

21. A Porter governor has arms 250 mm each and four rotating flyballs of mass 0.8 kg each. The sleeve movement is restricted to ± 20 mm from the height when the mean speed is 100 r.p.m. Calculate the central dead load and sensitiveness of the governor neglecting friction when the flyball exerts a centrifugal force of 9.81 N. Determine also the effort and power of the governor for 1 percent speed change. **[Ans. 11.76 N; 11.12; 0.196 N; 7.7 N-mm]**

22. The upper arms of a Porter governor are pivoted on the axis of rotation and the lower arms are pivoted to the sleeve at a distance of 30 mm from the axis of rotation. The length of each arm is 300 mm and the mass of each ball is 6 kg. If the equilibrium speed is 200 r.p.m. when the radius of rotation is 200 mm, find the required mass on the sleeve. If the friction is equivalent to a force of 40 N at the sleeve, find the coefficient of insensitiveness at 200 mm radius. **[Ans. 61.1 kg. ; 6%]**

23. In a spring controlled governor, the radial force acting on the balls was 4500 N when the centre of balls was 200 mm from the axis and 7500 N when at 300 mm. Assuming that the force varies directly as the radius, find the radius of the ball path when the governor runs at 270 r.p.m. Also find what alteration in spring load is required in order to make the governor isochronous and the speed at which it would then run. The mass of each ball is 30 kg. **[Ans. 250 mm ; 1500 N ; 301.5 r.p.m.]**

DO YOU KNOW ?

1. What is the function of a governor ? How does it differ from that of a flywheel ?

2. State the different types of governors. What is the difference between centrifugal and inertia type governors ? Why is the former preferred to the latter ?

3. Explain the term height of the governor. Derive an expression for the height in the case of a Watt governor. What are the limitations of a Watt governor ?

4. What are the effects of friction and of adding a central weight to the sleeve of a Watt governor ?

5. Discuss the controlling force and stability of a governor and show that the stability of a governor depends on the slope of the curve connecting the controlling force (F_C) and radius of rotation (r) and the value (F_C/r).

6. What is stability of a governor ? Sketch the controlling force *versus* radius diagrams for a stable, unstable and isochronous governor. Derive the conditions for stability.

7. Explain clearly how would you determine from the controlling force curve whether a governor is stable, unstable or isochronous. Show also how the effect of friction may be indicated on the curve.

8. Define and explain the following terms relating to governors :

   1. Stability,   2. Sensitiveness,   3. Isochronism, and   4. Hunting.

9. Explain the terms and derive expressions for 'effort' and 'power' of a Porter governor.

10. Prove that the sensitiveness of a Proell governor is greater than that of a Porter governor.

11. Write short note on 'coefficient of insensitiveness' of governors.

OBJECTIVE TYPE QUESTIONS

1. The height of a Watt's governor (in metres) in equal to

   (a) $8.95/N^2$ (b) $89.5/N^2$ (c) $895/N^2$ (d) $8950/N^2$

   where N = Speed of the arm and ball about the spindle axis.

2. The ratio of the height of a Porter governor (when the length of arms and links are equal) to the height of a Watt's governor is

(a) $\dfrac{m}{m+M}$ (b) $\dfrac{M}{m+M}$ (c) $\dfrac{m+M}{m}$ (d) $\dfrac{m+M}{M}$

where m = Mass of the ball, and

            M = Mass of the load on the sleeve.

3. When the sleeve of a Porter governor moves upwards, the governor speed

   (a) increases   (b) decreases   (c) remains unaffected

4. A Hartnell governor is a

   (a) pendulum type governor   (b) spring loaded governor

   (c) dead weight governor   (d) inertia governor

5. Which of the following governor is used to drive a gramophone ?

   (a) Watt governor   (b) Porter governor

   (c) Pickering governor   (d) Hartnell governor

6. Which of the following is a spring controlled governor?

   (a) Hartnell   (b) Hartung   (c) Pickering   (d) all of these

7. For two governors A and B, the lift of sleeve of governor A is more than that of governor B, for a given fractional change in speed. It indicates that

   (a) governor A is more sensitive than governor B

   (b) governor B is more sensitive than governor A

   (c) both governors A and B are equally sensitive

   (d) none of the above

8. The sensitiveness of a governor is given by

(a) $\dfrac{\omega_{mean}}{\omega_2 - \omega_1}$ (b) $\dfrac{\omega_2 - \omega_1}{\omega_{mean}}$ (c) $\dfrac{\omega_2 - \omega_1}{2\,\omega_{mean}}$ (d) none of these

where ω_1 and ω_2 = Minimum and maximum angular speed, and

            ω_{mean} = Mean angular speed.

9. In a Hartnell governor, if a spring of greater stiffness is used, then the governor will be

   (a) more sensitive   (b) less sensitive   (c) isochronous

10. A governor is said to be hunting, if the speed of the engine

    (a) remains constant at the mean speed

    (b) is above the mean speed

    (c) is below the mean speed

    (d) fluctuates continuously above and below the mean speed.

11. A hunting governor is

    (a) more stable   (b) less sensitive   (c) more sensitive   (d) none of these

12. Isochronism in a governor is desirable when

    (a) the engine operates at low speeds

    (b) the engine operates at high speeds

    (c) the engine operates at variable speeds

    (d) one speed is desired under one load

13. The power of a governor is equal to

(a) $\dfrac{c^2}{1+2c}(m+M)h$

(b) $\dfrac{2c^2}{1+2c}(m+M)h$

(c) $\dfrac{3c^2}{1+2c}(m+M)h$

(d) $\dfrac{4c^2}{1+2c}(m+M)h$

where c = Percentage increase in speed.

14. When the relation between the controlling force (F_C) and radius of rotation (r) for a spring controlled governor is $F_C = a.r + b$, then the governor will be

(a) stable　　　(b) unstable　　　(c) isochronous

15. For a governor, if F_C is the controlling force, r is the radius of rotation of the balls, the stability of the governor will be ensured when

(a) $\dfrac{dF_C}{dr} > \dfrac{F_C}{r}$

(b) $\dfrac{dF_C}{dr} < \dfrac{F_C}{r}$

(c) $\dfrac{dF_C}{dr} = 0$

(d) none of these

ANSWERS

1.	(c)	2.	(c)	3.	(a)	4.	(b)	5.	(c)
6.	(d)	7.	(a)	8.	(b)	9.	(b)	10.	(d)
11.	(c)	12.	(d)	13.	(d)	14.	(b)	15.	(a)

19

Brakes and Dynamometers

19.1. Introduction

A *brake* is a device by means of which artificial frictional resistance is applied to a moving machine member, in order to retard or stop the motion of a machine. In the process of performing this function, the brake absorbs either kinetic energy of the moving member or potential energy given up by objects being lowered by hoists, elevators etc. The energy absorbed by brakes is dissipated in the form of heat. This heat is dissipated in the surrounding air (or water which is circulated through the passages in the brake drum) so that excessive heating of the brake lining does not take place. The capacity of a brake depends upon the following factors :

1. The unit pressure between the braking surfaces,
2. The coefficient of friction between the braking surfaces,
3. The peripheral velocity of the brake drum,
4. The projected area of the friction surfaces, and
5. The ability of the brake to dissipate heat equivalent to the energy being absorbed.

The major functional difference between a clutch and a brake is that a clutch is used to keep the driving and driven member moving together, whereas brakes are used to stop a moving member or to control its speed.

19.2. Materials for Brake Lining

The material used for the brake lining should have the following characteristics :

732

1. It should have high coefficient of friction with minimum fading. In other words, the coefficient of friction should remain constant with change in temperature.
2. It should have low wear rate.
3. It should have high heat resistance.
4. It should have high heat dissipation capacity.
5. It should have adequate mechanical strength.
6. It should not be affected by moisture and oil.

The materials commonly used for facing or lining of brakes and their properties are shown in the following table.

Table 19.1. Properties of materials for brake lining.

Material for braking lining	*Coefficient of friction* (μ)			*Allowable pressure* (*p*)
	Dry	*Greasy*	*Lubricated*	*N/mm²*
Cast iron on cast iron	0.15 – 0.2	0.06 – 0.10	0.05 – 0.10	1.0 – 1.75
Bronze on cast iron	–	0.05 – 0.10	0.05 – 0.10	0.56 – 0.84
Steel on cast iron	0.20 – 0.30	0.07 – 0.12	0.06 – 0.10	0.84 – 1.40
Wood on cast iron	0.20 – 0.35	0.08 – 0.12	–	0.40 – 0.62
Fibre on metal	–	0.10 – 0.20	–	0.07 – 0.28
Cork on metal	0.35	0.25 – 0.30	0.22 – 0.25	0.05 – 0.10
Leather on metal	0.30 – 0.5	0.15 – 0.20	0.12 – 0.15	0.07 – 0.28
Wire asbestos on metal	0.35 – 0.5	0.25 – 0.30	0.20 – 0.25	0.20 – 0.55
Asbestos blocks on metal	0.40 – 0.48	0.25 – 0.30	–	0.28 – 1.1
Asbestos on metal (Short action)	–	–	0.20 – 0.25	1.4 – 2.1
Metal on cast iron (Short action)	–	–	0.05 – 0.10	1.4 – 2.1

19.3. Types of Brakes

The brakes, according to the means used for transforming the energy by the braking elements, are classified as :

1. Hydraulic brakes *e.g.* pumps or hydrodynamic brake and fluid agitator,

2. Electric brakes *e.g.* generators and eddy current brakes, and

3. Mechanical brakes.

The hydraulic and electric brakes cannot bring the member to rest and are mostly used where large amounts of energy are to be transformed while the brake is retarding the load such as in laboratory dynamometers, high way trucks and electric locomotives. These brakes are also used for retarding or controlling the speed of a vehicle for down-hill travel.

The mechanical brakes, according to the direction of acting force, may be divided into the following two groups :

(*a*) *Radial brakes.* In these brakes, the force acting on the brake drum is in radial direction. The radial brakes may be

Simple bicycle brakes.

sub-divided into *external brakes* and *internal brakes.* According to the shape of the friction elements, these brakes may be *block* or *shoe brakes* and *band brakes.*

(b) *Axial brakes.* In these brakes, the force acting on the brake drum is in axial direction. The axial brakes may be disc brakes and cone brakes. The analysis of these brakes is similar to clutches.

Since we are concerned with only mechanical brakes, therefore, these are discussed, in detail, in the following pages.

19.4. Single Block or Shoe Brake

A single block or shoe brake is shown in Fig. 19.1. It consists of a block or shoe which is pressed against the rim of a revolving brake wheel drum. The block is made of a softer material than the rim of the wheel. This type of a brake is commonly used on railway trains and tram cars. The friction between the block and the wheel causes a tangential braking force to act on the wheel, which retard the rotation of the wheel. The block is pressed against the wheel by a force applied to one end of a lever to which the block is rigidly fixed as shown in Fig. 19.1. The other end of the lever is pivoted on a fixed fulcrum O.

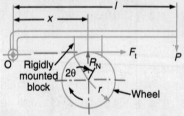 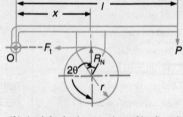

(a) Clockwise rotation of brake wheel.   (b) Anticlockwise rotation of brake wheel.
Fig. 19.1. Single block brake. Line of action of tangential force passes through the fulcrum of the lever.

Let P = Force applied at the end of the lever,

R_N = Normal force pressing the brake block on the wheel,

r = Radius of the wheel,

2θ = Angle of contact surface of the block,

μ = Coefficient of friction, and

F_t = Tangential braking force or the frictional force acting at the contact surface of the block and the wheel.

If the angle of contact is less than 60°, then it may be assumed that the normal pressure between the block and the wheel is uniform. In such cases, tangential braking force on the wheel,

$$F_t = \mu.R_N \qquad ...(i)$$

and the braking torque, $T_B = F_t.r = \mu.R_N.r \qquad ...(ii)$

Let us now consider the following three cases :

Case 1. When the line of action of tangential braking force (F_t) passes through the fulcrum O of the lever, and the brake wheel rotates clockwise as shown in Fig. 19.1 (a), then for equilibrium, taking moments about the fulcrum O, we have

$$R_N \times x = P \times l \quad \text{or} \quad R_N = \frac{P \times l}{x}$$

∴ Braking torque,

$$T_B = \mu.R_N.r = \mu \times \frac{P.l}{x} \times r = \frac{\mu.P.l.r}{x}$$

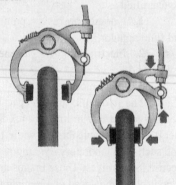

When brakes are on, the pads grip the wheel rim from either side, friction between the pads and the rim converts the cycle's kinetic energy into heat as they reduce its speed.

It may be noted that when the brake wheel rotates anticlockwise as shown in Fig. 19.1 (*b*), then the braking torque is same, *i.e.*

$$T_B = \mu.R_N.r = \frac{\mu.P.l.r}{x}$$

Case 2. When the line of action of the tangential braking force (F_t) passes through a distance '*a*' below the fulcrum *O*, and the brake wheel rotates clockwise as shown in Fig. 19.2 (*a*), then for equilibrium, taking moments about the fulcrum *O*,

$$R_N \times x + F_t \times a = P.l \quad \text{or} \quad R_N \times x + \mu R_N \times a = P.l \quad \text{or} \quad R_N = \frac{P.l}{x + \mu.a}$$

and braking torque,

$$T_B = \mu R_N.r = \frac{\mu.p.l.r}{x + \mu.a}$$

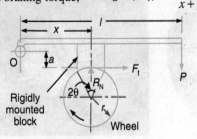

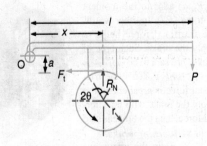

(*a*) Clockwise rotation of brake wheel.   (*b*) Anticlockwise rotation of brake wheel.

Fig. 19.2. Single block brake. Line of action of F_t passes below the fulcrum.

When the brake wheel rotates anticlockwise, as shown in Fig. 19.2 (*b*), then for equilibrium,

$$R_N.x = P.l + F_t.a = P.l + \mu.R_N.a \qquad \qquad ...(i)$$

or $\qquad\qquad R_N (x - \mu.a) = P.l \quad$ or $\quad R_N = \dfrac{P.l}{x - \mu.a}$

and braking torque, $\qquad T_B = \mu.R_N.r = \dfrac{\mu.P.l.r}{x - \mu.a}$

Case 3. When the line of action of the tangential braking force (F_t) passes through a distance '*a*' above the fulcrum *O*, and the brake wheel rotates clockwise as shown in Fig. 19.3 (*a*), then for equilibrium, taking moments about the fulcrum *O*, we have

$$R_N.x = P.l + F_t . a = P.l + \mu.R_N.a \qquad \qquad . . . (ii)$$

or $\qquad\qquad R_N (x - \mu.a) = P.l \quad$ or $\quad R_N = \dfrac{P.l}{x - \mu.a}$

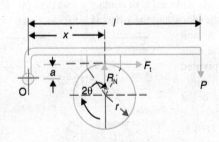

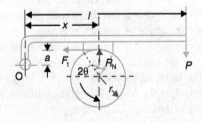

(*a*) Clockwise rotation of brake wheel.   (*b*) Anticlockwise rotation of brake wheel.

Fig. 19.3. Single block brake. Line of action of F_t passes above the fulcrum.

and braking torque, $\qquad T_B = \mu.R_N.r = \dfrac{\mu.P.l.r}{x - \mu.a}$

When the brake wheel rotates anticlockwise as shown in Fig. 19.3 (*b*), then for equilibrium, taking moments about the fulcrum *O*, we have

$$R_N \times x + F_t \times a = P.l \quad \text{or} \quad R_N \times x + \mu.R_N \times a = P.l \quad \text{or} \quad R_N = \frac{P.l}{x + \mu.a}$$

and braking torque, $\quad T_B = \mu.R_N.r = \dfrac{\mu.P.l.r}{x + \mu.a}$

Notes : 1. From above we see that when the brake wheel rotates anticlockwise in case 2 [Fig. 19.2 (*b*)] and when it rotates clockwise in case 3 [Fig. 19.3 (*a*)], the equations (*i*) and (*ii*) are same, *i.e.*

$$R_N \times x = P.l + \mu.R_N.a$$

From this we see that the moment of frictional force ($\mu.R_N.a$) adds to the moment of force ($P.l$). In other words, the frictional force helps to apply the brake. Such type of brakes are said to be *self energizing brakes*. When the frictional force is great enough to apply the brake with no external force, then the brake is said to be *self-locking brake*.

Shoe brakes of a racing car

From the above expression, we see that if $x \leq \mu.a$, then *P* will be negative or equal to zero. This means no external force is needed to apply the brake and hence the brake is self locking. Therefore the condition for the brake to be self locking is

$$x \leq \mu.a$$

The self locking brake is used only in back-stop applications.

2. The brake should be self energizing and not the self locking.

3. In order to avoid self locking and to prevent the brake from grabbing, *x* is kept greater than $\mu . a$.

4. If A_b is the projected bearing area of the block or shoe, then the bearing pressure on the shoe,

$$p_b = R_N / A_b$$

We know that $\quad A_b$ = Width of shoe × Projected length of shoe = $w(2r\sin\theta)$

5. When a single block or shoe brake is applied to a rolling wheel, an additional load is thrown on the shaft bearings due to heavy normal force (R_N) and produces bending of the shaft.

In order to overcome this drawback, a double block or shoe brake is used, as discussed in Art. 19.6.

19.5. Pivoted Block or Shoe Brake

We have discussed in the previous article that when the angle of contact is less than 60°, then it may be assumed that the normal pressure between the block and the wheel is uniform. But when the angle of contact is greater than 60°, then the unit pressure normal to the surface of contact is less at the ends than at the centre. In such cases, the block or shoe is pivoted to the lever, as shown in Fig. 19.4, instead of being rigidly attached to the lever. This gives uniform wear of the brake lining in the direction of the applied force. The braking torque for a pivoted block or shoe brake (*i.e.* when $2\theta > 60°$) is given by

Fig. 19.4. Pivoted block or shoe brake.

$$T_B = F_t \times r = \mu'.R_N.r$$

where $\quad \mu'$ = Equivalent coefficient of friction = $\dfrac{4\mu\sin\theta}{2\theta + \sin 2\theta}$, and

μ = Actual coefficient of friction.

These brakes have more life and may provide a higher braking torque.

Example 19.1. *A single block brake is shown in Fig. 19.5. The diameter of the drum is 250 mm and the angle of contact is 90°. If the operating force of 700 N is applied at the end of a lever and the coefficient of friction between the drum and the lining is 0.35, determine the torque that may be transmitted by the block brake.*

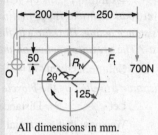

All dimensions in mm.
Fig. 19.5

Solution. Given : $d = 250$ mm or $r = 125$ mm ; $2\theta = 90°$ $= \pi/2$ rad ; $P = 700$ N ; $\mu = 0.35$

Since the angle of contact is greater than 60°, therefore equivalent coefficient of friction,

$$\mu' = \frac{4\mu \sin\theta}{2\theta + \sin 2\theta} = \frac{4 \times 0.35 \times \sin 45°}{\pi/2 + \sin 90°} = 0.385$$

Let R_N = Normal force pressing the block to the brake drum, and

F_t = Tangential braking force = $\mu'.R_N$

Taking moments about the fulcrum O, we have

$$700(250+200) + F_t \times 50 = R_N \times 200 = \frac{F_t}{\mu'} \times 200 = \frac{F_t}{0.385} \times 200 = 520\, F_t$$

or $\qquad 520\, F_t - 50 F_t = 700 \times 450 \quad$ or $\quad F_t = 700 \times 450/470 = 670$ N

We know that torque transmitted by the block brake,

$$T_B = F_t \times r = 670 \times 125 = 8\ 3750 \text{ N-mm} = 83.75\text{N-m} \textbf{ Ans.}$$

Example 19.2. *Fig. 19.6 shows a brake shoe applied to a drum by a lever AB which is pivoted at a fixed point A and rigidly fixed to the shoe. The radius of the drum is 160 mm. The coefficient of friction at the brake lining is 0.3. If the drum rotates clockwise, find the braking torque due to the horizontal force of 600 N at B.*

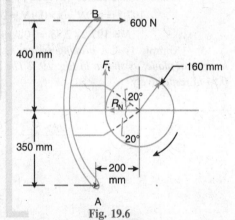

Fig. 19.6

Solution. Given : $r = 160$ mm = 0.16 m ; $\mu = 0.3$; $P = 600$ N

Since the angle subtended by the shoe at the centre of drum is 40°, therefore we need not to calculate the equivalent coefficient of friction μ'.

Let $\quad R_N$ = Normal force pressing the block to the brake drum, and

F_t = Tangential braking force = $\mu.R_N$

Taking moments about point A,

$$R_N \times 350 + F_t (200 - 160) = 600 (400 + 350)$$

$$\frac{F_t}{0.3} \times 350 + 40 F_t = 600 \times 750 \text{ or } 1207\, F_t = 450 \times 10^3$$

∴ $\qquad F_t = 450 \times 10^3/1207 = 372.8$ N

We know that braking torque,

$$T_B = F_t \times r = 372.8 \times 0.16 = 59.6 \text{ N-m Ans.}$$

Example 19.3. *A bicycle and rider of mass 100 kg are travelling at the rate of 16 km/h on a level road. A brake is applied to the rear wheel which is 0.9 m in diameter and this is the only resistance acting. How far will the bicycle travel and how many turns will it make before it comes to rest ? The pressure applied on the brake is 100 N and μ = 0.05.*

Solution. Given : $m = 100$ kg, $v = 16$ km / h $= 4.44$ m / s ; $D = 0.9$ m ; $R_N = 100$ N ; $\mu = 0.05$

Distance travelled by the bicycle before it comes to rest

Let $x =$ Distance travelled (in metres) by the bicycle before it comes to rest.

We know that tangential braking force acting at the point of contact of the brake and wheel,

$$F_t = \mu.R_N = 0.05 \times 100 = 5 \text{ N}$$

and work done $= F_t \times x = 5 \times x = 5x$ N-m ... (i)

We know that kinetic energy of the bicycle

$$= \frac{m.v^2}{2} = \frac{100(4.44)^2}{2}$$

$$= 986 \text{ N-m} \qquad ... (ii)$$

In order to bring the bicycle to rest, the work done against friction must be equal to kinetic energy of the bicycle. Therefore equating equations (i) and (ii),

$$5x = 986 \text{ or } x = 986/5 = 197.2 \text{ m Ans.}$$

Number of revolutions made by the bicycle before it comes to rest

Let $N =$ Required number of revolutions.

We know that distance travelled by the bicycle (x),

$$197.2 = \pi DN = \pi \times 0.9 N = 2.83N$$

∴ $N = 197.2 / 2.83 = 70$ Ans.

Shoe brake.

Example 19.4. *A braking system has its braking lever inclined at an angle of 30° to the horizontal plane, as shown in Fig. 19.7. The mass and diameter of the brake drum are 218 kg and 0.54 m respectively.*

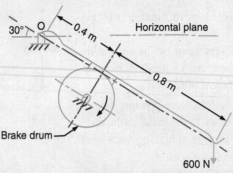

30° — O ← 0.4 m — Horizontal plane

0.8 m

Brake drum —

600 N

Fig. 19.7

At the instant the lever is pressed on the brake drum with a vertical force of 600 N, the drum is found to rotate at 2400 r.p.m. clockwise. The coefficient of friction between the brake shoe and the brake drum is 0.4. Assume that the lever and brake shoe are perfectly rigid and possess negligible weight. Find :

1. Braking torque, 2. Number of revolutions the drum will make before coming to rest from the instant of pressing the lever, and 3. Time taken for the drum to come to rest from the instant of pressing the lever.

Solution. Given : $m = 218$ kg ; $d = 0.54$ m or $r = 0.27$ m ; $P = 600$ N ; $N = 2400$ r.p.m.; $\mu = 0.4$

1. *Braking torque*

Let $\quad\quad R_N$ = Normal force pressing the block to the brake drum, and

$\quad\quad F_t$ = Tangential braking force.

The various forces acting on the braking system are shown in Fig. 19.8.

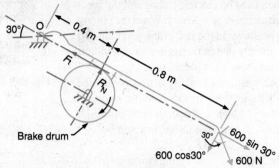

Fig. 19.8

Taking moments about the fulcrum O,

$$600 \cos 30° \times 1.2 = R_N \times 0.4 \quad \text{or} \quad 623.5 = 0.4\, R_N$$

$\therefore \quad\quad\quad\quad R_N = 623.5/0.4 = 1560$ N

and $\quad\quad\quad\quad F_t = \mu . R_N = 0.4 \times 1560 = 624$ N

We know that braking torque,

$$T_B = F_t \times r = 624 \times 0.27 = 168.5 \text{ N-m} \textbf{ Ans.}$$

2. *Number of revolutions the drum will make before coming to rest*

Let $\quad\quad n$ = Required number of revolutions.

We know that kinetic energy of the brake drum

$$= \frac{m.v^2}{2} = \frac{218}{2}\left(\frac{\pi\, d.N}{60}\right)^2 = 109\left(\frac{\pi \times 0.54 \times 2400}{60}\right)^2 \text{ N-m}$$

$$= 502 \times 10^3 \text{ N-m} \quad\quad\quad \ldots (i)$$

and work done by the brake drum due to braking torque

$$= T_B \times 2\pi n = 168.5 \times 2\pi n = 1060n \text{ N-m} \quad\quad\quad \ldots (ii)$$

Since the kinetic energy of the brake drum is used to overcome the work done due to braking torque, therefore equating equations (i) and (ii),

$$n = 502 \times 10^3/1060 = 474 \textbf{ Ans.}$$

3. *Time taken for the drum to come to rest*

We know that time taken for the drum to come to rest *i.e.* time required for 474 revolutions,

$$t = \frac{n}{N} = \frac{474}{2400} = 0.2 \min = 12 \text{ s} \textbf{ Ans.}$$

19.6. Double Block or Shoe Brake

When a single block brake is applied to a rolling wheel, an additional load is thrown on the shaft bearings due to the normal force (R_N). This produces bending of the shaft. In order to overcome this drawback, a double block or shoe brake, as shown in Fig. 19.9, is used. It consists of two brake blocks applied at the opposite ends of a diameter of the wheel which eliminate or reduces the unbalanced force on the shaft. The brake is set by a spring which pulls the upper ends of the brake arms together. When a force P is applied to the bell crank lever, the spring is compressed and the brake is released. This type of brake is often used on electric cranes and the force P is produced by an electromagnet or solenoid. When the current is switched off, there is no force on the bell crank lever and the brake is engaged automatically due to the spring force and thus there will be no downward movement of the load.

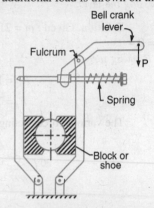

Fig. 19.9. Double block or shoe brake.

In a double block brake, the braking action is doubled by the use of two blocks and these blocks may be operated practically by the same force which will operate one. In case of double block or shoe brake, the braking torque is given by

$$T_B = (F_{t1} + F_{t2})\, r$$

where F_{t1} and F_{t2} are the braking forces on the two blocks.

Example 19.5. *A double shoe brake, as shown in Fig. 19.10, is capable of absorbing a torque of 1400 N-m. The diameter of the brake drum is 350 mm and the angle of contact for each shoe is 100°. If the coefficient of friction between the brake drum and lining is 0.4 ; find 1. the spring force necessary to set the brake ; and 2. the width of the brake shoes, if the bearing pressure on the lining material is not to exceed 0.3 N/mm².*

Solution. Given : $T_B = 1400$ N-m $= 1400 \times 10^3$ N-mm ; $d = 350$ mm or $r = 175$ mm ; $2\theta = 100° = 100 \times \pi/180 = 1.75$ rad; $\mu = 0.4$; $p_b = 0.3$ N/mm²

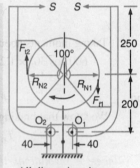

All dimensions in mm.

Fig. 19.10

1. Spring force necessary to set the brake

Let S = Spring force necessary to set the brake.

R_{N1} and F_{t1} = Normal reaction and the braking force on the right hand side shoe, and

R_{N2} and F_{t2} = Corresponding values on the left hand side shoe.

Since the angle of contact is greater than 60°, therefore equivalent coefficient of friction,

$$\mu' = \frac{4\mu \sin\theta}{2\theta + \sin 2\theta} = \frac{4 \times 0.4 \times \sin 50°}{1.75 + \sin 100°} = 0.45$$

Brakes on a railway coach.

Taking moments about the fulcrum O_1, we have

$$S \times 450 = R_{N1} \times 200 + F_{t1}(175 - 40) = \frac{F_{t1}}{0.45} \times 200 + F_{t1} \times 135 = 579.4\, F_{t1}$$

$$\dots \left(\text{Substituting } R_{N1} = \frac{F_{t1}}{\mu'} \right)$$

$\therefore \qquad\qquad F_{t1} = S \times 450 / 579.4 = 0.776\, S$

Again taking moments about O_2, we have

$$S \times 450 + F_{t2}(175 - 40) = R_{N2} \times 200 = \frac{F_{t2}}{0.45} \times 200 = 444.4\, F_{t2}$$

$$\dots \left(\text{Substituting } R_{N2} = \frac{F_{t2}}{\mu'} \right)$$

$$444.4\, F_{t2} - 135 F_{t2} = S \times 450 \qquad \text{or} \quad 309.4\, F_{t2} = S \times 450$$

$\therefore \qquad\qquad F_{t2} = S \times 450 / 309.4 = 1.454\, S$

We know that torque capacity of the brake (T_B),

$$1400 \times 10^3 = (F_{t1} + F_{t2})\, r = (0.776\, S + 1.454\, S)\, 175 = 390.25\, S$$

$\therefore \qquad\qquad S = 1400 \times 10^3 / 390.25 = 3587 \text{ N } \textbf{Ans.}$

2. *Width of the brake shoes*

Let $\qquad\qquad b = $ Width of the brake shoes in mm.

We know that projected bearing area for one shoe,

$$A_b = b\,(2r \sin\theta) = b\,(2 \times 175 \sin 50°) = 268\, b \text{ mm}^2$$

Normal force on the right hand side of the shoe,

$$R_{N1} = \frac{F_{t1}}{\mu'} = \frac{0.776 \times S}{0.45} = \frac{0.776 \times 3587}{0.45} = 6186 \text{ N}$$

and normal force on the left hand side of the shoe,

$$R_{N2} = \frac{F_{t2}}{\mu'} = \frac{1.454 \times S}{0.45} = \frac{1.454 \times 3587}{0.45} = 11\,590 \text{ N}$$

We see that the maximum normal force is on the left hand side of the shoe. Therefore we shall find the width of the shoe for the maximum normal force *i.e.* R_{N2}.

We know that the bearing pressure on the lining material (p_b),

$$0.3 = \frac{R_{N2}}{A_b} = \frac{11\,590}{268\, b} = \frac{43.25}{b}$$

$\therefore \qquad\qquad b = 43.25 / 0.3 = 144.2 \text{ mm } \textbf{Ans.}$

19.7. Simple Band Brake

A band brake consists of a flexible band of leather, one or more ropes, or a steel lined with friction material, which embraces a part of the circumference of the drum. A band brake, as shown in Fig. 19.11, is called a *simple band brake* in which one end of the band is attached to a fixed pin or fulcrum of the lever while the other end is attached to the lever at a distance b from the fulcrum.

When a force P is applied to the lever at C, the lever turns about the fulcrum pin O and tightens the band on the drum and hence the brakes are applied. The friction between the band and the drum provides the braking force. The force P on the lever at C may be determined as discussed below :

Let $\qquad\qquad T_1 = $ Tension in the tight side of the band,

$\qquad\qquad\qquad T_2 = $ Tension in the slack side of the band,

θ = Angle of lap (or embrace) of the band on the drum,

μ = Coefficient of friction between the band and the drum,

r = Radius of the drum,

t = Thickness of the band, and

r_e = Effective radius of the drum = $r + \dfrac{t}{2}$

Band brake

Bands of a brake shown separately

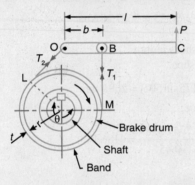

(a) Clockwise rotation of drum.   (b) Anticlockwise rotation of drum.

Fig. 19.11. Simple band brake.

We know that limiting ratio of the tensions is given by the relation,

$$\frac{T_1}{T_2} = e^{\mu\theta} \qquad \text{or} \qquad 2.3\log\left(\frac{T_1}{T_2}\right) = \mu.\theta$$

and braking force on the drum = $T_1 - T_2$

∴ Braking torque on the drum,

$$T_B = (T_1 - T_2)\, r \qquad \text{... (Neglecting thickness of band)}$$

$$= (T_1 - T_2)\, r_e \qquad \text{... (Considering thickness of band)}$$

Now considering the equilibrium of the lever *OBC*. It may be noted that when the drum rotates in the clockwise direction, as shown in Fig. 19.11 (*a*), the end of the band attached to the fulcrum *O* will be slack with tension T_2 and end of the band attached to *B* will be tight with tension T_1. On the other hand, when the drum rotates in the anticlockwise direction, as shown in Fig. 19.11 (*b*), the tensions in the band will reverse, *i.e.* the end of the band attached to the fulcrum *O* will be tight with tension T_1 and the end of the band attached to *B* will be slack with tension T_2. Now taking moments about the fulcrum *O*, we have

$$P.l = T_1.b \qquad \text{... (For clockwise rotation of the drum)}$$

and

$$P.l = T_2.b \qquad \text{... (For anticlockwise rotation of the drum)}$$

where l = Length of the lever from the fulcrum (OC), and

b = Perpendicular distance from O to the line of action of T_1 or T_2.

Notes : 1. When the brake band is attached to the lever, as shown in Fig. 19.11 (*a*) and (*b*), then the force (*P*) must act in the upward direction in order to tighten the band on the drum.

2. If the permissible tensile stress (σ) for the material of the band is known, then maximum tension in the band is given by

$$T_1 = \sigma.w.t$$

where w = Width of the band, and

t = thickness of the band.

Example 19.6. *A band brake acts on the 3/4th of circumference of a drum of 450 mm diameter which is keyed to the shaft. The band brake provides a braking torque of 225 N-m. One end of the band is attached to a fulcrum pin of the lever and the other end to a pin 100 mm from the fulcrum. If the operating force is applied at 500 mm from the fulcrum and the coefficient of friction is 0.25, find the operating force when the drum rotates in the (a) anticlockwise direction, and (b) clockwise direction.*

Solution. Given : $d = 450$ mm or $r = 225$ mm $= 0.225$ m ; $T_B = 225$ N-m ; $b = OB = 100$ mm $= 0.1$ m ; $l = 500$ mm $= 0.5$ m ; $\mu = 0.25$

Let P = Operating force.

(a) Operating force when drum rotates in anticlockwise direction

The band brake is shown in Fig. 19.11. Since one end of the band is attached to the fulcrum at O, therefore the operating force P will act upward and when the drum rotates anticlockwise, as shown in Fig. 19.11 (*b*), the end of the band attached to O will be tight with tension T_1 and the end of the band attached to B will be slack with tension T_2. First of all, let us find the tensions T_1 and T_2.

Drums for band brakes.

We know that angle of wrap,

$$\theta = \frac{3}{4} \text{th of circumference} = \frac{3}{4} \times 360° = 270°$$

$$= 270 \times \pi / 180 = 4.713 \text{ rad}$$

and $2.3 \log\left(\dfrac{T_1}{T_1}\right) = \mu.\theta = 0.25 \times 4.713 = 1.178$

$\therefore \qquad \log\left(\dfrac{T_1}{T_2}\right) = \dfrac{1.178}{2.3} = 0.5123 \text{ or } \dfrac{T_1}{T_2} = 3.253 \qquad \qquad \dots (i)$

$\dots$ (Taking antilog of 0.5123)

We know that braking torque (T_B),

$$225 = (T_1 - T_2)\, r = (T_1 - T_2)\, 0.225$$

$\therefore \qquad T_1 - T_2 = 225 / 0.225 = 1000 \text{ N} \qquad \qquad \dots (ii)$

From equations (*i*) and (*ii*), we have

$$T_1 = 1444 \text{ N; and} \quad T_2 = 444 \text{ N}$$

Now taking moments about the fulcrum O, we have

$$P \times l = T_2.b \qquad \text{or} \qquad P \times 0.5 = 444 \times 0.1 = 44.4$$

$\therefore \qquad P = 44.4 / 0.5 = 88.8 \text{ N } \textbf{Ans.}$

(b) Operating force when drum rotates in clockwise direction

When the drum rotates in clockwise direction, as shown in Fig.19.11 *(a)*, then taking moments about the fulcrum *O*, we have

$$P \times l = T_1 . b \quad \text{or} \quad P \times 0.5 = 1444 \times 0.1 = 144.4$$
$$\therefore \quad P = 144.4 / 0.5 = 288.8 \text{ N Ans.}$$

Example 19.7. *The simple band brake, as shown in Fig. 19.12, is applied to a shaft carrying a flywheel of mass 400 kg. The radius of gyration of the flywheel is 450 mm and runs at 300 r.p.m.*

If the coefficient of friction is 0.2 and the brake drum diameter is 240 mm, find :

1. the torque applied due to a hand load of 100 N,

2. the number of turns of the wheel before it is brought to rest, and

3. the time required to bring it to rest, from the moment of the application of the brake.

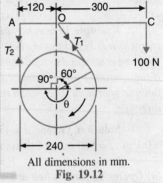

All dimensions in mm.
Fig. 19.12

Solution. Given : $m = 400$ kg ; $k = 450$ mm $= 0.45$ m ; $N = 300$ r.p.m. or $\omega = 2\pi \times 300/60 = 31.42$ rad/s ; $\mu = 0.2$; $d = 240$ mm $= 0.24$ m or $r = 0.12$ m

1. *Torque applied due to hand load*

First of all, let us find the tensions in the tight and slack sides of the band *i.e.* T_1 and T_2 respectively.

From the geometry of the Fig. 19.12, angle of lap of the band on the drum,

$$\theta = 360° - 150° = 210° = 210 \times \frac{\pi}{180} = 3.666 \text{ rad}$$

We know that

$$2.3 \log \left(\frac{T_1}{T_2} \right) = \mu . \theta = 0.2 \times 3.666 = 0.7332$$

$$\log \left(\frac{T_1}{T_2} \right) = \frac{0.7332}{2.3} = 0.3188 \quad \text{or} \quad \frac{T_1}{T_2} = 2.08 \qquad \ldots (i)$$

... (Taking antilog of 0.3188)

Taking moments about the fulcrum *O*,

$$T_2 \times 120 = 100 \times 300 = 30\,000 \quad \text{or} \quad T_2 = 30\,000/120 = 250 \text{ N}$$
$$\therefore \quad T_1 = 2.08 T_2 = 2.08 \times 250 = 520 \text{ N} \qquad \ldots \text{[From equation } (i)\text{]}$$

We know that torque applied,

$$T_B = (T_1 - T_2) r = (520 - 250)\, 0.12 = 32.4 \text{ N-m Ans.}$$

2. *Number of turns of the wheel before it is brought to rest*

Let $\quad n =$ Number of turns of the wheel before it is brought to rest.

We know that kinetic energy of rotation of the drum

$$= \frac{1}{2} \times I . \omega^2 = \frac{1}{2} \times m.k^2 . \omega^2 = \frac{1}{2} \times 400 (0.45)^2 (31.42)^2 = 40\,000 \text{ N-m}$$

This energy is used to overcome the work done due to the braking torque (T_B).

$$\therefore \quad 40\,000 = T_B \times 2\pi n = 32.4 \times 2\pi n = 203.6\, n$$

or $\quad n = 40\,000 / 203.6 = 196.5$ **Ans.**

3. Time required to bring the wheel to rest

We know that the time required to bring the wheel to rest

$$= n / N = 196.5 / 300 = 0.655 \text{ min} = 39.3 \text{ s} \textbf{ Ans.}$$

Example 19.8. *A simple band brake operates on a drum of 600 mm in diameter that is running at 200 r.p.m. The coefficient of friction is 0.25. The brake band has a contact of 270°, one end is fastened to a fixed pin and the other end to the brake arm 125 mm from the fixed pin. The straight brake arm is 750 mm long and placed perpendicular to the diameter that bisects the angle of contact.*

1. *What is the pull necessary on the end of the brake arm to stop the wheel if 35 kW is being absorbed ? What is the direction for this minimum pull ?*

2. *What width of steel band of 2.5 mm thick is required for this brake if the maximum tensile stress is not to exceed 50 N/mm² ?*

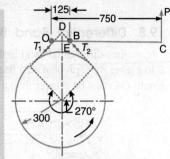

All dimensions in mm

Fig. 19.13

Solution. Given : $d = 600$ mm or $r = 300$ mm ;
$N = 200$ r.p.m. ; $\mu = 0.25$; $\theta = 270° = 270 \times \pi / 180 = 4.713$ rad ;
Power $= 35$ kW $= 35 \times 10^3$ W ; $t = 2.5$ mm ; $\sigma = 50$ N/mm²

1. Pull necessary on the end of the brake arm to stop the wheel

Let P = Pull necessary on the end of the brake arm to stop the wheel.

The simple band brake is shown in Fig. 19.13. Since one end of the band is attached to the fixed pin O, therefore the pull P on the end of the brake arm will act upward and when the wheel rotates anticlockwise, the end of the band attached to O will be tight with tension T_1 and the end of the band attached to B will be slack with tension T_2. First of all, let us find the tensions T_1 and T_2. We know that

$$2.3 \log \left(\frac{T_1}{T_2} \right) = \mu.\theta = 0.25 \times 4.713 = 1.178$$

$$\therefore \qquad \log \left(\frac{T_1}{T_2} \right) = \frac{1.178}{2.3} = 0.5122 \quad \text{or} \quad \frac{T_1}{T_2} = 3.25 \quad \text{... (Taking antilog of 0.5122) ... (i)}$$

Let T_B = Braking torque.

We know that power absorbed,

$$35 \times 10^3 = \frac{2\pi \times N.T_B}{60} = \frac{2\pi \times 200 \times T_B}{60} = 21 T_B$$

$$\therefore \qquad T_B = 35 \times 10^3 / 21 = 1667 \text{ N-m} = 1667 \times 10^3 \text{ N-mm}$$

We also know that braking torque (T_B),

$$1667 \times 10^3 = (T_1 - T_2) \ r = (T_1 - T_2) \ 300$$

$$\therefore \qquad T_1 - T_2 = 1167 \times 10^3 / 300 = 5556 \text{ N} \qquad \qquad \text{...(ii)}$$

From equations (*i*) and (*ii*), we find that

$$T_1 = 8025 \text{ N}; \quad \text{and} \quad T_2 = 2469 \text{ N}$$

Now taking moments about O, we have

$$P \times 750 = T_2 \times {}^*OD = T_2 \times 62.5\sqrt{2} = 2469 \times 88.4 = 218\ 260$$

$$\therefore \qquad P = 218260 / 750 = 291 \text{ N } \textbf{Ans.}$$

2. Width of steel band

Let $\qquad w$ = Width of steel band in mm.

We know that maximum tension in the band (T_1),

$$8025 = \sigma.w.t = 50 \times w \times 2.5 = 125\ w$$

$$\therefore \qquad w = 8025 / 125 = 64.2 \text{ mm } \textbf{Ans.}$$

19.8. Differential Band Brake

In a differential band brake, as shown in Fig. 19.14, the ends of the band are joined at A and B to a lever AOC pivoted on a fixed pin or fulcrum O. It may be noted that for the band to tighten, the length OA must be greater than the length OB.

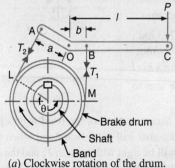 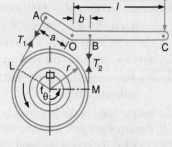

(a) Clockwise rotation of the drum.   (a) Anticlockwise rotation of the drum.

Fig. 19.14. Differential band brake.

The braking torque on the drum may be obtained in the similar way as discussed in simple band brake. Now considering the equilibrium of the lever AOC. It may be noted that when the drum rotates in the clockwise direction, as shown in Fig. 19.14 (a), the end of the band attached to A will be slack with tension T_2 and end of the band attached to B will be tight with tension T_1. On the other hand, when the drum rotates in the anticlockwise direction, as shown in Fig. 19.14 (b), the end of the band attached to A will be tight with tension T_1 and end of the band attached to B will be slack with tension T_2. Now taking moments about the fulcrum O, we have

$$P.l + T_1.b = T_2.a$$

... (For clockwise rotation of the drum)

or $\qquad P.l = T_2.a - T_1.b \qquad$ ... (i)

and $\qquad P.l + T_2.b = T_1.a$

... (For anticlockwise rotation of the drum)

or $\qquad P.l = T_1.a - T_2.b \qquad$ ... (ii)

Tractors are specially made to move on rough terrain and exert high power at low speeds.

Note : This picture is given as additional information.

---

* $\qquad OD$ = Perpendicular distance from O to the line of action of tension T_2.

$\qquad OE = EB = OB/2 = 125/2 = 62.5$ mm, and $\angle DOE = 45°$

$\therefore \qquad OD = OE \sec 45° = 62.5\sqrt{2}$ mm

We have discussed in block brakes (Art. 19.4), that when the frictional force helps to apply the brake, it is said to be self energizing brake. In case of differential band brake, we see from equations (*i*) and (*ii*) that the moment $T_1.b$ and $T_2.b$ helps in applying the brake (because it adds to the moment $P.l$) for the clockwise and anticlockwise rotation of the drum respectively.

We have also discussed that when the force P is negative or zero, then brake is self locking. Thus for differential band brake and for clockwise rotation of the drum, the condition for self locking is

$$T_2.a \leq T_1.b \qquad \text{or} \qquad T_2/T_1 \leq b/a$$

and for anticlockwise rotation of the drum, the condition for self locking is

$$T_1.a \leq T_2.b \qquad \text{or} \qquad T_1/T_2 \leq b/a$$

Notes : 1. The condition for self locking may also be written as follows :
For clockwise rotation of the drum,

$$T_1.b \geq T_2.a \qquad \text{or} \qquad T_1/T_2 \geq a/b$$

and for anticlockwise rotation of the drum,

$$T_2.b \geq T_1.a \qquad \text{or} \qquad T_2/T_1 \geq a/b$$

2. When in Fig. 19.14 (*a*) and (*b*), the length *OB* is greater than *OA*, then the force *P* must act in the upward direction in order to apply the brake. The tensions in the band, *i.e.* T_1 and T_2 will remain unchanged.

Example 19.9. *In a winch, the rope supports a load W and is wound round a barrel 450 mm diameter. A differential band brake acts on a drum 800 mm diameter which is keyed to the same shaft as the barrel. The two ends of the bands are attached to pins on opposite sides of the fulcrum of the brake lever and at distances of 25 mm and 100 mm from the fulcrum. The angle of lap of the brake band is 250° and the coefficient of friction is 0.25. What is the maximum load W which can be supported by the brake when a force of 750 N is applied to the lever at a distance of 3000 mm from the fulcrum ?*

Solution. Given : $D = 450$ mm or $R = 225$ mm ; $d = 800$ mm or $r = 400$ mm ; $OB = 25$ mm ; $OA = 100$ mm ; $\theta = 250° = 250 \times \pi/180 = 4.364$ rad ; $\mu = 0.25$; $P = 750$ N ; $l = OC = 3000$ mm

Since *OA* is greater than *OB*, therefore the operating force ($P = 750$ N) will act downwards.

First of all, let us consider that the drum rotates in clockwise direction.

We know that when the drum rotates in clockwise direction, the end of band attached to *A* will be slack with tension T_2 and the end of the band attached to *B* will be tight with tension T_1, as shown in Fig. 19.15. Now let us find out the values of tensions T_1 and T_2. We know that

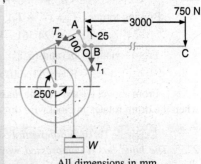

All dimensions in mm.
Fig. 19.15

$$2.3 \log\left(\frac{T_1}{T_2}\right) = \mu.\theta = 0.25 \times 4.364 = 1.091$$

$$\therefore \quad \log\left(\frac{T_1}{T_2}\right) = \frac{1.091}{2.3} = 0.4743 \text{ or } \frac{T_1}{T_2} = 2.98 \qquad \text{... (Taking antilog of 0.4743)}$$

and $\qquad\qquad T_1 = 2.98\, T_2 \qquad\qquad$ ... (*i*)

Now taking moments about the fulcrum *O*,

$$750 \times 3000 + T_1 \times 25 = T_2 \times 100$$

or $T_2 \times 100 - 2.98\, T_2 \times 25 = 2250 \times 10^3$ ... ($\because T_1 = 2.98\, T_2$)

$\qquad\qquad 25.5\, T_2 = 2250 \times 10^3$ or $T_2 = 2250 \times 10^3/25.5 = 88 \times 10^3$ N

and $\qquad\qquad T_1 = 2.98 T_2 = 2.98 \times 88 \times 10^3 = 262 \times 10^3$ N

We know that braking torque,

$$T_B = (T_1 - T_2)\, r$$
$$= (262 \times 10^3 - 88 \times 10^3)\,400 = 69.6 \times 10^6 \text{ N-mm} \qquad\qquad ...(i)$$

and the torque due to load W newtons,

$$T_W = W.R = W \times 225 = 225\,W \text{ N-mm} \qquad\qquad ... (ii)$$

Since the braking torque must be equal to the torque due to load W newtons, therefore from equations (i) and (ii),

$$W = 69.6 \times 10^6/225 = 309 \times 10^3 \text{ N} = 309 \text{ kN}$$

Now let us consider that the drum rotates in anticlockwise direction. We know that when the drum rotates in anticlockwise direction, the end of the band attached to A will be tight with tension T_1 and end of the band attached to B will be slack with tension T_2, as shown in Fig. 19.16. The ratio of tensions T_1 and T_2 will be same as calculated above, *i.e.*

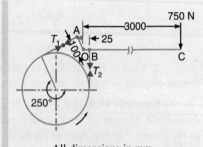

All dimensions in mm.
Fig. 19.16

$$\frac{T_1}{T_2} = 2.98 \text{ or } T_1 = 2.98\, T_2$$

Now taking moments about the fulcrum O,

$$750 \times 3000 + T_2 \times 25 = T_1 \times 100$$

or $2.98\, T_2 \times 100 - T_2 \times 25 = 2250 \times 10^3$ ... ($\because T_1 = 2.98\, T_2$)

$\qquad\qquad 273\, T_2 = 2250 \times 10^3$ or $T_2 = 2250 \times 10^3/273 = 8242$ N

and $\qquad\qquad T_1 = 2.98\, T_2 = 2.98 \times 8242 = 24\,561$ N

$\therefore$ Braking torque, $T_B = (T_1 \times T_2)\, r$
$$= (24\,561 - 8242)400 = 6.53 \times 10^6 \text{ N-mm} \qquad\qquad ...(iii)$$

From equations (ii) and (iii),

$$W = 6.53 \times 10^6/225 = 29 \times 10^3 \text{ N} = 29 \text{ kN}$$

From above, we see that the maximum load (W) that can be supported by the brake is 309 kN, when the drum rotates in clockwise direction. **Ans.**

Example 19.10. *A differential band brake, as shown in Fig. 19.17, has an angle of contact of 225°. The band has a compressed woven lining and bears against a cast iron drum of 350 mm diameter. The brake is to sustain a torque of 350 N-m and the coefficient of friction between the band and the drum is 0.3. Find : 1. The necessary force (P) for the clockwise and anticlockwise rotation of the drum; and 2. The value of 'OA' for the brake to be self locking, when the drum rotates clockwise.*

Solution. Given: $\theta = 225° = 225 \times \pi/180 = 3.93$ rad ; $d = 350$ mm   or $r = 175$ mm ; $T = 350$ N-m $= 350 \times 10^3$ N-mm ; $M = 0.3$

1. Necessary force (P) for the clockwise and anticlockwise rotation of the drum

When the drum rotates in the clockwise direction, the end of the band attached to A will be slack with tension T_2 and the end of the band attached to B will be tight with tension T_1, as shown in Fig. 19.18. First of all, let us find the values of tensions T_1 and T_2.

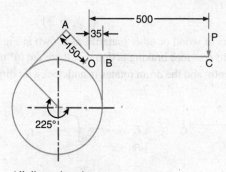

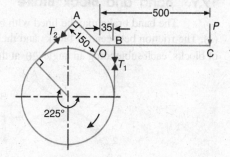

All dimensions in mm.

Fig. 19.17   **Fig. 19.18**

We know that

$$2.3 \log\left(\frac{T_1}{T_2}\right) = \mu.\theta = 0.3 \times 3.93 = 1.179$$

$$\therefore \quad \log\left(\frac{T_1}{T_2}\right) = \frac{1.179}{2.3} = 0.5126 \quad \text{or} \quad \frac{T_1}{T_2} = 3.255 \quad \text{... (Taking antilog of 0.5126) ... (i)}$$

and braking torque (T_B),

$$350 \times 10^3 = (T_1 - T_2)r = (T_1 - T_2)\,175$$

$$\therefore \qquad T_1 - T_2 = 350 \times 10^3/175 = 2000 \text{ N} \qquad \qquad \text{... (ii)}$$

From equations (*i*) and (*ii*), we find that

$$T_1 = 2887 \text{ N} \text{ ; and } T_2 = 887 \text{ N}$$

Now taking moments about the fulcrum O, we have

$$P \times 500 = T_2 \times 150 - T_1 \times 35 = 887 \times 150 - 2887 \times 35 = 32 \times 10^3$$

$$\therefore \qquad P = 32 \times 10^3/500 = 64 \text{ N } \textbf{Ans.}$$

When the drum rotates in the anticlockwise direction, the end of the band attached to A will be tight with tension T_1 and end of the band attached to B will be slack with tension T_2, as shown in Fig. 19.19. Taking moments about the fulcrum O, we have

$$P \times 500 = T_1 \times 150 - T_2 \times 35$$

$$= 2887 \times 150 - 887 \times 35$$

$$= 402 \times 10^3$$

$$P = 402 \times 10^3/500 = 804 \text{ N } \textbf{Ans.}$$

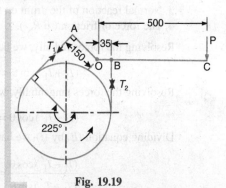

Fig. 19.19

2. Value of 'OA' for the brake to be self locking, when the drum rotates clockwise

The clockwise rotation of the drum is shown in Fig 19.18.

For clockwise rotation of the drum, we know that

$$P \times 500 = T_2 \times OA - T_1 \times OB$$

For the brake to be self locking, P must be equal to zero. Therefore

$$T_2 \times OA = T_1 \times OB$$

and

$$OA = \frac{T_1 \times OB}{T_2} = \frac{2887 \times 35}{887} = 114 \text{ mm } \textbf{Ans.}$$

19.9. Band and Block Brake

The band brake may be lined with blocks of wood or other material, as shown in Fig. 19.20 (*a*). The friction between the blocks and the drum provides braking action. Let there are '*n*' number of blocks, each subtending an angle 2θ at the centre and the drum rotates in anticlockwise direction.

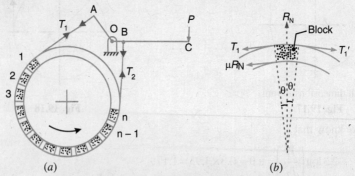

(*a*)   (*b*)

Fig. 19.20. Band and block brake.

Let T_1 = Tension in the tight side,

T_2 = Tension in the slack side,

μ = Coefficient of friction between the blocks and drum,

T_1' = Tension in the band between the first and second block,

T_2', T_3' etc.= Tensions in the band between the second and third block,

between the third and fourth block etc.

Consider one of the blocks (say first block) as shown in Fig. 19.20 (*b*). This is in equilibrium under the action of the following forces :

1. Tension in the tight side (T_1),

2. Tension in the slack side (T_1') or tension in the band between the first and second block,

3. Normal reaction of the drum on the block (R_N), and

4. The force of friction ($\mu.R_N$).

Resolving the forces radially, we have

$$(T_1 + T_1')\sin\theta = R_N \qquad \qquad \text{... (i)}$$

Resolving the forces tangentially, we have

$$(T_1 - T_1')\cos\theta = \mu.R_N \qquad \qquad \text{... (ii)}$$

Dividing equation (*ii*) by (*i*), we have

$$\frac{(T_1 - T_1')\cos\theta}{(T_1 + T_1')\sin\theta} = \frac{\mu.R_N}{R_N}$$

or

$$(T_1 - T_1') = \mu\tan\theta(T_1 + T_1')$$

∴

$$\frac{T_1}{T_1'} = \frac{1 + \mu\tan\theta}{1 - \mu\tan\theta}$$

Similarly, it can be proved for each of the blocks that

$$\frac{T_1'}{T_2'} = \frac{T_2'}{T_3'} = \frac{T_3'}{T_4'} = \dots \dots \frac{T_{n-1}}{T_2} = \frac{1 + \mu\tan\theta}{1 - \mu\tan\theta}$$

$$\therefore \quad \frac{T_1}{T_2} = \frac{T_1}{T_1'} \times \frac{T_1'}{T_2'} \times \frac{T_2'}{T_3'} \times \dots\dots\dots \times \frac{T_{n-1}}{T_2} = \left(\frac{1+\mu\tan\theta}{1-\mu\tan\theta}\right)^n \qquad \dots (iii)$$

Braking torque on the drum of effective radius r_e,

$$T_B = (T_1 - T_2)\, r_e$$
$$= (T_1 - T_2)\, r \qquad\qquad \dots \text{[Neglecting thickness of band]}$$

Note : For the first block, the tension in the tight side is T_1 and in the slack side is T_1' and for the second block, the tension in the tight side is T_1' and in the slack side is T_2'. Similarly for the third block, the tension in the tight side is T_2' and in the slack side is T_3' and so on. For the last block, the tension in the tight side is T_{n-1} and in the slack side is T_2.

Example 19.11. *In the band and block brake shown in Fig. 19.21, the band is lined with 12 blocks each of which subtends an angle of 15° at the centre of the rotating drum. The thickness of the blocks is 75 mm and the diameter of the drum is 850 mm. If, when the brake is in action, the greatest and least tensions in the brake strap are T_1 and T_2, show that*

$$\frac{T_1}{T_2} = \left(\frac{1+\mu\tan 7.5°}{1-\mu\tan 7.5°}\right)^{12}, \text{ where } \mu \text{ is the}$$

coefficient of friction for the blocks.

With the lever arrangement as shown in Fig.19.21, find the least force required at C for the blocks to absorb 225 kW at 240 r.p.m. The coefficient of friction between the band and blocks is 0.4.

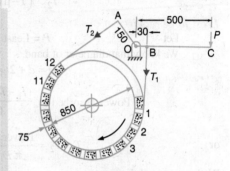

All dimensions in mm.

Fig. 19.21

Solution. Given : $n = 12$; $2\theta = 15°$ or $\theta = 7.5°$; $t = 75$ mm $= 0.075$ m ; $d = 850$ mm $= 0.85$ m ; Power $= 225$ kW $= 225 \times 10^3$ W ; $N = 240$ r.p.m.; $\mu = 0.4$

Since $OA > OB$, therefore the force at C must act downward. Also, the drum rotates clockwise, therefore the end of the band attached to A will be slack with tension T_2 (least tension) and the end of the band attached to B will be tight with tension T_1 (greatest tension).

Consider one of the blocks (say first block) as shown in Fig. 19.22. This is in equilibrium under the action of the following four forces :

1. Tension in the tight side (T_1),
2. Tension in the slack side (T_1') or the tension in the band between the first and second block,
3. Normal reaction of the drum on the block (R_N), and
4. The force of friction $(\mu.R_N)$.

Resolving the forces radially, we have

$$(T_1 + T_1')\sin 7.5° = R_N \qquad \dots (i)$$

Resolving the forces tangentially, we have

$$(T_1 - T_1')\cos 7.5° = \mu.R_N \qquad \dots (ii)$$

Dividing equation (ii) by (i), we have

$$\frac{(T_1 - T_1')\cos 7.5°}{(T_1 + T_1')\sin 7.5°} = \mu \quad \text{ or } \quad \frac{T_1 - T_1'}{T_1 + T_1'} = \mu\tan 7.5°$$

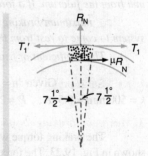

Fig. 19.22

$$\therefore \qquad T_1 - T_1' = T_1.\mu \tan 7.5° + T_1'.\mu \tan 7.5°$$

or $\qquad T_1(1 - \mu \tan 7.5°) = T_1'(1 + \mu \tan 7.5°)$

$$\therefore \qquad \frac{T_1}{T_1'} = \left(\frac{1 + \mu \tan 7.5°}{1 - \mu \tan 7.5°}\right)$$

Similarly, for the other blocks, the ratio of tensions $\dfrac{T_1'}{T_2'} = \dfrac{T_2'}{T_3'}$ etc. remains constant.

Therefore for 12 blocks having greatest tension T_1 and least tension T_2 is

$$\frac{T_1}{T_2} = \left(\frac{1 + \mu \tan 7.5°}{1 - \mu \tan 7.5°}\right)^{12}$$

Least force required at C

Let $\qquad\qquad\qquad P = $ Least force required at C.

We know that diameter of band,

$$D = d + 2t = 0.85 + 2 \times 0.075 = 1 \text{ m}$$

$\therefore \qquad$ Power absorbed $= \dfrac{(T_1 - T_2)\pi D.N}{60}$

or $\qquad T_1 - T_2 = \dfrac{\text{Power} \times 60}{\pi\, DN} = \dfrac{225 \times 10^3 \times 60}{\pi \times 1 \times 240} = 17\,900 \text{ N}$ ... (iii)

We have proved that

$$\frac{T_1}{T_2} = \left(\frac{1 + \mu \tan 7.5°}{1 - \mu \tan 7.5°}\right)^{12} = \left(\frac{1 + 0.4 \times 0.1317}{1 - 0.4 \times 0.1317}\right)^{12} = \left(\frac{1.0527}{0.9473}\right)^{12} = 3.55$$

... (iv)

From equations (iii) and (iv), we find that

$$T_1 = 24\,920 \text{ N, and } T_2 = 7020 \text{ N}$$

Now taking moments about O, we have

$$P \times 500 = T_2 \times 150 - T_1 \times 30 = 7020 \times 150 - 24\,920 \times 30 = 305\,400$$

$\therefore \qquad\qquad P = 305\,400 \,/\, 500 = 610.8 \text{ N } \textbf{Ans.}$

Example 19.12. *A band and block brake, having 14 blocks each of which subtends an angle of 15° at the centre, is applied to a drum of 1 m effective diameter. The drum and flywheel mounted on the same shaft has a mass of 2000 kg and a combined radius of gyration of 500 mm. The two ends of the band are attached to pins on opposite sides of the brake lever at distances of 30 mm and 120 mm from the fulcrum. If a force of 200 N is applied at a distance of 750 mm from the fulcrum, find:*

1. maximum braking torque, 2. angular retardation of the drum, and 3. time taken by the system to come to rest from the rated speed of 360 r.p.m.

The coefficient of friction between blocks and drum may be taken as 0.25.

Solution. Given : $n = 14$; $2\theta = 15°$ or $\theta = 7.5°$; $d = 1$ m or $r = 0.5$ m ; $m = 2000$ kg ; $k = 500$ mm $= 0.5$ m ; $P = 200$ N ; $N = 360$ r.p.m. ; $l = 750$ mm ; $\mu = 0.25$

1. Maximum braking torque

The braking torque will be maximum when $OB > OA$ and the drum rotates anticlockwise as shown in Fig. 19.23. The force P must act upwards and the end of the band attached to A is tight under tension T_1 and the end of the band attached to B is slack under tension T_2.

Taking moments about O,

$$200 \times 750 + T_1 \times 30 = T_2 \times 120$$

$$12 T_2 - 3T_1 = 15\ 000 \qquad \ldots (i)$$

We know that
$$\frac{T_1}{T_2} = \left(\frac{1 + \mu \tan \theta}{1 - \mu \tan \theta} \right)^n$$

$$= \left(\frac{1 + 0.25 \tan 7.5°}{1 - 0.25 \tan 7.5°} \right)^{14}$$

$$= \left(\frac{1 + 0.25 \times 0.1317}{1 - 0.25 \times 0.1317} \right)^{14}$$

$$= (1.068)^{14} = 2.512 \ldots (ii)$$

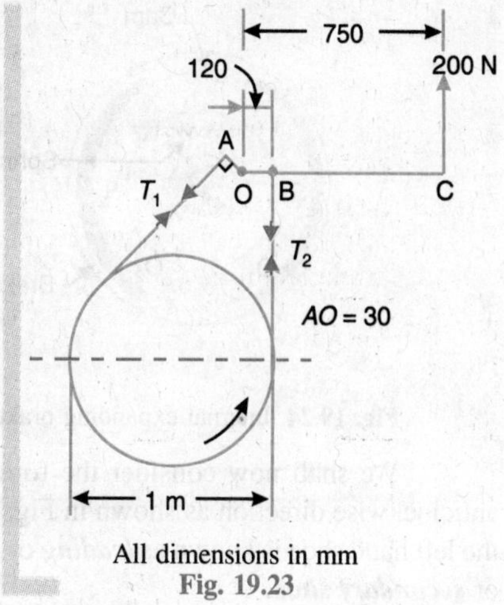

From equations (i) and (ii),

All dimensions in mm

Fig. 19.23

$$T_1 = 8440 \text{ N, and } T_2 = 3360 \text{ N}$$

We know that maximum braking torque,

$$T_B = (T_1 - T_2)\, r = (8440 - 3360)0.5 = 2540 \text{ N-m} \quad \textbf{Ans.}$$

2. Angular retardation of the drum

Let α = Angular retardation of the drum.

We know that braking torque (T_B),

$$2540 = I.\alpha = m.k^2.\alpha = 2000(0.5)^2 \alpha = 500\alpha$$

$$\therefore \qquad \alpha = 2540 / 500 = 5.08 \text{ rad/s}^2 \text{ \textbf{Ans.}}$$

3. Time taken by the system to come to rest

Let t = Required time.

Since the system is to come to rest from the rated speed of 360 r.p.m., therefore

Initial angular speed, $\omega_1 = 2\pi \times 360 / 60 = 37.7$ rad/s

and final angular speed, $\omega_2 = 0$

We know that
$$\omega_2 = \omega_1 - \alpha.t \qquad \ldots (- \text{ve sign due to retardation })$$

$$\therefore \qquad t = \omega_1 / \alpha = 37.7 / 5.08 = 7.42 \text{ s} \text{ \textbf{Ans.}}$$

19.10. Internal Expanding Brake

An internal expanding brake consists of two shoes S_1 and S_2 as shown in Fig. 19.24. The outer surface of the shoes are lined with some friction material (usually with Ferodo) to increase the coefficient of friction and to prevent wearing away of the metal. Each shoe is pivoted at one end about a fixed fulcrum O_1 and O_2 and made to contact a cam at the other end. When the cam rotates, the shoes are pushed outwards against the rim of the drum. The friction between the shoes and the drum produces the braking torque and hence reduces the speed of the drum. The shoes are normally held in off position by a spring as shown in Fig. 19.24. The drum encloses the entire mechanism to keep out dust and moisture. This type of brake is commonly used in motor cars and light trucks.

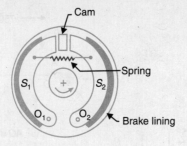

Fig. 19.24. Internal expanding brake.

Fig. 19.25. Forces on an internal expanding brake.

We shall now consider the forces acting on such a brake, when the drum rotates in the anticlockwise direction as shown in Fig. 19.25. It may be noted that for the anticlockwise direction, the left hand shoe is known as *leading* or *primary shoe* while the right hand shoe is known as *trailing* or *secondary shoe*.

Let r = Internal radius of the wheel rim,

   b = Width of the brake lining,

   p_1 = Maximum intensity of normal pressure,

   p_N = Normal pressure,

   F_1 = Force exerted by the cam on the leading shoe, and

   F_2 = Force exerted by the cam on the trailing shoe.

Consider a small element of the brake lining AC subtending an angle $\delta\theta$ at the centre. Let OA makes an angle θ with OO_1 as shown in Fig. 19.25. It is assumed that the pressure distribution on the shoe is nearly uniform, however the friction lining wears out more at the free end. Since the shoe turns about O_1, therefore the rate of wear of the shoe lining at A

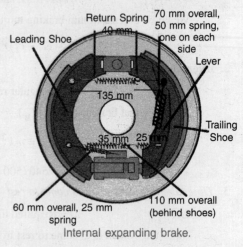

Internal expanding brake.

will be proportional to the radial displacement of that point. The rate of wear of the shoe lining varies directly as the perpendicular distance from O_1 to OA, *i.e.* O_1B. From the geometry of the figure,

$$O_1B = OO_1 \sin\theta$$

and normal pressure at A,

$$p_N \propto \sin\theta \quad \text{or} \quad p_N = p_1 \sin\theta$$

∴   Normal force acting on the element,

$$\delta R_N = \text{Normal pressure} \times \text{Area of the element}$$

$$= p_N(b.r.\delta\theta) = p_1 \sin\theta(b.r.\delta\theta)$$

and braking or friction force on the element,

$$\delta F = \mu \times \delta R_N = \mu.p_1 \sin\theta(b.r.\delta\theta)$$

∴   Braking torque due to the element about O,

$$\delta T_B = \delta F \times r = \mu.p_1 \sin\theta(b.r.\delta\theta)r = \mu.p_1 b\, r^2 (\sin\theta.\delta\theta)$$

and total braking torque about O for whole of one shoe,

$$T_B = \mu \, p_1 b \, r^2 \int_{\theta_1}^{\theta_2} \sin\theta \, d\theta = \mu \, p_1 b \, r^2 \left[-\cos\theta\right]_{\theta_1}^{\theta_2}$$

$$= \mu \, p_1 b r^2 (\cos\theta_1 - \cos\theta_2)$$

Moment of normal force δR_N of the element about the fulcrum O_1,

$$\delta M_N = \delta R_N \times O_1 B = \delta R_N (OO_1 \sin\theta)$$

$$= p_1 \sin\theta (b.r.\delta\theta)(OO_1 \sin\theta) = p_1 \sin^2\theta (b.r.\delta\theta) OO_1$$

∴ Total moment of normal forces about the fulcrum O_1,

$$M_N = \int_{\theta_1}^{\theta_2} p_1 \sin^2\theta (b.r.\delta\theta) OO_1 = p_1.b.r.OO_1 \int_{\theta_1}^{\theta_2} \sin^2\theta \, d\theta$$

Internal exparding brake.

$$= p_1.b.r.OO_1 \int_{\theta_1}^{\theta_2} \frac{1}{2}(1 - \cos 2\theta) d\theta \qquad \ldots \left[\because \sin^2\theta = \frac{1}{2}(1 - \cos 2\theta)\right]$$

$$= \frac{1}{2} p_1.b.r.OO_1 \left[\theta - \frac{\sin 2\theta}{2}\right]_{\theta_1}^{\theta_2}$$

$$= \frac{1}{2} p_1.b.r.OO_1 \left[\theta_2 - \frac{\sin 2\theta_2}{2} - \theta_1 + \frac{\sin 2\theta_1}{2}\right]$$

$$= \frac{1}{2} p_1.b.r.OO_1 \left[(\theta_2 - \theta_1) + \frac{1}{2}(\sin 2\theta_1 - \sin 2\theta_2)\right]$$

Moment of frictional force δF about the fulcrum O_1,

$$\delta M_F = \delta F \times AB = \delta F (r - OO_1 \cos\theta) \qquad \ldots (\because AB = r - OO_1 \cos\theta)$$

$$= \mu \, p_1 \sin\theta (b.r.\delta\theta)(r - OO_1 \cos\theta)$$

$$= \mu.p_1.b.r(r \sin\theta - OO_1 \sin\theta \cos\theta)\delta\theta$$

$$= \mu.p_1.b.r\left(r \sin\theta - \frac{OO_1}{2} \sin 2\theta\right)\delta\theta \qquad \ldots (\because 2\sin\theta\cos\theta = \sin 2\theta)$$

∴ Total moment of frictional force about the fulcrum O_1,

$$M_F = \mu \, p_1 b \, r \int_{\theta_1}^{\theta_2} \left(r \sin\theta - \frac{OO_1}{2} \sin 2\theta\right) d\theta$$

$$= \mu \, p_1 b \, r \left[-r \cos\theta + \frac{OO_1}{4} \cos 2\theta\right]_{\theta_1}^{\theta_2}$$

$$= \mu \, p_1 b \, r \left[-r \cos\theta_2 + \frac{OO_1}{4} \cos 2\theta_2 + r \cos\theta_1 - \frac{OO_1}{4} \cos 2\theta_1\right]$$

$$= \mu \, p_1 b \, r \left[r(\cos\theta_1 - \cos\theta_2) + \frac{OO_1}{4}(\cos 2\theta_2 - \cos 2\theta_1)\right]$$

Now for leading shoe, taking moments about the fulcrum O_1,
$$F_1 \times l = M_N - M_F$$
and for trailing shoe, taking moments about the fulcrum O_2,
$$F_2 \times l = M_N + M_F$$
Note : If $M_F > M_N$, then the brake becomes self locking.

Example 19.13. *The arrangement of an internal expanding friction brake, in which the brake shoe is pivoted at 'C' is shown in Fig. 19.26. The distance 'CO' is 75 mm, O being the centre of the drum. The internal radius of the brake drum is 100 mm. The friction lining extends over an arc AB, such that the angle AOC is 135° and angle BOC is 45°. The brake is applied by means of a force at Q, perpendicular to the line CQ, the distance CQ being 150 mm.*

The local rate of wear on the lining may be taken as proportional to the normal pressure on an element at an angle of 'θ' with OC and may be taken as equal to $p_1 \sin \theta$, where p_1 is the maximum intensity of normal pressure.

The coefficient of friction may be taken as 0.4 and the braking torque required is 21 N-m. Calculate the force Q required to operate the brake when 1. The drum rotates clockwise, and 2. The drum rotates anticlockwise.

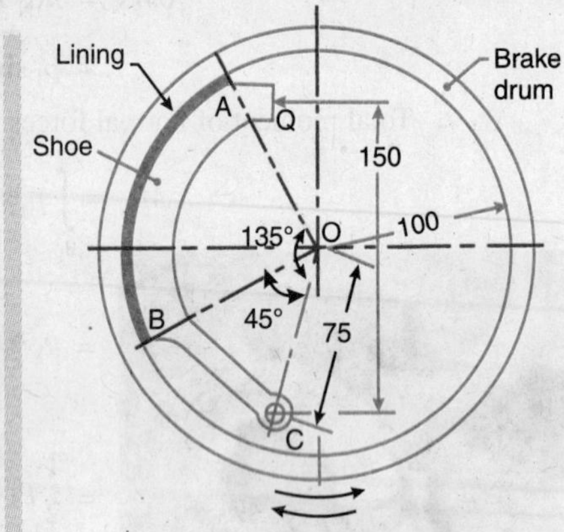

All dimensions in mm

Fig. 19.26

Solution. Given : $OC = 75$ mm ; $r = 100$ mm ;

$\theta_2 = 135° = 135 \times \pi / 180 = 2.356$ rad ; $\theta_1 = 45° = 45 \times \pi/180 = 0.786$ rad ; $l = 150$ mm ; $\mu = 0.4$; $T_B = 21$ N-m $= 21 \times 10^3$ N-mm

1. Force 'Q' required to operate the brake when drum rotates clockwise

We know that total braking torque due to shoe (T_B),

$$21 \times 10^3 = \mu.p_1.b.r^2 (\cos\theta_1 - \cos\theta_2)$$

$$= 0.4 \times p_1 \times b(100)^2 (\cos 45° - \cos 135°) = 5656 \, p_1 b$$

$\therefore \qquad p_1.b = 21 \times 10^3 / 5656 = 3.7$

Total moment of normal forces about the fulcrum C,

$$M_N = \frac{1}{2} p_1.b.r.OC \left[(\theta_2 - \theta_1) + \frac{1}{2}(\sin 2\theta_1 - \sin 2\theta_2) \right]$$

$$= \frac{1}{2} \times 3.7 \times 100 \times 75 \left[(2.356 - 0.786) + \frac{1}{2}(\sin 90° - \sin 270°) \right]$$

$$= 13\,875\,(1.57 + 1) = 35\,660 \text{ N-mm}$$

and total moment of friction force about the fulcrum C,

$$M_F = \mu.p_1 b.r \left[r(\cos\theta_1 - \cos\theta_2) + \frac{OC}{4}(\cos 2\theta_2 - \cos 2\theta_1) \right]$$

$$= 0.4 \times 3.7 \times 100 \left[100\,(\cos 45° - \cos 135°) + \frac{75}{4}(\cos 270° - \cos 90°) \right]$$

$$= 148 \times 141.4 = 20\,930 \text{ N-mm}$$

Taking moments about the fulcrum C, we have
$$Q \times 150 = M_N + M_F = 35\ 660 + 20\ 930 = 56\ 590$$
∴ $$Q = 56\ 590\ /\ 150 = 377\ N\ \textbf{Ans.}$$

2. Force 'Q' required to operate the brake when drum rotates anticlockwise

Taking moments about the fulcrum C, we have
$$Q \times 150 = M_N - M_F = 35\ 660 - 20\ 930 = 14\ 730$$
∴ $$Q = 14\ 730/150 = 98.2\ N\ \textbf{Ans.}$$

19.11. Braking of a Vehicle

In a four wheeled moving vehicle, the brakes may be applied to
1. the rear wheels only,
2. the front wheels only, and
3. all the four wheels.

In all the above mentioned three types of braking, it is required to determine the retardation of the vehicle when brakes are applied. Since the vehicle retards, therefore it is a problem of dynamics. But it may be reduced to an equivalent problem of statics by including the inertia force in the system of forces actually applied to the vehicle. The inertia force is equal and opposite to the braking force causing retardation.

Now, consider a vehicle moving up an inclined plane, as shown in Fig. 19.27.

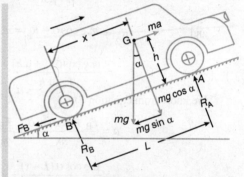

Fig. 19.27. Motion of vehicle up the inclined plane and brakes are applied to rear wheels only.

Let
α = Angle of inclination of the plane to the horizontal,

m = Mass of the vehicle in kg (such that its weight is $m.g$ newtons),

h = Height of the C.G. of the vehicle above the road surface in metres,

x = Perpendicular distance of C.G. from the rear axle in metres,

L = Distance between the centres of the rear and front wheels (also called wheel base) of the vehicle in metres,

R_A = Total normal reaction between the ground and the front wheels in newtons,

R_B = Total normal reaction between the ground and the rear wheels in newtons,

μ = Coefficient of friction between the tyres and road surface, and

a = Retardation of the vehicle in m/s^2.

We shall now consider the above mentioned three cases of braking, one by one. In all these cases, the braking force acts in the opposite direction to the direction of motion of the vehicle.

1. When the brakes are applied to the rear wheels only

It is a common way of braking the vehicle in which the braking force acts at the rear wheels only.

Let
F_B = Total braking force (in newtons) acting at the rear wheels due to the application of the brakes. Its maximum value is $\mu.R_B$.

The various forces acting on the vehicle are shown in Fig. 19.27. For the equilibrium of the vehicle, the forces acting on the vehicle must be in equilibrium.

Resolving the forces parallel to the plane,
$$F_B + m.g.\sin \alpha = m.a \qquad \qquad \dots (i)$$

Resolving the forces perpendicular to the plane,

$$R_A + R_B = m.g \cos \alpha \qquad \text{...(ii)}$$

Taking moments about G, the centre of gravity of the vehicle,

$$F_B \times h + R_B \times x = R_A (L - x) \qquad \text{...(iii)}$$

Substituting the value of $F_B = \mu.R_B$, and $R_A = m.g \cos \alpha - R_B$ [from equation (ii)] in the above expression, we have

$$\mu.R_B \times h + R_B \times x = (m.g \cos \alpha - R_B)(L - x)$$
$$R_B (L + \mu.h) = m.g \cos \alpha (L - x)$$

$$\therefore \qquad R_B = \frac{m.g \cos \alpha (L - x)}{L + \mu.h}$$

and

$$R_A = m.g \cos \alpha - R_B = m.g \cos \alpha - \frac{m.g \cos \alpha (L - x)}{L + \mu.h}$$

$$= \frac{m.g \cos \alpha (x + \mu.h)}{L + \mu.h}$$

We know from equation (i),

$$a = \frac{F_B + m.g \sin \alpha}{m} = \frac{F_B}{m} + g \sin \alpha = \frac{\mu.R_B}{m} + g \sin \alpha$$

$$= \frac{\mu.g \cos \alpha (L - x)}{L + \mu.h} + g \sin \alpha \qquad \text{... (Substituting the value of } R_B)$$

Notes : 1. When the vehicle moves on a level track, then $\alpha = 0$.

$$\therefore \qquad R_B = \frac{m.g(L - x)}{L + \mu.h} \ ; \ R_A = \frac{m.g(x + \mu.h)}{L + \mu.h} \quad \text{and} \quad a = \frac{\mu.g(L - x)}{L + \mu.h}$$

2. If the vehicle moves down the plane, then equation (i) becomes

$$F_B - m.g \sin \alpha = m.a$$

$$\therefore \qquad a = \frac{F_B}{m} - g.\sin \alpha = \frac{\mu.R_B}{m} - g.\sin \alpha = \frac{\mu.g \cos \alpha (L - x)}{L + \mu.h} - g \sin \alpha$$

2. *When the brakes are applied to front wheels only*

It is a very rare way of braking the vehicle, in which the braking force acts at the front wheels only.

Let F_A = Total braking force (in newtons) acting at the front wheels due to the application of brakes. Its maximum value is $\mu.R_A$.

The various forces acting on the vehicle are shown in Fig. 19.28.

Resolving the forces parallel to the plane,

$$F_A + m.g \sin \alpha = m.a \qquad \text{...(i)}$$

Resolving the forces perpendicular to the plane,

$$R_A + R_B = m.g \cos \alpha \qquad \text{...(ii)}$$

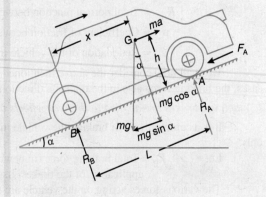

Fig. 19.28. Motion of the vehicle up the inclined plane and brakes are applied to front wheels only.

Taking moments about G, the centre of gravity of the vehicle,

$$F_A \times h + R_B \times x = R_A (L - x)$$

Substituting the value of $F_A = \mu.R_A$ and $R_B = m.g \cos \alpha - R_A$ [from equation (ii)] in the above expression, we have

$$\mu.R_A \times h + (m.g \cos \alpha - R_A) x = R_A (L - x)$$

$$\mu.R_A \times h + m.g \cos \alpha \times x = R_A \times L$$

$$\therefore \qquad R_A = \frac{m.g \cos \alpha \times x}{L - \mu.h}$$

and

$$R_B = m.g \cos \alpha - R_A = m.g \cos \alpha - \frac{m.g \cos \alpha \times x}{L - \mu.h}$$

$$= m.g \cos \alpha \left(1 - \frac{x}{L - \mu.h} \right) = m.g \cos \alpha \left(\frac{L - \mu.h - x}{L - \mu.h} \right)$$

We know from equation (i),

$$a = \frac{F_A + m.g \sin \alpha}{m} = \frac{\mu.R_A + m.g \sin \alpha}{m}$$

$$= \frac{\mu.m.g \cos \alpha \times x}{(L - \mu.h)m} + \frac{m.g \sin \alpha}{m} \qquad \dots \text{(Substituting the value of } R_A)$$

$$= \frac{\mu.g \cos \alpha \times x}{L - \mu.h} + g \sin \alpha$$

Notes : 1. When the vehicle moves on a level track, then $\alpha = 0$.

$$\therefore \qquad R_A = \frac{m.g \times x}{L - \mu.h} ; \quad R_B = \frac{m.g(L - \mu.h - x)}{L - \mu.h} ; \quad \text{and} \quad a = \frac{\mu.g \cdot x}{L - \mu.h}$$

2. When the vehicle moves down the plane, then equation (i) becomes

$$F_A - m.g \sin \alpha = m.a$$

$$\therefore \qquad a = \frac{F_A}{m} - g.\sin \alpha = \frac{\mu.R_A}{m} - g.\sin \alpha = \frac{\mu.g \cos \alpha \times x}{L - \mu.h} - g \sin \alpha$$

3. *When the brakes are applied to all the four wheels*

This is the most common way of braking the vehicle, in which the braking force acts on both the rear and front wheels.

Let F_A = Braking force provided by the front wheels = $\mu.R_A$, and

F_B = Braking force provided by the rear wheels = $\mu.R_B$.

A little consideration will show that when the brakes are applied to all the four wheels, the braking distance (i.e. the distance in which the vehicle is brought to rest after applying the brakes) will be the least. It is due to this reason that the brakes are applied to all the four wheels.

The various forces acting on the vehicle are shown in Fig. 19.29.

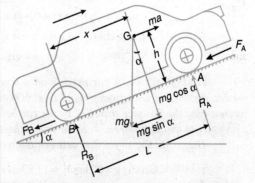

Fig. 19.29. Motion of the vehicle up the inclined plane and the brakes are applied to all the four wheels.

Resolving the forces parallel to the plane,

$$F_A + F_B + m.g \sin \alpha = m.a \qquad \qquad \dots (i)$$

Resolving the forces perpendicular to the plane,

$$R_A + R_B = m.g \cos \alpha \qquad \qquad \dots (ii)$$

Taking moments about G, the centre of gravity of the vehicle,

$$(F_A + F_B)h + R_B \times x = R_A(L - x) \qquad \qquad \dots (iii)$$

Substituting the value of $F_A = \mu.R_A$, $F_B = \mu.R_B$ and $R_B = m.g \cos \alpha - R_A$ [From equation (ii)] in the above expression,

$$\mu(R_A + R_B)h + (m.g \cos \alpha - R_A)x = R_A(L - x)$$

$$\mu(R_A + m.g \cos \alpha - R_A)h + (m.g \cos \alpha - R_A)x = R_A(L - x)$$

$$\mu.m.g \cos \alpha \times h + m.g \cos \alpha \times x = R_A \times L$$

$$\therefore \qquad R_A = \frac{m.g \cos \alpha(\mu.h + x)}{L}$$

and

$$R_B = m.g \cos \alpha - R_A = m.g \cos \alpha - \frac{mg \cos \alpha(\mu.h + x)}{L}$$

$$= m.g \cos \alpha \left[1 - \frac{\mu.h + x}{L} \right] = m.g \cos \alpha \left(\frac{L - \mu.h - x}{L} \right)$$

Now from equation (i),

$$\mu.R_A + \mu R_B + m.g \sin \alpha = m.a$$

$$\mu(R_A + R_B) + m.g \sin \alpha = m.a$$

$$\mu.m.g.\cos \alpha + m.g \sin \alpha = m.a \qquad \qquad \dots [\text{From equation (ii)}]$$

$$\therefore \qquad a = g(\mu.\cos \alpha + \sin \alpha)$$

Notes : 1. When the vehicle moves on a level track, then $\alpha = 0$.

$$\therefore \qquad R_A = \frac{m.g(\mu.h + x)}{L} ; \quad R_B = m.g \left(\frac{L - \mu.h - x}{L} \right); \text{ and } a = g.\mu$$

2. If the vehicle moves down the plane, then equation (i) may be written as

$$F_A + F_B - m.g \sin \alpha = m.a$$

or

$$\mu(R_A + R_B) - m.g \sin \alpha = m.a$$

$$\mu.m.g \cos \alpha - m.g \sin \alpha = m.a$$

and

$$a = g(\mu.\cos \alpha - \sin \alpha)$$

Example 19.14. *A car moving on a level road at a speed 50 km/h has a wheel base 2.8 metres, distance of C.G. from ground level 600 mm, and the distance of C.G. from rear wheels 1.2 metres. Find the distance travelled by the car before coming to rest when brakes are applied,*

1. to the rear wheels, 2. to the front wheels, and 3. to all the four wheels.

The coefficient of friction between the tyres and the road may be taken as 0.6.

Solution. Given : $u = 50$ km/h $= 13.89$ m/s ; $L = 2.8$ m ; $h = 600$ mm $= 0.6$ m ; $x = 1.2$ m ; $\mu = 0.6$

Let $s = $ Distance travelled by the car before coming to rest.

1. When brakes are applied to the rear wheels

Since the vehicle moves on a level road, therefore retardation of the car,

$$a = \frac{\mu.g(L - x)}{L + \mu.h} = \frac{0.6 \times 9.81(2.8 - 1.2)}{2.8 + 0.6 \times 0.6} = 2.98 \text{ m/s}^2$$

We know that for uniform retardation,

$$s = \frac{u^2}{2a} = \frac{(13.89)^2}{2 \times 2.98} = 32.4 \text{ m Ans.}$$

2. When brakes are applied to the front wheels

Since the vehicle moves on a level road, therefore retardation of the car,

$$a = \frac{\mu.g.x}{L - \mu.h} = \frac{0.6 \times 9.18 \times 1.2}{2.8 - 0.6 \times 0.6} = 2.9 \text{ m/s}^2$$

We know that for uniform retardation,

$$s = \frac{u^2}{2a} = \frac{(13.89)^2}{2 \times 2.9} = 33.26 \text{ m Ans.}$$

3. When the brakes are applied to all the four wheels

Since the vehicle moves on a level road, therefore retardation of the car,

$$a = g.\mu = 9.81 \times 0.6 = 5.886 \text{ m/s}^2$$

We know that for uniform retardation,

$$s = \frac{u^2}{2a} = \frac{(13.89)^2}{2 \times 5.886} = 16.4 \text{ m Ans.}$$

Example 19.15. *A vehicle moving on a rough plane inclined at 10° with the horizontal at a speed of 36 km/h has a wheel base 1.8 metres. The centre of gravity of the vehicle is 0.8 metre from the rear wheels and 0.9 metre above the inclined plane. Find the distance travelled by the vehicle before coming to rest and the time taken to do so when 1. The vehicle moves up the plane, and 2. The vehicle moves down the plane.*

The brakes are applied to all the four wheels and the coefficient of friction is 0.5.

Solution. Given : $\alpha = 10°$; $u = 36$ km/h $= 10$ m/s ; $L = 1.8$ m ; $x = 0.8$ m ; $h = 0.9$ m ; $\mu = 0.5$

Let $s =$ Distance travelled by the vehicle before coming to rest, and

$t =$ Time taken by the vehicle in coming to rest.

1. When the vehicle moves up the plane and brakes are applied to all the four wheels

Since the vehicle moves up the inclined plane, therefore retardation of the vehicle,

$$a = g (\mu \cos \alpha + \sin \alpha)$$

$$= 9.81 (0.5 \cos 10° + \sin 10°) = 9.81(0.5 \times 0.9848 + 0.1736) = 6.53 \text{ m/s}^2$$

We know that for uniform retardation,

$$s = \frac{u^2}{2a} = \frac{(10)^2}{2 \times 6.53} = 7.657 \text{ m Ans.}$$

and final velocity of the vehicle (v),

$$0 = u + a.t = 10 - 6.53 \ t \qquad \text{...(Minus sign due to retardation)}$$

∴ $t = 10 / 6.53 = 1.53$ s Ans.

2. When the vehicle moves down the plane and brakes are applied to all the four wheels

Since the vehicle moves down the inclined plane, therefore retardation of the vehicle,

$$a = g (\mu \cos \alpha - \sin \alpha)$$

$$= 9.81(0.5 \cos 10° - \sin 10°) = 9.81(0.5 \times 0.9848 - 0.1736) = 3.13 \text{ m/s}^2$$

We know that for uniform retardation,

$$s = \frac{u^2}{2a} = \frac{(10)^2}{2 \times 3.13} = 16 \text{ m Ans.}$$

and final velocity of the vehicle (v),

$$0 = u + a.t = 10 - 3.13\ t \qquad \text{... (Minus sign due to retardation)}$$

$$\therefore \qquad t = 10/3.13 = 3.2 \text{ s Ans.}$$

Example 19.16. *The wheel base of a car is 3 metres and its centre of gravity is 1.2 metres ahead the rear axle and 0.75 m above the ground level. The coefficient of friction between the wheels and the road is 0.5. Determine the maximum deceleration of the car when it moves on a level road, if the braking force on all the wheels is the same and no wheel slip occurs.*

Solution. Given : $L = 3$ m ; $x = 1.2$ m ; $h = 0.75$ m ; $\mu = 0.5$

Let $\quad a$ = Maximum deceleration of the car,

$\quad m$ = Mass of the car,

F_A and F_B = Braking forces at the front and rear wheels respectively, and

R_A and R_B = Normal reactions at the front and rear wheels respectively.

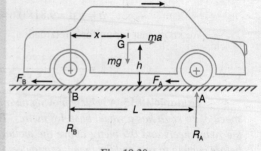

Fig. 19.30

The various forces acting on the car are shown in Fig. 19.30.

We shall consider the following two cases:

(a) When the slipping is imminent at the rear wheels

We know that when the brakes are applied to all the four wheels and the vehicle moves on a level road, then

$$R_B = m.g\left(\frac{L - \mu.h - x}{L}\right) = m \times 9.81\left(\frac{3 - 0.5 \times 0.75 - 1.2}{3}\right) = 4.66\ m \text{ N}$$

and $\qquad F_A + F_B = m.a \qquad$ or $\qquad 2\mu.\ R_B = m.a \qquad$ ... ($\because F_B = F_A$ and $F_B = \mu.R_B$)

$\therefore \qquad 2 \times 0.5 \times 4.66\ m = m.a \qquad$ or $\qquad a = 4.66 \text{ m/s}^2$

(b) When the slipping is imminent at the front wheels

We know that when the brakes are applied to all the four wheels and the vehicle moves on a level road, then

$$R_A = \frac{m.g(\mu.h + x)}{L} = \frac{m \times 9.81(0.5 \times 0.75 + 1.2)}{3} = 5.15\ m \text{ N}$$

and $\qquad F_A + F_B = m.a \qquad$ or $\qquad 2\mu.\ R_A = m.a \qquad$ ... ($\because F_A = F_B$ and $F_A = \mu.R_A$)

$\therefore \qquad 2 \times 0.5 \times 5.15\ m = m.a \qquad$ or $\qquad a = 5.15 \text{ m/s}^2$

Hence the maximum possible deceleration is 4.66 m/s^2 and slipping would occur first at the rear wheels. Ans.

19.12. Dynamometer

A dynamometer is a brake but in addition it has a device to measure the frictional resistance. Knowing the frictional resistance, we may obtain the torque transmitted and hence the power of the engine.

19.13. Types of Dynamometers

Following are the two types of dynamometers, used for measuring the brake power of an engine.

1. Absorption dynamometers, and **2.** Transmission dynamometers.

In the *absorption dynamometers*, the entire energy or power produced by the engine is absorbed by the friction resistances of the brake and is transformed into heat, during the process of measurement. But in the *transmission dynamometers*, the energy is not wasted in friction but is used for doing work. The energy or power produced by the engine is transmitted through the dynamometer to some other machines where the power developed is suitably measured.

Dynamometers measure the power of the engines.

19.14. Classification of Absorption Dynamometers

The following two types of absorption dynamometers are important from the subject point of view :

1. Prony brake dynamometer, and **2.** Rope brake dynamometer.

These dynamometers are discussed, in detail, in the following pages.

19.15. Prony Brake Dynamometer

A simplest form of an absorption type dynamometer is a prony brake dynamometer, as shown in Fig. 19.31. It consists of two wooden blocks placed around a pulley fixed to the shaft of an engine whose power is required to be measured. The blocks are clamped by means of two bolts and nuts, as shown in Fig. 19.31. A helical spring is provided between the nut and the upper block to adjust the pressure on the pulley to control its speed. The upper block has a long lever attached to it and carries a weight W at its outer end. A counter weight is placed at the other end of the lever which balances the brake when unloaded. Two stops S, S are provided to limit the motion of the lever.

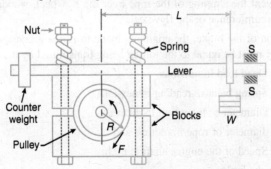

Fig. 19.31. Prony brake dynamometer.

When the brake is to be put in operation, the long end of the lever is loaded with suitable weights W and the nuts are tightened until the engine shaft runs at a constant speed and the lever is in horizontal position. Under these conditions, the moment due to the weight W must balance the moment of the frictional resistance between the blocks and the pulley.

Let W = Weight at the outer end of the lever in newtons,

        L = Horizontal distance of the weight W from the centre of the pulley in metres,

        F = Frictional resistance between the blocks and the pulley in newtons,

        R = Radius of the pulley in metres, and

        N = Speed of the shaft in r.p.m.

We know that the moment of the frictional resistance or torque on the shaft,

$$T = W.L = F.R \text{ N-m}$$

Work done in one revolution

$$= \text{Torque} \times \text{Angle turned in radians}$$

$$= T \times 2\pi \text{ N-m}$$

∴ Work done per minute

$$= T \times 2\pi N \text{ N-m}$$

We know that brake power of the engine,

Another dynamo

$$B.P. = \frac{\text{Work done per min.}}{60} = \frac{T \times 2\pi N}{60} = \frac{W.L \times 2\pi N}{60} \text{ watts}$$

Notes : 1. From the above expression, we see that while determining the brake power of engine with the help of a prony brake dynamometer, it is not necessary to know the radius of the pulley, the coefficient of friction between the wooden blocks and the pulley and the pressure exerted by tightening of the nuts.

2. When the driving torque on the shaft is not uniform, this dynamometer is subjected to severe oscillations.

19.16. Rope Brake Dynamometer

It is another form of absorption type dynamometer which is most commonly used for measuring the brake power of the engine. It consists of one, two or more ropes wound around the flywheel or rim of a pulley fixed rigidly to the shaft of an engine. The upper end of the ropes is attached to a spring balance while the lower end of the ropes is kept in position by applying a dead weight as shown in Fig. 19.32. In order to prevent the slipping of the rope over the flywheel, wooden blocks are placed at intervals around the circumference of the flywheel.

In the operation of the brake, the engine is made to run at a constant speed. The frictional torque, due to the rope, must be equal to the torque being transmitted by the engine.

Let W = Dead load in newtons,

        S = Spring balance reading in newtons,

        D = Diameter of the wheel in metres,

        d = diameter of rope in metres, and

        N = Speed of the engine shaft in r.p.m.

∴ Net load on the brake

$$= (W - S) \text{ N}$$

We know that distance moved in one revolution

$$= \pi(D + d) \text{ m}$$

∴ Work done per revolution

$$= (W - S)\pi(D + d) \text{ N-m}$$

and work done per minute

$$= (W - S)\pi(D + d) N \text{ N-m}$$

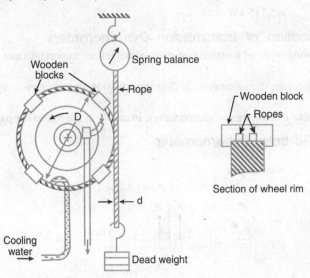

Wooden blocks

Spring balance

Rope

Wooden block

Ropes

D

Section of wheel rim

d

Cooling water

Dead weight

Fig. 19.32. Rope brake dynamometer.

∴ Brake power of the engine,

$$\text{B.P} = \frac{\text{Work done per min}}{60} = \frac{(W - S)\,\pi\,(D + d)N}{60} \text{ watts}$$

If the diameter of the rope (d) is neglected, then brake power of the engine,

$$\text{B.P.} = \frac{(W - S)\pi D\, N}{60} \text{ watts}$$

Note: Since the energy produced by the engine is absorbed by the frictional resistances of the brake and is transformed into heat, therefore it is necessary to keep the flywheel of the engine cool with soapy water. The flywheels have their rims made of a channel section so as to receive a stream of water which is being whirled round by the wheel. The water is kept continually flowing into the rim and is drained away by a sharp edged scoop on the other side, as shown in Fig. 19.32.

Example 19.17. *In a laboratory experiment, the following data were recorded with rope brake:*

Diameter of the flywheel 1.2 m; diameter of the rope 12.5 mm; speed of the engine 200 r.p.m.; dead load on the brake 600 N; spring balance reading 150 N. Calculate the brake power of the engine.

Solution. Given : $D = 1.2$ m ; $d = 12.5$ mm $= 0.0125$ m ; $N = 200$ r.p.m ; $W = 600$ N ; $S = 150$ N

An engine is being readied for testing on a dynamometer

We know that brake power of the engine,

$$\text{B.P.} = \frac{(W-S)\,\pi\,(D+d)N}{60} = \frac{(600-150)\,\pi\,(1.2+0.0125)200}{60} = 5715 \text{ W}$$

$$= 5.715 \text{ kW Ans.}$$

19.17. Classification of Transmission Dynamometers

The following types of transmission dynamometers are important from the subject point of view :

1. Epicyclic-train dynamometer, 2. Belt transmission dynamometer, and 3. Torsion dynamometer.

We shall now discuss these dynamometers, in detail, in the following pages.

19.18. Epicyclic-train Dynamometer

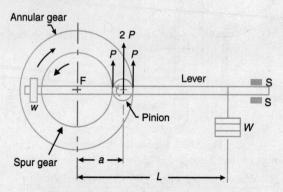

Fig. 19.33. Epicyclic train dynamometer.

An epicyclic-train dynamometer, as shown in Fig. 19.33, consists of a simple epicyclic train of gears, *i.e.* a spur gear, an annular gear (a gear having internal teeth) and a pinion. The spur gear is keyed to the engine shaft (*i.e.* driving shaft) and rotates in anticlockwise direction. The annular gear is also keyed to the driving shaft and rotates in clockwise direction. The pinion or the intermediate gear meshes with both the spur and annular gears. The pinion revolves freely on a lever which is pivoted to the common axis of the driving and driven shafts. A weight w is placed at the smaller end of the lever in order to keep it in position. A little consideration will show that if the friction of the pin on which the pinion rotates is neglected, then the tangential effort P exerted by the spur gear on the pinion and the tangential reaction of the annular gear on the pinion are equal.

Since these efforts act in the upward direction as shown, therefore total upward force on the lever acting through the axis of the pinion is $2P$. This force tends to rotate the lever about its fulcrum and it is balanced by a dead weight W at the end of the lever. The stops S, S are provided to control the movement of the lever.

For equilibrium of the lever, taking moments about the fulcrum F,

$$2P \times a = W.L \quad \text{or} \quad P = W.L/2a$$

Let $\qquad R$ = Pitch circle radius of the spur gear in metres, and

$\qquad N$ = Speed of the engine shaft in r.p.m.

$\therefore$ Torque transmitted, $T = P.R$

and power transmitted

$$= \frac{T \times 2\pi N}{60} = \frac{P.R \times 2\pi N}{60} \text{ watts}$$

19.19. Belt Transmission Dynamometer-Froude or Throneycroft Transmission Dynamometer

When the belt is transmitting power from one pulley to another, the tangential effort on the driven pulley is equal to the difference between the tensions in the tight and slack sides of the belt. A belt dynamometer is introduced to measure directly the difference between the tensions of the belt, while it is running.

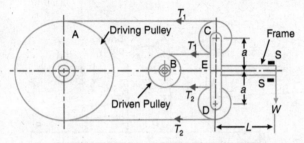

Fig. 19.34. Froude or Throneycroft transmission dynamometer.

A belt transmission dynamometer, as shown in Fig. 19.34, is called a Froude or Throneycroft transmission dynamometer. It consists of a pulley A (called driving pulley) which is rigidly fixed to the shaft of an engine whose power is required to be measured. There is another pulley B (called driven pulley) mounted on another shaft to which the power from pulley A is transmitted. The pulleys A and B are connected by means of a continuous belt passing round the two loose pulleys C and D which are mounted on a T-shaped frame. The frame is pivoted at E and its movement is controlled by two stops S,S. Since the tension in the tight side of the belt (T_1) is greater than the tension in the slack side of the belt (T_2), therefore the total force acting on the pulley C (*i.e.* $2T_1$) is greater than the total force acting on the pulley D (*i.e.* $2T_2$). It is thus obvious that the frame causes movement about E in the anticlockwise direction. In order to balance it, a weight W is applied at a distance L from E on the frame as shown in Fig. 19.34.

Now taking moments about the pivot E, neglecting friction,

$$2T_1 \times a = 2T_2 \times a + W.L \qquad \text{or} \qquad T_1 - T_2 = \frac{W.L}{2a}$$

Let

D = Diameter of the pulley A in metres, and

N = Speed of the engine shaft in r.p.m.

∴ Work done in one revolution = $(T_1 - T_2) \pi D$ N-m

and workdone per minute = $(T_1 - T_2) \pi DN$ N-m

∴ Brake power of the engine, B.P. = $\dfrac{(T_1 - T_2) \pi DN}{60}$ watts

Example 19.18. *The essential features of a transmission dynamometer are shown in Fig. 19.35. A is the driving pulley which runs at 600 r.p.m. B and C are jockey pulleys mounted on a horizontal beam pivoted at D, about which point the complete beam is balanced when at rest. E is the driven pulley and all portions of the belt between the pulleys are vertical. A, B and C are each 300 mm diameter and the thickness and weight of the belt are neglected. The length DF is 750 mm.*

Find : 1. the value of the weight W to maintain the beam in a horizontal position when 4.5 kW is being transmitted, and 2. the value of W, when the belt just begins to slip on pulley A. The coefficient of friction being 0.2 and maximum tension in the belt 1.5 kN.

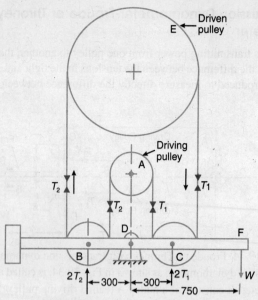

Fig. 19.35. All dimensions in mm.

Solution. Given : $N_A = 600$ r.p.m. : $D_A = D_B = D_C = 300$ mm $= 0.3$ m

1. Value of the weight W to maintain the beam in a horizontal position

Given : Power transmitted $(P) = 4.5$ kW $= 4500$ W

Let $T_1 =$ Tension in the tight side of the belt on pulley A, and

$T_2 =$ Tension in the slack side of the belt on pulley A.

∴ Force acting upwards on the pulley $C = 2T_1$

and force acting upwards on the pulley $B = 2T_2$

Now taking moments about the pivot D,

$$W \times 750 = 2T_1 \times 300 - 2T_2 \times 300 = 600 (T_1 - T_2)$$

∴ $T_1 - T_2 = W \times 750 / 600 = 1.25$ W N

We know that the power transmitted (P),

$$4500 = \frac{(T_1 - T_2) \pi D_A N_A}{60} = \frac{1.25 W \times \pi \times 0.3 \times 600}{60} = 11.78 W$$

∴ $W = 4500 / 11.78 = 382$ N **Ans.**

2. Value of W, when the belt just begins to slip on A

Given : $\mu = 0.2$; $T_1 = 1.5$ kN $= 1500$ N

We know that

$$2.3 \log\left(\frac{T_1}{T_2}\right) = \mu.\theta = 0.2 \times \pi = 0.6284 \qquad \ldots (\because \theta = 180° = \pi \text{ rad})$$

$$\log\left(\frac{T_1}{T_2}\right) = \frac{0.6284}{2.3} = 0.2732 \quad \text{or} \quad \frac{T_1}{T_2} = 1.876 \qquad \ldots \text{(Taking antilog of 0.2732)}$$

∴ $T_2 = T_1 / 1.876 = 1500 / 1.876 = 800$ N

Now taking moments about the pivot D,

$$W \times 750 = 2T_1 \times 300 - 2T_2 \times 300 = 2 \times 1500 \times 300 - 2 \times 800 \times 300$$

$$= 420 \times 10^3$$

∴ $W = 420 \times 10^3 / 750 = 560$ N **Ans.**

19.20. Torsion Dynamometer

A torsion dynamometer is used for measuring large powers particularly the power transmitted along the propeller shaft of a turbine or motor vessel. A little consideration will show that when the power is being transmitted, then the driving end of the shaft twists through a small angle relative to the driven end of the shaft. The amount of twist depends upon many factors such as torque acting on the shaft (T), length of the shaft (l), diameter of the shaft (D) and modulus of rigidity (C) of the material of the shaft. We know that the torsion equation is

$$\frac{T}{J} = \frac{C.\theta}{l}$$

where
$$\theta = \text{Angle of twist in radians, and}$$
$$J = \text{Polar moment of inertia of the shaft.}$$

For a solid shaft of diameter D, the polar moment of inertia

$$J = \frac{\pi}{32} \times D^4$$

and for a hollow shaft of external diameter D and internal diameter d, the polar moment of inertia,

$$J = \frac{\pi}{32}(D^4 - d^4)$$

From the above torsion equation,

$$T = \frac{C.J}{l} \times \theta = k.\theta$$

where $k = C.J/l$ is a constant for a particular shaft. Thus, the torque acting on the shaft is proportional to the angle of twist. This means that if the angle of twist is measured by some means, then the torque and hence the power transmitted may be determined.

We know that the power transmitted

$$P = \frac{T \times 2\pi N}{60} \text{ watts, where } N \text{ is the speed in r.p.m.}$$

A number of dynamometers are used to measure the angle of twist, one of which is discussed in Art. 19.21. Since the angle of twist is measured for a small length of the shaft, therefore some magnifying device must be introduced in the dynamometer for accurate measurement.

Example 19.19. *A torsion dynamometer is fitted to a propeller shaft of a marine engine. It is found that the shaft twists 2° in a length of 20 metres at 120 r.p.m. If the shaft is hollow with 400 mm external diameter and 300 mm internal diameter, find the power of the engine. Take modulus of rigidity for the shaft material as 80 GPa.*

Solution. Given : $\theta = 2° = 2 \times \pi /180 = 0.035$ rad ; $l = 20$ m ; $N = 120$ r.p.m. ; $D = 400$ mm $= 0.4$ m ; $d = 300$ mm $= 0.3$ m ; $C = 80$ GPa $= 80 \times 10^9$ N/m^2

We know that polar moment of inertia of the shaft,

$$J = \frac{\pi}{32}(D^4 - d^4) = \frac{\pi}{32}\left[(0.4)^4 - (0.3)^4\right] = 0.0017 \text{m}^4$$

and torque applied to the shaft,

$$T = \frac{C.J}{l} \times \theta = \frac{80 \times 10^9 \times 0.0017}{20} \times 0.035 = 238 \times 10^3 \text{ N-m}$$

We know that power of the engine,

$$P = \frac{T \times 2\pi N}{60} = \frac{238 \times 10^3 \times 2\pi \times 120}{60} = 2990 \times 10^3 \text{ W} = 2990 \text{ kW Ans.}$$

19.21. Bevis-Gibson Flash Light Torsion Dynamometer

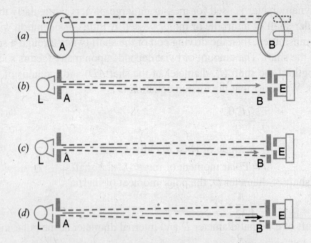

Fig. 19.36. Bevis-Gibson flash light torsion dynamometer.

It depends upon the fact that the light travels in a straight line through air of uniform density and the velocity of light is infinite. It consists of two discs A and B fixed on a shaft at a convenient distance apart, as shown in Fig. 19.36 (*a*). Each disc has a small radial slot and these two slots are in the same line when no power is transmitted and there is no torque on the shaft. A bright electric lamp L, behind the disc A, is fixed on the bearing of the shaft. This lamp is masked having a slot directly opposite to the slot of disc A. At every revolution of the shaft, a flash of light is projected through the slot in the disc A towards the disc B in a direction parallel to the shaft. An eye piece E is fitted behind the disc B on the shaft bearing and is capable of slight circumferential adjustment.

When the shaft does not transmit any torque (*i.e.* at rest), a flash of light may be seen after every revolution of the shaft, as the positions of the slit do not change relative to one another as shown in Fig. 19.36 (*b*). Now when the torque is transmitted, the shaft twists and the slot in the disc B changes its position, though the slots in L, A and E are still in line. Due to this, the light does not reach to the eye piece as shown in Fig. 19.36 (*c*). If the eye piece is now moved round by an amount equal to the lag of disc B, then the slot in the eye piece will be opposite to the slot in disc B as shown in Fig. 19.36 (*d*) and hence the eye piece receives flash of light. The eye piece is moved by operating a micrometer spindle and by means of scale and vernier, the angle of twist may be measured upto 1/100th of a degree.

The torsion meter discussed above gives the angle of twist of the shaft, when the uniform torque is transmitted during each revolution as in case of turbine shaft. But when the torque varies during each revolution as in reciprocating engines, it is necessary to measure the angle of twist at several different angular positions. For this, the discs A and B are perforated with slots arranged in the form of spiral as shown in Fig. 19.37. The lamp and the eye piece must be moved radially so as to bring them into line with each corresponding pair of slots in the discs.

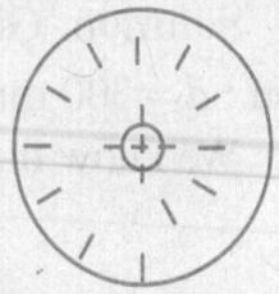

Fig. 19.37. Perforated disc.

EXERCISES

1. A single block brake, as shown in Fig. 19.38, has the drum diameter 250 mm. The angle of contact is 90° and the coefficient of friction between the drum and the lining is 0.35. If the operating force of 650 N is applied at the end of the lever, determine the torque that may be transmitted by the block brake. [Ans. 65.6 N-m]

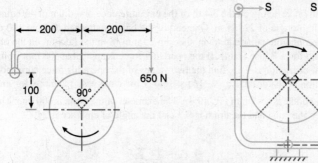

All dimensions in mm.

| Fig. 19.38 | Fig. 19.39 |

2. The layout and dimensions of a double shoe brake is shown in Fig. 19.39. The diameter of the brake drum is 300 mm and the contact angle for each shoe is 90°. If the coefficient of friction for the brake lining and the drum is 0.4, find the spring force necessary to transmit a torque of 30 N-m. Also determine the width of the brake shoes, if the bearing pressure on the lining material is not to exceed 0.28 N/mm². **[Ans. 98.4 N ; 5 mm]**

3. The arrangements of a transmission brake is shown in Fig. 19.40. The arms are pivoted at O_1 and O_2 and when force is applied at the end of a hand lever, the screw AB rotates. The left and right hand threads working in nuts on the ends of the arms move the arms together and thus apply the brake. The force on the hand lever is applied 400 mm from the axis of the screw.

   The drum is 240 mm in diameter and the angle subtended by each is 90°. The screw has six square threads with a mean diameter of 20 mm and a lead of 55 mm. Assuming a coefficient of friction for the braking surface as 0.3 and for the threads 0.15, determine the force on the hand lever required to set the brake when the torque on the drum is 245 N-m. **[Ans. 86.5 N]**

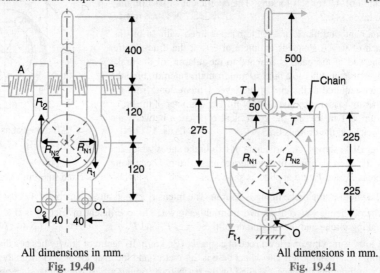

| All dimensions in mm. | All dimensions in mm. |
| Fig. 19.40 | Fig. 19.41 |

4. The layout and dimensions of the block brake are shown in Fig. 19.41. The diameter of the wheel is 300 mm and the contact angle for each block is 90°. If the coefficient of friction for the brake lining and wheel is 0.4 and the torque on the wheel is 30 N-m, find the force P on the operating arm required to set the brake for anticlockwise rotation of the wheel. **[Ans. 10 N]**

5. A simple band brake is operated by a lever of length 500 mm. The brake drum has a diameter of 500 mm and the brake band embraces 5/8 of the circumference. One end of the band is attached to the fulcrum of the lever while the other end is attached to a pin on the lever 100 mm from the fulcrum. If the effort applied to the end of the lever is 2 kN and the coefficient of friction is 0.25, find the maximum braking torque on the drum. **[Ans. 4.2 kN-m]**

6. A differential band brake acting on the 3/4 th of the circumference of a drum of 450 mm diameter, is to provide a braking torque of 225 N-m. One end of the band is attached to a pin 100 mm from the fulcrum of the lever and the other end to another pin 25 mm from the fulcrum on the other side of it where the operating force is also acting. If the operating force is applied at 500 mm from the fulcrum and the coefficient of friction is 0.25, find the two values of the operating force corresponding to two directions of rotation of the drum. **[Ans. 16.6 N for clockwise ; 266.6 N for anticlockwise]**

7. A differential band brake is shown in Fig. 19.42. The diameter of the drum is 800 mm. The coefficient of friction between the band and the drum is 0.3 and the angle of embrace is 240°.

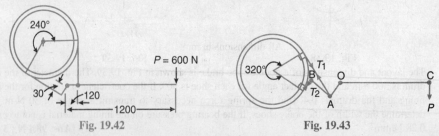

Fig. 19.42 Fig. 19.43

When a force of 600 N is applied at the free end of the lever, find for clockwise and anticlockwise rotation of the drum: 1. the maximum and minimum forces in the band ; and 2. the torque which can be applied by the brake. **[Ans. 176 kN, 50 kN, 50.4 kN-m ; 6.46 kN, 1.835 kN, 1.85 kN-m]**

8. A differential band brake is shown in Fig. 19.43. The diameter of the drum is 1 metre and rotates at 1200 r.p.m. in the anticlockwise direction. The angle of contact is 320°. The various lengths are : $OA = 30$ mm; $AB = 150$ mm and $OC = 700$ mm. Find the pull required at the end C of a lever to absorb 40 kW. Also find the length of AB for self locking. The coefficient of friction may be taken as 0.2. **[Ans. 25.7 N ; 91.8 mm]**

9. In a band and block brake, the band is lined with 14 blocks, each of which subtends an angle of 20° at the drum centre. One end of the band is attached to the fulcrum of the brake lever and the other to a pin 150 mm from the fulcrum. Find the force required at the end of the lever 1 metre long from the fulcrum to give a torque of 4 kN-m. The diameter of the brake drum is 1 metre and the coefficient of friction between the blocks and the drum is 0.25. **[Ans. 1712 N]**

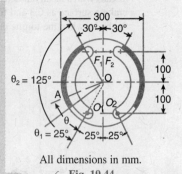

All dimensions in mm.

Fig. 19.44

10. Fig. 19.44 shows the particulars of two brake shoes which act on the internal surface of a cylindrical brake drum. The braking forces F_1 and F_2 are applied as shown, and each shoe pivots on its fixed fulcrum O_1 and O_2.

The width of the brake lining is 35 mm. The intensity of pressure at any point A is 0.4 sin θ N/mm^2, where θ is measured as shown from either pivot. The coefficient of friction is 0.4. Determine the braking torque and the magnitude of the forces F_1 and F_2. **[Ans. 373 N-m ; 685 N, 2323 N]**

11. A lorry is moving on a level road at a speed of 36 km/h. Its centre of gravity lies at a distance of 0.6 m from the ground level. The wheel base is 2.4 metres and the distance of C.G. from the rear wheels is 0.9 m. Find the distance travelled by the car before coming to rest when brakes are applied,
(a) to the rear wheels, (b) to the front wheels, and (c) to all the four wheels.
The coefficient of friction between the tyres and the road surface is 0.45.
[Ans. 21.55 m; 26.82 m; 11.36 m]

12. A torsion dynamometer is fitted on a turbine shaft to measure the angle of twist. It is observed that the shaft twists 1.5° in a length of 5 metres at 500 r.p.m. The shaft is solid and has a diameter of 200 mm. If the modulus of rigidity for the shaft material is 85 GPa, find the power transmitted by the turbine.
[Ans. 3662 kW]

DO YOU KNOW ?

1. Distinguish between brakes and dynamometers.
2. Discuss the various types of the brakes.
3. Show that, in a band and block brake, the ratio of the maximum and minimum tensions in the brake straps is

$$\frac{T_0}{T_n} = \left(\frac{1+\mu \cdot \tan \theta}{1-\mu \tan \theta}\right)^n$$

   where
   T_0 = Maximum tension,
   T_n = Minimum tension
   μ = Coefficient of friction between the blocks and drum, and
   2θ = Angle subtended by each block at the centre of the drum.

4. Describe with the help of a neat sketch the principles of operation of an internal expanding shoe. Derive the expression for the braking torque.
5. What are the leading and trailing shoes of an internal expanding shoe brake ?
6. What is the difference between absorption and transmission dynamometers ? What are torsion dynamometers ?
7. Describe the construction and operation of a prony brake or rope brake absorption dynamometer.
8. Describe with sketches one form of torsion dynamometer and explain with detail the calculations involved in finding the power transmitted.
9. Explain with neat sketches the Bevis-Gibson flash light dynamometer.

OBJECTIVE TYPE QUESTIONS

1. The brakes commonly used in railway trains is
   - (a) shoe brake
   - (b) band brake
   - (c) band and block brake
   - (d) internal expanding brake
2. The brake commonly used in motor cars is
   - (a) shoe brake
   - (b) band brake
   - (c) band and block brake
   - (d) internal expanding brake
3. In a differential band brake, as shown in Fig. 19.45, the length OA is greater than OB. In order to apply the brake, the force P at C should
   - (a) be zero
   - (b) act in upward direction
   - (c) act in downward direction

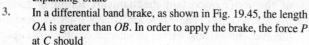

4. For the brake to be self locking, the force P at C as shown in Fig. 19.45, should
   - (a) be zero
   - (b) act in upward direction
   - (c) act in downward direction

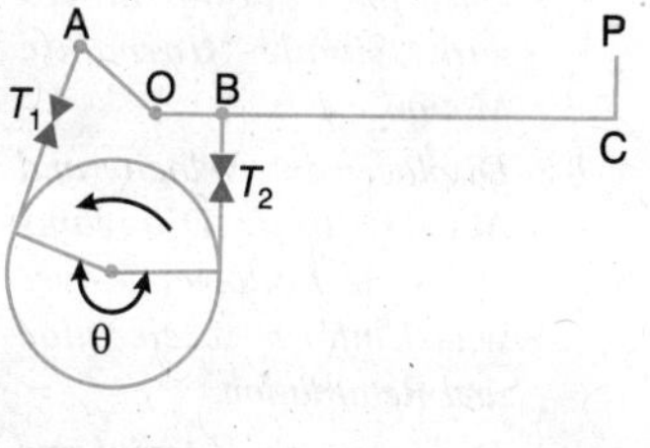

Fig. 19.45

5. When brakes are applied to all the four wheels of a moving car, the distance travelled by the car before it is brought to rest, will be
   - (a) maximum
   - (b) minimum
6. Which of the following is an absorption type dynamometer ?
   - (a) prony brake dynamometer
   - (b) rope brake dynamometer
   - (c) epicyclic-train dynamometer
   - (d) torsion dynamometer

ANSWERS

| 1. (a) | 2. (d) | 3. (c) | 4. (a) | 5. (b) | 6. (a), (b) |

20

Cams

20.1. Introduction

A *cam* is a rotating machine element which gives reciprocating or oscillating motion to another element known as *follower*. The cam and the follower have a line contact and constitute a higher pair. The cams are usually rotated at uniform speed by a shaft, but the follower motion is predetermined and will be according to the shape of the cam. The cam and follower is one of the simplest as well as one of the most important mechanisms found in modern machinery today. The cams are widely used for operating the inlet and exhaust valves of internal combustion engines, automatic attachment of machineries, paper cutting machines, spinning and weaving textile machineries, feed mechanism of automatic lathes etc.

20.2. Classification of Followers

The followers may be classified as discussed below :

1. *According to the surface in contact.* The followers, according to the surface in contact, are as follows :

(a) *Knife edge follower.* When the contacting end of the follower has a sharp knife edge, it is called a knife edge follower, as shown in Fig. 20.1 (a). The sliding motion takes place between the contacting surfaces (*i.e.* the knife edge and the cam surface). It is seldom used in practice because the small area of contacting surface results in excessive wear. In knife edge followers, a considerable side thrust exists between the follower and the guide.

774

(b) *Roller follower.* When the contacting end of the follower is a roller, it is called a roller follower, as shown in Fig. 20.1 (b). Since the rolling motion takes place between the contacting surfaces (*i.e.* the roller and the cam), therefore the rate of wear is greatly reduced. In roller followers also the side thrust exists between the follower and the guide. The roller followers are extensively used where more space is available such as in stationary gas and oil engines and aircraft engines.

(c) *Flat faced or mushroom follower.* When the contacting end of the follower is a perfectly flat face, it is called a flat-faced follower, as shown in Fig. 20.1 (c). It may be noted that the side thrust between the follower and the guide is much reduced in case of flat faced followers. The only side thrust is due to friction between the contact surfaces of the follower and the cam. The relative motion between these surfaces is largely of sliding nature but wear may be reduced by off-setting the axis of the follower, as shown in Fig. 20.1 (f) so that when the cam rotates, the follower also rotates about its own axis. The flat faced followers are generally used where space is limited such as in cams which operate the valves of automobile engines.

Note : When the flat faced follower is circular, it is then called a mushroom follower.

(d) *Spherical faced follower.* When the contacting end of the follower is of spherical shape, it is called a spherical faced follower, as shown in Fig. 20.1 (d). It may be noted that when a flat-faced follower is used in automobile engines, high surface stresses are produced. In order to minimise these stresses, the flat end of the follower is machined to a spherical shape.

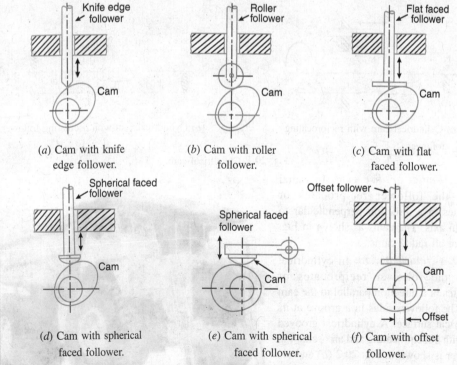

(a) Cam with knife edge follower.

(b) Cam with roller follower.

(c) Cam with flat faced follower.

(d) Cam with spherical faced follower.

(e) Cam with spherical faced follower.

(f) Cam with offset follower.

Fig. 20.1. Classification of followers.

2. *According to the motion of the follower.* The followers, according to its motion, are of the following two types:

(a) *Reciprocating or translating follower.* When the follower reciprocates in guides as the cam rotates uniformly, it is known as reciprocating or translating follower. The followers as shown in Fig. 20.1 (a) to (d) are all reciprocating or translating followers.

(b) *Oscillating or rotating follower.* When the uniform rotary motion of the cam is converted into predetermined oscillatory motion of the follower, it is called oscillating or rotating follower. The follower, as shown in Fig 20.1 (e), is an oscillating or rotating follower.

3. *According to the path of motion of the follower.* The followers, according to its path of motion, are of the following two types:

(a) *Radial follower.* When the motion of the follower is along an axis passing through the centre of the cam, it is known as radial follower. The followers, as shown in Fig. 20.1 (a) to (e), are all radial followers.

(b) *Off-set follower.* When the motion of the follower is along an axis away from the axis of the cam centre, it is called off-set follower. The follower, as shown in Fig. 20.1 (f), is an off-set follower.

Note : In all cases, the follower must be constrained to follow the cam. This may be done by springs, gravity or hydraulic means. In some types of cams, the follower may ride in a groove.

20.3. Classification of Cams

Though the cams may be classified in many ways, yet the following two types are important from the subject point of view :

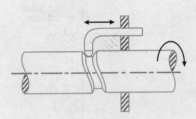

(a) Cylindrical cam with reciprocating follower.

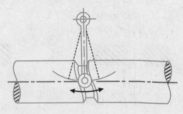

(b) Cylindrical cam with oscillating follower.

Fig. 20.2. Cylindrical cam.

1. *Radial or disc cam.* In radial cams, the follower reciprocates or oscillates in a direction perpendicular to the cam axis. The cams as shown in Fig. 20.1 are all radial cams.

2. *Cylindrical cam.* In cylindrical cams, the follower reciprocates or oscillates in a direction parallel to the cam axis. The follower rides in a groove at its cylindrical surface. A cylindrical grooved cam with a reciprocating and an oscillating follower is shown in Fig. 20.2 (a) and (b) respectively.

Note : In actual practice, radial cams are widely used. Therefore our discussion will be only confined to radial cams.

In IC engines, cams are widely used to operate valves.

20.4. Terms Used in Radial Cams

Fig. 20.3 shows a radial cam with reciprocating roller follower. The following terms are important in order to draw the cam profile.

1. *Base circle.* It is the smallest circle that can be drawn to the cam profile.

2. *Trace point.* It is a reference point on the follower and is used to generate the *pitch curve.* In case of knife edge follower, the knife edge represents the trace point and the pitch curve corresponds to the cam profile. In a roller follower, the centre of the roller represents the trace point.

3. *Pressure angle.* It is the angle between the direction of the follower motion and a normal to the pitch curve. This angle is very important in designing a cam profile. If the pressure angle is too large, a reciprocating follower will jam in its bearings.

4. *Pitch point.* It is a point on the pitch curve having the maximum pressure angle.

5. *Pitch circle.* It is a circle drawn from the centre of the cam through the pitch points.

6. *Pitch curve.* It is the curve generated by the trace point as the follower moves relative to the cam. For a knife edge follower, the pitch curve and the cam profile are same whereas for a roller follower, they are separated by the radius of the roller.

7. *Prime circle.* It is the smallest circle that can be drawn from the centre of the cam and tangent to the pitch curve. For a knife edge and a flat face follower, the prime circle and the base circle are identical. For a roller follower, the prime circle is larger than the base circle by the radius of the roller.

8. *Lift or stroke.* It is the maximum travel of the follower from its lowest position to the topmost position.

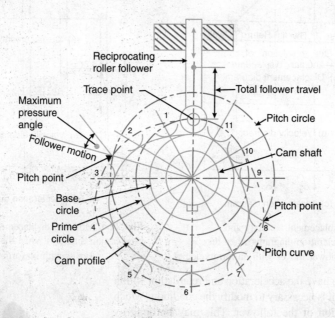

Fig. 20.3. Terms used in radial cams.

20.5. Motion of the Follower

The follower, during its travel, may have one of the following motions.

1. Uniform velocity, **2.** Simple harmonic motion, **3.** Uniform acceleration and retardation, and **4.** Cycloidal motion.

We shall now discuss the displacement, velocity and acceleration diagrams for the cam when the follower moves with the above mentioned motions.

20.6. Displacement, Velocity and Acceleration Diagrams when the Follower Moves with Uniform Velocity

The displacement, velocity and acceleration diagrams when a knife-edged follower moves with uniform velocity are shown in Fig. 20.4 (a), (b) and (c) respectively. The abscissa (base) represents the time (i.e. the number of seconds required for the cam to complete one revolution) or it may represent the angular displacement of the cam in degrees. The ordinate represents the displacement, or velocity or acceleration of the follower.

Since the follower moves with uniform velocity during its rise and return stroke, therefore the slope of the displacement curves must be constant. In other words, AB_1 and C_1D must be straight lines. A little consideration will show that the follower remains at rest during part of the cam rotation. The periods during which the follower remains at rest are known as *dwell periods*, as shown by lines B_1C_1 and DE in Fig. 20.4 (a). From Fig. 20.4 (c), we see that the acceleration or retardation of the follower at the beginning and at the end of each stroke is infinite. This is due to the fact that the follower is required to start from rest and has to gain a velocity within no time. This is only possible if the acceleration or retardation at the beginning and at the end of each stroke is infinite. These conditions are however, impracticable.

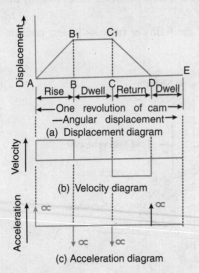

Fig. 20.4. Displacement, velocity and acceleration diagrams when the follower moves with uniform velocity.

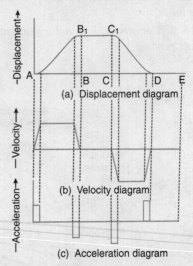

Fig. 20.5. Modified displacement, velocity and acceleration diagrams when the follower moves with uniform velocity.

In order to have the acceleration and retardation within the finite limits, it is necessary to modify the conditions which govern the motion of the follower. This may be done by rounding off the sharp corners of the displacement diagram at the beginning and at the end of each stroke, as shown in Fig. 20.5 (a). By doing so, the velocity of the follower increases gradually to its maximum value at the beginning of each stroke and decreases gradually to zero at the end of each stroke as shown in Fig. 20.5 (b). The modified

Camshaft of an IC engine.

displacement, velocity and acceleration diagrams are shown in Fig. 20.5. The round corners of the displacement diagram are usually parabolic curves because the parabolic motion results in a very low acceleration of the follower for a given stroke and cam speed.

20.7. Displacement, Velocity and Acceleration Diagrams when the Follower Moves with Simple Harmonic Motion

The displacement, velocity and acceleration diagrams when the follower moves with simple harmonic motion are shown in Fig. 20.6 (*a*), (*b*) and (*c*) respectively. The displacement diagram is drawn as follows :

1. Draw a semi-circle on the follower stroke as diameter.
2. Divide the semi-circle into any number of even equal parts (say eight).
3. Divide the angular displacements of the cam during out stroke and return stroke into the same number of equal parts.
4. The displacement diagram is obtained by projecting the points as shown in Fig. 20.6 (*a*).

The velocity and acceleration diagrams are shown in Fig. 20.6 (*b*) and (*c*) respectively. Since the follower moves with a simple harmonic motion, therefore velocity diagram consists of a sine curve and the acceleration diagram is a cosine curve. We see from Fig. 20.6 (*b*) that the velocity of the follower is zero at the beginning and at the end of its stroke and increases gradually to a maximum at mid-stroke. On the other hand, the acceleration of the follower is maximum at the beginning and at the ends of the stroke and diminishes to zero at mid-stroke.

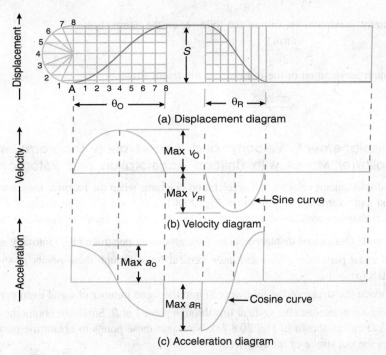

Fig. 20.6. Displacement, velocity and acceleration diagrams when the follower moves with simple harmonic motion.

Let S = Stroke of the follower,

θ_O and θ_R = Angular displacement of the cam during out stroke and return stroke of the follower respectively, in radians, and

ω = Angular velocity of the cam in rad/s.

∴ Time required for the out stroke of the follower in seconds,

$$t_O = \theta_O / \omega$$

Consider a point P moving at a uniform speed ω_P radians per sec round the circumference of a circle with the stroke S as diameter, as shown in Fig. 20.7. The point P' (which is the projection of a point P on the diameter) executes a simple harmonic motion as the point P rotates. The motion of the follower is similar to that of point P'.

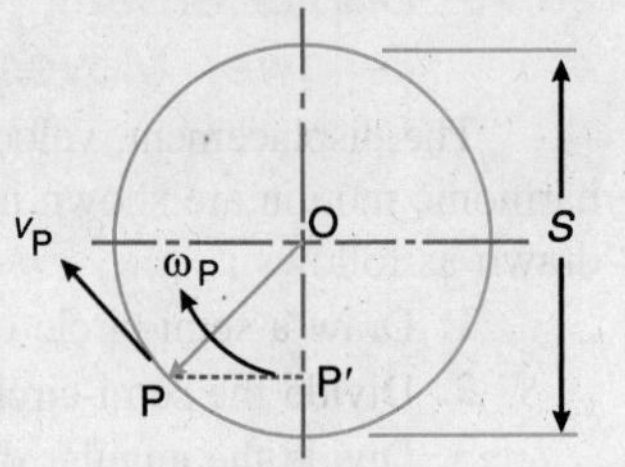

∴ Peripheral speed of the point P',

$$v_P = \frac{\pi S}{2} \times \frac{1}{t_O} = \frac{\pi S}{2} \times \frac{\omega}{\theta_O}$$

and maximum velocity of the follower on the outstroke,

$$v_O = v_P = \frac{\pi S}{2} \times \frac{\omega}{\theta_O} = \frac{\pi \omega S}{2\theta_O}$$

Fig. 20.7. Motion of a point.

We know that the centripetal acceleration of the point P,

$$a_P = \frac{(v_P)^2}{OP} = \left(\frac{\pi \omega S}{2\theta_O}\right)^2 \times \frac{2}{S} = \frac{\pi^2 \omega^2 . S}{2(\theta_O)^2}$$

∴ Maximum acceleration of the follower on the outstroke,

$$a_O = a_P = \frac{\pi^2 \omega^2 . S}{2(\theta_O)^2}$$

Similarly, maximum velocity of the follower on the return stroke,

$$v_R = \frac{\pi \omega . S}{2\theta_R}$$

and maximum acceleration of the follower on the return stroke,

$$a_R = \frac{\pi^2 \omega^2 . S}{2(\theta_R)^2}$$

20.8. Displacement, Velocity and Acceleration Diagrams when the Follower Moves with Uniform Acceleration and Retardation

The displacement, velocity and acceleration diagrams when the follower moves with uniform acceleration and retardation are shown in Fig. 20.8 (a), (b) and (c) respectively. We see that the displacement diagram consists of a parabolic curve and may be drawn as discussed below :

1. Divide the angular displacement of the cam during outstroke (θ_O) into any even number of equal parts (say eight) and draw vertical lines through these points as shown in Fig. 20.8 (a).

2. Divide the stroke of the follower (S) into the same number of equal even parts.

3. Join Aa to intersect the vertical line through point 1 at B. Similarly, obtain the other points C, D etc. as shown in Fig. 20.8 (a). Now join these points to obtain the parabolic curve for the out stroke of the follower.

4. In the similar way as discussed above, the displacement diagram for the follower during return stroke may be drawn.

Since the acceleration and retardation are uniform, therefore the velocity varies directly with the time. The velocity diagram is shown in Fig. 20.8 (b).

Let S = Stroke of the follower,

θ_O and θ_R = Angular displacement of the cam during out stroke and return stroke
of the follower respectively, and

ω = Angular velocity of the cam.

We know that time required for the follower during outstroke,

$$t_O = \theta_O / \omega$$

and time required for the follower during return stroke,

$$t_R = \theta_R / \omega$$

Mean velocity of the follower during outstroke

$$= S/t_O$$

and mean velocity of the follower during return stroke

$$= S/t_R$$

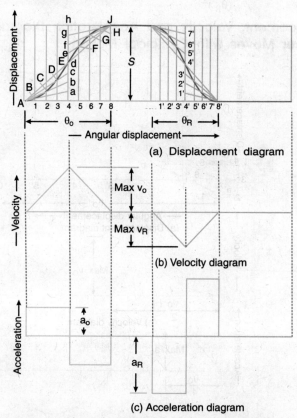

(a) Displacement diagram

(b) Velocity diagram

(c) Acceleration diagram

Fig. 20.8. Displacement, velocity and acceleration diagrams when the follower moves
with uniform acceleration and retardation.

Since the maximum velocity of follower is equal to twice the mean velocity, therefore maximum velocity of the follower during outstroke,

$$v_O = \frac{2S}{t_O} = \frac{2\omega S}{\theta_O}$$

Similarly, maximum velocity of the follower during return stroke,

$$v_R = \frac{2\omega S}{\theta_R}$$

We see from the acceleration diagram, as shown in Fig. 20.8 (c), that during first half of the outstroke there is uniform acceleration and during the second half of the out stroke there is uniform retardation. Thus, the maximum velocity of the follower is reached after the time $t_O/2$ (during out stroke) and $t_R/2$ (during return stroke).

∴ Maximum acceleration of the follower during outstroke,

$$a_O = \frac{v_O}{t_O/2} = \frac{2 \times 2\omega.S}{t_O.\theta_O} = \frac{4\omega^2.S}{(\theta_O)^2} \qquad \dots (\because \ t_O = \theta_O/\omega)$$

Similarly, maximum acceleration of the follower during return stroke,

$$a_R = \frac{4\omega^2.S}{(\theta_R)^2}$$

20.9. Displacement, Velocity and Acceleration Diagrams when the Follower Moves with Cycloidal Motion

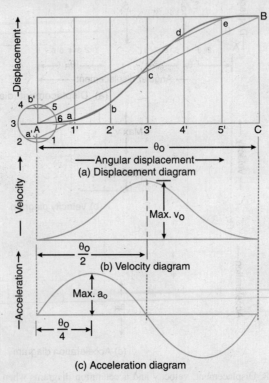

(a) Displacement diagram

(b) Velocity diagram

(c) Acceleration diagram

Fig. 20.9. Displacement, velocity and acceleration diagrams when the follower moves with cycloidal motion.

The displacement, velocity and acceleration diagrams when the follower moves with cycloidal motion are shown in Fig. 20.9 (a), (b) and (c) respectively. We know that cycloid is a curve traced by a point on a circle when the circle rolls without slipping on a straight line.

In case of cams, this straight line is a stroke of the follower which is translating and the circumference of the rolling circle is equal to the stroke (S) of the follower. Therefore the radius of the rolling circle is $S/2\pi$. The displacement diagram is drawn as discussed below :

1. Draw a circle of radius $S/2\pi$ with A as centre.

2. Divide the circle into any number of equal even parts (say six). Project these points horizontally on the vertical centre line of the circle. These points are shown by a' and b' in Fig. 20.9 (a).

3. Divide the angular displacement of the cam during outstroke into the same number of equal even parts as the circle is divided. Draw vertical lines through these points.

4. Join AB which intersects the vertical line through $3'$ at c.

   From a' draw a line parallel to AB intersecting the vertical lines through $1'$ and $2'$ at a and b respectively.

5. Similarly, from b' draw a line parallel to AB intersecting the vertical lines through $4'$ and $5'$ at d and e respectively.

Cams are used in Jet and aircraft engines. The above picture shows an aircraft engine.

6. Join the points $A\ a\ b\ c\ d\ e\ B$ by a smooth curve. This is the required cycloidal curve for the follower during outstroke.

Let $\qquad \theta$ = Angle through which the cam rotates in time t seconds, and

$\qquad \omega$ = Angular velocity of the cam.

We know that displacement of the follower after time t seconds,

$$x = S\left[\frac{\theta}{\theta_O} - \frac{1}{2\pi}\sin\left(\frac{2\pi\theta}{\theta_O}\right)\right] \qquad \ldots (i)$$

∴ Velocity of the follower after time t seconds,

$$\frac{dx}{dt} = S\left[\frac{1}{\theta_O} \times \frac{d\theta}{dt} - \frac{2\pi}{2\pi\theta_O}\cos\left(\frac{2\pi\theta}{\theta_O}\right)\frac{d\theta}{dt}\right]$$

$$\ldots \text{[Differentiating equation } (i)]$$

$$= \frac{S}{\theta_O} \times \frac{d\theta}{dt}\left[1 - \cos\left(\frac{2\pi\theta}{\theta_O}\right)\right] = \frac{\omega S}{\theta_O}\left[1 - \cos\left(\frac{2\pi\theta}{\theta_O}\right)\right] \qquad \ldots (ii)$$

The velocity is maximum, when

$$\cos\left(\frac{2\pi\theta}{\theta_O}\right) = -1 \quad \text{or} \quad \frac{2\pi\theta}{\theta_O} = \pi \quad \text{or} \quad \theta = \theta_O/2$$

Substituting $\theta = \theta_O/2$ in equation (ii), we have maximum velocity of the follower during outstroke,

$$v_O = \frac{\omega.S}{\theta_O}(1+1) = \frac{2\,\omega.S}{\theta_O}$$

Similarly, maximum velocity of the follower during return stroke,

$$v_R = \frac{2\,\omega.S}{\theta_R}$$

Now, acceleration of the follower after time t sec,

$$\frac{d^2x}{dt^2} = \frac{\omega.S}{\theta_O}\left[\frac{2\pi}{\theta_O}\sin\left(\frac{2\pi\theta}{\theta_O}\right)\frac{d\theta}{dt}\right] \qquad \ldots\text{[Differentiating equation (ii)]}$$

$$= \frac{2\pi\omega^2.S}{(\theta_O)^2}\sin\left(\frac{2\pi\theta}{\theta_O}\right) \qquad \ldots\left(\because \frac{d\theta}{dt} = \omega\right) \quad \ldots\text{(iii)}$$

The acceleration is maximum, when

$$\sin\left(\frac{2\pi\theta}{\theta_O}\right) = 1 \quad \text{or} \quad \frac{2\pi\theta}{\theta_O} = \frac{\pi}{2} \quad \text{or} \quad \theta = \theta_O/4$$

Substituting $\theta = \theta_O/4$ in equation (iii), we have maximum acceleration of the follower during outstroke,

$$a_O = \frac{2\pi\omega^2.S}{(\theta_O)^2}$$

Similarly, maximum acceleration of the follower during return stroke,

$$a_R = \frac{2\pi\omega^2.S}{(\theta_R)^2}$$

The velocity and acceleration diagrams are shown in Fig. 20.9 (b) and (c) respectively.

20.10. Construction of Cam Profile for a Radial Cam

In order to draw the cam profile for a radial cam, first of all the displacement diagram for the given motion of the follower is drawn. Then by constructing the follower in its proper position at each angular position, the profile of the working surface of the cam is drawn.

In constructing the cam profile, the principle of kinematic inversion is used, i.e. the cam is imagined to be stationary and the follower is allowed to rotate in the *opposite direction* to the *cam rotation.*

The construction of cam profiles for different types of follower with different types of motions are discussed in the following examples.

Example 20.1. *A cam is to give the following motion to a knife-edged follower :*

1. Outstroke during 60° of cam rotation ; 2. Dwell for the next 30° of cam rotation ; 3. Return stroke during next 60° of cam rotation, and 4. Dwell for the remaining 210° of cam rotation.

The stroke of the follower is 40 mm and the minimum radius of the cam is 50 mm. The follower moves with uniform velocity during both the outstroke and return strokes. Draw the profile of the cam when (a) the axis of the follower passes through the axis of the cam shaft, and (b) the axis of the follower is offset by 20 mm from the axis of the cam shaft.

Construction

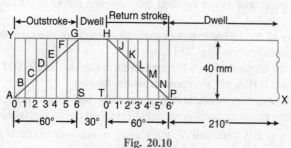

Fig. 20.10

First of all, the displacement diagram, as shown in Fig. 20.10, is drawn as discussed in the following steps :

1. Draw a horizontal line $AX = 360°$ to some suitable scale. On this line, mark $AS = 60°$ to represent outstroke of the follower, $ST = 30°$ to represent dwell, $TP = 60°$ to represent return stroke and $PX = 210°$ to represent dwell.

2. Draw vertical line AY equal to the stroke of the follower (*i.e.* 40 mm) and complete the rectangle as shown in Fig. 20.10.

3. Divide the angular displacement during outstroke and return stroke into any equal number of even parts (say six) and draw vertical lines through each point.

4. Since the follower moves with uniform velocity during outstroke and return stroke, therefore the displacement diagram consists of straight lines. Join AG and HP.

5. The complete displacement diagram is shown by $AGHPX$ in Fig. 20.10.

(*a*) *Profile of the cam when the axis of follower passes through the axis of cam shaft*

The profile of the cam when the axis of the follower passes through the axis of the cam shaft, as shown in Fig. 20.11, is drawn as discussed in the following steps :

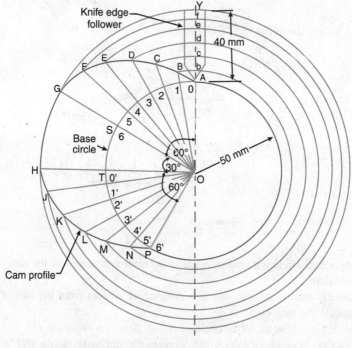

Fig. 20.11

1. Draw a base circle with radius equal to the minimum radius of the cam (*i.e.* 50 mm) with O as centre.
2. Since the axis of the follower passes through the axis of the cam shaft, therefore mark trace point A, as shown in Fig. 20.11.
3. From OA, mark angle AOS = 60° to represent outstroke, angle SOT = 30° to represent dwell and angle TOP = 60° to represent return stroke.
4. Divide the angular displacements during outstroke and return stroke (*i.e.* angle AOS and angle TOP) into the same number of equal even parts as in displacement diagram.
5. Join the points 1, 2, 3 ...etc. and $0', 1', 2', 3', ...$ etc. with centre O and produce beyond the base circle as shown in Fig. 20.11.
6. Now set off 1B, 2C, 3D ... etc. and $0'H, 1'J$ ... etc. from the displacement diagram.
7. Join the points A, B, C,... M, N, P with a smooth curve. The curve AGHPA is the complete profile of the cam.

Notes : The points B, C, D .... L, M, N may also be obtained as follows :

1. Mark AY = 40 mm on the axis of the follower, and set of Ab, Ac, Ad... etc. equal to the distances 1B, 2C, 3D... etc. as in displacement diagram.

2. From the centre of the cam O, draw arcs with radii Ob, Oc, Od etc. The arcs intersect the produced lines O1, O2... etc. at B, C, D ... L, M, N.

(b) *Profile of the cam when the axis of the follower is offset by 20 mm from the axis of the cam shaft*

The profile of the cam when the axis of the follower is offset from the axis of the cam shaft, as shown in Fig. 20.12, is drawn as discussed in the following steps :

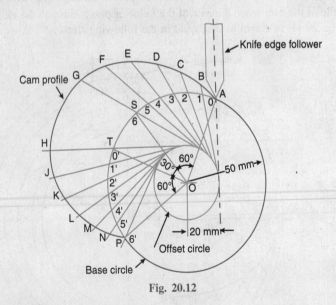

Fig. 20.12

1. Draw a base circle with radius equal to the minimum radius of the cam (*i.e.* 50 mm) with O as centre.
2. Draw the axis of the follower at a distance of 20 mm from the axis of the cam, which intersects the base circle at A.
3. Join AO and draw an offset circle of radius 20 mm with centre O.
4. From OA, mark angle AOS = 60° to represent outstroke, angle SOT = 30° to represent dwell and angle TOP = 60° to represent return stroke.

5. Divide the angular displacement during outstroke and return stroke (*i.e.* angle *AOS* and angle *TOP*) into the same number of equal even parts as in displacement diagram.

6. Now from the points 1, 2, 3 ... etc. and $0', 1', 2', 3'$ ... etc. on the base circle, draw tangents to the offset circle and produce these tangents beyond the base circle as shown in Fig. 20.12.

7. Now set off $1B, 2C, 3D$ ... etc. and $0'H, 1'J$ ... etc. from the displacement diagram.

8. Join the points *A, B, C ...M, N, P* with a smooth curve. The curve *AGHPA* is the complete profile of the cam.

Example 20.2. *A cam is to be designed for a knife edge follower with the following data :*
1. *Cam lift = 40 mm during 90° of cam rotation with simple harmonic motion.*
2. *Dwell for the next 30°.*
3. *During the next 60° of cam rotation, the follower returns to its original position with simple harmonic motion.*
4. *Dwell during the remaining 180°.*
Draw the profile of the cam when
(a) the line of stroke of the follower passes through the axis of the cam shaft, and
(b) the line of stroke is offset 20 mm from the axis of the cam shaft.
The radius of the base circle of the cam is 40 mm. Determine the maximum velocity and acceleration of the follower during its ascent and descent, if the cam rotates at 240 r.p.m.

Solution. Given : $S = 40$ mm $= 0.04$ m; $\theta_O = 90° = \pi/2$ rad $= 1.571$ rad ; $\theta_R = 60° = \pi/3$ rad $= 1.047$ rad ; $N = 240$ r.p.m.

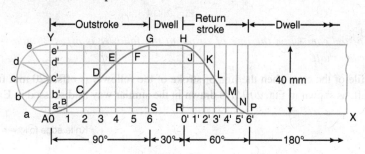

Fig. 20.13

First of all, the displacement diagram, as shown in Fig 20.13, is drawn as discussed in the following steps :

1. Draw horizontal line *AX* = 360° to some suitable scale. On this line, mark *AS* = 90° to represent out stroke ; *SR* = 30° to represent dwell ; *RP* = 60° to represent return stroke and *PX* = 180° to represent dwell.

2. Draw vertical line *AY* = 40 mm to represent the cam lift or stroke of the follower and complete the rectangle as shown in Fig. 20.13.

3. Divide the angular displacement during out stroke and return stroke into any equal number of even parts (say six) and draw vertical lines through each point.

4. Since the follower moves with simple harmonic motion, therefore draw a semicircle with *AY* as diameter and divide into six equal parts.

5. From points *a, b, c* ... etc. draw horizontal lines intersecting the vertical lines drawn through 1, 2, 3 ... etc. and $0', 1', 2'$ ...etc. at *B, C, D ... M, N, P.*

6. Join the points *A, B, C* ... etc. with a smooth curve as shown in Fig. 20.13. This is the required displacement diagram.

(a) *Profile of the cam when the line of stroke of the follower passes through the axis of the cam shaft*

The profile of the cam when the line of stroke of the follower passes through the axis of the cam shaft, as shown in Fig. 20.14, is drawn in the similar way as is discussed in Example 20.1.

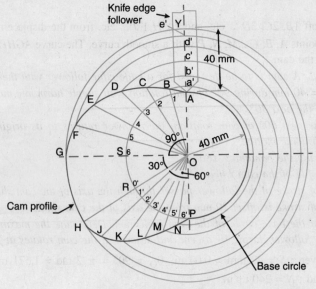

Fig. 20.14

(b) *Profile of the cam when the line of stroke of the follower is offset 20 mm from the axis of the cam shaft*

The profile of the cam when the line of stroke of the follower is offset 20 mm from the axis of the cam shaft, as shown in Fig. 20.15, is drawn in the similar way as discussed in Example 20.1.

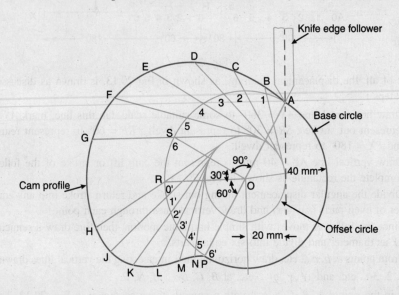

Fig. 20.15

Maximum velocity of the follower during its ascent and descent

We know that angular velocity of the cam,

$$\omega = \frac{2\pi N}{60} = \frac{2\pi \times 240}{60} = 25.14 \text{ rad/s}$$

We also know that the maximum velocity of the follower during its ascent,

$$v_O = \frac{\pi \omega S}{2\theta_O} = \frac{\pi \times 25.14 \times 0.04}{2 \times 1.571} = 1 \text{ m/s Ans.}$$

and maximum velocity of the follower during its descent,

$$v_R = \frac{\pi \omega S}{2\theta_R} = \frac{\pi \times 25.14 \times 0.04}{2 \times 1.047} = 1.51 \text{ m/s Ans.}$$

Maximum acceleration of the follower during its ascent and descent

We know that the maximum acceleration of the follower during its ascent,

Role of cams in piston movement.

$$a_O = \frac{\pi^2 \omega^2 . S}{2(\theta_O)^2} = \frac{\pi^2 (25.14)^2 0.04}{2(1.571)^2} = 50.6 \text{ m/s}^2 \text{ Ans.}$$

and maximum acceleration of the follower during its descent,

$$a_R = \frac{\pi^2 \omega^2 . S}{2(\theta_R)^2} = \frac{\pi^2 (25.14)^2 0.04}{2(1.047)^2} = 113.8 \text{ m/s}^2 \text{ Ans.}$$

Example 20.3. *A cam, with a minimum radius of 25 mm, rotating clockwise at a uniform speed is to be designed to give a roller follower, at the end of a valve rod, motion described below :*

1. To raise the valve through 50 mm during 120° rotation of the cam ;

2. To keep the valve fully raised through next 30°;

3. To lower the valve during next 60°; and

4. To keep the valve closed during rest of the revolution i.e. 150° ;

The diameter of the roller is 20 mm and the diameter of the cam shaft is 25 mm.

Draw the profile of the cam when (a) the line of stroke of the valve rod passes through the axis of the cam shaft, and (b) the line of the stroke is offset 15 mm from the axis of the cam shaft.

The displacement of the valve, while being raised and lowered, is to take place with simple harmonic motion. Determine the maximum acceleration of the valve rod when the cam shaft rotates at 100 r.p.m.

Draw the displacement, the velocity and the acceleration diagrams for one complete revolution of the cam.

Solution. Given : $S = 50$ mm $= 0.05$ m ; $\theta_O = 120° = 2\ \pi/3$ rad $= 2.1$ rad ; $\theta_R = 60° = \pi/3$ rad $= 1.047$ rad ; $N = 100$ r.p.m.

Since the valve is being raised and lowered with simple harmonic motion, therefore the displacement diagram, as shown in Fig. 20.16 (*a*), is drawn in the similar manner as discussed in the previous example.

(a) *Profile of the cam when the line of stroke of the valve rod passes through the axis of the cam shaft*

The profile of the cam, as shown in Fig. 20.17, is drawn as discussed in the following steps :

1. Draw a base circle with centre O and radius equal to the minimum radius of the cam (*i.e.* 25 mm).

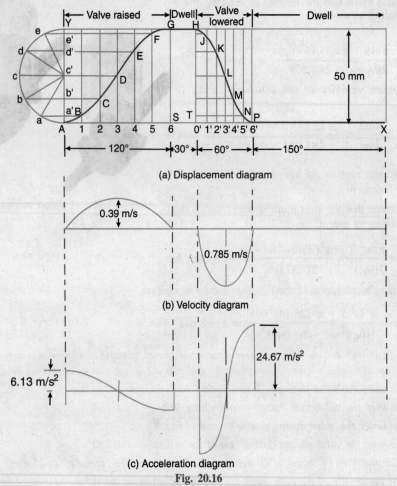

Fig. 20.16

2. Draw a prime circle with centre O and radius,

$$OA = \text{Min. radius of cam} + \frac{1}{2} \text{ Dia. of roller} = 25 + \frac{1}{2} \times 20 = 35 \text{ mm}$$

3. Draw angle $AOS = 120°$ to represent raising or out stroke of the valve, angle $SOT = 30°$ to represent dwell and angle $TOP = 60°$ to represent lowering or return stroke of the valve.

4. Divide the angular displacements of the cam during raising and lowering of the valve (*i.e.* angle AOS and TOP) into the same number of equal even parts as in displacement diagram.

5. Join the points 1, 2, 3, etc. with the centre O and produce the lines beyond prime circle as shown in Fig. 20.17.

6. Set off $1B$, $2C$, $3D$ etc. equal to the displacements from displacement diagram.

7. Join the points A, B, C ... N, P, A. The curve drawn through these points is known as *pitch curve*.

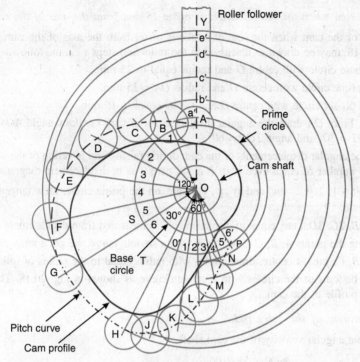

Fig. 20.17

8. From the points *A, B, C ... N, P*, draw circles of radius equal to the radius of the roller.
9. Join the bottoms of the circles with a smooth curve as shown in Fig. 20.17. This is the required profile of the cam.

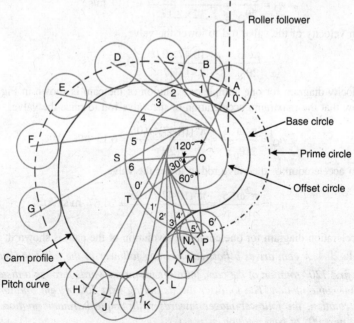

Fig. 20.18

(b) Profile of the cam when the line of stroke is offset 15 mm from the axis of the cam shaft

The profile of the cam when the line of stroke is offset from the axis of the cam shaft, as shown in Fig. 20.18, may be drawn as discussed in the following steps :

1. Draw a base circle with centre O and radius equal to 25 mm.
2. Draw a prime circle with centre O and radius $OA = 35$ mm.
3. Draw an off-set circle with centre O and radius equal to 15 mm.
4. Join OA. From OA draw the angular displacements of cam *i.e.* draw angle $AOS = 120°$, angle $SOT = 30°$ and angle $TOP = 60°$.
5. Divide the angular displacements of the cam during raising and lowering of the valve into the same number of equal even parts (*i.e.* six parts) as in displacement diagram.
6. From points 1, 2, 3 .... etc. and $0', 1', 3'$, ...etc. on the prime circle, draw tangents to the offset circle.
7. Set off $1B$, $2C$, $3D$... etc. equal to displacements as measured from displacement diagram.
8. By joining the points A, B, C ... M, N, P, with a smooth curve, we get a *pitch curve*.
9. Now A, B, C...etc. as centre, draw circles with radius equal to the radius of roller.
10. Join the bottoms of the circles with a smooth curve as shown in Fig. 20.18. This is the required profile of the cam.

Maximum acceleration of the valve rod

We know that angular velocity of the cam shaft,

$$\omega = \frac{2\pi N}{60} = \frac{2\pi \times 100}{60} = 10.47 \text{ rad/s}$$

We also know that maximum velocity of the valve rod to raise valve,

$$v_O = \frac{\pi \omega . S}{2\theta_O} = \frac{\pi \times 10.47 \times 0.05}{2 \times 2.1} = 0.39 \text{ m/s}$$

and maximum velocity of the valve rod to lower the valve,

$$v_R = \frac{\pi \omega . S}{2\theta_R} = \frac{\pi \times 10.47 \times 0.05}{2 \times 1.047} = 0.785 \text{ m/s}$$

The velocity diagram for one complete revolution of the cam is shown in Fig. 20.16 (*b*). We know that the maximum acceleration of the valve rod to raise the valve,

$$a_O = \frac{\pi^2 \omega^2 . S}{2(\theta_O)^2} = \frac{\pi^2 (10.47)^2 0.05}{2(2.1)^2} = 6.13 \text{ m/s}^2 \text{ Ans.}$$

and maximum acceleration of the valve rod to lower the valve,

$$a_R = \frac{\pi^2 \omega^2 . S}{2(\theta_R)^2} = \frac{\pi^2 (10.47)^2 0.05}{2(1.047)^2} = 24.67 \text{ m/s}^2 \text{ Ans.}$$

The acceleration diagram for one complete revolution of the cam is shown in Fig. 20.16 (*c*).

Example 20.4. *A cam drives a flat reciprocating follower in the following manner :*

During first 120° rotation of the cam, follower moves outwards through a distance of 20 mm with simple harmonic motion. The follower dwells during next 30° of cam rotation. During next 120° of cam rotation, the follower moves inwards with simple harmonic motion. The follower dwells for the next 90° of cam rotation.

The minimum radius of the cam is 25 mm. Draw the profile of the cam.

Construction

Since the follower moves outwards and inwards with simple harmonic motion, therefore the displacement diagram, as shown in Fig. 20.19, is drawn in the similar manner as discussed earlier.

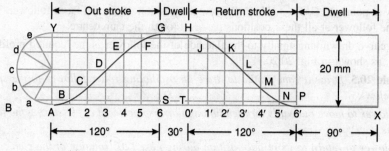

Fig. 20.19

Now the profile of the cam driving a flat reciprocating follower, as shown in Fig. 20.20, is drawn as discussed in the following steps :

1. Draw a base circle with centre *O* and radius *OA* equal to the minimum radius of the cam (*i.e.* 25 mm).
2. Draw angle *AOS* = 120° to represent the outward stroke, angle *SOT* = 30° to represent dwell and angle *TOP* = 120° to represent inward stroke.
3. Divide the angular displacement during outward stroke and inward stroke (*i.e.* angles *AOS* and *TOP*) into the same number of equal even parts as in the displacement diagram.

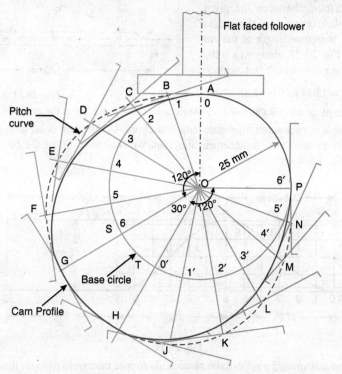

Fig. 20.20

4. Join the points 1, 2, 3 . . . etc. with centre O and produce beyond the base circle.

5. From points 1, 2, 3 . . . etc., set off $1B$, $2C$, $3D$ . . . etc. equal to the distances measured from the displacement diagram.

6. Now at points B, C, D . . . M, N, P, draw the position of the flat-faced follower. The axis of the follower at all these positions passes through the cam centre.

7. The curve drawn tangentially to the flat side of the follower is the required profile of the cam, as shown in Fig. 20.20.

Example 20.5. *Draw a cam profile to drive an oscillating roller follower to the specifications given below :*

(a) Follower to move outwards through an angular displacement of 20° during the first 120° rotation of the cam ;

(b) Follower to return to its initial position during next 120° rotation of the cam ;

(c) Follower to dwell during the next 120° of cam rotation.

The distance between pivot centre and roller centre = 120 mm ; distance between pivot centre and cam axis = 130 mm ; minimum radius of cam = 40 mm ; radius of roller = 10 mm ; inward and outward strokes take place with simple harmonic motion.

Construction

We know that the angular displacement of the roller follower

$$= 20° = 20 \times \pi / 180 = \pi / 9 \text{ rad}$$

Since the distance between the pivot centre and the roller centre (*i.e.* the radius $A_1 A$) is 120 mm, therefore length of the arc AA_2, as shown in Fig. 20.21, along which the displacement of the roller actually takes place

$$= 120 \times \pi / 9 = 41.88 \text{ mm}$$

. . . (∵ Length of arc = Radius of arc × Angle subtended by the arc at the centre in radians)

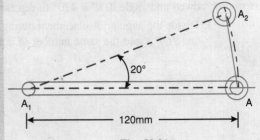

Fig. 20.21

Since the angle is very small, therefore length of chord AA_2 is taken equal to the length of arc AA_2. Thus in order to draw the displacement diagram, we shall take lift of the follower equal to length of chord AA_2 *i.e.* 41.88 mm.

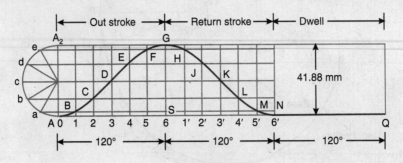

Fig. 20.22

The outward and inward strokes take place with simple harmonic motion, therefore the displacement diagram, as shown in Fig. 20.22, is drawn in the similar way as discussed in Example 20.4.

The profile of the cam to drive an oscillating roller follower, as shown in Fig. 20.23, is drawn as discussed in the following steps :

1. First of all, draw a base circle with centre O and radius equal to the minimum radius of the cam (*i.e.* 40 mm)

2. Draw a prime circle with centre O and radius OA

$$= \text{Min. radius of cam + radius of roller} = 40 + 10 = 50 \text{ mm}$$

3. Now locate the pivot centre A_1 such that $OA_1 = 130$ mm and $AA_1 = 120$ mm. Draw a pivot circle with centre O and radius $OA_1 = 130$ mm.

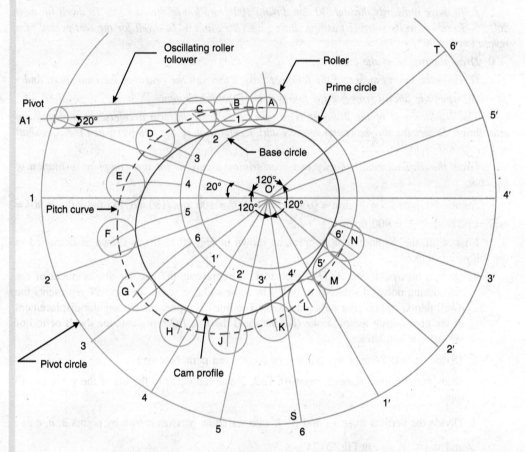

Fig. 20.23

4. Join OA_1. Draw angle $A_1OS = 120°$ to represent the outward stroke of the follower, angle $SOT = 120°$ to represent the inward stroke of the follower and angle $TOA_1 = 120°$ to represent the dwell.

5. Divide angles A_1OS and SOT into the same number of equal even parts as in the displacement diagram and mark points 1, 2, 3 . . . $4', 5', 6'$ on the pivot circle.

6. Now with points 1, 2, 3 . . . $4', 5', 6'$ (on the pivot circle) as centre and radius equal to A_1A (*i.e.* 120 mm) draw circular arcs to intersect the prime circle at points 1, 2, 3 . . . $4', 5', 6'$.

7. Set off the distances 1B, 2C, 3D... 4'L, 5'M along the arcs drawn equal to the distances as measured from the displacement diagram.

8. The curve passing through the points A, B, C....L, M, N is known as pitch curve.

9. Now draw circles with A, B, C, D....L, M, N as centre and radius equal to the radius of roller.

10. Join the bottoms of the circles with a smooth curve as shown in Fig. 20.23. This is the required profile of the cam.

Example 20.6. *A cam, with a minimum radius of 50 mm, rotating clockwise at a uniform speed, is required to give a knife edge follower the motion as described below :*

1. To move outwards through 40 mm during 100° rotation of the cam ; 2. To dwell for next 80° ; 3. To return to its starting position during next 90°, and 4. To dwell for the rest period of a revolution i.e. 90°.

Draw the profile of the cam

(i) when the line of stroke of the follower passes through the centre of the cam shaft, and

(ii) when the line of stroke of the follower is off-set by 15 mm.

The displacement of the follower is to take place with uniform acceleration and uniform retardation. Determine the maximum velocity and acceleration of the follower when the cam shaft rotates at 900 r.p.m.

Draw the displacement, velocity and acceleration diagrams for one complete revolution of the cam.

Solution. Given : $S = 40$ mm $= 0.04$ m; $\theta_o = 100° = 100 \times \pi/180 = 1.745$ rad ; $\theta_R = 90° = \pi/2 = 1.571$ rad ; $N = 900$ r.p.m.

First of all, the displacement diagram, as shown in Fig. 20.24 (*a*), is drawn as discussed in the following steps :

1. Draw a horizontal line ASTPQ such that AS represents the angular displacement of the cam during outward stroke (*i.e.* 100°) to some suitable scale. The line ST represents the dwell period of 80° after outward stroke. The line TP represents the angular displacement of the cam during return stroke (*i.e.* 90°) and the line PQ represents the dwell period of 90° after return stroke.

2. Divide AS and TP into any number of equal even parts (say six).

3. Draw vertical lines through points 0, 1, 2, 3 etc. and equal to the lift of the valve *i.e.* 40 mm.

4. Divide the vertical lines 3-*f* and 3'- *f'* into six equal parts as shown by points *a, b, c* . . . and a', b', c' . . . in Fig. 20.24 (*a*).

5. Since the follower moves with equal uniform acceleration and uniform retardation, therefore the displacement diagram of the outward and return stroke consists of a double parabola.

6. Join A*a*, A*b* and A*c* intersecting the vertical lines through 1, 2 and 3 at B, C and D respectively.

7. Join the points B, C and D with a smooth curve. This is the required parabola for the half outstroke of the valve. Similarly the other curves may be drawn as shown in Fig. 20.24.

8. The curve A B C . . . N P Q is the required displacement diagram.

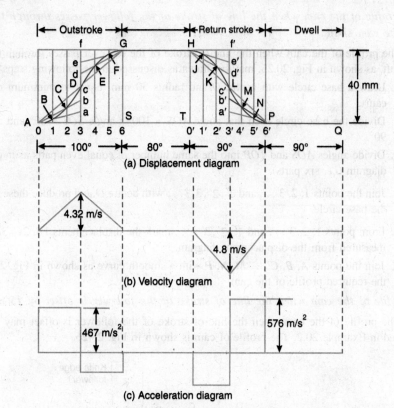

(a) Displacement diagram

(b) Velocity diagram

(c) Acceleration diagram

Fig. 20.24

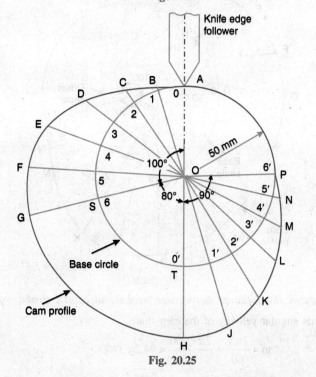

Fig. 20.25

(i)   Profile of the cam when the line of stroke of the follower passes through the centre of the cam shaft

The profile of the cam when the line of stroke of the follower passes through the centre of cam shaft, as shown in Fig. 20.25, may be drawn as discussed in the following steps :

1. Draw a base circle with centre O and radius 50 mm (equal to minimum radius of the cam).

2. Divide the base circle such that angle $AOS = 100°$; angle $SOT = 80°$ and angle $TOP = 90°$.

3. Divide angles AOS and TOP into the same number of equal even parts as in displacement diagram (*i.e.* six parts).

4. Join the points 1, 2, 3 ... and 1′, 2′, 3′, ... with centre O and produce these lines beyond the base circle.

5. From points 1, 2, 3 ... and 1′, 2′, 3′, ... mark the displacements 1B, 2C, 3D ... etc. as measured from the displacement diagram.

6. Join the points $A, B, C ... M, N, P$ with a smooth curve as shown in Fig. 20.25. This is the required profile of the cam.

(ii) Profile of the cam when the line of stroke of the follower is offset by 15 mm

The profile of the cam when the line of stroke of the follower is offset may be drawn as discussed in Example 20.2. The profile of cam is shown in Fig. 20.26.

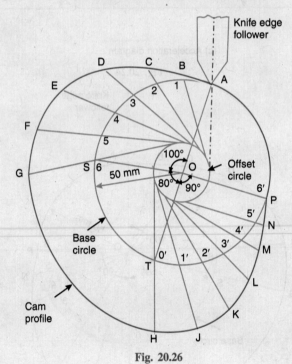

Fig. 20.26

Maximum velocity of the follower during out stroke and return stroke

We know that angular velocity of the cam shaft,

$$\omega = \frac{2\pi N}{60} = \frac{2\pi \times 900}{60} = 94.26 \text{ rad/s}$$

We also know that the maximum velocity of the follower during out stroke,

$$v_O = \frac{2\omega.S}{\theta_O} = \frac{2 \times 94.26 \times 0.04}{1.745} = 4.32 \text{ m/s Ans.}$$

and maximum velocity of the follower during return stroke,

$$v_R = \frac{2\omega.S}{\theta_R} = \frac{2 \times 94.26 \times 0.04}{1.571} = 4.8 \text{ m/s Ans.}$$

The velocity diagram is shown in Fig. 20.24 (*b*).

A type of roller follower.

Maximum acceleration of the follower during out stroke and return stroke

We know that the maximum acceleration of the follower during out stroke,

$$a_O = \frac{4\omega^2.S}{(\theta_O)^2} = \frac{4(94.26)^2 0.04}{(1.745)^2} = 467 \text{ m/s}^2 \text{ Ans.}$$

and maximum acceleration of the follower during return stroke,

$$a_R = \frac{4\omega^2.S}{(\theta_R)^2} = \frac{4(94.26)^2 0.04}{(1.571)^2} = 576 \text{ m/s}^2 \text{ Ans.}$$

The acceleration diagram is shown in Fig. 20.24 (*c*).

Example 20.7. *Design a cam for operating the exhaust valve of an oil engine. It is required to give equal uniform acceleration and retardation during opening and closing of the valve each of which corresponds to 60° of cam rotation. The valve must remain in the fully open position for 20° of cam rotation.*

The lift of the valve is 37.5 mm and the least radius of the cam is 40 mm. The follower is provided with a roller of radius 20 mm and its line of stroke passes through the axis of the cam.

Construction

First of all, the displacement diagram, as shown in Fig. 20.27, is drawn as discussed in the following steps :

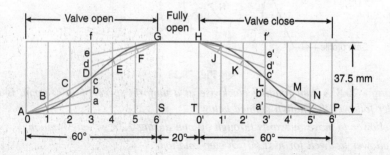

Fig. 20.27

1. Draw a horizontal line *ASTP* such that *AS* represents the angular displacement of the cam during opening (*i.e.* out stroke) of the valve (equal to 60°), to some suitable scale. The line *ST* represents the dwell period of 20° *i.e.* the period during which the valve remains

fully open and *TP* represents the angular displacement during closing (*i.e.* return stroke) of the valve which is equal to 60°.

2. Divide *AS* and *TP* into any number of equal even parts (say six).

3. Draw vertical lines through points 0, 1, 2, 3 etc. and equal to lift of the valve *i.e.* 37.5 mm.

4. Divide the vertical lines 3*f* and 3′ *f*′ into six equal parts as shown by the points *a, b, c* . . . and *a′, b′, c′* . . . in Fig. 20.27.

5. Since the valve moves with equal uniform acceleration and retardation, therefore the displacement diagram for opening and closing of a valve consists of double parabola.

6. Complete the displacement diagram as shown in Fig. 20.27.

Now the profile of the cam, with a roller follower when its line of stroke passes through the axis of cam, as shown in Fig. 20.28, is drawn in the similar way as discussed in Example 20.3.

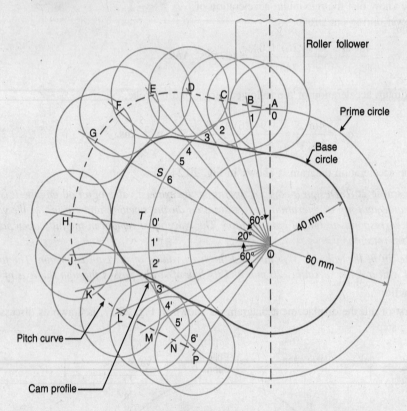

Fig. 20.28

Example 20.8. *A cam rotating clockwise at a uniform speed of 1000 r.p.m. is required to give a roller follower the motion defined below :*

1. Follower to move outwards through 50 mm during 120° of cam rotation,

2. Follower to dwell for next 60° of cam rotation,

3. Follower to return to its starting position during next 90° of cam rotation,

4. Follower to dwell for the rest of the cam rotation.

The minimum radius of the cam is 50 mm and the diameter of roller is 10 mm. The line of stroke of the follower is off-set by 20 mm from the axis of the cam shaft. If the displacement of the follower takes place with uniform and equal acceleration and retardation on both the outward and return strokes, draw profile of the cam and find the maximum velocity and acceleration during out stroke and return stroke.

Solution. Given : $N = 1000$ r.p.m. ; $S = 50$ mm $= 0.05$ m ; $\theta_O = 120° = 2\,\pi/3$ rad $= 2.1$ rad ; $\theta_R = 90° = \pi/2$ rad $= 1.571$ rad

Since the displacement of the follower takes place with uniform and equal acceleration and retardation on both outward and return strokes, therefore the displacement diagram, as shown in Fig. 20.29, is drawn in the similar manner as discussed in the previous example. But in this case, the angular displacement and stroke of the follower is divided into eight equal parts.

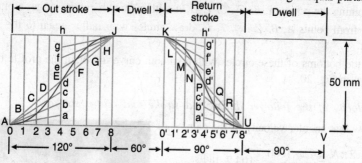

Fig. 20.29

Now, the profile of the cam, as shown in Fig. 20.30, is drawn as discussed in the following steps :

1. Draw a base circle with centre O and radius equal to the minimum radius of the cam (*i.e.* 50 mm).

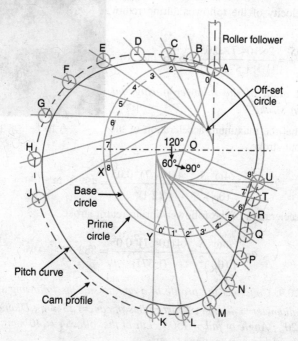

Fig. 20.30

2. Draw a prime circle with centre O and radius

$$OA = \text{Minimum radius of the cam} + \text{radius of roller} = 50 + 5 = 55 \text{ mm}$$

3. Draw an off-set circle with centre O and radius equal to 20 mm.

4. Divide the angular displacements of the cam during out stroke and return stroke into eight equal parts as shown by points $0, 1, 2 \dots$ and $0', 1', 2' \dots$ etc. on the prime circle in Fig. 20.30.

5. From these points draw tangents to the off-set circle.

6. Set off $1B, 2C, 3D \dots$ etc. equal to the displacements as measured from the displacement diagram.

7. By joining the points $A, B, C \dots T, U, A$ with a smooth curve, we get a pitch curve.

8. Now from points $A, B, C \dots T, U$, draw circles with radius equal to the radius of the roller.

9. Join the bottoms of these circles with a smooth curve to obtain the profile of the cam as shown in Fig. 20.30.

Maximum velocity of the follower during out stroke and return stroke

We know that angular velocity of the cam,

$$\omega = \frac{2\pi N}{60} = \frac{2\pi \times 1000}{60} = 104.7 \text{ rad/s.}$$

We also know that the maximum velocity of the follower during outstroke,

$$v_O = \frac{2\omega.S}{\theta_O} = \frac{2 \times 104.7 \times 0.05}{2.1} = 5 \text{ m/s Ans.}$$

and maximum velocity of the follower during return stroke,

$$v_R = \frac{2\omega.S}{\theta_R} = \frac{2 \times 104.7 \times 0.05}{1.571} = 6.66 \text{ m/s Ans.}$$

Maximum acceleration of the follower during out stroke and return stroke

We know that the maximum acceleration of the follower during out stroke,

A rocker using a cam.

$$a_O = \frac{4\omega^2.S}{(\theta_O)^2} = \frac{4(104.7)^2 0.05}{(2.1)^2} = 497.2 \text{ m/s}^2 \text{ Ans.}$$

and maximum acceleration of the follower during return stroke,

$$a_R = \frac{4\omega^2.S}{(\theta_R)^2} = \frac{4(104.7)^2 0.05}{(1.571)^2} = 888 \text{ m/s}^2 \text{ Ans.}$$

Example 20.9. *Construct the profile of a cam to suit the following specifications :*

Cam shaft diameter = 40 mm ; Least radius of cam = 25 mm ; Diameter of roller = 25 mm; Angle of lift = 120° ; Angle of fall = 150° ; Lift of the follower = 40 mm ; Number of pauses are two of equal interval between motions.

During the lift, the motion is S.H.M. During the fall the motion is uniform acceleration and deceleration. The speed of the cam shaft is uniform. The line of stroke of the follower is off-set 12.5 mm from the centre of the cam.

Construction

First of all the displacement diagram, as shown in Fig. 20.31, is drawn as discussed in the following steps :

1. Since the follower moves with simple harmonic motion during lift (*i.e.* for 120° of cam rotation), therefore draw the displacement curve *ADG* in the similar manner as discussed in Example 20.2.

2. Since the follower moves with uniform acceleration and deceleration during fall (*i.e.* for 150° of cam rotation), therefore draw the displacement curve *HLP* consisting of double parabola as discussed in Example 20.6.

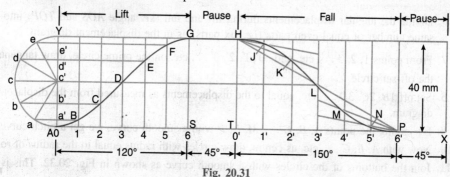

Fig. 20.31

Now the profile of the cam, when the line of stroke of the follower is off-set 12.5 mm from the centre of the cam, as shown in Fig. 20.32, is drawn as discussed in the following steps :

1. Draw a base circle with centre *O* and radius equal to the least radius of cam (*i.e.* 25 mm).

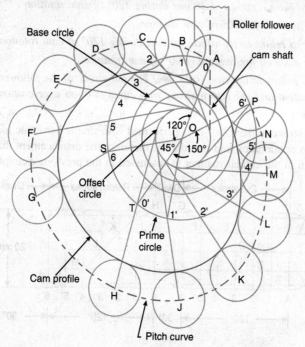

Fig. 20.32

2. Draw a prime circle with centre O and radius,

$$OA = \text{Least radius of cam} + \text{radius of roller} = 25 + 25/2 = 37.5 \text{ mm}$$

3. Draw a circle with centre O and radius equal to 20 mm to represent the cam shaft.

4. Draw an offset circle with centre O and radius equal to 12.5 mm.

5. Join OA. From OA draw angular displacements of the cam, *i.e.* draw angle $AOS = 120°$ to represent lift of the follower, angle $SOT = 45°$ to represent pause, angle $TOP = 150°$ to represent fall of the follower and angle $POA = 45°$ to represent pause.

Note. Since the number of pauses are two of equal interval between motions (*i.e.* between lift and fall of the follower), therefore angular displacement of each pause

$$= \frac{360° - (120° + 150°)}{2} = 45°$$

6. Divide the angular displacements during lift and fall (*i.e.* angle AOS and TOP) into the same number of equal even parts (*i.e.* six parts) as in the displacement diagram.

7. From points 1, 2, 3 . . . etc. and 0′, 1′, 2′, 3′ . . . etc. on the prime circle, draw tangents to the off-set circle.

8. Set off $1B$, $2C$, $3D$ . . . etc. equal to the displacements as measured from the displacement diagram.

9. By joining the points A, B, C . . . M, N, P with a smooth curve, we get a pitch curve.

10. Now with A, B, C . . . etc. as centre, draw circles with radius equal to the radius of roller.

11. Join the bottoms of the circles with a smooth curve as shown in Fig. 20.32. This is the required profile of the cam.

Example 20.10. *It is required to set out the profile of a cam to give the following motion to the reciprocating follower with a flat mushroom contact face :*

(i) Follower to have a stroke of 20 mm during 120° of cam rotation ;

(ii) Follower to dwell for 30° of cam rotation ;

(iii) Follower to return to its initial position during 120° of cam rotation ; and

(iv) Follower to dwell for remaining 90° of cam rotation.

The minimum radius of the cam is 25 mm. The out stroke of the follower is performed with simple harmonic motion and the return stroke with equal uniform acceleration and retardation.

Construction

Since the out stroke of the follower is performed with simple harmonic motion and the return stroke with uniform acceleration and retardation, therefore the displacement diagram, as shown in Fig. 20.33, is drawn in the similar manner as discussed in the previous example.

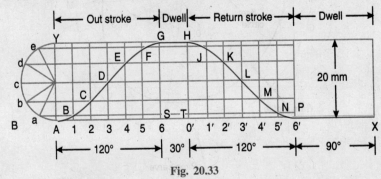

Fig. 20.33

The profile of the cam with a flat mushroom contact face reciprocating follower, as shown in Fig. 20.34, is drawn in the similar way as discussed in Example 20.4.

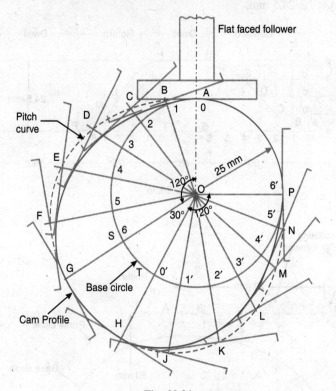

Fig. 20.34

Example 20.11. *It is required to set out the profile of a cam with oscillating follower for the following motion :*

(a) Follower to move outward through an angular displacement of 20° during 90° of cam rotation ; (b) Follower to dwell for 45° of cam rotation ; (c) Follower to return to its original position of zero displacement in 75° of cam rotation ; and (d) Follower to dwell for the remaining period of the revolution of the cam.

The distance between the pivot centre and the follower roller centre is 70 mm and the roller diameter is 20 mm. The minimum radius of the cam corresponds to the starting position of the follower as given in (a). The location of the pivot point is 70 mm to the left and 60 mm above the axis of rotation of the cam. The motion of the follower is to take place with S.H.M. during out stroke and with uniform acceleration and retardation during return stroke.

Construction

We know that the angular displacement of the roller follower,

$$= 20° = 20 \times \pi / 180 = \pi / 9 \text{ rad}$$

Since the distance between the pivot centre and the roller centre (*i.e.* radius A_1A) is 70 mm, therefore length of arc AA_2, as shown in Fig. 20.35, along which the displacement of the roller actually takes place

$$= 70 \times \pi / 9 = 24.5 \text{ mm}$$

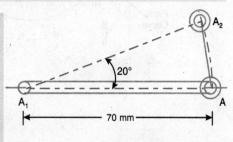

Fig. 20.35

Since the angle is very small, therefore length of chord AA_2 is taken equal to the length of arc AA_2. Thus in order to draw the displacement diagram, we shall take lift of the follower equal to the length of chord AA_2 i.e. 24.5 mm.

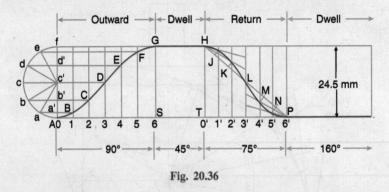

Fig. 20.36

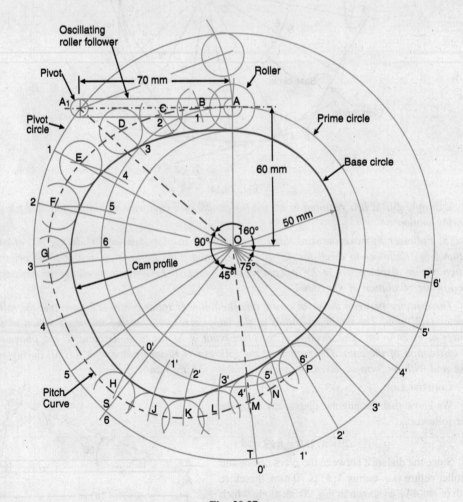

Fig. 20.37

The follower moves with simple harmonic motion during out stroke and with uniform acceleration and retardation during return stroke. Therefore, the displacement diagram, as shown in Fig. 20.36, is drawn in the similar way as discussed in the previous example.

The profile of the cam, as shown in Fig. 20.37, is drawn as discussed in the following steps :

1. First of all, locate the pivot point A_1 which is 70 mm to the left and 60 mm above the axis of the cam.

2. Since the distance between the pivot centre A_1 and the follower roller centre A is 70 mm and the roller diameter is 20 mm, therefore draw a circle with centre A and radius equal to the radius of roller *i.e.* 10 mm.

3. We find that the minimum radius of the cam

$$= 60 - 10 = 50 \text{ mm}$$

∴ Radius of the prime circle,

OA = Min. radius of cam + Radius of roller = 50 + 10 = 60 mm

4. Now complete the profile of the cam in the similar way as discussed in Example 20.5.

Example 20.12. *Draw the profile of the cam when the roller follower moves with cycloidal motion during out stroke and return stroke, as given below :*

1. Out stroke with maximum displacement of 31.4 mm during 180° of cam rotation,

2. Return stroke for the next 150° of cam rotation,

3. Dwell for the remaining 30° of cam rotation.

The minimum radius of the cam is 15 mm and the roller diameter of the follower is 10 mm. The axis of the roller follower is offset by 10 mm towards right from the axis of cam shaft.

Construction

First of all, the displacement diagram, as shown in Fig. 20.38, is drawn as discussed in the following steps :

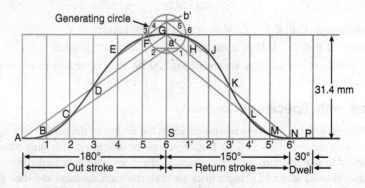

Fig. 20.38

1. Draw horizontal line ASP such that AS = 180° to represent the out stroke, SN = 150° to represent the return stroke and NP = 30° to represent the dwell period.

2. Divide AS and SN into any number of even equal parts (say six).

3. From the points 1, 2, 3 . . . etc. draw vertical lines and set-off equal to the stroke of the follower.

4. From a point G draw a generating circle of radius,

$$r = \frac{\text{Stroke}}{2\pi} = \frac{31.4}{2\pi} = 5 \text{ mm}$$

5. Divide the generating circle into six equal parts and from these points draw horizontal lines to meet the vertical diameter at a', G and b'.

6. Join AG and GN. From point a', draw lines parallel to AG and GN to intersect the vertical lines drawn through 1, 2, 4' and 5' at B, C, L and M respectively. Similarly draw parallel lines from b' intersecting the vertical lines through 4, 5, 1' and 2' at E, F, H and J respectively.

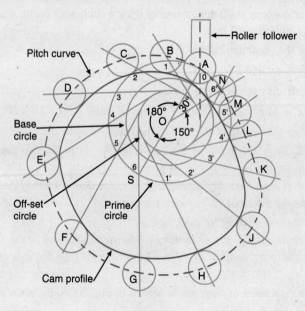

Fig. 20.39

7. Join the points A, B, C . . . L, M, N with a smooth curve.

8. The curve $A\ B\ C$ . . . $L\ M\ N$ is the required displacement diagram.

Now the profile of the cam, as shown in Fig. 20.39, may be drawn in the similar way as discussed in Example 20.9.

20.11. Cams with Specified Contours

In the previous articles, we have discussed about the design of the profile of a cam when the follower moves with the specified motion. But, the shape of the cam profile thus obtained may be difficult and costly to manufacture. In actual practice, the cams with specified contours (cam profiles consisting of circular arcs and straight lines are preferred) are assumed and then motion of the follower is determined.

20.12. Tangent Cam with Reciprocating Roller Follower

When the flanks of the cam are straight and tangential to the base circle and nose circle, then the cam is known as a *tangent cam*, as shown in Fig. 20.40. These cams are usually symmetrical about the centre line of the cam shaft. Such type of cams are used for operating the inlet and exhaust valves of internal combustion engines. We shall now derive the expressions for displacement, velocity and acceleration of the follower for the following two cases :

1. When the roller has contact with the straight flanks ; and

2. When the roller has contact with the nose.

Let r_1 = Radius of the base circle or minimum radius of the cam,

r_2 = Radius of the roller,

r_3 = Radius of nose,

α = Semi-angle of action of cam or angle of ascent,

θ = Angle turned by the cam from the beginning of the roller displacement,

ϕ = Angle turned by the cam for contact of roller with the straight flank, and

ω = Angular velocity of the cam.

1. *When the roller has contact with straight flanks.* A roller having contact with straight flanks is shown in Fig. 20.40. The point *O* is the centre of cam shaft and the point *K* is the centre of nose. *EG* and *PQ* are straight flanks of the cam. When the roller is in lowest position, (*i.e.* when the roller has contact with the straight flank at *E*), the centre of roller lies at *B* on the pitch curve. Let the cam has turned through an angle* θ (less than ϕ) for the roller to have contact at any point (say *F*) between the straight flanks *EG*. The centre of roller at this stage lies at *C*. Therefore displacement (or lift or stroke) of the roller from its lowest position is given by

$$x = OC - OB = \frac{OB}{\cos \theta} - OB = OB \left(\frac{1 - \cos \theta}{\cos \theta} \right)$$

$$= (r_1 + r_2) \left(\frac{1 - \cos \theta}{\cos \theta} \right) \qquad \dots (\because OB = OE + EB = r_1 + r_2) \dots (i)$$

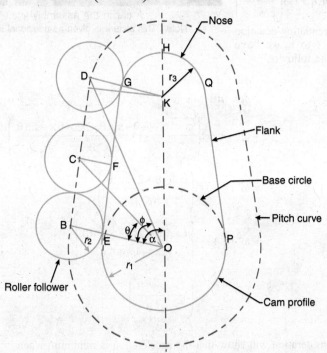

Fig. 20.40. Tangent cam with reciprocating roller follower having contact with straight flanks.

---

* Since the cam is assumed to be stationary, the angle θ is turned by the roller.

Differentiating equation (*i*) with respect to *t*, we have velocity of the follower,

$$v = \frac{dx}{dt} = \frac{dx}{d\theta} \times \frac{d\theta}{dt} = (r_1 + r_2)\left(\frac{\sin\theta}{\cos^2\theta}\right)\frac{d\theta}{dt}$$

$$= \omega(r_1 + r_2)\left(\frac{\sin\theta}{\cos^2\theta}\right) \qquad \dots (\because \ d\theta/dt = \omega) \ \dots (ii)$$

From equation (*ii*), we see that when θ increases, sin θ increases and cos θ decreases. In other words, $\sin\theta/\cos^2\theta$ increases. Thus the velocity is maximum where θ is maximum. This happens when θ = φ *i.e.* when the roller just leaves contact with the straight flank at *G* or when the straight flank merges into a circular nose.

∴ Maximum velocity of the follower,

$$v_{max} = \omega(r_1 + r_2)\left(\frac{\sin\phi}{\cos^2\phi}\right)$$

Now differentiating equation (*ii*) with respect to *t*, we have acceleration of the follower,

A car in the assembly line.
Note : This picture is given as additional information.

$$a = \frac{dv}{dt} = \frac{dv}{d\theta} \times \frac{d\theta}{dt}$$

$$= \omega(r_1 + r_2)\left(\frac{\cos^2\theta.\cos\theta - \sin\theta \times 2\cos\theta \times -\sin\theta}{\cos^4\theta}\right)\frac{d\theta}{dt}$$

$$= \omega^2(r_1 + r_2)\left(\frac{\cos^2\theta + 2\sin^2\theta}{\cos^3\theta}\right) \qquad \dots \left(\because \frac{d\theta}{dt} = \omega\right)$$

$$= \omega^2(r_1 + r_2)\left[\frac{\cos^2\theta + 2(1 - \cos^2\theta)}{\cos^3\theta}\right]$$

$$= \omega^2(r_1 + r_2)\left(\frac{2 - \cos^2\theta}{\cos^3\theta}\right) \qquad \dots (iii)$$

A little consideration will show that the acceleration is minimum when $\dfrac{2 - \cos^2\theta}{\cos^3\theta}$ is minimum. This is only possible when $(2 - \cos^2\theta)$ is minimum and $\cos^3\theta$ is maximum. This happens when $\theta = 0°$, *i.e.* when the roller is at the beginning of its lift along the straight flank (or when the roller has contact with the straight flank at E).

∴ Minimum acceleration of the follower,

$$a_{min} = \omega^2(r_1 + r_2)$$

The acceleration is maximum when $\theta = \phi$, *i.e.* when the roller just leaves contact with the straight flank at G or when the straight flank merges into a circular nose.

∴ Maximum acceleration of the follower,

$$a_{max} = \omega^2(r_1 + r_2)\left(\frac{2 - \cos^2\phi}{\cos^3\phi}\right)$$

2. When the roller has contact with the nose. A roller having contact with the circular nose at G is shown in Fig 20.41. The centre of roller lies at D on the pitch curve. The displacement is usually measured from the top position of the roller, *i.e.* when the roller has contact at the apex of the nose (point H) and the centre of roller lies at J on the pitch curve.

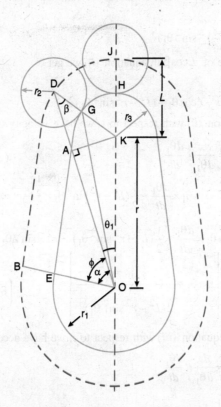

Fig. 20.41. Tangent cam with reciprocating roller follower having contact with the nose.

Let θ_1 = Angle turned by the cam measured from the position when the roller is at the top of the nose.

The displacement of the roller is given by

$$x = OJ - OD = OJ - (OA + AD) = (OK + KJ) - (OA + AD)$$

Substituting $OK = r$ and $KJ = KH + HJ = r_3 + r_2 = L$, we have

$$x = (r + L) - (OK \times \cos\theta_1 + DK\cos\beta)$$

$$= (r + L) - (r\cos\theta_1 + L\cos\beta) \qquad \ldots (\because DK = KJ = r_3 + r_2 = L)$$

$$= L + r - r\cos\theta_1 - L\cos\beta \qquad \ldots (i)$$

Now from right angled triangles OAK and DAK,

$$AK = DK\sin\beta = OK\sin\theta_1$$

or
$$L\sin\beta = r\sin\theta_1$$

Squaring both sides,

$$L^2\sin^2\beta = r^2\sin^2\theta_1 \quad \text{or} \quad L^2(1 - \cos^2\beta) = r^2\sin^2\theta_1$$

$$L^2 - L^2\cos^2\beta = r^2\sin^2\theta_1 \quad \text{or} \quad L^2\cos^2\beta = L^2 - r^2\sin^2\theta_1$$

$$\therefore \qquad L\cos\beta = (L^2 - r^2\sin^2\theta_1)^{\frac{1}{2}}$$

Substituting the value of $L\cos\beta$ in equation (i), we get

$$x = L + r - r\cos\theta_1 - (L^2 - r^2\sin^2\theta_1)^{\frac{1}{2}} \qquad \ldots (ii)$$

Differentiating equation (ii) with respect to t, we have velocity of the follower,

$$v = \frac{dx}{dt} = \frac{dx}{d\theta_1} \times \frac{d\theta_1}{dt}$$

$$= -r \times -\sin\theta_1 \times \frac{d\theta_1}{dt} - \frac{1}{2}(L^2 - r^2\sin^2\theta_1)^{-\frac{1}{2}}(-r^2 \times 2\sin\theta_1\cos\theta_1)\frac{d\theta_1}{dt}$$

$$= r\sin\theta_1 \times \frac{d\theta_1}{dt} + \frac{1}{2}(L^2 - r^2\sin^2\theta_1)^{-\frac{1}{2}}r^2 \times \sin 2\theta_1 \times \frac{d\theta_1}{dt}$$

$$= \omega.r\left[\sin\theta_1 + \frac{r\sin 2\theta_1}{2(L^2 - r^2\sin^2\theta_1)^{\frac{1}{2}}}\right] \qquad \ldots \left(\text{Substituting } \frac{d\theta_1}{dt} = \omega\right) \ldots (iii)$$

Now differentiating equation (iii) with respect to t, we have acceleration of the follower,

$$a = \frac{dv}{dt} = \frac{dv}{d\theta_1} \times \frac{d\theta_1}{dt}$$

$$= \omega.r\left[\cos\theta_1 + \frac{(L^2 - r^2\sin^2\theta_1)^{\frac{1}{2}}(r \times 2\cos 2\theta_1 + r\sin 2\theta_1 \times \frac{1}{2}(L^2 - r^2\sin^2\theta_1)^{-\frac{1}{2}}(r^2 \times 2\sin\theta_1\cos\theta_1)}{2(L^2 - r^2\sin^2\theta_1)}\right]\frac{d\theta_1}{dt}$$

Substituting $\dfrac{d\theta_1}{dt} = \omega$ and multiplying the numerator and denominator of second term by

$(L^2 - r^2 \sin^2 \theta_1)^{\frac{1}{2}}$, we have

$$a = \omega^2 . r \left[\cos \theta_1 + \frac{(L^2 - r^2 \sin^2 \theta_1)(2r\cos 2\theta_1) + \dfrac{1}{2} \times r^3 \sin^2 2\theta_1}{2(L^2 - r^2 \sin^2 \theta_1)^{3/2}} \right]$$

$$= \omega^2 . r \left[\cos \theta_1 + \frac{L^2 \times 2r\cos 2\theta_1 - 2r^3 \sin^2 \theta_1 . \cos 2\theta_1 + \dfrac{1}{2} \times r^3 (2\sin \theta_1 \cos \theta_1)^2}{2(L^2 - r^2 \sin^2 \theta_1)^{3/2}} \right]$$

$$= \omega^2 . r \left[\cos \theta_1 + \frac{2L^2 . r\cos 2\theta_1 - 2r^3 . \sin^2 \theta_1 (1 - 2\sin^2 \theta_1) + 2r^3 \sin^2 \theta_1 (1 - \sin^2 \theta_1)}{2(L^2 - r^2 \sin^2 \theta_1)^{3/2}} \right]$$

$$= \omega^2 . r \left[\cos \theta_1 + \frac{L^2 . r\cos 2\theta_1 + r^3 \sin^4 \theta_1}{(L^2 - r^2 \sin^2 \theta_1)^{3/2}} \right]$$

Notes : 1. Since θ_1 is measured from the top position of the roller, therefore for the roller to have contact at the apex of the nose (*i.e.* at point *H*), then $\theta_1 = 0$, and for the roller to have contact where straight flank merges into a nose (*i.e.* at point *G*), then $\theta_1 = \alpha - \phi$.

2. The velocity is zero at *H* and maximum at *G*.

3. The acceleration is minimum at *H* and maximum at *G*.

4. From Fig 20.41, we see that the distances *OK* and *KD* remains constant for all positions of the roller when it moves along the circular nose. In other words, a tangent cam operating a roller follower and having contact with the nose is equivalent to a slider crank mechanism (*i.e.* *ODK*) in which the roller is assumed equivalent to the slider *D*, crank *OK* and connecting rod *DK*. Therefore the velocity and acceleration of the roller follower may be obtained graphically as discussed in Chapters 7 and 8.

Example 20.13. *In a symmetrical tangent cam operating a roller follower, the least radius of the cam is 30 mm and roller radius is 17.5 mm. The angle of ascent is 75° and the total lift is 17.5 mm. The speed of the cam shaft is 600 r.p.m. Calculate : 1. the principal dimensions of the cam ; 2. the accelerations of the follower at the beginning of the lift, where straight flank merges into the circular nose and at the apex of the circular nose. Assume that there is no dwell between ascent and descent.*

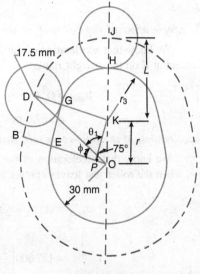

Fig. 20.42

Solution. Given : $r_1 = 30$ mm ; $r_2 = 17.5$ mm ; $\alpha = 75°$; Total lift = 17.5 mm ; $N = 600$ r.p.m. or $\omega = 2\pi \times 600/60 = 62.84$ rad/s

1. Principal dimensions of the cam

Let $r = OK =$ Distance between cam centre and nose centre,

$r_3 =$ Nose radius, and

$\phi =$ Angle of contact of cam with straight flanks.

From the geometry of Fig. 20.42,

$$r + r_3 = r_1 + \text{Total lift}$$

$$= 30 + 17.5 = 47.5 \text{ mm}$$

∴ $\qquad r = 47.5 - r_3$ $\qquad\qquad ...(i)$

Also, $\qquad OE = OP + PE \qquad$ or $\qquad r_1 = OP + r_3$

∴ $\qquad OP = r_1 - r_3 = 30 - r_3$ $\qquad\qquad ...(ii)$

Now from right angled triangle OKP,

$$OP = OK \times \cos\alpha \qquad\qquad ...(\because \cos\alpha = OP/OK)$$

or $\qquad 30 - r_3 = (47.5 - r_3)\cos 75° = (47.5 - r_3)0.2588 = 12.3 - 0.2588\, r_3$

$$...(\because OK = r)$$

∴ $\qquad r_3 = 23.88 \text{ mm } \textbf{Ans.}$

and $\qquad r = OK = 47.5 - r_3 = 47.5 - 23.88 = 23.62 \text{ mm } \textbf{Ans.}$

Again, from right angled triangle ODB,

$$\tan\phi = \frac{DB}{OB} = \frac{KP}{OB} = \frac{OK \sin\alpha}{r_1 + r_2} = \frac{23.62 \sin 75°}{30 + 17.5} = 0.4803$$

∴ $\qquad \phi = 25.6° \textbf{ Ans.}$

2. Acceleration of the follower at the beginning of the lift

We know that acceleration of the follower at the beginning of the lift, *i.e.* when the roller has contact at E on the straight flank,

$$a_{min} = \omega^2 (r_1 + r_2) = (62.84)^2 (30 + 17.5)^2 = 187\,600 \text{ mm/s}^2$$

$$= 187.6 \text{ m/s}^2 \textbf{ Ans.}$$

Acceleration of the follower where straight flank merges into a circular nose

We know that acceleration of the follower where straight flank merges into a circular nose *i.e.* when the roller just leaves contact at G,

$$a_{max} = \omega^2 (r_1 + r_2) \left[\frac{2 - \cos^2\phi}{\cos^3\phi}\right] = (62.84)^2 (30 + 17.5)\left(\frac{2 - \cos^2 25.6°}{\cos^3 25.6°}\right)$$

$$= 187\,600 \left(\frac{2 - 0.813}{0.733}\right) = 303\,800 \text{ mm/s}^2 = 303.8 \text{ m/s}^2 \textbf{ Ans.}$$

Acceleration of the follower at the apex of the circular nose

We know that acceleration of the follower for contact with the circular nose,

$$a = \omega^2 . r \left[\cos \theta_1 + \frac{L^2 . r \cos 2\theta_1 + r^3 \sin^4 \theta_1}{(L^2 - r^2 \sin^2 \theta_1)^{3/2}} \right]$$

Since θ_1 is measured from the top position of the follower, therefore for the follower to have contact at the apex of the circular nose (*i.e.* at point H), $\theta_1 = 0$.

∴ Acceleration of the follower at the apex of the circular nose,

$$a = \omega^2 . r \left(1 + \frac{L^2 . r}{L^3} \right) = \omega^2 . r \left(1 + \frac{r}{L} \right) = \omega^2 . r \left(1 + \frac{r}{r_2 + r_3} \right)$$

$$= (62.84)^2 \, 23.62 \left(1 + \frac{23.62}{17.5 + 23.88} \right) = 146\ 530 \text{ mm/s}^2 \quad \dots (\because L = r_2 + r_3)$$

$$= 146.53 \text{ m/s}^2 \text{ Ans.}$$

Example 20.14. *A cam has straight working faces which are tangential to a base circle of diameter 90 mm. The follower is a roller of diameter 40 mm and the centre of roller moves along a straight line passing through the centre line of the cam shaft. The angle between the tangential faces of the cam is 90° and the faces are joined by a nose circle of 10 mm radius. The speed of rotation of the cam is 120 revolutions per min.*

Find the acceleration of the roller centre 1. when during the lift, the roller is just about to leave the straight flank ; and 2. when the roller is at the outer end of its lift.

Solution. Given : $d_1 = 90$ mm or $r_1 = 45$ mm ; $d_2 = 40$ mm or $r_2 = 20$ mm ; 2 α = 90° or α = 45° ; $r_3 = 10$ mm ; $N = 120$ r.p.m. or ω = 2 π × 120/60 = 12.57 rad/s

The tangent cam operating a roller follower is shown in Fig. 20.43.

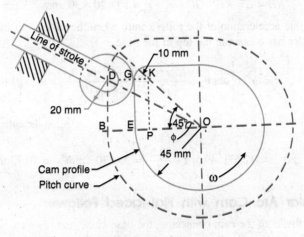

Fig. 20.43

First of all, let us find the *angle turned by the cam (ϕ) when the roller is just about to leave the straight flank at G. The centre of roller at this position lies at D.

---

* Since the cam is assumed to be stationary, ϕ is the angle turned by the roller when it is just about to leave the straight flank at G.

From the geometry of the figure,

$$BD = PK = OP = OE - PE$$

$$= OE - KG$$

$$= r_1 - r_3 = 45 - 10 = 35 \text{ mm}$$

Now from triangle OBD,

$$\tan \phi = \frac{BD}{OB} = \frac{BD}{OE + EB}$$

$$= \frac{BD}{r_1 + r_2} = \frac{35}{45 + 20} = 0.5385$$

In aircraft engines roller followers are widely used.

$$\therefore \qquad \phi = 28.3°$$

1. Acceleration of the roller centre when roller is just about to leave the straight flank

We know that acceleration of the roller centre when the roller is just about to leave the straight flank,

$$a = \omega^2 (r_1 + r_2) \left(\frac{2 - \cos^2 \phi}{\cos^3 \phi} \right) = (12.57)^2 (45 + 20) \left(\frac{2 - \cos^2 28.3°}{\cos^3 28.3°} \right)$$

$$= 18\ 500 \text{ mm/s}^2 = 18.5 \text{ m/s}^2 \text{ Ans.}$$

2. Acceleration of the roller centre when the roller is at the outer end of the lift

First of all, let us find the values of OK and KD. From the geometry of the figure,

$$OK = r = \sqrt{(OP)^2 + (PK)^2} = \sqrt{2} \times OP \qquad \qquad \ldots (\because OP = PK)$$

$$= \sqrt{2}(OE - EP) = \sqrt{2}(45 - 10) = 49.5 \text{ mm}$$

$$KD = L = KG + GD = r_3 + r_2 = 10 + 20 = 30 \text{ mm}$$

We know that acceleration of the roller centre when the roller is at the outer end of the lift, *i.e.* when the roller has contact at the top of the nose,

$$a = \omega^2 . r \left[\cos \theta_1 + \frac{L^2 . r \cos 2\theta_1 + r^3 \sin^4 \theta_1}{(L^2 - r^2 \sin^2 \theta_1)^{3/2}} \right] = \omega^2 . r \left(1 + \frac{r}{L} \right)$$

$$\ldots (\because \text{ At the outer end of the lift, } \theta_1 = 0)$$

$$= (12.57)^2 49.5 \left(1 + \frac{49.5}{30} \right) = 20\ 730 \text{ mm/s}^2 = 20.73 \text{ m/s}^2 \text{ Ans.}$$

20.13. Circular Arc Cam with Flat-faced Follower

When the flanks of the cam connecting the base circle and nose are of convex circular arcs, then the cam is known as *circular arc cam.* A symmetrical circular arc cam operating a flat-faced follower is shown in Fig. 20.44, in which O and Q are the centres of cam and nose respectively. EF and GH are two circular flanks whose centres lie at P and P' respectively. The centres * P and P'

---

* The centres P and P' may also be obtained by drawing arcs with centres O and Q and radii equal to OP and PQ respectively. The circular flanks EF and GH are now drawn with centres P and P' and radius equal to PE.

lie on lines *EO* and *GO* produced.

Let
r_1 = Minimum radius of the cam or radius of the base circle = *OE*,

r_2 = Radius of nose,

R = Radius of circular flank = *PE*,

2α = Total angle of action of cam = angle *EOG*,

α = Semi-angle of action of cam or angle of ascent = angle *EOK*, and

φ = Angle of action of cam on the circular flank.

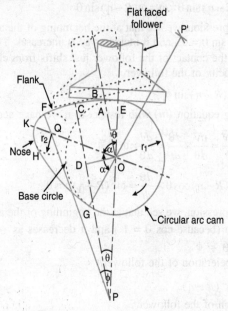

Fig. 20.44. Circular arc cam with flat face of the follower having contact with the circular flank.

We shall consider the following two cases :

1. When the flat face of the follower has contact on the circular flank, and

2. When the flat face of the follower has contact on the nose.

In deriving the expressions for displacement, velocity and acceleration of the follower for the above two cases, it is assumed that the cam is fixed and the follower rotates in the opposite sense to that of the cam. In Fig. 20.44, the cam is rotating in the clockwise direction and the follower rotates in the counter-clockwise direction.

1. *When the flat face of the follower has contact on the circular flank.* First of all, let us consider that the flat face of the follower has contact at *E* (*i.e.* at the junction of the circular flank and base circle). When the cam turns through an angle θ (less than φ) relative to the follower, the contact of the flat face of the follower will shift from *E* to *C* on the circular flank, such that flat face of the follower is perpendicular to *PC*. Since *OB* is perpendicular to *BC*, therefore *OB* is parallel to *PC*. From *O*, draw *OD* perpendicular to *PC*.

From the geometry of the figure, the displacement or lift of the follower (*x*) at any instant for contact on the circular flank, is given by

$$x = BA = BO - AO = CD - EO \qquad \ldots (i)$$

We know that

$$CD = PC - PD = PE - OP \cos \theta$$

$$= OP + OE - OP \cos \theta = OE + OP (1 - \cos \theta)$$

Substituting the value of CD in equation (i),

$$x = OE + OP(1 - \cos \theta) - EO = OP(1 - \cos \theta)$$

$$= (PE - OE)(1 - \cos \theta) = (R - r_1)(1 - \cos \theta) \qquad \ldots (ii)$$

Differentiating equation (ii) with respect to t, we have velocity of the follower,

$$v = \frac{dx}{dt} = \frac{dx}{d\theta} \times \frac{d\theta}{dt} = \frac{dx}{d\theta} \times \omega \qquad \ldots \left(\text{substituting } \frac{d\theta}{dt} = \omega \right)$$

$$= (R - r_1) \sin \theta \times \omega = \omega(R - r_1) \sin \theta \qquad \ldots (iii)$$

From the above expression, we see that at the beginning of the ascent (*i.e.* when $\theta = 0$), the velocity is zero (because $\sin 0 = 0$) and it increases as θ increases. The velocity will be maximum when $\theta = \phi$, *i.e.* when the contact of the follower just shifts from circular flank to circular nose. Therefore maximum velocity of the follower,

$$v_{max} = \omega(R - r_1) \sin \phi$$

Now differentiating equation (iii) with respect to t, we have acceleration of the follower,

$$a = \frac{dv}{dt} = \frac{dv}{d\theta} \times \frac{d\theta}{dt} = \frac{dv}{d\theta} \times \omega$$

$$= \omega(R - r_1) \cos \theta \times \frac{d\theta}{dt} = \omega^2 (R - r_1) \cos \theta \qquad \ldots \left(\because \frac{d\theta}{dt} = \omega \right) \ldots (iv)$$

From the above expression, we see that at the beginning of the ascent (*i.e.* when $\theta = 0$), the acceleration is maximum (because $\cos 0 = 1$) and it decreases as θ increases. The acceleration will be minimum when $\theta = \phi$.

∴   Maximum acceleration of the follower,

$$a_{max} = \omega^2 (R - r_1)$$

and minimum acceleration of the follower,

$$a_{min} = \omega^2 (R - r_1) \cos \phi$$

2. When the flat face of the follower has contact on the nose. The flat face of the follower having contact on the nose at C is shown in Fig. 20.45. The centre of curvature of the nose lies at Q. In this case, the displacement or lift of the follower at any instant when the cam has turned through an angle θ (greater than ϕ) is given by

$$x = AB = OB - OA = CD - OA \qquad \ldots (\because \ OB = CD) \ldots (i)$$

But $CD = CQ + QD = CQ + OQ \cos(\alpha - \theta)$

Substituting the value of CD in equation (i), we have

$$x = CQ + OQ \cos(\alpha - \theta) - OA \qquad \ldots (ii)$$

The displacement or lift of the follower when the contact is at the apex K of the nose *i.e.* when $\alpha - \theta = 0$ is

$$^* x = CQ + OQ - OA = r_2 + OQ - r_1$$

---

*   From the geometry of Fig. 20.45, we also find that lift of the follower when the contact is at the apex K of the nose is

$$x = JK = OQ + QK - OJ = OQ + r_2 - r_1$$

Differentiating equation (*ii*) with respect to *t*, we have velocity of the follower,

$$v = \frac{dx}{dt} = \frac{dx}{d\theta} \times \frac{d\theta}{dt} = \frac{dx}{d\theta} \times \omega$$

$$= OQ \sin(\alpha - \theta)\omega = \omega \times OQ \sin(\alpha - \theta) \qquad \ldots (iii)$$

$$\ldots (\because \ CQ, OQ, OA \text{ and } \alpha \text{ are constant})$$

From the above expression, we see that the velocity is zero when $\alpha - \theta = 0$ or $\alpha = \theta$ *i.e.* when the follower is at the apex *K* of the nose. The velocity will be maximum when $(\alpha - \theta)$ is maximum. This happens when the follower changes contact from circular flank to circular nose at point *F*, *i.e.* when $(\alpha - \theta) = \phi$.

Now differentiating equation (*iii*) with respect to *t*, we have acceleration of the follower,

$$a = \frac{dv}{dt} = \frac{dv}{d\theta} \times \frac{d\theta}{dt} = \frac{dv}{d\theta} \times \omega$$

$$= -\omega \times OQ \cos(\alpha - \theta)\omega = -\omega^2 \times OQ \cos(\alpha - \theta) \qquad \ldots (iv)$$

The negative sign in the above expression shows that there is a retardation when the follower is in contact with the nose of the cam.

From the above expression, we see that retardation is maximum when $\alpha - \theta = 0$ or $\theta = \alpha$, *i.e.* when the follower is at the apex *K* of the nose.

∴ Maximum retardation $= \omega^2 \times OQ$

The retardation is minimum when $\alpha - \theta$ is maximum. This happens when the follower changes contact from circular flank to circular nose at point *F i.e.* when $\theta = \phi$.

∴ Minimum retardation $= \omega^2 \times OQ \cos(\alpha - \phi)$

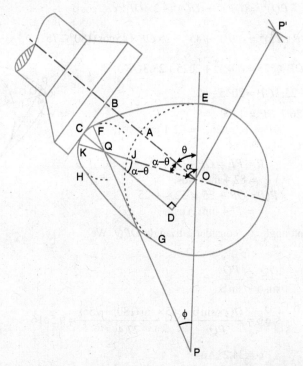

Fig. 20.45. Circular arc cam with flat face of the follower having contact on the nose.

Example 20.15. *A symmetrical circular cam operating a flat-faced follower has the following particulars :*

Minimum radius of the cam = 30 mm ; Total lift = 20 mm ; Angle of lift = 75° ; Nose radius = 5 mm ; Speed = 600 r.p.m. Find : 1. the principal dimensions of the cam, and 2. the acceleration of the follower at the beginning of the lift, at the end of contact with the circular flank , at the beginning of contact with nose and at the apex of the nose.

Solution. Given : $r_1 = OE = 30$ mm ; $x = JK = 20$ mm ; $\alpha = 75°$; $r_2 = QF = QK = 5$ mm ; $N = 600$ r.p.m. or $\omega = 2\pi \times 600/60 = 62.84$ rad/s

1. Principal dimensions of the cam

A symmetrical circular cam operating a flat faced follower is shown in Fig. 20.46.

Let OQ = Distance between cam centre and nose centre,

$R = PE$ = Radius of circular flank, and

ϕ = Angle of contact on the circular flank.

We know that lift of the follower (x),

$$20 = OQ + r_2 - r_1 = OQ + 5 - 30 = OQ - 25$$

∴ $$OQ = 20 + 25 = 45 \text{ mm } \textbf{Ans.}$$

We know that $$PQ = PF - FQ = PE - FQ = OP + OE - FQ$$

$$= OP + 30 - 5 = (OP + 25) \text{ mm}$$

Now from a triangle OPQ,

$$(PQ)^2 = (OP)^2 + (OQ)^2 - 2 \times OP \times OQ \cos\beta$$

$$(OP + 25)^2 = (OP)^2 + 45^2 - 2 \times OP \times 45 \cos(180° - 75°)$$

$$(OP)^2 + 50\,OP + 625 = (OP)^2 + 2025 + 23.3\,OP$$

$$50\,OP - 23.3\,OP = 2025 - 625$$

or $$26.7 \; OP = 1400$$

and $$OP = 1400/26.7 = 52.4 \text{ mm}$$

∴ Radius of circular flanks,

$$R = PE = OP + OE = 52.4 + 30$$

$$= 82.4 \text{ mm } \textbf{Ans.}$$

and $$PQ = OP + 25 = 52.4 + 25$$

$$= 77.4 \text{ mm } \textbf{Ans.}$$

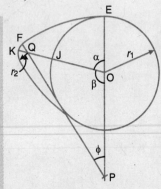

Fig. 20.46

In order to find angle ϕ, consider a triangle OPQ. We know that

$$\frac{OQ}{\sin\phi} = \frac{PQ}{\sin\beta}$$

or $$\sin\phi = \frac{OQ \times \sin\beta}{PQ} = \frac{45 \times \sin(180° - 75°)}{77.4} = 0.5616$$

∴ $$\phi = 34.2° \textbf{ Ans.}$$

2. Acceleration of the follower

We know that acceleration of the follower at the beginning of the lift,

$$a = \omega^2 (R - r_1) \cos\theta = \omega^2 (R - r_1) \quad \dots (\because \text{At the beginning of lift, } \theta = 0°)$$

$$= (62.84)^2 (82.4 - 30) = 206\ 930 \text{ mm/s} = 206.93 \text{ m/s}^2 \text{ **Ans.**}$$

Acceleration of the follower at the end of contact with the circular flank,

$$a = \omega^2 (R - r_1) \cos\theta = \omega^2 (R - r_1) \cos\phi$$

$$\dots (\because \text{ At the end of contact with the circular flank, } \theta = \phi)$$

$$= (62.84)^2 (82.4 - 30) \cos 34.2° = 171\ 130 \text{ mm/s}^2 = 171.13 \text{ m/s}^2 \text{ **Ans.**}$$

Acceleration of the follower at the beginning of contact with nose,

$$a = -\omega^2 \times OQ \cos(\alpha - \theta) = -\omega^2 \times OQ \cos(\alpha - \phi)$$

$$\dots (\because \text{ At the beginning of contact with nose, } \theta = \phi)$$

$$= -(62.84)^2\ 45 \cos(75° - 34.2°) = -134\ 520 \text{ mm/s}^2 = -134.52 \text{ m/s}^2$$

$$= 134.52 \text{ m/s}^2 \text{ **(Retardation) Ans.**}$$

and acceleration of the follower at the apex of nose,

$$a = -\omega^2 \times OQ \cos(\alpha - \theta) = -\omega^2 \times OQ \quad \dots (\because \text{At the apex of nose, } \alpha - \theta = 0)$$

$$= -(62.84)^2\ 45 = -177\ 700 \text{ mm/s}^2 = -177.7 \text{ m/s}^2$$

$$= 177.7 \text{ m/s}^2 \text{ **(Retardation) Ans.**}$$

Example 20.16. *A symmetrical cam with convex flanks operates a flat-footed follower. The lift is 8 mm, base circle radius 25 mm and the nose radius 12 mm. The total angle of the cam action is 120°.*

1. Find the radius of convex flanks, 2. Draw the profile of the cam, and 3. Determine the maximum velocity and the maximum acceleration when the cam shaft rotates at 500 r.p.m.

Solution. Given : $x = JK = 8$ mm ; $r_1 = OE = OJ = 25$ mm ; $r_2 = QF = QK = 12$ mm ; $2\alpha = \angle EOG = 120°$ or $\alpha = \angle EOK = 60°$; $N = 500$ r.p.m. or $\omega = 2\pi \times 500/60 = 52.37$ rad/s

1. Radius of convex flanks

Let R = Radius of convex flanks = $PE = P'G$

A symmetrical cam with convex flanks operating a flat footed follower is shown in Fig. 20.47. From the geometry of the figure,

$$OQ = OJ + JK - QK = r_1 + x - r_2$$

$$= 25 + 8 - 12 = 21 \text{ mm}$$

$$PQ = PF - QF = PE - QF = (R - 12) \text{ mm}$$

and

$$OP = PE - OE = (R - 25) \text{ mm}$$

Now consider the triangle OPQ. We know that

$$(PQ)^2 = (OP)^2 + (OQ)^2 - 2\,OP \times OQ \times \cos\beta$$

$$(R-12)^2 = (R-25)^2 + (21)^2 - 2(R-25)21\cos(180°-60°)$$

$$R^2 - 24R + 144 = R^2 - 50R + 625 + 441 + 21R - 525$$

$$-24R + 144 = -29R + 541 \text{ or } 5R = 397$$

$$\therefore \qquad R = 397/5 = 79.4 \text{ mm } \textbf{Ans.}$$

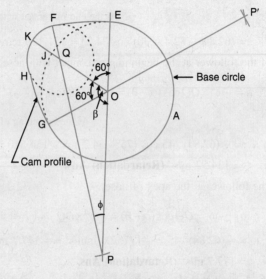

Fig. 20.47

2. Profile of the cam

The profile of the cam, as shown in Fig. 20.47, is drawn as discussed in the following steps :

(a) First of all, draw a base circle with centre O and radius $OE = r_1 = 25$ mm.

(b) Draw angle $EOK = 60°$ and angle $KOG = 60°$ such that the total angle of cam action is 120°.

(c) On line OK mark $OQ = 21$ mm (as calculated above). Now Q as centre, draw a circle of radius equal to the nose radius $r_2 = QK = QF = 12$ mm. This circle cuts the line OK at J. Now JK represents the lift of the follower (*i.e.* 8 mm).

(d) Produce EO and GO as shown in Fig. 20.47. Now with Q as centre and radius equal to $PQ = R - r_2 = 79.4 - 12 = 67.4$ mm, draw arcs intersecting the lines EO and GO produced at P and P' respectively. The centre P' may also be obtained by drawing arcs with centres O and Q and radii OP and PQ respectively.

(e) Now with P and P' as centres and radius equal to $R = 79.4$ mm, draw arcs EF and GH which represent the convex flanks. $EFKHGAE$ is the profile of the cam.

3. Maximum velocity and maximum acceleration

First of all, let us find the angle ϕ. From triangle OPQ,

$$\frac{OQ}{\sin\phi} = \frac{PQ}{\sin\beta}$$

or
$$\sin\phi = \frac{OQ}{PQ} \times \sin\beta = \frac{21}{79.4-12} \times \sin(180° - 60°) = 0.2698$$

$$\ldots (\because \ PQ = R - 12\ )$$

$$\therefore \qquad \phi = 15.65°$$

We know that maximum velocity,

$$v_{max} = \omega(R - r_1)\sin\phi = 52.37(79.4-25)\sin 15.65° = 770 \ \text{mm/s}$$
$$= 0.77 \ \text{m/s} \ \textbf{Ans.}$$

and maximum acceleration,

$$a_{max} = \omega^2(R - r_1) = (52.37)^2(79.4-25) = 149\,200 \ \text{mm/s}^2 = 149.2 \ \text{m/s}^2 \ \textbf{Ans.}$$

Example 20.17. *The following particulars relate to a symmetrical circular cam operating a flat faced follower :*

Least radius = 16 mm, nose radius = 3.2 mm, distance between cam shaft centre and nose centre = 25 mm, angle of action of cam = 150°, and cam shaft speed = 600 r.p.m.

Assuming that there is no dwell between ascent or descent, determine the lift of the valve, the flank radius and the acceleration and retardation of the follower at a point where circular nose merges into circular flank.

Solution. Given : $r_1 = OE = OJ = 16$ mm ; $r_2 = QK = QF = 3.2$ mm ; $OQ = 25$ mm ; $2\ \alpha = 150°$ or $\alpha = 75°$; $N = 600$ r.p.m. or $\omega = 2\pi \times 600/60 = 62.84$ rad/s

Lift of the valve

A symmetrical circular cam operating a flat faced follower is shown in Fig. 20.48.

We know that lift of the valve,

$$x = JK = OK - OJ$$

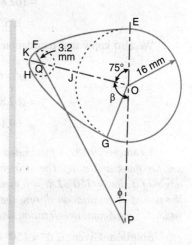

$$= OQ + QK - OJ = OQ + r_2 - r_1$$
$$= 25 + 3.2 - 16 = 12.2 \ \text{mm} \ \textbf{Ans.}$$

Flank radius

Let $\qquad R = PE =$ Flank radius.

First of all, let us find out the values of OP and PQ. From the geometry of Fig. 20.48,

$$OP = PE - OE = R - 16$$

and $\qquad PQ = PF - FQ = R - 3.2$

Fig. 20.48

Now consider the triangle OPQ. We know that

$$(PQ)^2 = (OP)^2 + (OQ)^2 - 2OP \times OQ \times \cos\beta$$

Substituting the values of OP and PQ in the above expression,

$$(R - 3.2)^2 = (R - 16)^2 + (25)^2 - 2(R - 16) \times 25 \cos(180° - 75°)$$

$$R^2 - 6.4R + 10.24 = R^2 - 32R + 256 + 625 - (50R - 800)(-0.2588)$$

$$-6.4R + 10.24 = -19.06R + 673.96 \quad \text{or} \quad 12.66\,R = 663.72$$

∴ $\qquad\qquad\qquad R = 52.43$ mm **Ans.**

Acceleration and retardation of the follower at a point where circular nose merges into circular flank

From Fig. 20.48 we see that at a point F, the circular nose merges into a circular flank. Let ϕ be the angle of action of cam at point F. From triangle OPQ,

$$\frac{OQ}{\sin\phi} = \frac{PQ}{\sin\beta}$$

or $\qquad\qquad \sin\phi = \dfrac{OQ}{PQ} \times \sin(180° - 75°) = \dfrac{OQ}{PF - FQ} \times \sin 105°$

$$= \frac{25}{52.43 - 3.2} \times 0.966 = 0.4907$$

∴ $\qquad\qquad\qquad \phi = 29.4°$

We know that acceleration of the follower,

$$a = \omega^2 \times OP \times \cos\theta = \omega^2 (R - r_1)\cos\phi \qquad \dots(\because \quad \theta = \phi)$$

$$= (62.84)^2 (52.43 - 16) \cos 29.4° = 125\,330 \text{ mm/s}^2$$

$$= 125.33 \text{ m/s}^2 \text{ **Ans.**}$$

We also know that retardation of the follower,

$$a = \omega^2 \times OQ \cos(\alpha - \theta) = \omega^2 \times OQ \cos(\alpha - \phi) \qquad \dots(\because \quad \theta = \phi)$$

$$= (62.84)^2\, 25 \cos(75° - 29.4°) = 69\,110 \text{ mm/s}^2$$

$$= 69.11 \text{ m/s}^2 \text{ **Ans.**}$$

Example 20.18. *A flat ended valve tappet is operated by a symmetrical cam with circular arc for flank and nose. The straight line path of the tappet passes through the cam axis. Total angle of action = 150°. Lift = 6 mm. Base circle diameter = 30 mm. Period of acceleration is half the period of retardation during the lift. The cam rotates at 1250 r.p.m. Find : 1. flank and nose radii ; 2. maximum acceleration and retardation during the lift.*

Solution. Given : $2\alpha = 150°$ or $\alpha = 75°$; $x = JK = 6$ mm ; $d_1 = 30$ mm or $r_1 = OE = OJ = 15$ mm ; $N = 1250$ r.p.m. or $\omega = 2\pi \times 1250/60 = 131$ rad/s

1. *Flank and nose radii*

The circular arc cam operating a flat ended valve tappet is shown in Fig. 20.49.

Let $\qquad\qquad R = PE = $ Flank radius, and

$\qquad\qquad r_2 = QF = QK = $ Nose radius.

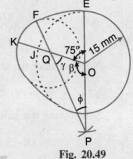

Fig. 20.49

First of all, let us find the values of *OP*, *OQ* and *PQ*. The acceleration takes place while the follower is on the flank and retardation while the follower is on nose. Since the period of acceleration is half the period of retardation during the lift, therefore

$$\phi = \frac{1}{2}\gamma \qquad \qquad \dots (i)$$

We know that $\qquad \beta = 180° - \alpha = 180° - 75° = 105°$

∴ $\qquad \qquad \phi + \gamma = 75° = 180° - \beta = 180° - 105° = 75° \qquad \qquad \dots (ii)$

From equations (*i*) and (*ii*),

$$\phi = 25° \text{ , } \quad \text{and} \quad \gamma = 50°$$

Now from the geometry of Fig. 20.49,

$$OQ = OJ + JK - QK = r_1 + x - r_2 = 15 + 6 - r_2 = 21 - r_2 \qquad \dots (iii)$$

and $\qquad \qquad PQ = PF - FQ = PE - FQ = (OP + OE) - FQ = OP + 15 - r_2 \qquad \dots (iv)$

Now from triangle *OPQ*,

$$\frac{OP}{\sin\gamma} = \frac{OQ}{\sin\phi} = \frac{PQ}{\sin\beta}$$

or $\qquad \qquad \dfrac{OP}{\sin 50°} = \dfrac{21 - r_2}{\sin 25°} = \dfrac{OP + 15 - r_2}{\sin 105°}$

∴ $\qquad \qquad OP = \dfrac{21 - r_2}{\sin 25°} \times \sin 50° = \dfrac{21 - r_2}{0.4226} \times 0.766 = 38 - 1.8\, r_2 \qquad \dots (v)$

Also $\qquad \qquad OP = \dfrac{OP + 15 - r_2}{\sin 105°} \times \sin 50° = \dfrac{OP + 15 - r_2}{0.966} \times 0.766$

$$= 0.793 \times OP + 11.9 - 0.793\, r_2$$

∴ $\qquad 0.207\, OP = 11.9 - 0.793\, r_2 \quad \text{or} \quad OP = 57.5 - 3.83\, r_2 \qquad \dots (vi)$

From equations (*v*) and (*vi*),

$$38 - 1.8\, r_2 = 57.5 - 3.83\, r_2 \quad \text{or} \quad 2.03\, r_2 = 19.5$$

∴ $\qquad \qquad r_2 = 9.6 \text{ mm **Ans.**}$

We know that $\qquad OP = 38 - 1.8\, r_2 = 38 - 1.8 \times 9.6 = 20.7 \text{ mm} \qquad \dots \text{[From equation (v)]}$

∴ $\qquad \qquad R = PE = OP + OE = 20.7 + 15 = 35.7 \text{ mm **Ans.**}$

2. Maximum acceleration and retardation during the lift

We know that maximum acceleration

$$= \omega^2 (R - r_1) = \omega^2 \times OP = (131)^2\, 20.7 = 355\,230 \text{ mm/s}^2$$
$$= 355.23 \text{ m/s}^2 \text{ **Ans.**}$$

and maximum retardation, $\quad = \omega^2 \times OQ = \omega^2 (21 - r_2) \qquad \dots \text{[From equation (iii)]}$

$$= (131)^2 (21 - 9.6) = 195\,640 \text{ mm/s}^2 = 195.64 \text{ m/s}^2 \text{ **Ans.**}$$

Example 20.19. *A cam consists of a circular disc of diameter 75 mm with its centre displaced 25 mm from the camshaft axis. The follower has a flat surface (horizontal) in contact with the cam and the line of action of the follower is vertical and passes through the shaft axis as shown in Fig. 20.50. The mass of the follower is 2.3 kg and is pressed downwards by a spring which has a stiffness of 3.5 N/mm. In the lowest position the spring force is 45 N.*

1. Derive an expression for the acceleration of the follower in terms of the angle of rotation from the beginning of the lift.

2. As the cam shaft speed is gradually increased, a value is reached at which the follower begins to lift from the cam surface. Determine the camshaft speed for this condition.

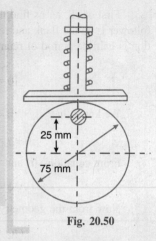

Fig. 20.50

Solution. Given : $d = 75$ mm   or $r = OA = 37.5$ mm ; $OQ = 25$ mm ; $m = 2.3$ kg ; $s = 3.5$ N/mm ; $S = 45$ N

1. *Expression for the acceleration of the follower*

The cam in its lowest position is shown by full lines in Fig. 20.51 and by dotted lines when it has rotated through an angle θ.

From the geometry of the figure, the displacement of the follower,

$$x = AB = OS = OQ - QS$$

$$= OQ - PQ\cos\theta$$

$$= OQ - OQ\cos\theta \qquad ... (\because PQ = OQ)$$

$$= OQ(1 - \cos\theta) = 25(1 - \cos\theta) \qquad ... (i)$$

Differentiating equation (*i*) with respect to *t*, we get velocity of the follower,

$$v = \frac{dx}{dt} = \frac{dx}{d\theta} \times \frac{d\theta}{dt} = \frac{dx}{d\theta} \times \omega$$

$$... \text{(Substituting } d\theta/dt = \omega)$$

$$= 25\sin\theta \times \omega = 25\,\omega\sin\theta \qquad ... (ii)$$

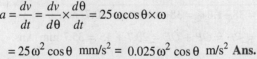

Fig. 20.51

Now differentiating equation (*ii*) with respect to *t*, we get acceleration of the follower,

$$a = \frac{dv}{dt} = \frac{dv}{d\theta} \times \frac{d\theta}{dt} = 25\,\omega\cos\theta \times \omega$$

$$= 25\,\omega^2\cos\theta \ \text{mm/s}^2 = 0.025\,\omega^2\cos\theta \ \text{m/s}^2 \ \textbf{Ans.}$$

2. *Cam shaft speed*

Let N = Cam shaft speed in r.p.m.

We know that accelerating force

$$= m.a = 2.3 \times 0.025\,\omega^2\cos\theta = 0.0575\,\omega^2\cos\theta \ \text{N}$$

Now for any value of θ, the algebraic sum of the spring force, weight of the follower and the accelerating force is equal to the vertical reaction between the cam and follower. When this reaction is zero, then the follower will just begin to leave the cam.

$$\therefore \qquad S + s.x + m.g + m.a = 0$$

$$45 + 3.5 \times 25 (1 - \cos\theta) + 2.3 \times 9.81 + 0.0575\,\omega^2 \cos\theta = 0$$

$$45 + 87.5 - 87.5 \cos\theta + 22.56 + 0.0575\,\omega^2 \cos\theta = 0$$

$$155.06 - 87.5 \cos\theta + 0.0575\,\omega^2 \cos\theta = 0$$

$$2697 - 1522 \cos\theta + \omega^2 \cos\theta = 0 \qquad \qquad \dots (\text{Dividing by } 0.0575)$$

$$\omega^2 \cos\theta = 1522 \cos\theta - 2697 \text{ or } \omega^2 = 1522 - 2697 \sec\theta$$

Since $\sec\theta \geq +1$ or, ≤ -1, therefore the minimum value of ω^2 occurs when $\theta = 180°$ therefore

$$\omega^2 = 1522 - (-2697) = 4219 \qquad \qquad \dots [\text{Substituting } \sec\theta = -1\,]$$

$$\therefore \qquad \omega = 65 \text{ rad/s}$$

and maximum allowable cam shaft speed,

$$N = \frac{\omega \times 60}{2\pi} = \frac{65 \times 60}{2\pi} = 621 \text{ r.p.m. Ans.}$$

EXERCISES

1. A disc cam is to give uniform motion to a knife edge follower during out stroke of 50 mm during the first half of the cam revolution. The follower again returns to its original position with uniform motion during the next half of the revolution. The minimum radius of the cam is 50 mm and the diameter of the cam shaft is 35 mm. Draw the profile of the cam when 1. the axis of follower passes through the axis of cam shaft, and 2. the axis of follower is offset by 20 mm from the axis of the cam shaft.

2. A cam operating a knife-edged follower has the following data :

   (a) Follower moves outwards through 40 mm during 60° of cam rotation.

   (b) Follower dwells for the next 45°.

   (c) Follower returns to its original position during next 90°.

   (d) Follower dwells for the rest of the rotation.

   The displacement of the follower is to take place with simple harmonic motion during both the outward and return strokes. The least radius of the cam is 50 mm. Draw the profile of the cam when 1. the axis of the follower passes through the cam axis, and 2. the axis of the follower is offset 20 mm towards right from the cam axis. If the cam rotates at 300 r.p.m., determine maximum velocity and acceleration of the follower during the outward stroke and the return stroke.

   [Ans. **1.88 m/s, 1.26 m/s ; 177.7 m/s², 79 m/s²**]

3. A disc cam rotating in a clockwise direction is used to move a reciprocating roller with simple harmonic motion in a radial path, as given below :

   (i) Outstroke with maximum displacement of 25 mm during 120° of cam rotation,

   (ii) Dwell for 60° of cam rotation,

   (iii) Return stroke with maximum displacement of 25 mm during 90° of cam rotation, and

   (iv) Dwell during remaining 90° of cam rotation.

   The line of reciprocation of follower passes through the camshaft axis. The maximum radius of cam is 20 mm. If the cam rotates at a uniform speed of 300 r.p.m. find the maximum velocity and acceleration during outstroke and return stroke. The roller diameter is 8 mm.

Draw the profile of the cam when the line of reciprocation of the follower is offset by 20 mm towards right from the cam shaft axis. [Ans. **0.59 m/s, 0.786 m/s ; 27.8 m/s², 49.4 m/s²**]

4. Design a cam to raise a valve with simple harmonic motion through 50 mm in 1/3 of a revolution, keep if fully raised through 1/12 revolution and to lower it with harmonic motion in 1/6 revolution. The valve remains closed during the rest of the revolution. The diameter of the roller is 20 mm and the minimum radius of the cam is 25 mm. The diameter of the camshaft is 25 mm. The axis of the valve rod passes through the axis of the camshaft. If the camshaft rotates at uniform speed of 100 r.p.m. ; find the maximum velocity and acceleration of a valve during raising and lowering.

[Ans. **0.39 m/s, 0.78 m/s ; 6.17 m/s², 24.67 m/s²**]

5. A cam rotating clockwise with a uniform speed is to give the roller follower of 20 mm diameter with the following motion :

   (a) Follower to move outwards through a distance of 30 mm during 120° of cam rotation ;

   (b) Follower to dwell for 60° of cam rotation ;

   (c) Follower to return to its initial position during 90° of cam rotation ; and

   (d) Follower to dwell for the remaining 90° of cam rotation.

   The minimum radius of the cam is 45 mm and the line of stroke of the follower is offset 15 mm from the axis of the cam and the displacement of the follower is to take place with simple harmonic motion on both the outward and return strokes. Draw the cam profile.

6. A cam rotating clockwise at a uniform speed of 100 r.p.m. is required to give motion to knife-edge follower as below :

   (a) Follower to move outwards through 25 mm during 120° of cam rotation,

   (b) Follower to dwell for the next 60° of cam rotation,

   (c) Follower to return to its starting position during next 90° of cam rotation, and

   (d) Follower to dwell for the rest of the cam rotation.

   The minimum radius of the cam is 50 mm and the line of stroke of the follower passes through the axis of the cam shaft. If the displacement of the follower takes place with uniform and equal acceleration and retardation on both the outward and return strokes, find the maximum velocity and acceleration during outstroke and return stroke. [Ans. **0.25 m/s, 0.33 m/s ; 2.5 m/s² , 4.44 m/s²**]

7. A cam with 30 mm as minimum diameter is rotating clockwise at a uniform speed of 1200 r.p.m. and has to give the following motion to a roller follower 10 mm in diameter:

   (a) Follower to complete outward stroke of 25 mm during 120° of cam rotation with equal uniform acceleration and retardation ;

   (b) Follower to dwell for 60° of cam rotation ;

   (c) Follower to return to its initial position during 90° of cam rotation with equal uniform acceleration and retardation ;

   (d) Follower to dwell for the remaining 90° of cam rotation.

   Draw the cam profile if the axis of the roller follower passes through the axis of the cam.

   Determine the maximum velocity of the follower during the outstroke and return stroke and also the uniform acceleration of the follower on the out stroke and the return stoke.

   [Ans. **3 m/s , 4 m/s ; 360.2 m/s², 640.34 m/s²**]

8. A cam rotating clockwise at a uniform speed of 200 r.p.m. is required to move an offset roller follower with a uniform and equal acceleration and retardation on both the outward and return strokes. The angle of ascent, the angle of dwell (between ascent and descent) and the angle of descent is 120°, 60° and 90° respectively. The follower dwells for the rest of cam rotation. The least radius of the cam is 50 mm, the lift of the follower is 25 mm and the diameter of the roller is 10 mm. The line of stroke of the follower is offset by 20 mm from the axis of the cam. Draw the cam profile and find the maximum velocity and acceleration of the follower during the outstroke.

9. A flat faced reciprocating follower has the following motion :

(*i*) The follower moves out for 80° of cam rotation with uniform acceleration and retardation, the acceleration being twice the retardation.

(*ii*) The follower dwells for the next 80° of cam rotation.

(*iii*) It moves in for the next 120° of cam rotation with uniform acceleration and retardation, the retardation being twice the acceleration.

(*iv*) The follower dwells for the remaining period.

The base circle diameter of the cam is 60 mm and the stroke of the follower is 20 mm. The line of movement of the follower passes through the cam centre.

Draw the displacement diagram and the profile of the cam very neatly showing all constructional details.

10. From the following data, draw the profile of a cam in which the follower moves with simple harmonic motion during ascent while it moves with uniformly accelerated motion during descent :

Least radius of cam = 50 mm ; Angle of ascent = 48° ; Angle of dwell between ascent and descent = 42° ; Angle of descent = 60° ; Lift of follower = 40 mm ; Diameter of roller = 30 mm ; Distance between the line of action of follower and the axis of cam = 20 mm.

If the cam rotates at 360 r.p.m. anticlockwise, find the maximum velocity and acceleration of the follower during descent. [Ans. 2.88 m/s ; 207.4 m/s²]

11. Draw the profile of a cam with oscillating roller follower for the following motion :

(*a*) Follower to move outwards through an angular displacement of 20° during 120° of cam rotation.

(*b*) Follower to dwell for 50° of cam rotation.

(*c*) Follower to return to its initial position in 90° of cam rotation with uniform acceleration and retardation.

(*d*) Follower to dwell for the remaining period of cam rotation.

The distance between the pivot centre and the roller centre is 130 mm and the distance between the pivot centre and cam axis is 150 mm. The minimum radius of the cam is 80 mm and the diameter of the roller is 50 mm.

12. Draw the profile of the cam when the roller follower moves with cycloidal motion as given below :

(*a*) Outstroke with maximum displacement of 44 mm during 180° of cam rotation.

(*b*) Return stroke for the next 150° of cam rotation.

(*c*) Dwell for the remaining 30° of cam rotation.

The minimum radius of the cam is 20 mm and the diameter of the roller is 10 mm. The axis of the roller follower passes through the cam shaft axis.

13. A symmetrical tangent cam operating a roller follower has the following particulars :

Radius of base circle of cam = 40 mm, roller radius = 20 mm, angle of ascent = 75°, total lift = 20 mm, speed of cam shaft = 300 r.p.m.

Determine : 1. the principal dimensions of the cam, 2. the equation for the displacement curve, when the follower is in contact with the straight flank, and 3. the acceleration of the follower when it is in contact with the straight flank where it merges into the circular nose.

[Ans. r_3 = 33 mm ; θ = 23.5° ; 89.4 m/s²]

14. A cam profile consists of two circular arcs of radii 24 mm and 12 mm, joined by straight lines, giving the follower a lift of 12 mm. The follower is a roller of 24 mm radius and its line of action is a straight line passing through the cam shaft axis. When the cam shaft has a uniform speed of 500 rev/min, find the maximum velocity and acceleration of the follower while in contact with the straight flank of the cam. [Ans. 1.2 m/s ; 198 m/s²]

15. The following particulars relate to a symmetrical tangent cam operating a roller follower :-

Least radius = 30 mm, nose radius = 24 mm, roller radius = 17.5 mm, distance between cam shaft and nose centre = 23.5 mm, angle of action of cam = 150°, cam shaft speed = 600 r.p.m.

Assuming that there is no dwell between ascent and descent, determine the lift of the valve and the acceleration of the follower at a point where straight flank merges into the circular nose.

[**Ans. 17.5 mm ; 304.5 m/s^2**]

16. Following is the data for a circular arc cam working with a flat faced reciprocating follower :

Minimum radius of the cam = 30 mm ; Total angle of cam action = 120° ; Radius of the circular arc = 80 mm ; Nose radius = 10 mm.

1. Find the distance of the centre of nose circle from the cam axis ; 2. Draw the profile of the cam to full scale; 3. Find the angle through which the cam turns when the point of contact moves from the junction of minimum radius arc and circular arc to the junction of nose radius arc and circular arc ; and 4. Find the velocity and acceleration of the follower when the cam has turned through an angle of θ = 20°. The angle θ is measured from the point where the follower just starts moving away from the cam. The angular velocity of the cam is 10 rad/s.

[**Ans. 30 mm ; 22°; 68.4 mm/s ; 1880 mm/s^2**]

17. The suction valve of a four stroke petrol engine is operated by a circular arc cam with a flat faced follower. The lift of the follower is 10 mm ; base circle diameter of the cam is 40 mm and the nose radius is 2.5 mm. The crank angle when suction valve opens is 4° after top dead centre and when the suction valve closes, the crank angle is 50° after bottom dead centre. If the cam shaft rotates at 600 r.p.m., determine: 1. maximum velocity of the valve, and 2. maximum acceleration and retardation of the valve.

[**Ans. 1.22 m/s ; 383 m/s^2, 108.6 m/s^2**]

[**Hint.** Total angle turned by the crankshaft when valve is open

= 180° − 4° + 50° = 226°

Since the engine is a four stroke cycle, therefore speed of cam shaft is half of the speed of the crank shaft.

∴ Total angle turned by the cam shaft during opening of valve, 2 α = 226/2 = 113° or α = 56.5°].

18. The following particulars relate to a symmetrical circular cam operating a flat-faced follower :

Least radius = 25 mm ; nose radius = 8 mm, lift of the valve = 10 mm, angle of action of cam = 120°, cam shaft speed = 1000 r.p.m.

Determine the flank radius and the maximum velocity, acceleration and retardation of the follower. If the mass of the follower and valve with which it is in contact is 4 kg, find the minimum force to be exerted by the spring to overcome inertia of the valve parts.

[**Ans. 88 mm ; 1.93 m/s, 690.6 m/s^2, 296 m/s^2 ; 1184 N**]

DO YOU KNOW ?

1. Write short notes on cams and followers.
2. Explain with sketches the different types of cams and followers.
3. Why a roller follower is preferred to that of a knife-edged follower ?
4. Define the following terms as applied to cam with a neat sketch :-
   (a) Base circle, (b) Pitch circle, (c) Pressure angle, and (d) Stroke of the follower.
5. What are the different types of motion with which a follower can move ?
6. Draw the displacement, velocity and acceleration diagrams for a follower when it moves with simple harmonic motion. Derive the expression for velocity and acceleration during outstroke and return stroke of the follower.
7. Draw the displacement, velocity and acceleration diagrams for a follower when it moves with uniform acceleration and retardation. Derive the expression for velocity and acceleration during outstroke and return stroke of the follower.
8. Derive expressions for displacement, velocity and acceleration for a tangent cam operating on a radial-translating roller follower :

(*i*) when the contact is on straight flank, and

(*ii*) when the contact is on circular nose.

9. Derive the expressions for displacement, velocity and acceleration for a circular arc cam operating a flat-faced follower

(*i*) when the contact is on the circular flank, and

(*ii*) when the contact is on circular nose.

OBJECTIVE TYPE QUESTIONS

1. The size of a cam depends upon .

   (*a*) base circle   (*b*) pitch circle   (*c*) prime circle   (*d*) pitch curve

2. The angle between the direction of the follower motion and a normal to the pitch curve is called

   (*a*) pitch angle   (*b*) prime angle

   (*c*) base angle   (*d*) pressure angle

3. A circle drawn with centre as the cam centre and radius equal to the distance between the cam centre and the point on the pitch curve at which the pressure angle is maximum, is called

   (*a*) base circle   (*b*) pitch circle

   (*c*) prime circle   (*d*) none of these

4. The cam follower generally used in automobile engines is

   (*a*) knife edge follower   (*b*) flat faced follower

   (*c*) spherical faced follower   (*d*) roller follower

5. The cam follower extensively used in air-craft engines is

   (*a*) knife edge follower   (*b*) flat faced follower

   (*c*) spherical faced follower   (*d*) roller follower

6. In a radial cam, the follower moves

   (*a*) in a direction perpendicular to the cam axis

   (*b*) in a direction parallel to the cam axis

   (*c*) in any direction irrespective of the cam axis

   (*d*) along the cam axis

7. A radial follower is one

   (*a*) that reciprocates in the guides   (*b*) that oscillates

   (*c*) in which the follower translates along an axis passing through the cam centre of rotation.

   (*d*) none of the above

8. Offet is provided to a cam follower mechanism to

   (*a*) minimise the side thrust   (*b*) accelerate

   (*c*) avoid jerk   (*d*) none of these

9. For low and moderate speed engines, the cam follower should move with

   (*a*) uniform velocity   (*b*) simple harmonic motion

   (*c*) uniform acceleration and retardation   (*d*) cycloidal motion

10. For high speed engines, the cam follower should move with

    (*a*) uniform velocity   (*b*) simple harmonic motion

    (*c*) uniform acceleration and retardation   (*d*) cycloidal motion

11. Which of the following displacement diagrams should be chosen for better dynamic performance of a cam-follower mechanism ?

    (*a*) simple hormonic motion   (*b*) parabolic motion

    (*c*) cycloidal motion   (*d*) none of these

12. For a given lift of the follower of a cam follower mechanism, a smaller base circle diameter is desired.

    (a) because it will give a steeper cam and higher pressure angle.

    (b) because it will give a profile with lower pressure angle

    (c) because it will avoid jumping

    (d) none of the above.

13. The linear velocity of the reciprocating roller follower when it has contact with the straight flanks of the tangent cam, is given by

    (a) $\omega(r_1 - r_2)\sin\theta$

    (b) $\omega(r_1 - r_2)\cos\theta$

    (c) $\omega(r_1 + r_2)\sin\theta\sec^2\theta$

    (d) $\omega(r_1 + r_2)\cos\theta\csc^2\theta$

    where ω = Angular velocity of the cam shaft,

    r_1 = Minimum radius of the cam,

    r_2 = Radius of the roller, and

    θ = Angle turned by the cam from the beginning of the displacement for contact

    of roller with the straight flanks.

14. The displacement of a flat faced follower when it has contact with the flank of a circular arc cam, is given by

    (a) $R(1 - \cos\theta)$

    (b) $R(1 - \sin\theta)$

    (c) $(R - r_1)(1 - \cos\theta)$

    (d) $(R - r_1)(1 - \sin\theta)$

    where. R = Radius of the flank,

    r_1 = Minimum radius of the cam, and

    θ = Angle turned by the cam for contact with the circular flank.

15. The retardation of a flat faced follower when it has contact at the apex of the nose of a circular arc cam, is given by

    (a) $\omega^2 \times OQ$

    (b) $\omega^2 \times OQ\sin\theta$

    (c) $\omega^2 \times OQ\cos\theta$

    (d) $\omega^2 \times OQ\tan\theta$

    where OQ = Distance between the centre of circular flank and centre of nose.

ANSWERS

1. (a)	2. (d)	3. (b)	4. (c)	5. (d)
6. (a)	7. (a)	8. (a)	9. (b)	10. (d)
11. (c)	12. (d)	13. (c)	14. (c)	15. (a)

21

Features

Balancing of Rotating Masses

21.1. Introduction

The high speed of engines and other machines is a common phenomenon now-a-days. It is, therefore, very essential that all the rotating and reciprocating parts should be completely balanced as far as possible. If these parts are not properly balanced, the dynamic forces are set up. These forces not only increase the loads on bearings and stresses in the various members, but also produce unpleasant and even dangerous vibrations. In this chapter we shall discuss the balancing of unbalanced forces caused by rotating masses, in order to minimise pressure on the main bearings when an engine is running.

21.2. Balancing of Rotating Masses

We have already discussed, that whenever a certain mass is attached to a rotating shaft, it exerts some centrifugal force, whose effect is to bend the shaft and to produce vibrations in it. In order to prevent the effect of centrifugal force, another mass is attached to the opposite side of the shaft, at such a position so as to balance the effect of the centrifugal force of the first mass. This is done in such a way that the centrifugal force of both the masses are made to be equal and opposite. The process of providing the second mass in order to counteract the effect of the centrifugal force of the first mass, is called *balancing of rotating masses.*

The following cases are important from the subject point of view:

1. Balancing of a single rotating mass by a single mass rotating in the same plane.
2. Balancing of a single rotating mass by two masses rotating in different planes.
3. Balancing of different masses rotating in the same plane.
4. Balancing of different masses rotating in different planes.

We shall now discuss these cases, in detail, in the following pages.

21.3. Balancing of a Single Rotating Mass By a Single Mass Rotating in the Same Plane

Consider a disturbing mass m_1 attached to a shaft rotating at ω rad/s as shown in Fig. 21.1. Let r_1 be the radius of rotation of the mass m_1 (*i.e.* distance between the axis of rotation of the shaft and the centre of gravity of the mass m_1).

We know that the centrifugal force exerted by the mass m_1 on the shaft,

$$F_{C1} = m_1 \cdot \omega^2 \cdot r_1 \qquad \ldots (i)$$

This centrifugal force acts radially outwards and thus produces bending moment on the shaft. In order to counteract the effect of this force, a balancing mass (m_2) may be attached in the same plane of rotation as that of disturbing mass (m_1) such that the centrifugal forces due to the two masses are equal and opposite.

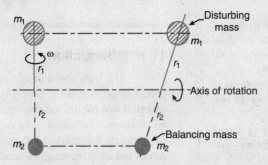

Fig. 21.1. Balancing of a single rotating mass by a single mass rotating in the same plane.

Let r_2 = Radius of rotation of the balancing mass m_2 (*i.e.* distance between the axis of rotation of the shaft and the centre of gravity of mass m_2).

∴ Centrifugal force due to mass m_2,

$$F_{C2} = m_2 \cdot \omega^2 \cdot r_2 \qquad \ldots (ii)$$

Equating equations (*i*) and (*ii*),

$$m_1 \cdot \omega^2 \cdot r_1 = m_2 \cdot \omega^2 \cdot r_2 \quad \text{or} \quad m_1 \cdot r_1 = m_2 \cdot r_2$$

Notes : 1. The product $m_2 . r_2$ may be split up in any convenient way. But the radius of rotation of the balancing mass (m_2) is generally made large in order to reduce the balancing mass m_2.

2. The centrifugal forces are proportional to the product of the mass and radius of rotation of respective masses, because ω^2 is same for each mass.

21.4. Balancing of a Single Rotating Mass By Two Masses Rotating in Different Planes

We have discussed in the previous article that by introducing a single balancing mass in the same plane of rotation as that of disturbing mass, the centrifugal forces are balanced. In other words, the two forces are equal in magnitude and opposite in direction. But this type of arrangement for balancing gives rise to a couple which tends to rock the shaft in its bearings. Therefore in order to put the system in complete balance, two balancing masses are placed in two different planes, parallel to the plane of rotation of the disturbing mass, in such a way that they satisfy the following two conditions of equilibrium.

1. The net dynamic force acting on the shaft is equal to zero. This requires that the line of action of three centrifugal forces must be the same. In other words, the centre of the masses of the system must lie on the axis of rotation. This is the condition for *static balancing.*

2. The net couple due to the dynamic forces acting on the shaft is equal to zero. In other words, the algebraic sum of the moments about any point in the plane must be zero.

The conditions (1) and (2) together give *dynamic balancing.* The following two possibilities may arise while attaching the two balancing masses :

1. The plane of the disturbing mass may be in between the planes of the two balancing masses, and

2. The plane of the disturbing mass may lie on the left or right of the two planes containing the balancing masses.

We shall now discuss both the above cases one by one.

The picture shows a diesel engine. All diesel, petrol and steam engines have reciprocating and rotating masses inside them which need to be balanced.

1. *When the plane of the disturbing mass lies in between the planes of the two balancing masses*

Consider a disturbing mass m lying in a plane A to be balanced by two rotating masses m_1 and m_2 lying in two different planes L and M as shown in Fig. 21.2. Let r, r_1 and r_2 be the radii of rotation of the masses in planes A, L and M respectively.

Let l_1 = Distance between the planes A and L,

l_2 = Distance between the planes A and M, and

l = Distance between the planes L and M.

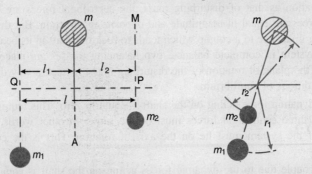

Fig. 21.2. Balancing of a single rotating mass by two rotating masses in different planes when the plane of single rotating mass lies in between the planes of two balancing masses.

We know that the centrifugal force exerted by the mass m in the plane A,

$$F_C = m \cdot \omega^2 \cdot r$$

Similarly, the centrifugal force exerted by the mass m_1 in the plane L,

$$F_{C1} = m_1 \cdot \omega^2 \cdot r_1$$

and, the centrifugal force exerted by the mass m_2 in the plane M,

$$F_{C2} = m_2 \cdot \omega^2 \cdot r_2$$

Since the net force acting on the shaft must be equal to zero, therefore the centrifugal force on the disturbing mass must be equal to the sum of the centrifugal forces on the balancing masses, therefore

$$F_C = F_{C1} + F_{C2} \qquad \text{or} \qquad m \cdot \omega^2 \cdot r = m_1 \cdot \omega^2 \cdot r_1 + m_2 \cdot \omega^2 \cdot r_2$$

∴ $$m \cdot r = m_1 \cdot r_1 + m_2 \cdot r_2 \qquad \qquad \dots (i)$$

Now in order to find the magnitude of balancing force in the plane L (or the dynamic force at the bearing Q of a shaft), take moments about P which is the point of intersection of the plane M and the axis of rotation. Therefore

$$F_{C1} \times l = F_C \times l_2 \qquad \text{or} \qquad m_1 \cdot \omega^2 \cdot r_1 \times l = m \cdot \omega^2 \cdot r \times l_2$$

∴ $$m_1 \cdot r_1 \cdot l = m \cdot r \cdot l_2 \qquad \text{or} \qquad m_1 \cdot r_1 = m \cdot r \times \frac{l_2}{l} \qquad \dots (ii)$$

Similarly, in order to find the balancing force in plane M (or the dynamic force at the bearing P of a shaft), take moments about Q which is the point of intersection of the plane L and the axis of rotation. Therefore

$$F_{C2} \times l = F_C \times l_1 \qquad \text{or} \qquad m_2 \cdot \omega^2 \cdot r_2 \times l = m \cdot \omega^2 \cdot r \times l_1$$

∴ $$m_2 \cdot r_2 \cdot l = m \cdot r \cdot l_1 \qquad \text{or} \qquad m_2 \cdot r_2 = m \cdot r \times \frac{l_1}{l} \qquad \dots (iii)$$

It may be noted that equation (i) represents the condition for static balance, but in order to achieve dynamic balance, equations (ii) or (iii) must also be satisfied.

2. *When the plane of the disturbing mass lies on one end of the planes of the balancing masses*

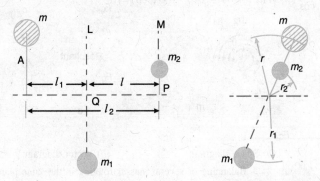

Fig. 21.3. Balancing of a single rotating mass by two rotating masses in different planes, when the plane of single rotating mass lies at one end of the planes of balancing masses.

In this case, the mass m lies in the plane A and the balancing masses lie in the planes L and M, as shown in Fig. 21.3. As discussed above, the following conditions must be satisfied in order to balance the system, *i.e.*

$$F_C + F_{C2} = F_{C1} \quad \text{or} \quad m \cdot \omega^2 \cdot r + m_2 \cdot \omega^2 \cdot r_2 = m_1 \cdot \omega^2 \cdot r_1$$

$$\therefore \qquad m \cdot r + m_2 \cdot r_2 = m_1 . r_1 \qquad \qquad \dots (iv)$$

Now, to find the balancing force in the plane L (or the dynamic force at the bearing Q of a shaft), take moments about P which is the point of intersection of the plane M and the axis of rotation. Therefore

$$F_{C1} \times l = F_C \times l_2 \quad \text{or} \quad m_1 \cdot \omega^2 \cdot r_1 \times l = m \cdot \omega^2 \cdot r \times l_2$$

$$\therefore \qquad m_1 \cdot r_1 \cdot l = m \cdot r \cdot l_2 \quad \text{or} \quad m_1 \cdot r_1 = m \cdot r \times \frac{l_2}{l} \qquad \dots (v)$$

$$\dots \text{[Same as equation } (ii)]$$

Similarly, to find the balancing force in the plane M (or the dynamic force at the bearing P of a shaft), take moments about Q which is the point of intersection of the plane L and the axis of rotation. Therefore

$$F_{C2} \times l = F_C \times l_1 \quad \text{or} \quad m_2 \cdot \omega^2 \cdot r_2 \times l = m \cdot \omega^2 \cdot r \times l_1$$

$$m_2 \cdot r_2 \cdot l = m \cdot r \cdot l_1 \quad \text{or} \quad m_2 \cdot r_2 = m \cdot r \times \frac{l_1}{l} \qquad \dots (vi)$$

$$\dots \text{[Same as equation } (iii)]$$

21.5. Balancing of Several Masses Rotating in the Same Plane

Consider any number of masses (say four) of magnitude m_1, m_2, m_3 and m_4 at distances of r_1, r_2, r_3 and r_4 from the axis of the rotating shaft. Let $\theta_1, \theta_2, \theta_3$ and θ_4 be the angles of these masses with the horizontal line OX, as shown in Fig. 21.4 (a). Let these masses rotate about an axis through O and perpendicular to the plane of paper, with a constant angular velocity of ω rad/s.

The magnitude and position of the balancing mass may be found out analytically or graphically as discussed below :

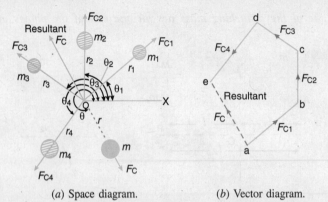

(*a*) Space diagram.	(*b*) Vector diagram.

Fig. 21.4. Balancing of several masses rotating in the same plane.

1. *Analytical method*

The magnitude and direction of the balancing mass may be obtained, analytically, as discussed below :

1. First of all, find out the centrifugal force* (or the product of the mass and its radius of rotation) exerted by each mass on the rotating shaft.

A car assembly line.

Note : This picture is given as additional information.

---

* Since ω^2 is same for each mass, therefore the magnitude of the centrifugal force for each mass is proportional to the product of the respective mass and its radius of rotation.

2. Resolve the centrifugal forces horizontally and vertically and find their sums, *i.e.* ΣH and ΣV. We know that

Sum of horizontal components of the centrifugal forces,

$$\Sigma H = m_1 \cdot r_1 \cos\theta_1 + m_2 \cdot r_2 \cos\theta_2 + \ldots\ldots$$

and sum of vertical components of the centrifugal forces,

$$\Sigma V = m_1 \cdot r_1 \sin\theta_1 + m_2 \cdot r_2 \sin\theta_2 + \ldots\ldots$$

3. Magnitude of the resultant centrifugal force,

$$F_C = \sqrt{(\Sigma H)^2 + (\Sigma V)^2}$$

4. If θ is the angle, which the resultant force makes with the horizontal, then

$$\tan\theta = \Sigma V / \Sigma H$$

5. The balancing force is then equal to the resultant force, but in *opposite direction*.

6. Now find out the magnitude of the balancing mass, such that

$$F_C = m \cdot r$$

where $\qquad m$ = Balancing mass, and

$\qquad\qquad r$ = Its radius of rotation.

2. *Graphical method*

The magnitude and position of the balancing mass may also be obtained graphically as discussed below :

1. First of all, draw the space diagram with the positions of the several masses, as shown in Fig. 21.4 (*a*).

2. Find out the centrifugal force (or product of the mass and radius of rotation) exerted by each mass on the rotating shaft.

3. Now draw the vector diagram with the obtained centrifugal forces (or the product of the masses and their radii of rotation), such that *ab* represents the centrifugal force exerted by the mass m_1 (or $m_1.r_1$) in magnitude and direction to some suitable scale. Similarly, draw *bc*, *cd* and *de* to represent centrifugal forces of other masses m_2, m_3 and m_4 (or $m_2.r_2$, $m_3.r_3$ and $m_4.r_4$).

4. Now, as per polygon law of forces, the closing side *ae* represents the resultant force in magnitude and direction, as shown in Fig. 21.4 (*b*).

5. The balancing force is, then, equal to the resultant force, but in *opposite direction*.

6. Now find out the magnitude of the balancing mass (*m*) at a given radius of rotation (*r*), such that

$$m \cdot \omega^2 \cdot r = \text{Resultant centrifugal force}$$

or $\qquad\qquad m.r = \text{Resultant of } m_1.r_1, m_2.r_2, m_3.r_3 \text{ and } m_4.r_4$

Example 21.1. *Four masses m_1, m_2, m_3 and m_4 are 200 kg, 300 kg, 240 kg and 260 kg respectively. The corresponding radii of rotation are 0.2 m, 0.15 m, 0.25 m and 0.3 m respectively and the angles between successive masses are 45°, 75° and 135°. Find the position and magnitude of the balance mass required, if its radius of rotation is 0.2 m.*

Solution. Given : m_1 = 200 kg ; m_2 = 300 kg ; m_3 = 240 kg ; m_4 = 260 kg ; r_1 = 0.2 m ; r_2 = 0.15 m ; r_3 = 0.25 m ; r_4 = 0.3 m ; θ_1 = 0° ; θ_2 = 45° ; θ_3 = 45° + 75° = 120° ; θ_4 = 45° + 75° + 135° = 255° ; r = 0.2 m

Let m = Balancing mass, and

θ = The angle which the balancing mass makes with m_1.

Since the magnitude of centrifugal forces are proportional to the product of each mass and its radius, therefore

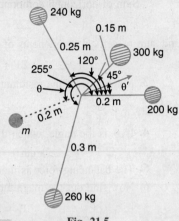

$$m_1 \cdot r_1 = 200 \times 0.2 = 40 \, \text{kg-m}$$

$$m_2 \cdot r_2 = 300 \times 0.15 = 45 \, \text{kg-m}$$

$$m_3 \cdot r_3 = 240 \times 0.25 = 60 \, \text{kg-m}$$

$$m_4 \cdot r_4 = 260 \times 0.3 = 78 \, \text{kg-m}$$

The problem may, now, be solved either analytically or graphically. But we shall solve the problem by both the methods one by one.

Fig. 21.5

1. Analytical method

The space diagram is shown in Fig. 21.5.

Resolving $m_1.r_1$, $m_2.r_2$, $m_3.r_3$ and $m_4.r_4$ horizontally,

$$\Sigma H = m_1 \cdot r_1 \cos\theta_1 + m_2 \cdot r_2 \cos\theta_2 + m_3 \cdot r_3 \cos\theta_3 + m_4 \cdot r_4 \cos\theta_4$$

$$= 40 \cos 0° + 45 \cos 45° + 60 \cos 120° + 78 \cos 255°$$

$$= 40 + 31.8 - 30 - 20.2 = 21.6 \, \text{kg-m}$$

Now resolving vertically,

$$\Sigma V = m_1 \cdot r_1 \sin\theta_1 + m_2 \cdot r_2 \sin\theta_2 + m_3 \cdot r_3 \sin\theta_3 + m_4 \cdot r_4 \sin\theta_4$$

$$= 40 \sin 0° + 45 \sin 45° + 60 \sin 120° + 78 \sin 255°$$

$$= 0 + 31.8 + 52 - 75.3 = 8.5 \, \text{kg-m}$$

$\therefore$ Resultant, $R = \sqrt{(\Sigma H)^2 + (\Sigma V)^2} = \sqrt{(21.6)^2 + (8.5)^2} = 23.2 \, \text{kg-m}$

We know that

$$m \cdot r = R = 23.2 \quad \text{or} \quad m = 23.2/r = 23.2/0.2 = 116 \, \text{kg} \; \textbf{Ans.}$$

and $\tan\theta' = \Sigma V / \Sigma H = 8.5/21.6 = 0.3935 \quad \text{or} \quad \theta' = 21.48°$

Since θ' is the angle of the resultant R from the horizontal mass of 200 kg, therefore the angle of the balancing mass from the horizontal mass of 200 kg,

$$\theta = 180° + 21.48° = 201.48° \; \textbf{Ans.}$$

2. Graphical method

The magnitude and the position of the balancing mass may also be found graphically as discussed below :

1. First of all, draw the space diagram showing the positions of all the given masses as shown in Fig 21.6 (a).
2. Since the centrifugal force of each mass is proportional to the product of the mass and radius, therefore

$$m_1.r_1 = 200 \times 0.2 = 40 \, \text{kg-m}$$

$$m_2.r_2 = 300 \times 0.15 = 45 \, \text{kg-m}$$

$$m_3.r_3 = 240 \times 0.25 = 60 \text{ kg-m}$$
$$m_4.r_4 = 260 \times 0.3 = 78 \text{ kg-m}$$

3. Now draw the vector diagram with the above values, to some suitable scale, as shown in Fig. 21.6 (*b*). The closing side of the polygon *ae* represents the resultant force. By measurement, we find that *ae* = 23 kg-m.

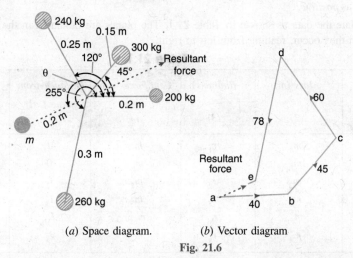

(*a*) Space diagram.   (*b*) Vector diagram

Fig. 21.6

4. The balancing force is equal to the resultant force, but *opposite* in direction as shown in Fig. 21.6 (*a*). Since the balancing force is proportional to *m.r*, therefore

$$m \times 0.2 = \text{vector } ea = 23 \text{ kg-m} \quad \text{or} \quad m = 23/0.2 = \textbf{115 kg Ans.}$$

By measurement we also find that the angle of inclination of the balancing mass (*m*) from the horizontal mass of 200 kg,

$$\theta = 201° \text{ Ans.}$$

21.6. Balancing of Several Masses Rotating in Different Planes

When several masses revolve in different planes, they may be transferred to a *reference plane* (briefly written as *R.P*), which may be defined as the plane passing through a point on the axis of rotation and perpendicular to it. The effect of transferring a revolving mass (in one plane) to a reference plane is to cause a force of magnitude equal to the centrifugal force of the revolving mass to act in the reference plane, together with a couple of magnitude equal to the product of the force and the distance between the plane of rotation and the reference plane. In order to have a complete balance of the several revolving masses in different planes, the following two conditions must be satisfied :

1. The forces in the reference plane must balance, *i.e.* the resultant force must be zero.

2. The couples about the reference plane must balance, *i.e.* the resultant couple must be zero.

Let us now consider four masses m_1, m_2, m_3 and m_4 revolving in planes 1, 2, 3 and 4 respectively as shown in

Diesel engine.

Fig. 21.7 (*a*). The relative angular positions of these masses are shown in the end view [Fig. 21.7 (*b*)]. The magnitude of the balancing masses m_L and m_M in planes L and M may be obtained as discussed below :

1. Take one of the planes, say L as the reference plane (*R.P.*). The distances of all the other planes to the left of the reference plane may be regarded as *negative*, and those to the right as *positive*.

2. Tabulate the data as shown in Table 21.1. The planes are tabulated in the same order in which they occur, reading from left to right.

Table 21.1

Plane (1)	Mass (m) (2)	Radius(r) (3)	Cent.force ÷ ω² (m.r) (4)	Distance from plane L (l) (5)	Couple ÷ ω² (m.r.l) (6)
1	m_1	r_1	$m_1.r_1$	$-l_1$	$-m_1.r_1.l_1$
L(R.P.)	m_L	r_L	$m_L.r_L$	0	0
2	m_2	r_2	$m_2.r_2$	l_2	$m_2.r_2.l_2$
3	m_3	r_3	$m_3.r_3$	l_3	$m_3.r_3.l_3$
M	m_M	r_M	$m_M.r_M$	l_M	$m_M.r_M.l_M$
4	m_4	r_4	$m_4.r_4$	l_4	$m_4.r_4.l_4$

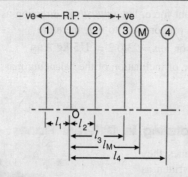

(*a*) Position of planes of the masses.

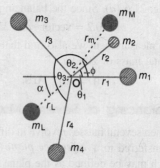

(*b*) Angular position of the masses.

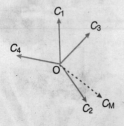

(*c*) Couple vector. (*d*) Couple vectors turned counter clockwise through a right angle.

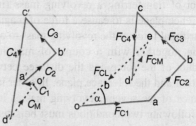

(*e*) Couple polygon. (*f*) Force polygon.

Fig. 21.7. Balancing of several masses rotating in different planes.

3. A couple may be represented by a vector drawn perpendicular to the plane of the couple. The couple C_1 introduced by transferring m_1 to the reference plane through O is propor-

tional to $m_1.r_1.l_1$ and acts in a plane through Om_1 and perpendicular to the paper. The vector representing this couple is drawn in the plane of the paper and perpendicular to Om_1 as shown by OC_1 in Fig. 21.7 (c). Similarly, the vectors OC_2, OC_3 and OC_4 are drawn perpendicular to Om_2, Om_3 and Om_4 respectively and in the plane of the paper.

4. The couple vectors as discussed above, are turned counter clockwise through a right angle for convenience of drawing as shown in Fig. 21.7 (d). We see that their relative positions remains unaffected. Now the vectors OC_2, OC_3 and OC_4 are parallel and in the same direction as Om_2, Om_3 and Om_4, while the vector OC_1 is parallel to Om_1 but in *opposite direction. Hence the *couple vectors are drawn radially outwards for the masses on one side of the reference plane and radially inward for the masses on the other side of the reference plane.*

5. Now draw the couple polygon as shown in Fig. 21.7 (e). The vector $d'o'$ represents the balanced couple. Since the balanced couple C_M is proportional to $m_M.r_M.l_M$, therefore

$$C_M = m_M \cdot r_M \cdot l_M = \text{vector } d'o' \qquad \text{or} \qquad m_M = \frac{\text{vector } d'o'}{r_M \cdot l_M}$$

From this expression, the value of the balancing mass m_M in the plane M may be obtained, and the angle of inclination ϕ of this mass may be measured from Fig. 21.7 (b).

6. Now draw the force polygon as shown in Fig. 21.7 (f). The vector eo (in the direction from e to o) represents the balanced force. Since the balanced force is proportional to $m_L.r_L$, therefore,

$$m_L \cdot r_L = \text{vector } eo \qquad \text{or} \qquad m_L = \frac{\text{vector } eo}{r_L}$$

From this expression, the value of the balancing mass m_L in the plane L may be obtained and the angle of inclination α of this mass with the horizontal may be measured from Fig. 21.7 (b).

Example 21.2. *A shaft carries four masses A, B, C and D of magnitude 200 kg, 300 kg, 400 kg and 200 kg respectively and revolving at radii 80 mm, 70 mm, 60 mm and 80 mm in planes measured from A at 300 mm, 400 mm and 700 mm. The angles between the cranks measured anticlockwise are A to B 45°, B to C 70° and C to D 120°. The balancing masses are to be placed in planes X and Y. The distance between the planes A and X is 100 mm, between X and Y is 400 mm and between Y and D is 200 mm. If the balancing masses revolve at a radius of 100 mm, find their magnitudes and angular positions.*

Solution. Given : $m_A = 200$ kg ; $m_B = 300$ kg ; $m_C = 400$ kg ; $m_D = 200$ kg ; $r_A = 80$ mm $= 0.08$ m ; $r_B = 70$ mm $= 0.07$ m ; $r_C = 60$ mm $= 0.06$ m ; $r_D = 80$ mm $= 0.08$ m ; $r_X = r_Y = 100$ mm $= 0.1$ m

Let $\qquad m_X =$ Balancing mass placed in plane X, and

$\qquad\qquad m_Y =$ Balancing mass placed in plane Y.

The position of planes and angular position of the masses (assuming the mass A as horizontal) are shown in Fig. 21.8 (a) and (b) respectively.

Assume the plane X as the reference plane (R.P.). The distances of the planes to the right of plane X are taken as + ve while the distances of the planes to the left of plane X are taken as – ve. The data may be tabulated as shown in Table 21.2.

---

* From Table 21.1 (column 6) we see that the couple is $- m_1.r_1.l_1$.

Table 21.2

Plane (1)	Mass (m) kg (2)	Radius (r) m (3)	Cent.force $\div \omega^2$ (m.r) kg-m (4)	Distance from Plane x(l) m (5)	Couple $\div \omega^2$ (m.r.l) kg-m^2 (6)
A	200	0.08	16	– 0.1	– 1.6
X(R.P.)	m_X	0.1	0.1 m_X	0	0
B	300	0.07	21	0.2	4.2
C	400	0.06	24	0.3	7.2
Y	m_Y	0.1	0.1 m_Y	0.4	0.04 m_Y
D	200	0.08	16	0.6	9.6

The balancing masses m_X and m_Y and their angular positions may be determined graphically as discussed below :

1. First of all, draw the couple polygon from the data given in Table 21.2 (column 6) as shown in Fig. 21.8 (c) to some suitable scale. The vector $d'o'$ represents the balanced couple. Since the balanced couple is proportional to 0.04 m_Y, therefore by measurement,

$$0.04\,m_Y = \text{vector } d'o' = 7.3 \text{ kg-m}^2 \quad \text{or} \quad m_Y = 182.5 \text{ kg} \text{ Ans.}$$

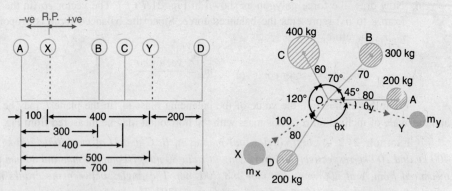

(a) Position of planes. (b) Angular position of masses.

All dimensions in mm.

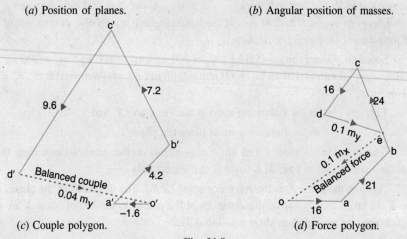

(c) Couple polygon. (d) Force polygon.

Fig. 21.8

The angular position of the mass m_Y is obtained by drawing Om_Y in Fig. 21.8 (*b*), parallel to vector $d' o'$. By measurement, the angular position of m_Y is $\theta_Y = 12°$ in the clockwise direction from mass m_A (*i.e.* 200 kg). **Ans.**

2. Now draw the force polygon from the data given in Table 21.2 (column 4) as shown in Fig. 21.8 (*d*). The vector *eo* represents the balanced force. Since the balanced force is proportional to 0.1 m_X, therefore by measurement,

$$0.1 \, m_X = \text{vector } eo = 35.5 \text{ kg-m} \quad \text{or} \quad m_X = \textbf{355 kg Ans.}$$

The angular position of the mass m_X is obtained by drawing Om_X in Fig. 21.8 (*b*), parallel to vector *eo*. By measurement, the angular position of m_X is $\theta_X = 145°$ in the clockwise direction from mass m_A (*i.e.* 200 kg). **Ans.**

Example 21.3. *Four masses A, B, C and D as shown below are to be completely balanced.*

	A	*B*	*C*	*D*
Mass (kg)	—	*30*	*50*	*40*
Radius (mm)	*180*	*240*	*120*	*150*

The planes containing masses B and C are 300 mm apart. The angle between planes containing B and C is 90°. B and C make angles of 210° and 120° respectively with D in the same sense. Find :

1. The magnitude and the angular position of mass A ; and

2. The position of planes A and D.

Solution. Given : r_A = 180 mm = 0.18 m ; m_B = 30 kg ; r_B = 240 mm = 0.24 m ; m_C = 50 kg ; r_C = 120 mm = 0.12 m ; m_D = 40 kg ; r_D = 150 mm = 0.15 m ; $\angle BOC = 90°$; $\angle BOD = 210°$; $\angle COD = 120°$

1. *The magnitude and the angular position of mass A*

Let $\qquad m_A$ = Magnitude of Mass A,

$\qquad\qquad x$ = Distance between the planes B and D, and

$\qquad\qquad y$ = Distance between the planes A and B.

The position of the planes and the angular position of the masses is shown in Fig. 21.9 (*a*) and (*b*) respectively.

Assuming the plane B as the reference plane (R.P.) and the mass B (m_B) along the horizontal line as shown in Fig. 21.9 (*b*), the data may be tabulated as below :

Table 21.3

Plane (1)	*Mass* (*m*) *kg* (2)	*Radius* (*r*) *m* (3)	*Cent.force ÷ ω^2* (*m.r*) *kg-m* (4)	*Distance from plane B (l) m* (5)	*Couple ÷ ω^2* (*m.r.l*) *kg-m²* (6)
A	m_A	0.18	0.08 m_A	– *y*	– 0.18 $m_A y$
B (R.P)	30	0.24	7.2	0	0
C	50	0.12	6	0.3	1.8
D	40	0.15	6	*x*	6*x*

The magnitude and angular position of mass A may be determined by drawing the force polygon from the data given in Table 21.3 (Column 4), as shown in Fig. 21.9 (*c*), to some suitable scale. Since the masses are to be completely balanced, therefore the force polygon must be a closed figure. The closing side (*i.e.* vector *do*) is proportional to $0.18\ m_A$. By measurement,

$$0.18\ m_A = \text{Vector } do = 3.6\ \text{kg-m} \quad \text{or} \quad m_A = 20\ \text{kg Ans.}$$

In order to find the angular position of mass A, draw OA in Fig. 21.9 (*b*) parallel to vector *do*. By measurement, we find that the angular position of mass A from mass B in the anticlockwise direction is $\angle AOB = 236°$ **Ans**.

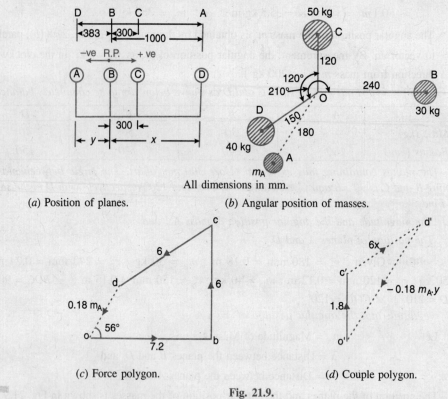

(*a*) Position of planes. (*b*) Angular position of masses.

All dimensions in mm.

(*c*) Force polygon. (*d*) Couple polygon.

Fig. 21.9.

2. Position of planes A and D

The position of planes A and D may be obtained by drawing the couple polygon, as shown in Fig. 21.9 (*d*), from the data given in Table 21.3 (column 6). The couple polygon is drawn as discussed below :

1. Draw vector $o'c'$ parallel to OC and equal to 1.8 kg-m², to some suitable scale.

2. From points c' and o', draw lines parallel to OD and OA respectively, such that they intersect at point d'. By measurement, we find that

$$6\,x = \text{vector } c'd' = 2.3\ \text{kg-m}^2 \text{ or } x = 0.383\ \text{m}$$

We see from the couple polygon that the direction of vector $c'd'$ is opposite to the direction of mass D. Therefore the plane of mass D is 0.383 m or 383 mm towards left of plane B and not towards right of plane B as already assumed. **Ans**.

Again by measurement from couple polygon,

$$- 0.18 \, m_A.y = \text{vector } o' \, d' = 3.6 \text{ kg-m}^2$$

$$- 0.18 \times 20 \, y = 3.6 \quad \text{or} \quad y = - 1 \text{ m}$$

The negative sign indicates that the plane A is not towards left of B as assumed but it is 1 m or 1000 mm towards right of plane B. **Ans.**

Example 21.4. *A, B, C and D are four masses carried by a rotating shaft at radii 100, 125, 200 and 150 mm respectively. The planes in which the masses revolve are spaced 600 mm apart and the mass of B, C and D are 10 kg, 5 kg, and 4 kg respectively.*

Find the required mass A and the relative angular settings of the four masses so that the shaft shall be in complete balance.

Solution. Given : $r_A = 100$ mm $= 0.1$ m ; $r_B = 125$ mm $= 0.125$ m ; $r_C = 200$ mm $= 0.2$ m ; $r_D = 150$ mm $= 0.15$ m ; $m_B = 10$ kg ; $m_C = 5$ kg ; $m_D = 4$ kg

The position of planes is shown in Fig. 21.10 (*a*). Assuming the plane of mass A as the reference plane (*R.P.*), the data may be tabulated as below :

Table 21.4

Plane (1)	Mass (m) kg (2)	Radius (r) m (3)	Cent. Force ÷ ω^2 (m.r)kg-m (4)	Distance from plane A (l)m (5)	Couple ÷ ω^2 (m.r.l) kg-m^2 (6)
A(R.P.)	m_A	0.1	0.1 m_A	0	0
B	10	0.125	1.25	0.6	0.75
C	5	0.2	1	1.2	1.2
D	4	0.15	0.6	1.8	1.08

First of all, the angular setting of masses C and D is obtained by drawing the couple polygon from the data given in Table 21.4 (column 6). Assume the position of mass B in the horizontal direction OB as shown in Fig. 21.10 (*b*). Now the couple polygon as shown in Fig. 21.10 (*c*) is drawn as discussed below :

1. Draw vector $o' \, b'$ in the horizontal direction (*i.e.* parallel to OB) and equal to 0.75 kg-m^2, to some suitable scale.
2. From points o' and b', draw vectors $o' \, c'$ and $b' \, c'$ equal to 1.2 kg-m^2 and 1.08 kg-m^2 respectively. These vectors intersect at c'.
3. Now in Fig. 21.10 (*b*), draw OC parallel to vector $o' \, c'$ and OD parallel to vector $b' \, c'$.

By measurement, we find that the angular setting of mass C from mass B in the anticlockwise direction, *i.e.*

$$\angle BOC = 240° \text{ Ans.}$$

and angular setting of mass D from mass B in the anticlockwise direction, *i.e.*

$$\angle BOD = 100° \text{ Ans.}$$

In order to find the required mass A (m_A) and its angular setting, draw the force polygon to some suitable scale, as shown in Fig. 21.10 (*d*), from the data given in Table 21.4 (column 4).

Since the closing side of the force polygon (vector do) is proportional to 0.1 m_A, therefore by measurement,

$$0.1 \, m_A = 0.7 \text{ kg-m}^2 \quad \text{or} \quad m_A = 7 \text{ kg Ans.}$$

Now draw *OA* in Fig. 21.10 (*b*), parallel to vector *do*. By measurement, we find that the angular setting of mass *A* from mass *B* in the anticlockwise direction, *i.e.*

$$\angle\,BOA\;=\;155°\;\text{ Ans.}$$

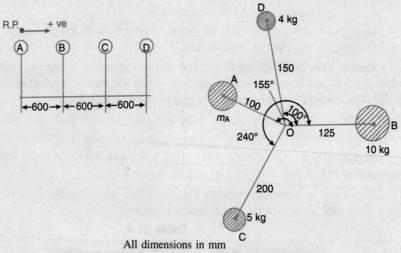

(*a*) Position of planes.

(*b*) Angular position of masses.

All dimensions in mm

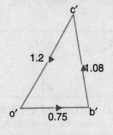

(*c*) Couple polygon.

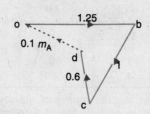

(*d*) Force polygon.

Fig. 21.10

Example 21.5. *A shaft carries four masses in parallel planes A, B, C and D in this order along its length. The masses at B and C are 18 kg and 12.5 kg respectively, and each has an eccentricity of 60 mm. The masses at A and D have an eccentricity of 80 mm. The angle between the masses at B and C is 100° and that between the masses at B and A is 190°, both being measured in the same direction. The axial distance between the planes A and B is 100 mm and that between B and C is 200 mm. If the shaft is in complete dynamic balance, determine :*

1.The magnitude of the masses at A and D ; 2.the distance between planes A and D ; and 3.the angular position of the mass at D.

Solution. Given : $m_B = 18$ kg ; $m_C = 12.5$ kg ; $r_B = r_C = 60$ mm $= 0.06$ m ; $r_A = r_D = 80$ mm $= 0.08$ m ; $\angle BOC = 100°$; $\angle BOA = 190°$

1. *Magnitude of the masses at A and D*

Let $\quad\quad\quad\quad M_A = $ Mass at A,

$\quad\quad\quad\quad\quad\quad M_D = $ Mass at D, and

$\quad\quad\quad\quad\quad\quad x = $ Distance between planes A and D.

The position of the planes and angular position of the masses is shown in Fig. 21.11 (*a*) and (*b*) respectively. The position of mass *B* is assumed in the horizontal direction, *i.e.* along *OB*. Taking the plane of mass *A* as the reference plane, the data may be tabulated as below :

Table 21.5

Plane	Mass	Eccentricity	Cent. force $\div \omega^2$	Distance from	Couple $\div \omega^2$
	(m) kg	(r) m	(m.r) kg-m	plane A(l)m	(m.r.l) kg-m²
(1)	(2)	(3)	(4)	(5)	(6)
A (R.P.)	m_A	0.08	0.08 m_A	0	0
B	18	0.06	1.08	0.1	0.108
C	12.5	0.06	0.75	0.3	0.225
D	m_D	0.08	0.08 m_D	x	0.08 m_D . x

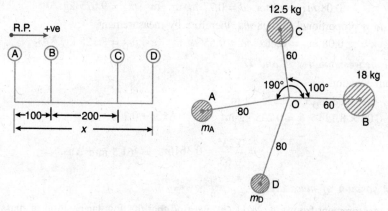

All dimensions in mm.

(*a*) Position of planes. (*b*) Angular position of masses.

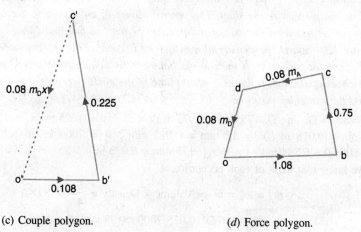

(*c*) Couple polygon. (*d*) Force polygon.

Fig. 21.11

First of all, the direction of mass *D* is fixed by drawing the couple polygon to some suitable scale, as shown in Fig. 21.11 (*c*), from the data given in Table 21.5 (column 6). The closing side of the couple polygon (vector $c'o'$) is proportional to $0.08\ m_D.x$. By measurement, we find that

$$0.08\ m_D.x = \text{vector } c'o' = 0.235 \text{ kg-m}^2 \qquad \ldots (i)$$

In Fig. 21.11 (b), draw OD parallel to vector $c'o'$ to fix the direction of mass D.

Now draw the force polygon, to some suitable scale, as shown in Fig. 21.11 (d), from the data given in Table 21.5 (column 4), as discussed below :

1. Draw vector ob parallel to OB and equal to 1.08 kg-m.
2. From point b, draw vector bc parallel to OC and equal to 0.75 kg-m.
3. For the shaft to be in complete dynamic balance, the force polygon must be a closed figure. Therefore from point c, draw vector cd parallel to OA and from point o draw vector od parallel to OD. The vectors cd and od intersect at d. Since the vector cd is proportional to $0.08\ m_A$, therefore by measurement

$$0.08\ m_A = \text{vector } cd = 0.77 \text{ kg-m} \quad \text{or} \quad m_A = 9.625 \text{ kg } \textbf{Ans.}$$

and vector do is proportional to $0.08\ m_D$, therefore by measurement,

$$0.08\ m_D = \text{vector } do = 0.65 \text{ kg-m} \quad \text{or} \quad m_D = 8.125 \text{ kg } \textbf{Ans.}$$

2. *Distance between planes A and D*

From equation (i),

$$0.08\ m_D.x = 0.235 \text{ kg-m}^2$$
$$0.08 \times 8.125 \times x = 0.235 \text{ kg-m}^2 \quad \text{or} \quad 0.65\ x = 0.235$$

$$\therefore \qquad x = \frac{0.235}{0.65} = 0.3615 \text{m} = 361.5 \text{ mm } \textbf{Ans.}$$

3. *Angular position of mass at D*

By measurement from Fig. 21.11 (b), we find that the angular position of mass at D from mass B in the anticlockwise direction, *i.e.* $\angle BOD = 251°$ **Ans.**

Example 21.6. *A shaft has three eccentrics, each 75 mm diameter and 25 mm thick, machined in one piece with the shaft. The central planes of the eccentric are 60 mm apart. The distance of the centres from the axis of rotation are 12 mm, 18 mm and 12 mm and their angular positions are 120° apart. The density of metal is 7000 kg/m³. Find the amount of out-of-balance force and couple at 600 r.p.m. If the shaft is balanced by adding two masses at a radius 75 mm and at distances of 100 mm from the central plane of the middle eccentric, find the amount of the masses and their angular positions.*

Solution. Given : $D = 75$ mm $= 0.075$ m ; $t = 25$ mm $= 0.025$ m ; $r_A = 12$ mm $= 0.012$ m ; $r_B = 18$ mm $= 0.018$ m ; $r_C = 12$ mm $= 0.012$ mm ; $\rho = 7000$ kg/m³ ; $N = 600$ r.p.m. or $\omega = 2\pi \times 600/60 = 62.84$ rad/s ; $r_L = r_M = 75$ mm $= 0.075$ m

We know that mass of each eccentric,

$$m_A = m_B = m_C = \text{Volume} \times \text{Density} = \frac{\pi}{4} \times D^2 \times t \times \rho$$

$$= \frac{\pi}{4}(0.075)^2(0.025)7000 = 0.77 \text{ kg}$$

Let L and M be the planes at distances of 100 mm from the central plane of middle eccentric. The position of the planes and the angular position of the three eccentrics is shown in Fig. 21.12 (a) and (b) respectively. Assuming L as the reference plane and mass of the eccentric A in the vertical direction, the data may be tabulated as below :

Table 21.6.

Plane	Mass	Radius	Cent. force $\div \omega^2$	Distance from	Couple $\div \omega^2$
	(m) kg	(r) m	(m.r) kg-m	plane L.(l)m	(m.r.l) kg-m^2
(1)	(2)	(3)	(4)	(5)	(6)
L (R.P.)	m_L	0.075	$75 \times 10^{-3}\, m_L$	0	0
A	0.77	0.012	9.24×10^{-3}	0.04	0.3696×10^{-3}
B	0.77	0.018	13.86×10^{-3}	0.1	1.386×10^{-3}
C	0.77	0.012	9.24×10^{-3}	0.16	1.4784×10^{-3}
M	m_M	0.075	$75 \times 10^{-3}\, m_M$	0.20	$15 \times 10^{-3}\, m_M$

Out-of-balance force

The out-of-balance force is obtained by drawing the force polygon, as shown in Fig. 21.12 (c), from the data given in Table 21.6 (column 4). The resultant *oc* represents the out-of-balance force.

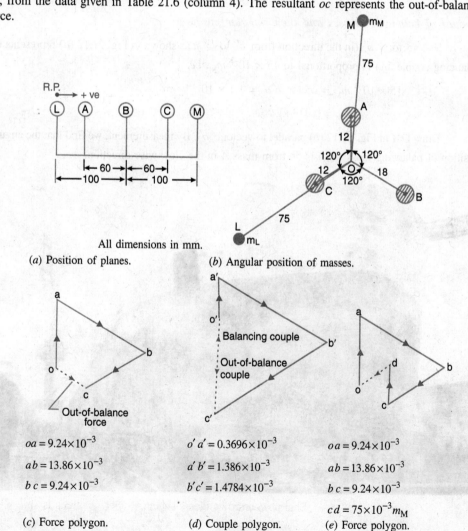

All dimensions in mm.

(a) Position of planes.　　　(b) Angular position of masses.

$oa = 9.24 \times 10^{-3}$

$ab = 13.86 \times 10^{-3}$

$bc = 9.24 \times 10^{-3}$

$o'a' = 0.3696 \times 10^{-3}$

$a'b' = 1.386 \times 10^{-3}$

$b'c' = 1.4784 \times 10^{-3}$

$oa = 9.24 \times 10^{-3}$

$ab = 13.86 \times 10^{-3}$

$bc = 9.24 \times 10^{-3}$

$cd = 75 \times 10^{-3}\, m_M$

(c) Force polygon.　　　(d) Couple polygon.　　　(e) Force polygon.

Fig. 21.12

Since the centrifugal force is proportional to the product of mass and radius (*i.e. m.r*), therefore by measurement.

Out-of-balance force = vector $oc = 4.75 \times 10^{-3}$ kg-m

$$= 4.75 \times 10^{-3} \times \omega^2 = 4.75 \times 10^{-3} (62.84)^2 = 18.76 \text{ N Ans.}$$

Out-of-balance couple

The out-of-balance couple is obtained by drawing the couple polygon from the data given in Table 21.6 (column 6), as shown in Fig. 21.12 (*d*). The resultant $o'c'$ represents the out-of-balance couple. Since the couple is proportional to the product of force and distance (*m.r.l*), therefore by measurement,

Out-of-balance couple = vector $o'c' = 1.1 \times 10^{-3}$ kg-m^2

$$= 1.1 \times 10^{-3} \times \omega^2 = 1.1 \times 10^{-3} (62.84)^2 = 4.34 \text{ N-m Ans.}$$

Amount of balancing masses and their angular positions

The vector $c'o'$ (in the direction from c' to o'), as shown in Fig. 21.12 (*d*) represents the balancing couple and is proportional to $15 \times 10^{-3} m_M$, *i.e.*

$$15 \times 10^{-3} m_M = \text{vector } c'o' = 1.1 \times 10^{-3} \text{ kg-m}^2$$

or $$m_M = 0.073 \text{ kg Ans.}$$

Draw *OM* in Fig. 21.12 (*b*) parallel to vector $c'o'$. By measurement, we find that the angular position of balancing mass (m_M) is 5° from mass *A* in the clockwise direction. **Ans.**

Ship powered by a diesel engine.

In order to find the balancing mass (m_L), a force polygon as shown in Fig. 21.12 (*e*) is drawn. The closing side of the polygon *i.e.* vector *do* (in the direction from *d* to *o*) represents the balancing force and is proportional to $75 \times 10^{-3} \, m_L$. By measurement, we find that

$$75 \times 10^{-3} \, m_L = \text{vector } do = 5.2 \times 10^{-3} \text{ kg-m}$$

or $\qquad\qquad m_L = 0.0693 \text{ kg } \textbf{Ans.}$

Draw *OL* in Fig. 21.12 (*b*), parallel to vector *do*. By measurement, we find that the angular position of mass (m_L) is 124° from mass *A* in the clockwise direction. **Ans.**

Example 21.7. *A shaft is supported in bearings 1.8 m apart and projects 0.45 m beyond bearings at each end. The shaft carries three pulleys one at each end and one at the middle of its length. The mass of end pulleys is 48 kg and 20 kg and their centre of gravity are 15 mm and 12.5 mm respectively from the shaft axis. The centre pulley has a mass of 56 kg and its centre of gravity is 15 mm from the shaft axis. If the pulleys are arranged so as to give static balance, determine :*
1. relative angular positions of the pulleys, and 2. dynamic forces produced on the bearings when the shaft rotates at 300 r.p.m.

Solution. Given : $m_A = 48$ kg ; $m_C = 20$ kg ; $r_A = 15$ mm $= 0.015$ m ; $r_C = 12.5$ mm $= 0.0125$ m ; $m_B = 56$ kg ; $r_B = 15$ mm $= 0.015$ m ; $N = 300$ *r.p.m.* or $\omega = 2 \pi \times 300/60 = 31.42$ rad/s

1. *Relative angular position of the pulleys*

The position of the shaft and pulleys is shown in Fig. 21.13 (*a*).

Let $\qquad\quad m_L$ and m_M = Mass at the bearings *L* and *M*, and

$\qquad\qquad r_L$ and r_M = Radius of rotation of the masses at *L* and *M* respectively.

Assuming the plane of bearing *L* as reference plane, the data may be tabulated as below :

Table 21.7.

Plane (1)	Mass (m) kg (2)	Radius (r) m (3)	Cent. force ÷ ω^2 (m.r) kg-m (4)	Distance from plane L(l)m (5)	Couple ÷ ω^2 (m.r.l) kg-m^2 (6)
A	48	0.015	0.72	− 0.45	− 0.324
L(R.P)	m_L	r_L	$m_L \cdot r_L$	0	0
B	56	0.015	0.84	0.9	0.756
M	m_M	r_M	$m_M \cdot r_M$	1.8	1.8 $m_M \cdot r_M$
C	20	0.0125	0.25	2.25	0.5625

First of all, draw the force polygon to some suitable scale, as shown in Fig. 21.13 (*c*), from the data given in Table 21.7 (column 4). It is assumed that the mass of pulley *B* acts in vertical direction. We know that for the static balance of the pulleys, the centre of gravity of the system must lie on the axis of rotation. Therefore a force polygon must be a closed figure. Now in Fig. 21.13 (*b*), draw *OA* parallel to vector *bc* and *OC* parallel to vector *co*. By measurement, we find that

$\qquad\qquad$ Angle between pulleys *B* and *A* = 161° **Ans.**

$\qquad\qquad$ Angle between pulleys *A* and *C* = 76° **Ans.**

and $\qquad\qquad$ Angle between pulleys *C* and *B* = 123° **Ans.**

2. *Dynamic forces at the two bearings*

In order to find the dynamic forces (or reactions) at the two bearings *L* and *M*, let us first calculate the values of $m_L \cdot r_L$ and $m_M \cdot r_M$ as discussed below :

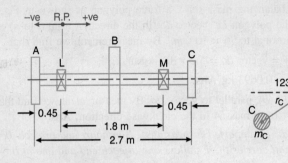

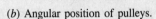

(a) Position of shaft and pulleys.　　　　(b) Angular position of pulleys.

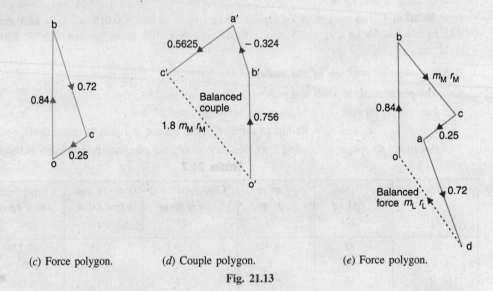

(c) Force polygon.　　　(d) Couple polygon.　　　(e) Force polygon.

Fig. 21.13

1. Draw the couple polygon to some suitable scale, as shown in Fig. 21.13 (d), from the data given in Table 21.7 (column 6). The closing side of the polygon (vector $c'o'$) represents the balanced couple and is proportional to $1.8\,m_M.r_M$. By measurement, we find that

$$1.8\,m_M.r_M = \text{vector } c'o' = 0.97 \text{ kg-m}^2 \qquad \text{or} \qquad m_M.r_M = 0.54 \text{ kg-m}$$

∴ Dynamic force at the bearing M

$$= m_M.r_M.\omega^2 = 0.54\,(31.42)^2 = 533 \text{ N Ans.}$$

2. Now draw the force polygon, as shown in Fig. 21.13 (e), from the data given in Table 21.7 (column 4) and taking $m_M.r_M = 0.54$ kg-m. The closing side of the polygon (vector do) represents the balanced force and is proportional to $m_L.r_L$. By measurement, we find that

$$m_L.r_L = 0.54 \text{ kg-m}$$

∴ Dynamic force at the bearing L

$$= m_L.r_L.\omega^2 = 0.54\,(31.42)^2 = 533 \text{ N Ans.}$$

Notes : **1.** The dynamic force at the two bearings are equal in magnitude but opposite in direction.

2. The dynamic force at the two bearings may also be obtained as discussed below :

From couple polygon as shown in Fig. 21.13 (*d*), we see that the vector $o'c'$ in the direction from o' to c' represents the out-of-balance couple.

By measurement, we find that

Out-of-balance couple

$$= \text{vector } o'c' = 0.97 \text{ kg-m}^2$$

$$= 0.97 \times \omega^2 = 0.97 \ (31.42)^2 = 957.6 \text{ N-m}$$

Since the shaft is in static balance, therefore it is only subjected to an unbalanced couple which is same about all planes and the bearing reactions are then equal and opposite. We know that

Dynamic force on each bearing

$$= \frac{\text{Out-of-balance couple}}{\text{Distance between bearings}} = \frac{957.6}{1.8} = 532 \text{ N Ans.}$$

A spiral elevator conveyor for material handling.
Note : This picture is given as additional information.

EXERCISES

1. Four masses *A*, *B*, *C* and *D* are attached to a shaft and revolve in the same plane. The masses are 12 kg, 10 kg, 18 kg and 15 kg respectively and their radii of rotations are 40 mm, 50 mm, 60 mm and 30 mm. The angular position of the masses *B*, *C* and *D* are 60°, 135° and 270° from the mass *A*. Find the magnitude and position of the balancing mass at a radius of 100 mm.

   [Ans. 7.56 kg ; 87° clockwise from *A*]

2. Four masses *A*, *B*, *C* and *D* revolve at equal radii and are equally spaced along a shaft. The mass *B* is 7 kg and the radii of *C* and *D* make angles of 90° and 240° respectively with the radius of *B*. Find the magnitude of the masses *A*, *C* and *D* and the angular position of *A* so that the system may be completely balanced.

   [Ans. 5 kg ; 6 kg ; 4.67 kg ; 205° from mass *B* in anticlockwise direction]

3. A rotating shaft carries four masses *A*, *B*, *C* and *D* which are radially attached to it. The mass centres are 30 mm, 38 mm, 40 mm and 35 mm respectively from the axis of rotation. The masses *A*, *C* and *D* are 7.5 kg, 5 kg and 4 kg respectively. The axial distances between the planes of rotation of *A* and *B* is 400 mm and between *B* and *C* is 500 mm. The masses *A* and *C* are at right angles to each other. Find for a complete balance,

   1. the angles between the masses *B* and *D* from mass *A*,

   2. the axial distance between the planes of rotation of *C* and *D*,

   3. the magnitude of mass *B*.   **[Ans. 162.5°, 47.5° ; 511 mm : 9.24 kg]**

4. A rotating shaft carries four unbalanced masses 18 kg, 14 kg, 16 kg and 12 kg at radii 50 mm, 60 mm, 70 mm and 60 mm respectively. The 2nd, 3rd and 4th masses revolve in planes 80 mm, 160 mm and 280 mm respectively measured from the plane of the first mass and are angularly located at 60°, 135° and 270° respectively measured clockwise from the first mass looking from this mass end of the shaft. The shaft is dynamically balanced by two masses, both located at 50 mm radii and revolving in planes mid-way between those of 1st and 2nd masses and midway between those of 3rd and 4th masses. Determine, graphically or otherwise, the magnitudes of the masses and their respective angular positions.

   [Ans. 13.3 kg and 10.4 kg at 25° and 275° from mass *A* in anticlockwise direction]

5. A shaft carries five masses A, B, C, D and E which revolve at the same radius in planes which are equidistant from one another. The magnitude of the masses in planes A, C and D are 50 kg, 40 kg and 80 kg respectively. The angle between A and C is 90° and that between C and D is 135°. Determine the magnitude of the masses in planes B and E and their positions to put the shaft in complete rotating balance.

    [**Ans.** 12 kg, 15 kg ; 130° and 24° from mass A in anticlockwise direction]

6. A shaft with 3 metres span between two bearings carries two masses of 10 kg and 20 kg acting at the extremities of the arms 0.45 m and 0.6 m long respectively. The planes in which these masses rotate are 1.2 m and 2.4 m respectively from the left end bearing supporting the shaft. The angle between the arms is 60°. The speed of rotation of the shaft is 200 r.p.m. If the masses are balanced by two counter-masses rotating with the shaft acting at radii of 0.3 m and placed at 0.3 m from each bearing centres, estimate the magnitude of the two balance masses and their orientation with respect to the X-axis, *i.e.* mass of 10 kg.

    [**Ans.** 10 kg and 41 kg at 190° and 235° from X-axis in the anticlockwise direction]

7. A, B, C and D are four masses carried by a rotating shaft at radii 100 mm, 150 mm, 150 mm and 200 mm respectively. The planes in which the masses rotate are spaced at 500 mm apart and the magnitude of the masses B, C and D are 9 kg, 5 kg and 4 kg respectively. Find the required mass A and the relative angular settings of the four masses so that the shaft shall be in complete balance.

    [**Ans.** 10 kg ; Between B and A 165°, Between B and C 295°, Between B and D 145°]

8. A 3.6 m long shaft carries three pulleys, two at its two ends and third at the mid-point. The two end pulleys has mass of 79 kg and 40 kg and their centre of gravity are 3 mm and 5 mm respectively from the axis of the shaft. The middle pulley mass is 50 kg and its centre of gravity is 8 mm from the shaft axis. The pulleys are so keyed to the shaft that the assembly is in static balance. The shaft rotates at 300 r.p.m. in two bearings 2.4 m apart with equal overhang on either side. Determine : 1. the relative angular positions of the pulleys, and 2. dynamic reactions at the two bearings.

9. The camshaft of high speed pump consists of a parallel shaft 25 mm diameter and 480 mm long. It carries three eccentrics, each of diameter 60 mm and a uniform thickness of 18 mm. The assembly is symmetrical as shown in Fig. 21.14 and the bearings are at A and B. The angle between the eccentrics is 120° and the eccentricity of each is 12.5 mm. The material density is 7000 kg/m³, and the speed of rotation is 1430 r.p.m.

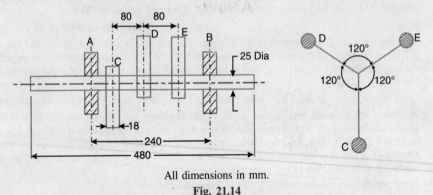

All dimensions in mm.

Fig. 21.14

Find : 1. dynamic load on each bearing due to the out-of-balance couple ; and 2. kinetic energy of the complete assembly.

[**Ans.** 6.12 kg ; 8.7 N-m]

DO YOU KNOW ?

1. Why is balancing of rotating parts necessary for high speed engines ?

2. Explain clearly the terms 'static balancing' and 'dynamic balancing'. State the necessary conditions to achieve them.

3. Discuss how a single revolving mass is balanced by two masses revolving in different planes.

4.   Explain the method of balancing of different masses revolving in the same plane.

5.   How the different masses rotating in different planes are balanced ?

OBJECTIVE TYPE QUESTIONS

1.   The balancing of rotating and reciprocating parts of an engine is necessary when it runs at

    (*a*) slow speed   (*b*) medium speed   (*c*) high speed

2.   A disturbing mass m_1 attached to a rotating shaft may be balanced by a single mass m_2 attached in the same plane of rotation as that of m_1 such that

    (*a*) $m_1.r_2 = m_2.r_1$ (*b*) $m_1.r_1 = m_2.r_2$ (*c*) $m_1. m_2 = r_1.r_2$

3.   For static balancing of a shaft,

    (*a*) the net dynamic force acting on the shaft is equal to zero

    (*b*) the net couple due to the dynamic forces acting on the shaft is equal to zero

    (*c*) both (*a*) and (*b*)

    (*d*) none of the above

4.   For dynamic balancing of a shaft,

    (*a*) the net dynamic force acting on the shaft is equal to zero

    (*b*) the net couple due to dynamic forces acting on the shaft is equal to zero

    (*c*) both (*a*) and (*b*)

    (*d*) none of the above

5.   In order to have a complete balance of the several revolving masses in different planes

    (*a*) the resultant force must be zero

    (*b*) the resultant couple must be zero

    (*c*) both the resultant force and couple must be zero

    (*d*) none of the above

ANSWERS

    1. (*c*)   **2.** (*b*)   **3.** (*a*)   **4.** (*c*)   **5.** (*c*)

22

Balancing of Reciprocating Masses

22.1. Introduction

We have discussed in Chapter 15 (Art. 15.10), the various forces acting on the reciprocating parts of an engine. The resultant of all the forces acting on the body of the engine due to inertia forces only is known as *unbalanced force* or *shaking force*. Thus if the resultant of all the forces due to inertia effects is zero, then there will be no unbalanced force, but even then an unbalanced couple or shaking couple will be present.

Consider a horizontal reciprocating engine mechanism as shown in Fig. 22.1.

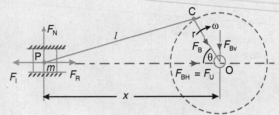

Fig. 22.1. Reciprocating engine mechanism.

Let F_R = Force required to accelerate the reciprocating parts,

F_I = Inertia force due to reciprocating parts,

F_N = Force on the sides of the cylinder walls or normal force acting on the cross-head guides, and

F_B = Force acting on the crankshaft bearing or main bearing.

Since F_R and F_I are equal in magnitude but opposite in direction, therefore they balance each other. The horizontal component of F_B (*i.e.* F_{BH}) acting along the line of reciprocation is also equal and opposite to F_I. This force $F_{BH} = F_U$ is an unbalanced force or shaking force and required to be properly balanced.

The force on the sides of the cylinder walls (F_N) and the vertical component of F_B (*i.e.* F_{BV}) are equal and opposite and thus form a shaking couple of magnitude $F_N \times x$ or $F_{BV} \times x$.

From above we see that the effect of the reciprocating parts is to produce a shaking force and a shaking couple. Since the shaking force and a shaking couple vary in magnitude and direction during the engine cycle, therefore they cause very objectionable vibrations.

Thus the purpose of balancing the reciprocating masses is to eliminate the shaking force and a shaking couple. In most of the mechanisms, we can reduce the shaking force and a shaking couple by adding appropriate balancing mass, but it is usually not practical to eliminate them completely. In other words, the reciprocating masses are only partially balanced.

Note : The masses rotating with the crankshaft are normally balanced and they do not transmit any unbalanced or shaking force on the body of the engine.

22.2. Primary and Secondary Unbalanced Forces of Reciprocating Masses

Consider a reciprocating engine mechanism as shown in Fig. 22.1.

Let m = Mass of the reciprocating parts,

l = Length of the connecting rod PC,

r = Radius of the crank OC,

θ = Angle of inclination of the crank with the line of stroke PO,

ω = Angular speed of the crank,

n = Ratio of length of the connecting rod to the crank radius = l / r.

We have already discussed in Art. 15.8 that the acceleration of the reciprocating parts is approximately given by the expression,

$$a_R = \omega^2 \cdot r \left(\cos\theta + \frac{\cos 2\theta}{n} \right)$$

∴ Inertia force due to reciprocating parts or force required to accelerate the reciprocating parts,

$$F_I = F_R = \text{Mass} \times \text{acceleration} = m \cdot \omega^2 \cdot r \left(\cos\theta + \frac{\cos 2\theta}{n} \right)$$

We have discussed in the previous article that the horizontal component of the force exerted on the crank shaft bearing (*i.e.* F_{BH}) is equal and opposite to inertia force (F_I). This force is an unbalanced one and is denoted by F_U.

∴   Unbalanced force,

$$F_U = m \cdot \omega^2 \cdot r \left(\cos\theta + \frac{\cos 2\theta}{n} \right) = m.\omega^2 \cdot r \cos\theta + m \cdot \omega^2 \cdot r \times \frac{\cos 2\theta}{n} = F_P + F_S$$

The expression $(m \cdot \omega^2 \cdot r \cos\theta)$ is known as *primary unbalanced force* and $\left(m \cdot \omega^2 \cdot r \times \dfrac{\cos 2\theta}{n} \right)$ is called *secondary unbalanced force*.

∴ Primary unbalanced force, $F_P = m \cdot \omega^2 \cdot r \cos\theta$

and secondary unbalanced force, $\qquad F_S = m \cdot \omega^2 \cdot r \times \dfrac{\cos 2\theta}{n}$

Notes: 1. The primary unbalanced force is maximum, when $\theta = 0°$ or $180°$. Thus, the primary force is maximum twice in one revolution of the crank. The maximum primary unbalanced force is given by

$$F_{P(max)} = m \cdot \omega^2 \cdot r$$

2. The secondary unbalanced force is maximum, when $\theta = 0°$, $90°$, $180°$ and $360°$. Thus, the secondary force is maximum four times in one revolution of the crank. The maximum secondary unbalanced force is given by

$$F_{S(max)} = m \cdot \omega^2 \times \dfrac{r}{n}$$

3. From above we see that maximum secondary unbalanced force is $1/n$ times the maximum primary unbalanced force.

4. In case of moderate speeds, the secondary unbalanced force is so small that it may be neglected as compared to primary unbalanced force.

5. The unbalanced force due to reciprocating masses varies in magnitude but constant in direction while due to the revolving masses, the unbalanced force is constant in magnitude but varies in direction.

22.3. Partial Balancing of Unbalanced Primary Force in a Reciprocating Engine

The primary unbalanced force $(m \cdot \omega^2 \cdot r \cos\theta)$ may be considered as the component of the centrifugal force produced by a rotating mass m placed at the crank radius r, as shown in Fig. 22.2.

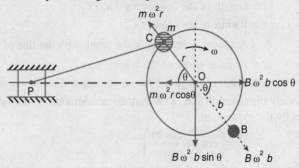

Fig. 22.2. Partial balancing of unbalanced primary force in a reciprocating engine.

The primary force acts from O to P along the line of stroke. Hence, balancing of primary force is considered as equivalent to the balancing of mass m rotating at the crank radius r. This is balanced by having a mass B at a radius b, placed diametrically opposite to the crank pin C.

We know that centrifugal force due to mass B,

$$= B \cdot \omega^2 \cdot b$$

and horizontal component of this force acting in opposite direction of primary force

$$= B \cdot \omega^2 \cdot b \cos\theta$$

The primary force is balanced, if

$$B \cdot \omega^2 \cdot b \cos\theta = m \cdot \omega^2 \cdot r \cos\theta \quad \text{or} \quad B.b = m.r$$

A little consideration will show, that the primary force is completely balanced if $B.b = m.r$, but the centrifugal force produced due to the revolving mass B, has also a vertical component (perpendicular to the line of stroke) of magnitude $B \cdot \omega^2 \cdot b \sin\theta$. This force remains unbalanced. The maximum value of this force is equal to $B \cdot \omega^2 \cdot b$ when θ is 90° and 270°, which is same as the maximum value of the primary force $m \cdot \omega^2 \cdot r$.

From the above discussion, we see that in the first case, the primary unbalanced force acts along the line of stroke whereas in the second case, the unbalanced force acts along the perpendicular to the line of stroke. The maximum value of the force remains same in both the cases. It is thus obvious, that the effect of the above method of balancing is to change the direction of the maximum unbalanced force from the line of stroke to the perpendicular of line of stroke. As a compromise let a fraction 'c' of the reciprocating masses is balanced, such that

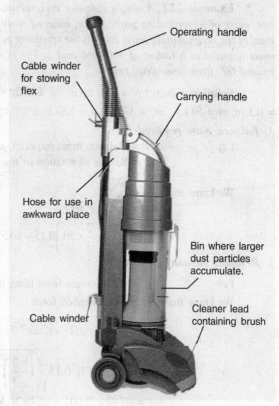

Cyclone cleaner.

$$c.m.r = B.b$$

∴ Unbalanced force along the line of stroke

$$= m \cdot \omega^2 \cdot r \cos\theta - B \cdot \omega^2 \cdot b \cos\theta$$

$$= m \cdot \omega^2 \cdot r \cos\theta - c \cdot m \cdot \omega^2 \cdot r \cos\theta \qquad \text{...} (\because \ B.b = c.m.r)$$

$$= (1-c)m \cdot \omega^2 \cdot r \cos\theta$$

and unbalanced force along the perpendicular to the line of stroke

$$= B \cdot \omega^2 \cdot b \sin\theta = c \cdot m \cdot \omega^2 \cdot r \sin\theta$$

∴ Resultant unbalanced force at any instant

$$= \sqrt{\left[(1-c)m \cdot \omega^2 \cdot r \cos\theta \right]^2 + \left[c \cdot m \cdot \omega^2 \cdot r \sin\theta \right]^2}$$

$$= m \cdot \omega^2 \cdot r \sqrt{(1-c)^2 \cos^2\theta + c^2 \sin^2\theta}$$

Note : If the balancing mass is required to balance the revolving masses as well as reciprocating masses, then

$$B.b = m_1 \cdot r + c \cdot m \cdot r = (m_1 + c \cdot m)r$$

where
m_1 = Magnitude of the revolving masses, and

m = magnitude of the reciprocating masses.

Example 22.1. *A single cylinder reciprocating engine has speed 240 r.p.m., stroke 300 mm, mass of reciprocating parts 50 kg, mass of revolving parts at 150 mm radius 37 kg. If two-third of the reciprocating parts and all the revolving parts are to be balanced, find : **1.** The balance mass required at a radius of 400 mm, and **2.** The residual unbalanced force when the crank has rotated 60° from inner dead centre.*

Solution. Given : N = 240 r.p.m. or $\omega = 2\pi \times 240/60$ = 25.14 rad/s ; Stroke = 300 mm = 0.3 m; m = 50 kg ; m_1 = 37 kg ; r = 150 mm = 0.15 m ; c = 2/3

1. Balance mass required

Let $\qquad$ B = Balance mass required, and

$\qquad$ b = Radius of rotation of the balance mass = 400 mm = 0.4 m

$\qquad\qquad\qquad\qquad\qquad\qquad\qquad\qquad\qquad\qquad\qquad$ ... (Given)

We know that

$$B.b = (m_1 + c.m) \, r$$

$$B \times 0.4 = \left(37 + \frac{2}{3} \times 50\right) 0.15 = 10.55 \quad \text{or} \quad B = 26.38 \text{ kg } \textbf{Ans.}$$

2. Residual unbalanced force

Let $\qquad$ θ = Crank angle from inner dead centre = 60° $\qquad\qquad$ ... (Given)

We know that residual unbalanced force

$$= m \cdot \omega^2 \cdot r \sqrt{(1-c)^2 \cos^2 \theta + c^2 \sin^2 \theta}$$

$$= 50 (25.14)^2 0.15 \sqrt{\left(1 - \frac{2}{3}\right)^2 \cos^2 60° + \left(\frac{2}{3}\right)^2 \sin^2 60°} \text{ N}$$

$$= 4740 \times 0.601 = 2849 \text{ N } \textbf{Ans.}$$

22.4. Partial Balancing of Locomotives

The locomotives, usually, have two cylinders with cranks placed at right angles to each other in order to have uniformity in turning moment diagram. The two cylinder locomotives may be classified as :

1. Inside cylinder locomotives ; and **2.** Outside cylinder locomotives.

In the *inside cylinder locomotives*, the two cylinders are placed in between the planes of two driving wheels as shown in Fig. 22.3 (*a*) ; whereas in the *outside cylinder locomotives*, the two cylinders are placed outside the driving wheels, one on each side of the driving wheel, as shown in Fig. 22.3 (*b*). The locomotives may be

(*a*) Single or uncoupled locomotives ; and (*b*) Coupled locomotives.

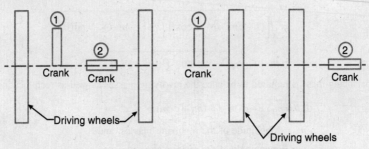

$\qquad\quad$ (*a*) Inside cylinder locomotives. $\qquad\qquad$ (*b*) Outside cylinder locomotives.

Fig. 22.3

A *single* or *uncoupled locomotive* is one, in which the effort is transmitted to one pair of the wheels only ; whereas in *coupled locomotives,* the driving wheels are connected to the leading and trailing wheel by an outside coupling rod.

22.5. Effect of Partial Balancing of Reciprocating Parts of Two Cylinder Locomotives

We have discussed in the previous article that the reciprocating parts are only partially balanced. Due to this partial balancing of the reciprocating parts, there is an unbalanced primary force along the line of stroke and also an unbalanced primary force perpendicular to the line of stroke. The effect of an unbalanced primary force along the line of stroke is to produce;

1. Variation in tractive force along the line of stroke ; and **2.** Swaying couple.

The effect of an unbalanced primary force perpendicular to the line of stroke is to produce variation in pressure on the rails, which results in hammering action on the rails. The maximum magnitude of the unbalanced force along the perpendicular to the line of stroke is known as a *hammer blow*. We shall now discuss the effects of an unbalanced primary force in the following articles.

22.6. Variation of Tractive Force

The resultant unbalanced force due to the two cylinders, along the line of stroke, is known as *tractive force*. Let the crank for the first cylinder be inclined at an angle θ with the line of stroke, as shown in Fig. 22.4. Since the crank for the second cylinder is at right angle to the first crank, therefore the angle of inclination for the second crank will be $(90° + \theta)$.

Let m = Mass of the reciprocating parts per cylinder, and

c = Fraction of the reciprocating parts to be balanced.

We know that unbalanced force along the line of stroke for cylinder 1

$$= (1-c)m.\omega^2.r\cos\theta$$

Similarly, unbalanced force along the line of stroke for cylinder 2,

$$= (1-c)m.\omega^2 \cdot r\cos(90°+\theta)$$

∴ As per definition, the tractive force,

F_T = Resultant unbalanced force along the line of stroke

$$= (1-c)m.\omega^2.r\cos\theta$$

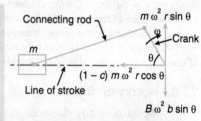

Fig. 22.4. Variation of tractive force.

$$+ (1-c)m.\omega^2.r\cos(90°+\theta)$$

$$= (1-c)m.\omega^2.r(\cos\theta-\sin\theta)$$

The tractive force is maximum or minimum when $(\cos\theta - \sin\theta)$ is maximum or minimum. For $(\cos\theta - \sin\theta)$ to be maximum or minimum,

$$\frac{d}{d\theta}(\cos\theta-\sin\theta)=0 \quad \text{or} \quad -\sin\theta-\cos\theta=0 \quad \text{or} \quad -\sin\theta=\cos\theta$$

∴ $\tan\theta=-1$ or $\theta=135°$ or $315°$

Thus, the tractive force is maximum or minimum when $\theta = 135°$ or $315°$.

∴ Maximum and minimum value of the tractive force or the variation in tractive force

$$= \pm(1-c)m.\omega^2.r(\cos135°-\sin135°)=\pm\sqrt{2}(1-c)m.\omega^2.r$$

22.7. Swaying Couple

The unbalanced forces along the line of stroke for the two cylinders constitute a couple about the centre line *YY* between the cylinders as shown in Fig. 22.5.

This couple has swaying effect about a vertical axis, and tends to sway the engine alternately in clockwise and anticlockwise directions. Hence the couple is known as *swaying couple.*

Let a = Distance between the centre lines of the two cylinders.

∴ Swaying couple

$$= (1-c)m.\omega^2.r\cos\theta \times \frac{a}{2}$$

$$- (1-c)m.\omega^2.r\cos(90°+\theta)\frac{a}{2}$$

$$= (1-c)m.\omega^2.r \times \frac{a}{2}(\cos\theta + \sin\theta)$$

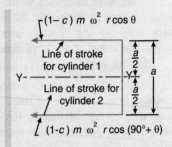

Fig. 22.5. Swaying couple.

The swaying couple is maximum or minimum when $(\cos\theta + \sin\theta)$ is maximum or minimum. For $(\cos\theta + \sin\theta)$ to be maximum or minimum,

$$\frac{d}{d\theta}(\cos\theta + \sin\theta) = 0 \quad \text{or} \quad -\sin\theta + \cos\theta = 0 \quad \text{or} \quad -\sin\theta = -\cos\theta$$

$$\therefore \qquad \tan\theta = 1 \quad \text{or} \quad \theta = 45° \quad \text{or} \quad 225°$$

Thus, the swaying couple is maximum or minimum when $\theta = 45°$ or $225°$.

∴ Maximum and minimum value of the swaying couple

$$= \pm(1-c)m.\omega^2.r \times \frac{a}{2}(\cos 45° + \sin 45°) = \pm\frac{a}{\sqrt{2}}(1-c)m.\omega^2.r$$

Note : In order to reduce the magnitude of the swaying couple, revolving balancing masses are introduced. But, as discussed in the previous article, the revolving balancing masses cause unbalanced forces to act at right angles to the line of stroke. These forces vary the downward pressure of the wheels on the rails and cause oscillation of the locomotive in a vertical plane about a horizontal axis. Since a swaying couple is more harmful than an oscillating couple, therefore a value of 'c' from 2/3 to 3/4, in two-cylinder locomotives with two pairs of coupled wheels, is usually used. But in large four cylinder locomotives with three or more pairs of coupled wheels, the value of 'c' is taken as 2/5.

22.8. Hammer Blow

We have already discussed that the maximum magnitude of the unbalanced force along the perpendicular to the line of stroke is known as *hammer blow.*

We know that the unbalanced force along the perpendicular to the line of stroke due to the balancing mass B, at a radius b, in order to balance reciprocating parts only is $B.\omega^2.b\sin\theta$. This force will be maximum when $\sin\theta$ is unity, *i.e.* when $\theta = 90°$ or $270°$.

$$\therefore \qquad \text{Hammer blow} = B.\omega^2.b \qquad\qquad \text{(Substituiting } \sin\theta = 1\text{)}$$

The effect of hammer blow is to cause the variation in pressure between the wheel and the rail. This variation is shown in Fig. 22.6, for one revolution of the wheel.

Let P be the downward pressure on the rails (or static wheel load).

∴ Net pressure between the wheel and the rail

$$= P \pm B.\omega^2.b$$

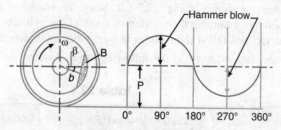

Fig. 22.6. Hammer blow.

If $(P - B.\omega^2.b)$ is *negative,* then the wheel will be lifted from the rails. Therefore the limiting condition in order that the wheel does not lift from the rails is given by

$$P = B.\omega^2.b$$

and the permissible value of the angular speed,

$$\omega = \sqrt{\frac{P}{B.b}}$$

Example 22.2. *An inside cylinder locomotive has its cylinder centre lines 0.7 m apart and has a stroke of 0.6 m. The rotating masses per cylinder are equivalent to 150 kg at the crank pin, and the reciprocating masses per cylinder to 180 kg. The wheel centre lines are 1.5 m apart. The cranks are at right angles.*

The whole of the rotating and 2/3 of the recipro-cating masses are to be balanced by masses placed at a radius of 0.6 m. Find the magnitude and direction of the balancing masses.

Find the fluctuation in rail pressure under one wheel, variation of tractive effort and the magnitude of swaying couple at a crank speed of 300 r.p.m.

Solution. Given : $a = 0.7$ m; $l_B = l_C = 0.6$ m or $r_B = r_C = 0.3$ m; $m_1 = 150$ kg; $m_2 = 180$ kg; $c = 2/3$; $r_A = r_D = 0.6$ m; $N = 300$ r.p.m. or $\omega = 2\pi \times 300/60 = 31.42$ rad/s

We know that the equivalent mass of the rotating parts to be balanced per cylinder at the crank pin,

This Brinel hardness testing machine is used to test the hardness of the metal.

Note : This picture is given as additional information.

$$m = m_B = m_C = m_1 + c.m_2 = 150 + \frac{2}{3} \times 180 = 270 \text{ kg}$$

Magnitude and direction of the balancing masses

Let m_A and m_D = Magnitude of the balancing masses

θ_A and θ_D = Angular position of the balancing masses m_A and m_D from the first crank B.

The magnitude and direction of the balancing masses may be determined graphically as discussed below :

1. First of all, draw the space diagram to show the positions of the planes of the wheels and the cylinders, as shown in Fig. 22.7 (*a*). Since the cranks of the cylinders are at right angles, therefore assuming the position of crank of the cylinder *B* in the horizontal direction, draw *OC* and *OB* at right angles to each other as shown in Fig. 22.7 (*b*).

2. Tabulate the data as given in the following table. Assume the plane of wheel *A* as the reference plane.

Table 22.1

Plane (1)	mass. (m) kg (2)	Radius (r)m (3)	Cent. force $\div \omega^2$ (m.r) kg-m (4)	Distance from plane A (l)m (5)	Couple $\div \omega^2$ (m.r.l) kg-m² (6)
A (R.P.)	m_A	0.6	$0.6\, m_A$	0	0
B	270	0.3	81	0.4	32.4
C	270	0.3	81	1.1	89.1
D	m_D	0.6	$0.6 m_D$	1.5	$0.9\, m_D$

3. Now, draw the couple polygon from the data given in Table 22.1 (column 6), to some suitable scale, as shown in Fig 22.7 (*c*). The closing side $c'o'$ represents the balancing couple and it is proportional to $0.9\, m_D$. Therefore, by measurement,

$$0.9\, m_D = \text{vector } c'o' = 94.5 \text{ kg-m}^2 \quad \text{or} \quad m_D = 105 \text{ kg} \quad \textbf{Ans.}$$

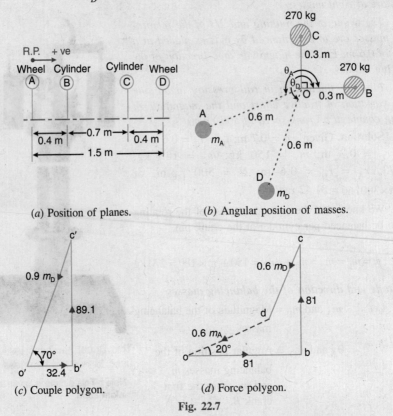

(*a*) Position of planes.

(*b*) Angular position of masses.

(*c*) Couple polygon.

(*d*) Force polygon.

Fig. 22.7

4. To determine the angular position of the balancing mass *D*, draw *OD* in Fig. 22.7 (*b*) parallel to vector *c'o'*. By measurement,

$$\theta_D = 250° \text{ Ans.}$$

5. In order to find the balancing mass *A*, draw the force polygon from the data given in · Table 22.1 (column 4), to some suitable scale, as shown in Fig. 22.7 (*d*), The vector *do* represents the balancing force and it is proportional to 0.6 *m*$_A$. Therefore by measurement,

$$0.6 \, m_A = \text{vector } do = 63 \text{ kg-m or } m_A = 105 \text{ kg Ans.}$$

6. To determine the angular position of the balancing mass *A*, draw *OA* in Fig. 22.7 (*b*) parallel to vector *do*. By measurement,

$$\theta_A = 200° \text{ Ans.}$$

Fluctuation in rail pressure

We know that each balancing mass
$$= 105 \text{ kg}$$
∴   Balancing mass for rotating masses,

$$= \frac{m_1}{m} \times 105 = \frac{150}{270} \times 105 = 58.3 \text{ kg}$$

and balancing mass for reciprocating masses,

$$B = \frac{c.m_2}{m} \times 105 = \frac{2}{3} \times \frac{180}{270} \times 105 = 46.6 \text{ kg}$$

This balancing mass of 46.6 kg for reciprocating masses gives rise to the centrifugal force.
∴ Fluctuation in rail pressure or hammer blow

$$= B.\omega^2.b = 46.6 \, (31.42)^2 \, 0.6 = 27\,602 \text{ N Ans.} \qquad \dots (\because b = r_A = r_D)$$

Variation of tractive effort

We know that maximum variation of tractive effort

$$= \pm\sqrt{2}(1-c)m_2.\omega^2.r = \pm\sqrt{2}\left(1 - \frac{2}{3}\right)180(31.42)^2\,0.3\,\text{N}$$

$$= \pm 25\,127 \text{ N Ans.} \qquad \dots (\because r = r_B = r_C)$$

Swaying couple

We know that maximum swaying couple

$$= \frac{a(1-c)}{\sqrt{2}} \times m_2.\omega^2.r = \frac{0.7\left(1 - \frac{2}{3}\right)}{\sqrt{2}} \times 180(31.42)^2\,0.3 \text{ N-m}$$

$$= 8797 \text{ N-m Ans.}$$

Example 22.3 *The three cranks of a three cylinder locomotive are all on the same axle and are set at 120°. The pitch of the cylinders is 1 metre and the stroke of each piston is 0.6 m. The reciprocating masses are 300 kg for inside cylinder and 260 kg for each outside cylinder and the planes of rotation of the balance masses are 0.8 m from the inside crank.*

If 40% of the reciprocating parts are to be balanced, find :

1. the magnitude and the position of the balancing masses required at a radius of 0.6 m ;

and

2. the hammer blow per wheel when the axle makes 6 r.p.s.

Solution. Given : $\angle AOB = \angle BOC = \angle COA = 120°$; $l_A = l_B = l_C = 0.6$ m or $r_A = r_B$ $= r_C = 0.3$ m ; $m_1 = 300$ kg ; $m_O = 260$ kg ; $c = 40\% = 0.4$; $b_1 = b_2 = 0.6$ m ; $N = 6$ r.p.s. $= 6 \times 2\pi = 37.7$ rad/s

Since 40% of the reciprocating masses are to be balanced, therefore mass of the reciprocating parts to be balanced for each outside cylinder,

$$m_A = m_C = c \times m_O = 0.4 \times 260 = 104 \text{ kg}$$

and mass of the reciprocating parts to be balanced for inside cylinder,

$$m_B = c \times m_1 = 0.4 \times 300 = 120 \text{ kg}$$

1. Magnitude and position of the balancing masses

Let B_1 and B_2 = Magnitude of the balancing masses in kg,

θ_1 and θ_2 = Angular position of the balancing masses B_1 and B_2 from crank A.

The magnitude and position of the balancing masses may be determined graphically as discussed below :

1. First of all, draw the position of planes and cranks as shown in Fig. 22.8 (a) and (b) respectively. The position of crank A is assumed in the horizontal direction.
2. Tabulate the data as given in the following table. Assume the plane of balancing mass B_1 (i.e. plane 1) as the reference plane.

Table 22.2

Plane (1)	Mass (m)kg (2)	Radius (r) m (3)	Cent. force $\div \omega^2$ (m.r) kg-m (4)	Distance from plane1 (l)m (5)	Couple $\div \omega^2$ (m.r.l.) kg-m^2 (6)
A	104	0.3	31.2	– 0.2	– 6.24
1 (R.P.)	B_1	0.6	0.6 B_1	0	0
B	120	0.3	36	0.8	28.8
2	B_2	0.6	0.6 B_2	1.6	0.96 B_2
C	104	0.3	31.2	1.8	56.16

3. Now draw the couple polygon with the data given in Table 22.2 (column 6), to some suitable scale, as shown in Fig. 22.8 (c). The closing side $c'o'$ represents the balancing couple and it is proportional to 0.96 B_2. Therefore, by measurement,

$$0.96 B_2 = \text{vector } c'o' = 55.2 \text{ kg-m}^2 \text{ or } B_2 = 57.5 \text{ kg Ans.}$$

4. To determine the angular position of the balancing mass B_2, draw OB_2 parallel to vector $c'o'$ as shown in Fig. 22.8 (b). By measurement,

$$\theta_2 = 24° \text{ Ans.}$$

5. In order to find the balance mass B_1, draw the force polygon with the data given in Table 22.2 (column 4), to some suitable scale, as shown in Fig. 22.8 (d). The closing side co represents the balancing force and it is proportional to 0.6 B_1. Therefore, by measurement,

$$0.6 B_1 = \text{vector } co = 34.5 \text{ kg-m} \quad \text{or} \quad B_1 = 57.5 \text{ kg Ans.}$$

6. To determine the angular position of the balancing mass B_1, draw OB_1 parallel to vector co, as shown in Fig. 22.8 (b). By measurement,

$$\theta_1 = 215° \text{ Ans.}$$

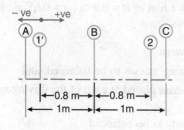

(a) Position of planes.

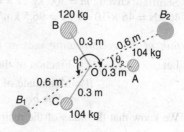

(b) Position of cranks.

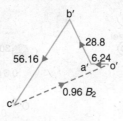

(c) Couple polygon.

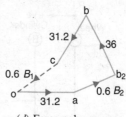

(d) Force polygon.

Fig. 22.8

2. Hammer blow per wheel

We know that hammer blow per wheel

$$= B_1.\omega^2.b_1 = 57.5 \ (37.7)^2 \ 20.6 = 49 \ 035 \ \text{N Ans.}$$

This chamber is used to test the acoustics of a vehicle so that the noise it produces can be reduced. The panels in the walls and ceiling of the room absorb the sound which is monitored (above)

Note : This picture is given as additional information.

Example 22.4. *The following data refer to two cylinder locomotive with cranks at 90° :*

Reciprocating mass per cylinder = 300 kg ; Crank radius = 0.3 m ; Driving wheel diameter = 1.8 m ; Distance between cylinder centre lines = 0.65 m ; Distance between the driving wheel central planes = 1.55 m.

Determine : 1. the fraction of the reciprocating masses to be balanced, if the hammer blow is not to exceed 46 kN at 96.5 km. p.h. ; 2. the variation in tractive effort ; and 3. the maximum swaying couple.

Solution. Given : $m = 300$ kg ; $r = 0.3$ m ; $D = 1.8$ m or $R = 0.9$ m ; $a = 0.65$ m ; Hammer blow = 46 kN = 46×10^3 N ; $v = 96.5$ km/h = 26.8 m/s

1. *Fraction of the reciprocating masses to be balanced*

Let
c = Fraction of the reciprocating masses to be balanced, and

B = Magnitude of balancing mass placed at each of the driving wheels at radius b.

We know that the mass of the reciprocating parts to be balanced

$$= c.m = 300c \text{ kg}$$

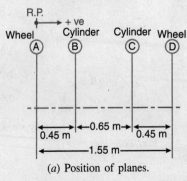
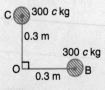

(a) Position of planes.   (b) Position of cranks.

Fig. 22.9

The position of planes of the wheels and cylinders is shown in Fig. 22.9 (a), and the position of cranks is shown in Fig 22.9 (b). Assuming the plane of wheel A as the reference plane, the data may be tabulated as below :

Table 22.3

Plane (1)	Mass (m) kg (2)	Radius (r) m (3)	Cent. force ÷ ω^2 (m.r) kg-m (4)	Distance from plane A (l)m (5)	Couple ÷ ω^2 (m.r.l.) kg-m^2 (6)
A (R.P.)	B	b	B.b	0	0
B	300 c	0.3	90 c	0.45	40.5 c
C	300 c	0.3	90 c	1.1	99 c
D	B	b	B.b	1.55	1.55 B.b

Now the couple polygon, to some suitable scale, may be drawn with the data given in Table 22.3 (column 6), as shown in Fig. 22.10. The closing side of the polygon (vector $c'o'$) represents the balancing couple and is proportional to 1.55 B.b.

From the couple polygon,

$$1.55\, B.b = \sqrt{(40.5c)^2 + (99c)^2} = 107c$$

∴ $\qquad B.b = 107\, c\, /\, 1.55 = 69\, c$

We know that angular speed,

$$\omega = v/R = 26.8/0.9 = 29.8 \text{ rad/s}$$

∴ Hammer blow,

$$46 \times 10^3 = B.\, \omega^2\, .b$$
$$= 69\, c\, (29.8)^2 = 61\,275\, c$$

∴ $\qquad c = 46 \times 10^3/61\,275 = 0.751$ **Ans.**

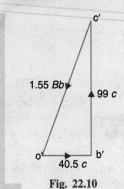

Fig. 22.10

2. *Variation in tractive effort*

We know that variation in tractive effort

$$= \pm\sqrt{2}(1-c)\, m.\omega^2 .r = \pm\sqrt{2}(1-0.751)\, 300\,(29.8)^2 0.3$$

$$= 28\ 140 \text{ N} = 28.14 \text{ kN } \textbf{Ans.}$$

Maximum swaying couple

We know the maximum swaying couple

$$= \frac{a(1-c)}{\sqrt{2}} \times m.\omega^2 .r = \frac{0.65(1-0.751)}{\sqrt{2}} \times 300\,(29.8)^2\, 0.3 = 9148 \text{ N-m}$$

$$= 9.148 \text{ kN-m } \textbf{Ans.}$$

Example 22.5. *The following data apply to an outside cylinder uncoupled locomotive :*

Mass of rotating parts per cylinder = 360 kg ; Mass of reciprocating parts per cylinder = 300 kg ; Angle between cranks = 90° ; Crank radius = 0.3 m ; Cylinder centres = 1.75 m ; Radius of balance masses = 0.75 m ; Wheel centres = 1.45 m.

If whole of the rotating and two-thirds of reciprocating parts are to be balanced in planes of the driving wheels, find :

1. Magnitude and angular positions of balance masses,

2. Speed in kilometres per hour at which the wheel will lift off the rails when the load on each driving wheel is 30 kN and the diameter of tread of driving wheels is 1.8 m, and

3. Swaying couple at speed arrived at in (2) above.

Solution : Given : $m_1 = 360$ kg ; $m_2 = 300$ kg ; $\angle AOD = 90°$; $r_A = r_D = 0.3$ m ; $a = 1.75$ m ; $r_B = r_C = 0.75$ m ; $c = 2/3$.

We know that the equivalent mass of the rotating parts to be balanced per cylinder,

$$m = m_A = m_D = m_1 + c.m_2 = 360 + \frac{2}{3} \times 300 = 560 \text{ kg}$$

1. *Magnitude and angular position of balance masses*

Let $\quad m_B$ and m_C = Magnitude of the balance masses, and

$\quad\quad \theta_B$ and θ_C = angular position of the balance masses m_B and m_C from the crank A.

The magnitude and direction of the balance masses may be determined, graphically, as discussed below :

1. First of all, draw the positions of the planes of the wheels and the cylinders as shown in Fig. 22.11 (*a*). Since the cranks of the two cylinders are at right angles, therefore assuming the position of the cylinder A in the horizontal direction, draw OA and OD at right angles to each other as shown in Fig. 22.11 (*b*).

2. Assuming the plane of wheel B as the reference plane, the data may be tabulated as below:

Table 22.4

Plane (1)	Mass (m) kg (2)	Radius (r) m (3)	Cent. force $\div \omega^2$ (m.r) kg-m (4)	Distance from plane B(l) m (5)	Couple $\div \omega^2$ (m.r.l) kg-m² (6)
A	560	0.3	168	– 0.15	– 25.2
B (R.P)	m_B	0.75	0.75 m_B	0	0
C	m_C	0.75	0.75 m_C	1.45	1.08 m_C
D	560	0.3	168	1.6	268.8

3. Now draw the couple polygon with the data given in Table 22.4 column (6), to some suitable scale as shown in Fig. 22.11(c). The closing side $d'o'$ represents the balancing couple and it is proportional to 1.08 m_C. Therefore, by measurement,

$$1.08 \ m_C = 269.6 \text{ kg-m}^2 \quad \text{or} \quad m_C = 249 \text{ kg} \quad \textbf{Ans.}$$

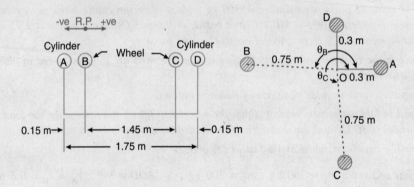

(a) Position of planes.   (b) Position of masses.

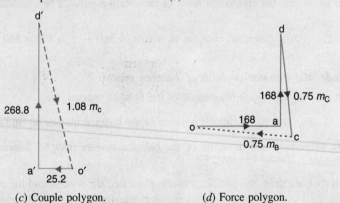

(c) Couple polygon.   (d) Force polygon.

Fig. 22.11

4. To determine the angular position of the balancing mass C, draw OC parallel to vector $d'o'$ as shown in Fig. 22.11 (b). By measurement,

$$\theta_C = 275° \quad \textbf{Ans.}$$

5. In order to find the balancing mass B, draw the force polygon with the data given in Table 22.4 column (4), to some suitable scale, as shown in Fig. 22.11 (d). The vector co represents

the balancing force and it is proportional to 0.75 m_B. Therefore, by measurement,

$$0.75\ m_B = 186.75\ \text{kg-m} \quad \text{or} \quad m_B = 249\ \text{kg Ans.}$$

6. To determine the angular position of the balancing mass B, draw OB parallel to vector oc as shown Fig. 22.11 (*b*). By measurement,

$$\theta_B = 174.5° \text{ Ans.}$$

2. *Speed at which the wheel will lift off the rails*

Given : $P = 30\ \text{kN} = 30 \times 10^3\ \text{N} ; D = 1.8\ \text{m}$

Let ω = Angular speed at which the wheels will lift off the rails in rad/s, and

v = Corresponding linear speed in km/h.

We know that each balancing mass,

$$m_B = m_C = 249\ \text{kg}$$

∴   Balancing mass for reciprocating parts,

$$B = \frac{c.m_2}{m} \times 249 = \frac{2}{3} \times \frac{300}{560} \times 249 = 89\ \text{kg}$$

We know that $\omega = \sqrt{\dfrac{P}{B.b}} = \sqrt{\dfrac{30 \times 10^3}{89 \times 0.75}} = 21.2\ \text{rad/s}$ ...(∵ $b = r_B = r_C$)

and $v = \omega \times D / 2 = 21.2 \times 1.8 / 2 = 19.08\ \text{m/s}$

$$= 19.08 \times 3600/ 1000 = 68.7\ \text{km/h Ans.}$$

3. *Swaying couple at speed* $\omega = 21.1\ rad/s$

We know that the swaying couple

$$= \frac{a(1-c)}{\sqrt{2}} \times m_2.\omega^2.r = \frac{1.75\left[1 - \dfrac{2}{3}\right]}{\sqrt{2}} \times 300(21.2)^2 0.3\ \text{N-m}$$

$$= 16\ 687\ \text{N-m} = 16.687\ \text{kN-m Ans.}$$

22.9. Balancing of Coupled Locomotives

The uncoupled locomotives as discussed in the previous article, are obsolete now-a-days. In a coupled locomotive, the driving wheels are connected to the leading and trailing wheels by an outside coupling rod. By such an arrangement, a greater portion of the engine mass is utilised by tractive purposes. In coupled locomotives, the coupling rod cranks are placed diametrically opposite to the adjacent main cranks (*i.e.* driving cranks). The coupling rods together with cranks and pins may be treated as rotating masses

A dynamo converts mechanical energy into electrical energy.

Note : This picture is given as additional information.

and completely balanced by masses in the respective wheels. Thus in a coupled engine, the rotating and reciprocating masses must be treated separately and the balanced masses for the two systems are suitably combined in the wheel.

It may be noted that the variation of pressure between the wheel and the rail (*i.e.* hammer blow) may be reduced by equal distribution of balanced mass (*B*) between the driving, leading and trailing wheels respectively.

Example 22.6. *The following particulars relate to a two-cylinder locomotive with two coupled wheels on each side :*

Stroke	*= 650 mm*
Mass of reciprocating parts per cylinder	*= 240 kg*
Mass of revolving parts per cylinder	*= 200 kg*
Mass of each coupling rod	*= 250 kg*
Radius of centre of coupling rod pin	*= 250 mm*
Distances between cylinders	*= 0.6 m*
Distance between wheels	*= 1.5 m*
Distance between coupling rods	*= 1.8 m*

The main cranks are at right angles and the coupling rod pins are at 180° to their respective main cranks. The balance masses are to be placed in the wheels at a mean radius of 675 mm in order to balance whole of the revolving and 3/4th of the reciprocating masses. The balance mass for the reciprocating masses is to be divided equally between the driving wheels and the coupled wheels. Find : 1. The magnitudes and angular positions of the masses required for the driving and trailing wheels, and 2. The hammer blow at 120 km/h, if the wheels are 1.8 metre diameter.

Solution. Given : $L_C = L_D = 650$ mm or $r_C = r_D = 325$ mm $= 0.325$ m ; $m_1 = 240$ kg ; $m_2 = 200$ kg ; $m_3 = 250$ kg ; $r_A = r_F = 250$ mm $= 0.25$ m ; $CD = 0.6$ m ; $BE = 1.5$ m ; $AF = 1.8$ m ; $r_B = r_E = 675$ mm $= 0.675$ m ; $c = 3/4$

The position of planes for the driving wheels *B* and *E*, cylinders *C* and *D*, and coupling rods *A* and *F*, are shown in Fig. 22.12 (*a*).

The angular position of cranks *C* and *D* and coupling pins *A* and *F* are shown in Fig. 22.12(*b*).

We know that mass of the reciprocating parts per cylinder to be balanced

$$= c.m_1 = \frac{3}{4} \times 240 = 180 \text{ kg}$$

Since the reciprocating masses are to be divided equally between the driving wheels and trailing wheels, therefore 90 kg is taken for driving wheels and 90 kg for trailing wheels. Now for each driving wheel, the following masses are to be balanced :

1. Half of the mass of coupling rod *i.e.* $\frac{1}{2} \times 250 = 125$ kg . In other words, the masses at the coupling rods *A* and *F* to be balanced for each driving wheel are

$$m_A = m_F = 125 \text{ kg}$$

2. Whole of the revolving mass *i.e.* 200 kg and the mass of the reciprocating parts *i.e.* 90 kg. In other words, total mass at the cylinders C and D to be balanced for each driving wheel are

$$m_C = m_D = 200 + 90 = 290 \text{ kg}$$

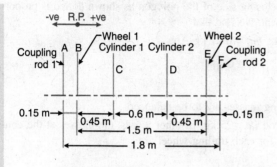

(*a*) Position of planes.

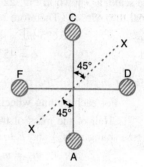

(*b*) Angular position of cranks and coupling pins.

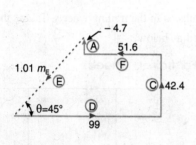

(*c*) Couple polygon : Driving wheel *E*.

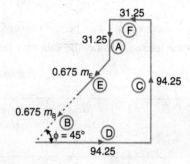

(*d*) Force polygon : Driving wheel *B*.

Fig. 22.12

Balanced masses in the driving wheels

Let m_B and m_E be the balance masses placed in the driving wheels B and E respectively. Taking the plane of B as reference plane, the data may be tabulated as below :

Table 22.5. (For driving wheels)

Plane	Mass	Radius	Cent. force $\div \omega^2$	Distance from	Couple $\div \omega^2$
	(m) kg	(r) m	(m.r) kg-m	Plane B(l) m	(m.r.l) kg-m^2
(1)	(2)	(3)	(4)	(5)	(6)
A	125	0.25	31.25	– 0.15	– 4.7
B (R.P.)	m_B	0.675	0.675 m_B	0	0
C	290	0.325	94.25	0.45	42.4
D	290	0.325	94.25	1.05	99
E	m_E	0.675	0.675 m_E	1.5	1.01 m_E
F	125	0.25	31.25	1.65	51.6

In order to find the balance mass m_E in the driving wheel E, draw a couple polygon from the data given in Table 22.5 (column 6), to some suitable scale as shown in Fig 22.12 (*c*). The closing side of polygon as shown dotted is proportional to 1.01 m_E, Therefore by measurement, we find that

$$1.01 \, m_E = 67.4 \text{ kg-m}^2 \quad \text{or} \quad m_E = 66.7 \text{ kg Ans.}$$

and
$$\theta = 45° \text{ Ans.}$$

Now draw the force polygon from the data given in Table 22.5 (column 4), to some suitable scale, as shown in Fig. 22.12 (d). The closing side of the polygon as shown dotted is proportional to $0.675 \, m_B$. Therefore by measurement, we find that

$$0.675 \, m_B = 45 \text{ kg-m} \quad \text{or} \quad m_B = 66.7 \text{ kg Ans.}$$

and
$$\phi = 45° \text{ Ans.}$$

Balance masses in the trailing wheels

For each trailing wheel, the following masses are to be balanced :

1. Half of the mass of the coupling rod *i.e.* 125 kg. In other words, the masses at the coupling rods A and F to be balanced for each trailing wheel are

$$m_A = m_F = 125 \text{ kg}$$

2. Mass of the reciprocating parts *i.e.* 90 kg. In other words, the mass at the cylinders C and D to be balanced for each trailing wheel are

$$m_C = m_D = 90 \text{ kg}$$

Let m_B' and m_E' be the balanced masses placed in the trailing wheels. Taking the plane of B as the reference plane, the data may be tabulated as below :

Table 22.6. (For trailing wheels)

Plane (1)	Mass (m) kg (2)	Radius (r) m (3)	Cent. force ÷ ω^2 (m.r) kg-m (4)	Distance from plane B (l) m (5)	Couple ÷ ω^2 (m.r.l) kg-m² (6)
A	125	0.25	31.25	– 0.15	– 4.7
B (R.P.)	m_B'	0.675	0.675 m_B'	0	0
C	90	0.325	29.25	0.45	13.2
D	90	0.325	29.25	1.05	30.7
E	m_E'	0.675	0.675 m_E'	1.5	1.01 m_E'
F	125	0.25	31.25	1.65	51.6

In order to find the balance mass m_E' in the trailing wheel E, draw a couple polygon from the data given in Table 22.6 (column 6), to some suitable scale, as shown in Fig. 22.13 (a). The closing side of the polygon as shown dotted is proportional to $1.01 \, m_E'$. Therefore by measurement, we find that

$$1.01 \, m_E' = 27.5 \text{ m}^2 \quad \text{or} \quad m_E' = 27.5 \text{ kg Ans.}$$

and
$$\alpha = 40° \text{ Ans.}$$

Now draw the force polygon from the data given in Table 22.6 (column 4), to some suitable scale, as shown in Fig. 22.13 (b). The closing side of the polygon as shown dotted is proportional to $0.675 \, m_B'$. Therefore by measurement, we find that

$$0.675 \, m_B' = 18.35 \text{ kg-m} \quad \text{or} \quad m_B' = 27.2 \text{ kg Ans.}$$

and
$$\beta = 50° \text{ Ans.}$$

Fig. 22.14 shows the balance masses in the four wheels and it will be seen that the balance masses for the driving wheels are symmetrical about the axis *X-X* [Fig. 22.12 (*b*)]. Similarly the balance masses for the trailing wheels are symmetrical about the axis *X-X*.

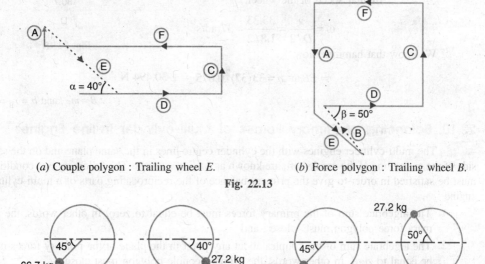

(a) Couple polygon : Trailing wheel E.   (b) Force polygon : Trailing wheel B.

Fig. 22.13

Driving wheel E.   Trailing wheel E.   Driving wheel B.   Trailing wheel B.
(a)   (b)   (c)   (d)

Fig. 22.14

Hammer blow

In order to find the hammer blow, we must find the balance mass required for reciprocating masses only. For this, the data may be tabulated as below. Let m''_B and m''_E be the balanced masses required for the reciprocating masses.

Table 22.7. (For hammer blow)

Plane (1)	Mass (m) kg (2)	Radius (r) m (3)	Cent. force $\div \omega^2$ (m.r) kg-m (4)	Distance from Plane B(l) m (5)	Couple $\div \omega^2$ (m.r.l) kg-m^2 (6)
B(R.P.)	m''_B	0.675	0.675 m''_B	0	0
C	90	0.325	29.25	0.45	13.2
D	90	0.325	29.25	1.05	30.7
E	m''_E	0.675	0.675 m''_E	1.5	1.01 m''_E

Now the couple polygon and the force polygon may be drawn, but due to symmetry we shall only draw the couple polygon from the data given in Table 22.7 (column 6), to some suitable scale as shown in Fig 22.15.

From Fig. 22.15,

$$1.01 \, m''_E = \sqrt{(30.7)^2 + (13.2)^2} = 33.4$$

∴ $$m''_E = 33 \text{ kg}$$

We know that linear speed of the wheel,
$$v = 120 \text{ km/h} = 33.33 \text{ m/s}$$
and diameter of the wheel, $D = 1.8$ m

∴ Angular speed of the wheel

Fig. 22.15

$$\omega = \frac{v}{D/2} = \frac{33.33}{1.8/2} = 37 \text{rad/s}$$

We know that hammer blow

$$= \pm B.\omega^2.b = 33(37)^2 0.675 = \pm 30.494 \text{ N Ans.}$$

$$\dots (\because B = m''_E, \text{ and } b = r_B = r_E)$$

22.10. Balancing of Primary Forces of Multi-cylinder In-line Engines

The multi-cylinder engines with the cylinder centre lines in the same plane and on the same side of the centre line of the crankshaft, are known as *In-line engines*. The following two conditions must be satisfied in order to give the primary balance of the reciprocating parts of a multi-cylinder engine :

1. The algebraic sum of the primary forces must be equal to zero. In other words, the primary force polygon must *close ; and

2. The algebraic sum of the couples about any point in the plane of the primary forces must be equal to zero. In other words, the primary couple polygon must close.

We have already discussed, that the primary unbalanced force due to the reciprocating masses is equal to the component, parallel to the line of stroke, of the centrifugal force produced by the equal mass placed at the crankpin and revolving with it. Therefore, in order to give the *primary balance of the reciprocating parts of a multi-cylinder engine, it is convenient to imagine the reciprocating masses to be transferred to their respective crankpins and to treat the problem as one of revolving masses.*

The speedometer is an instrument which shows how fast a car is moving. It works with a magnet that spins around as the car moves.

Note : This picture is given as additional information.

Notes : 1. For a two cylinder engine with cranks at 180°, condition (1) may be satisfied, but this will result in an unbalanced couple. Thus the above method of primary balancing cannot be applied in this case.

2. For a three cylinder engine with cranks at 120° and if the reciprocating masses per cylinder are same, then condition (1) will be satisfied because the forces may be represented by the sides of an equilateral triangle. However, by taking a reference plane through one of the cylinder centre lines, two couples with non-parallel axes will remain and these cannot vanish vectorially. Hence the above method of balancing fails in this case also.

---

* The closing side of the primary force polygon gives the maximum unbalanced primary force and the closing side of the primary couple polygon gives the maximum unbalanced primary couple.

3. For a four cylinder engine, similar reasoning will show that complete primary balance is possible and it follows that

'**For a multi-cylinder engine, the primary forces may be completely balanced by suitably arranging the crank angles, provided that the number of cranks are not less than four**'.

22.11. Balancing of Secondary Forces of Multi-cylinder In-line Engines

When the connecting rod is not too long (*i.e.* when the obliquity of the connecting rod is considered), then the secondary disturbing force due to the reciprocating mass arises.

We have discussed in Art. 22.2, that the secondary force,

$$F_S = m.\omega^2.r \times \frac{\cos 2\theta}{n}$$

This expression may be written as

$$F_S = m.(2\omega)^2 \times \frac{r}{4n} \times \cos 2\theta$$

As in case of primary forces, the secondary forces may be considered to be equivalent to the component, parallel to the line of stroke, of the centrifugal force produced by an equal mass placed at the imaginary crank of length $r/4n$ and revolving at twice the speed of the actual crank (*i.e.* 2ω) as shown in Fig. 22.16.

Thus, in multi-cylinder in-line engines, each imaginary secondary crank with a mass attached to the crankpin is inclined to the line of stroke at twice the angle of the actual crank. The values of the secondary forces and couples may be obtained by considering the revolving mass. This is done in the similar way as discussed for primary forces. The following two conditions must be satisfied in order to give a complete secondary balance of an engine :

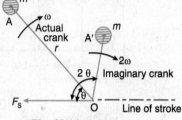

Fig. 22.16. Secondary force.

1. The algebraic sum of the secondary forces must be equal to zero. In other words, the secondary force polygon must close, and
2. The algebraic sum of the couples about any point in the plane of the secondary forces must be equal to zero. In other words, the secondary couple polygon must close.

Note : The closing side of the secondary force polygon gives the maximum unbalanced secondary force and the closing side of the secondary couple polygon gives the maximum unbalanced secondary couple.

Example 22.7. *A four cylinder vertical engine has cranks 150 mm long. The planes of rotation of the first, second and fourth cranks are 400 mm, 200 mm and 200 mm respectively from the third crank and their reciprocating masses are 50 kg, 60 kg and 50 kg respectively. Find the mass of the reciprocating parts for the third cylinder and the relative angular positions of the cranks in order that the engine may be in complete primary balance.*

Solution. Given $r_1 = r_2 = r_3 = r_4 = 150$ mm $= 0.15$ m ; $m_1 = 50$ kg ; $m_2 = 60$ kg ; $m_4 = 50$ kg

We have discussed in Art. 22.10 that in order to give the primary balance of the reciprocating parts of a multi-cylinder engine, the problem may be treated as that of revolving masses with the reciprocating masses transferred to their respective crank pins.

The position of planes is shown in Fig. 22.17 (*a*). Assuming the plane of third cylinder as the reference plane, the data may be tabulated as given in Table 22.8.

Table 22.8

Plane (m) kg (1)	Mass (m) kg (2)	Radius (r) m (3)	Cent. force ÷ ω² (m.r) kg-m (4)	Distance from plane 3(l) m (5)	Couple ÷ ω² (m.r.l) kg-m² (6)
1	50	0.15	7.5	– 0.4	– 3
2	60	0.15	9	– 0.2	– 1.8
3(R.P.)	m_3	0.15	$0.15m_3$	0	0
4	50	0.15	7.5	0.2	1.5

First of all, the angular position of cranks 2 and 4 are obtained by drawing the couple polygon from the data given in Table 22.8 (column 6). Assume the position of crank 1 in the horizontal direction as shown in Fig 22.17 (*b*), The couple polygon, as shown in Fig. 22.17 (*c*), is drawn as discussed below:

1. Draw vector $o'a'$ in the horizontal direction (*i.e.* parallel to $O1$) and equal to – 3 kg-m², to some suitable scale.

2. From point o' and a', draw vectors $o'b'$ and $a'b'$ equal to – 1.8 kg-m² and 1.5 kg-m² respectively. These vectors intersect at b'.

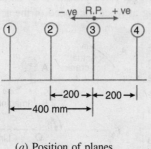

(*a*) Position of planes.

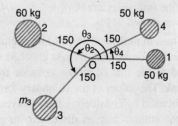

(*b*) Angular position of cranks.

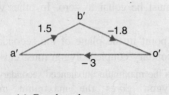

(*c*) Couple polygon.

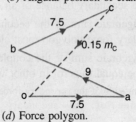

(*d*) Force polygon.

Fig. 22.17

3. Now in Fig. 22.17 (*b*), draw $O2$ parallel to vector $o'b'$ and $O4$ parallel to vector $a'b'$.

By measurement, we find that the angular position of crank 2 from crank 1 in the anticlockwise direction is

$$\theta_2 = 160° \text{ Ans.}$$

and the angular position of crank 4 from crank 1 in the anticlockwise direction is

$$\theta_4 = 26° \text{ Ans.}$$

In order to find the mass of the third cylinder (m_3) and its angular position, draw the force polygon, to some suitable scale, as shown in Fig. 22.17 (*d*), from the data given in Table 22.8 (column 4). Since the closing side of the force polygon (vector co) is proportional to 0.15 m_3, therefore by measurement,

$$0.15m_3 = 9 \text{ kg-m} \quad \text{or} \quad m_3 = 60 \text{ kg Ans.}$$

Now draw $O3$ in Fig 22.17 (b), parallel to vector co. By measurement, we find that the angular position of crank 3 from crank 1 in the anticlockwise direction is

$$\theta_3 = 227° \text{ Ans.}$$

Example 22.8. *A four crank engine has the two outer cranks set at 120° to each other, and their reciprocating masses are each 400 kg. The distance between the planes of rotation of adjacent cranks are 450 mm, 750 mm and 600 mm. If the engine is to be in complete primary balance, find the reciprocating mass and the relative angular position for each of the inner cranks.*

If the length of each crank is 300 mm, the length of each connecting rod is 1.2 m and the speed of rotation is 240 r.p.m., what is the maximum secondary unbalanced force ?

Solution. Given : $m_1 = m_4 = 400$ kg ; $r = 300$ mm $= 0.3$ m ; $l = 1.2$ m ; $N = 240$ r.p.m. or $\omega = 2\pi \times 240/60 = 25.14$ rad/s

Reciprocating mass and the relative angular position for each of the inner cranks

Let m_2 and m_3 = Reciprocating mass for the inner cranks 2 and 3 respectively, and

            θ_2 and θ_3 = Angular positions of the cranks 2 and 3 with respect to crank 1 respectively.

The position of the planes of rotation of the cranks and their angular setting are shown in Fig. 22.18 (a) and (b) respectively. Taking the plane of crank 2 as the reference plane, the data may be tabulated as below :

Table 22.9

Plane (1)	Mass (m) kg (2)	Radius (r) m (3)	Cent. force $\div \omega^2$ (m.r) kg-m (4)	Distance from plane (2) (l) m (5)	Couple $\div \omega^2$ (m.r.l.) kg-m² (6)
1	400	0.3	120	− 0.45	− 54
2(R.P.)	m_2	0.3	$0.3\ m_2$	0	0
3	m_3	0.3	$0.3\ m_3$	0.75	$0.225\ m_3$
4	400	0.3	120	1.35	162

Since the engine is to be in complete primary balance, therefore the primary couple polygon and the primary force polygon must close. First of all, the primary couple polygon, as shown in Fig. 22.18 (c), is drawn to some suitable scale from the data given in Table 22.9 (column 6), in order to find the reciprocating mass for crank 3. Now by measurement, we find that

$$0.225\, m_3 = 196\, \text{kg-m}^2 \quad \text{or} \quad m_3 = 871 \text{ kg Ans.}$$

and its angular position with respect to crank 1 in the anticlockwise direction,

$$\theta_3 = 326° \text{ Ans.}$$

Now in order to find the reciprocating mass for crank 2, draw the primary force polygon, as shown in Fig. 22.18 (d), to some suitable scale from the data given in Table 22.9 (column 4). Now by measurement, we find that

$$0.3\, m_2 = 284 \text{ kg-m} \quad \text{or} \quad m_2 = 947 \text{ kg Ans.}$$

and its angular position with respect to crank 1 in the anticlockwise direction,

$$\theta_2 = 168° \text{ Ans.}$$

Maximum secondary unbalanced force

The secondary crank positions obtained by rotating the primary cranks at twice the angle, is shown in Fig. 22.18 (*e*). Now draw the secondary force polygon, as shown in Fig. 22.18 (*f*), to some suitable scale, from the data given in Table 22.9 (column 4). The closing side of the polygon shown dotted in Fig. 22.18 (*f*) represents the maximum secondary unbalanced force. By measurement, we find that the maximum secondary unbalanced force is proportional to 582 kg-m.

∴ Maximum secondary unbalanced force

$$= 582 \times \frac{\omega^2}{n} = \frac{582(25.14)^2}{1.2/0.3} = 91\,960\text{N} = 91.96 \text{ kN } \textbf{Ans.} \quad \ldots (\because n = l/r)$$

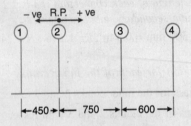

(*a*) Positions of planes.

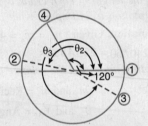

(*b*) Primary crank positions.

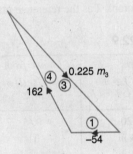

(*c*) Primary couple polygon.

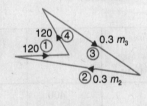

(*d*) Primary force polygon.

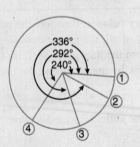

(*e*) Secondary crank positions.

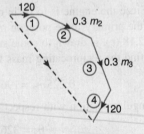

(*f*) Secondary force polygon.

Fig. 22.18

Example 22.9. *The cranks and connecting rods of a 4-cylinder in-line engine running at 1800 r.p.m. are 60 mm and 240 mm each respectively and the cylinders are spaced 150 mm apart. If the cylinders are numbered 1 to 4 in sequence from one end, the cranks appear at intervals of 90° in an end view in the order 1-4-2-3. The reciprocating mass corresponding to each cylinder is 15 kg.*

Determine : 1. Unbalanced primary and secondary forces, if any, and 2. Unbalanced primary and secondary couples with reference to central plane of the engine.

Solution. Given : N = 1800 r.p.m. or $\omega = 2\pi \times 1800/60$ = 188.52 rad/s ; r = 60 mm = 0.06 m ; l = 240 mm = 0.24 m ; m = 15 kg

1. *Unbalanced primary and secondary forces*

The position of the cylinder planes and cranks is shown in Fig.22.19 (*a*) and (*b*) respectively. With reference to central plane of the engine, the data may be tabulated as below :

Table 22.10

Plane (1)	Mass (m) kg (2)	Radius (r) m (3)	Cent. force ÷ ω^2 (m.r) kg-m (4)	Distance from ref. plane 3 (l) m (5)	Couple ÷ ω^2 (m.r.l.) kg-m^2 (6)
1	15	0.06	0.9	– 0.225	– 0.2025
2	15	0.06	0.9	– 0.075	– 0.0675
3	15	0.06	0.9	+ 0.075	+ 0.0675
4	15	0.06	0.9	+ 0.225	+ 0.2025

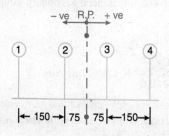

(*a*) Cylinder plane positions.

(*b*) Primary crank positions.

(*c*) Primary force polygon.

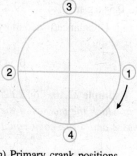

(*d*) Primary couple polygon.

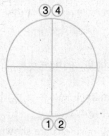

(*e*) Secondary crank positions.

(*f*) Secondary force polygon.

(*g*) Secondary couple polygon.

Fig. 22.19

The primary force polygon from the data given in Table 22.10 (column 4) is drawn as shown in Fig. 22.19 (c). Since the primary force polygon is a closed figure, therefore there are no unbalanced primary forces. **Ans.**

The secondary crank positions, taking crank 3 as the reference crank, is shown in Fig. 22.19 (e). From the secondary force polygon as shown in Fig. 22.19 (f), we see that it is a closed figure. Therefore there are no unbalanced secondary forces. **Ans.**

2. Unbalanced primary and secondary couples

The primary couple polygon from the data given in Table 22.10 (column 6) is drawn as shown in Fig. 22.19 (d). The closing side of the polygon, shown dotted in the figure, represents unbalanced primary couple. By measurement, we find the unbalanced primary couple is proportional to 0.19 kg-m^2.

∴ Unbalanced primary couple,

$$U.P.C = 0.19 \times \omega^2 = 0.19 \, (188.52)^2 = 6752 \text{ N-m } \textbf{Ans.}$$

The secondary couple polygon is shown in Fig. 22.1 (g). The unbalanced secondary couple is shown by dotted line. By measurement, we find that unbalanced secondary couple is proportional to 0.54 kg-m^2.

∴ Unbalanced secondary couple,

$$U.S.C. = 0.54 \times \frac{\omega^2}{n} = 0.54 \times \frac{(188.52)^2}{0.24/0.6} = 4798 \text{ N-m } \textbf{Ans.} \qquad \dots (\because \ n = l/r)$$

Example 22.10. *Fig. 22.20 shows the arrangement of the cranks in a four crank symmetrical engine in which the masses of the reciprocating parts at cranks 1 and 4 are each equal to m_1 and at cranks 2 and 3 are each equal to m_2.*

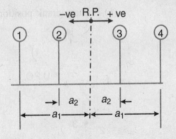
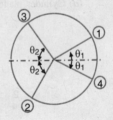

Fig. 22.20

Show that the arrangement is balanced for primary forces and couples and for secondary forces provided that

$$\frac{m_1}{m_2} = \frac{\cos\theta_2}{\cos\theta_1} \ ; \quad \frac{a_1}{a_2} = \frac{\tan\theta_2}{\tan\theta_1}, \quad and \quad \cos\theta_1 . \cos\theta_2 = \frac{1}{2}.$$

Solution. Given : Mass of reciprocating parts at cranks 1 and 4 = m_1 ; Mass of the reciprocating parts at cranks 2 and 3 = m_2

The position of planes and primary and secondary crank positions are shown in Fig. 22.21 (a), (b) and (c) respectively. Assuming the reference plane midway between the planes of rotation of cranks 2 and 3, the data may be tabulated as below :

Table 22.11

Plane (1)	Mass (m) (2)	Radius (r) (3)	Cent. force ÷ ω^2 (m.r) (4)	Distance from ref. plane (l) (5)	Couple ÷ ω^2 (m.r.l) (6)
1	m_1	r	$m_1.r$	$-a_1$	$-m_1.r.a_1$
2	m_2	r	$m_2.r$	$-a_2$	$-m_2.r.a_2$
3	m_2	r	$m_2.r$	$+a_2$	$+m_2.r.a_2$
4	m_1	r	$m_1.r$	$+a_1$	$+m_1.r.a_1$

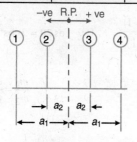

(a) Position of planes.

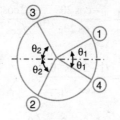

(b) Primary crank positions.

(c) Secondary crank Positions.

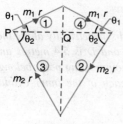

(d) Primary force polygon.

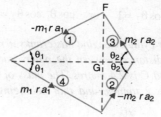

(e) Primary couple polygon.

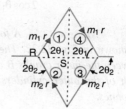

(f) Secondary force polygon.

Fig. 22.21

In order to balance the arrangement for primary forces and couples, the primary force and couple polygons must close. Fig. 22.21 (d) and (e) show the primary force and couple polygons, which are closed figures. From Fig. 22.21 (d),

$$PQ = m_1.r\cos\theta_1 = m_2.r\cos\theta_2 \qquad \text{or} \qquad \frac{m_1}{m_2} = \frac{\cos\theta_2}{\cos\theta_1} \quad \textbf{Ans.}$$

From Fig. 22.21 (e),

$$FG = m_1.r.a_1 \sin\theta_1 = m_2.r.a_2 \sin\theta_2$$

or

$$m_1.a_1 \sin\theta_1 = m_2.a_2 \sin\theta_2$$

$$\frac{m_1}{m_2} \times \frac{a_1}{a_2} = \frac{\sin\theta_2}{\sin\theta_1} \qquad \text{or} \qquad \frac{\cos\theta_2}{\cos\theta_1} \times \frac{a_1}{a_2} = \frac{\sin\theta_2}{\sin\theta_1} \qquad \dots \left(\because \frac{m_1}{m_2} = \frac{\cos\theta_2}{\cos\theta_1} \right)$$

$$\therefore \qquad \frac{a_1}{a_2} = \frac{\sin\theta_2}{\sin\theta_1} \times \frac{\cos\theta_1}{\cos\theta_2} = \frac{\tan\theta_2}{\tan\theta_1} \quad \text{Ans.}$$

In order to balance the arrangement for secondary forces, the secondary force polygon must close. The position of the secondary cranks is shown in Fig. 22.21 (c) and the secondary force polygon is shown in Fig. 22.21 (f).

Now from Fig. 22.21 (f),

$$RS = m_1.r\cos 2\theta_1 = m_2.r\cos(180° - 2\theta_2)$$

or

$$m_1.\cos 2\theta_1 = -m_2.\cos 2\theta_2$$

$$\therefore \qquad \frac{m_1}{m_2} = \frac{-\cos 2\theta_2}{\cos 2\theta_1} = \frac{-(2\cos^2\theta_2 - 1)}{2\cos^2\theta_1 - 1} \quad \dots (\because \cos 2\theta = 2\cos^2\theta - 1)$$

$$\frac{\cos\theta_2}{\cos\theta_1} = \frac{(1 - 2\cos^2\theta_2)}{2\cos^2\theta_1 - 1} \qquad \dots \left[\because \frac{m_1}{m_2} = \frac{\cos\theta_2}{\cos\theta_1}\right]$$

$$2\cos^2\theta_1.\cos\theta_2 - \cos\theta_2 = \cos\theta_1 - 2\cos^2\theta_2.\cos\theta_1$$

$$2\cos\theta_1.\cos\theta_2(\cos\theta_1 + \cos\theta_2) = \cos\theta_1 + \cos\theta_2$$

$$2\cos\theta_1.\cos\theta_2 = 1 \quad \text{or} \quad \cos\theta_1.\cos\theta_2 = \frac{1}{2} \quad \text{Ans.}$$

Example 22.11. *A four cylinder engine has cranks arranged symmetrically along the shaft as shown in Fig. 22.22. The distance between the outer cranks A and D is 5.4 metres and that between the inner cranks B and C is 2.4 metres. The mass of the reciprocating parts belonging to each of the outer cylinders is 2 tonnes, and that belonging to each of the inner cylinders is m tonnes.*

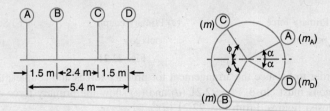

Fig. 22.22

If the primary and secondary forces are to be balanced and also the primary couples, determine the crank angle positions and the mass of the reciprocating parts (m) corresponding to the inner cylinders.

Find also the maximum value of the unbalanced secondary couple, if the stroke is 1 metre, the connecting rod length 2 metres, and the speed of the engine is 110 r.p.m.

Solution. Given : $AD = 5.4$ m ; $BC = 2.4$ m ; $m_A = m_D = 2$ t ; $L = 1$ m or $r = L/2 = 0.5$ m ; $l = 2$ m ; $N = 110$ r.p.m. or $\omega = 2\pi \times 110/60 = 11.52$ rad/s

Fig. 22.23 (a) shows the position of planes and Fig. 22.23 (b) shows the end view of the cranks with primary crank angles α and ϕ which are to be determined. Assuming the reference plane mid-way between the planes of rotation of cranks *A* and *D*, the data may be tabulated as below :

Table 22.12

Plane (1)	Mass (m) t (2)	Radius (r) m (3)	Cent. force $\div \omega^2$ (m.r) t-m (3)	Distance from ref. plane (l) m (4)	Couple $\div \omega^2$ (m.r.l) t-m² (5)
A	2	0.5	1	– 2.7	– 2.7
B	m	0.5	0.5 m	– 1.2	– 0.6 m
C	m	0.5	0.5 m	+ 1.2	+ 0.6 m
D	2	0.5	1	+ 2.7	+ 2.7

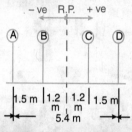

(a) Positions of planes.

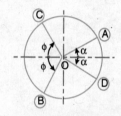

(b) Primary crank positions.

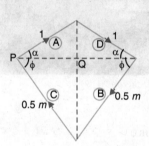

(c) Primary force polygon.

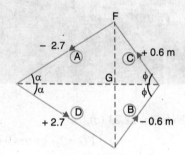

(d) Primary couple polygon.

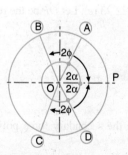

(e) Secondary crank positions.

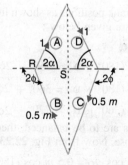

(f) Secondary force polygon.

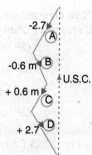

(g) Secondary couple polygon.

Fig. 22.23

Since the primary forces and couples are to be balanced, therefore the primary force and couple polygons, drawn from the data given in Table 22.12 column (4) and (6) respectively, as shown in Fig. 22.23 (c) and (d), must close.

From Fig. 22.23 (c),

$$PQ = 1\cos\alpha = 0.5\,m\cos\phi$$

$$\therefore \qquad \cos\phi = \frac{1\cos\alpha}{0.5\,m} = \frac{2\cos\alpha}{m} \qquad \ldots (i)$$

A Steam-powered ship.

From Fig. 22.23 (d),

$$FG = 2.7\sin\alpha = 0.6\,m\sin\phi$$

$$\therefore \qquad \sin\alpha = \frac{0.6\,m\,\sin\phi}{2.7} = \frac{m\sin\phi}{4.5} \qquad \ldots (ii)$$

Now draw the secondary crank positions as shown in Fig. 22.23 (e). Let OP be the reference line. The secondary crank angles are given below :

$$OP \text{ to } OA = 2\alpha$$

$$OP \text{ to } OC = 2\,(180° - \phi) = 360° - 2\phi$$

$$OP \text{ to } OB = 2\,(180° + \phi) = 360° + 2\phi$$

$$OP \text{ to } OD = 2\,(360° - \alpha) = 720° - 2\alpha$$

Since the secondary forces are to be balanced, therefore the secondary force polygon, as shown in Fig. 22.23 (f), must close. Now from Fig. 22.23 (f),

$$RS = 1\cos 2\alpha = 0.5\,m\cos(180° - 2\phi)$$

or

$$\frac{1}{0.5m} = \frac{-\cos 2\phi}{\cos 2\alpha} = \frac{-(2\cos^2\phi - 1)}{2\cos^2\alpha - 1} \qquad \ldots (\because \cos 2\phi = 2\cos^2\phi - 1)$$

$$2\cos^2\alpha - 1 = 0.5m(1 - 2\cos^2\phi) = 0.5m\left[1 - 2\left(\frac{2\cos\alpha}{m}\right)^2\right] \qquad \ldots \text{[From equation (i)]}$$

$$= 0.5m\left[1 - \frac{8\cos^2\alpha}{m^2}\right] = 0.5m - \frac{4\cos^2\alpha}{m}$$

$$2\cos^2\alpha + \frac{4\cos^2\alpha}{m} = 1 + 0.5m \quad \text{or} \quad \cos^2\alpha\left(\frac{2m+4}{m}\right) = 1 + 0.5m$$

$$\therefore \qquad\qquad \cos^2\alpha = (1+0.5m) \times \frac{m}{2m+4} = \frac{m}{4} \qquad\qquad \ldots (iii)$$

Now from equation (ii)

$$\sin^2\alpha = \left(\frac{m\sin\phi}{4.5}\right)^2$$

or $\qquad 1 - \cos^2\alpha = \frac{m^2\sin^2\phi}{20.25} = \frac{m^2}{20.25}(1-\cos^2\phi) = \frac{m^2}{20.25}\left[1 - \left(\frac{2\cos\alpha}{m}\right)^2\right]$

$$\ldots \text{[From equations (i)]}$$

$$1 - \frac{m}{4} = \frac{m^2}{20.25}\left(1 - \frac{4}{m^2} \times \frac{m}{4}\right) = \frac{m^2}{20.25}\left(1 - \frac{1}{m}\right) = \frac{m^2}{20.25} - \frac{m}{20.25}$$

$$\ldots \text{[From equation (iii)]}$$

or $\qquad \dfrac{m^2}{20.25} - \dfrac{m}{20.25} + \dfrac{m}{4} - 1 = 0 \quad \text{or} \quad m^2 + 4.0625m - 20.25 = 0$

$$\therefore \qquad\qquad m = \frac{-4.0625 \pm \sqrt{(4.0625)^2 + 4\times 20.25}}{2} = 2.9 \text{ t}$$

We know that $\cos^2\alpha = \dfrac{m}{4} = \dfrac{2.9}{4} = 0.725$

$$\therefore \qquad\qquad \cos\alpha = 0.851 \quad \text{or} \quad \alpha = 31.6° \text{ Ans.}$$

Also $\qquad\qquad \cos\phi = \dfrac{2\cos\alpha}{m} = \dfrac{2\times 0.851}{2.9} = 0.5869 \quad \text{or} \quad \phi = 54.06° \text{ Ans.}$

Maximum unbalanced secondary couple

The secondary couple polygon is shown in Fig. 22.23 (g). The maximum unbalanced secondary couple is shown by a dotted line. By measurement, we find that the maximum unbalanced secondary couple is proportional to 8 t-m².

∴ Maximum unbalanced secondary couple,

$$U.S.C = 8 \times \frac{\omega^2}{n} = 8 \times \frac{(11.52)^2}{2/0.5} = 265.4 \text{ kN-m Ans.} \qquad \ldots (\because \ n = l/r)$$

Example 22.12. *A five cylinder in-line engine running at 750 r.p.m. has successive cranks 144° apart, the distance between the cylinder centre lines being 375 mm. The piston stroke is 225 mm and the ratio of the connecting rod to the crank is 4. Examine the engine for balance of primary and secondary forces and couples. Find the maximum values of these and the position of the central crank at which these maximum values occur. The reciprocating mass for each cylinder is 15 kg.*

Solution. Given : $N = 750$ r.p.m. or $\omega = 2\pi \times 750/60 = 78.55$ rad/s ; $L = 225$ mm $= 0.225$ m or $r = 0.1125$ m ; $n = l/r = 4$; $m = 15$ kg

Assuming the engine to be a vertical engine, the positions of the cylinders and the cranks are shown in Fig. 22.24 (a), (b) and (c). The plane 3 may be taken as the reference plane and the crank 3 as the reference crank. The data may be tabulated as given in the following table.

Table 22.13

Plane (1)	Mass (m) kg (2)	Radius (r) m (3)	Cent. force ÷ ω² (m.r) kg-m (4)	Distance from ref. Plane 3 (l) m (5)	Couple ÷ ω² (m.r.l) kg-m² (6)
1	15	0.1125	1.6875	– 0.75	– 1.265
2	15	0.1125	1.6875	– 0.375	– 0.6328
3(R.P.)	15	0.1125	1.6875	0	0
4	15	0.1125	1.6875	+ 0.375	+ 0.6328
5	15	0.1125	1.6875	+ 0.75	+ 1.265

Now, draw the force and couple polygons for primary and secondary cranks as shown in Fig. 22.24 (d), (e), (f), and (g). Since the primary and secondary force polygons are close, therefore the engine is balanced for primary and secondary forces. **Ans.**

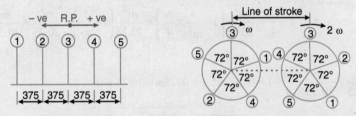

(a) Position of planes.   (b) Primary crank positions.   (c) Secondary crank positions.

(d) Primary force polygon.

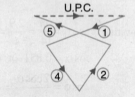

(e) Primary couple polygon.

(f) Secondary force polygon.

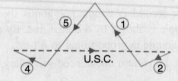

(g) Secondary couple polygon.

Fig. 22.24

Maximum unbalanced primary couple

We know that the closing side of the primary couple polygon [shown dotted in Fig. 22.24 (e)] gives the maximum unbalanced primary couple. By measurement, we find that maximum unbalanced primary couple is proportional to 1.62 kg-m².

∴ Maximum unbalanced primary couple,

$$U.P.C. = 1.62 \times \omega^2 = 1.62 \, (78.55)^2 = 9996 \text{ N-m } \textbf{Ans.}$$

We see from Fig. 22.24 (*e*) [shown by dotted line] that the maximum unbalanced primary couple occurs when crank 3 is at 90° from the line of stroke.

Maximum unbalanced secondary couple

We know that the closing side of the secondary couple polygon [shown dotted in Fig. 22.24 (*g*)] gives the maximum unbalanced secondary couple. By measurement, we find that maximum unbalanced secondary couple is proportional to 2.7 kg-m².

∴ Maximum unbalanced secondary couple.

$$U.S.C = 2.7 \times \frac{\omega^2}{n} = 2.7 \times \frac{(78.55)^2}{4} = 4165 \text{ N-m } \textbf{Ans.}$$

We see from Fig. 22.24 (*g*) that if the vector representing the unbalanced secondary couple (shown by dotted line) is rotated through 90°, it will coincide with the line of stroke. Hence the original crank will be rotated through 45°. Therefore, the maximum unbalanced secondary couple occurs when crank 3 is at 45° and at successive intervals of 90° (*i.e.* 135°, 225° and 315°) from the line of stroke.

Example 22.13. *The firing order in a 6 cylinder vertical four stroke in-line engine is 1-4-2-6-3-5. The piston stroke is 100 mm and the length of each connecting rod is 200 mm. The pitch distances between the cylinder centre lines are 100 mm, 100 mm, 150 mm, 100 mm, and 100 mm respectively. The reciprocating mass per cylinder is 1 kg and the engine runs at 3000 r.p.m.*

Determine the out-of-balance primary and secondary forces and couples on this engine, taking a plane midway between the cylinder 3 and 4 as the reference plane.

Solution. Given : $L = 100$ mm or $r = L / 2 = 50$ mm $= 0.05$ m ; $l = 200$ mm ; $m = 1$ kg ; $N = 3000$ r.p.m.

The position of the cylinders and the cranks are shown in Fig. 22.25 (*a*), (*b*) and (*c*). With the reference plane midway between the cylinders 3 and 4, the data may be tabulated as given in the following table :

Table 22.14

Plane (1)	Mass (m) kg (2)	Radius (r) m (3)	Cent. force ÷ ω² (m.r) kg-m (4)	Distance from plane 3 (l)m (5)	Couple ÷ ω² (m.r.l) kg-m² (6)
1	1	0.05	0.05	– 0.275	– 0.01375
2	1	0.05	0.05	– 0.175	– 0.00875
3	1	0.05	0.05	– 0.075	– 0.00375
4	1	0.05	0.05	+ 0.075	+ 0.00375
5	1	0.05	0.05	+ 0.175	+ 0.00875
6	1	0.05	0.05	+ 0.275	+ 0.01375

Now, draw the force and couple polygons for the primary and secondary cranks as shown in Fig. 22.25 (*d*), (*e*), (*f*) and (*g*).

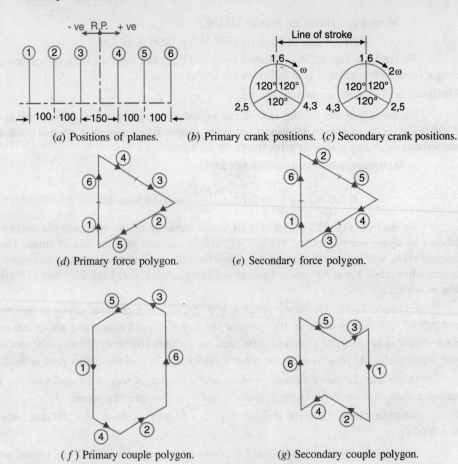

(a) Positions of planes. (b) Primary crank positions. (c) Secondary crank positions.

(d) Primary force polygon. (e) Secondary force polygon.

(f) Primary couple polygon. (g) Secondary couple polygon.

Fig. 22.25

From Fig. 22.25 (d) and (e), we see that the primary and secondary force polygons are closed figures, therefore there are no out-of-balance primary and secondary forces. Thus the engine is balanced for primary and secondary forces. Also, the primary and secondary couple polygons, as shown in Fig. 22.25 (f) and (g) are closed figures, therefore there are no out-of-balance primary and secondary couples. Thus the engine is balanced for primary and secondary couples. **Ans.**

Example 22.14. *In an in-line six cylinder engine working on two stroke cycle, the cylinder centre lines are spaced at 600 mm. In the end view, the cranks are 60° apart and in the order 1-4-5-2-3-6. The stroke of each piston is 400 mm and the connecting rod length is 1 metre. The mass of the reciprocating parts is 200 kg per cylinder and that of rotating parts 100 kg per crank. The engine rotates at 300 r.p.m. Examine the engine for the balance of primary and secondary forces and couples. Find the maximum unbalanced forces and couples.*

Solution. Given : $L = 400$ mm or $r = L/2 = 200$ mm $= 0.2$ m ; $l = 1$ m ; $m_1 = 200$ kg ; $m_2 = 100$ kg ; $N = 300$ r.p.m. or $\omega = 2\pi \times 300/60 = 31.42$ rad/s

Assuming the engine to be a vertical engine, the position of planes of cylinders and the angular position of primary and secondary cranks (assuming the crank 1 coinciding with the line of stroke *i.e.* in the vertical direction) are shown in Fig. 22.26 (a), (b) and (c) respectively. It may be noted that the mass of rotating parts (m_2) at each crank pin is included with the mass of reciprocating parts (m_1) for primary forces and couples only. Taking the reference plane between the cylinders 3 and 4, the data may be tabulated as below:

Table 22.15. (For primary forces and couples only)

Plane *(1)*	*Mass (m) kg* $m = m_1 + m_2$ *(2)*	*Radius* *(r) m* *(3)*	*Cent. force $\div \omega^2$* *(m.r)kg-m* *(4)*	*Distance from* *ref. plane (1) m* *(5)*	*Couple $\div \omega^2$* *(m.r.l) kg-m²* *(6)*
1	300	0.2	60	– 1.5	– 90
2	300	0.2	60	– 0.9	– 54
3	300	0.2	60	– 0.3	– 18
4	300	0.2	· 60	+ 0.3	+ 18
5	300	0.2	60	+ 0.9	+ 54
6	300	0.2	60	+ 1.5	+ 90

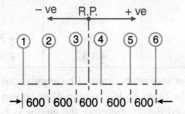 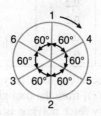 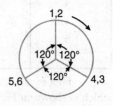

(*a*) Positions of planes of cylinders.   (*b*) Primary crank positions. (*c*) Secondary crank positions.

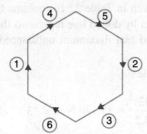 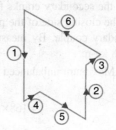

(*d*) Primary force polygon.   (*e*) Primary couple polygon.

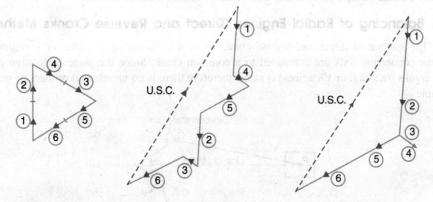

(*f*) Secondary force polygon.   (*g*) Secondary couple polygon.   (*h*) Secondary couple polygon.

Fig. 22.26

Now draw the force polygon and couple polygon for primary cranks from the data given in Table 22.15 (column 4 and 6) respectively, as shown in Fig. 22.26 (*d*) and (*e*). Since the force and couple polygons are closed figures, therefore the engine is balanced for primary force and couple (*i.e.* there is no unbalanced primary force and couple).

The data for the secondary forces and couples, taking $m = m_1 = 200$ kg, may be tabulated as below :

Table 22.16. (For secondary forces and couples)

Plane	Mass (m) kg $m = m_1$	Radius (r) m	Cent. force $\div \omega^2$ (m.r) kg-m	Distance from ref. plane (l) m	Couple $\div \omega^2$ (m.r.l) kg-m²
1	200	0.2	40	– 1.5	– 60
2	200	0.2	40	– 0.9	– 36
3	200	0.2	40	– 0.3	– 12
4	200	0.2	40	+ 0.3	+ 12
5	200	0.2	40	+ 0.9	+ 36
6	200	0.2	40	+ 1.5	+ 60

First of all, draw the secondary force polygon for secondary cranks [the angular position of which is shown in Fig. 22.26 (*c*)] from the data given in Table 22.16 (column 4) as shown in Fig. 22.26 (*f*). Since the secondary force polygon is a closed figure, therefore the engine is balanced for secondary forces (*i.e.* there is no unbalanced secondary forces.) Now draw the secondary couple polygon for the secondary cranks from the data given in Table 22.16 (column 6) as shown in Fig. 22.26 (*g*). The closing side of the polygon as shown by dotted line represents the maximum unbalanced secondary couple. By measurement, we find that maximum unbalanced couple is proportional to 168 kg-m².

∴ Maximum unbalanced secondary couple

$$= 168 \times \frac{\omega^2}{n} = 168 \times \frac{(31.42)^2}{1/0.2} = 33\ 170 \text{ N-m} = 33.17 \text{ kN-m } \textbf{Ans.}$$

$$\ldots (\because n = l/r)$$

Note : The secondary couple polygon may also be drawn as shown in Fig. 22.26 (*h*).

22.12. Balancing of Radial Engines (Direct and Reverse Cranks Method)

The method of direct and reverse cranks is used in balancing of radial or *V*-engines, in which the connecting rods are connected to a common crank. Since the plane of rotation of the various cranks (in radial or *V*-engines) is same, therefore there is no unbalanced primary or secondary couple.

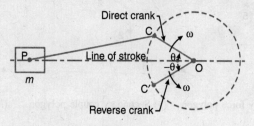

Fig. 22.27. Reciprocating engine mechanism.

Consider a reciprocating engine mechanism as shown in Fig. 22.27. Let the crank *OC* (known as the direct crank) rotates uniformly at ω radians per second in a clockwise direction. Let at any instant the crank makes an angle θ with the line of stroke *OP*. The indirect or reverse crank *OC'* is the image of the direct crank *OC*, when seen through the mirror placed at the line of stroke. A little consideration will show that when the direct crank revolves in a clockwise direction, the reverse crank will revolve in the anticlockwise direction. We shall now discuss the primary and secondary forces due to the mass (*m*) of the reciprocating parts at *P*.

Considering the primary forces

We have already discussed that primary force is $m.\omega^2.r\cos\theta$. This force is equal to the component of the centrifugal force along the line of stroke, produced by a mass (*m*) placed at the crank pin *C*. Now let us suppose that the mass (*m*) of the reciprocating parts is divided into two parts, each equal to *m* / 2.

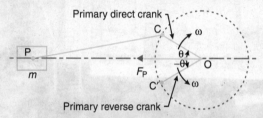

Fig. 22.28. Primary forces on reciprocating engine mechanism.

It is assumed that *m* / 2 is fixed at the *direct crank* (termed as *primary direct crank*) pin *C* and *m* / 2 at the *reverse crank* (termed as *primary reverse crank*) pin *C'*, as shown in Fig. 22.28.

We know that the centrifugal force acting on the primary direct and reverse crank

$$= \frac{m}{2} \times \omega^2.r$$

∴ Component of the centrifugal force acting on the primary direct crank

$$= \frac{m}{2} \times \omega^2.r\cos\theta \qquad \text{... (in the direction from } O \text{ to } P)$$

and, the component of the centrifugal force acting on the primary reverse crank

$$= \frac{m}{2} \times \omega^2.r\cos\theta \qquad \text{... (in the direction from } O \text{ to } P)$$

∴ Total component of the centrifugal force along the line of stroke

$$= 2 \times \frac{m}{2} \times \omega^2.r\cos\theta = m.\omega^2.r\cos\theta = \text{Primary force, } F_P$$

Hence, for primary effects, the mass m of the reciprocating parts at P may be replaced by two masses at C and C' each of magnitude m/2.

Note : The component of the centrifugal forces of the direct and reverse cranks, in a direction perpendicular to the line of stroke, are each equal to $\frac{m}{2} \times \omega^2.r\sin\theta,$, but opposite in direction. Hence these components are balanced.

Considering secondary forces

We know that the secondary force

$$= m(2\omega)^2 \frac{r}{4n} \times \cos 2\theta = m.\omega^2 r \times \frac{\cos 2\theta}{n}$$

A diesel train engine.

In the similar way as discussed above, it will be seen that for the secondary effects, the mass (m) of the reciprocating parts may be replaced by two masses (each $m/2$) placed at D and D' such that $OD = OD' = r/4n$. The crank OD is the *secondary direct crank* and rotates at 2ω rad/s in the clockwise direction, while the crank OD' is the *secondary reverse crank* and rotates at 2ω rad/s in the anticlockwise direction as shown in Fig. 22.29.

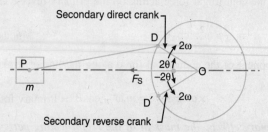

Fig. 22.29. Secondary force on reciprocating engine mechanism.

Example 22.15. *The three cylinders of an air compressor have their axes 120° to one another, and their connecting rods are coupled to a single crank. The stroke is 100 mm and the length of each connecting rod is 150 mm. The mass of the reciprocating parts per cylinder is 1.5 kg. Find the maximum primary and secondary forces acting on the frame of the compressor when running at 3000 r.p.m. Describe clearly a method by which such forces may be balanced.*

Solution. Given : $L = 100$ mm or $r = L / 2 = 50$ mm $= 0.05$ m ; $l = 150$ mm $= 0.15$ m ; $m = 1.5$ kg ; $N = 3000$ r.p.m. or $\omega = 2\pi \times 3000/60 = 314.2$ rad/s

The position of three cylinders is shown in Fig. 22.30. Let the common crank be along the inner dead centre of cylinder 1. Since common crank rotates clockwise, therefore θ is positive when measured clockwise.

Maximum primary force acting on the frame of the compressor

The primary direct and reverse crank positions as shown in Fig. 22.31 (*a*) and (*b*), are obtained as discussed below :

1. Since $\theta = 0°$ for cylinder 1, therefore both the primary direct and reverse cranks will coincide with the common crank.

2. Since $\theta = \pm120°$ for cylinder 2, therefore the primary direct crank is 120° clockwise and the primary reverse crank is 120° anti-clockwise from the line of stroke of cylinder 2.

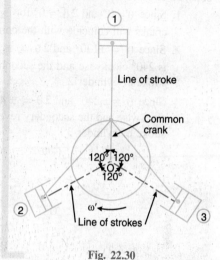

Fig. 22.30

3. Since $\theta = \pm 240°$ for cylinder 3, therefore the primary direct crank is 240° clockwise and the primary reverse crank is 240° anti-clockwise from the line of stroke of cylinder 3.

From Fig. 22.31 (*b*), we see that the primary reverse cranks form a balanced system. Therefore there is no unbalanced primary force due to the reverse cranks. From Fig. 22.31 (*a*), we see that the resultant primary force is equivalent to the centrifugal force of a mass 3 *m*/2 attached to the end of the crank.

$\therefore$ Maximum primary force $= \dfrac{3m}{2} \times \omega^2 . r = \dfrac{3 \times 1.5}{2}(314.2)^2 0.05 = 11\,106$ N $= 11.106$ kN **Ans.**

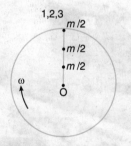

(*a*) Direct primary cranks.

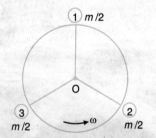

(*b*) Reverse primary cranks.

Fig. 22.31

The maximum primary force may be balanced by a mass attached diametrically opposite to the crank pin and rotating with the crank, of magnitude B_1 at radius b_1 such that

$$B_1.b_1 = \frac{3m}{2} \times r = \frac{3 \times 1.5}{2} \times 0.05 = 0.1125 \text{ N-m } \textbf{Ans.}$$

Maximum secondary force acting on the frame of the compressor

The secondary direct and reverse crank positions as shown in Fig. 22.32 (*a*) and (*b*), are obtained as discussed below :

1. Since $\theta = 0°$ and $2\theta = 0°$ for cylinder 1, therefore both the secondary direct and reverse cranks will coincide with the common crank.

2. Since $\theta = \pm120°$ and $2\theta = \pm 240°$ for cylinder 2, therefore the secondary direct crank is 240° clockwise and the secondary reverse crank is 240° anticlockwise from the line of stroke of cylinder 2.

3. Since $\theta = \pm 240°$ and $2\theta = \pm 480°$, therefore the secondary direct crank is 480° or 120° clockwise and the secondary reverse crank is 480° or 120° anti-clockwise from the line of stroke of cylinder 3.

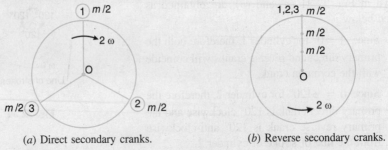

(*a*) Direct secondary cranks.　　　　　(*b*) Reverse secondary cranks.

Fig. 22.32

From Fig. 22.32 (*a*), we see that the secondary direct cranks form a balanced system. Therefore there is no unbalanced secondary force due to the direct cranks. From Fig. 22.32 (*b*), we see that the resultant secondary force is equivalent to the centrifugal force of a mass 3 $m/2$ attached at a crank radius of $r/4n$ and rotating at a speed of 2ω rad/s in the opposite direction to the crank.

Submarines are powered by diesel or nuclear powered engines which have reciprocating and rotating parts.

∴ Maximum secondary force

$$= \frac{3m}{2}(2\omega)^2\left(\frac{r}{4n}\right) = \frac{3\times1.5}{2}(2\times314.2)^2\left[\frac{0.05}{4\times0.15/0.05}\right]N$$

...($\because$ $n = l/r$)

$$= 3702 \text{ N Ans.}$$

This maximum secondary force may be balanced by a mass B_2 at radius b_2, attached diametrically opposite to the crankpin, and rotating anti-clockwise at twice the crank speed, such that

$$B_2.b_2 = \frac{3m}{2}\times\frac{r}{4n} = \frac{3\times1.5}{2}\times\frac{0.05}{4\times0.15/0.05} = 0.009\ 375 \text{ N-m Ans.}$$

Notes : 1. Proceeding in the same way as discussed in the above example, we may prove that in a radial engine with an odd number of cylinders, the primary forces may be balanced by attaching single mass of magnitude $\frac{1}{2}K.m$ (*K* being the number of cylinders), at crank radius diametrically opposite to the crank pin.

2. For a radial engine containing four or more cylinders, the secondary direct and reverse cranks form a balanced system, *i.e.* the secondary forces are in complete balance.

22.13. Balancing of V-engines

Consider a symmetrical two cylinder *V*-engine as shown in Fig. 22.33, The common crank *OC* is driven by two connecting rods *PC* and *QC*. The lines of stroke *OP* and *OQ* are inclined to the vertical *OY*, at an angle α as shown in Fig 22.33.

Let
m = Mass of reciprocating parts per cylinder,
l = Length of connecting rod,
r = Radius of crank,
n = Ratio of length of connecting rod to crank radius = l / r
θ = Inclination of crank to the vertical at any instant,
ω = Angular velocity of crank.

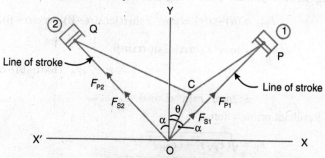

Fig.22.33. Balancing of V-engines.

We know that inertia force due to reciprocating parts of cylinder 1, along the line of stroke

$$= m.\omega^2.r\left[\cos(\alpha-\theta) + \frac{\cos 2(\alpha-\theta)}{n}\right]$$

and the inertia force due to reciprocating parts of cylinder 2, along the line of stroke

$$= m.\omega^2.r\left[\cos(\alpha+\theta) + \frac{\cos 2(\alpha+\theta)}{n}\right]$$

The balancing of *V*-engines is only considered for primary and secondary forces* as discussed below :

Considering primary forces

We know that primary force acting along the line of stroke of cylinder 1,

$$F_{P1} = m.\omega^2.r\cos(\alpha - \theta)$$

∴ Component of F_{P1} along the vertical line *OY*,

$$= F_{P1}\cos\alpha = m.\omega^2 r.\cos(\alpha - \theta)\cos\alpha \qquad \qquad \text{... (i)}$$

and component of F_{P1} along the horizontal line *OX*

$$= F_{P1}\sin\alpha = m.\omega^2 r\cos(\alpha - \theta)\sin\alpha \qquad \qquad \text{... (ii)}$$

Similarly, primary force acting along the line of stroke of cylinder 2,

$$F_{P2} = m.\omega^2.r\cos(\alpha + \theta)$$

∴ Component of F_{P2} along the vertical line *OY*

$$= F_{P2}\cos\alpha = m.\omega^2.r\cos(\alpha + \theta)\cos\alpha \qquad \qquad \text{... (iii)}$$

and component of F_{P2} along the horizontal line *OX'*

$$= F_{P2}\sin\alpha = m.\omega^2.r\cos(\alpha + \theta)\sin\alpha \qquad \qquad \text{... (iv)}$$

Total component of primary force along the vertical line *OY*

$$F_{PV} = (i) + (iii) = m.\omega^2.r\cos\alpha\,[\cos(\alpha - \theta) + \cos(\alpha + \theta)]$$

$$= m.\omega^2.r\cos\alpha \times 2\cos\alpha\cos\theta$$

$$\text{... } [\because\ \cos(\alpha - \theta) + \cos(\alpha + \theta) = 2\cos\alpha\cos\theta]$$

$$= 2\,m.\omega^2.r\cos^2\alpha.\cos\theta$$

and total component of primary force along the horizontal line *OX*

$$F_{PH} = (ii) - (iv) = m.\omega^2.r\sin\alpha[\cos(\alpha - \theta) - \cos(\alpha + \theta)]$$

$$= m.\omega^2.r\sin\alpha \times 2\sin\alpha\sin\theta$$

$$\text{... } [\because\ \cos(\alpha - \theta) - \cos(\alpha + \theta) = 2\sin\alpha\sin\theta]$$

$$= 2m.\omega^2.r\sin^2\alpha.\sin\theta$$

∴ Resultant primary force,

$$F_P = \sqrt{(F_{PV})^2 + (F_{PH})^2}$$

$$= 2m.\omega^2.r\sqrt{(\cos^2\alpha.\cos\theta)^2 + (\sin^2\alpha.\sin\theta)^2} \qquad \qquad \text{... (v)}$$

Notes : The following results, derived from equation (*v*), depending upon the value of α may be noted :

1. When $2\alpha = 60°$ or $\alpha = 30°$,

$$F_P = 2m.\omega^2.r\sqrt{(\cos^2 30°\cos\theta)^2 + (\sin^2 30°\sin\theta)^2}$$

---

* Since the plane of rotation of the crank is same, therefore there are no unbalanced primary and secondary couples.

$$= 2m.\omega^2.r\sqrt{\left(\frac{3}{4}\cos\theta\right)^2 + \left(\frac{1}{4}\sin\theta\right)^2} = \frac{m}{2}\times\omega^2.r\sqrt{9\cos^2\theta + \sin^2\theta} \qquad ...(vi)$$

2. When $2\alpha = 90°$ or $\alpha = 45°$

$$F_P = 2m.\omega^2.r\sqrt{(\cos^2 45°\cos\theta)^2 + (\sin^2 45°\sin\theta)^2}$$

$$= 2m.\omega^2.r\sqrt{\left(\frac{1}{2}\cos\theta\right)^2 + \left(\frac{1}{2}\sin\theta\right)^2} = m.\omega^2.r \qquad \dots (vii)$$

3. When $2\alpha = 120°$ or $\alpha = 60°$,

$$F_P = 2m.\omega^2.r\sqrt{(\cos^2 60°\cos\theta)^2 + (\sin^2 60°\sin\theta)^2}$$

$$= 2m.\omega^2.r\sqrt{\left(\frac{1}{4}\cos\theta\right)^2 + \left(\frac{3}{4}\sin\theta\right)^2} = \frac{m}{2}\times\omega^2.r\sqrt{\cos^2\theta + 9\sin^2\theta} \qquad \dots (viii)$$

Considering secondary forces

We know that secondary force acting along the line of stroke of cylinder 1,

$$F_{S1} = m.\omega^2.r\times\frac{\cos 2(\alpha-\theta)}{n}$$

∴ Component of F_{S1} along the vertical line OY

$$= F_{S1}\cos\alpha = m.\omega^2.r\times\frac{\cos 2(\alpha-\theta)}{n}\times\cos\alpha \qquad \dots (ix)$$

and component of F_{S1} along the horizontal line OX

$$= F_{S1}\sin\alpha = m.\omega^2.r\times\frac{\cos 2(\alpha-\theta)}{n}\times\sin\alpha \qquad \dots (x)$$

Similarly, secondary force acting along the line of stroke of cylinder 2,

$$F_{S2} = m.\omega^2 r\times\frac{\cos 2(\alpha+\theta)}{n}$$

∴ Component of F_{S2} along the vertical line OY

$$= F_{S2}\cos\alpha = m.\omega^2.r\times\frac{\cos 2(\alpha+\theta)}{n}\times\cos\alpha \qquad \dots (xi)$$

and component of F_{S2} along the horizontal line OX'

$$= F_{S2}\sin\alpha = m.\omega^2.r\times\frac{\cos 2(\alpha+\theta)}{n}\times\sin\alpha \qquad \dots (xii)$$

Total component of secondary force along the vertical line OY,

$$F_{SV} = (ix) + (xi) = \frac{m}{n}\times\omega^2.r\cos\alpha\,[\cos 2(\alpha-\theta)+\cos 2(\alpha+\theta)]$$

$$= \frac{m}{n}\times\omega^2.r\cos\alpha\times 2\cos 2\alpha\cos 2\theta = \frac{2m}{n}\times\omega^2.r\cos\alpha.\cos 2\alpha\cos 2\theta$$

and total component of secondary force along the horizontal line OX,

$$F_{SH} = (x) - (xii) = \frac{m}{n}\times\omega^2.r\sin\alpha\,[\cos 2(\alpha-\theta)-\cos 2(\alpha+\theta)]$$

$$= \frac{m}{n}\times\omega^2.r\sin\alpha\times 2\sin 2\alpha.\sin 2\theta$$

$$= \frac{2m}{n}\times\omega^2.r\sin\alpha.\sin 2\alpha.\sin 2\theta$$

∴   Resultant secondary force,

$$F_S = \sqrt{(F_{SV})^2 + (F_{SH})^2}$$

$$= \frac{2m}{n} \times \omega^2 . r \sqrt{(\cos\alpha.\cos 2\alpha.\cos 2\theta)^2 + (\sin\alpha.\sin 2\alpha.\sin 2\theta)^2}$$

. . .(*xiii*)

Notes : The following results, derived from equation (*xiii*), depending upon the value of α, may be noted.

1. When $2\alpha = 60°$ or $\alpha = 30°$,

$$F_S = \frac{2m}{n} \times \omega^2 . r \sqrt{(\cos 30° \cos 60° \cos 2\theta)^2 + (\sin 30° \sin 60° \sin 2\theta)^2}$$

$$= \frac{2m}{n} \times \omega^2 . r \sqrt{\left[\frac{\sqrt{3}}{2} \times \frac{1}{2}\cos 2\theta\right]^2 + \left[\frac{1}{2} \times \frac{\sqrt{3}}{2}\sin 2\theta\right]^2}$$

$$= \frac{\sqrt{3}}{2} \times \frac{m}{n} \times \omega^2 . r$$

. . . (*xiv*)

2. When $2\alpha = 90°$ or $\alpha = 45°$,

$$F_S = \frac{2m}{n} \times \omega^2 . r \sqrt{(\cos 45° \cos 90° \cos 2\theta)^2 + (\sin 45° \sin 90° \sin 2\theta)^2}$$

$$= \frac{2m}{n} \times \omega^2 . r \sqrt{0 + \left[\frac{1}{\sqrt{2}} \times 1 \times \sin 2\theta\right]^2} = \frac{\sqrt{2}m}{n} \times \omega^2 . r \sin 2\theta$$

. . . (*xv*)

Automated Guided Vehicles, AGVs, operate in many factories. They ferry goods and materials along carefully marked routes. Many AGVs are guided by signals from electrical loops buried under factory floors.

Note : This picture is given as additional information.

3. When $2\alpha = 120°$ or $\alpha = 60°$

$$F_S = \frac{2m}{n} \times \omega^2 . r \sqrt{(\cos 60° \cos 120° \cos 2\theta)^2 + (\sin 60° \sin 120° \sin 2\theta)^2}$$

$$= \frac{2m}{n} \times \omega^2 . r \sqrt{\left[\frac{1}{2} \times -\frac{1}{2} \times \cos 2\theta\right]^2 + \left[\frac{\sqrt{3}}{2} \times \frac{\sqrt{3}}{2} \times \sin 2\theta\right]^2}$$

$$= \frac{m}{2n} \times \omega^2 . r \sqrt{\cos^2 2\theta + 9 \sin^2 2\theta} \qquad \qquad \ldots (xvi)$$

Example 22.16. *A vee-twin engine has the cylinder axes at right angles and the connecting rods operate a common crank. The reciprocating mass per cylinder is 11.5 kg and the crank radius is 75 mm. The length of the connecting rod is 0.3 m. Show that the engine may be balanced for primary forces by means of a revolving balance mass.*

If the engine speed is 500 r.p.m. What is the value of maximum resultant secondary force ?

Solution. Given : $2\alpha = 90°$ or $\alpha = 45°$; $m = 11.5$ kg ; $r = 75$ mm $= 0.075$ m ; $l = 0.3$ m ; $N = 500$ r.p.m. or $\omega = 2\pi \times 500 / 60 = 52.37$ rad/s

We know that resultant primary force,

$$F_P = 2m.\omega^2 . r \sqrt{(\cos^2 \alpha \cos \theta)^2 + (\sin^2 \alpha \sin \theta)^2}$$

$$= 2m.\omega^2 . r \sqrt{(\cos^2 45° \cos \theta)^2 + (\sin^2 45° \sin \theta)^2}$$

$$= 2m.\omega^2 . r \sqrt{\left[\frac{\cos \theta}{2}\right]^2 + \left[\frac{\sin \theta}{2}\right]^2} = m.\omega^2 . r$$

Since the resultant primary force $m.\omega^2 . r$ is the centrifugal force of a mass m at the crank radius r when rotating at ω rad / s, therefore, the engine may be balanced by a rotating balance mass.

Maximum resultant secondary force

We know that resultant secondary force,

$$F_S = \sqrt{2} \times \frac{m}{n} \times \omega^2 . r \sin 2\theta \qquad \qquad \ldots (\text{When } 2\alpha = 90°)$$

This is maximum, when $\sin 2\theta$ is maximum *i.e.* when $\sin 2\theta = \pm 1$ or $\theta = 45°$ or $135°$.

∴ Maximum resultant secondary force,

$$F_{S_{max}} = \sqrt{2} \times \frac{m}{n} \times \omega^2 . r \qquad \qquad \ldots (\text{Substituting } \theta = 45°)$$

$$= \sqrt{2} \times \frac{11.5}{0.3 / 0.075} (52.37)^2 0.075 = 836 \text{ N Ans.} \qquad \ldots (\because n = l / r)$$

Example 22.17. *The reciprocating mass per cylinder in a 60° V-twin engine is 1.5 kg. The stroke and connecting rod length are 100 mm and 250 mm respectively. If the engine runs at 2500 r.p.m., determine the maximum and minimum values of the primary forces. Also find out the resultant secondary force.*

Solution. Given $2\alpha = 60°$ or $\alpha = 30°$, $m = 1.5$ kg ; Stroke $= 100$ mm or $r = 100/2$ $= 50$ mm $= 0.05$ m ; $l = 250$ mm $= 0.25$ m ; $N = 250$ r.p.m. or $\omega = 2\pi \times 2500 / 60 = 261.8$ rad/s

Maximum and minimum values of primary forces

We know that the resultant primary force,

$$F_P = 2m.\omega^2.r\sqrt{(\cos^2\alpha \cdot \cos\theta)^2 + (\sin^2\alpha \cdot \sin\theta)^2}$$

$$= 2m.\omega^2.r\sqrt{(\cos^2 30°\cos\theta)^2 + (\sin^2 30°\sin\theta)^2}$$

$$= 2m\omega^2 r\sqrt{\left(\frac{3}{4}\cos\theta\right)^2 + \left(\frac{1}{4}\sin\theta\right)^2}$$

$$= \frac{m}{2}\times\omega^2 r\sqrt{9\cos^2\theta + \sin^2\theta} \qquad ...(i)$$

The primary force is maximum, when $\theta = 0°$. Therefore substituting $\theta = 0°$ in equation (i), we have maximum primary force,

$$F_{P(max)} = \frac{m}{2}\times\omega^2 r\times 3 = \frac{1.5}{2}(261.8)^2 0.05\times 3 = 7710.7 \text{ N } \textbf{Ans.}$$

The primary force is minimum, when $\theta = 90°$. Therefore substituting $\theta = 90°$ in equation (i), we have minimum primary force,

$$F_{P(min)} = \frac{m}{2}\times\omega^2 r = \frac{1.5}{2}(261.8)^2 0.05 = 2570.2 \text{ N } \textbf{Ans.}$$

Resultant secondary force

We know that resultant secondary force.

$$F_S = \frac{2m}{n}\times\omega^2\sqrt{(\cos\alpha\cos 2\alpha\cos 2\theta)^2 + (\sin\alpha\sin 2\alpha\sin 2\theta)^2}$$

$$= \frac{2m}{n}\times\omega^2 r\sqrt{(\cos 30°\cos 60°\cos 2\theta)^2 + (\sin 30°\sin 60°\sin 2\theta)^2}$$

$$= \frac{2m}{n}\times\omega^2 r\sqrt{\left(\frac{\sqrt{3}}{2}\times\frac{1}{2}\cos 2\theta\right)^2 + \left(\frac{1}{2}\times\frac{\sqrt{3}}{2}\sin 2\theta\right)^2}$$

$$= \frac{\sqrt{3}}{2}\times\frac{m}{n}\times\omega^2 r$$

$$= \frac{\sqrt{3}}{2}\times\frac{1.5}{0.25/0.05}(261.8)^2 0.05 \qquad ... (\because n = l / r)$$

$$= 890.3 \text{ N } \textbf{Ans.}$$

EXERCISES

1. A single cylinder horizontal engine runs at 120 r.p.m. The length of stroke is 400 mm. The mass of the revolving parts assumed concentrated at the crank pin is 100 kg and mass of the reciprocating parts is 150 kg. Determine the magnitude of the balancing mass required to be placed opposite to the crank at a radius of 150mm which is equivalent to all the revolving and 2/3rd of the reciprocating masses. If the crank turns 30° from the inner dead centre, find the magnitude of the unbalanced force due to the balancing mass. **[Ans. 212.4 kg]**

2. A single cylinder engine runs at 250 r.p.m. and has a stroke of 180 mm. The reciprocating parts has a mass of 120 kg and the revolving parts are equivalent to a mass of 70 kg at a radius of 90 mm. A mass is placed opposite to the crank at a radius of 150 mm to balance the whole of the revolving mass and two-thirds of the reciprocating mass. Determine the magnitude of the balancing mass and the resultant residual unbalance force when the crank has turned 30° from the inner dead centre, neglect the obliquity of the connecting rod. **[Ans. 90 kg ; 3.264 kN]**

3. A two cylinder uncoupled locomotive has inside cylinders 0.6 m apart. The radius of each crank is 300 mm and are at right angles. The revolving mass per cylinder is 250 kg and the reciprocating mass per cylinder is 300 kg. The whole of the revolving and two-third of the reciprocating masses are to be balanced and the balanced masses are placed, in the planes of rotation of the driving wheels, at a radius of 0.8 m. The driving wheels are 2 m in diameter and 1.5 m apart. If the speed of the engine is 80 km. p.h. ; find hammer blow, maximum variation in tractive effort and maximum swaying couple. **[Ans. 18.30 kN, 16.92 kN, 16.2 kN-m]**

4. A two cylinder uncoupled locomotive with cranks at 90° has a crank radius of 325 mm. The distance between the centres of driving wheels is 1.5 m. The pitch of cylinders is 0.6 m. The diameter of treads of driving wheels is 1.8 m. The radius of centres of gravity of balance masses is 0.65 m. The pressure due to dead load on each wheel is 40 kN. The masses of reciprocating and rotating parts per cylinder are 330 kg and 300 kg respectively. The speed of the locomotive is 60 km. p.h. find :
   1. The balancing masses both in magnitude and position required to be placed is the planes of driving wheels to balance whole of the revolving and two-third of the reciprocating masses ; 2. The swaying couple ; 3.The variation is tractive force ; 4. The maximum and minimum pressure on rails ; and 5. The maximum speed at which it is possible to run the locomotive, in order that the wheels are not lifted from the rails.
   [Ans. 200 kg ; 13 kN-m ; 17.34 kN ; 58.86 kN, 21.14 kN ; 87.54 km/h]

5. Two locomotives are built with similar sets of reciprocating parts. One is an inside cylinder engine with two cylinders with centre lines at 0.6 m apart. The other is an outside cylinder with centre lines at 1.98 m apart. The distance between the driving wheel centres is 1.5 m in both the cases. The inside cylinder locomotive runs at 0.8 times the speed of the outside cylinder locomotive and the hammer blow of the inside cylinder locomotive is 1.2 times the hammer blow of the outside cylinder locomotive.
   If the diameter of the driving wheel of the outside cylinder locomotive is 1.98 m, calculate the diameter of the driving wheel of the inside cylinder locomotive. Compare also the variation in the swaying couples of the two engines. Assume that the same fraction of the reciprocating masses are balanced in both the cases. **[Ans. 1.184 m, 1.185]**

6. An air compressor has four vertical cylinders 1,2,3 and 4 in line and the driving cranks at 90° intervals reach their upper most positions in this order. The cranks are of 150 mm radius, the connecting rods 500 mm long and the cylinder centre line 400 mm apart. The mass of the reciprocating parts for each cylinder is 22.5 kg and the speed of rotation is 400 r.p.m. Show that there are no out-of-balance primary or secondary forces and determine the corresponding couples, indicating the positions of No. 1 crank for maximum values. The central plane of the machine may be taken as reference plane. **[Ans. Primary couple = 6.7 kN-m at 45° and 225° ;**
   Secondary couple = 1.4 kN-m at 0°, 90°, 180°, 270°]

7. A four cylinder engine has the two outer cranks at 120° to each other and their reciprocating masses are each 400 kg. The distance between the planes of rotation of adjacent cranks are 400 mm, 700 mm, 700 mm and 500 mm. Find the reciprocating mass and the relative angular position for each of the inner cranks, if the engine is to be in complete primary balance. Also find the maximum

unbalanced secondary force, if the length of each crank is 350 mm, the length of each connecting rod 1.7 m and the engine speed 500 r.p.m.

[Ans. 800 kg at 163° counter clockwise from crank 1, 830 kg at 312° counter clockwise from crank 1 ; 397.3 kN]

8. The reciprocating masses of the first three cylinders of a four cylinder engine are 4.1, 6.2 and 7.4 tonnes respectively. The centre lines of the three cylinders are 5.2 m, 3.2 m and 1.2 m from the fourth cylinder. If the cranks for all the cylinders are equal, determine the reciprocating mass of the fourth cylinder and the angular position of the cranks such that the system is completely balanced for the primary force and couple.

If the cranks are 0.8 m long, the connecting rods 3.8 m, and the speed of the engine 75 r.p.m. ; find the maximum unbalanced secondary force and the crank angle at which it occurs.

[Ans. 6.19 t ; 7.5 kN, 33° clockwise from I.D.C.]

9. In a four cylinder petrol engine equally spaced, the cranks, numbered from the front end are 1,2,3, and 4. The cranks 1 and 4 are in phase and 180° ahead of cranks 2 and 3. The reciprocating mass of each cylinder is 1 kg. The cranks are 50 mm radius and the connecting rod 200 mm long.

What are the resultant unbalanced forces and couples, primary and secondary, when cranks 1 and 4 are on top dead centre position ? The engine is rotating at 1500 r.p.m. in a clockwise direction when viewed from the front. Take the reference plane midway between cylinder 2 and 3.

10. A four cylinder inline marine oil engine has cranks at angular displacement of 90°. The outer cranks are 3 m apart and inner cranks are 1.2 m apart. The inner cranks are placed symmetrically between the outer cranks. The length of each crank is 450 mm. If the engine runs at 90 r.p.m. and the mass of reciprocating parts for each cylinder is 900 kg, find the firing order of the cylinders for the best primary balancing force of reciprocating masses. Determine the maximum unbalanced primary couple for the best arrangement. [Ans. 1-4-2-3 ; 45.7 kN-m]

11. In a four crank symmetrical engine, the reciprocating masses of the two outside cylinders A and D are each 600 kg and those of the two inside cylinders B and C are each 900 kg. The distance between the cylinder axes of A and D is 5.4 metres. Taking the reference line to bisect the angle between the cranks A and D, and the reference plane to bisect the distance between the cylinder axes of A and D, find the angles between the cranks and the distance between the cylinder axes of B and C for complete balance except for secondary couples.

Determine the maximum value of the unbalanced secondary couple if the length of the crank is 425 mm, length of connecting rod 1.8 m and speed is 150 r.p.m.

[Ans. A = 210°, B = 54.7°, C = 305.3°, D =150°; 2.2 m ; 67 N-m]

12. In a four cylinder inline engine, the cylinders are placed symmetrically along the longitudinal axis, with a centre distance of 2.4 m between the outside cylinders and 0.6 m between the inside cylinders. The cranks between the two inside cylinders are at 90° to each other and the mass of reciprocating parts of each of these is 225 kg. All the four cranks are of 0.3 m radius. If the system is to be completely balanced for the primary effects, determine 1. The mass of the reciprocating parts of each of the outside cranks, and 2. The angular position of the outside cranks with reference to the nearest inside cranks, measured in clockwise direction and draw an end view of the four primary cranks marking these angles therein.

With the above arrangement, evaluate the secondary unbalanced effects completely, with reference to a plane through the centre line of cylinder no. 1 and show by means of an end view the angular position of these with reference to secondary crank no. 1. The engine is running at 180 r.p.m. and the length of each connecting rod is 1.2 m.

[Ans. 164 kg each ; 128° and 148° ; 814 kN and 12.7 kN-m]

13. A six-cylinder, single acting, two stroke Diesel engine is arranged with cranks at 60° for the firing sequence 1-4-5-2-3-6. The cylinders, numbered 1 to 6 in succession are pitched 1.5 m apart, except cylinders 3 and 4 which are 1.8 m apart. The reciprocating and revolving masses per line are 2.2 tonnes and 1.6 tonnes respectively. The crank length is 375 mm, the connecting rod length is 1.6 m, and the speed is 120 r.p.m.

Determine the maximum and minimum values of the primary couple due to the reciprocating and revolving parts. Also find the maximum secondary couple and angular position relative to crank No. 1. Take the plane between the cylinders 3 and 4 as the reference plane.

14. A three cylinder radial engine driven by a common crank has the cylinders spaced at 120°. The stroke is 125 mm, length of the connecting rod 225 mm and the mass of the reciprocating parts per cylinder 2 kg. Calculate the primary and secondary forces at crank shaft speed of 1200 r.p.m.

[Ans. 3000 N ; 830 N]

15. The pistons of a 60° twin *V*-engine has strokes of 120 mm. The connecting rods driving a common crank has a length of 200 mm. The mass of the reciprocating parts per cylinder is 1 kg and the speed of the crank shaft is 2500 r.p.m. Determine the magnitude of the primary and secondary forces.

[Ans. 6.3 kN ; 1.1 kN]

16. A twin cylinder *V*-engine has the cylinders set at an angle of 45°, with both pistons connected to the single crank. The crank radius is 62.5 mm and the connecting rods are 275 mm long. The reciprocating mass per line is 1.5 kg and the total rotating mass is equivalent to 2 kg at the crank radius. A balance mass fitted opposite to the crank, is equivalent to 2.25 kg at a radius of 87.5 mm. Determine for an engine speed of 1800 r.p.m. ; the maximum and minimum values of the primary and secondary forces due to the inertia of reciprocating and rotating masses.

[Ans. Primary forces : 3240 N (max.) and 1830 N (min.)
Secondary forces : 1020 N (max.) and 470 N (min.)]

DO YOU KNOW ?

1. Write a short note on primary and secondary balancing.
2. Explain why only a part of the unbalanced force due to reciprocating masses is balanced by revolving mass.
3. Derive the following expressions, for an uncoupled two cylinder locomotive engine :
   (*a*) Variation is tractive force ; (*b*) Swaying couple ; and (*c*) Hammer blow.
4. What are in-line engines ? How are they balanced ? Is it possible to balance them completely ?
5. Explain the 'direct and reverse crank' method for determining unbalanced forces in radial engines.
6. Discuss the balancing of *V*-engines.

OBJECTIVE TYPE QUESTIONS

1. The primary unbalanced force is maximum when the angle of inclination of the crank with the line of stroke is
   (*a*) 0°   (*b*) 90°   (*c*) 180°   (*d*) 360°

2. The partial balancing means
   (*a*) balancing partially the revolving masses
   (*b*) balancing partially the reciprocating masses
   (*c*) best balancing of engines
   (*d*) all of the above

3. In order to facilitate the starting of locomotive in any position, the cranks of a locomotive, with two cylinders, are placed at . . . . . . to each other.
   (*a*) 45°   (*b*) 90°   (*c*) 120°   (*d*) 180°

4. In a locomotive, the ratio of the connecting rod length to the crank radius is kept very large in order to
   (*a*) minimise the effect of primary forces   (*b*) minimise the effect of secondary forces
   (*c*) have perfect balancing   (*d*) start the locomotive quickly

5. If *c* be the fraction of the reciprocating parts of mass *m* to be balanced per cyclinder of a steam locomotive with crank radius *r*, angular speed ω, distance between centre lines of two cylinders *a*, then the magnitude of the maximum swaying couple is given by

   (*a*) $\dfrac{1-c}{2} \times mr\omega^2 a$ (*b*) $\dfrac{1-c}{\sqrt{2}} \times mr\omega^2 a$

   (*c*) $\sqrt{2}(1-c)\, mr\omega^2 a$ (*d*) none of these

6. The swaying couple is maximum or minimum when the angle of inclination of the crank to the line of stroke (θ) is equal to

    (*a*) 45° and 135°   (*b*) 90° and 135°

    (*c*) 135° and 225°   (*d*) 45° and 225°

7. The tractive force is maximum or minimum when the angle of inclination of the crank to the line of stroke (θ) is equal to

    (*a*) 90° and 225°   (*b*) 135° and 180°   (*c*) 180° and 225° (*d*) 135° and 315°

8. The swaying couple is due to the

    (*a*) primary unbalanced force   (*b*) secondary unbalanced force

    (*c*) two cylinders of locomotive   (*d*) partial balancing

9. In a locomotive, the maximum magnitude of the unbalanced force along the perpendicular to the line of stroke, is known as

    (*a*) tractive force   (*b*) swaying couple   (*c*) hammer blow (*d*) none of these

10. The effect of hammer blow in a locomotive can be reduced by

    (*a*) decreasing the speed

    (*b*) using two or three pairs of wheels coupled together

    (*c*) balancing whole of the reciprocating parts

    (*d*) both (*a*) and (*b*)

11. Multi-cylinder engines are desirable because

    (*a*) only balancing problems are reduced   (*b*) only flywheel size is reduced

    (*c*) both (*a*) and (*b*)   (*d*) none of these

12. When the primary direct crank of a reciprocating engine makes an angle θ with the line of stroke, then the secondary direct crank will make an angle of . . . . . with the line of stroke.

    (*a*) $\theta/2$ (*b*) θ (*c*) 2θ (*d*) 4θ

13. Secondary forces in reciprocating mass on engine frame are

    (*a*) of same frequency as of primary forces

    (*b*) twice the frequency as of primary forces

    (*c*) four times the frequency as of primary forces

    (*d*) none of the above

14. The secondary unbalanced force produced by the reciprocating parts of a certain cylinder of a given engine with crank radius r and connecting rod length l can be considered as equal to primary unbalanced force produced by the same weight having

    (*a*) an equivalent crank radius $r^2/4l$ and rotating at twice the speed of the engine

    (*b*) $r^2/4l$ as equivalent crank radius and rotating at engine speed

    (*c*) equivalent crank length of $r^2/4l$ and rotating at engine speed

    (*d*) none of the above

15. Which of the following statement is correct?

    (*a*) In any engine, 100% of the reciprocating masses can be balanced dynamically

    (*b*) In the case of balancing of multicylinder engine, the value of secondary force is higher than the value of the primary force

    (*c*) In the case of balancing of multimass rotating systems, dynamic balancing can be directly started without static balancing done to the system

    (*d*) none of the above.

ANSWERS

1. (*c*)	**2.** (*b*)	**3.** (*b*)	**4.** (*b*)	**5.** (*b*)
6. (*d*)	**7.** (*d*)	**8.** (*a*)	**9.** (*c*)	**10.** (*d*)
11. (*c*)	**12.** (*c*)	**13.** (*b*)	**14.** (*a*)	**15.** (*c*)

23
Longitudinal and Transverse Vibrations

23.1. Introduction

When elastic bodies such as a spring, a beam and a shaft are displaced from the equilibrium position by the application of external forces, and then released, they execute a *vibratory motion*. This is due to the reason that, when a body is displaced, the internal forces in the form of elastic or strain energy are present in the body. At release, these forces bring the body to its original position. When the body reaches the equilibrium position, the whole of the elastic or strain energy is converted into kinetic energy due to which the body continues to move in the opposite direction. The whole of the kinetic energy is again converted into strain energy due to which the body again returns to the equilibrium position. In this way, the vibratory motion is repeated indefinitely.

23.2. Terms Used in Vibratory Motion

The following terms are commonly used in connection with the vibratory motions :

1. *Period of vibration or time period.* It is the time interval after which the motion is repeated itself. The period of vibration is usually expressed in seconds.

2. *Cycle.* It is the motion completed during one time period.

3. *Frequency.* It is the number of cycles described in one second. In S.I. units, the frequency is expressed in hertz (briefly written as Hz) which is equal to one cycle per second.

23.3. Types of Vibratory Motion

The following types of vibratory motion are important from the subject point of view :

1. *Free or natural vibrations.* When no external force acts on the body, after giving it an initial displacement, then the body is said to be under *free or natural vibrations*. The frequency of the free vibrations is called *free or natural frequency*.

2. *Forced vibrations.* When the body vibrates under the influence of external force, then the body is said to be under *forced vibrations*. The external force applied to the body is a periodic disturbing force created by unbalance. The vibrations have the same frequency as the applied force.

Note : When the frequency of the external force is same as that of the natural vibrations, resonance takes place.

3. *Damped vibrations.* When there is a reduction in amplitude over every cycle of vibration, the motion is said to be *damped vibration*. This is due to the fact that a certain amount of energy possessed by the vibrating system is always dissipated in overcoming frictional resistances to the motion.

23.4. Types of Free Vibrations

The following three types of free vibrations are important from the subject point of view :

1. Longitudinal vibrations, **2.** Transverse vibrations, and **3.** Torsional vibrations.

Consider a weightless constraint (spring or shaft) whose one end is fixed and the other end carrying a heavy disc, as shown in Fig. 23.1. This system may execute one of the three above mentioned types of vibrations.

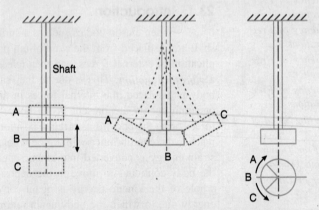

B = Mean position ; *A* and *C* = Extreme positions.

(*a*) Longitudinal vibrations.   (*b*) Transverse vibrations.   (*c*) Torsional vibrations.

Fig. 23.1. Types of free vibrations.

1. *Longitudinal vibrations.* When the particles of the shaft or disc moves parallel to the axis of the shaft, as shown in Fig. 23.1 (*a*), then the vibrations are known as *longitudinal vibrations*. In this case, the shaft is elongated and shortened alternately and thus the tensile and compressive stresses are induced alternately in the shaft.

2. Transverse vibrations. When the particles of the shaft or disc move approximately perpendicular to the axis of the shaft, as shown in Fig. 23.1 (*b*), then the vibrations are known as *transverse vibrations*. In this case, the shaft is straight and bent alternately and bending stresses are induced in the shaft.

Bridges should be built taking vibrations into account.

3. Torsional vibrations*. When the particles of the shaft or disc move in a circle about the axis of the shaft, as shown in Fig. 23.1 (*c*), then the vibrations are known as *torsional vibrations*. In this case, the shaft is twisted and untwisted alternately and the torsional shear stresses are induced in the shaft.

Note : If the limit of proportionality (*i.e.* stress proportional to strain) is not exceeded in the three types of vibrations, then the restoring force in longitudinal and transverse vibrations or the restoring couple in torsional vibrations which is exerted on the disc by the shaft (due to the stiffness of the shaft) is directly proportional to the displacement of the disc from its equilibrium or mean position. Hence it follows that the acceleration towards the equilibrium position is directly proportional to the displacement from that position and the vibration is, therefore, simple harmonic.

23.5. Natural Frequency of Free Longitudinal Vibrations

The natural frequency of the free longitudinal vibrations may be determined by the following three methods :

1. *Equilibrium Method*

Consider a constraint (*i.e.* spring) of negligible mass in an unstrained position, as shown in Fig. 23.2 (*a*).

Let s = Stiffness of the constraint. It is the force required to produce unit displacement in the direction of vibration. It is usually expressed in N/m.

m = Mass of the body suspended from the constraint in kg,

W = Weight of the body in newtons = $m.g$,

---

* The torsional vibrations are separately discussed in chapter 24.

δ = Static deflection of the spring in metres due to weight W newtons, and

x = Displacement given to the body by the external force, in metres.

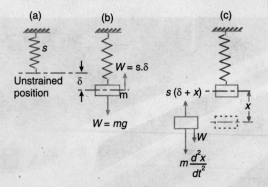

Fig. 23.2. Natural frequency of free longitudinal vibrations.

In the equilibrium position, as shown in Fig. 23.2 (b), the gravitational pull $W = m.g$, is balanced by a force of spring, such that $W = s.\delta$.

Since the mass is now displaced from its equilibrium position by a distance x, as shown in Fig. 23.2 (c), and is then released, therefore after time t,

Restoring force $\qquad = W - s(\delta + x) = W - s.\delta - s.x$

$\qquad\qquad\qquad\qquad = s.\delta - s.\delta - s.x = -s.x \qquad\qquad (\because W = s.\delta) \qquad \ldots (i)$

$\qquad\qquad\qquad\qquad\qquad\qquad\qquad\qquad\qquad \ldots \text{(Taking upward force as negative)}$

and $\qquad\qquad$ Accelerating force = Mass × Acceleration

$$= m \times \frac{d^2x}{dt^2} \ldots \text{(Taking downward force as positive)} \ldots (ii)$$

Equating equations (i) and (ii), the equation of motion of the body of mass m after time t is

$$m \times \frac{d^2x}{dt^2} = -s.x \quad \text{or} \quad m \times \frac{d^2x}{dt^2} + s.x = 0$$

$\therefore \qquad\qquad \dfrac{d^2x}{dt^2} + \dfrac{s}{m} \times x = 0 \qquad\qquad\qquad\qquad\qquad\qquad\qquad \ldots (iii)$

We know that the fundamental equation of simple harmonic motion is

$$\frac{d^2x}{dt^2} + \omega^2.x = 0 \qquad\qquad\qquad\qquad\qquad\qquad \ldots (iv)$$

Comparing equations (iii) and (iv), we have

$$\omega = \sqrt{\frac{s}{m}}$$

$\therefore \qquad$ Time period, $\qquad t_p = \dfrac{2\pi}{\omega} = 2\pi\sqrt{\dfrac{m}{s}}$

and natural frequency,

$$f_n = \frac{1}{t_p} = \frac{1}{2\pi}\sqrt{\frac{s}{m}} = \frac{1}{2\pi}\sqrt{\frac{g}{\delta}} \qquad \qquad \dots (\because \ m.g = s.\delta)$$

Taking the value of g as 9.81 m/s² and δ in metres,

$$f_n = \frac{1}{2\pi}\sqrt{\frac{9.81}{\delta}} = \frac{0.4985}{\sqrt{\delta}}\,\text{Hz}$$

Note : The value of static deflection δ may be found out from the given conditions of the problem. For longitudinal vibrations, it may be obtained by the relation,

$$\frac{\text{Stress}}{\text{Strain}} = E \quad \text{or} \quad \frac{W}{A}\times\frac{l}{\delta} = E \quad \text{or} \quad \delta = \frac{W.l}{E.A}$$

where

$\quad\quad\quad\quad \delta$ = Static deflection *i.e.* extension or compression of the constraint,

$\quad\quad\quad\quad W$ = Load attached to the free end of constraint,

$\quad\quad\quad\quad l$ = Length of the constraint,

$\quad\quad\quad\quad E$ = Young's modulus for the constraint, and

$\quad\quad\quad\quad A$ = Cross-sectional area of the constraint.

2. *Energy method*

We know that the kinetic energy is due to the motion of the body and the potential energy is with respect to a certain datum position which is equal to the amount of work required to move the body from the datum position. In the case of vibrations, the datum position is the mean or equilibrium position at which the potential energy of the body or the system is zero.

In the free vibrations, no energy is transferred to the system or from the system. Therefore the summation of kinetic energy and potential energy must be a constant quantity which is same at all the times. In other words,

This industrial compressor uses compressed air to power heavy-duty construction tools. Compressors are used for jobs, such as breaking up concrete or paving, drilling, pile driving, sand-blasting and tunnelling. A compressor works on the same principle as a pump. A piston moves backwards and forwards inside a hollow cylinder, which compresses the air and forces it into a hollow chamber. A pipe or hose connected to the chamber channels the compressed air to the tools.

Note : This picture is given as additional information.

$$\therefore \quad \frac{d}{dt}(K.E.+P.E.) = 0$$

We know that kinetic energy,

$$K.E. = \frac{1}{2}\times m\left(\frac{dx}{dt}\right)^2$$

and potential energy,
$$P.E. = \left(\frac{0 + s.x}{2}\right) x = \frac{1}{2} \times s.x^2$$

$$\dots (\because P.E. = \text{Mean force} \times \text{Displacement})$$

$$\therefore \qquad \frac{d}{dt}\left[\frac{1}{2} \times m \left(\frac{dx}{dt}\right)^2 + \frac{1}{2} \times s.x^2\right] = 0$$

$$\frac{1}{2} \times m \times 2 \times \frac{dx}{dt} \times \frac{d^2x}{dt^2} + \frac{1}{2} \times s \times 2x \times \frac{dx}{dt} = 0$$

or
$$m \times \frac{d^2x}{dt^2} + s.x = 0 \quad \text{or} \quad \frac{d^2x}{dt^2} + \frac{s}{m} \times x = 0 \qquad \dots \text{(Same as before)}$$

The time period and the natural frequency may be obtained as discussed in the previous method.

3. Rayleigh's method

In this method, the maximum kinetic energy at the mean position is equal to the maximum potential energy (or strain energy) at the extreme position. Assuming the motion executed by the vibration to be simple harmonic, then

$$x = X \sin \omega.t \qquad \dots (i)$$

where
$$x = \text{Displacement of the body from the mean position after time } t$$
$$\text{seconds, and}$$
$$X = \text{Maximum displacement from mean position to extreme position.}$$

Now, differentiating equation (i), we have

$$\frac{dx}{dt} = \omega \times X \cos \omega.t$$

Since at the mean position, $t = 0$, therefore maximum velocity at the mean position,

$$v = \frac{dx}{dt} = \omega.X$$

$\therefore$ Maximum kinetic energy at mean position

$$= \frac{1}{2} \times m.v^2 = \frac{1}{2} \times m.\omega^2.X^2 \qquad \dots (ii)$$

and maximum potential energy at the extreme position

$$= \left(\frac{0 + s.X}{2}\right) X = \frac{1}{2} \times s.X^2 \qquad \dots (iii)$$

Equating equations (ii) and (iii),

$$\frac{1}{2} \times m.\omega^2.X^2 = \frac{1}{2} \times s.X^2 \quad \text{or} \quad \omega^2 = \frac{s}{m} \text{ , and } \omega = \sqrt{\frac{s}{m}}$$

$\therefore$ Time period,
$$t_p = \frac{2\pi}{\omega} = 2\pi \sqrt{\frac{s}{m}} \qquad \dots \text{(Same as before)}$$

and natural frequency, $\quad f_n = \dfrac{1}{t_p} = \dfrac{\omega}{2\pi} = \dfrac{1}{2\pi}\sqrt{\dfrac{s}{m}}$ $\qquad$ . . . (Same as before)

Note : In all the above expressions, ω is known as **natural circular frequency** and is generally denoted by ω_n.

23.6. Natural Frequency of Free Transverse Vibrations

Consider a shaft of negligible mass, whose one end is fixed and the other end carries a body of weight W, as shown in Fig. 23.3.

Let $\qquad\qquad$ s = Stiffness of shaft,

$\qquad\qquad\qquad$ δ = Static deflection due to weight of the body,

$\qquad\qquad\qquad$ x = Displacement of body from mean position after time t.

$\qquad\qquad\qquad$ m = Mass of body = W/g

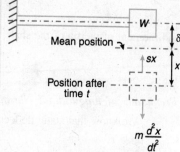

Fig. 23.3. Natural frequency of free transverse vibrations.

As discussed in the previous article,

$\qquad$ Restoring force $\quad = -s.x$ $\qquad$ . . . (i)

and accelerating force $\qquad = m \times \dfrac{d^2 x}{dt^2}$ $\qquad$ . . . (ii)

Equating equations (i) and (ii), the equation of motion becomes

$$m \times \dfrac{d^2 x}{dt^2} = -s.x \qquad \text{or} \qquad m \times \dfrac{d^2 x}{dt^2} + s.x = 0$$

$\therefore \qquad \dfrac{d^2 x}{dt^2} + \dfrac{s}{m} \times x = 0$ $\qquad\qquad\qquad$ . . . (Same as before)

Hence, the time period and the natural frequency of the transverse vibrations are same as that of longitudinal vibrations. Therefore

Time period, $\qquad t_p = 2\pi\sqrt{\dfrac{m}{s}}$

and natural frequency, $\qquad f_n = \dfrac{1}{t_p} = \dfrac{1}{2\pi}\sqrt{\dfrac{s}{m}} = \dfrac{1}{2\pi}\sqrt{\dfrac{g}{\delta}}$

Note : The shape of the curve, into which the vibrating shaft deflects, is identical with the static deflection curve of a cantilever beam loaded at the end. It has been proved in the text book on Strength of Materials, that the static deflection of a cantilever beam loaded at the free end is

$$\delta = \dfrac{W l^3}{3EI} \quad \text{(in metres)}$$

where $\qquad\qquad$ W = Load at the free end, in newtons,

$\qquad\qquad\quad$ l = Length of the shaft or beam in metres,

$\qquad\qquad\quad$ E = Young's modulus for the material of the shaft or beam in N/m², and

$\qquad\qquad\quad$ I = Moment of inertia of the shaft or beam in m⁴.

Example 23.1. *A cantilever shaft 50 mm diameter and 300 mm long has a disc of mass 100 kg at its free end. The Young's modulus for the shaft material is 200 GN/m². Determine the frequency of longitudinal and transverse vibrations of the shaft.*

Solution. Given : $d = 50$ mm $= 0.05$ m ; $l = 300$ mm $= 0.03$ m ; $m = 100$ kg ; $E = 200$ GN/m² $= 200 \times 10^9$ N/m²

We know that cross-sectional area of the shaft,

$$A = \frac{\pi}{4} \times d^2 = \frac{\pi}{4}(0.05)^2 = 1.96 \times 10^{-3} \, \text{m}^2$$

and moment of inertia of the shaft,

$$I = \frac{\pi}{64} \times d^4 = \frac{\pi}{64}(0.05)^4 = 0.3 \times 10^{-6} \, \text{m}^4$$

Frequency of longitudinal vibration

We know that static deflection of the shaft,

$$\delta = \frac{W.l}{A.E} = \frac{100 \times 9.81 \times 0.3}{1.96 \times 10^{-3} \times 200 \times 10^9} = 0.751 \times 10^{-6} \, \text{m}$$

$$\dots (\because W = m.g)$$

∴ Frequency of longitudinal vibration,

$$f_n = \frac{0.4985}{\sqrt{\delta}} = \frac{0.4985}{\sqrt{0.751 \times 10^{-6}}} = 575 \, \text{Hz} \quad \textbf{Ans.}$$

Frequency of transverse vibration

We know that static deflection of the shaft,

$$\delta = \frac{W\,l^3}{3\,E.I} = \frac{100 \times 9.81 \times (0.3)^3}{3 \times 200 \times 10^9 \times 0.3 \times 10^{-6}} = 0.147 \times 10^{-3} \, \text{m}$$

∴ Frequency of transverse vibration,

$$f_n = \frac{0.4985}{\sqrt{\delta}} = \frac{0.4985}{\sqrt{0.147 \times 10^{-3}}} = 41 \, \text{Hz} \, \textbf{Ans.}$$

23.7. Effect of Inertia of the Constraint in Longitudinal and Transverse Vibrations

In deriving the expressions for natural frequency of longitudinal and transverse vibrations, we have neglected the inertia of the constraint *i.e.* shaft. We shall now discuss the effect of the inertia of the constraint, as below :

1. Longitudinal vibration

Consider the constraint whose one end is fixed and other end is free as shown in Fig. 23.4.

Let $\quad m_1$ = Mass of the constraint per unit length,

$\qquad l$ = Length of the constraint,

$\qquad m_C$ = Total mass of the constraint = $m_1 . l$, and

$\qquad v$ = Longitudinal velocity of the free end.

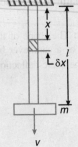

Fig. 23.4. Effect of inertia of the constraint in longitudinal vibrations.

Consider a small element of the constraint at a distance x from the fixed end and of length δx.

∴ Velocity of the small element

$$= \frac{x}{l} \times v$$

and kinetic energy possessed by the element

$$= \frac{1}{2} \times \text{Mass (velocity)}^2$$

$$= \frac{1}{2} \times m_1 . \delta x \left(\frac{x}{l} \times v \right)^2 = \frac{m_1 . v^2 \, x^2}{2 l^2} \times \delta x$$

∴ Total kinetic energy possessed by the constraint,

$$= \int_0^l \frac{m_1 . v^2 x^2}{2 l^2} \times dx = \frac{m_1 . v^2}{2 l^2} \left[\frac{x^3}{3} \right]_0^l$$

$$= \frac{m_1 . v^2}{2 l^2} \times \frac{l^3}{3} = \frac{1}{2} \times m_1 . v^2 \times \frac{l}{3} = \frac{1}{2} \left(\frac{m_1 l}{3} \right) v^2 = \frac{1}{2} \left(\frac{m_C}{3} \right) v^2 \quad \dots (i)$$

$$\dots \text{(Substituting } m_1 . l = m_C)$$

If a mass of $\frac{m_C}{3}$ is placed at the free end and the constraint is assumed to be of negligible mass, then

Total kinetic energy possessed by the constraint

$$= \frac{1}{2} \left(\frac{m_C}{3} \right) v^2 \qquad \dots \text{[Same as equation } (i)] \dots (ii)$$

Hence the two systems are dynamically same. Therefore, inertia of the constraint may be allowed for by adding one-third of its mass to the disc at the free end.

From the above discussion, we find that when the mass of the constraint m_C and the mass of the disc m at the end is given, then natural frequency of vibration,

$$f_n = \frac{1}{2\pi} \sqrt{\frac{s}{m + \frac{m_C}{3}}}$$

2. Transverse vibration

Consider a constraint whose one end is fixed and the other end is free as shown in Fig. 23.5.

Let m_1 = Mass of constraint per unit length,

l = Length of the constraint,

m_C = Total mass of the constraint = $m_1.l$, and

v = Transverse velocity of the free end.

Consider a small element of the constraint at a distance x from the fixed end and of length δx. The velocity of this element is

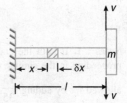

Fig. 23.5. Effect of inertia of the constraint in transverse vibrations.

given by $\left[\dfrac{3l.x^2 - x^3}{2l^3} \times v\right]$.

∴ Kinetic energy of the element

$$= \frac{1}{2} \times m_1.\delta x \left(\frac{3l.x^2 - x^3}{2l^3} \times v\right)^2$$

and total kinetic energy of the constraint,

$$= \int_0^l \frac{1}{2} \times m_1 \left(\frac{3l.x^2 - x^3}{2l^3} \times v\right)^2 dx = \frac{m_1.v^2}{8l^6} \int_0^l (9l^2.x^4 - 6l.x^5 + x^6)\, dx$$

$$= \frac{m_1.v^2}{8l^6} \left[\frac{9l^2.x^5}{5} - \frac{6l.x^6}{6} + \frac{x^7}{7}\right]_0^l$$

$$= \frac{m_1.v^2}{8l^6} \left[\frac{9l^7}{5} - \frac{6l^7}{6} + \frac{l^7}{7}\right] = \frac{m_1.v^2}{8l^6} \left(\frac{33l^7}{35}\right)$$

$$= \frac{33}{280} \times m_1.l.v^2 = \frac{1}{2}\left(\frac{33}{140} \times m_1.l\right) v^2 = \frac{1}{2}\left(\frac{33}{140} \times m_C\right) v^2 \qquad \ldots (i)$$

$$\ldots \text{(Substituting } m_1.l = m_C)$$

If a mass of $\dfrac{33 m_C}{140}$ is placed at the free end and the constraint is assumed to be of negligible mass, then

Total kinetic energy possessed by the constraint

$$= \frac{1}{2}\left(\frac{33 m_C}{140}\right) v^2 \qquad \ldots \text{[Same as equation } (i)]$$

Hence the two systems are dynamically same. Therefore the inertia of the constraint may be allowed for by adding $\dfrac{33}{140}$ of its mass to the disc at the free end.

From the above discussion, we find that when the mass of the constraint m_C and the mass of the disc m at the free end is given, then natural frequency of vibration,

$$f_n = \frac{1}{2\pi} \sqrt{\frac{s}{m + \dfrac{33 m_C}{140}}}$$

Notes : 1. If both the ends of the constraint are fixed, and the disc is situated in the middle of it, then proceeding in the similar way as discussed above, we may prove that the inertia of the constraint may be allowed for by adding $\dfrac{13}{35}$ of its mass to the disc.

2. If the constraint is like a simply supported beam, then $\dfrac{17}{35}$ of its mass may be added to the mass of the disc.

23.8. Natural Frequency of Free Transverse Vibrations Due to a Point Load Acting Over a Simply Supported Shaft

Consider a shaft AB of length l, carrying a point load W at C which is at a distance of l_1 from A and l_2 from B, as shown in Fig. 23.6. A little consideration will show that when the shaft is deflected and suddenly released, it will make transverse vibrations. The deflection of the shaft is proportional to the load W and if the beam is deflected beyond the static equilibrium position then the load will vibrate with simple harmonic motion (as by a helical spring). If δ is the static deflection due to load W, then the natural frequency of the free transverse vibration is

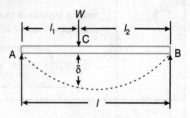

Fig. 23.6. Simply supported beam with a point load.

$$f_n = \frac{1}{2\pi}\sqrt{\frac{g}{\delta}} = \frac{0.4985}{\sqrt{\delta}} \text{ Hz} \qquad \dots \text{(Substituting, } g = 9.81 \text{ m/s}^2\text{)}$$

Some of the values of the static deflection for the various types of beams and under various load conditions are given in the following table.

Table 23.1. Values of static deflection (δ) for the various types of beams and under various load conditions.

S.No.	Type of beam	Deflection (δ)
1.	Cantilever beam with a point load W at the free end.	$\delta = \dfrac{Wl^3}{3EI}$ (at the free end)
2.	Cantilever beam with a uniformly distributed load of w per unit length.	$\delta = \dfrac{wl^4}{8EI}$ (at the free end)
3.	Simply supported beam with an eccentric point load W.	$\delta = \dfrac{Wa^2b^2}{3EIl}$ (at the point load)
4.	Simply supported beam with a central point load W.	$\delta = \dfrac{Wl^3}{48EI}$ (at the centre)

S.No.	Type of beam	Deflection (δ)
5.	Simply supported beam with a uniformly distributed load of w per unit length. w/ unit length $\leftarrow$ l $\rightarrow$	$\delta = \dfrac{5}{384} \times \dfrac{wl^4}{EI}$ (at the centre)
6.	Fixed beam with an eccentric point load W. W $\leftarrow a \rightarrow\leftarrow\quad b\quad \rightarrow$ $\leftarrow\qquad l\qquad \rightarrow$	$\delta = \dfrac{a\,a^3\,b^3}{3a\,aa^3}$ (at the point load)
7.	Fixed beam with a central point load W. W $\leftarrow l/2 \rightarrow\leftarrow l/2 \rightarrow$ $\leftarrow\quad l\quad \rightarrow$	$\delta = \dfrac{Wl^3}{192EI}$ (at the centre)
8.	Fixed beam with a uniformly distributed load of w per unit length. w/ unit length $\leftarrow\quad l\quad \rightarrow$	$\delta = \dfrac{wl^4}{384EI}$ (at the centre)

Example 23.2. *A shaft of length 0.75 m, supported freely at the ends, is carrying a body of mass 90 kg at 0.25 m from one end. Find the natural frequency of transverse vibration. Assume E = 200 GN/m² and shaft diameter = 50 mm.*

Solution. Given : $l = 0.75$ m ; $m = 90$ kg ; $a = AC = 0.25$ m ; $E = 200$ GN/m² $= 200 \times 10^9$ N/m²; $d = 50$ mm $= 0.05$ m

The shaft is shown in Fig. 23.7.

We know that moment of inertia of the shaft,

$$I = \frac{\pi}{64} \times d^4 = \frac{\pi}{64}(0.05)^4 \, \text{m}^4$$

$$= 0.307 \times 10^{-6} \, \text{m}^4$$

and static deflection at the load point (*i.e.* at point C),

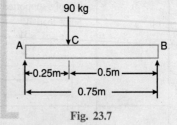

Fig. 23.7

$$\delta = \frac{Wa^2b^2}{3EIl} = \frac{90 \times 9.81(0.25)^2(0.5)^2}{3 \times 200 \times 10^9 \times 0.307 \times 10^{-6} \times 0.75} = 0.1 \times 10^{-3} \text{ m}$$

$$\dots (\because b = BC = 0.5 \text{ m})$$

We know that natural frequency of transverse vibration,

$$f_n = \frac{0.4985}{\sqrt{\delta}} = \frac{0.4985}{\sqrt{0.1 \times 10^{-3}}} = 49.85 \text{ Hz} \quad \textbf{Ans.}$$

Example 23.3. *A flywheel is mounted on a vertical shaft as shown in Fig. 23.8. The both ends of the shaft are fixed and its diameter is 50 mm. The flywheel has a mass of 500 kg. Find the natural frequencies of longitudinal and transverse vibrations. Take E = 200 GN/m².*

Solution. Given : $d = 50$ mm $= 0.05$ m ; $m = 500$ kg ; $E = 200$ GN/m² $= 200 \times 10^9$ N/m²

We know that cross-sectional area of shaft,

$$A = \frac{\pi}{4} \times d^2 = \frac{\pi}{4}(0.05)^2 = 1.96 \times 10^{-3} \text{ m}^2$$

and moment of inertia of shaft,

$$I = \frac{\pi}{64} \times d^4 = \frac{\pi}{64}(0.05)^4 = 0.307 \times 10^{-6} \text{ m}^4$$

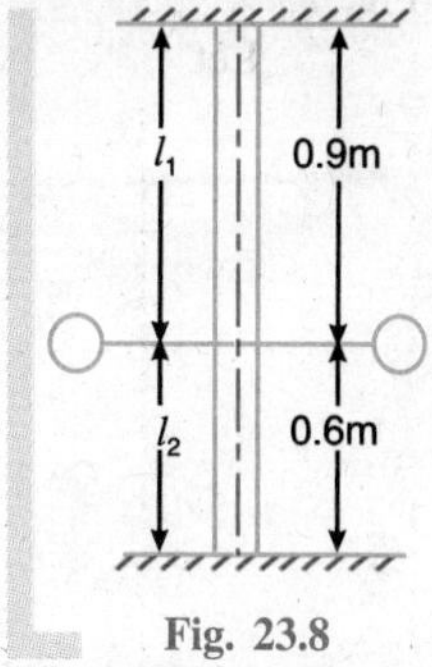

Fig. 23.8

Natural frequency of longitudinal vibration

Let $m_1 =$ Mass of flywheel carried by the length l_1.

∴ $m - m_1 =$ Mass of flywheel carried by length l_2.

We know that extension of length l_1

$$= \frac{W_1 l_1}{A.E} = \frac{m_1.g.l_1}{A.E} \qquad \ldots (i)$$

Similarly, compression of length l_2

$$= \frac{(W - W_1) l_2}{A.E} = \frac{(m - m_1) g.l_2}{A.E} \qquad \ldots (ii)$$

Since extension of length l_1 must be equal to compression of length l_2, therefore equating equations (i) and (ii),

$$m_1 l_1 = (m - m_1) l_2$$

$$m_1 \times 0.9 = (500 - m_1) 0.6 = 300 - 0.6 m_1 \quad \text{or} \quad m_1 = 200 \text{ kg}$$

∴ Extension of length l_1,

$$\delta = \frac{m_1.g.l_1}{A.E} = \frac{200 \times 9.81 \times 0.9}{1.96 \times 10^{-3} \times 200 \times 10^9} = 4.5 \times 10^{-6} \text{ m}$$

We know that natural frequency of longitudinal vibration,

$$f_n = \frac{0.4985}{\sqrt{\delta}} = \frac{0.4985}{\sqrt{4.5 \times 10^{-6}}} = 235 \text{ Hz} \quad \textbf{Ans.}$$

Natural frequency of transverse vibration

We know that the static deflection for a shaft fixed at both ends and carrying a point load is given by

$$\delta = \frac{W a^3 b^3}{3E \, I l^3} = \frac{500 \times 9.81 (0.9)^3 (0.6)^3}{3 \times 200 \times 10^9 \times 0.307 \times 10^{-6} (1.5)^3} = 1.24 \times 10^{-3} \text{ m}$$

$$\ldots \text{(Substituting } W = m.g \text{ ; } a = l_1, \text{ and } b = l_2)$$

We know that natural frequency of transverse vibration,

$$f_n = \frac{0.4985}{\sqrt{\delta}} = \frac{0.4985}{\sqrt{1.24 \times 10^{-3}}} = 14.24 \text{ Hz} \quad \textbf{Ans.}$$

23.9. Natural Frequency of Free Transverse Vibrations Due to Uniformly Distributed Load Acting Over a Simply Supported Shaft

Consider a shaft AB carrying a uniformly distributed load of w per unit length as shown in Fig. 23.9.

Let
y_1 = Static deflection at the middle of the shaft,

a_1 = Amplitude of vibration at the middle of the shaft, and

w_1 = Uniformly distributed load per unit static deflection at the middle of the shaft = w/y_1.

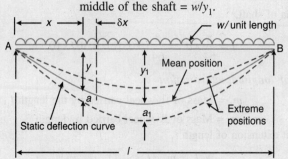

Fig. 23.9. Simply supported shaft carrying a uniformly distributed load.

Now, consider a small section of the shaft at a distance x from A and length δx.

Let
y = Static deflection at a distance x from A, and

a = Amplitude of its vibration.

∴ Work done on this small section

$$= \frac{1}{2} \times w_1 . a_1 . \delta x \times a = \frac{1}{2} \times \frac{w}{y_1} \times a_1 . \delta x \times a = \frac{1}{2} \times w \times \frac{a_1}{y_1} \times a \times \delta x$$

Since the maximum potential energy at the extreme position is equal to the amount of work done to move the beam from the mean position to one of its extreme positions, therefore Maximum potential energy at the extreme position

$$= \int_0^l \frac{1}{2} \times w \times \frac{a_1}{y_1} \times a . dx \qquad \qquad \dots (i)$$

Assuming that the shape of the curve of a vibrating shaft is similar to the static deflection curve of a beam, therefore

$$\frac{a_1}{y_1} = \frac{a}{y} = \text{Constant}, C \quad \text{or} \quad \frac{a_1}{y_1} = C \text{ and } a = y.C$$

Substituting these values in equation (i), we have maximum potential energy at the extreme position

$$= \int_0^l \frac{1}{2} \times w \times C \times y.C . dx = \frac{1}{2} \times w.C^2 \int_0^l y . dx \qquad \dots (ii)$$

Since the maximum velocity at the mean position is $\omega.a_1$, where ω is the circular frequency of vibration, therefore

Maximum kinetic energy at the mean position

$$= \int_0^l \frac{1}{2} \times \frac{w.dx}{g} (\omega a)^2 = \frac{w}{2g} \times \omega^2 \times C^2 \int_0^l y^2.dx \qquad \dots (iii)$$

$$\dots (\text{Substituting } a = y.C)$$

We know that the maximum potential energy at the extreme position is equal to the maximum kinetic energy at the mean position, therefore equating equations (*ii*) and (*iii*),

$$\frac{1}{2} \times w \times C^2 \int_0^l y.dx = \frac{w}{2g} \times \omega^2 \times C^2 \int_0^l y^2.dx$$

$$\therefore \qquad \omega^2 = \frac{g \int_0^l y.dx}{\int_0^l y^2.dx} \qquad \text{or} \qquad \omega = \sqrt{\frac{g \int_0^l y.dx}{\int_0^l y^2.dx}} \qquad \dots (iv)$$

When the shaft is a simply supported, then the static deflection at a distance x from A is

$$* \quad y = \frac{w}{24\,EI} (x^4 - 2l\,x^3 + l^3 x) \qquad \dots (v)$$

where

w = Uniformly distributed load unit length,

E = Young's modulus for the material of the shaft, and

I = Moment of inertia of the shaft.

---

* It has been proved in books on 'Strength of Materials' that maximum bending moment at a distance x from A is

$$(B.M.)_{max} = EI \frac{d^2 y}{dx^2} = \frac{wx^2}{2} - \frac{wl\,x}{2}$$

Integrating this expression,

$$EI. \frac{dy}{dx} = \frac{wx^3}{2 \times 3} - \frac{wl.x^2}{2 \times 2} + C_1$$

On further integrating,

$$E.I.y = \frac{wx^4}{2 \times 3 \times 4} - \frac{wl.x^3}{2 \times 2 \times 3} + C_1 x + C_2$$

$$= \frac{wx^4}{24} - \frac{wlx^3}{12} + C_1 x + C_2$$

where C_1 and C_2 are the constants of integration and may be determined from the given conditions of the problem. Here

when $\qquad\qquad x = 0, y = 0 ; \qquad\qquad \therefore \qquad C_2 = 0$

and when $\qquad\qquad x = 1, y = 0 ; \qquad\qquad \therefore \qquad C_1 = \dfrac{wl^3}{24}$

Substituting the value of C_1, we get

$$y = \frac{w}{24\,EI} (x^4 - 2l\,x^3 + l^3 x)$$

A railway bridge.

Now integrating the above equation (v) within the limits from 0 to l,

$$\int_0^l y\,dx = \frac{w}{24\,EI}\int_0^l (x^4 - 2lx^3 + l^3 x)\,dx = \frac{w}{24\,EI}\left[\frac{x^5}{5} - \frac{2lx^4}{4} + \frac{l^3 x^2}{2}\right]_0^l$$

$$= \frac{w}{24\,EI}\left[\frac{l^5}{5} - \frac{2l^5}{4} + \frac{l^5}{2}\right] = \frac{w}{24\,EI}\times\frac{l^5}{5} = \frac{w.l^5}{120\,E.I} \qquad \dots (vi)$$

Now

$$\int_0^l y^2\,dx = \int_0^l \left[\frac{w}{24\,EI}(x^4 - 2l\,x^3 + l^3 x)\right]^2 dx$$

$$= \left(\frac{w}{24\,EI}\right)^2 \int_0^l (x^8 + 4l^2 x^6 + l^6 x^2 - 4l\,x^7 - 4l^4 x^4 + 2l^3 x^5)\,dx$$

$$= \frac{w^2}{576\,E^2 I^2}\cdot\left[\frac{x^9}{9} + \frac{4l^2 x^7}{7} + \frac{l^6 x^3}{3} - \frac{4lx^8}{8} - \frac{4l^4 x^5}{5} + \frac{2l^3 x^6}{6}\right]_0^l$$

$$= \frac{w^2}{576\,E^2 I^2}\left[\frac{l^9}{9} + \frac{4l^9}{7} + \frac{l^9}{3} - \frac{4l^9}{8} - \frac{4l^9}{5} + \frac{2l^9}{6}\right]$$

$$= \frac{w^2}{576\,E^2 I^2}\times\frac{31l^9}{630} \qquad \dots (vii)$$

Substituting the value in equation (iv) from equations (vi) and (vii), we get circular frequency due to uniformly distributed load,

$$\omega = \sqrt{g\left(\frac{wl^5}{120\,EI}\times\frac{576\,E^2 I^2 \times 630}{w^2 \times 31 l^9}\right)}$$

$$= \sqrt{\frac{24\,EI}{wl^4} \times \frac{630}{155}\,g} = \pi^2 \sqrt{\frac{EI\,g}{wl^4}} \qquad \ldots (viii)$$

∴   Natural frequency due to uniformly distributed load,

$$f_n = \frac{\omega}{2\pi} = \frac{\pi^2}{2\pi}\sqrt{\frac{EI\,g}{wl^4}} = \frac{\pi}{2}\sqrt{\frac{EIg}{wl^4}} \qquad \ldots (ix)$$

We know that the static deflection of a simply supported shaft due to uniformly distributed load of *w* per unit length, is

$$\delta_S = \frac{5\,wl^4}{384\,EI} \qquad \text{or} \qquad \frac{EI}{wl^4} = \frac{5}{384\,\delta_S}$$

Equation (*ix*) may be written as

$$f_n = \frac{\pi}{2}\sqrt{\frac{5\,g}{384\,\delta_S}} = \frac{0.5615}{\sqrt{\delta_S}}\ \text{Hz} \qquad \ldots (\text{Substituting, } g = 9.81\ \text{m/s}^2)$$

23.10. Natural Frequency of Free Transverse Vibrations of a Shaft Fixed at Both Ends Carrying a Uniformly Distributed Load

Consider a shaft *AB* fixed at both ends and carrying a uniformly distributed load of *w* per unit length as shown in Fig. 23.10.

We know that the static deflection at a distance *x* from *A* is given by

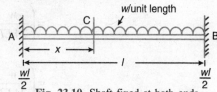

Fig. 23.10. Shaft fixed at both ends carrying a uniformly distributed load.

$$* \ y = \frac{w}{24\,EI}(x^4 + l^2x^2 - 2lx^3) \ \ldots (i)$$

---

*   It has been proved in books on 'Strength of Materials' that the bending moment at a distance *x* from *A* is

$$M = EI\frac{d^2y}{dx^2} = \frac{wl^2}{12} + \frac{wx^2}{2} - \frac{wlx}{2}$$

Integrating this equation,

$$EI\frac{dy}{dx} = \frac{wl^2}{12}x + \frac{wx^3}{2\times3} - \frac{wlx^2}{2\times2} + C_1$$

where C_1 is the constant of integration. We know that when $x = 0, \dfrac{dy}{dx} = 0$. Therefore $C_1 = 0$.

or

$$EI\frac{dy}{dx} = \frac{wl^2}{12}x + \frac{wx^3}{6} - \frac{wlx^2}{4}$$

Integrating the above equation,

$$EI.y = \frac{wl^2x^2}{12\times2} + \frac{wx^4}{6\times4} - \frac{wl}{4}\times\frac{x^3}{3} + C = \frac{wl^2x^2}{24} + \frac{wx^4}{24} - \frac{wlx^3}{12} + C_2$$

where C_2 is the constant of integration. We know that when $x = 0$, $y = 0$. Therefore $C_2 = 0$.

or

$$EI.y = \frac{w}{24}(l^2x^2 + x^4 - 2lx^3)$$

or

$$y = \frac{w}{24\,EI}(x^4 + l^2x^2 - 2lx^3)$$

Integrating the above equation within limits from 0 to l,

$$\int_0^l y \, dx = \frac{w}{24 \, EI} \int_0^l (x^4 + l^2 x^2 - 2l \, x^3) \, dx$$

$$= \frac{w}{24 \, EI} \left[\frac{x^5}{5} + \frac{l^2 x^3}{3} - \frac{2l \, x^4}{4} \right]_0^l = \frac{w}{24 \, EI} \left[\frac{l^5}{5} + \frac{l^5}{3} - \frac{2l^5}{4} \right]$$

$$= \frac{w}{24 \, EI} \times \frac{l^5}{30} = \frac{wl^5}{720 \, EI}$$

Now integrating y^2 within the limits from 0 to l,

$$\int_0^l y^2 \, dx = \left(\frac{w}{24 \, EI} \right)^2 \int_0^l (x^4 + l^2 x^2 - 2l \, x^3)^2 \, dx$$

$$= \left(\frac{w}{24 \, EI} \right)^2 \int_0^l (x^8 + l^4 x^4 + 4l^2 x^6 + 2l^2 x^6 - 4l \, x^7 - 2l^3 x^5) \, dx$$

$$= \left(\frac{w}{24 \, EI} \right)^2 \int_0^l (x^8 + l^4 x^4 + 6l^2 x^6 + 4l \, x^7 - 2l^3 x^5) \, dx$$

$$= \left(\frac{w}{24 \, EI} \right)^2 \left[\frac{x^9}{9} + \frac{l^4 x^5}{5} + \frac{6l^2 x^7}{7} - \frac{4l \, x^8}{8} - \frac{2l^3 x^6}{6} \right]_0^l$$

$$= \left(\frac{w}{24 \, EI} \right)^2 \left[\frac{l^9}{9} + \frac{l^9}{5} + \frac{6l^9}{7} - \frac{4l^9}{8} - \frac{2l^9}{6} \right] = \left(\frac{w}{24 \, EI} \right)^2 \frac{l^9}{630}$$

We know that

$$\omega^2 = \frac{g \int_0^l y \, dx}{\int_0^l y^2 \, dx} = g \times \frac{wl^5}{720 \, EI} \times \frac{(24 \, EI)^2 \times 630}{w^2 l^9} = \frac{504 \, EIg}{wl^4}$$

$$\therefore \qquad \omega = \sqrt{\frac{504 \, EIg}{wl^4}}$$

and natural frequency,

$$f_n = \frac{\omega}{2\pi} = \frac{1}{2\pi} \sqrt{\frac{504 \, EIg}{wl^4}} = 3.573 \sqrt{\frac{EI \, g}{wl^4}}$$

Since the static deflection of a shaft fixed at both ends and carrying a uniformly distributed load is

$$\delta_S = \frac{wl^4}{384 \, EI} \qquad \text{or} \qquad \frac{EI}{wl^4} = \frac{1}{384 \, \delta_S}$$

$$\therefore \qquad f_n = 3.573 \sqrt{\frac{g}{384 \, \delta_S}} = \frac{0.571}{\sqrt{\delta_S}} \text{ Hz} \qquad \dots \text{(Substituting, } g = 9.81 \text{ m/s}^2\text{)}$$

23.11. Natural Frequency of Free Transverse Vibrations For a Shaft Subjected to a Number of Point Loads

Consider a shaft AB of negligible mass loaded with point loads W_1, W_2, W_3 and W_4 etc. in newtons, as shown in Fig. 23.11. Let m_1, m_2, m_3 and m_4 etc. be the corresponding masses in kg. The natural frequency of such a shaft may be found out by the following two methods :

1. *Energy (or Rayleigh's) method*

Let y_1, y_2, y_3, y_4 etc. be total deflection under loads W_1, W_2, W_3 and W_4 etc. as shown in Fig. 23.11.

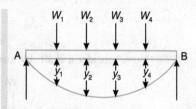

Fig. 23.11. Shaft carrying a number of point loads.

We know that maximum potential energy

$$= \frac{1}{2} \times m_1.g.y_1 + \frac{1}{2} \times m_2.g.y_2 + \frac{1}{2} m_3.g.y_3 + \frac{1}{2} \times m_4.g.y_4 + ...$$

$$= \frac{1}{2} \Sigma m.g.y$$

and maximum kinetic energy

$$= \frac{1}{2} \times m_1 (\omega.y_1)^2 + \frac{1}{2} \times m_2 (\omega.y_2)^2 + \frac{1}{2} \times m_3 (\omega.y_3)^2 + \frac{1}{2} \times m_4 (\omega.y_4)^2 + ...$$

$$= \frac{1}{2} \times \omega^2 \left[m_1 (y_1)^2 + m_2 (y_2)^2 + m_3 (y_3)^2 + m_4 (y_4)^2 + ... \right]$$

$$= \frac{1}{2} \times \omega^2 \Sigma m.y^2 \qquad \qquad ... (\text{where } \omega = \text{Circular frequency of vibration})$$

Equating the maximum kinetic energy to the maximum potential energy, we have

$$\frac{1}{2} \times \omega^2 \Sigma m.y^2 = \frac{1}{2} \Sigma m.g.y$$

∴ $$\omega^2 = \frac{\Sigma m.g.y}{\Sigma m.y^2} = \frac{g \Sigma m.y}{\Sigma m.y^2} \qquad \text{or} \qquad \omega = \sqrt{\frac{g \Sigma m.y}{\Sigma m.y^2}}$$

∴ Natural frequency of transverse vibration,

$$f_n = \frac{\omega}{2\pi} = \frac{1}{2\pi} \sqrt{\frac{g \Sigma m.y}{\Sigma m.y^2}}$$

2. *Dunkerley's method*

The natural frequency of transverse vibration for a shaft carrying a number of point loads and uniformly distributed load is obtained from Dunkerley's empirical formula. According to this

$$\frac{1}{(f_n)^2} = \frac{1}{(f_{n1})^2} + \frac{1}{(f_{n2})^2} + \frac{1}{(f_{n3})^2} + ... + \frac{1}{(f_{ns})^2}$$

where f_n = Natural frequency of transverse vibration of the shaft carrying point loads and uniformly distributed load.

f_{n1}, f_{n2}, f_{n3}, etc. = Natural frequency of transverse vibration of each point load.

f_{ns} = Natural frequency of transverse vibration of the uniformly distributed load (or due to the mass of the shaft).

Now, consider a shaft AB loaded as shown in Fig. 23.12.

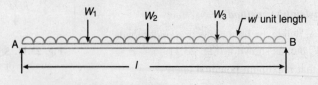

Fig. 23.12. Shaft carrying a number of point loads and a uniformly distributed load.

Let $\delta_1, \delta_2, \delta_3$, etc. = Static deflection due to the load W_1, W_2, W_3 etc. when considered separately.

δ_S = Static deflection due to the uniformly distributed load or due to the mass of the shaft.

We know that natural frequency of transverse vibration due to load W_1,

$$f_{n_1} = \frac{0.4985}{\sqrt{\delta_1}} \text{ Hz}$$

Similarly, natural frequency of transverse vibration due to load W_2,

$$f_{n_2} = \frac{0.4985}{\sqrt{\delta_2}} \text{ Hz}$$

and, natural frequency of transverse vibration due to load W_3,

$$f_{n_3} = \frac{0.4985}{\sqrt{\delta_3}} \text{ Hz}$$

Also natural frequency of transverse vibration due to uniformly distributed load or weight of the shaft,

$$f_{ns} = \frac{0.5615}{\sqrt{\delta_S}} \text{ Hz}$$

Suspension spring of an automobile.

Note : This picture is given as additional information.

Therefore, according to Dunkerley's empirical formula, the natural frequency of the whole system,

$$\frac{1}{(f_n)^2} = \frac{1}{(f_{n1})^2} + \frac{1}{(f_{n2})^2} + \frac{1}{(f_{n3})^3} + \ldots + \frac{1}{(f_{ns})^2}$$

$$= \frac{\delta_1}{(0.4985)^2} + \frac{\delta_2}{(0.4985)^2} + \frac{\delta_3}{(0.4985)^2} + \ldots + \frac{\delta_S}{(0.5615)^2}$$

$$= \frac{1}{(0.4985)^2}\left[\delta_1 + \delta_2 + \delta_3 + \ldots + \frac{\delta_S}{1.27}\right]$$

or
$$f_n = \frac{0.4985}{\sqrt{\delta_1 + \delta_2 + \delta_3 + ... + \dfrac{\delta_S}{1.27}}} \text{ Hz}$$

Notes : 1. When there is no uniformly distributed load or mass of the shaft is negligible, then $\delta_S = 0$.

∴
$$f_n = \frac{0.4985}{\sqrt{\delta_1 + \delta_2 + \delta_3 + ...}} \text{ Hz}$$

2. The value of $\delta_1, \delta_2, \delta_3$ etc. for a simply supported shaft may be obtained from the relation

$$\delta = \frac{W a^2 b^2}{3 E I l}$$

where
δ = Static deflection due to load W,

a and b = Distances of the load from the ends,

E = Young's modulus for the material of the shaft,

I = Moment of inertia of the shaft, and

l = Total length of the shaft.

Example 23.4. *A shaft 50 mm diameter and 3 metres long is simply supported at the ends and carries three loads of 1000 N, 1500 N and 750 N at 1 m, 2 m and 2.5 m from the left support. The Young's modulus for shaft material is 200 GN/m². Find the frequency of transverse vibration.*

Solution. Given : $d = 50$ mm $= 0.05$ m ; $l = 3$ m, $W_1 = 1000$ N ; $W_2 = 1500$ N ; $W_3 = 750$ N; $E = 200$ GN/m² $= 200 \times 10^9$ N/m²

The shaft carrying the loads is shown in Fig. 23.13

We know that moment of inertia of the shaft,

$$I = \frac{\pi}{64} \times d^4 = \frac{\pi}{64} (0.05)^4 = 0.307 \times 10^{-6} \text{ m}^4$$

and the static deflection due to a point load W,

$$\delta = \frac{W a^2 b^2}{3 E I l}$$

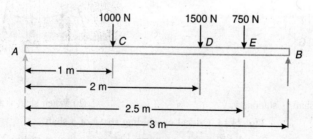

Fig. 23.13

∴ Static deflection due to a load of 1000 N,

$$\delta_1 = \frac{1000 \times 1^2 \times 2^2}{3 \times 200 \times 10^9 \times 0.307 \times 10^{-6} \times 3} = 7.24 \times 10^{-3} \text{ m}$$

... (Here $a = 1$ m, and $b = 2$ m)

Similarly, static deflection due to a load of 1500 N,

$$\delta_2 = \frac{1500 \times 2^2 \times 1^2}{3 \times 200 \times 10^9 \times 0.307 \times 10^{-6} \times 3} = 10.86 \times 10^{-3} \text{ m}$$

$\qquad$ ... (Here $a = 2$ m, and $b = 1$ m)

and static deflection due to a load of 750 N,

$$\delta_3 = \frac{750(2.5)^2 (0.5)^2}{3 \times 200 \times 10^9 \times 0.307 \times 10^{-6} \times 3} = 2.12 \times 10^{-3} \text{ m}$$

$\qquad$ ... (Here $a = 2.5$ m, and $b = 0.5$ m)

We know that frequency of transverse vibration,

$$f_n = \frac{0.4985}{\sqrt{\delta_1 + \delta_2 + \delta_3}} = \frac{0.4985}{\sqrt{7.24 \times 10^{-3} + 10.86 \times 10^{-3} + 2.12 \times 10^{-3}}}$$

$$= \frac{0.4985}{0.1422} = 3.5 \text{ Hz Ans.}$$

23.12. Critical or Whirling Speed of a Shaft

In actual practice, a rotating shaft carries different mountings and accessories in the form of gears, pulleys, etc. When the gears or pulleys are put on the shaft, the centre of gravity of the pulley or gear does not coincide with the centre line of the bearings or with the axis of the shaft, when the shaft is stationary. This means that the centre of gravity of the pulley or gear is at a certain distance from the axis of rotation and due to this, the shaft is subjected to centrifugal force. This force will bent the shaft which will further increase the distance of centre of gravity of the pulley or gear from the axis of rotation. This correspondingly increases the value of centrifugal force, which further increases the distance of centre of gravity from the axis of rotation. This effect is cumulative and ultimately the shaft fails. The bending of shaft not only depends upon the value of eccentricity (distance between centre of gravity of the pulley and the axis of rotation) but also depends upon the speed at which the shaft rotates.

The speed at which the shaft runs so that the additional deflection of the shaft from the axis of rotation becomes infinite, is known as *critical* or *whirling speed.*

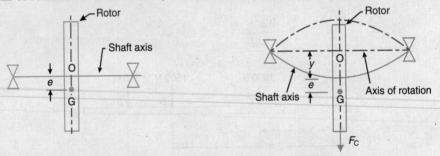

(a) When shaft is stationary. $\qquad\qquad$ (b) When shaft is rotating.

Fig. 23.14. Critical or whirling speed of a shaft.

Consider a shaft of negligible mass carrying a rotor, as shown in Fig.23.14 (a). The point O is on the shaft axis and G is the centre of gravity of the rotor. When the shaft is stationary, the centre line of the bearing and the axis of the shaft coincides. Fig. 23.14 (b) shows the shaft when rotating about the axis of rotation at a uniform speed of ω rad/s.

$\qquad$ Let $\qquad\qquad\qquad m =$ Mass of the rotor,

$\qquad\qquad\qquad\qquad e =$ Initial distance of centre of gravity of the rotor from the centre line of the bearing or shaft axis, when the shaft is stationary,

y = Additional deflection of centre of gravity of the rotor when the shaft starts rotating at ω rad/s, and

s = Stiffness of the shaft *i.e.* the load required per unit deflection of the shaft.

Since the shaft is rotating at ω rad/s, therefore centrifugal force acting radially outwards through G causing the shaft to deflect is given by

$$F_C = m.\omega^2 (y + e)$$

The shaft behaves like a spring. Therefore the force resisting the deflection y,

$$= s.y$$

For the equilibrium position,

$$m.\omega^2 (y + e) = s.y$$

or $\qquad m.\omega^2.y + m.\omega^2.e = s.y \qquad$ or $\qquad y(s - m.\omega^2) = m.\omega^2.e$

$\therefore \qquad$
$$y = \frac{m.\omega^2.e}{s - m.\omega^2} = \frac{\omega^2.e}{s/m - \omega^2} \qquad \qquad \text{... (i)}$$

We know that circular frequency,

$$\omega_n = \sqrt{\frac{s}{m}} \qquad \text{or} \qquad y = \frac{\omega^2.e}{(\omega_n)^2 - \omega^2} \qquad \text{... [From equation (i)]}$$

A little consideration will show that when $\omega > \omega_n$, the value of y will be negative and the shaft deflects is the opposite direction as shown dotted in Fig 23.14 (b).

In order to have the value of y always positive, both *plus* and *minus* signs are taken.

$\therefore \qquad$
$$y = \pm \frac{\omega^2 e}{(\omega_n)^2 - \omega^2} = \frac{\pm e}{\left(\dfrac{\omega_n}{\omega}\right)^2 - 1} = \frac{\pm e}{\left(\dfrac{\omega_c}{\omega}\right)^2 - 1}$$

... (Substituting $\omega_n = \omega_c$)

We see from the above expression that when $\omega_n = \omega_c$, the value of y becomes infinite. Therefore ω_c is the **critical or whirling speed.**

$\therefore \qquad$ Critical or whirling speed,

$$\omega_c = \omega_n = \sqrt{\frac{s}{m}} = \sqrt{\frac{g}{\delta}} \text{ Hz} \qquad \qquad \cdots \left(\because \delta = \frac{m.g}{s} \right)$$

If N_c is the critical or whirling speed in r.p.s., then

$$2\pi N_c = \sqrt{\frac{g}{\delta}} \qquad \text{or} \qquad N_c = \frac{1}{2\pi}\sqrt{\frac{g}{\delta}} = \frac{0.4985}{\sqrt{\delta}} \text{r.p.s.}$$

where $\qquad \qquad \delta$ = Static deflection of the shaft in metres.

Hence the **critical or whirling speed is the same as the natural frequency of transverse vibration but its unit will be revolutions per second.**

Notes : 1. When the centre of gravity of the rotor lies between the centre line of the shaft and the centre line of the bearing, e is taken negative. On the other hand, if the centre of gravity of the rotor does not lie between the centre line of the shaft and the centre line of the bearing (as in the above article) the value of e is taken positive.

2. To determine the critical speed of a shaft which may be subjected to point loads, uniformly distributed load or combination of both, find the frequency of transverse vibration which is equal to critical speed of a shaft in r.p.s. The Dunkerley's method may be used for calculating the frequency.

3. A shaft supported is short bearings (or ball bearings) is assumed to be a simply supported shaft while the shaft supported in long bearings (or journal bearings) is assumed to have both ends fixed.

Example 23.5. *Calculate the whirling speed of a shaft 20 mm diameter and 0.6 m long carrying a mass of 1 kg at its mid-point. The density of the shaft material is 40 Mg/m³, and Young's modulus is 200 GN/m². Assume the shaft to be freely supported.*

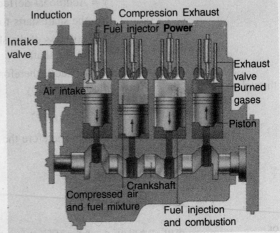

Induction   Compression Exhaust

Fuel injector **Power**

Intake valve

Air intake

Exhaust valve

Burned gases

Piston

Crankshaft

Compressed air and fuel mixture

Fuel injection and combustion

Diesel engines have several advantages over petrol engines. They do not need an electrical ignition system; they use cheaper fuel; and they do not need a carburettor. Diesel engines also have a greater ability to convert the stored energy in the fuel into mechanical energy, or work.

Note : This picture is given as additional information.

Solution. Given : $d = 20$ mm $= 0.02$ m ; $l = 0.6$ m ; $m_1 = 1$ kg ; $\rho = 40$ Mg/m³ $= 40 \times 10^6$ g/m³ $= 40 \times 10^3$ kg/m³ ; $E = 200$ GN/m² $= 200 \times 10^9$ N/m²

The shaft is shown in Fig. 23.15.

We know that moment of inertia of the shaft,

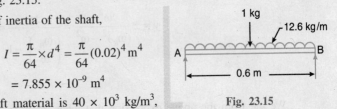

1 kg

12.6 kg/m

A ⟋⟋⟋⟋⟋⟋⟋⟋⟋⟋ B

0.6 m

$$I = \frac{\pi}{64} \times d^4 = \frac{\pi}{64} (0.02)^4 \, m^4$$

$$= 7.855 \times 10^{-9} \, m^4$$

Since the density of shaft material is 40×10^3 kg/m³, therefore mass of the shaft per metre length,

Fig. 23.15

$$m_S = \text{Area} \times \text{length} \times \text{density} = \frac{\pi}{4} (0.02)^2 \times 1 \times 40 \times 10^3 = 12.6 \text{ kg/m}$$

We know that static deflection due to 1 kg of mass at the centre,

$$\delta = \frac{Wl^3}{48 \, EI} = \frac{1 \times 9.81 (0.6)^3}{48 \times 200 \times 10^9 \times 7.855 \times 10^{-9}} = 28 \times 10^{-6} \text{ m}$$

and static deflection due to mass of the shaft,

$$\delta_S = \frac{5 \, wl^4}{384 \, EI} = \frac{5 \times 12.6 \times 9.81 (0.6)^4}{384 \times 200 \times 10^9 \times 7.855 \times 10^{-9}} = 0.133 \times 10^{-3} \text{ m}$$

∴ Frequency of transverse vibration,

$$f_n = \frac{0.4985}{\sqrt{\delta + \dfrac{\delta_S}{1.27}}} + \frac{0.4985}{\sqrt{28 \times 10^{-6} + \dfrac{0.133 \times 10^{-3}}{1.27}}}$$

$$= \frac{0.4985}{11.52 \times 10^{-3}} = 43.3 \text{ Hz}$$

Let $N_c =$ Whirling speed of a shaft.

We know that whirling speed of a shaft in r.p.s. is equal to the frequency of transverse vibration in Hz , therefore

$$N_c = 43.3 \text{ r.p.s.} = 43.3 \times 60 = 2598 \text{ r.p.m. } \textbf{Ans.}$$

Example 23.6. *A shaft 1.5 m long, supported in flexible bearings at the ends carries two wheels each of 50 kg mass. One wheel is situated at the centre of the shaft and the other at a distance of 375 mm from the centre towards left. The shaft is hollow of external diameter 75 mm and internal diameter 40 mm. The density of the shaft material is 7700 kg/m³ and its modulus of elasticity is 200 GN/m². Find the lowest whirling speed of the shaft, taking into account the mass of the shaft.*

Solution. $l = 1.5$ m ; $m_1 = m_2 = 50$ kg ;
$d_1 = 75$ mm $= 0.075$ m ; $d_2 = 40$ mm $= 0.04$ m ;
$\rho = 7700$ kg/m³ ; $E = 200$ GN/m² $= 200 \times 10^9$ N/m²

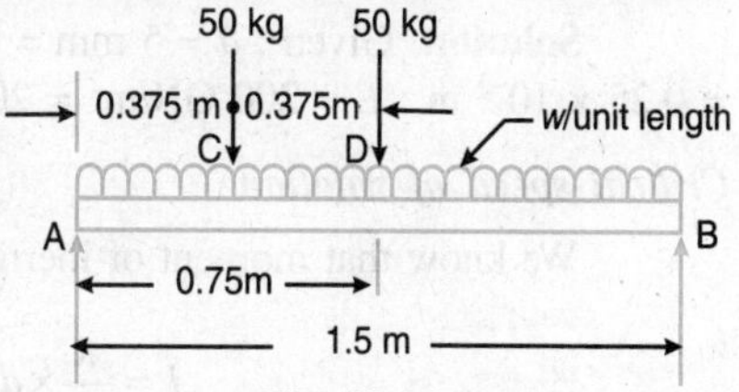

The shaft is shown in Fig. 23.16.

We know that moment of inertia of the shaft,

Fig. 23.16

$$I = \frac{\pi}{64}\left[(d_1)^4 - (d_2)^4\right] = \frac{\pi}{64}\left[(0.075)^4 - (0.04)^4\right] = 1.4 \times 10^{-6} \text{ m}^4$$

Since the density of shaft material is 7700 kg/m³, therefore mass of the shaft per metre length,

$$m_S = \text{Area} \times \text{length} \times \text{density}$$

$$= \frac{\pi}{4}\left[(0.075)^2 - (0.04)^2\right] \times 1 \times 7700 = 24.34 \text{ kg/m}$$

We know that the static deflection due to a load W

$$= \frac{Wa^2 b^2}{3\,EIl} = \frac{m.ga^2 b^2}{3\,EIl}$$

∴ Static deflection due to a mass of 50 kg at C,

$$\delta_1 = \frac{m_1 ga^2 b^2}{3\,EIl} = \frac{50 \times 9.81 (0.375)^2 (1.125)^2}{3 \times 200 \times 10^9 \times 1.4 \times 10^{-6} \times 1.5} = 70 \times 10^{-6} \text{ m}$$

... (Here $a = 0.375$ m, and $b = 1.125$ m)

Similarly, static deflection due to a mass of 50 kg at D

$$\delta_2 = \frac{m_2 ga^2 b^2}{3\,EIl} = \frac{50 \times 9.81 (0.75)^2 (0.75)^2}{3 \times 200 \times 10^9 \times 1.4 \times 10^{-6} \times 1.5} = 123 \times 10^{-6} \text{ m}$$

... (Here $a = b = 0.75$ m)

We know that static deflection due to uniformly distributed load or mass of the shaft,

$$\delta_S = \frac{5}{384} \times \frac{wl^4}{EI} = \frac{5}{384} \times \frac{24.34 \times 9.81(1.5)^4}{200 \times 10^9 \times 1.4 \times 10^{-6}} = 56 \times 10^{-6} \text{ m}$$

. . . (Substituting, $w = m_S \times g$)

We know that frequency of transverse vibration,

$$f_n = \frac{0.4985}{\sqrt{\delta_1 + \delta_2 + \dfrac{\delta_S}{1.27}}} = \frac{0.4985}{\sqrt{70 \times 10^{-6} + 123 \times 10^{-6} + \dfrac{56 \times 10^{-6}}{1.27}}} \text{ Hz}$$

$$= 32.4 \text{ Hz}$$

Since the whirling speed of shaft (N_c) in r.p.s. is equal to the frequency of transverse vibration in Hz, therefore

$$N_c = 32.4 \text{ r.p.s.} = 32.4 \times 60 = 1944 \text{ r.p.m. } \textbf{Ans.}$$

Example 23.7. *A vertical shaft of 5 mm diameter is 200 mm long and is supported in long bearings at its ends. A disc of mass 50 kg is attached to the centre of the shaft. Neglecting any increase in stiffness due to the attachment of the disc to the shaft, find the critical speed of rotation and the maximum bending stress when the shaft is rotating at 75% of the critical speed. The centre of the disc is 0.25 mm from the geometric axis of the shaft. E = 200 GN/m².*

Solution. Given : $d = 5$ mm $= 0.005$ m ; $l = 200$ mm $= 0.2$ m ; $m = 50$ kg ; $e = 0.25$ mm $= 0.25 \times 10^{-3}$ m ; $E = 200$ GN/m² $= 200 \times 10^9$ N/m²

Critical speed of rotation

We know that moment of inertia of the shaft,

$$I = \frac{\pi}{64} \times d^4 = \frac{\pi}{64}(0.005)^4 = 30.7 \times 10^{-12} \text{ m}^4$$

Since the shaft is supported in long bearings, it is assumed to be fixed at both ends. We know that the static deflection at the centre of the shaft due to a mass of 50 kg,

$$\delta = \frac{Wl^3}{192 \, EI} = \frac{50 \times 9.81(0.2)^3}{192 \times 200 \times 10^9 \times 30.7 \times 10^{-12}} = 3.33 \times 10^{-3} \text{ m}$$

. . . ($\because W = m.g$)

We know that critical speed of rotation (or natural frequency of transverse vibrations),

$$N_c = \frac{0.4985}{\sqrt{3.33 \times 10^{-3}}} = 8.64 \text{ r.p.s. } \textbf{Ans.}$$

Maximum bending stress

Let $\quad\sigma$ = Maximum bending stress in N/m², and

N = Speed of the shaft = 75% of critical speed = $0.75 \, N_c$ . . . (Given)

When the shaft starts rotating, the additional dynamic load (W_1) to which the shaft is subjected, may be obtained by using the bending equation,

$$\frac{M}{I} = \frac{\sigma}{y_1} \quad \text{or} \quad M = \frac{\sigma.I}{y_1}$$

We know that for a shaft fixed at both ends and carrying a point load (W_1) at the centre, the maximum bending moment

$$M = \frac{W_1.l}{8}$$

$\therefore$

$$\frac{W_1 l}{8} = \frac{\sigma \cdot I}{d/2} \qquad \qquad \dots(\because y_1 = d/2)$$

and

$$W_1 = \frac{\sigma.I}{d/2} \times \frac{8}{l} = \frac{\sigma \times 30.7 \times 10^{-12}}{0.005/2} \times \frac{8}{0.2} = 0.49 \times 10^{-6} \sigma \text{ N}$$

$\therefore$ Additional deflection due to load W_1,

$$y = \frac{W_1}{W} \times \delta = \frac{0.49 \times 10^{-6} \sigma}{50 \times 9.81} \times 3.33 \times 10^{-3} = 3.327 \times 10^{-12} \sigma$$

We know that

$$y = \frac{\pm e}{\left(\dfrac{\omega_c}{\omega}\right)^2 - 1} = \frac{\pm e}{\left(\dfrac{N_c}{N}\right)^2 - 1} \qquad \dots \text{(Substituting } \omega_c = N_c \text{ and } \omega = N \text{)}$$

$$3.327 \times 10^{-12} \sigma = \frac{\pm 0.25 \times 10^{-3}}{\left(\dfrac{N_c}{0.75 N_c}\right)^2 - 1} = \pm 0.32 \times 10^{-3}$$

$$\sigma = 0.32 \times 10^{-3} / 3.327 \times 10^{-12} = 0.0962 \times 10^9 \text{ N}/\text{m}^2 \quad \dots(\text{Taking} + \text{ve sign})$$

$$= 96.2 \times 10^6 \text{ N/m}^2 = 96.2 \text{ MN/m}^2 \text{ Ans.}$$

Example 23.8. *A vertical steel shaft 15 mm diameter is held in long bearings 1 metre apart and carries at its middle a disc of mass 15 kg. The eccentricity of the centre of gravity of the disc from the centre of the rotor is 0.30 mm.*

The modulus of elasticity for the shaft material is 200 GN/m² and the permissible stress is 70 MN/m². Determine : 1. The critical speed of the shaft and 2. The range of speed over which it is unsafe to run the shaft. Neglect the mass of the shaft.

[For a shaft with fixed end carrying a concentrated load (W) at the centre assume $\delta = \dfrac{Wl^3}{192 \, EI}$,

and $M = \dfrac{W.l}{8}$, *where* δ *and* M *are maximum deflection and bending moment respectively].*

Solution. Given : $d = 15$ mm $= 0.015$ m ; $l = 1$ m ; $m = 15$ kg ; $e = 0.3$ mm $= 0.3 \times 10^{-3}$ m ; $E = 200$ GN/m² $= 200 \times 10^9$ N/m² ; $\sigma = 70$ MN/m² $= 70 \times 10^6$ N/m²

We know that moment of inertia of the shaft,

$$I = \frac{\pi}{64} \times d^4 = \frac{\pi}{64} (0.015)^4 = 2.5 \times 10^{-9} \text{ m}^4$$

1. Critical speed of the shaft

Since the shaft is held in long bearings, therefore it is assumed to be fixed at both ends. We know that the static deflection at the centre of shaft,

$$\delta = \frac{Wl^3}{192 \, EI} = \frac{15 \times 9.81 \times 1^3}{192 \times 200 \times 10^9 \times 2.5 \times 10^{-9}} = 1.5 \times 10^{-3} \text{m} \qquad \dots(\because W = m.g)$$

∴ Natural frequency of transverse vibrations,

$$f_n = \frac{0.4985}{\sqrt{\delta}} = \frac{0.4985}{\sqrt{1.5 \times 10^{-3}}} = 12.88 \,\text{Hz}$$

We know that the critical speed of the shaft in r.p.s. is equal to the natural frequency of transverse vibrations in Hz.

∴ Critical speed of the shaft,

$$N_c = 12.88 \,\text{r.p.s.} = 12.88 \times 60 = 772.8 \,\text{r.p.m. Ans.}$$

2. Range of speed

Let N_1 and N_2 = Minimum and maximum speed respectively.

When the shaft starts rotating, the additional dynamic load ($W_1 = m_1.g$) to which the shaft is subjected may be obtained from the relation

$$\frac{M}{I} = \frac{\sigma}{y_1} \quad \text{or} \quad M = \frac{\sigma.I}{y_1}$$

Since $M = \frac{W_1.l}{8} = \frac{m_1.g.l}{8}$, and $y_1 = \frac{d}{2}$, therefore

$$\frac{m_1.g.l}{8} = \frac{\sigma.I}{d/2}$$

or

$$m_1 = \frac{8 \times 2 \times \sigma \times I}{d.g.l} = \frac{8 \times 2 \times 70 \times 10^6 \times 2.5 \times 10^{-9}}{0.015 \times 9.81 \times 1} = 19 \,\text{kg}$$

∴ Additional deflection due to load $W_1 = m_1 g$,

$$y = \frac{W_1}{W} \times \delta = \frac{m_1}{m} \times \delta = \frac{19}{15} \times 1.5 \times 10^{-3} = 1.9 \times 10^{-3} \,\text{m}$$

We know that,

$$y = \frac{\pm e}{\left(\dfrac{\omega_c}{\omega}\right)^2 - 1} \quad \text{or} \quad \pm \frac{y}{e} = \frac{1}{\left(\dfrac{N_c}{N}\right)^2 - 1}$$

... (Substituting, $\omega_c = N_c$, and $\omega = N$)

∴

$$\pm \frac{1.9 \times 10^{-3}}{0.3 \times 10^{-3}} = \frac{1}{\left(\dfrac{N_c}{N}\right)^2 - 1} \quad \text{or} \quad \left(\frac{N_c}{N}\right)^2 - 1 = \pm \frac{0.3}{1.9} = \pm 0.16$$

$$\left(\frac{N_c}{N}\right)^2 = 1 \pm 0.16 = 1.16 \quad \text{or} \quad 0.84$$

... (Taking first plus sign and then negative sign)

or

$$N = \frac{N_c}{\sqrt{1.16}} \quad \text{or} \quad \frac{N_c}{\sqrt{0.84}}$$

$$\therefore \quad N_1 = \frac{N_c}{\sqrt{1.16}} = \frac{772.8}{\sqrt{1.16}} = 718 \text{ r.p.m.}$$

and

$$N_2 = \frac{N_c}{\sqrt{0.84}} = \frac{772.8}{\sqrt{0.84}} = 843 \text{ r.p.m.}$$

Hence the range of speed is from 718 r.p.m. to 843 r.p.m. **Ans.**

23.13. Frequency of Free Damped Vibrations (Viscous Damping)

We have already discussed that the motion of a body is resisted by frictional forces. In vibrating systems, the effect of friction is referred to as damping. The damping provided by fluid resistance is known as *viscous damping*.

We have also discussed that in damped vibrations, the amplitude of the resulting vibration gradually diminishes. This is due to the reason that a certain amount of energy is always dissipated to overcome the frictional resistance. The resistance to the motion of the body is provided partly by the medium in which the vibration takes place and partly by the internal friction, and in some cases partly by a dash pot or other external damping device.

Consider a vibrating system, as shown in Fig. 23.17, in which a mass is suspended from one end of the spiral spring and the other end of which is fixed. A damper is provided between the mass and the rigid support.

Let
- m = Mass suspended from the spring,
- s = Stiffness of the spring,
- x = Displacement of the mass from the mean position at time t,
- δ = Static deflection of the spring
  - $= m.g/s$, and
- c = Damping coefficient or the damping force per unit velocity.

Since in viscous damping, it is assumed that the frictional resistance to the motion of the body is directly proportional to the speed of the movement, therefore

Damping force or frictional force on the mass acting in *opposite* direction to the motion of the mass

$$= c \times \frac{dx}{dt}$$

Accelerating force on the mass, acting *along* the motion of the mass

$$= m \times \frac{d^2 x}{dt^2}$$

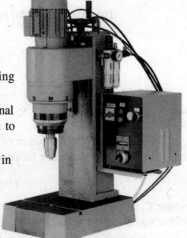

Fig. 23.17. Frequency of free damped vibrations.

Riveting Machine

Note : This picture is given as additional information.

and spring force on the mass, acting in *opposite* direction to the motion of the mass,

$$= s.x$$

Therefore the equation of motion becomes

$$m \times \frac{d^2x}{dt^2} = -\left(c \times \frac{dx}{dt} + s.x\right)$$

...(Negative sign indicates that the force opposes the motion)

or

$$m \times \frac{d^2x}{dt^2} + c \times \frac{dx}{dt} + s.x = 0$$

or

$$* \frac{d^2x}{dt^2} + \frac{c}{m} \times \frac{dx}{dt} + \frac{s}{m} \times x = 0$$

This is a differential equation of the second order. Assuming a solution of the form $x = e^{k\,t}$ where k is a constant to be determined. Now the above differential equation reduces to

$$k^2.e^{kt} + \frac{c}{m} \times k.e^{kt} + \frac{s}{m} \times e^{kt} = 0 \qquad \cdots \left[\because \frac{dx}{dt} = ke^{kt}, \text{ and } \frac{d^2x}{dt^2} = k^2.e^{kt}\right]$$

or

$$k^2 + \frac{c}{m} \times k + \frac{s}{m} = 0 \qquad \qquad \cdots (i)$$

and

$$k = \frac{-\dfrac{c}{m} \pm \sqrt{\left(\dfrac{c}{m}\right)^2 - 4 \times \dfrac{s}{m}}}{2}$$

$$= -\frac{c}{2m} \pm \sqrt{\left(\frac{c}{2m}\right)^2 - \frac{s}{m}}$$

∴   The two roots of the equation are

$$k_1 = -\frac{c}{2m} + \sqrt{\left(\frac{c}{2m}\right)^2 - \frac{s}{m}}$$

and

$$k_2 = -\frac{c}{2m} - \sqrt{\left(\frac{c}{2m}\right)^2 - \frac{s}{m}}$$

The most general solution of the differential equation (*i*) with its right hand side equal to zero has only complementary function and it is given by

$$x = C_1 e^{k_1 t} + C_2 e^{k_2 t} \qquad \qquad \cdots (ii)$$

where C_1 and C_2 are two arbitrary constants which are to be determined from the initial conditions of the motion of the mass.

It may be noted that the roots k_1 and k_2 may be real, complex conjugate (imaginary) or equal. We shall now discuss these three cases as below :

---

*   A system described by this equation is said to be a single degree of freedom harmonic oscillator with viscous damping.

1. *When the roots are real (overdamping)*

If $\left(\dfrac{c}{2m}\right)^2 > \dfrac{s}{m}$, then the roots k_1 and k_2 are real but negative. This is a case of *overdamping*

or *large damping* and the mass moves slowly to the equilibrium position. This motion is known as *aperiodic*. When the roots are real, the most general solution of the differential equation is

$$x = C_1 e^{k_1 t} + C_2 e^{k_2 t}$$

$$= C_1 e^{\left[-\frac{c}{2m} + \sqrt{\left(\frac{c}{2m}\right)^2 - \frac{s}{m}}\right]t} + C_2 e^{\left[-\frac{c}{2m} - \sqrt{\left(\frac{c}{2m}\right)^2 - \frac{s}{m}}\right]t}$$

Note : In actual practice, the overdamped vibrations are avoided.

2. *When the roots are complex conjugate (underdamping)*

If $\dfrac{s}{m} > \left(\dfrac{c}{2m}\right)^2$, then the radical (*i.e.* the term under the square root) becomes negative.

The two roots k_1 and k_2 are then known as complex conjugate. This is a most practical case of damping and it is known as *underdamping* or *small damping*. The two roots are

$$k_1 = -\frac{c}{2m} + i\sqrt{\frac{s}{m} - \left(\frac{c}{2m}\right)^2}$$

and

$$k_2 = -\frac{c}{2m} - i\sqrt{\frac{s}{m} - \left(\frac{c}{2m}\right)^2}$$

where i is a Greek letter known as iota and its value is $\sqrt{-1}$. For the sake of mathematical calculations, let

$$\frac{c}{2m} = a; \quad \frac{s}{m} = (\omega_n)^2; \quad \text{and} \quad \sqrt{\frac{s}{m} - \left(\frac{c}{2m}\right)^2} = \omega_d = \sqrt{(\omega_n)^2 - a^2}$$

Therefore the two roots may be written as

$$k_1 = -a + i\omega_d \; ; \quad \text{and} \quad k_2 = -a - i\omega_d$$

We know that the general solution of a differential equation is

$$x = C_1 e^{k_1 t} + C_2 e^{k_2 t} = C_1 e^{(-a + i\omega_d)t} + C_2 e^{(-a - i\omega_d)t}$$

$$= e^{-at}(C_1 e^{i\omega_d t} + C_2 e^{-i\omega_d t}) \quad \text{...(Using } e^{m+n} = e^m \times e^n) \text{ ...(}iii\text{)}$$

Now according to Euler's theorem

$$e^{+i\theta} = \cos\theta + i\sin\theta \; ; \text{ and } e^{-i\theta} = \cos\theta - i\sin\theta$$

Therefore the equation (*iii*) may be written as

$$x = e^{-at}\left[C_1(\cos\omega_d t + i\sin\omega_d t) + C_2(\cos\omega_d t - i\sin\omega_d t)\right]$$

$$= e^{-at}\left[(C_1 + C_2)\cos\omega_d t + i(C_1 - C_2)\sin\omega_d t)\right]$$

Let

$$C_1 + C_2 = A, \quad \text{and} \quad i(C_1 - C_2) = B$$

$\therefore$ $\qquad$ $x = e^{-at}(A\cos\omega_d t + B\sin\omega_d t)$ $\qquad$ ... (iv)

Again, let $A = C\cos\theta$, and $B = C\sin\theta$, therefore

$$C = \sqrt{A^2 + B^2} \text{ , and } \tan\theta = \frac{B}{A}$$

Now the equation (iv) becomes

$$x = e^{-at}(C\cos\theta\cos\omega_d t + C\sin\theta\sin\omega_d t)$$

$$= Ce^{-at}\cos(\omega_d t - \theta) \qquad \text{... (v)}$$

If t is measured from the instant at which the mass m is released after an initial displacement A, then

$$A = C\cos\theta \qquad \text{... [Substituting } x = A \text{ and } t = 0 \text{ in equation (v)]}$$

and $\qquad$ when $\theta = 0$, then $A = C$

$\therefore$ The equation (v) may be written as

$$x = Ae^{-at}\cos\omega_d t \qquad \text{... (vi)}$$

where $\qquad$ $\omega_d = \sqrt{\dfrac{s}{m} - \left(\dfrac{c}{2m}\right)^2} = \sqrt{(\omega_n)^2 - a^2}$; and $a = \dfrac{c}{2m}$

We see from equation (vi), that the motion of the mass is simple harmonic whose circular damped frequency is ω_d and the amplitude is Ae^{-at} which diminishes exponentially with time as shown in Fig. 23.18. Though the mass eventually returns to its equilibrium position because of its inertia, yet it overshoots and the oscillations may take some considerable time to die away.

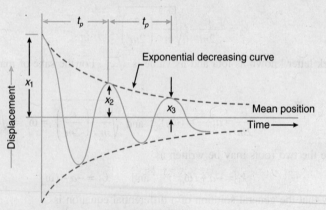

Fig. 23.18. Underdamping or small damping.

We know that the periodic time of vibration,

$$t_p = \frac{2\pi}{\omega_d} = \frac{2\pi}{\sqrt{\dfrac{s}{m} - \left(\dfrac{c}{2m}\right)^2}} = \frac{2\pi}{\sqrt{(\omega_n)^2 - a^2}}$$

and frequency of damped vibration,

$$f_d = \frac{1}{t_p} = \frac{\omega_d}{2\pi} = \frac{1}{2\pi}\sqrt{(\omega_n)^2 - a^2} = \frac{1}{2\pi}\sqrt{\dfrac{s}{m} - \left(\dfrac{c}{2m}\right)^2} \qquad \text{... (vii)}$$

Note : When no damper is provided in the system, then $c = 0$. Therefore the frequency of the undamped vibration,

$$f_n = \frac{1}{2\pi}\sqrt{\frac{s}{m}}$$

... [Substituting $c = 0$, in equation (*vii*)]

It is the same as discussed under free vibrations.

3. *When the roots are equal (critical damping)*

If $\left(\dfrac{c}{2m}\right)^2 = \dfrac{s}{m}$, then the radical becomes zero and the two roots k_1 and k_2 are equal. This is a case of **critical damping.** In other words, the critical damping is said to occur when frequency of damped vibration (f_d) is zero (*i.e.* motion is aperiodic). This type of damping is also avoided because the mass moves back rapidly to its equilibrium position, in the shortest possible time.

In a disc brake, hydraulic pressure forces friction pads to squeeze a metal disc that rotates on the same axle as the wheel. Here a disc brake is being tested.

Note : This picture is given as additional information.

For critical damping, equation (*ii*) may be written as

$$x = (C_1 + C_2)\, e^{-\frac{c}{2m}t} = (C_1 + C_2)\, e^{-\omega_n t} \qquad \cdots \left[\because \frac{c}{2m} = \sqrt{\frac{s}{m}} = \omega_n\right]$$

Thus the motion is again aperiodic. The critical damping coefficient (c_c) may be obtained by substituting c_c for c in the condition for critical damping, *i.e.*

$$\left(\frac{c_c}{2m}\right)^2 = \frac{s}{m} \qquad \text{or} \qquad c_c = 2m\sqrt{\frac{s}{m}} = 2m \times \omega_n$$

The critical damping coefficient is the amount of damping required for a system to be critically damped.

23.14. Damping Factor or Damping Ratio

The ratio of the actual damping coefficient (c) to the critical damping coefficient (c_c) is known as *damping factor* or *damping ratio.* Mathematically,

Damping factor $= \dfrac{c}{c_c} = \dfrac{c}{2m.\omega_n}$ ... $(\because c_c = 2\pi.\omega_n)$

The damping factor is the measure of the relative amount of damping in the existing system with that necessary for the critical damped system.

23.15. Logarithmic Decrement

It is defined as the natural logarithm of the amplitude reduction factor. The amplitude reduction factor is the ratio of any two successive amplitudes on the same side of the mean position.

If x_1 and x_2 are successive values of the amplitude on the same side of the mean position, as shown in Fig. 23.18, then amplitude reduction factor,

$$\frac{x_1}{x_2} = \frac{Ae^{-at}}{Ae^{-a(t+t_p)}} = e^{at_p} = \text{constant}$$

where t_p is the period of forced oscillation or the time difference between two consecutive amplitudes. As per definition, logarithmic decrement,

$$\delta = \log\left(\frac{x_1}{x_2}\right) = \log e^{at_p}$$

or

$$\delta = \log_e\left(\frac{x_1}{x_2}\right) = a.t_p = a \times \frac{2\pi}{\omega_d} = \frac{a \times 2\pi}{\sqrt{(\omega_n)^2 - a^2}}$$

$$\ldots \left[\because \omega_d = \sqrt{(\omega_n)^2 - a^2}\right]$$

$$= \frac{\dfrac{c}{2m} \times 2\pi}{\sqrt{(\omega_n)^2 - \left(\dfrac{c}{2m}\right)^2}} \qquad \ldots \left(\because a = \frac{c}{2m}\right)$$

$$= \frac{\dfrac{c}{2m} \times 2\pi}{\omega_n \sqrt{1 - \left(\dfrac{c}{2m.\omega_n}\right)^2}} = \frac{c \times 2\pi}{c_c \sqrt{1 - \left(\dfrac{c}{c_c}\right)^2}} \qquad \ldots (\because c_c = 2m.\omega_n)$$

$$= \frac{2\pi \times c}{\sqrt{(c_c)^2 - c^2}}$$

In general, amplitude reduction factor,

$$\frac{x_1}{x_2} = \frac{x_2}{x_3} = \frac{x_3}{x_4} = \ldots = \frac{x_n}{x_{n+1}} = e^{at_p} = \text{constant}$$

∴ Logarithmic decrement,

$$\delta = \log_e\left(\frac{x_n}{x_{n+1}}\right) = a.t_p = \frac{2\pi \times c}{\sqrt{(c_c)^2 - c^2}}$$

Example 23.9. *A vibrating system consists of a mass of 200 kg, a spring of stiffness 80 N/mm and a damper with damping coefficient of 800 N/m/s. Determine the frequency of vibration of the system.*

Solution. Given : $m = 200$ kg ; $s = 80$ N/mm $= 80 \times 10^3$ N/m ; $c = 800$ N/m/s

We know that circular frequency of undamped vibrations,

$$\omega_n = \sqrt{\frac{s}{m}} = \sqrt{\frac{80 \times 10^3}{200}} = 20 \text{ rad/s}$$

and circular frequency of damped vibrations,

$$\omega_d = \sqrt{(\omega_n)^2 - a^2} = \sqrt{(\omega_n)^2 - (c/2m)^2} \qquad \ldots(\because \ a = c/2m)$$

$$= \sqrt{(20)^2 - (800/2 \times 200)^2} = 19.9 \ \text{rad/s}$$

∴ Frequency of vibration of the system,

$$f_d = \omega_d / 2\pi = 19.9/2\pi = 3.17 \ \text{Hz} \ \textbf{Ans.}$$

Example 23.10. *The following data are given for a vibratory system with viscous damping:*

Mass = 2.5 kg ; spring constant = 3 N/mm and the amplitude decreases to 0.25 of the initial value after five consecutive cycles.

Determine the damping coefficient of the damper in the system.

Solution. Given : $m = 2.5$ kg ; $s = 3$ N/mm = 3000 N/m ; $x_6 = 0.25 \, x_1$

We know that natural circular frequency of vibration,

$$\omega_n = \sqrt{\frac{s}{m}} = \sqrt{\frac{3000}{2.5}} = 34.64 \ \text{rad/s}$$

Let c = Damping coefficient of the damper in N/m/s,

x_1 = Initial amplitude, and

x_6 = Final amplitude after five consecutive cycles = $0.25 \, x_1$ ...(Given)

We know that

$$\frac{x_1}{x_2} = \frac{x_2}{x_3} = \frac{x_3}{x_4} = \frac{x_4}{x_5} = \frac{x_5}{x_6}$$

or

$$\frac{x_1}{x_6} = \frac{x_1}{x_2} \times \frac{x_2}{x_3} \times \frac{x_3}{x_4} \times \frac{x_4}{x_5} \times \frac{x_5}{x_6} = \left(\frac{x_1}{x_2}\right)^5$$

∴

$$\frac{x_1}{x_2} = \left(\frac{x_1}{x_6}\right)^{1/5} = \left(\frac{x_1}{0.25 \, x_1}\right)^{1/5} = (4)^{1/5} = 1.32$$

We know that

$$\log_e\left(\frac{x_1}{x_2}\right) = a \times \frac{2\pi}{\sqrt{(\omega_n)^2 - a^2}}$$

$$\log_e(1.32) = a \times \frac{2\pi}{\sqrt{(34.64)^2 - a^2}} \qquad \text{or} \qquad 0.2776 = \frac{a \times 2\pi}{\sqrt{1200 - a^2}}$$

Squaring both sides,

$$0.077 = \frac{39.5 \, a^2}{1200 - a^2} \qquad \text{or} \qquad 92.4 - 0.077 \, a^2 = 39.5 \, a^2$$

∴ $a^2 = 2.335$ or $a = 1.53$

We know that $a = c/2m$ or $c = a \times 2m = 1.53 \times 2 \times 2.5 = 7.65$ N/m/s **Ans.**

Example 23.11. *An instrument vibrates with a frequency of 1 Hz when there is no damping. When the damping is provided, the frequency of damped vibrations was observed to be 0.9 Hz. Find 1. the damping factor, and 2. logarithmic decrement.*

Solution. Given : $f_n = 1$ Hz ; $f_d = 0.9$ Hz

1. *Damping factor*

Guitar

Let m = Mass of the instrument in kg,

     c = Damping coefficient or damping force per unit velocity in N/m/s, and

     c_c = Critical damping coefficient in N/m/s.

We know that natural circular frequency of undamped vibrations,

$$\omega_n = 2\pi \times f_n = 2\pi \times 1 = 6.284 \text{ rad/s}$$

and circular frequency of damped vibrations,

$$\omega_d = 2\pi \times f_d = 2\pi \times 0.9 = 5.66 \text{ rad/s}$$

We also know that circular frequency of damped vibrations (ω_d),

$$5.66 = \sqrt{(\omega_n)^2 - a^2} = \sqrt{(6.284)^2 - a^2}$$

Squaring both sides,

$$(5.66)^2 = (6.284)^2 - a^2 \text{ or } 32 = 39.5 - a^2$$

∴ $a^2 = 7.5$ or $a = 2.74$

We know that, $a = c/2m$ or $c = a \times 2m = 2.74 \times 2m = 5.48 \ m$ N/m/s

and $c_c = 2m.\omega_n = 2m \times 6.284 = 12.568 \ m$ N/m/s

∴   Damping factor,

$$c/c_c = 5.48m/12.568m = 0.436 \text{ Ans.}$$

2. *Logarithmic decrement*

We know that logarithmic decrement,

$$\delta = \frac{2\pi c}{\sqrt{(c_c)^2 - c^2}} = \frac{2\pi \times 5.48 m}{\sqrt{(12.568 m)^2 - (5.48 m)^2}} = \frac{34.4}{11.3} = 3.04 \text{ Ans.}$$

Example 23.12. *The measurements on a mechanical vibrating system show that it has a mass of 8 kg and that the springs can be combined to give an equivalent spring of stiffness 5.4 N/mm. If the vibrating system have a dashpot attached which exerts a force of 40 N when the mass has a velocity of 1 m/s, find : 1. critical damping coefficient, 2. damping factor, 3. logarithmic decrement, and 4. ratio of two consecutive amplitudes.*

Solution. Given : $m = 8$ kg ; $s = 5.4$ N/mm = 5400 N/m

Since the force exerted by dashpot is 40 N, and the mass has a velocity of 1 m/s , therefore

Damping coefficient (actual),

$$c = 40 \text{ N/m/s}$$

1. *Critical damping coefficient*

We know that critical damping coefficient,

$$c_c = 2m.\omega_n = 2m \times \sqrt{\frac{s}{m}} = 2 \times 8 \sqrt{\frac{5400}{8}} = 416 \text{ N/m/s Ans.}$$

2. *Damping factor*

We know that damping factor

$$= \frac{c}{c_c} = \frac{40}{416} = 0.096 \text{ Ans.}$$

3. *Logarithmic decrement*

We know that logarithmic decrement,

$$\delta = \frac{2\pi c}{\sqrt{(c_c)^2 - c^2}} = \frac{2\pi \times 40}{\sqrt{(416)^2 - (40)^2}} = 0.6 \text{ Ans.}$$

4. *Ratio of two consecutive amplitudes*

Let x_n and x_{n+1} = Magnitude of two consecutive amplitudes,

We know that logarithmic decrement,

$$\delta = \log_e \left[\frac{x_n}{x_{n+1}} \right] \text{ or } \frac{x_n}{x_{n+1}} = e^\delta = (2.7)^{0.6} = 1.82 \text{ Ans.}$$

Example 23.13. *A mass suspended from a helical spring vibrates in a viscous fluid medium whose resistance varies directly with the speed. It is observed that the frequency of damped vibration is 90 per minute and that the amplitude decreases to 20 % of its initial value in one complete vibration. Find the frequency of the free undamped vibration of the system.*

Helical spring suspension of a two-wheeler.

Note : This picture is given as additional information.

Solution. Given : f_d = 90/min = 90/60 = 1.5 Hz

We know that time period,

$$t_p = 1/f_d = 1/1.5 = 0.67 \text{ s}$$

Let x_1 = Initial amplitude, and

x_2 = Final amplitude after one complete vibration

$$= 20\% \; x_1 = 0.2 \; x_1 \qquad \qquad \dots \text{(Given)}$$

We know that

$$\log_e \left(\frac{x_1}{x_2} \right) = a.t_p \quad \text{ or } \quad \log_e \left(\frac{x_1}{0.2 \, x_1} \right) = a \times 0.67$$

∴ $\log_e 5 = 0.67 \, a$ or $1.61 = 0.67 \, a$ or $a = 2.4$ $\dots (\because \log_e 5 = 1.61)$

We also know that frequency of free damped vibration,

$$f_d = \frac{1}{2\pi}\sqrt{(\omega_n)^2 - a^2}$$

or $\qquad (\omega_n)^2 = (2\pi \times f_d)^2 + a^2 \qquad \qquad \text{... (By squaring and arranging)}$

$$= (2\pi \times 1.5)^2 + (2.4)^2 = 94.6$$

$\therefore \qquad \omega_n = 9.726 \text{ rad/s}$

We know that frequency of undamped vibration,

$$f_n = \frac{\omega_n}{2\pi} = \frac{9.726}{2\pi} = 1.55 \text{ Hz Ans.}$$

Example 23.14. *A coil of spring stiffness 4 N/mm supports vertically a mass of 20 kg at the free end. The motion is resisted by the oil dashpot. It is found that the amplitude at the beginning of the fourth cycle is 0.8 times the amplitude of the previous vibration. Determine the damping force per unit velocity. Also find the ratio of the frequency of damped and undamped vibrations.*

Solution. Given : $s = 4 \text{ N/mm} = 4000 \text{ N/m}$; $m = 20 \text{ kg}$

Damping force per unit velocity

Let $\qquad \qquad \qquad c$ = Damping force in newtons per unit velocity *i.e.* in N/m/s

$\qquad \qquad \qquad x_n$ = Amplitude at the beginning of the third cycle,

$\qquad \qquad \qquad x_{n+1}$ = Amplitude at the beginning of the fourth cycle = $0.8 \, x_n$

$\qquad \qquad \qquad \qquad \qquad \qquad \qquad \qquad \qquad \qquad \qquad \text{... (Given)}$

We know that natural circular frequency of motion,

$$\omega_n = \sqrt{\frac{s}{m}} = \sqrt{\frac{4000}{20}} = 14.14 \text{ rad/s}$$

and $\qquad \qquad \log_e\left(\dfrac{x_n}{x_n + 1}\right) = a \times \dfrac{2\pi}{\sqrt{(\omega_n)^2 - a^2}}$

or $\qquad \qquad \log_e\left(\dfrac{x_n}{0.8\, x_n}\right) = a \times \dfrac{2\pi}{\sqrt{(14.14)^2 - a^2}}$

$$\log_e 1.25 = a \times \frac{2\pi}{\sqrt{200 - a^2}} \qquad \text{or} \qquad 0.223 = a \times \frac{2\pi}{\sqrt{200 - a^2}}$$

Squaring both sides

$$0.05 = \frac{a^2 \times 4\pi^2}{200 - a^2} = \frac{39.5\, a^2}{200 - a^2}$$

$$0.05 \times 200 - 0.05\, a^2 = 39.5 a^2 \qquad \text{or} \qquad 39.55\, a^2 = 10$$

$\therefore \qquad \qquad \qquad a^2 = 10 / 39.55 = 0.25 \quad \text{or} \quad a = 0.5$

We know that $\qquad \qquad a = c / 2m$

$\therefore \qquad \qquad c = a \times 2m = 0.5 \times 2 \times 20 = 20 \text{ N/m/s Ans.}$

Ratio of the frequencies

Let $\qquad \qquad \qquad f_{n_1}$ = Frequency of damped vibrations = $\dfrac{\omega_d}{2\pi}$

$$f_{n2} = \text{Frequency of undamped vibrations} = \frac{\omega_n}{2\pi}$$

∴

$$\frac{f_{n1}}{f_{n2}} = \frac{\omega_d}{2\pi} \times \frac{2\pi}{\omega_n} = \frac{\omega_d}{\omega_n} = \sqrt{\frac{(\omega_n)^2 - a^2}{\omega_n}} = \sqrt{\frac{(14.14)^2 - (0.5)^2}{14.14}}$$

$$\dots \left(\because \omega_d = \sqrt{(\omega_n)^2 - a^2} \right)$$

$$= 0.999 \ \textbf{Ans.}$$

Example 23.15. *A machine of mass 75 kg is mounted on springs and is fitted with a dashpot to damp out vibrations. There are three springs each of stiffness 10 N/mm and it is found that the amplitude of vibration diminishes from 38.4 mm to 6.4 mm in two complete oscillations. Assuming that the damping force varies as the velocity, determine : 1. the resistance of the dashpot at unit velocity ; 2. the ratio of the frequency of the damped vibration to the frequency of the undamped vibration ; and 3. the periodic time of the damped vibration.*

Solution. Given : m = 75 kg ; s = 10 N/mm = 10×10^3 N/m ; x_1 = 38.4 mm = 0.0384 m ; x_3 = 6.4 mm = 0.0064 m

Since the stiffness of each spring is 10×10^3 N/m and there are 3 springs, therefore total stiffness,

$$s = 3 \times 10 \times 10^3 = 30 \times 10^3 \ \text{N/m}$$

We know that natural circular frequency of motion,

$$\omega_n = \sqrt{\frac{s}{m}} = \sqrt{\frac{30 \times 10^3}{75}} = 20 \ \text{rad/s}$$

1. Resistance of the dashpot at unit velocity

Let c = Resistance of the dashpot in newtons at unit velocity *i.e.* in N/m/s,

                    x_2 = Amplitude after one complete oscillation in metres, and

                    x_3 = Amplitude after two complete oscillations in metres.

We know that $\dfrac{x_1}{x_2} = \dfrac{x_2}{x_3}$

∴

$$\left(\frac{x_1}{x_2} \right)^2 = \frac{x_1}{x_3} \qquad \dots \left[\because \frac{x_1}{x_3} = \frac{x_1}{x_2} \times \frac{x_2}{x_3} = \frac{x_1}{x_2} \times \frac{x_1}{x_2} = \left(\frac{x_1}{x_2} \right)^2 \right]$$

or

$$\frac{x_1}{x_2} = \left(\frac{x_1}{x_3} \right)^{1/2} = \left(\frac{0.0384}{0.0064} \right)^{1/2} = 2.45$$

We also know that

$$\log_e \left(\frac{x_1}{x_2} \right) = a \times \frac{2\pi}{\sqrt{(\omega_n)^2 - a^2}}$$

$$\log_e 2.45 = a \times \frac{2\pi}{\sqrt{(20)^2 - a^2}}$$

$$0.8951 = \frac{a \times 2\pi}{\sqrt{400 - a^2}} \quad \text{or} \quad 0.8 = \frac{a^2 \times 39.5}{400 - a^2} \quad \text{... (Squaring both sides)}$$

$$\therefore \qquad a^2 = 7.94 \qquad \text{or} \quad a = 2.8$$

We know that $\qquad a = c / 2m$

$$\therefore \qquad c = a \times 2m = 2.8 \times 2 \times 75 = 420 \text{ N/m/s } \textbf{Ans.}$$

2. Ratio of the frequency of the damped vibration to the frequency of undamped vibration

Let $\qquad f_{n1}$ = Frequency of damped vibration = $\dfrac{\omega_d}{2\pi}$

$\qquad f_{n2}$ = Frequency of undamped vibration = $\dfrac{\omega_n}{2\pi}$

$$\therefore \qquad \frac{f_{n1}}{f_{n2}} = \frac{\omega_d}{2\pi} \times \frac{2\pi}{\omega_n} = \frac{\omega_d}{\omega_n} = \frac{\sqrt{(\omega_n)^2 - a^2}}{\omega_n} = \frac{\sqrt{(20)^2 - (2.8)^2}}{20} = 0.99 \textbf{ Ans.}$$

3. Periodic time of damped vibration

We know that periodic time of damped vibration

$$= \frac{2\pi}{\omega_d} = \frac{2\pi}{\sqrt{(\omega_n)^2 - a^2}} = \frac{2\pi}{\sqrt{(20)^2 - (2.8)^2}} = 0.32 \text{ s } \textbf{Ans.}$$

Example 23.16. *The mass of a single degree damped vibrating system is 7.5 kg and makes 24 free oscillations in 14 seconds when disturbed from its equilibrium position. The amplitude of vibration reduces to 0.25 of its initial value after five oscillations. Determine : 1. stiffness of the spring, 2. logarithmic decrement, and 3. damping factor, i.e. the ratio of the system damping to critical damping.*

Solution. Given : $m = 7.5$ kg

Since 24 oscillations are made in 14 seconds, therefore frequency of free vibrations,

$$f_n = 24/14 = 1.7$$

and $\qquad \omega_n = 2\pi \times f_n = 2\pi \times 1.7 = 10.7 \text{ rad/s}$

1. Stiffness of the spring

Let $\qquad s$ = Stiffness of the spring in N/m.

We know that $\qquad (\omega_n)^2 = s / m$ or $s = (\omega_n)^2 m = (10.7)^2 7.5 = 860 \text{ N/m } \textbf{Ans.}$

2. Logarithmic decrement

Let $\qquad x_1$ = Initial amplitude,

$\qquad x_6$ = Final amplitude after five oscillations = $0.25\, x_1$ $\qquad$ ... (Given)

$$\therefore \qquad \frac{x_1}{x_6} = \frac{x_1}{x_2} \times \frac{x_2}{x_3} \times \frac{x_3}{x_4} \times \frac{x_4}{x_5} \times \frac{x_5}{x_6} = \left(\frac{x_1}{x_2}\right)^5 \quad \dots \left[\because \frac{x_1}{x_2} = \frac{x_2}{x_3} = \frac{x_3}{x_4} = \frac{x_4}{x_5} = \frac{x_5}{x_6} \right]$$

or
$$\frac{x_1}{x_2} = \left(\frac{x_1}{x_6}\right)^{1/5} = \left(\frac{x_1}{0.25\,x_1}\right)^{1/5} = (4)^{1/5} = 1.32$$

We know that logarithmic decrement,
$$\delta = \log_e\left(\frac{x_1}{x_2}\right) = \log_e 1.32 = 0.28 \text{ Ans.}$$

3. *Damping factor*

Let c = Damping coefficient for the actual system, and

               c_c = Damping coefficient for the critical damped system.

We know that logarithmic decrement (δ),

$$0.28 = \frac{a \times 2\pi}{\sqrt{(\omega_n)^2 - a^2}} = \frac{a \times 2\pi}{\sqrt{(10.7)^2 - a^2}}$$

$$0.0784 = \frac{a^2 \times 39.5}{114.5 - a^2} \qquad \qquad \text{. . . (Squaring both sides)}$$

$$8.977 - 0.0784\, a^2 = 39.5\, a^2 \quad \text{or} \quad a^2 = 0.227 \quad \text{or} \quad a = 0.476$$

We know that $a = c/2m$ or $c = a \times 2m = 0.476 \times 2 \times 7.5 = 7.2$ N/m/s Ans.

and $c_c = 2m.\omega_n = 2 \times 7.5 \times 10.7 = 160.5$ N/m/s Ans.

∴   Damping factor = $c/c_c = 7.2 / 160.5 = 0.045$ Ans.

23.16. Frequency of Under Damped Forced Vibrations

Consider a system consisting of spring, mass and damper as shown in Fig. 23.19. Let the system is acted upon by an external periodic (*i.e.* simple harmonic) disturbing force,

$$F_x = F \cos \omega t$$

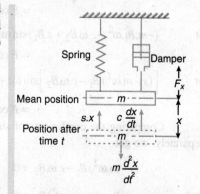

where F = Static force, and

           ω = Angular velocity of the periodic disturbing force.

When the system is constrained to move in vertical guides, it has only one degree of freedom. Let at sometime t, the mass is displaced downwards through a distance x from its mean position.

Fig. 23.19. Frequency of under damped forced vibrations.

Using the symbols as discussed in the previous article, the equation of motion may be written as

$$m \times \frac{d^2x}{dt^2} = -c \times \frac{dx}{dt} - s.x + F \cos \omega t$$

or $m \times \dfrac{d^2x}{dt^2} + c \times \dfrac{dx}{dt} + s.x = F \cos \omega t$ . . . (*i*)

This equation of motion may be solved either by differential equation method or by graphical method as discussed below :

1. *Differential equation method*

The equation (i) is a differential equation of the second degree whose right hand side is some function in t. The solution of such type of differential equation consists of two parts ; one part is the complementary function and the second is particular integral. Therefore the solution may be written as

$$x = x_1 + x_2$$

where
$$x_1 = \text{Complementary function, and}$$
$$x_2 = \text{Particular integral.}$$

The complementary function is same as discussed in the previous article, *i.e.*

$$x_1 = C e^{-at} \cos(\omega_d t - \theta) \qquad \ldots (ii)$$

where C and θ are constants. Let us now find the value of particular integral as discussed below :

Let the particular integral of equation (i) is given by

$$x_2 = B_1 \sin \omega t + B_2 \cos \omega t \qquad \ldots \text{(where } B_1 \text{ and } B_2 \text{ are constants)}$$

$$\therefore \qquad \frac{dx}{dt} = B_1.\omega \cos \omega t - B_2.\omega \sin \omega t$$

and
$$\frac{d^2 x}{dt^2} = -B_1.\omega^2 \sin \omega t - B_2.\omega^2 \cos \omega t$$

Substituting these values in the given differential equation (i), we get

$$m(-B_1.\omega^2 \sin \omega t - B_2.\omega^2 \cos \omega t) + c(B_1.\omega \cos \omega t - B_2.\omega \sin \omega t) + s(B_1 \sin \omega t + B_2 \cos \omega t)$$
$$= F \cos \omega t$$

or
$$(-m.B_1.\omega^2 - c.\omega.B_2 + s.B_1) \sin \omega t + (-m.\omega^2.B_2 + c.\omega.B_1 + s.B_2) \cos \omega t$$
$$= F \cos \omega t$$

or
$$\left[(s - m.\omega^2) B_1 - c.\omega.B_2 \right] \sin \omega t + \left[c.\omega.B_1 + (s - m.\omega^2) B_2 \right] \cos \omega t$$
$$= F \cos \omega t + 0 \sin \omega t$$

Comparing the coefficients of $\sin \omega t$ and $\cos \omega t$ on the left hand side and right hand side separately, we get

$$(s - m.\omega^2) B_1 - c.\omega.B_2 = 0 \qquad \ldots (iii)$$

and
$$c.\omega.B_1 + (s - m.\omega^2) B_2 = F \qquad \ldots (iv)$$

Now from equation (iii)

$$(s - m.\omega^2) B_1 = c.\omega.B_2$$

$$\therefore \qquad B_2 = \frac{s - m.\omega^2}{c.\omega} \times B_1 \qquad \ldots (v)$$

Substituting the value of B_2 in equation (iv)

$$c.\omega.B_1 + \frac{(s - m.\omega^2)(s - m.\omega^2)}{c.\omega} \times B_1 = F$$

$$c^2.\omega^2.B_1 + (s - m.\omega^2)^2 B_1 = c.\omega.F$$

$$B_1 \left[c^2.\omega^2 + (s - m.\omega^2)^2 \right] = c.\omega.F$$

$$\therefore \quad B_1 = \frac{c.\omega.F}{c^2.\omega^2 + (s - m.\omega^2)^2}$$

and

$$B_2 = \frac{s - m.\omega^2}{c.\omega} \times \frac{c.\omega.F}{c^2.\omega^2 + (s - m.\omega^2)^2} \qquad \text{... [From equation (v)]}$$

$$= \frac{F(s - m.\omega^2)}{c^2.\omega^2 + (s - m.\omega^2)^2}$$

∴ The particular integral of the differential equation (*i*) is

$$x_2 = B_1 \sin \omega t + B_2 \cos \omega t$$

$$= \frac{c.\omega.F}{c^2.\omega^2 + (s - m.\omega^2)^2} \times \sin \omega t + \frac{F(s - m.\omega^2)}{c^2.\omega^2 + (s - m.\omega^2)^2} \times \cos \omega t$$

$$= \frac{F}{c^2.\omega^2 + (s - m.\omega^2)^2} \left[c.\omega \sin \omega t + (s - m.\omega^2) \cos \omega t \right] \qquad \text{... (vi)}$$

Let $c.\omega = X \sin \phi$; and $s - m.\omega^2 = X \cos \phi$

$$\therefore \qquad X = \sqrt{c^2.\omega^2 + (s - m.\omega^2)^2} \qquad \text{... (By squaring and adding)}$$

This machine performs pressing operation, welding operation and material handling.
Note : This picture is given as additional information.

and
$$\tan\phi = \frac{c.\omega}{s - m.\omega^2} \quad \text{or} \quad \phi = \tan^{-1}\left(\frac{c.\omega}{s - m.\omega^2}\right)$$

Now the equation (vi) may be written as.

$$x_2 = \frac{F}{c^2.\omega^2 + (s - m.\omega^2)^2}\left[X\sin\phi.\sin\omega t + X\cos\phi\cos\omega t\right]$$

$$= \frac{F.X}{c^2.\omega^2 + (s - m.\omega^2)^2} \times \cos(\omega t - \phi)$$

$$= \frac{F\sqrt{c^2.\omega^2 + (s - m.\omega^2)^2}}{c^2.\omega^2 + (s - m.\omega^2)^2} \times \cos(\omega t - \phi)$$

$$= \frac{F}{\sqrt{c^2.\omega^2 + (s - m.\omega^2)^2}} \times \cos(\omega t - \phi)$$

∴ The complete solution of the differential equation (i) becomes

$$x = x_1 + x_2$$

$$= C.e^{-at}\cos(\omega_d.t - \theta) + \frac{F}{\sqrt{c^2.\omega^2 + (s - m.\omega^2)^2}} \times \cos(\omega t - \phi)$$

In actual practice, the value of the complementary function x_1 at any time t is much smaller as compared to particular integral x_2. Therefore, the displacement x, at any time t, is given by the particular integral x_2 only.

∴
$$x = \frac{F}{\sqrt{c^2.\omega^2 + (s - m.\omega^2)^2}} \times \cos(\omega t - \phi) \qquad \ldots (vii)$$

This equation shows that motion is simple harmonic whose circular frequency is ω and the

amplitude is $\dfrac{F}{\sqrt{c^2.\omega^2 + (s - m.\omega^2)^2}}$.

A little consideration will show that the frequency of forced vibration is equal to the angular velocity of the periodic force and the amplitude of the forced vibration is equal to the maximum displacement of vibration.

∴ Maximum displacement or the amplitude of forced vibration,

$$x_{max} = \frac{F}{\sqrt{c^2.\omega^2 + (s - m.\omega^2)^2}} \qquad \ldots (viii)$$

Notes : 1. The equations (vii) and (viii) hold good when steady vibrations of constant amplitude takes place.

2. The equation (viii) may be written as

$$x_{max} = \frac{F/s}{\sqrt{\dfrac{c^2.\omega^2}{s^2} + \dfrac{(s - m.\omega^2)^2}{s^2}}}$$

... (Dividing the numerator and denominator by s)

$$= \frac{x_o}{\sqrt{\frac{c^2.\omega^2}{s^2} + \left(1 - \frac{m.\omega^2}{s}\right)^2}}$$

. . . (Substituting $F/s = x_o$)

where x_o is the deflection of the system under the static force F. We know that the natural frequency of free vibrations is given by

$$(\omega_n)^2 = s / m$$

$$\therefore \qquad x_{max} = \frac{x_o}{\sqrt{\frac{c^2.\omega^2}{s^2} + \left(1 - \frac{\omega^2}{(\omega_n)^2}\right)^2}}$$

. . . (ix)

3. When damping is negligible, then $c = 0$.

$$\therefore \qquad x_{max} = \frac{x_o}{1 - \frac{\omega^2}{(\omega_n)^2}} = \frac{x_o (\omega_n)^2}{(\omega_n)^2 - \omega^2} = \frac{x_o \times s / m}{(\omega_n)^2 - \omega^2}$$

. . . $\left[\because (\omega_n)^2 = s / m \right]$

$$\therefore \qquad = \frac{F}{m\left[(\omega_n)^2 - \omega^2\right]}$$

. . . $(\because F = x_o.s)$ . . . (x)

4. At resonance $\omega = \omega_n$. Therefore the angular speed at which the resonance occurs is

$$\omega = \omega_n = \sqrt{\frac{s}{m}} \ \text{ rad/s}$$

and $\qquad x_{max} = x_o \times \frac{s}{c.\omega_n} = \frac{F}{c.\omega_n}$

. . . [From equation (ix)]

2. Graphical method

The solution of the equation of motion for a forced and damped vibration may be easily obtained by graphical method as discussed below :

Let us assume that the displacement of the mass (m) in the system, as shown in Fig. 23.19, under the action of the applied simple harmonic force $F \cos \omega t$ is itself simple harmonic, so that it can be represented by the equation,

$$x = A \cos (\omega t - \phi)$$

where A is the amplitude of vibration.

Now differentiating the above equation,

$$\frac{dx}{dt} = -\omega.A \sin (\omega t - \phi) = \omega.A \cos \left[90° + (\omega t - \phi)\right]$$

and $\qquad \dfrac{d^2 x}{dt^2} = -\omega^2.A \cos (\omega t - \phi) = \omega^2.A \cos \left[180° + (\omega t - \phi)\right]$

∴ Elastic force *i.e.* the force required to extend the spring

$$= s.x = s.A \cos(\omega t - \phi)$$

Disturbing force *i.e.* the force required to overcome the resistance of dashpot

$$= c \times \frac{dx}{dt} = c.\omega.A \cos[90° + (\omega t - \phi)]$$

and inertia force *i.e.* the force required to accelerate the mass *m*

$$= m \times \frac{d^2 x}{dt^2} = m.\omega^2.A \cos[180° + (\omega t - \phi)]$$

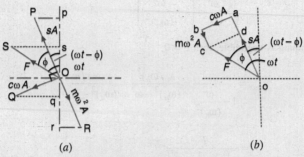

(a)   (b)

Fig. 23.20. Graphical method.

The algebraic sum of these three forces at any given instant must be equal to the applied force $F \cos \omega t$. These forces are represented graphically in Fig. 23.20 (*a*). The vector *OP* represents, to some suitable scale, the elastic force (of maximum value *s.A*), at an inclination $(\omega t - \phi)$ to the vertical. The vector *OQ* (of maximum value $c\omega.A$) and vector *OR* (of maximum value $m.\omega^2 A$) represents, to the same scale, the disturbing force and inertia force respectively. The vectors *OP*, *OQ* and *OR* are at successive intervals of 90°.

The projected lengths *Op*, *Oq* and *Or* represent the instantaneous values of these forces at time *t* and *Os* (the algebraic sum of *Op*, *Oq* and *Or*) must represent the value $F \cos \omega t$ of the applied force at the same instant. Thus the force vector *OS* must be the vector sum of *OP*, *OQ* and *OR* or force *F* must be the vector sum of *s.A*, $c.\omega.A$ and $m.\omega^2.A$, as shown in Fig. 23.20 (*b*). From the geometry of the figure,

$$F = oc = \sqrt{(od)^2 + (cd)^2} = \sqrt{(oa - ad)^2 + (cd)^2}$$

$$= \sqrt{(s.A - m.\omega^2.A)^2 + (c.\omega.A)^2} = A\sqrt{(s - m.\omega^2)^2 + c^2.\omega^2}$$

∴ $$A \,(or\ x_{max}) = \frac{F}{\sqrt{(s - m.\omega^2)^2 + c^2.\omega^2}} \qquad \text{... (Same as before)}$$

and $$\tan \phi = \frac{cd}{od} = \frac{c.\omega.A}{s.A - m.\omega^2.A} = \frac{c.\omega^2}{s - m.\omega^2} \qquad \text{... (Same as before)}$$

23.17. Magnification Factor or Dynamic Magnifier

It is the ratio of *maximum displacement of the forced vibration* (x_{max}) *to the deflection due to the static force* $F(x_o)$. We have proved in the previous article that the maximum displacement or the amplitude of forced vibration,

$$x_{max} = \frac{x_o}{\sqrt{\dfrac{c^2 . \omega^2}{s^2} + \left(1 - \dfrac{\omega^2}{(\omega_n)^2}\right)^2}}$$

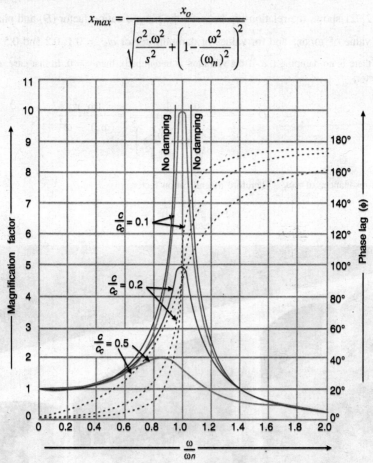

Fig. 23.21. Relationship between magnification factor and phase angle for different values of ω / ω_n.

∴   Magnification factor or dynamic magnifier,

$$D = \frac{x_{max}}{x_o} = \frac{1}{\sqrt{\dfrac{c^2 . \omega^2}{s^2} + \left(1 - \dfrac{\omega^2}{(\omega_n)^2}\right)^2}} \qquad \qquad \dots (i)$$

$$= \frac{1}{\sqrt{\left(\dfrac{2c . \omega}{c_c . \omega_n}\right)^2 + \left(1 - \dfrac{\omega^2}{(\omega_n)^2}\right)^2}}$$

$$\dots \left[\because \frac{c . \omega}{s} = \frac{2c . \omega}{2m \times \dfrac{s}{m}} = \frac{2c . \omega}{2m(\omega_n)^2} = \frac{2c . \omega}{c_c . \omega_n} \right]$$

The magnification factor or dynamic magnifier gives the factor by which the static deflection produced by a force F (*i.e.* x_o) must be multiplied in order to obtain the maximum amplitude of the forced vibration (*i.e.* x_{max}) by the harmonic force $F \cos \omega t$

∴ $$x_{max} = x_o \times D$$

Fig. 23.21 shows the relationship between the magnification factor (D) and phase angle ϕ for different value of ω / ω_n and for values of damping factor $c/c_c = 0.1, 0.2$ and 0.5.

Notes : 1. If there is no damping (*i.e.* if the vibration is undamped), then $c = 0$. In that case, magnification factor,

$$D = \frac{x_{max}}{x_o} = \frac{1}{\sqrt{\left(1 - \frac{\omega^2}{(\omega_n)^2}\right)^2}} = \frac{(\omega_n)^2}{(\omega_n)^2 - \omega^2}$$

2. At resonance, $\omega = \omega_n$. Therefore magnification factor,

$$D = \frac{x_{max}}{x_o} = \frac{s}{c.\omega_n}$$

Depending upon the case bridges can be treated as beams subjected to uniformly distributed leads and point loads.

Example 23.17. *A single cylinder vertical petrol engine of total mass 300 kg is mounted upon a steel chassis frame and causes a vertical static deflection of 2 mm. The reciprocating parts of the engine has a mass of 20 kg and move through a vertical stroke of 150 mm with simple harmonic motion. A dashpot is provided whose damping resistance is directly proportional to the velocity and amounts to 1.5 kN per metre per second.*

Considering that the steady state of vibration is reached ; determine : 1. the amplitude of forced vibrations, when the driving shaft of the engine rotates at 480 r.p.m., and 2. the speed of the driving shaft at which resonance will occur.

Solution : Given. $m = 300$ kg; $\delta = 2$ mm $= 2 \times 10^{-3}$ m ; $m_1 = 20$ kg ; $l = 150$ mm $= 0.15$ m ; $c = 1.5$ kN/m/s $= 1500$ N/m/s ; $N = 480$ r.p.m. or $\omega = 2\pi \times 480/60 = 50.3$ rad/s

1. *Amplitude of the forced vibrations*

We know that stiffness of the frame,

$$s = m.g \, / \, \delta \ = 300 \times 9.81/2 \times 10^{-3} = 1.47 \times 10^6 \text{ N/m}$$

Since the length of stroke (l) = 150 mm = 0.15 m, therefore radius of crank,

$$r = l \, / \, 2 = 0.15 \, / \, 2 = 0.075 \text{ m}$$

We know that the centrifugal force due to the reciprocating parts or the static force,

$$F = m_1.\omega^2.r \ = 20 \, (50.3)^2 \, 0.075 = 3795 \text{ N}$$

∴   Amplitude of the forced vibration (maximum),

$$x_{max} = \frac{F}{\sqrt{c^2.\omega^2 + (s - m.\omega^2)^2}}$$

$$= \frac{3795}{\sqrt{(1500)^2 (50.3)^2 + [1.47 \times 10^6 - 300 \, (50.3)^2]^2}}$$

$$= \frac{3795}{\sqrt{5.7 \times 10^9 + 500 \times 10^9}} = \frac{3795}{710 \times 10^3} = 5.3 \times 10^{-3} \text{ m}$$

$$= 5.3 \text{ mm Ans.}$$

2. *Speed of the driving shaft at which the resonance occurs*

Let N = Speed of the driving shaft at which the resonance occurs in r.p.m.

We know that the angular speed at which the resonance occurs,

$$\omega = \omega_n = \sqrt{\frac{s}{m}} = \sqrt{\frac{1.47 \times 10^6}{300}} = 70 \text{ rad/s}$$

∴ $$N = \omega \times 60 \, / \, 2\pi = 70 \times 60 \, / \, 2\pi \ = 668.4 \text{ r.p.m. Ans.}$$

Example 23.18. *A mass of 10 kg is suspended from one end of a helical spring, the other end being fixed. The stiffness of the spring is 10 N/mm. The viscous damping causes the amplitude to decrease to one-tenth of the initial value in four complete oscillations. If a periodic force of 150 cos 50 t N is applied at the mass in the vertical direction, find the amplitude of the forced vibrations. What is its value of resonance ?*

Solution. Given : m = 10 kg ; s = 10 N/mm = 10×10^3 N/m ; $x_s = \dfrac{x_1}{10}$

Since the periodic force, $F_x = F \cos \omega t = 150 \cos 50 t$, therefore

Static force, F = 150 N

and angular velocity of the periodic disturbing force,

$$\omega = 50 \text{ rad/s}$$

We know that angular speed or natural circular frequency of free vibrations,

$$\omega_n = \sqrt{\frac{s}{m}} = \sqrt{\frac{10 \times 10^3}{10}} = 31.6 \text{ rad/s}$$

Amplitude of the forced vibrations

Since the amplitude decreases to 1/10th of the initial value in four complete oscillations, therefore, the ratio of initial amplitude (x_1) to the final amplitude after four complete oscillations (x_5) is given by

$$\frac{x_1}{x_5} = \frac{x_1}{x_2} \times \frac{x_2}{x_3} \times \frac{x_3}{x_4} \times \frac{x_4}{x_5} = \left(\frac{x_1}{x_2}\right)^4 \qquad \cdots \left(\because \frac{x_1}{x_2} = \frac{x_2}{x_3} = \frac{x_3}{x_4} = \frac{x_4}{x_5} \right)$$

$$\therefore \qquad \frac{x_1}{x_2} = \left(\frac{x_1}{x_5}\right)^{1/4} = \left(\frac{x_1}{x_1/10}\right)^{1/4} = (10)^{1/4} = 1.78 \qquad \cdots \left(x_5 = \frac{x_1}{10} \right)$$

We know that

$$\log_e \left(\frac{x_1}{x_2}\right) = a \times \frac{2\pi}{\sqrt{(\omega_n)^2 - a^2}}$$

$$\log_e 1.78 = a \times \frac{2\pi}{\sqrt{(31.6)^2 - a^2}} \quad \text{or} \quad 0.576 = \frac{a \times 2\pi}{\sqrt{1000 - a^2}}$$

Squaring both sides and rearranging,

$$39.832 \ a^2 = 332 \quad \text{or} \quad a^2 = 8.335 \quad \text{or} \quad a = 2.887$$

We know that $a = c/2m$ or $c = a \times 2m = 2.887 \times 2 \times 10 = 57.74$ N/m/s and deflection of the system produced by the static force F,

$$x_o = F/s = 150/10 \times 10^3 = 0.015 \text{ m}$$

We know that amplitude of the forced vibrations,

$$x_{max} = \frac{x_o}{\sqrt{\dfrac{c^2 . \omega^2}{s^2} + \left[1 - \dfrac{\omega^2}{(\omega_n)^2}\right]^2}}$$

$$= \frac{0.015}{\sqrt{\dfrac{(57.74)^2 (50)^2}{(10 \times 10^3)^2} + \left[1 - \left(\dfrac{50}{31.6}\right)^2\right]^2}} = \frac{0.015}{\sqrt{0.083 + 2.25}}$$

$$= \frac{0.015}{1.53} = 9.8 \times 10^{-3} \text{ m} = 9.8 \text{ mm Ans.}$$

Amplitude of forced vibrations at resonance

We know that amplitude of forced vibrations at resonance,

$$x_{max} = x_0 \times \frac{s}{c . \omega_n} = 0.015 \times \frac{10 \times 10^3}{57.54 \times 31.6} = 0.0822 \text{ m} = 82.2 \text{ mm Ans.}$$

Example 23.19. *A body of mass 20 kg is suspended from a spring which deflects 15 mm under this load. Calculate the frequency of free vibrations and verify that a viscous damping force amounting to approximately 1000 N at a speed of 1 m/s is just-sufficient to make the motion aperiodic.*

If when damped to this extent, the body is subjected to a disturbing force with a maximum value of 125 N making 8 cycles/s, find the amplitude of the ultimate motion.

Solution . Given : $m = 20$ kg ; $\delta = 15$ mm $= 0.015$ m ; $c = 1000$ N/m/s ; $F = 125$ N ; $f = 8$ cycles/s

Frequency of free vibrations

We know that frequency of free vibrations,

$$f_n = \frac{1}{2\pi}\sqrt{\frac{g}{\delta}} = \frac{1}{2\pi}\sqrt{\frac{9.81}{0.015}} = 4.07 \text{ Hz} \quad \textbf{Ans.}$$

The critical damping to make the motion aperiodic is such that damped frequency is zero, *i.e.*

$$\left(\frac{c}{2m}\right)^2 = \frac{s}{m}$$

$\therefore$

$$c = \sqrt{\frac{s}{m} \times 4m^2} = \sqrt{4\,s.m} = \sqrt{4 \times \frac{m.g}{\delta} \times m} \qquad \dots \left(\because s = \frac{m.g}{\delta}\right)$$

$$= \sqrt{4 \times \frac{20 \times 9.81}{0.015} \times 20} = 1023 \text{ N/m/s}$$

This means that the viscous damping force is 1023 N at a speed of 1 m/s. Therefore a viscous damping force amounting to approximately 1000 N at a speed of 1 m/s is just sufficient to make the motion aperiodic. **Ans.**

Amplitude of ultimate motion

We know that angular speed of forced vibration,

$$\omega = 2\pi \times f = 2\pi \times 8 = 50.3 \text{ rad/s}$$

and stiffness of the spring, $\quad s = m.g/\delta = 20 \times 9.81 / 0.015 = 13.1 \times 10^3$ N/m

$\therefore$ Amplitude of ultimate motion *i.e.* maximum amplitude of forced vibration,

$$x_{max} = \frac{F}{\sqrt{c^2.\omega^2 + (s - m.\omega^2)^2}}$$

$$= \frac{125}{\sqrt{(1023)^2 (50.3)^2 + [13.1 \times 10^3 - 20(50.3)^2]^2}}$$

$$= \frac{125}{\sqrt{2600 \times 10^6 + 1406 \times 10^6}} = \frac{125}{63.7 \times 10^3} = 1.96 \times 10^{-3} \text{ m}$$

$$= 1.96 \text{ mm} \quad \textbf{Ans.}$$

Example 23.20. *A machine part of mass 2 kg vibrates in a viscous medium. Determine the damping coefficient when a harmonic exciting force of 25 N results in a resonant amplitude of 12.5 mm with a period of 0.2 second. If the system is excited by a harmonic force of frequency 4 Hz what will be the percentage increase in the amplitude of vibration when damper is removed as compared with that with damping.*

Solution . Given : $m = 2$ kg ; $F = 25$ N ; Resonant $x_{max} = 12.5$ mm $= 0.0125$ m ; $t_p = 0.2$ s ; $f = 4$ Hz

Damping coefficient

Let c = Damping coefficient in N/m/s.

We know that natural circular frequency of the exciting force,

$$\omega_n = 2\pi/t_p = 2\pi/0.2 = 31.42 \text{ rad/s}$$

We also know that the maximum amplitude of vibration at resonance (x_{max}),

$$0.0125 = \frac{F}{c.\omega_n} = \frac{25}{c \times 31.42} = \frac{0.796}{c} \quad \text{or} \quad c = 63.7 \text{ N/m/s Ans.}$$

Percentage increase in amplitude

Since the system is excited by a harmonic force of frequency (f) = 4 Hz, therefore corresponding circular frequency

$$\omega = 2\pi \times f = 2\pi \times 4 = 25.14 \text{ rad/s}$$

We know that maximum amplitude of vibration with damping,

$$x_{max} = \frac{F}{\sqrt{c^2.\omega^2 + (s - m.\omega^2)^2}}$$

$$= \frac{25}{\sqrt{(63.7)^2(25.14)^2 + [2(31.42)^2 - 2(25.14)^2]^2}}$$

$$\ldots \left[\because (\omega_n)^2 = s/m \quad \text{or} \quad s = m(\omega_n)^2 \right]$$

$$= \frac{25}{\sqrt{2.56 \times 10^6 + 0.5 \times 10^6}} = \frac{25}{1749} = 0.0143 \text{ m} = 14.3 \text{ mm}$$

and the maximum amplitude of vibration when damper is removed,

$$x_{max} = \frac{F}{m\left[(\omega_n)^2 - \omega^2\right]} = \frac{25}{2[(31.42)^2 - (25.14)^2]} = \frac{25}{710} = 0.0352 \text{ m}$$

$$= 35.2 \text{ mm}$$

∴ Percentage increase in amplitude

$$= \frac{35.2 - 14.3}{14.3} = 1.46 \quad \text{or} \quad 146\% \text{ Ans.}$$

Example 23.21. *The time of free vibration of a mass hung from the end of a helical spring is 0.8 second. When the mass is stationary, the upper end is made to move upwards with a displacement y metre such that y = 0.018 sin 2 πt, where t is the time in seconds measured from the beginning of the motion. Neglecting the mass of the spring and any damping effects, determine the vertical distance through which the mass is moved in the first 0.3 second.*

Solution. Given : $t_p = 0.8$ s ; $y = 0.018 \sin 2\pi t$

Let m = Mass hung to the spring in kg, and

s = Stiffness of the spring in N/m.

We know that time period of free vibrations (t_p),

$$0.8 = 2\pi\sqrt{\frac{m}{s}} \quad \text{or} \quad \frac{m}{s} = \left(\frac{0.8}{2\pi}\right)^2 = 0.0162$$

If x metres is the upward displacement of mass m from its equilibrium position after time t seconds, the equation of motion is given by

$$m \times \frac{d^2 x}{dt^2} = s(y - x) \qquad \text{or} \qquad \frac{m}{s} \times \frac{d^2 x}{dt^2} + x = y = 0.018 \sin 2\pi t$$

The solution of this differential equation is

$$x = A \sin \sqrt{\frac{s}{m}} \times t + B \cos \sqrt{\frac{s}{m}} \times t + \frac{0.018 \sin 2\pi t}{1 - \left(\dfrac{2\pi}{\sqrt{s/m}} \right)^2}$$

. . . (where A and B are constants)

$$= A \sin \frac{t}{\sqrt{0.0162}} + B \cos \frac{t}{\sqrt{0.0162}} + \frac{0.018 \sin 2\pi t}{1 - 4\pi^2 \times 0.0162}$$

$$= A \sin 7.85 t + B \cos 7.85 t + 0.05 \sin 2\pi t \qquad \text{. . . } (i)$$

Now when $t = 0$, $x = 0$, then from equation (i), $B = 0$.

Again when $t = 0$, $dx/dt = 0$.

Therefore differentiating equation (i) and equating to zero, we have

$$dx / dt = 7.85 A \cos 7.85 t + 0.05 \times 2\pi \cos 2\pi t = 0 \qquad \text{. . . } (\because \quad B = 0)$$

or $\qquad 7.85 A \cos 7.85 t = -0.05 \times 2\pi \cos 2\pi t$

$\therefore \qquad\qquad A = -0.05 \times 2\pi / 7.85 = -0.04 \qquad \text{. . . } (\because \quad t = 0)$

Now the equation (i) becomes

$$x = -0.04 \sin 7.85 t + 0.05 \sin 2\pi t \qquad \text{. . . } (\because \quad B = 0) \text{ . . . } (ii)$$

$\therefore$ Vertical distance through which the mass is moved in the first 0.3 second (*i.e.* when $t = 0.3$ s),

$$= -0.04 \sin (7.85 \times 0.3) + 0.05 \sin (2\pi \times 0.3)$$

. . . [Substituting $t = 0.3$ in equation (ii)]

$$= -0.04 \times 0.708 + 0.05 \times 0.951 = -0.0283 + 0.0476 = 0.0193 \text{ m}$$

$$= 19.3 \text{ mm } \textbf{Ans.}$$

23.18. Vibration Isolation and Transmissibility

A little consideration will show that when an unbalanced machine is installed on the foundation, it produces vibration in the foundation. In order to prevent these vibrations or to minimise the transmission of forces to the foundation, the machines are mounted on springs and dampers or on some vibration isolating material, as shown in Fig. 23.22. The arrangement is assumed to have one degree of freedom, *i.e.* it can move up and down only.

It may be noted that when a periodic (*i.e.* simple harmonic) disturbing force $F \cos \omega t$ is applied to a machine

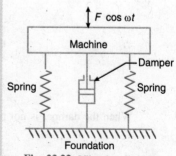

Fig. 23.22. Vibration isolation.

of mass m supported by a spring of stiffness s, then the force is transmitted by means of the spring and the damper or dashpot to the fixed support or foundation.

The ratio of the force transmitted (F_T) to the force applied (F) is known as the *isolation factor* or *transmissibility ratio* of the spring support.

We have discussed above that the force transmitted to the foundation consists of the following two forces :

1. Spring force or elastic force which is equal to $s. x_{max}$, and

2. Damping force which is equal to $c. \omega. x_{max}$.

Since these two forces are perpendicular to one another, as shown in Fig.23.23, therefore the force transmitted,

$$F_T = \sqrt{(s.x_{max})^2 + (c.\omega.x_{max})^2}$$

$$= x_{max} \sqrt{s^2 + c^2.\omega^2}$$

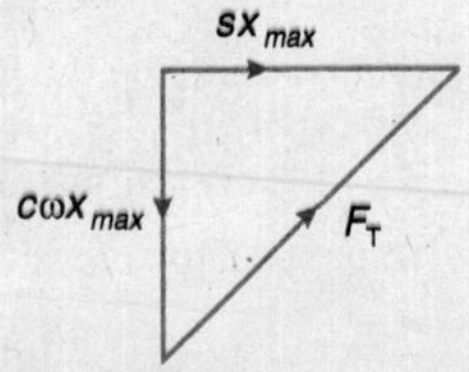

∴ Transmissibility ratio,

$$\varepsilon = \frac{F_T}{F} = \frac{x_{max} \sqrt{s^2 + c^2.\omega^2}}{F}$$

We know that

$$x_{max} = x_o \times D = \frac{F}{s} \times D \qquad \qquad \cdots \left(\because x_o = \frac{F}{s} \right)$$

∴

$$\varepsilon = \frac{D}{s} \sqrt{s^2 + c^2.\omega^2} = D \sqrt{1 + \frac{c^2.\omega^2}{s^2}}$$

$$= D \sqrt{1 + \left(\frac{2c}{c_c} \times \frac{\omega}{\omega_n} \right)^2} \qquad \qquad \cdots \left(\because \frac{c.\omega}{s} = \frac{2c}{c_c} \times \frac{\omega}{\omega_n} \right)$$

We have seen in Art. 23.17 that the magnification factor,

$$D = \frac{1}{\sqrt{\left(\frac{2c.\omega}{c_c.\omega_n} \right)^2 + \left(1 - \frac{\omega^2}{(\omega_n)^2} \right)^2}}$$

∴

$$\varepsilon = \frac{\sqrt{1 + \left(\frac{2c.\omega}{c_c.\omega_n} \right)^2}}{\sqrt{\left(\frac{2c.\omega}{c_c.\omega_n} \right)^2 + \left(1 - \frac{\omega^2}{(\omega_n)^2} \right)^2}} \qquad \cdots (i)$$

When the damper is not provided, then $c = 0$, and

$$\varepsilon = \frac{1}{1 - (\omega/\omega_n)^2} \qquad \cdots (ii)$$

Fig. 23.23

From above, we see that when $\omega/\omega_n > 1$, ε is negative. This means that there is a phase difference of 180° between the transmitted force and the disturbing force ($F\cos\omega t$). The value of ω/ω_n must be greater than $\sqrt{2}$ if ε is to be less than 1 and it is the numerical value of ε, independent of any phase difference between the forces that may exist which is important. It is therefore more convenient to use equation (*ii*) in the following form, *i.e.*

$$\varepsilon = \frac{1}{(\omega/\omega_n)^2 - 1} \qquad \qquad \dots(iii)$$

Fig. 23.24 is the graph for different values of damping factor c/c_c to show the variation of transmissibility ratio (ε) against the ratio ω/ω_n.

1. When $\omega/\omega_n = \sqrt{2}$, then all the curves pass through the point $\varepsilon = 1$ for all values of damping factor c/c_c.

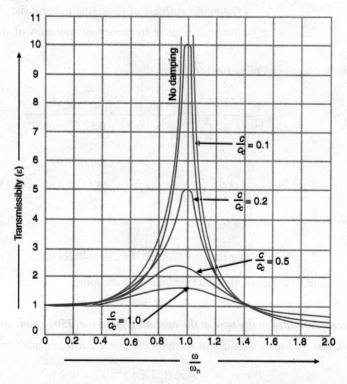

Fig. 23.24. Graph showing the variation of transmissibility ratio.

2. When $\omega/\omega_n < \sqrt{2}$, then $\varepsilon > 1$ for all values of damping factor c/c_c. This means that the force transmitted to the foundation through elastic support is greater than the force applied.

3. When $\omega/\omega_n > \sqrt{2}$, then $\varepsilon < 1$ for all values of damping factor c/c_c. This shows that the force transmitted through elastic support is less than the applied force. Thus vibration isolation is possible only in the range of $\omega/\omega_n > \sqrt{2}$.

We also see from the curves in Fig. 23.24 that the damping is detrimental beyond $\omega/\omega_n > \sqrt{2}$ and advantageous only in the region $\omega/\omega_n < \sqrt{2}$. It is thus concluded that for the vibration isolation, dampers need not to be provided but in order to limit resonance amplitude, stops may be provided.

Example 23.22. *The mass of an electric motor is 120 kg and it runs at 1500 r.p.m. The armature mass is 35 kg and its C.G. lies 0.5 mm from the axis of rotation. The motor is mounted on five springs of negligible damping so that the force transmitted is one-eleventh of the impressed force. Assume that the mass of the motor is equally distributed among the five springs.*

Determine : 1. stiffness of each spring; 2. dynamic force transmitted to the base at the operating speed; and 3. natural frequency of the system.

Solution. Given $m_1 = 120$ kg ; $m_2 = 35$ kg; $r = 0.5$ mm $= 5 \times 10^{-4}$ m; $\varepsilon = 1/11$; $N = 1500$ r.p.m. or $\omega = 2\pi \times 1500/60 = 157.1$ rad/s ;

1. Stiffness of each spring

Let $\qquad s =$ Combined stiffness of the spring in N-m, and

$\qquad \omega_n =$ Natural circular frequency of vibration of the machine in rad/s.

We know that transmissibility ratio (ε),

$$\frac{1}{11} = \frac{1}{\left(\dfrac{\omega}{\omega_n}\right)^2 - 1} = \frac{(\omega_n)^2}{\omega^2 - (\omega_n)^2} = \frac{(\omega_n)^2}{(157.1)^2 - (\omega_n)^2}$$

or $\qquad (157.1)^2 - (\omega_n)^2 = 11(\omega_n)^2$ or $(\omega_n)^2 = 2057$ or $\omega_n = 45.35$ rad/s

We know that $\qquad \omega_n = \sqrt{s/m_1}$

$$s = m_1(\omega_n)^2 = 120 \times 2057 = 246\,840 \text{ N/m}$$

Since these are five springs, therefore stiffness of each spring

$$= 246\,840/5 = 49\,368 \text{ N/m} \quad \textbf{Ans.}$$

2. Dynamic force transmitted to the base at the operating speed (i.e. 1500 r.p.m. or 157.1 rad/s)

We know that maximum unbalanced force on the motor due to armature mass,

$$F = m_2\,\omega^2 \cdot r = 35(157.1)^2\,5 \times 10^{-4} = 432 \text{ N}$$

$\therefore$ Dynamic force transmitted to the base,

$$F_T = \varepsilon.F = \frac{1}{11} \times 432 = 39.27 \text{ N} \quad \textbf{Ans.}$$

3. Natural frequency of the system

We have calculated above that the natural frequency of the system,

$$\omega_n = 45.35 \text{ rad/s} \quad \textbf{Ans.}$$

Example 23.23. *A machine has a mass of 100 kg and unbalanced reciprocating parts of mass 2 kg which move through a vertical stroke of 80 mm with simple harmonic motion. The machine is mounted on four springs, symmetrically arranged with respect to centre of mass, in such a way that the machine has one degree of freedom and can undergo vertical displacements only.*

Neglecting damping, calculate the combined stiffness of the spring in order that the force transmitted to the foundation is 1/25 th of the applied force, when the speed of rotation of machine crank shaft is 1000 r.p.m.

When the machine is actually supported on the springs, it is found that the damping reduces the amplitude of successive free vibrations by 25%. Find : 1. the force transmitted to foundation at 1000 r.p.m., 2. the force transmitted to the foundation at resonance, and 3. the amplitude of the forced vibration of the machine at resonance.

Solution. Given : $m_1 = 100$ kg ; $m_2 = 2$ kg ; $l = 80$ mm $= 0.08$ m ; $\varepsilon = 1/25$; $N = 1000$ r.p.m. or $\omega = 2\pi \times 1000/60 = 104.7$ rad/s

Combined stiffness of springs

Let $\qquad$ s = Combined stiffness of springs in N/m, and

$\qquad \omega_n$ = Natural circular frequency of vibration of the machine in rad/s.

We know that transmissibility ratio (ε),

$$\frac{1}{25} = \frac{1}{\left(\dfrac{\omega}{\omega_n}\right)^2 - 1} = \frac{(\omega_n)^2}{\omega^2 - (\omega_n)^2} = \frac{(\omega_n)^2}{(104.7)^2 - (\omega_n)^2}$$

or $\qquad (104.7)^2 - (\omega_n)^2 = 25(\omega_n)^2 \qquad$ or $\qquad (\omega_n)^2 = 421.6$ or $\omega_n = 20.5$ rad/s

We know that $\qquad \omega_n = \sqrt{s/m_1}$

$\therefore \qquad s = m_1 (\omega_n)^2 = 100 \times 421.6 = 42\ 160$ N/m **Ans.**

1. *Force transmitted to the foundation at 1000 r.p.m.*

Let $\qquad F_T$ = Force transmitted, and

$\qquad x_1$ = Initial amplitude of vibration.

Since the damping reduces the amplitude of successive free vibrations by 25%, therefore final amplitude of vibration,

$$x_2 = 0.75\, x_1$$

We know that

$$\log_e \left(\frac{x_1}{x_2}\right) = \frac{a \times 2\pi}{\sqrt{(\omega_n)^2 - a^2}} \qquad \text{or} \qquad \log_e \left(\frac{x_1}{0.75 x_1}\right) = \frac{a \times 2\pi}{\sqrt{421.6 - a^2}}$$

Squaring both sides,

$$(0.2877)^2 = \frac{a^2 \times 4\pi^2}{421.6 - a^2} \qquad \text{or} \qquad 0.083 = \frac{39.5\, a^2}{421.6 - a^2}$$

$$\dots \left[\because \log_e \left(\frac{1}{0.75}\right) = \log_e 1.333 = 0.2877 \right]$$

$$35 - 0.083\, a^2 = 39.5\, a^2 \qquad \text{or} \qquad a^2 = 0.884 \qquad \text{or} \qquad a = 0.94$$

We know that damping coefficient or damping force per unit velocity,

$$c = a \times 2m_1 = 0.94 \times 2 \times 100 = 188 \text{ N/m/s}$$

and critical damping coefficient,

$$c_c = 2m.\omega_n = 2 \times 100 \times 20.5 = 4100 \text{ N/m/s}$$

∴   Actual value of transmissibility ratio,

$$\varepsilon = \frac{\sqrt{1 + \left(\dfrac{2c.\omega}{c_c.\omega_n}\right)^2}}{\sqrt{\left(\dfrac{2c.\omega}{c_c.\omega_n}\right)^2 + \left(1 - \dfrac{\omega^2}{(\omega_n)^2}\right)^2}}$$

$$= \frac{\sqrt{1 + \left(\dfrac{2 \times 188 \times 104.7}{4100 \times 20.5}\right)^2}}{\sqrt{\left(\dfrac{2 \times 188 \times 104.7}{4100 \times 20.5}\right)^2 + \left[1 - \left(\dfrac{104.7}{20.5}\right)^2\right]^2}} = \frac{\sqrt{1 + 0.22}}{\sqrt{0.22 + 629}}$$

$$= \frac{1.104}{25.08} = 0.044$$

We know that the maximum unbalanced force on the machine due to reciprocating parts,

$$F = m_2.\omega^2.r = 2(104.7)^2 (0.08/2) = 877 \text{ N} \qquad \ldots (\because \quad r = l/2)$$

∴   Force transmitted to the foundation,

$$F_T = \varepsilon.F = 0.044 \times 877 = 38.6 \text{ N \textbf{Ans.}} \qquad \ldots (\because \quad \varepsilon = F_T/F)$$

2. Force transmitted to the foundation at resonance

Since at resonance, $\omega = \omega_n$, therefore transmissibility ratio,

$$\varepsilon = \frac{\sqrt{1 + \left(\dfrac{2c}{c_c}\right)^2}}{\sqrt{\left(\dfrac{2c}{c_c}\right)^2}} = \frac{\sqrt{1 + \left(\dfrac{2 \times 188}{4100}\right)^2}}{\sqrt{\left(\dfrac{2 \times 188}{4100}\right)^2}} = \frac{\sqrt{1 + 0.0084}}{0.092} = 10.92$$

and maximum unbalanced force on the machine due to reciprocating parts at resonance speed ω_n,

$$F = m_2 (\omega_n)^2 r = 2(20.5)^2 (0.08/2) = 33.6 \text{ N} \quad \ldots (\because \quad r = l/2)$$

∴   Force transmitted to the foundation at resonance,

$$F_T = \varepsilon.F = 10.92 \times 33.6 = 367 \text{ N \textbf{Ans.}}$$

3. Amplitude of the forced vibration of the machine at resonance

We know that amplitude of the forced vibration at resonance

$$= \frac{\text{Force transmitted at resonance}}{\text{Combined stiffness}} = \frac{367}{42\,160} = 8.7 \times 10^{-3} \text{ m}$$

$$= 8.7 \text{ mm \textbf{Ans.}}$$

Example 23.24. *A single-cylinder engine of total mass 200 kg is to be mounted on an elastic support which permits vibratory movement in vertical direction only. The mass of the piston is 3.5 kg and has a vertical reciprocating motion which may be assumed simple harmonic with a stroke of 150 mm. It is desired that the maximum vibratory force transmitted through the elastic support to the foundation shall be 600 N when the engine speed is 800 r.p.m. and less than this at all higher speeds.*

1. Find the necessary stiffness of the elastic support, and the amplitude of vibration at 800 r.p.m., and

2. If the engine speed is reduced below 800 r.p.m. at what speed will the transmitted force again becomes 600 N?

Solution. Given : $m_1 = 200$ kg ; $m_2 = 3.5$ kg ; $l = 150$ mm $= 0.15$ m or $r = l/2 = 0.075$ m ; $F_T = 600$ N ; $N = 800$ r.p.m. or $\omega = 2\pi \times 800 / 60 = 83.8$ rad/s

We know that the disturbing force at 800 r.p.m.,

$$F = \text{Centrifugal force on the piston}$$

$$= m_2 . \omega^2 . r = 3.5 \, (83.8)^2 \, 0.075 = 1843 \text{ N}$$

1. Stiffness of elastic support and amplitude of vibration

Let $s = $ Stiffness of elastic support in N/m, and

$x_{max} = $ Max. amplitude of vibration in metres.

Since the max. vibratory force transmitted to the foundation is equal to the force on the elastic support (neglecting damping), therefore

Max. vibratory force transmitted to the foundation,

$$F_T = \text{Force on the elastic support}$$

$$= \text{Stiffness of elastic support} \times \text{Max. amplitude of vibration}$$

$$= s \times x_{max} = s \times \frac{F}{m\left[\omega^2 - (\omega_n)^2\right]}$$

$$= s \times \frac{F}{m\left(\omega^2 - \dfrac{s}{m}\right)} = \frac{F.s}{m.\omega^2 - s} \qquad \dots \left[\because (\omega_n)^2 = \frac{s}{m}\right]$$

$$\therefore \qquad 600 = \frac{1843 \times s}{200\,(83.8)^2 - s} = \frac{1843\,s}{1.4 \times 10^6 - s} \qquad \dots \text{(Substituting } m = m_1)$$

---

* The equation (*x*) of Art. 23.16 is

$$x_{max} = \frac{F}{m\left[(\omega_n)^2 - \omega^2\right]}$$

Since the max. vibratory force transmitted to the foundation through the elastic support decreases at all higher speeds (*i.e.* above $N = 800$ r.p.m. or $\omega = 83.8$ rad/s), therefore we shall use

$$x_{max} = \frac{F}{m\left[\omega^2 - (\omega_n)^2\right]}$$

or
$$840 \times 10^6 - 600\,s = 1843\,s$$

∴
$$s = 0.344 \times 10^6 = 344 \times 10^3 \text{ N/m Ans.}$$

and maximum amplitude of vibration,

$$x_{max} = \frac{F}{m.\omega^2 - s} = \frac{1843}{200\,(83.8)^2 - 344 \times 10^3} = \frac{1843}{1056 \times 10^3} \text{ m}$$

$$= 1.745 \times 10^{-3} \text{ m} = 1.745 \text{ mm Ans.}$$

2. Speed at the which the transmitted force again becomes 600 N

The transmitted force will rise as the speed of the engine falls and passes through resonance. There will be a speed below resonance at which the transmitted force will again equal to 600 N. Let this speed be ω_1 rad/s (or N_1 r.p.m.).

∴ Disturbing force, $F = m_2\,(\omega_1)^2\,r = 3.5\,(\omega_1)^2\,0.075 = 0.2625\,(\omega_1)^2\,\text{N}$

Since the engine speed is reduced below $N_1 = 800$ r.p.m., therefore in this case, max, amplitude of vibration,

$$x_{max} = \frac{F}{m\left[(\omega_n)^2 - (\omega_1)^2\right]} = \frac{F}{m\left[\dfrac{s}{m} - (\omega_1)^2\right]} = \frac{F}{s - m\,(\omega_1)^2}$$

and
$$\text{Force transmitted} = s \times \frac{F}{s - m\,(\omega_1)^2}$$

∴
$$600 = 344 \times 10^3 \times \frac{0.2625\,(\omega_1)^2}{344 \times 10^3 - 200\,(\omega_1)^2} = \frac{90.3 \times 10^3\,(\omega_1)^2}{344 \times 10^3 - 200\,(\omega_1)^2}$$

. . . (Substituting $m = m_1$)

$$206.4 \times 10^6 - 120 \times 10^3\,(\omega_1)^2 = 90.3 \times 10^3\,(\omega_1)^2 \quad \text{or} \quad (\omega_1)^2 = 981$$

∴
$$\omega_1 = 31.32 \text{ rad/s} \quad \text{or} \quad N_1 = 31.32 \times 60/2\pi = 299 \text{ r.p.m. Ans.}$$

EXERCISES

1. A shaft of 100 mm diameter and 1 metre long is fixed at one end and other end carries a flywheel of mass 1 tonne. Taking Young's modulus for the shaft material as 200 GN/m^2, find the natural frequency of longitudinal and transverse vibrations. **[Ans. 200 Hz ; 8.6 Hz]**

2. A beam of length 10 m carries two loads of mass 200 kg at distances of 3 m from each end together with a central load of mass 1000 kg. Calculate the frequency of transverse vibrations. Neglect the mass of the beam and take $I = 10^9$ mm^4 and $E = 205 \times 10^3$ N/mm^2. **[Ans. 13.8 Hz]**

3. A steel bar 25 mm wide and 50 mm deep is freely supported at two points 1 m apart and carries a mass of 200 kg in the middle of the bar. Neglecting the mass of the bar, find the frequency of transverse vibration.

   If an additional mass of 200 kg is distributed uniformly over the length of the shaft, what will be the frequency of vibration ? Take $E = 200$ GN/m^2. **[Ans. 17.8 Hz ; 14.6 Hz]**

4. A shaft 1.5 m long is supported in flexible bearings at the ends and carries two wheels each of 50 kg mass. One wheel is situated at the centre of the shaft and the other at a distance of 0.4 m from the centre towards right. The shaft is hollow of external diameter 75 mm and inner diameter 37.5 mm. The density of the shaft material is 8000 kg/m^3. The Young's modulus for the shaft material is 200 GN/m^2. Find the frequency of transverse vibration. **[Ans. 33.2 Hz]**

5.	A shaft of diameter 10 mm carries at its centre a mass of 12 kg. It is supported by two short bearings, the centre distance of which is 400 mm. Find the whirling speed : 1. neglecting the mass of the shaft, and 2. taking the mass of the shaft also into consideration. The density of shaft material is 7500 kg/m^3.	[Ans. 748 r.p.m.; 744 r.p.m.]

6.	A shaft 180 mm diameter is supported in two bearings 2.5 metres apart. It carries three discs of mass 250 kg, 500 kg and 200 kg at 0.6 m, 1.5 m and 2 m from the left hand. Assuming the mass of the shaft 190 kg/m, determine the critical speed of the shaft. Young's modulus for the material of the shaft is 211 GN/m^2.	[Ans. 18.8 r.p.m.]

7.	A shaft 12.5 mm diameter rotates in long bearings and a disc of mass 16 kg is secured to a shaft at the middle of its length. The span of the shaft between the bearing is 0.5 m. The mass centre of the disc is 0.5 mm from the axis of the shaft. Neglecting the mass of the shaft and taking $E = 200$ GN/m^2, find : 1 critical speed of rotation in r.p.m., and 2. the range of speed over which the stress in the shaft due to bending will not exceed 120 MN/m^2. Take the static deflection of the shaft for a beam fixed at both ends, *i.e.* $\delta = \dfrac{Wl^3}{192 EI}$.	[Ans. 1450 r.p.m. ; 1184 to 2050 r.p.m.]

8.	A vertical shaft 25 mm diameter and 0.75 m long is mounted in long bearings and carries a pulley of mass 10 kg midway between the bearings. The centre of pulley is 0.5 mm from the axis of the shaft. Find (*a*) the whirling speed, and (*b*) the bending stress in the shaft, when it is rotating at 1700 r.p.m. Neglect the mass of the shaft and $E = 200$ GN/m^2.	[Ans. 3996 r.p.m ; 12.1 MN/m^2]

9.	A shaft 12 mm in diameter and 600 mm long between long bearings carries a central mass of 4 kg. If the centre of gravity of the mass is 0.2 mm from the axis of the shaft, compute the maximum flexural stress in the shaft when it is running at 90 per cent of its critical speed. The value of Young's modulus of the material of the shaft is 200 GN/m^2.	[Ans. 14.8 kN/m^2]

10.	A vibrating system consists of a mass of 8 kg, spring of stiffness 5.6 N/mm and a dashpot of damping coefficient of 40 N/m/s. Find (*a*) damping factor, (*b*) logarithmic decrement, and (*c*) ratio of the two consecutive amplitudes.	[Ans. 0.094 ; 0.6 ; 1.82]

11.	A body of mass of 50 kg is supported by an elastic structure of stiffness 10 kN/m. The motion of the body is controlled by a dashpot such that the amplitude of vibration decreases to one-tenth of its original value after two complete vibrations. Determine : 1. the damping force at 1 m/s ; 2. the damping ratio, and 3. the natural frequency of vibration.	[Ans. 252 N/m/s ; 0.178 ; 2.214 Hz]

12.	A mass of 85 kg is supported on springs which deflect 18 mm under the weight of the mass. The vibrations of the mass are constrained to be linear and vertical and are damped by a dashpot which reduces the amplitude to one quarter of its initial value in two complete oscillations. Find : 1. the magnitude of the damping force at unit speed, and 2. the periodic time of damped vibration.	[Ans. 435 N/m/s ; 0.27 s]

13.	The mass of a machine is 100 kg. Its vibrations are damped by a viscous dash pot which diminishes amplitude of vibrations from 40 mm to 10 mm in three complete oscillations. If the machine is mounted on four springs each of stiffness 25 kN/m, find (*a*) the resistance of the dash pot at unit velocity, and (*b*) the periodic time of the damped vibration.	[Ans. 6.92 N/m/s ; 0.2 s]

14.	A mass of 7.5 kg hangs from a spring and makes damped oscillations. The time for 60 oscillations is 35 seconds and the ratio of the first and seventh displacement is 2.5. Find (*a*) the stiffness of the spring, and (*b*) the damping resistance in N/m/s. If the oscillations are critically damped, what is the damping resistance required in N/m/s ?	[Ans. 870 N/m ; 3.9 N/m/s ; 162 N/m/s]

15.	A mass of 5 kg is supported by a spring of stiffness 5 kN/m. In addition, the motion of mass is controlled by a damper whose resistance is proportional to velocity. The amplitude of vibration reduces to 1/15th of the initial amplitude in four complete cycles. Determine the damping force per unit velocity and the ratio of the frequencies of the damped and undamped vibrations.	[Ans. 34 N/m/s : 0.994]

16.	A mass of 50 kg suspended from a spring produces a statical deflection of 17 mm and when in motion it experiences a viscous damping force of value 250 N at a velocity of 0.3 m/s. Calculate the periodic time of damped vibration. If the mass is then subjected to a periodic disturbing force having a maximum value of 200 N and making 2 cycles/s, find the amplitude of ultimate motion.	[Ans. 0.262 s ; 8.53 mm]

17. A mass of 50 kg is supported by an elastic structure of total stiffness 20 kN/m. The damping ratio of the system is 0.2. A simple harmonic disturbing force acts on the mass and at any time t seconds, the force is 60 cos 10 t newtons. Find the amplitude of the vibrations and the phase angle caused by the damping. **[Ans. 3.865 mm ; 14.93°]**

18. A machine of mass 100 kg is supported on openings of total stiffness 800 kN/m and has a rotating unbalanced element which results in a disturbing force of 400 N at a speed of 3000 r.p.m. Assuming the damping ratio as 0.25, determine : 1. the amplitude of vibrations due to unbalance ; and 2. the transmitted force. **[Ans. 0.04 mm ; 35.2 N]**

19. A mass of 500 kg is mounted on supports having a total stiffness of 100 kN/m and which provides viscous damping, the damping ratio being 0.4. The mass is constrained to move vertically and is subjected to a vertical disturbing force of the type $F \cos \omega t$. Determine the frequency at which resonance will occur and the maximum allowable value of F if the amplitude at resonance is to be restricted to 5 mm. **[Ans. 2.25 Hz ; 400 N]**

20. A machine of mass 75 kg is mounted on springs of stiffness 1200 kN/m and with an assumed damping factor of 0.2. A piston within the machine of mass 2 kg has a reciprocating motion with a stroke of 80 mm and a speed of 3000 cycles/min. Assuming the motion to be simple harmonic, find : 1. the amplitude of motion of the machine, 2. its phase angle with respect to the exciting force, 3. the force transmitted to the foundation, and 4. the phase angle of transmitted force with respect to the exciting force. **[Ans. 1.254 mm ; 169.05° ; 2132 N ; 44.8°]**

DO YOU KNOW ?

1. What are the causes and effects of vibrations ?
2. Define, in short, free vibrations, forced vibrations and damped vibrations.
3. Discuss briefly with neat sketches the longitudinal, transverse and torsional free vibrations.
4. Derive an expression for the natural frequency of free transverse and longitudinal vibrations by equilibrium method.
5. Discuss the effect of inertia of the shaft in longitudinal and transverse vibrations.
6. Deduce an expression for the natural frequency of free transverse vibrations for a simply supported shaft carrying uniformly distributed mass of m kg per unit length.
7. Deduce an expression for the natural frequency of free transverse vibrations for a beam fixed at both ends and carrying a uniformly distributed mass of m kg per unit length.
8. Establish an expression for the natural frequency of free transverse vibrations for a simply supported beam carrying a number of point loads, by (a) Energy method ; and (b) Dunkerley's method.
9. Explain the term 'whirling speed' or 'critical speed' of a shaft. Prove that the whirling speed for a rotating shaft is the same as the frequency of natural transverse vibration.
10. Derive the differential equation characterising the motion of an oscillation system subject to viscous damping and no periodic external force. Assuming the solution to the equation, find the frequency of oscillation of the system.
11. Explain the terms 'under damping, critical damping' and 'over damping'
12. A thin plate of area A and mass m is attached to the end of a spring and is allowed to oscillate in a viscous fluid, as shown in Fig. 23.25. Show that

Fig. 23.25

$$\mu = \frac{m}{A}\sqrt{\omega^2 - (\omega_d)^2}$$

where the damping force on the plate is equal to $\mu.A.v$; v being the velocity.

The symbols ω and ω_d indicate the undamped and damped natural circular frequencies of oscillations.

13. Explain the term 'Logarithmic decrement' as applied to damped vibrations.
14. Establish an expression for the amplitude of forced vibrations.
15. Explain the term 'dynamic magnifier'.
16. What do you understand by transmissibility ?

OBJECTIVE TYPE QUESTIONS

1. When there is a reduction in amplitude over every cycle of vibration, then the body is said to have
   (a) free vibration   (b) forced vibration   (c) damped vibration

2. Longitudinal vibrations are said to occur when the particles of a body moves
   (a) perpendicular to its axis   (b) parallel to its axis
   (c) in a circle about its axis

3. When a body is subjected to transverse vibrations, the stress induced in a body will be
   (a) shear stress   (b) tensile stress   (c) compressive stress

4. The natural frequency (in Hz) of free longitudinal vibrations is equal to

   (a) $\dfrac{1}{2\pi}\sqrt{\dfrac{s}{m}}$ (b) $\dfrac{1}{2\pi}\sqrt{\dfrac{g}{\delta}}$ (c) $\dfrac{0.4985}{\sqrt{\delta}}$

   (d) any one of these
   where m = Mass of the body in kg,
         s = Stiffness of the body in N/m, and
         δ = Static deflection of the body in metres.

5. The factor which affects the critical speed of a shaft is
   (a) diameter of the disc   (b) span of the shaft
   (c) eccentricity   (d) all of these

6. The equation of motion for a vibrating system with viscous damping is

   $$\frac{d^2x}{dt^2} + \frac{c}{m} \times \frac{dx}{dt} + \frac{s}{m} \times x = 0$$

   If the roots of this equation are real, then the system will be
   (a) over damped   (b) under damped   (c) critically damped

7. In under damped vibrating system, if x_1 and x_2 are the successive values of the amplitude on the same side of the mean position, then the logarithmic decrement is equal to
   (a) x_1/x_2 (b) log (x_1/x_2) (c) $\log_e (x_1/x_2)$ (d) log $(x_1.x_2)$

8. The ratio of the maximum displacement of the forced vibration to the deflection due to the static force, is known as
   (a) damping factor   (b) damping coefficient
   (c) logarithmic decrement   (d) magnification factor

9. In vibration isolation system, if ω/ω_n is less than $\sqrt{2}$, then for all values of the damping factor, the transmissibility will be
   (a) less than unity   (b) equal to unity   (c) greater than unity   (d) zero
   where ω = Circular frequency of the system in rad/s, and
         ω_n = Natural circular frequency of vibration of the system in rad/s.

10. In vibration isolation system, if $\omega/\omega_n > 1$, then the phase difference between the transmitted force and the disturbing force is
    (a) 0°   (b) 90°   (c) 180°   (d) 270°

ANSWERS

1. (c)	**2.** (b)	**3.** (b)	**4.** (d)	**5.** (d)
6. (a)	**7.** (b)	**8.** (d)	**9.** (c)	**10.** (c)

24

Torsional Vibrations

24.1. Introduction

We have already discussed in the previous chapter that when the particles of a shaft or disc move in a circle about the axis of a shaft, then the vibrations are known as *torsional vibrations*. In this case, the shaft is twisted and untwisted alternately and torsional shear stresses are induced in the shaft. In this chapter, we shall now discuss the frequency of torsional vibrations of various systems.

24.2. Natural Frequency of Free Torsional Vibrations

Consider a shaft of negligible mass whose one end is fixed and the other end carrying a disc as shown in Fig. 24.1.

Let θ = Angular displacement of the shaft from mean position after time t in radians,

m = Mass of disc in kg,

I = Mass moment of inertia of disc in kg-m^2 = $m.k^2$,

k = Radius of gyration in metres,

q = Torsional stiffness of the shaft in N-m.

∴   Restoring force $= q.\theta$ ... (*i*)

and accelerating force $= I \times \dfrac{d^2\theta}{dt^2}$ ... (*ii*)

Equating equations (*i*) and (*ii*), the equation of motion is

$$I \times \frac{d^2\theta}{dt^2} = -q.\theta$$

or $$I \times \frac{d^2\theta}{dt^2} + q.\theta = 0$$

∴ $$\frac{d^2\theta}{dt^2} + \frac{q}{I} \times \theta = 0$$ ... (*iii*)

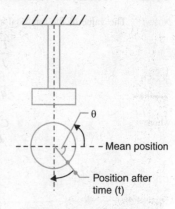

Fig 24.1. Natural frequency of free torsional vibrations.

The fundamental equation of the simple harmonic motion is

$$\frac{d^2\theta}{dt^2} + \omega^2 . x = 0$$ ... (*iv*)

Comparing equations (*iii*) and (*iv*),

$$\omega = \sqrt{\frac{q}{I}}$$

∴   Time period, $$t_p = \frac{2\pi}{\omega} = 2\pi \sqrt{\frac{I}{q}}$$

and natural frequency , $$f_n = \frac{1}{t_p} = \frac{1}{2\pi}\sqrt{\frac{q}{I}}$$

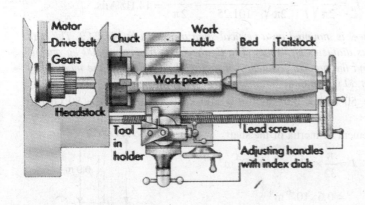

Note : This picture is given as additional information.

A modern lathe can create an artificial hip joint from information fed into it by a computer. Accurate drawings of the joint are first made on a computer and the information about the dimensions fed is directly into the lathe.

Note : The value of the torsional stiffness q may be obtained from the torsion equation,

$$\frac{T}{J} = \frac{C.\theta}{l} \quad \text{or} \quad \frac{T}{\theta} = \frac{C.J}{l}$$

$$\therefore \qquad q = \frac{C.J}{l} \qquad \qquad \dots \left(\because \frac{T}{\theta} = q \right)$$

where
C = Modulus of rigidity for the shaft material,

J = Polar moment of inertia of the shaft cross-section,

$$= \frac{\pi}{32} d^4 \; ; d \text{ is the diameter of the shaft, and}$$

l = Length of the shaft.

Example 24.1. *A shaft of 100 mm diameter and 1 metre long has one of its end fixed and the other end carries a disc of mass 500 kg at a radius of gyration of 450 mm. The modulus of rigidity for the shaft material is 80 GN/m². Determine the frequency of torsional vibrations.*

Solution. Given : $d = 100$ mm $= 0.1$ m ; $l = 1$ m ; $m = 500$ kg ; $k = 450$ mm $= 0.45$ m ; $C = 80$ GN/m² $= 80 \times 10^9$ N/m²

We know that polar moment of inertia of the shaft,

$$J = \frac{\pi}{32} \times d^4 = \frac{\pi}{32} (0.1)^4 = 9.82 \times 10^{-6} \, \text{m}^4$$

$\therefore$ Torsional stiffness of the shaft,

$$q = \frac{C.J}{l} = \frac{80 \times 10^9 \times 9.82 \times 10^{-6}}{1} = 785.6 \times 10^3 \, \text{N-m}$$

We know that mass moment of inertia of the shaft,

$$I = m.k^2 = 500(0.45)^2 = 101.25 \; \text{kg-m}^2$$

$\therefore$ Frequency of torsional vibrations,

$$f_n = \frac{1}{2\pi} \sqrt{\frac{q}{I}} = \frac{1}{2\pi} \sqrt{\frac{785.6 \times 10^3}{101.25}} = \frac{88.1}{2\pi} = 14 \text{ Hz } \textbf{Ans.}$$

Example 24.2. *A flywheel is mounted on a vertical shaft as shown in Fig 24.2. The both ends of a shaft are fixed and its diameter is 50 mm. The flywheel has a mass of 500 kg and its radius of gyration is 0.5 m. Find the natural frequency of torsional vibrations, if the modulus of rigidity for the shaft material is 80 GN/m².*

Solution. Given : $d = 50$ mm $= 0.05$ m ; $m = 500$ kg ; $k = 0.5$m; $G = 80$ GN/m² $= 84 \times 10^9$ N/m²

We know that polar moment of inertia of the shaft,

$$J = \frac{\pi}{32} \times d^4 = \frac{\pi}{32} (0.05)^4 \, \text{m}^4$$

$$= 0.6 \times 10^{-6} \, \text{m}^4$$

$\therefore$ Torsional stiffness of the shaft for length l_1,

$$q_1 = \frac{C.J}{l_1} = \frac{84 \times 10^9 \times 0.6 \times 10^{-6}}{0.9}$$

$$= 56 \times 10^3 \, \text{N-m}$$

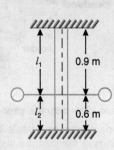

Fig 24.2

(l_1 — 0.9 m ; l_2 — 0.6 m)

Similarly torsional stiffness of the shaft for length l_2,

$$q_2 = \frac{C.J}{l_2} = \frac{84\times10^9 \times 0.6\times10^{-6}}{0.6} = 84 \times 10^3 \text{ N-m}$$

∴   Total torsional stiffness of the shaft,

$$q = q_1 + q_2 = 56\times10^3 + 84\times10^3 = 140\times10^3 \text{ N-m}$$

We know that mass moment of inertia of the flywheel,

$$I = m.k^2 = 500(0.5)^2 = 125 \text{ kg-m}^2$$

∴   Natural frequency of torsional vibration,

$$f_n = \frac{1}{2\pi}\sqrt{\frac{q}{I}} = \frac{1}{2\pi}\sqrt{\frac{140\times10^3}{125}} = \frac{33.5}{2\pi} = 5.32 \text{ Hz Ans.}$$

24.3. Effect of Inertia of the Constraint on Torsional Vibrations

Consider a constraint *i.e.* shaft whose one end is fixed and the other end free, as shown in Fig.24.3.

Let   ω = Angular velocity of free end,

m = Mass of constraint for unit length,

l = Length of constraint,

m_C = Total mass of constraint = $m.l$,

k = Radius of gyration of constraint,

I_C = Total mass moment of inertia of constraint

$$= m_C.k^2 = m.l.k^2.$$

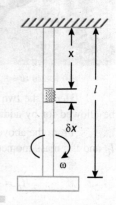

Fig 24.3. Effect of inertia of the constraint on torsional vibrations.

Consider a small element at a distance x from the fixed end and of length δx. Therefore,

Mass moment of inertia of the element

$$= (m.\delta x)k^2 = \frac{\delta x}{l}\times m.k^2.l$$

... (Dividing and multiplying by *l*)

$$= \frac{\delta x}{l}\times I_C$$

... (Substituting $m.k^2.l = I_C$)

and angular velocity of the element

$$= \frac{\omega}{l}\times x$$

Kinetic energy possessed by the element

$$= \frac{1}{2}\left(\frac{\delta x}{l}\times I_C\right)\left(\frac{\omega}{l}\times x\right)^2 = \frac{I_C.\omega^2.x^2}{2l^3}\times \delta x$$

∴   Total kinetic energy of the constraint

$$= \int_0^l \frac{I_C.\omega^2}{2l^3}\times x^2 \, dx = \frac{I_C.\omega^2}{2l^3}\left[\frac{x^3}{3}\right]_0^l = \frac{1}{2}\left(\frac{I_C}{3}\right)\omega^2 \qquad \text{... (i)}$$

If a mass whose mass moment of inertia is equal to $I_C/3$ is placed at the free end and the constraint is assumed to be of negligible mass, then

Total kinetic energy of the constraint

$$= \frac{1}{2}\left(\frac{I_C}{3}\right)\omega^2 \qquad \ldots \text{[Same as equation } (i)\text{]}$$

When loads are applied on the above two pulleys, the shaft is subject to torsional vibration

Hence the two systems are dynamically same. Therefore the inertia of the constraint may be allowed for by adding $I_C/3$ to the mass moment of inertia I of the disc at the free end.

From the above discussion, we find that when the mass moment of inertia of the constraint I_C and the mass moment of inertia of the disc I are known, then natural frequency of vibration,

$$f_n = \frac{1}{2\pi}\sqrt{\frac{q}{I + I_C/3}}$$

24.4. Free Torsional Vibrations of a Single Rotor System

We have already discussed that for a shaft fixed at one end and carrying a rotor at the free end as shown in Fig. 24.4, the natural frequency of torsional vibration,

$$f_n = \frac{1}{2\pi}\sqrt{\frac{q}{I}} = \frac{1}{2\pi}\sqrt{\frac{C.J}{l.I}}$$

$$\ldots \left(\because q = \frac{C.J}{l} \right)$$

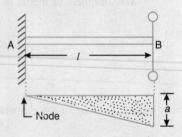

Fig 24.4. Free torsional vibrations of a single rotor system.

where C = Modulus of rigidity for shaft material,

J = Polar moment of inertia of shaft

$$= \frac{\pi}{32}\times d^4$$

d = Diameter of shaft,

l = Length of shaft,

m = Mass of rotor,

k = Radius of gyration of rotor, and

I = Mass moment of inertia of rotor = $m.k^2$

A little consideration will show that the amplitude of vibration is zero at A and maximum at B, as shown in Fig. 24.4. It may be noted that the point or the section of the shaft whose amplitude of torsional vibration is zero, is known as *node*. In other words, at the node, the shaft remains unaffected by the vibration.

24.5. Free Torsional Vibrations of a Two Rotor System

Consider a two rotor system as shown in Fig. 24.5. It consists of a shaft with two rotors at its ends. In this system, the torsional vibrations occur only when the two rotors A and B move in opposite directions *i.e.* if A moves in anticlockwise direction then B moves in clockwise direction at the same instant and *vice versa*. It may be noted that the two rotors must have the same frequency.

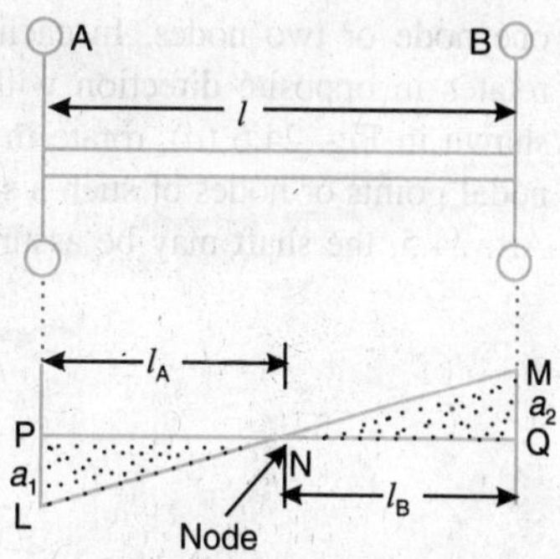

We see from Fig. 24.5 that the node lies at point N. This point can be safely assumed as a fixed end and the shaft may be considered as two separate shafts $N P$ and $N Q$ each fixed to one of its ends and carrying rotors at the free ends.

Let l = Length of shaft,

l_A = Length of part NP *i.e.* distance of node from rotor A,

l_B = Length of part NQ, *i.e.* distance of node from rotor B,

I_A = Mass moment of inertia of rotor A,

I_B = Mass moment of inertia of rotor B,

d = Diameter of shaft,

J = Polar moment of inertia of shaft, and

C = Modulus of rigidity for shaft material.

∴ Natural frequency of torsional vibration for rotor A,

Fig 24.5. Free torsional vibrations of a two rotor system.

$$f_{nA} = \frac{1}{2\pi}\sqrt{\frac{C.J}{l_A.I_A}} \qquad \ldots (i)$$

and natural frequency of torsional vibration for rotor B,

$$f_{nB} = \frac{1}{2\pi}\sqrt{\frac{C.J}{l_B.I_B}} \qquad \ldots (ii)$$

Since $f_{nA} = f_{nB}$, therefore

$$\frac{1}{2\pi}\sqrt{\frac{C.J}{l_A.I_A}} = \frac{1}{2\pi}\sqrt{\frac{C.J}{l_B.I_B}} \quad \text{or} \quad l_A \cdot I_A = l_B \cdot I_B \qquad \ldots (iii)$$

∴

$$l_A = \frac{l_B.I_B}{I_A}$$

We also know that

$$l = l_A + l_B \qquad \ldots (iv)$$

From equations (*iii*) and (*iv*), we may find the value of l_A and l_B and hence the position of node. Substituting the values of l_A or l_B in equation (*i*) or (*ii*), the natural frequency of torsional vibration for a two rotor system may be evaluated.

Note : The line *LNM* in Fig.24.5 is known as **elastic line** for the shaft.

24.6. Free Torsional Vibrations of a Three Rotor System

Consider a three rotor system as shown is Fig. 24.6 (*a*). It consists of a shaft and three rotors *A*, *B* and *C*. The rotors *A* and *C* are attached to the ends of a shaft, whereas the rotor *B* is attached in between *A* and *C*. The torsional vibrations may occur in two ways, that is with either one node or two nodes. In each case, the two rotors rotate in one direction and the third rotor rotates in opposite direction with the same frequency. Let the rotors *A* and *C* of the system, as shown in Fig. 24.6 (*a*), rotate in the same direction and the rotor *B* in opposite direction. Let the nodal points or nodes of such a system lies at N_1 and N_2 as shown in Fig. 24.6 (*b*). As discussed in Art. 24.5, the shaft may be assumed as a fixed end at the nodes.

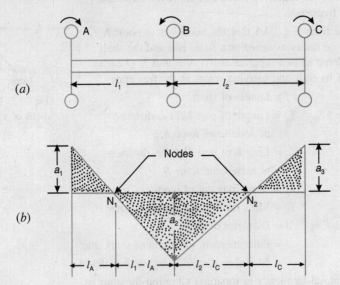

Fig. 24.6. Free torsional vibrations of a three rotor system.

Let l_1 = Distance between rotors *A* and *B*,

                 l_2 = Distance between rotors *B* and *C*,

                 l_A = Distance of node N_1 from rotor *A*,

                 l_C = Distance of node N_2 from rotor *C*,

                 I_A = Mass moment of inertia of rotor *A*,

                 I_B = Mass moment of inertia of rotor *B*,

                 I_C = Mass moment of inertia of rotor *C*,

                 d = Diameter of shaft,

                 J = Polar moment of inertia of shaft, and

                 C = Modulus of rigidity for shaft material.

∴   Natural frequency of torsional vibrations for rotor A,

$$f_{nA} = \frac{1}{2\pi}\sqrt{\frac{C.J}{l_A.I_A}}$$ ... (*i*)

Natural frequency of torsional vibrations for rotor B,

$$*f_{nB} = \frac{1}{2\pi}\sqrt{\frac{C.J}{I_B}\left(\frac{1}{l_1 - l_A} + \frac{1}{l_2 - l_C}\right)} \qquad \dots (ii)$$

and natural frequency of torsional vibrations for rotor C,

$$f_{nC} = \frac{1}{2\pi}\sqrt{\frac{C.J}{l_C.I_C}} \qquad \dots (iii)$$

Since $f_{nA} = f_{nB} = f_{nC,}$ therefore equating equations (i) and (iii)

$$\frac{1}{2\pi}\sqrt{\frac{C.J}{l_A.I_A}} = \frac{1}{2\pi}\sqrt{\frac{C.J}{l_C.I_C}} \qquad \text{or} \qquad l_A.I_A = l_C.I_C$$

$$\therefore \qquad l_A = \frac{l_C.I_C}{I_A} \qquad \dots (iv)$$

Now equating equations (ii) and (iii),

$$\frac{1}{2\pi}\sqrt{\frac{C.J}{I_B}\left(\frac{1}{l_1 - l_A} + \frac{1}{l_2 - l_C}\right)} = \frac{1}{2\pi}\sqrt{\frac{C.J}{l_C.I_C}}$$

or $\qquad \dfrac{1}{I_B}\left(\dfrac{1}{l_1 - l_A} + \dfrac{1}{l_2 - l_C}\right) = \dfrac{1}{l_C.I_C}$ $\qquad \dots (v)$

On substituting the value of l_A from equation (iv) in the above expression, a quadratic equation in l_C is obtained. Therefore, there are two values of l_C and correspondingly two values of l_A. One value of l_A and the corresponding value of l_C gives the position of two nodes. The frequency obtained by substituting the value of l_A or l_C in equation (i) or (iii) is known as *two node frequency*. But in the other pair of values, one gives the position of single node and the other is beyond the physical limits of the equation. In this case, the frequency obtained is known as *fundamental frequency* or *single node frequency*.

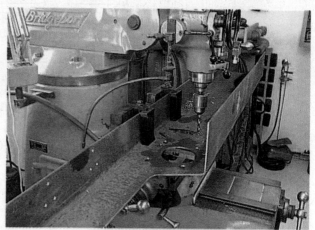

Inside view of a workshop.

Note : This picture is given as additional information.

---

* Since the resisting torque of the rotor B is supplied by two lengths $(l_1 - l_A)$ and $(l_2 - l_C)$ between the nodes N_1 and N_2, therefore the each length is twisted through the same angle and the combined torsional stiffness is equal to the sum of the separate stiffness.

We know that torsional stiffness due to $(l_1 - l_A)$ $= \dfrac{C.J}{l_1 - l_A}$

and torsional stiffness due to $(l_2 - l_C)$ $\qquad = \dfrac{C.J}{l_2 - l_C}$

$\therefore \qquad$ Total stiffness of the rotor B $\qquad = C.J\left(\dfrac{1}{l_1 - l_A} + \dfrac{1}{l_2 - l_C}\right)$

It may be noted that

1. When the rotors A and B rotate in the same direction and the rotor C in the opposite direction, then the torsional vibrations occur with a single node, as shown in Fig. 24.7 (b). In this case $l_A > l_1$ *i.e.* the node lies between the rotors B and C, but it does not give the actual value of the node.

2. When the rotors B and C rotate in the same direction and the rotor A in opposite direction, then the torsional vibrations also occur with a single node as shown in Fig. 24.7 (c). In this case $l_C > l_2$ *i.e* the node lies between the rotors A and B, but it does not give the actual value of the node.

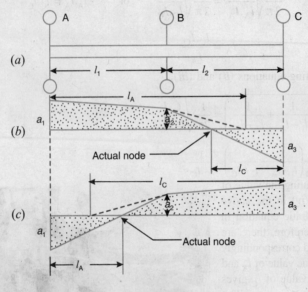

Fig 24.7

3. When the amplitude of vibration for the rotor A (a_1) is known, then the amplitude of rotor B,

$$a_2 = \frac{l_A - l_1}{l_A} \times a_1$$

and amplitude of rotor C, $\qquad a_3 = \frac{l_C}{l_C - l_2} \times a_2$

As there are two values of l_A and l_C, therefore there will be two values of amplitude for one node and two node vibrations.

24.7. Torsionally Equivalent Shaft

In the previous articles, we have assumed that the shaft is of uniform diameter. But in actual practice, the shaft may have variable diameter for different lengths. Such a shaft may, theoretically, be replaced by an equivalent shaft of uniform diameter.

Consider a shaft of varying diameters as shown in Fig. 24.8 (a). Let this shaft is replaced by an equivalent shaft of uniform diameter d and length l as shown in Fig.24.8 (b).These two shafts must have the same total angle of twist when equal opposing torques T are applied at their opposite ends.

Let d_1, d_2 and d_3 = Diameters for the lengths l_1, l_2 and l_3 respectively,

θ_1, θ_2 and θ_3 = Angle of twist for the lengths l_1, l_2 and l_3 respectively,

θ = Total angle of twist, and

J_1, J_2 and J_3 = Polar moment of inertia for the shafts of diameters d_1, d_2 and d_3 respectively.

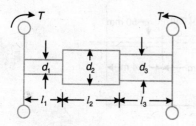

(*a*) Shaft of varying diameters.

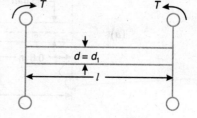

(*b*) Torsionally equivalent shaft.

Fig 24.8

Since the total angle of twist of the shaft is equal to the sum of the angle of twists of different lengths, therefore

$$\theta = \theta_1 + \theta_2 + \theta_3$$

or

$$\frac{T.l}{C.J} = \frac{T.l_1}{C.J_1} + \frac{T.l_2}{C.J_2} + \frac{T.l_3}{C.J_3}$$

$$\frac{l}{J} = \frac{l_1}{J_1} + \frac{l_2}{J_2} + \frac{l_3}{J_3}$$

$$\frac{l}{\dfrac{\pi}{32} \times d^4} = \frac{l_1}{\dfrac{\pi}{32}(d_1)^4} + \frac{l_2}{\dfrac{\pi}{32}(d_2)^4} + \frac{l_3}{\dfrac{\pi}{32}(d_3)^4}$$

$$\frac{l}{d^4} = \frac{l_1}{(d_1)^4} + \frac{l_2}{(d_2)^4} + \frac{l_3}{(d_3)^4}$$

In actual calculations, it is assumed that the diameter d of the equivalent shaft is equal to one of the diameter of the actual shaft. Let us assume that $d = d_1$.

$$\therefore \qquad \frac{l}{(d_1)^4} = \frac{l_1}{(d_1)^4} + \frac{l_2}{(d_2)^4} + \frac{l_3}{(d_3)^4}$$

or

$$l = l_1 + l_2 \left(\frac{d_1}{d_2}\right)^4 + l_3 \left(\frac{d_1}{d_3}\right)^4$$

This expression gives the length l of an equivalent shaft.

Example 24.3. *A steel shaft 1.5 m long is 95 mm in diameter for the first 0.6 m of its length, 60 mm in diameter for the next 0.5 m of the length and 50 mm in diameter for the remaining 0.4 m of its length. The shaft carries two flywheels at two ends, the first having a mass of 900 kg and 0.85 m radius of gyration located at the 95 mm diameter end and the second having a mass of 700 kg and 0.55 m radius of gyration located at the other end. Determine the location of the node and the natural frequency of free torsional vibration of the system. The modulus of rigidity of shaft material may be taken as 80 GN/m².*

Solution. Given : $L = 1.5$ m ; $d_1 = 95$ mm $= 0.095$ m ; $l_1 = 0.6$ m ; $d_2 = 60$ mm $= 0.06$ m ; $l_2 = 0.5$ m ; $d_3 = 50$ mm $= 0.05$ m ; $l_3 = 0.4$ m ; $m_A = 900$ kg ; $k_A = 0.85$ m ; $m_B = 700$ kg ; $k_B = 0.55$ m ; $C = 80$ GN/m² $= 80 \times 10^9$ N/m²

The actual shaft is shown in Fig. 24.9 (a). First of all, let us find the length of the equivalent shaft, assuming its diameter as $d_1 = 95$ mm as shown in Fig 24.9 (b).

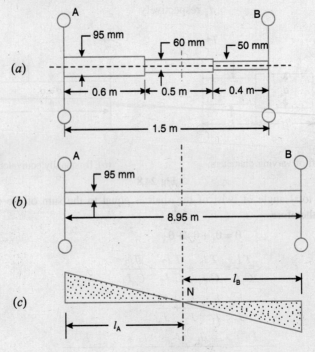

Fig. 24.9

We know that length of the equivalent shaft,

$$l = l_1 + l_2 \left(\frac{d_1}{d_2} \right)^4 + l_3 \left(\frac{d_1}{d_3} \right)^4 = 0.6 + 0.5 \left(\frac{0.095}{0.06} \right)^4 + 0.4 \left(\frac{0.095}{0.05} \right)^4$$

$$= 0.6 + 3.14 + 5.21 = 8.95 \text{ m}$$

Location of the node

Suppose the node of the equivalent shaft lies at N as shown in Fig. 24.9 (c).

Let l_A = Distance of the node from flywheel A, and

                  l_B = Distance of the node from flywheel B.

We know that mass moment of inertia of flywheel A,

$$I_A = m_A (k_A)^2 = 900 (0.85)^2 = 650 \text{ kg-m}^2$$

and mass moment of inertia of flywheel B,

$$I_B = m_B (k_B)^2 = 700 (0.55)^2 = 212 \text{ kg-m}^2$$

We know that $l_A . I_A = l_B . I_B$ or $l_A = \dfrac{l_B . I_B}{I_A} = \dfrac{l_B \times 212}{650} = 0.326 \, l_B$

Also, $l_A + l_B = l = 8.95$ m   or $0.326 \, l_B + l_B = 8.95$ or $l_B = 6.75$ m

and $l_A = 8.95 - 6.75 = 2.2$ m

Hence the node lies at 2.2 m from flywheel *A* or 6.75 m from flywheel *B* on the equivalent shaft.

∴ Position of node on the original shaft from flywheel *A*

$$= l_1 + (l_A - l_1)\left(\frac{d_2}{d_1}\right)^4 = 0.6 + (2.2 - 0.6)\left(\frac{0.06}{0.095}\right)^4 = 0.855 \text{ m } \textbf{Ans.}$$

Natural frequency of free torsional vibrations

We know that polar moment of inertia of the equivalent shaft,

$$J = \frac{\pi}{32}(d_1)^4 = \frac{\pi}{32}(0.095)^4 = 8 \times 10^{-6} \text{m}^4$$

Natural frequency of free torsional vibrations,

$$f_n = f_{nA} \quad \text{or} \quad f_{nB}$$

$$= \frac{1}{2\pi}\sqrt{\frac{C.J}{l_A.I_A}} = \frac{1}{2\pi}\sqrt{\frac{80 \times 10^9 \times 8 \times 10^{-6}}{2.2 \times 650}} = 3.37 \text{ Hz} \qquad \textbf{Ans.}$$

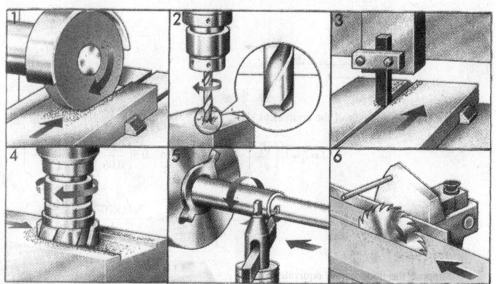

The above machine tools include grinding machine, drill, router, milling machines, lathe and a circular saw.

Note : This picture is given as additional information.

Example 24.4. *A steel shaft ABCD 1.5 m long has flywheel at its ends A and D. The mass of the flywheel A is 600 kg and has a radius of gyration of 0.6 m. The mass of the flywheel D is 800 kg and has a radius of gyration of 0.9 m. The connecting shaft has a diameter of 50 mm for the portion AB which is 0.4 m long ; and has a diameter of 60 mm for the portion BC which is 0.5 m long ; and has a diameter of d mm for the portion CD which is 0.6 m long. Determine :*

1. the diameter 'd' of the portion CD so that the node of the torsional vibration of the system will be at the centre of the length BC ; and 2. the natural frequency of the torsional vibrations.

The modulus of rigidity for the shaft material is 80 GN/m².

Solution. Given : $L = 1.5$ m ; $m_A = 600$ kg ; $k_A = 0.6$ m ; $m_D = 800$ kg ; $k_D = 0.9$ m ; $d_1 = 50$ mm $= 0.05$ m ; $l_1 = 0.4$ m ; $d_2 = 60$ mm $= 0.06$ m ; $l_2 = 0.5$ m ; $d_3 = d$; $l_3 = 0.6$ m ; $C = 80$ GN/m² $= 80 \times 10^9$ N/m²

The actual shaft is shown is Fig. 24.10 (a). First of all, let us find the length of the equivalent shaft, assuming its diameter as $d_1 = 50$ mm, as shown in Fig. 24.10 (b).

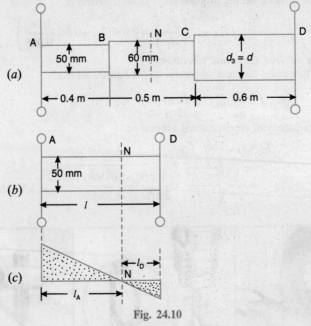

Fig. 24.10

We know that length of the equivalent shaft,

$$l = l_1 + l_2 \left(\frac{d_1}{d_2}\right)^4 + l_3 \left(\frac{d_1}{d_3}\right)^4 = 0.4 + 0.5 \left(\frac{0.05}{0.06}\right)^4 + 0.6 \left(\frac{0.05}{d}\right)^4$$

... [Substituting $d_3 = d$]

$$= 0.4 + 0.24 + \frac{3.75 \times 10^{-6}}{d^4} = 0.64 + \frac{3.75 \times 10^{-6}}{d^4} \qquad ... (i)$$

1. Diameter 'd' of the shaft CD

Suppose the node of the equivalent shaft lies at N as shown in Fig. 24.10 (c).

Let l_A = Distance of the node from flywheel A, and

l_D = Distance of the node from flywheel D.

We know that mass moment of inertia of flywheel A,

$$I_A = m_A (k_A)^2 = 600 (0.6)^2 = 216 \text{ kg-m}^2$$

and mass moment of inertia of flywheel D,

$$I_D = m_D (k_D)^2 = 800 (0.9)^2 = 648 \text{ kg-m}^2$$

A pulley is being processed at a turning centre.

Note : This picture is given as additional information.

We know that

$$l_A . I_A = l_D . I_D$$

or

$$l_D = \frac{l_A . I_A}{I_D} = \frac{l_A \times 216}{648} = \frac{l_A}{3}$$

Since the node lies in the centre of the length BC in an original system, therefore its equivalent length from rotor A,

$$l_A = l_1 + \frac{l_2}{2}\left(\frac{d_1}{d_2}\right)^4 = 0.4 + \frac{0.5}{2}\left(\frac{0.05}{0.06}\right)^4 = 0.52\,\text{m}$$

$\therefore$

$$l_D = \frac{l_A}{3} = \frac{0.52}{3} = 0.173\,\text{m}$$

We know that

$$l = l_A + l_D$$

or

$$0.64 + \frac{3.75 \times 10^{-6}}{d^4} = 0.52 + 0.173 \qquad \text{. . . [From equation (i)]}$$

$$\frac{3.75 \times 10^{-6}}{d^4} = 0.52 + 0.173 - 0.64 = 0.053$$

$\therefore$

$$d^4 = \frac{3.75 \times 10^{-6}}{0.053} = 70.75 \times 10^{-6}$$

or

$$d = 0.0917\,\text{m} = 91.7\,\text{mm} \text{ Ans.}$$

2. *Natural frequency of torsional vibrations*

We know that polar moment of inertia of the equivalent shaft,

$$J = \frac{\pi}{32}(d_1)^4 = \frac{\pi}{32}(0.05)^4 = 0.614 \times 10^{-6}\,\text{m}^4$$

$\therefore$ Natural frequency of torsional vibration,

$$f_n = f_{nA} \text{ or } f_{nD}$$

$$= \frac{1}{2\pi}\sqrt{\frac{C.J}{l_A . I_A}} = \frac{1}{2\pi}\sqrt{\frac{80 \times 10^9 \times 0.614 \times 10^{-6}}{0.52 \times 216}} \text{ Hz} = 3.33\,\text{Hz Ans.}$$

Example 24.5. *A single cylinder oil engine drives directly a centrifugal pump. The rotating mass of the engine, flywheel and the pump with the shaft is equivalent to a three rotor system as shown in Fig. 24.11.*

The mass moment of inertia of the rotors A, B and C are 0.15, 0.3 and 0.09 kg-m². Find the natural frequency of the torsional vibration. The modulus of rigidity for the shaft material is 84 kN/mm².

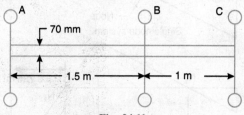

Fig. 24.11

Solution. Given : $I_A = 0.15$ kg-m² ; $I_B = 0.3$ kg-m² ; $I_C = 0.09$ kg-m² ; $d = 70$ mm $= 0.07$ m; $l_1 = 1.5$ m ; $l_2 = 1$ m ; $C = 84$ kN/mm² $= 84 \times 10^9$ N/m²

We know that

$$l_A . I_A = l_C . I_C$$

$$\therefore \qquad l_A = \frac{l_C \times I_C}{I_A} = l_C \times \frac{0.09}{0.15} = 0.6\, l_C$$

Also

$$\frac{1}{l_C . I_C} = \frac{1}{I_B}\left(\frac{1}{l_1 - l_A} + \frac{1}{l_2 - l_C}\right)$$

$$\frac{1}{l_C \times 0.09} = \frac{1}{0.3}\left(\frac{1}{1.5 - l_A} + \frac{1}{1 - l_C}\right)$$

$$\frac{0.3}{l_C \times 0.09} = \frac{1}{1.5 - 0.6 l_C} + \frac{1}{1 - l_C} \qquad \qquad \dots \text{(Substituting } l_A = 0.6\, l_C)$$

$$\frac{10}{3 l_C} = \frac{1 - l_C + 1.5 - 0.6 l_C}{(1.5 - 0.6 l_C)(1 - l_C)} = \frac{2.5 - 1.6 l_C}{1.5 - 2.1 l_C + 0.6 (l_C)^2}$$

On cross-multiplying and re-arranging,

$$10.8\,(l_C)^2 - 28.5\, l_C + 15 = 0$$

$$\therefore \qquad l_C = \frac{28.5 \pm \sqrt{(28.5)^2 - 4 \times 10.8 \times 15}}{2 \times 10.8} = \frac{28.5 \pm 12.8}{21.6}$$

$$= 1.91 \text{ m} \qquad \text{or} \qquad 0.726 \text{ m}$$

and
$$l_A = 0.6\, l_C = 1.146 \text{ m or } 0.4356 \text{ m}$$

Here we see that when $l_C = 1.91$ m, then $l_A = 1.146$ m. This gives the position of single node for $l_A = 1.146$ m, as shown in Fig. 24.12 (b). The value of $l_C = 0.726$ m and corresponding value of $l_A = 0.4356$ m gives the position of two nodes, as shown in Fig. 24.12 (c).

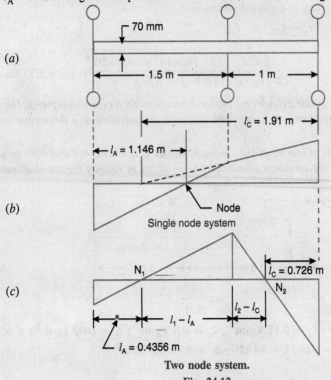

Fig. 24.12

We know that polar moment of inertia of the shaft,

$$J = \frac{\pi}{32} \times d^4 = \frac{\pi}{32}(0.07)^4 = 2.36 \times 10^{-6} \, \text{m}^4$$

∴ Natural frequency of torsional vibration for a single node system,

$$f_{n1} = \frac{1}{2\pi}\sqrt{\frac{C.J}{l_A.I_A}} = \frac{1}{2\pi}\sqrt{\frac{84 \times 10^9 \times 2.36 \times 10^{-6}}{1.146 \times 0.15}} \quad \text{Hz}$$

$$= 171 \, \text{Hz} \quad \textbf{Ans.} \qquad \qquad \dots \text{(Substituting } l_A = 1.146 \, \text{m)}$$

Similarly, natural frequency of torsional vibration for a two node system,

$$f_{n2} = \frac{1}{2\pi}\sqrt{\frac{C.J}{l_A.I_A}} = \frac{1}{2\pi}\sqrt{\frac{84 \times 10^9 \times 2.36 \times 10^{-6}}{0.4356 \times 0.15}} \quad \text{Hz}$$

$$= 277 \, \text{Hz} \quad \textbf{Ans.} \qquad \qquad \dots \text{(Substituting } l_A = 0.4356 \, \text{m)}$$

Example 24.6. *A motor generator set, as shown in Fig. 24.13, consists of two armatures A and C connected with flywheel between them at B. The modulus of rigidity of the connecting shaft is 84 GN/m². The system can vibrate torsionally with one node at 95 mm from A, the flywheel being at antinode. Find : 1. the position of another node ; 2. the natural frequency of vibration; and 3. the radius of gyration of the armature C.*

The other data are given below :

Particulars	A	B	C
Radius of gyration, mm	300	375	–
Mass, kg	400	500	300

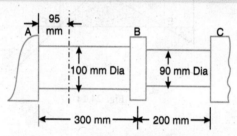

Fig. 24.13

Solution. Given : $C = 84 \, \text{GN/m}^2 = 84 \times 10^9 \, \text{N/m}^2$; $d_1 = 100 \, \text{mm} = 0.1 \, \text{m}$; $d_2 = 90 \, \text{mm} = 0.09 \, \text{m}$; $l_1 = 300 \, \text{mm} = 0.3 \, \text{m}$; $l_2 = 200 \, \text{mm} = 0.2 \, \text{m}$; $l_A = 95 \, \text{mm} = 0.095 \, \text{m}$; $m_A = 400 \, \text{kg}$; $k_A = 300 \, \text{mm} = 0.3 \, \text{m}$; $m_B = 500 \, \text{kg}$; $k_B = 375 \, \text{mm} = 0.375 \, \text{m}$; $m_C = 300 \, \text{kg}$

We know that mass moment of inertia of armature A,

$$I_A = m_A (k_A)^2 = 400 (0.3)^2 = 36 \, \text{kg-m}^2$$

and mass moment of inertia of flywheel B,

$$I_B = m_B (k_B)^2 = 500 (0.375)^2 = 70.3 \, \text{kg-m}^2$$

1. Position of another node

First of all, replace the original system, as shown in Fig. 24.14 (*a*), by an equivalent system as shown in Fig. 24.14 (*b*). It is assumed that the diameter of the equivalent shaft is $d_1 = 100$ mm $= 0.1$ m because the node lies in this portion. We know that the length of the equivalent shaft,

$$l = l_1 + l_2 \left(\frac{d_1}{d_2}\right)^4 = 0.3 + 0.2 \left(\frac{0.1}{0.09}\right)^4 = 0.605 \text{ m}$$

The first node lies at *E* at a distance 95 mm from rotor *A* i.e. $l_A = 95$ mm $= 0.095$ m, as shown in Fig. 24.14 (*c*).

Let l_C = Distance of node *F* in an equivalent system from rotor *C*, and

        l_3 = Distance between flywheel *B* and armature *C* in an equivalent system = $l - l_1 = 0.605 - 0.3 = 0.305$ m

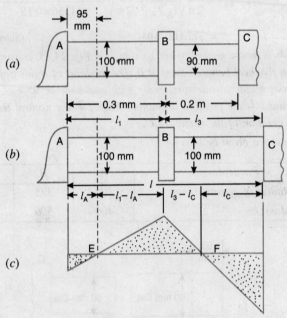

Fig. 24.14

We know that

$$\frac{1}{I_B}\left(\frac{1}{l_1 - l_A} + \frac{1}{l_3 - l_C}\right) = \frac{1}{l_A \cdot I_A}$$

$$\frac{1}{70.3}\left(\frac{1}{0.3 - 0.095} + \frac{1}{0.305 - l_C}\right) = \frac{1}{0.095 \times 36}$$

$$\frac{1}{0.205} + \frac{1}{0.305 - l_C} = \frac{70.3}{0.095 \times 36} = 20.56$$

$$\frac{1}{0.305 - l_C} = 20.56 - \frac{1}{0.205} = 15.68$$

$$0.305 - l_C = 1 / 15.68 = 0.064 \quad \text{or} \quad l_C = 0.21 \text{ m}$$

∴   Corresponding value of l_C in an original system from rotor C

$$= 0.21 \left(\frac{d_2}{d_1} \right)^4 = 0.21 \left(\frac{0.09}{0.1} \right)^4 = 0.13 \text{ m} \quad \textbf{Ans.}$$

2. Natural frequency of vibration

We know that polar moment of inertia of the equivalent shaft,

$$J = \frac{\pi}{32} (d_1)^4 = \frac{\pi}{32} (0.1)^4 = 9.82 \times 10^{-6} \, m^4$$

∴   Natural frequency of vibrations,

$$f_n = \frac{1}{2\pi} \sqrt{\frac{C.J}{l_A.I_A}} = \frac{1}{2\pi} \sqrt{\frac{84 \times 10^9 \times 9.82 \times 10^{-6}}{0.095 \times 36}} \text{ Hz}$$

$$= 78.1 \text{ Hz } \textbf{Ans.}$$

3. Radius of gyration of armature C

Let k_C = Radius of gyration of armature C in metres, and
                  I_C = Mass moment of inertia of armature $C = m_C (k_C)^2$ in kg-m².

We know that $l_A.I_A = l_C.I_C = l_C.m_C(k_C)^2$

or $(k_C)^2 = \dfrac{l_A.I_A}{l_C.m_C} = \dfrac{0.095 \times 36}{0.21 \times 300} = 0.0543 \, m^2$

∴ $k_C = 0.233 \text{ m } \textbf{Ans.}$

Example 24.7. *A 4-cylinder engine and flywheel coupled to a propeller are approximated to a 3-rotor system in which the engine is equivalent to a rotor of moment of inertia 800 kg-m², the flywheel to a second rotor of 320 kg-m² and the propeller to a third rotor of 20 kg-m². The first and the second rotors being connected by 50 mm diameter and 2 metre long shaft and the second and the third rotors being connected by a 25 mm diameter and 2 metre long shaft.*

Neglecting the inertia of the shaft and taking its modulus of rigidity as 80 GN/m², determine: 1. Natural frequencies of torsional oscillations, and 2. The positions of the nodes.

Solution. Given : $I_A = 800$ kg-m² ; $I_B = 320$ kg-m² ; $I_C = 20$ kg-m² ; $d_1 = 50$ mm = 0.05 m; $l_1 = 2$ m ; $d_2 = 25$ mm = 0.025 m ; $l_2 = 2$ m ; $C = 80 \times 10^9$ N/m²

1. Natural frequencies of torsional oscillations

First of all, replace the original system, as shown in Fig. 24.15 (*a*), by an equivalent system as shown in Fig. 24.15 (*b*). It is assumed that the diameter of equivalent shaft is $d_1 = 50$ mm = 0.05m.

We know that length of equivalent shaft,

$$l = l_1 + l_2 \left(\frac{d_1}{d_2} \right)^4 = 2 + 2 \left(\frac{0.05}{0.025} \right)^4 = 34 \, m$$

Now let us find the position of nodes for the equivalent system.

Let l_A = Distance of node N_1 from rotor A, and
                  l_C = Distance of node N_2 from rotor C.

We know that $l_A.I_A = l_C.I_C$

∴ $l_A = \dfrac{l_C.I_C}{I_A} = \dfrac{l_C \times 20}{800} = 0.025 \, l_C$

Also,
$$\frac{1}{l_C \cdot I_C} = \frac{1}{I_B}\left(\frac{1}{l_1 - l_A} + \frac{1}{l_3 - l_C}\right)$$

$$\frac{1}{l_C \times 20} = \frac{1}{320}\left(\frac{1}{2 - 0.025 l_C} + \frac{1}{32 - l_C}\right) \qquad \ldots (\because \; l_3 = l - l_1)$$

$$\frac{320}{l_C \times 20} = \frac{1}{2 - 0.025 l_C} + \frac{1}{32 - l_C}$$

$$\frac{16}{l_C} = \frac{32 - l_C + 2 - 0.025 l_C}{(2 - 0.025 l_C)(32 - l_C)} = \frac{34 - 1.025 l_C}{64 - 2.8 l_C + 0.025 (l_C)^2}$$

or $\quad 1.425 \, (l_C)^2 - 78.8 \, l_C + 1024 = 0$

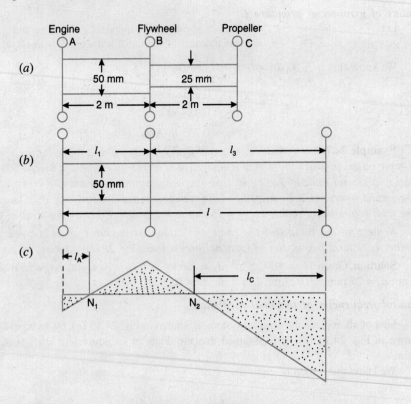

Fig. 24.15

$$\therefore \qquad l_C = \frac{78.8 \pm \sqrt{(78.8)^2 - 4 \times 1.425 \times 1024}}{2 \times 1.425} = \frac{78.8 \pm 19.3}{2.85}$$

$$= 34.42 \text{ m or } 20.88 \text{ m}$$

and $\qquad l_A = 0.025 \, l_C = 0.86 \text{ m or } 0.52 \text{ m}$

We see that when $l_C = 34.42$ m, then $l_A = 0.86$ m. This gives the position of single node for $l_A = 0.86$ m. The value of $l_C = 20.88$ m and corresponding value of $l_A = 0.52$ m gives the position of two nodes, as shown in Fig. 24.15 (c).

We know that polar moment of inertia of the equivalent shaft,

$$J = \frac{\pi}{32}(d_1)^4 = \frac{\pi}{32}(0.05)^4 = 0.614 \times 10^{-6} \, m^4$$

∴ Natural frequency of torsional vibrations for a single node system,

$$f_{n1} = \frac{1}{2\pi}\sqrt{\frac{C.J}{l_A.I_A}} = \frac{1}{2\pi}\sqrt{\frac{80 \times 10^9 \times 0.614 \times 10^{-6}}{0.86 \times 800}} \quad Hz$$

. . . (Substituting $l_A = 0.86$ m)

$$= 1.345 \text{ Hz Ans.}$$

Similarly natural frequency of torsional vibrations for a two node system,

$$f_{n2} = \frac{1}{2\pi}\sqrt{\frac{C.J}{l_A.I_A}} = \frac{1}{2\pi}\sqrt{\frac{80 \times 10^9 \times 0.614 \times 10^{-6}}{0.52 \times 800}} \quad Hz$$

. . . (Substituting $l_A = 0.52$ m)

$$= 1.73 \text{ Hz Ans.}$$

2. Position of the nodes

We have already calculated that for a two node system on an equivalent shaft, $l_C = 20.88$ m from the propeller.

∴ Corresponding value of l_C in an original system from the propeller

$$= 20.88\left(\frac{d_2}{d_1}\right)^4 = 20.88\left(\frac{0.025}{0.05}\right)^4 = 1.3 \text{ m}$$

Therefore one node occurs at a distance of $l_A = 0.52$ m from the engine and the other node at a distance of $l_C = 1.3$ m from the propeller. **Ans.**

24.8. Free Torsional Vibrations of a Geared System

Consider a geared system as shown in Fig. 24.16 (*a*). It consists of a driving shaft *C* which carries a rotor *A*. It drives a driven shaft *D* which carries a rotor *B*, through a pinion *E* and a gear wheel *F*. This system may be replaced by an equivalent system of continuous shaft carrying a rotor *A* at one end and rotor *B* at the other end, as shown in Fig. 24.16 (*b*). It is assumed that

1. the gear teeth are rigid and are always in contact,

2. there is no backlash in the gearing, and

3. the inertia of the shafts and gears is negligible.

Let d_1 and d_2 = Diameter of the shafts *C* and *D*,

         l_1 and l_2 = Length of the shafts *C* and *D*,

         I_A and I_B = Mass moment of inertia of the rotors *A* and *B*,

         ω_A and ω_B = Angular speed of the rotors *A* and *B*,

$$G = \text{Gear ratio} = \frac{\text{Speed of pinion } E}{\text{Speed of wheel } F} = \frac{\omega_A}{\omega_B}$$

. . . (∵ Speeds of *E* and *F* will be same as that of rotors *A* and *B*)

         d = Diameter of the equivalent shaft,

         l = Length of the equivalent shaft, and

         I_B' = Mass moment of inertia of the equivalent rotor *B'*.

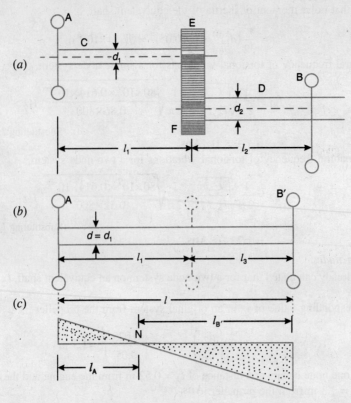

Fig. 24.16

The following two conditions must be satisfied by an equivalent system :

1. The kinetic energy of the equivalent system must be equal to the kinetic energy of the original system.

2. The strain energy of the equivalent system must be equal to the strain energy of the original system.

In order to satisfy the condition (**1**) for a given load,

K.E. of section l_1 + K.E. of section l_3

$$= \text{K.E. of section } l_1 + \text{K. E. of section } l_2$$

∴   K.E. of section l_3 = K.E. of section l_2

or $\dfrac{1}{2} \times I_B{}'(\omega_B{}')^2 = \dfrac{1}{2} \times I_B(\omega_B)^2$ or $I_B{}'(\omega_A)^2 = I_B(\omega_B)^2$ $\dots (\because \omega_B{}' = \omega_A)$

∴ $$I_B{}' = I_B\left(\dfrac{\omega_B}{\omega_A}\right)^2 = \dfrac{I_B}{G^2} \qquad \dots \left(\because G = \dfrac{\omega_A}{\omega_B}\right) \dots (i)$$

In order to satisfy the condition (**2**) for a given shaft diameter,

Strain energy of l_1 and l_3 = Strain energy of l_1 and l_2

∴   Strain energy of l_3 = Strain energy of l_2

or $$\dfrac{1}{2} \times T_3 \cdot \theta_3 = \dfrac{1}{2} \times T_2 \cdot \theta_2 \quad \text{or} \quad \dfrac{T_3}{T_2} = \dfrac{\theta_2}{\theta_3} \qquad \dots (ii)$$

where
T_2 and T_3 = Torque on the sections l_2 and l_3, and

θ_2 and θ_3 = Angle of twist on sections l_2 and l_3.

Assuming that the power transmitted in the sections l_3 and l_2 is same, therefore

$$T_3.\omega_A = T_2.\omega_B \quad \text{or} \quad \frac{T_3}{T_2} = \frac{\omega_B}{\omega_A} = \frac{1}{G} \qquad \qquad ...(iii)$$

Combining equations (ii) and (iii),

$$\frac{T_3}{T_2} = \frac{\theta_2}{\theta_3} = \frac{1}{G} \qquad \qquad ...(iv)$$

We know that torsional stiffness,

$$q = \frac{T}{\theta} = \frac{C.J}{l}$$

where
J = Polar moment of inertia of the shaft.

∴ For section l_3, $\dfrac{T_3}{\theta_3} = \dfrac{C.J_3}{l_3}$ $\qquad \qquad ...(v)$

and For section l_2, $\dfrac{T_2}{\theta_2} = \dfrac{C.J_2}{l_2}$ $\qquad \qquad ...(vi)$

Dividing equation (v) by equation (vi),

$$\frac{T_3}{T_2} \times \frac{\theta_2}{\theta_3} = \frac{J_3}{l_3} \times \frac{l_2}{J_2} \quad \text{or} \quad \frac{T_3}{T_2} = \frac{J_3.\theta_3 \cdot l_2}{J_2.\theta_2.l_3}$$

or
$$\frac{1}{G} = \frac{J_3}{J_2} \times G \times \frac{l_2}{l_3} \qquad \qquad \text{[From equation (iv)]}$$

∴
$$l_3 = \frac{J_3}{J_2} \times G^2 \times l_2 \qquad \qquad ...(vii)$$

Assuming the diameter of the equivalent shaft as that of shaft C i.e. $d = d_1$, therefore

$$J_3 = \frac{\pi}{32}(d_1)^4, \quad \text{and} \quad J_2 = \frac{\pi}{32}(d_2)^4$$

∴
$$\frac{J_3}{J_2} = \left(\frac{d_1}{d_2}\right)^4$$

Now the equation (vii) may be written as

$$l_3 = G^2 \cdot l_2 \left(\frac{d_1}{d_2}\right)^4 \qquad \qquad ...(viii)$$

Thus the single shaft is equivalent to the original geared system, if the mass moment of inertia of the rotor B' satisfies the equation (i) and the additional length of the equivalent shaft l_3 satisfies the equation (viii).

∴ Length of the equivalent shaft,

$$l = l_1 + l_3 = l_1 + G^2.l_2 \left(\frac{d_1}{d_2}\right)^4 \qquad \qquad ...(ix)$$

Now, the natural frequency of the torsional vibration of a geared system (which have been reduced to two rotor system) may be determined as discussed below :

Let the node of the equivalent system lies at N as shown in Fig. 24.16 (c), then the natural frequency of torsional vibration of rotor A,

$$f_{nA} = \frac{1}{2\pi}\sqrt{\frac{C.J}{l_A.I_A}}$$

and natural frequency of the torsional vibration of rotor B',

$$f_{nB'} = \frac{1}{2\pi}\sqrt{\frac{C.J}{l_B'.I_B'}}$$

We know that $f_{nA} = f_{nB}'$

$$\therefore \qquad \frac{1}{2\pi}\sqrt{\frac{C.J}{l_A.I_A}} = \frac{1}{2\pi}\sqrt{\frac{C.J}{l_B'.I_B'}}$$

CNC lathe ata turning centre.
Note : This picture is given as additional information.

or $\qquad l_A.I_A = l_B'.I_B'$

$$\cdots (x)$$

Also $\qquad l_A + l_B' = l$

$$\cdots (xi)$$

From these two equations (x) and (xi), the value of l_A and l_B' may be obtained and hence the natural frequency of the torsional vibrations is evaluated.

Note : When the inertia of the gearing is taken into consideration, then an additional rotor [shown dotted in Fig. 24.16 (b)] must be introduced to the equivalent system at a distance l_1 from the rotor A. This rotor will have a mass moment of inertia $I_E' = I_E + \dfrac{I_F}{G^2}$, where I_E and I_F are the moments of inertia of the pinion and wheel respectively. The system then becomes a three rotor system and the frequency of such a system may be obtained as discussed in the previous article.

Example 24.8. *A motor drives a centrifugal pump through gearing, the pump speed being one-third that of the motor. The shaft from the motor to the pinion is 60 mm diameter and 300 mm long. The moment of inertia of the motor is 400 kg-m². The impeller shaft is 100 mm diameter and 600 mm long. The moment of inertia of the impeller is 1500 kg-m². Neglecting inertia of the gears and the shaft, determine the frequency of torsional vibration of the system. The modulus of rigidity of the shaft material is 80 GN/m².*

Solution. Given : $G = N_A/N_B = 3$; $d_1 = 60$ mm $= 0.06$ m ; $l_1 = 300$ mm $= 0.3$ m ; $I_A = 400$ kg-m²; $d_2 = 100$ mm $= 0.1$ m ; $l_2 = 600$ mm $= 0.6$ m ; $I_B = 1500$ kg-m² ; $C = 80$ GN/m² $= 80 \times 10^9$ N/m²

The original and the equivalent system, neglecting the inertia of the gears, is shown in Fig. 24.17 (a) and (b) respectively. First of all, let us find the mass moment of inertia of the equivalent rotor B' and the additional length of the equivalent shaft, assuming its diameter as $d_1 = 60$ mm.

We know that mass moment of the equivalent rotor B',

$$I_B' = I_B / G^2 = 1500/3^2 = 166.7 \text{ kg–m}^2$$

and additional length of the equivalent shaft,

$$l_3 = G^2 l_2 \left(\frac{d_1}{d_2}\right)^4 = 3^2 \times 0.6 \left(\frac{0.06}{0.1}\right)^4 = 0.7 \text{m} = 700 \text{ mm}$$

∴ Total length of the equivalent shaft,

$$l = l_1 + l_3 = 300 + 700 = 1000 \text{ mm} = 1 \text{ m}$$

Let the node of the equivalent system lies at N, as shown in Fig. 24.17 (c). We know that

$$l_A . I_A = l_B' . I_B' \quad \text{or} \quad l_A \times 400 = (1 - l_A)166.7 \quad \ldots \quad (\because l_B' = l - l_A)$$

∴ $$l_A = 0.294 \text{ m} = 294 \text{ mm}$$

We know that polar moment of inertia of the equivalent shaft,

$$J = \frac{\pi}{32}(d_1)^4 = \frac{\pi}{32}(0.06)^4 = 1.27 \times 10^{-6} \text{ m}^4$$

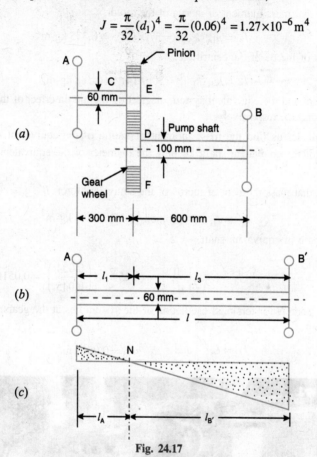

(a)

(b)

(c)

Fig. 24.17

∴ Frequency of torsional vibration,

$$f_n = \frac{1}{2\pi}\sqrt{\frac{C.J}{l_A . I_A}} = \frac{1}{2\pi}\sqrt{\frac{80 \times 10^9 \times 1.27 \times 10^{-6}}{0.294 \times 400}} \text{ Hz}$$

$$= 4.7 \text{ Hz Ans.}$$

Example 24.9. *An electric motor is to drive a centrifuge, running at four times the motor speed through a spur gear and pinion. The steel shaft from the motor to the gear wheel is 54 mm diameter and L metre long ; the shaft from the pinion to the centrifuge is 45 mm diameter and 400 mm long. The masses and radii of gyration of motor and centrifuge are respectively 37.5 kg, 100 mm ; 30 kg and 140 mm.*

Neglecting the inertia effect of the gears, find the value of L if the gears are to be at the node for torsional oscillation of the system and hence determine the frequency of torsional oscillation. Assume modulus of rigidity for material of shaft as 84 GN/m².

Solution. Given : $G = N_A/N_B = 1/4 = 0.25$; $d_1 = 54$ mm $= 0.054$ m ; $l_1 = L$ m ; $d_2 = 45$ mm $= 0.045$ m ; $l_2 = 400$ mm $= 0.4$ m ; $m_A = 37.5$ kg ; $k_A = 100$ mm $= 0.1$ m ; $m_B = 30$ kg ; $k_B = 140$ mm $= 0.14$ m; $C = 84$ GN/m² $= 84 \times 10^9$ N/m²

Value of L

We know that mass moment of inertia of the motor,

$$I_A = m_A (k_A)^2 = 37.5(0.1)^2 = 0.375 \text{ kg-m}^2$$

and mass moment of inertia of the centrifuge,

$$I_B = m_B (k_B)^2 = 30(0.14)^2 = 0.588 \text{ kg-m}^2$$

The original and the equivalent system, neglecting the inertia effect of the gears, is shown in Fig. 24.18 (*a*) and (*b*) respectively.

First of all, let us find the mass moment of inertia of the equivalent rotor B' and the additional length of the equivalent shaft, keeping the diameter of the equivalent shaft as $d_1 = 54$ mm.

We know that mass moment of inertia of the equivalent rotor B',

$$I_B' = I_B / G^2 = 0.588/(0.25)^2 = 9.4 \text{ kg-m}^2$$

and additional length of equivalent shaft,

$$l_3 = G^2 . l_2 \left(\frac{d_1}{d_2}\right)^4 = (0.25)^2 0.4 \left(\frac{0.054}{0.045}\right)^4 = 0.0518 \text{ m}$$

Since the node N for torsional oscillation of the system lies at the gears, as shown in Fig. 24.18 (*c*), therefore

$$l_A = L, \quad \text{and} \quad l_B' = l_3 = 0.0518 \text{ m}$$

Grinding is a commonly used method for removing the excess material from the cestings, forgings and weldments

Note : This picture is given as additional information.

We know that $\qquad l_A . I_A = l_B' . I_B'$

$\therefore \qquad L \times 0.375 = 0.0518 \times 9.4 = 0.487$ or $L = 1.3$ m **Ans.**

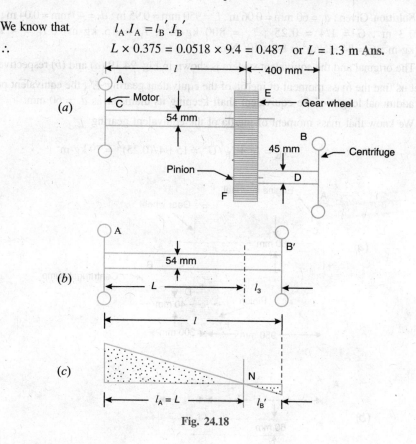

Fig. 24.18

Frequency of torsional oscillations

We know that polar moment of inertia of the equivalent shaft,

$$J = \frac{\pi}{32}(d_1)^4 = \frac{\pi}{32}(0.054)^4 = 0.835 \times 10^{-6} \, \text{m}^4$$

$\therefore$ Frequency of torsional oscillations,

$$f_n = \frac{1}{2\pi}\sqrt{\frac{C.J}{l_A.I_A}} = \frac{1}{2\pi}\sqrt{\frac{84 \times 10^9 \times 0.835 \times 10^{-6}}{1.3 \times 0.375}} = 60.4 \text{ Hz Ans.}$$

Example 24.10. *Determine the natural frequencies of torsional oscillation for the following system. The system is a reciprocating I.C. engine coupled to a centrifugal pump through a pair of gears. The shaft from the flywheel of the engine to the gear wheel is of 60 mm diameter and 950 mm length. The shaft from the pinion to the pump is of 40 mm diameter and 300 mm length. The engine speed is $\frac{1}{4}$th of the pump speed.*

Moment of inertia of the flywheel $\qquad = 800 \, kg\text{-}m^2$

Moment of inertia of the gear wheel $= 15 \, kg\text{-}m^2$

Moment of inertia of the pinion $\qquad = 4 \, kg\text{-}m^2$

Moment of inertia of the pump $\qquad = 17 \, kg\text{-}m^2$

Modulus of rigidity for shaft material is 84 GN/m².

Solution. Given : $d_1 = 60$ mm $= 0.06$ m ; $l_1 = 950$ mm $= 0.95$ m ; $d_2 = 40$ mm $= 0.04$ m ; $l_2 = 300$ mm $= 0.3$ m ; $G = 1/4 = 0.25$; $I_A = 800$ kg-m^2 ; $I_E = 15$ kg-m^2 ; $I_F = 4$ kg-m^2 ; $I_B = 17$ kg-m^2; $C = 84$ GN/m$^2 = 84 \times 10^9$ N/m^2

The original and the equivalent system is shown in Fig. 24.19 (a) and (b) respectively. First of all, let us find the mass moment of inertia of the equivalent gearing E', the equivalent pump B' and the additional length of the equivalent shaft keeping its diameter as $d_1 = 60$ mm.

We know that mass moment of inertia of the equivalent gearing E',

$$I_E' = I_E + I_F / G^2 = 15 + 4/(0.25)^2 = 79 \text{ kg-m}^2$$

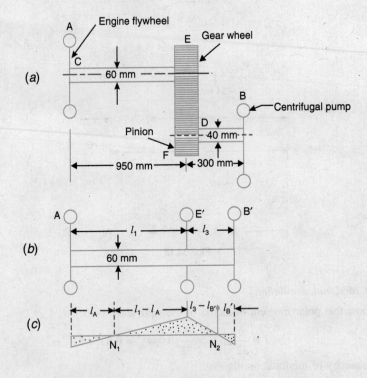

Fig. 24.19

Mass moment of inertia of the equivalent pump B',

$$I_B' = I_B / G^2 = 17/(0.25)^2 = 272 \text{ kg-m}^2$$

and additional length of the equivalent shaft,

$$l_3 = G^2 l_2 \left(\frac{d_1}{d_2}\right)^4 = (0.25)^2 0.3 \left(\frac{0.06}{0.04}\right)^4 = 0.095 \text{ m}$$

The original system is thus reduced to a three rotor system, as shown in 24.19 (b). Let us find the position of nodes for the equivalent system.

Let $\qquad l_A$ = Distance of node N_1 from rotor A, and

$\qquad\qquad l_B'$ = Distance of node N_2 from rotor B'.

We know that $$l_A . I_A = l_B' . I_B' \quad \text{or} \quad l_A = l_B' \times \frac{I_B'}{I_A} = l_B' \times \frac{272}{800} = 0.34 l_B'$$

Also $$\frac{1}{l_B' . I_B'} = \frac{1}{I_E'} \left(\frac{1}{l_1 - l_A} + \frac{1}{l_3 - l_B'} \right)$$

$$\frac{1}{l_B' \times 272} = \frac{1}{79} \left(\frac{1}{0.95 - 0.34 l_B'} + \frac{1}{0.095 - l_B'} \right)$$

$$\frac{79}{l_B' \times 272} = \frac{(0.095 - l_B' + 0.95 - 0.34 l_B')}{(0.95 - 0.34 l_B')(0.095 - l_B')}$$

$$\frac{0.29}{l_B'} = \frac{1.045 - 1.34 l_B'}{0.09 - 0.98 l_B' + 0.34 (l_B')^2}$$

$$0.026 - 0.28 l_B' + 0.1 (l_B')^2 = 1.045 l_B' - 1.34 (l_B')^2$$

$$1.44 (l_B')^2 - 1.325 l_B' + 0.026 = 0$$

$$\therefore \quad l_B' = \frac{1.325 \pm \sqrt{(1.325)^2 - 4 \times 1.44 \times 0.026}}{2 \times 1.44} = \frac{1.325 \pm 1.267}{2.88}$$

$$= 0.9 \text{ m} \quad \text{or} \quad 0.02 \text{ m}$$

and $$l_A = 0.34 l_B' = 0.306 \text{ m} \quad \text{or} \quad 0.0068 \text{ m}$$

We see that when $l_B' = 0.9$ m, then $l_A = 0.306$ m. This gives the position of single node for $l_A = 0.306$ m or 306 mm. When $l_B' = 0.02$ m, the corresponding value of $l_A = 0.0068$ m or 6.8 mm. This gives the position of two nodes as shown in Fig. 24.19 (c).

We know that polar moment of inertia of the equivalent shaft,

$$J = \frac{\pi}{32} (d_1)^4 = \frac{\pi}{32} (0.06)^4 = 1.27 \times 10^{-6} \text{ m}^4$$

∴ Natural frequency of torsional oscillations for a single node system,

$$f_{n1} = \frac{1}{2\pi} \sqrt{\frac{C.J}{l_A . I_A}} = \frac{1}{2\pi} \sqrt{\frac{84 \times 10^9 \times 1.27 \times 10^{-6}}{0.306 \times 800}} \text{ Hz}$$

$$= 3.32 \text{ Hz Ans.} \qquad \dots \text{(Substituting } l_A = 0.306 \text{ m)}$$

Similarly natural frequency of torsional oscillations for a two node system,

$$f_{n2} = \frac{1}{2\pi} \sqrt{\frac{C.J}{I_A . I_A}} = \frac{1}{2\pi} \sqrt{\frac{84 \times 10^9 \times 1.27 \times 10^{-6}}{0.0068 \times 800}} \text{ Hz}$$

$$= 22.3 \text{ Hz Ans.} \qquad \dots \text{(Substituting } l_A = 0.0068 \text{ m)}$$

EXERCISES

1. A shaft of 100 mm diameter and 1 metre long is fixed at one end and the other end carries a flywheel of mass 1 tonne. The radius of gyration of the flywheel is 0.5 m. Find the frequency of torsional vibrations, if the modulus of rigidity for the shaft material is 80 GN/m². **[Ans. 8.9 Hz]**

2. The flywheel of an engine driving a dynamo has a mass of 180 kg and a radius of gyration of 30 mm. The shaft at the flywheel end has an effective length of 250 mm and is 50 mm diameter. The armature mass is 120 kg and its radius of gyration is 22.5 mm. The dynamo shaft is 43 mm diameter and 200 mm effective length. Calculate the position of node and frequency of torsional oscillation. $C = 83$ kN/mm². **[Ans. 205 mm from flywheel, 218 Hz]**

3. The two rotors A and B are attached to the end of a shaft 500 mm long. The mass of the rotor A is 300 kg and its radius of gyration is 300 mm. The corresponding values of the rotor B are 500 kg and 450 mm respectively. The shaft is 70 mm in diameter for the first 250 mm ; 120 mm for the next 70 mm and 100 mm diameter for the remaining length. The modulus of rigidity for the shaft material is 80 GN/m². Find : 1. The position of the node, and 2. The frequency of torsional vibration. **[Ans. 225 mm from A ; 27.3 Hz]**

4. Three rotors A, B and C having moment of inertia of 2000 ; 6000 ; and 3500 kg-m² respectively are carried on a uniform shaft of 0.35 m diameter. The length of the shaft between the rotors A and B is 6 m and between B and C is 32 m. Find the natural frequency of the torsional vibrations. The modulus of rigidity for the shaft material is 80 GN/m². **[Ans. 6.16 Hz ; 18.27 Hz]**

5. A motor generator set consists of two armatures P and R as shown in Fig. 24.20, with a flywheel between them at Q. The modulus of rigidity of the material of the shaft is 84 GN/m². The system can vibrate with one node at 106.5 mm from P, the flywheel Q being at antinode. Using the data of rotors given below, find: 1. The position of the other node, 2. The natural frequency of the free torsional vibrations, for the given positions of the nodes, and 3. The radius of gyration of the rotor R.

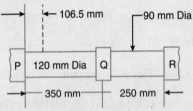

Data of rotors

Rotor	P	Q	R
Mass, kg	450	540	360
Radius of gyration, mm	250	300	–

Fig. 24.20   **[Ans. 225 mm from R ; 120 Hz ; 108 mm]**

6. An electric motor rotating at 1500 r.p.m. drives a centrifugal pump at 500 r.p.m. through a single stage reduction gearing. The moments of inertia of the electric motor and the pump impeller are 400 kg-m² and 1400 kg-m² respectively. The motor shaft is 45 mm in diameter and 180 mm long. The pump shaft is 90 mm in diameter and 450 mm long.
    Determine the frequency of torsional oscillations of the system, neglecting the inertia of the gears. The modulus of rigidity for the shaft material is 84 GN/m². **[Ans. 4.2 Hz]**

7. Two parallel shafts A and B of diameters 50 mm and 70 mm respectively are connected by a pair of gear wheels, the speed of A being 4 times that of B. The flywheel of mass moment of inertia 3 kg-m² is mounted on shaft A at a distance of 0.9 m from the gears. The shaft B also carries a flywheel of mass moment of inertia 16 kg-m² at a distance of 0.6 m from the gears. Neglecting the effect of the shaft and gear masses, calculate the fundamental frequency of free torsional oscillations and the position of node . Assume modulus of rigidity as 84 GN/m². **[Ans. 22.6 Hz ; 0.85 m from the flywheel on shaft A]**

8. A centrifugal pump is driven through a pair of spur wheels from an oil engine. The pump runs at 4 times the speed of the engine. The shaft from the engine flywheel to the gear is 75 mm diameter and 1.2 m long, while that from the pinion to the pump is 50 mm diameter and 400 mm long. The moment of inertia are as follows:
    Flywheel = 1000 kg-m², Gear = 25 kg m², Pinion = 10 kg-m², and Pump impeller = 40 kg-m².
    Find the natural frequencies of torsional oscillations of the system. Take $C = 84$ GN/m². **[Ans. 3.4 Hz ; 19.7 Hz]**

DO YOU KNOW ?

1. Derive an expression for the frequency of free torsional vibrations for a shaft fixed at one end and carrying a load on the free end.
2. Discuss the effect of inertia of a shaft on the free torsional vibrations.
3. How the natural frequency of torsional vibrations for a two rotor system is obtained ?
4. Describe the method of finding the natural frequency of torsional vibrations for a three rotor system.
5. What is meant by torsionally equivalent length of a shaft as referred to a stepped shaft? Derive the expression for the equivalent length of a shaft which have several steps.
6. Establish the expression to determine the frequency of torsional vibrations of a geared system.

OBJECTIVE TYPE QUESTIONS

1. The natural frequency of free torsional vibrations of a shaft is

   (a) $2\pi\sqrt{\dfrac{q}{I}}$ (b) $2\pi\sqrt{q.I}$ (c) $\dfrac{1}{2\pi}\sqrt{\dfrac{q}{I}}$ (d) $\dfrac{1}{2\pi}\sqrt{q.I}$

   where q = Torsional stiffness of the shaft, and

                 I = Mass moment of inertia of the disc attached at the end of the shaft.

2. At a nodal point in a shaft, the amplitude of torsional vibration is
       (a) zero   (b) minimum   (c) maximum
3. Two shafts A and B are shown in Fig. 24.21. The length of an equivalent shaft B is given by

   (a) $l = l_1 + l_2 + l_3$ (b) $l = l_1 + \left(\dfrac{d_2}{d_3}\right)^4$

   (c) $l = l_1 + l_2 \left(\dfrac{d_2}{d_2}\right)^4$ (d) $l = l_1 + l_2 \left(\dfrac{d_1}{d_2}\right)^4 + l_3 \left(\dfrac{d_1}{d_3}\right)^4$

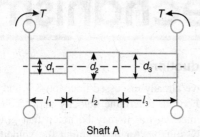

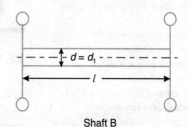

Shaft A   Shaft B

Fig. 24.21

4. A shaft carrying two rotors as its ends will have
       (a) no node   (b) one node   (c) two nodes   (d) three nodes
5. A shaft carrying three rotors will have
       (a) no node   (b) one node   (c) two nodes   (d) three nodes

ANSWERS

    1. (*c*)   **2.** (*a*)   **3.** (*d*)   **4.** (*b*)   **5.** (*c*)

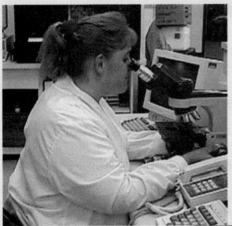

25

Features (Main)

Computer Aided Analysis and Synthesis of Mechanisms

25.1. Introduction

We have already discussed in chapters 7 and 8, the graphical methods to determine velocity and acceleration analysis of a mechanism. It may be noted that graphical method is only suitable for determining the velocity and acceleration of the links in a mechanism for a single position of the crank. In order to determine the velocity and acceleration of the links in a mechanism for different positions of the crank, we have to draw the velocity and acceleration diagrams for each position of the crank which is inconvenient. In this chapter, we shall discuss the analytical expressions for the displacement, velocity and acceleration in terms of general parameters of a mechanism and calculations may be performed either by a desk calculator or digital computer.

25.2. Computer Aided Analysis for Four Bar Mechanism (Freudenstein's Equation)

Consider a four bar mechanism *ABCD*, as shown in Fig. 25.1 (*a*), in which $AB = a$, $BC = b$, $CD = c$, and $DA = d$. The link *AD* is fixed and lies along *X*-axis. Let the links *AB* (input link), *BC* (coupler) and *DC* (output link) make angles θ, β and ϕ respectively along the *X*-axis or fixed link *AD*.

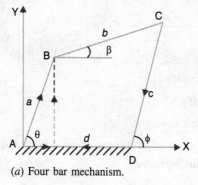

(*a*) Four bar mechanism.

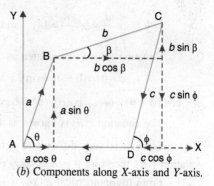

(*b*) Components along *X*-axis and *Y*-axis.

Fig. 25.1

The relation between the angles and link lengths may be developed by considering the links as vectors. The expressions for displacement, velocity and acceleration analysis are derived as discussed below :

1. *Displacement analysis*

For equilibrium of the mechanism, the sum of the components along *X*-axis and along *Y*-axis must be equal to zero. First of all, taking the sum of the components along *X*-axis as shown in Fig. 25.1 (*b*), we have

$$a \cos \theta + b \cos \beta - c \cos \phi - d = 0 \qquad \dots (i)$$

or $$b \cos \beta = c \cos \phi + d - a \cos \theta$$

Squaring both sides

$$b^2 \cos^2 \beta = (c \cos \phi + d - a \cos \theta)^2$$

$$= c^2 \cos^2 \phi + d^2 + 2c \, d \cos \phi + a^2 \cos^2 \theta$$

$$- 2a \, c \cos \phi \cos \theta - 2a \, d \cos \theta \qquad \dots (ii)$$

Now taking the sum of the components along *Y*-axis, we have

$$a \sin \theta + b \sin \beta - c \sin \phi = 0 \qquad \dots (iii)$$

or $$b \sin \beta = c \sin \phi - a \sin \theta$$

Squaring both sides,

$$b^2 \sin^2 \beta = (c \sin \phi - a \sin \theta)^2$$

$$= c^2 \sin^2 \phi + a^2 \sin^2 \theta - 2a \, c \sin \phi \sin \theta \qquad \dots (iv)$$

Adding equations (*ii*) and (*iv*),

$$b^2 (\cos^2 \beta + \sin^2 \beta) = c^2 (\cos^2 \phi + \sin^2 \phi) + d^2 + 2 \, c \, d \cos \phi + a^2 (\cos^2 \theta + \sin^2 \theta)$$

$$- 2 \, a \, c (\cos \phi \cos \theta + \sin \phi \sin \theta) - 2 \, a \, d \cos \theta$$

or
$$b^2 = c^2 + d^2 + 2\,c\,d\,\cos\phi + a^2 - 2\,a\,c(\cos\phi\cos\theta + \sin\phi\sin\theta) - 2\,a\,d\,\cos\theta$$

or
$$2\,a\,c(\cos\phi\cos\theta + \sin\phi\sin\theta) = a^2 - b^2 + c^2 + d^2 + 2\,c\,d\,\cos\phi - 2a\,d\,\cos\theta$$

$$\cos\phi\cos\theta + \sin\phi\sin\theta = \frac{a^2 - b^2 + c^2 + d^2}{2\,a\,c} + \frac{d}{a}\cos\phi - \frac{d}{c}\cos\theta \qquad \dots (v)$$

Let
$$\frac{d}{a} = k_1; \ \frac{d}{c} = k_2; \quad \text{and} \quad \frac{a^2 - b^2 + c^2 + d^2}{2\,a\,c} = k_3 \qquad \dots (vi)$$

Equation (v) may be written as

$$\cos\phi\cos\theta + \sin\phi\sin\theta = k_1\cos\phi - k_2\cos\theta + k_3 \qquad \dots (vii)$$

or $\cos(\phi - \theta)$ or $\cos(\theta - \phi) = k_1\cos\phi - k_2\cos\theta + k_3$

The equation (vii) is known as *Freudenstein's equation.*

Since it is very difficult to determine the value of ϕ for the given value of θ, from equation (vii), therefore it is necessary to simplify this equation.

From trigonometrical ratios, we know that

$$\sin\phi = \frac{2\tan(\phi/2)}{1 + \tan^2(\phi/2)} \quad \text{and} \quad \cos\phi = \frac{1 - \tan^2(\phi/2)}{1 + \tan^2(\phi/2)}$$

Substituting these values of $\sin\phi$ and $\cos\phi$ in equation (vii),

$$\frac{1 - \tan^2(\phi/2)}{1 + \tan^2(\phi/2)} \times \cos\theta + \frac{2\tan(\phi/2)}{1 + \tan^2(\phi/2)} \times \sin\theta$$

$$= k_1 \times \frac{1 - \tan^2(\phi/2)}{1 + \tan^2(\phi/2)} - k_2\cos\theta + k_3$$

$$\cos\theta\,[1 - \tan^2(\phi/2)] + 2\sin\theta\tan(\phi/2)$$

$$= k_1\,[1 - \tan^2(\phi/2)] - k_2\cos\theta\,[1 + \tan^2(\phi/2)] + k_3[1 + \tan^2(\phi/2)]$$

$$\cos\theta - \cos\theta\tan^2(\phi/2) + 2\sin\theta\tan(\phi/2)$$

$$= k_1 - k_1\tan^2(\phi/2) - k_2\cos\theta - k_2\cos\theta\tan^2(\phi/2) + k_3 + k_3\tan^2(\phi/2)$$

Rearranging this equation,

$$-\cos\theta\tan^2(\phi/2) + k_1\tan^2(\phi/2) + k_2\cos\theta\tan^2(\phi/2) - k_3\tan^2(\phi/2) + 2\sin\theta\tan(\phi/2)$$

$$= -\cos\theta + k_1 - k_2\cos\theta + k_3$$

$$-\tan^2(\phi/2)\,[\cos\theta - k_1 - k_2\cos\theta + k_3] + 2\sin\theta\tan(\phi/2) - k_1 - k_3 + \cos\theta(1 + k_2) = 0$$

$$[\,(1 - k_2)\cos\theta + k_3 - k_1]\tan^2\phi/2 + (-2\sin\theta)\tan\phi/2 + [k_1 + k_3 - (1 + k_2)\cos\theta] = 0$$

(By changing the sign)

or
$$A\tan^2(\phi/2) + B\tan(\phi/2) + C = 0 \qquad \dots (viii)$$

where
$$A = (1 - k_2)\cos\theta + k_3 - k_1,$$
$$B = -2\sin\theta, \text{and}$$
$$C = k_1 + k_3 - (1 + k_2)\cos\theta$$
... (*ix*)

Inner view of an aircraft engine.

Note : This picture is given as additional information.

The equation (*viii*) is a quadratic equation in $\tan(\phi/2)$. Its two roots are

$$\tan(\phi/2) = \frac{-B \pm \sqrt{B^2 - 4AC}}{2A}$$

or

$$\phi = 2\tan^{-1}\left[\frac{-B \pm \sqrt{B^2 - 4AC}}{2A}\right]$$
... (*x*)

From this equation (*x*), we can find the position of output link *CD* (*i.e.* angle ϕ) if the length of the links (*i.e. a, b, c* and *d*) and position of the input link *AB* (*i.e.* angle θ) is known.

If the relation between the position of input link *AB* (*i.e.* angle θ) and the position of coupler link *BC* (*i.e.* angle β) is required, then eliminate angle ϕ from the equations (*i*) and (*iii*).

The equation (*i*) may be written as

$$c\cos\phi = a\cos\theta + b\cos\beta - d$$
... (*xi*)

Squaring both sides,

$$c^2\cos^2\phi = a^2\cos^2\theta + b^2\cos^2\beta + 2\,a\,b\cos\theta\cos\beta$$
$$+ d^2 - 2\,a\,d\cos\theta - 2\,b\,d\,\cos\beta$$
... (*xii*)

Now equation (*iii*) may be written as

$$c\sin\phi = a\sin\theta + b\sin\beta$$
... (*xiii*)

Squaring both sides,

$$c^2 \sin^2 \phi = a^2 \sin^2 \theta + b^2 \sin^2 \beta + 2 a b \sin \theta \sin \beta \qquad \text{... (xiv)}$$

Adding equations (*xii*) and (*xiv*),

$$c^2 (\cos^2 \phi + \sin^2 \theta) = a^2 (\cos^2 \theta + \sin^2 \theta) + b^2 (\cos^2 \beta + \sin^2 \beta)$$

$$+ 2ab(\cos \theta \cos \beta + \sin \theta \sin \beta) + d^2 - 2 a d \cos \theta - 2 b d \cos \beta$$

or

$$c^2 = a^2 + b^2 + 2 a b(\cos \theta \cos \beta + \sin \theta \sin \beta)$$

$$+ d^2 - 2ad \cos \theta - 2 b d \cos \beta$$

or

$$2ab(\cos \theta \cos \beta + \sin \theta \sin \beta) = c^2 - a^2 - b^2 - d^2 + 2a d \cos \theta + 2 b d \cos \beta$$

$$\cos \theta \cos \beta + \sin \theta \sin \beta = \frac{c^2 - a^2 - b^2 - d^2}{2ab} + \frac{d}{b} \cos \theta + \frac{d}{a} \cos \beta \qquad \text{... (xv)}$$

Let

$$\frac{d}{a} = k_1 ; \frac{d}{b} = k_4 ; \quad \text{and} \quad \frac{c^2 - a^2 - b^2 - d^2}{2a b} = k_5 \qquad \text{... (xvi)}$$

∴ Equation (*xv*) may be written as

$$\cos \theta \cos \beta + \sin \theta \sin \beta = k_1 \cos \beta + k_4 \cos \theta + k_5 \qquad \text{... (xvii)}$$

From trigonometrical ratios, we know that

$$\sin \beta = \frac{2 \tan(\beta / 2)}{1 + \tan^2 (\beta / 2)}, \quad \text{and} \quad \cos \beta = \frac{1 - \tan^2 (\beta / 2)}{1 + \tan^2 (\beta / 2)}$$

Substituting these values of $\sin \beta$ and $\cos \beta$ in equation (*xvii*),

$$\cos \theta \left[\frac{1 - \tan^2 (\beta / 2)}{1 + \tan^2 (\beta / 2)} \right] + \sin \theta \left[\frac{2 \tan(\beta / 2)}{1 + \tan^2 (\beta / 2)} \right]$$

$$= k_1 \left[\frac{1 - \tan^2 (\beta / 2)}{1 + \tan^2 (\beta / 2)} \right] + k_4 \cos \theta + k_5$$

$$\cos \theta [1 - \tan^2 (\beta / 2)] + 2 \sin \theta \tan(\beta / 2)$$

$$= k_1 \left[1 - \tan^2 (\beta / 2) \right] + k_4 \cos \theta \left[1 + \tan^2 (\beta / 2) \right] + k_5 \left[1 + \tan^2 (\beta / 2) \right]$$

$$\cos \theta - \cos \theta \tan^2 (\beta / 2) + 2 \sin \theta \tan(\beta / 2)$$

$$= k_1 - k_1 \tan^2 (\beta / 2) + k_4 \cos \theta + k_4 \cos \theta \tan^2 (\beta / 2)$$

$$+ k_5 + k_5 \tan^2 (\beta / 2)$$

$$- \cos \theta \tan^2 (\beta / 2) + k_1 \tan^2 (\beta / 2) - k_4 \cos \theta \tan^2 (\beta / 2) - k_5 \tan^2 (\beta / 2)$$

$$+ 2 \sin \theta \tan(\beta / 2) - k_1 - k_4 \cos \theta - k_5 + \cos \theta = 0$$

$$- \tan^2 (\beta / 2)[(k_4 + 1) \cos \theta + k_5 - k_1] + 2 \sin \theta \tan(\beta / 2) - [(k_4 - 1) \cos \theta + k_5 + k_1] = 0$$

or $\qquad [(k_4+1)\cos\theta+k_5-k_1]\tan^2(\beta/2)+(-2\sin\theta)\tan(\beta/2)+[(k_4-1)\cos\theta+k_5+k_1]=0$

(By changing the sign)

or $\qquad\qquad D\tan^2(\beta/2)+E\tan(\beta/2)+F=0 \qquad\qquad$ ... (*xviii*)

where $\qquad\qquad \left.\begin{array}{l} D=(k_4+1)\cos\theta+k_5-k_1, \\ E=-2\sin\theta, \quad\text{and} \\ F=[(k_4-1)\cos\theta+k_5+k_1] \end{array}\right] \qquad\qquad$ ... (*xix*)

The equation (*xviii*) is a quadratic equation in $\tan(\beta/2)$. Its two roots are

$$\tan(\beta/2)=\frac{-E\pm\sqrt{E^2-4D\,F}}{2D}$$

or $\qquad\qquad \beta=2\tan^{-1}\left[\frac{-E\pm\sqrt{E^2-4DF}}{2\,D}\right] \qquad\qquad$ ... (*xx*)

From this equation (*xx*), we can find the position of coupler link BC (*i.e.* angle β).

Note: The angle α may be obtained directly from equation (*i*) or (*iii*) after determining the angle ϕ.

2. *Velocity analysis*

Let $\qquad\qquad \omega_1$ = Angular velocity of the link $AB=d\theta/dt$,

$\qquad\qquad\qquad \omega_2$ = Angular velocity of the link $BC=d\beta/dt$, and

$\qquad\qquad\qquad \omega_3$ = Angular velocity of the link $CD=d\phi/dt$.

Differentiating equation (*i*) with respect to time,

$$-a\sin\theta\times\frac{d\theta}{dt}-b\sin\beta\times\frac{d\beta}{dt}+c\sin\phi\times\frac{d\phi}{dt}=0$$

or $\qquad\qquad -a\omega_1\sin\theta-b\omega_2\sin\beta+c\omega_3\sin\phi=0 \qquad\qquad$ ... (*xxi*)

Again, differentiating equation (*iii*) with respect to time,

$$a\cos\theta\times\frac{d\theta}{dt}+b\cos\beta\times\frac{d\beta}{dt}-c\cos\phi\times\frac{d\phi}{dt}=0$$

or $\qquad\qquad a\omega_1\cos\theta+b\omega_2\cos\beta-c\omega_3\cos\phi=0 \qquad\qquad$ ... (*xxii*)

Multiplying the equation (*xxi*) by $\cos\beta$ and equation (*xxii*) by $\sin\beta$,

$\qquad -a\omega_1\sin\theta\cos\beta-b\omega_2\sin\beta\cos\beta+c\omega_3\sin\phi\cos\beta=0 \qquad$ ... (*xxiii*)

and $\qquad a\omega_1\cos\theta\sin\beta+b\omega_2\cos\beta\sin\beta-c\omega_3\cos\phi\sin\beta=0 \qquad$ ... (*xxiv*)

Adding equations (*xxiii*) and (*xxiv*),

$$a\omega_1\sin(\beta-\theta)+c\omega_3\sin(\phi-\beta)=0$$

$\therefore\qquad\qquad \omega_3=\dfrac{-a\omega_1\sin(\beta-\theta)}{c\sin(\phi-\beta)} \qquad\qquad$ ... (*xxv*)

Again, multiplying the equation (*xxi*) by $\cos\phi$ and equation (*xxii*) by $\sin\phi$,

$$-a\omega_1 \sin\theta\cos\phi - b\omega_2 \sin\beta\cos\phi + c\omega_3 \sin\phi\cos\phi = 0 \qquad \ldots (xxvi)$$

and
$$a\omega_1 \cos\theta\sin\phi + b\omega_2 \cos\beta\sin\phi - c\omega_3 \cos\phi\sin\phi = 0 \qquad \ldots (xxvii)$$

Adding equations (*xxvi*) and (*xxvii*),

$$a\omega_1 \sin(\phi-\theta) + b\omega_2 \sin(\phi-\beta) = 0$$

$$\therefore \qquad \omega_2 = \frac{-a\omega_1 \sin(\phi-\theta)}{b\sin(\phi-\beta)} \qquad \ldots (xxviii)$$

From equations (*xxv*) and (*xxviii*), we can find ω_3 and ω_2, if $a, b, c, \theta, \phi, \beta$ and ω_1 are known.

3. Acceleration analysis

Let $\quad \alpha_1$ = Angular acceleration of the link $AB = d\omega_1 / dt$,

$\quad \alpha_2$ = Angular acceleration of the link $BC = d\omega_2 / dt$, and

$\quad \alpha_3$ = Angular acceleration of the link $CD = d\omega_3 / dt$.

Differentiating equation (*xxi*) with respect to time,

$$-a\left[\omega_1 \cos\theta\times\frac{d\theta}{dt} + \sin\theta\times\frac{d\omega_1}{dt}\right] - b\left[\omega_2 \cos\beta\times\frac{d\beta}{dt} + \sin\beta\times\frac{d\omega_2}{dt}\right]$$

$$+c\left[\omega_3 \cos\phi\times\frac{d\phi}{dt} + \sin\phi\times\frac{d\omega_3}{dt}\right] = 0$$

$$\ldots\left[\because \frac{d}{dx}(uv) = u\times\frac{dv}{dx} + v\times\frac{du}{dx}\right]$$

or
$$-a\omega_1^2 \cos\theta - a\sin\theta\,\alpha_1 - b\omega_2^2 \cos\beta - b\sin\beta\,\alpha_2$$

$$+c\omega_3^2 \cos\phi + c\sin\phi\,\alpha_3 = 0 \qquad \ldots (xxix)$$

Again, differentiating equation (*xxii*) with respect to time,

$$a\left[\omega_1 \times-\sin\theta\times\frac{d\theta}{dt} + \cos\theta\times\frac{d\omega_1}{dt}\right] + b\left[\omega_2 \times-\sin\beta\times\frac{d\beta}{dt} + \cos\beta\times\frac{d\omega_2}{dt}\right]$$

$$-c\left[\omega_3 \times-\sin\phi\times\frac{d\phi}{dt} + \cos\phi\times\frac{d\omega_3}{dt}\right] = 0$$

or
$$-a\omega_1^2 \sin\theta + a\cos\theta\,\alpha_1 - b\omega_2^2 \sin\beta + b\cos\beta\,\alpha_2$$

$$+c\omega_3^2 \sin\phi - c\cos\phi\,\alpha_3 = 0 \qquad \ldots (xxx)$$

Multiplying equation (*xxix*) by $\cos\phi$, and equation (*xxx*) by $\sin\phi$,

$$-a\omega_1^2 \cos\theta\cos\phi - a\alpha_1 \sin\theta\cos\phi - b\omega_2^2 \cos\beta\cos\phi$$

$$-b\alpha_2 \sin\beta\cos\phi + c\omega_3^2 \cos^2\phi + c\alpha_3 \sin\phi\cos\phi = 0 \qquad \ldots (xxxi)$$

and $\quad -a\,\omega_1^2\sin\theta\sin\phi + a\,\alpha_1\cos\theta\sin\phi - b\,\omega_2^2\sin\beta\sin\phi$

$$+b\,\alpha_2\cos\beta\sin\phi + c\,\omega_3^2\sin^2\phi - c\,\alpha_3\cos\phi\sin\phi = 0 \qquad \dots (xxxii)$$

Adding equations (*xxxi*) and (*xxxii*),

$$-a\,\omega_1^2(\cos\phi\cos\theta + \sin\phi\sin\theta) + a\,\alpha_1(\sin\phi\cos\theta - \cos\phi\sin\theta)$$

$$-b\,\omega_2^2(\cos\phi\cos\beta + \sin\phi\sin\beta) + b\,\alpha_2(\sin\phi\cos\beta - \cos\phi\sin\beta)$$

$$+c\,\omega_3^2(\cos^2\phi + \sin^2\phi) = 0$$

$$-a\,\omega_1^2\cos(\phi-\theta) + a\,\alpha_1\sin(\phi-\theta) - b\,\omega_2^2\cos(\phi-\beta) + b\,\alpha_2\sin(\phi-\beta) + c\,\omega_3^2 = 0$$

$$\therefore \quad \alpha_2 = \frac{-a\,\alpha_1\sin(\phi-\theta) + a\,\omega_1^2\cos(\phi-\theta) + b\,\omega_2^2\cos(\phi-\beta) - c\,\omega_3^2}{b\sin(\phi-\beta)} \qquad \dots (xxxiii)$$

Again multiplying equation (*xxix*) by $\cos\beta$ and equation (*xxx*) by $\sin\beta$,

$$-a\,\omega_1^2\cos\theta\cos\beta - a\,\alpha_1\sin\theta\cos\beta - b\,\omega_2^2\cos^2\beta - b\,\alpha_2\sin\beta\cos\beta$$

$$+c\,\omega_3^2\cos\phi\cos\beta + c\,\alpha_3\sin\phi\cos\beta = 0 \qquad \dots (xxxiv)$$

and $\quad -a\,\omega_1^2\sin\theta\sin\beta + a\,\alpha_1\cos\theta\sin\beta - b\,\omega_2^2\sin^2\beta + b\,\alpha_2\cos\beta\sin\beta$

$$+c\,\omega_3^2\sin\phi\sin\beta - c\,\alpha_3\cos\phi\sin\beta = 0 \qquad \dots (xxxv)$$

Adding equations (*xxxiv*) and (*xxxv*),

$$-a\,\omega_1^2(\cos\beta\cos\theta + \sin\beta\sin\theta) + a\,\alpha_1(\sin\beta\cos\theta - \cos\beta\sin\theta) - b\,\omega_2^2(\cos^2\beta + \sin^2\beta)$$

$$+c\,\omega_3^2(\cos\phi\cos\beta + \sin\phi\sin\beta) + c\,\alpha_3(\sin\phi\cos\beta - \cos\phi\sin\beta) = 0$$

$$-a\,\omega_1^2\cos(\beta-\theta) + a\,\alpha_1\sin(\beta-\theta) - b\,\omega_2^2 + c\,\omega_3^2\cos(\phi-\beta) + c\,\alpha_3\sin(\phi-\beta) = 0$$

$$\therefore \quad \alpha_3 = \frac{-a\,\alpha_1\sin(\beta-\theta) + a\,\omega_1^2\cos(\beta-\theta) + b\,\omega_2^2 - c\,\omega_3^2\cos(\phi-\beta)}{c\sin(\phi-\beta)} \qquad \dots (xxxvi)$$

From equations (*xxxiii*) and (*xxxvi*), the angular acceleration of the links *BC* and *CD* (*i.e.* α_2 and α_3) may be determined.

25.3. Programme for Four Bar Mechanism

The following is a programme in Fortran for determining the velocity and acceleration of the links in a four bar mechanism for different position of the crank.

```
C       PROGRAM TO FIND THE VELOCITY AND ACCELERATION IN A FOUR-BAR
C       MECHANISM
        DIMENSION PH (2), PHI (2), PP (2), BET (2), BT (2), VELC (2), VELB (2), ACCC (2),
        ACCB (2), C1 (2), C2 (2), C3 (2), C4 (2), B1 (2), B2 (2), B3 (2), B4 (2)

        READ (*, *) A, B, C, D, VELA, ACCA, THETA
        PI = 4.0 * ATAN (1.0)
        THET = 0
        IHT = 180/THETA
        DTHET = PI/IHT
```

```
         DO 10 J = 1, 2 * IHT
         THET = (J – 1) * DTHET
         AK = (A * A – B * B + C * C + D * D) * 0.5)
         TH = THET * 180/PI
         AA = AK – A * (D – C) * COS (THET) – (C * D)
         BB = – 2.0 * A* C * SIN (THET)
         CC = AK – A * (D + C) * COS (THET) + (C * D)
         AB = BB * * 2 – 4 * AA * CC
         IF    (AB . LT . 0) GO TO 10
         PHH = SQRT (AB)
         PH (1) = – BB + PHH
         PH (2) = – BB – PHH
         DO 9 I =  1, 2
         PHI (I) = ATAN (PH (I) * 0.5/AA) * 2
         PP (I) = PHI (I) * 180/PI
         BET (I) = ASIN ((C * SIN (PHI (I)) – A * SIN (THET)) / B)
         BT (I) = BET (I) * 180/PI
         VELC (I) = A * VELA * SIN (BET (I) – THET) / (C * SIN (BET (I) – PHI (I)))
         VELB (I) = (A * VELA * SIN (PHI (I) – THET) ) / (B * SIN (BET (I) – PHI (I))))
         C1 (I) = A * ACCA * SIN (BET (I) – THET)
         C2 (I) = A * VELA * * 2 * COS (BET (I) – THET) + B * VELB (I) * * 2
         C3 (I) = C * VELC (I) * * 2 * COS (PHI (I) – BET (I) )
         C4 (I) = C * SIN (BET (I) – PHI (I))
         ACCC (I) = (C1 (I) – C2 (I) + C3 (I) ) / C4 (I)
         B1 (I) = A* ACCA* SIN (PHI (I) – THET )
         B2 (I) = A * VELA * * 2 * COS (PHI (I) – THET )
         B3 (I) = B * VELB (I) * * 2 * COS (PHI (I) – BET (I) ) – C * VELC (I) * * 2
         B4 (I) = B * (SIN (BET (I) – PHI (I))))
9        ACCB (I) = (B1 (I) – B2 (I) – B3 (I)) / B4 (I)
         IF (J . NE . 1) GO TO 8
         WRITE (*, 7)
7        FORMAT (4X,' THET', 4X,' PHI', 4X,' BETA', 4X,' VELC', 4X,' VELB', 4X,' ACCC', 4X,'
         ACCB')
8        WRITE (*, 6) TH, PP (1), BT (1), VELC (1), VELB (1), ACCC (1), ACCB (1)
6        FORMAT (8F8 . 2)
         WRITE (*, 5) PP (2), BT (2), VELC (2), VELB (2), ACCC (2), ACCB (2)
5        FORMAT (8X, 8F8 . 2)
10       CONTINUE
         STOP
         END
```

The various input variables are

    A, B, C, D = Lengths of the links *AB, BC, CD,* and *DA* respectively in mm,

        THETA = Interval of the input angle in degrees,

        VELA = Angular Velocity of the input link *AB* in rad/s, and

        ACCA = Angular acceleration of the input link in rad/s^2.

The output variables are :

        THET = Angular displacement of the input link *AB* in degrees,

        PHI = Angular displacement of the output link *DC* in degrees,

        BETA = Angular displacement of the coupler link *BC* in degrees,

        VELC = Angular velocity of the output link *DC* in rad/s,

        VELB = Angular velocity of the coupler link *BC* in rad/s,

        ACCC = Angular acceleration of the output link *DC* in rad/s^2,

        ACCB = Angular acceleration of the coupler link *BC* in rad/s^2.

Example 25.1. *ABCD is a four bar mechanism, with link AD fixed. The lengths of the links are*

$$AB = 300 \ mm; \ BC = 360 \ mm; \ CD = 360 \ mm \ and \ AD = 600 \ mm.$$

The crank AB has an angular velocity of 10 rad/s and an angular retardation of 30 rad/s², both anticlockwise. Find the angular displacements, velocities and accelerations of the links BC and CD, for an interval of 30° of the crank AB.

Solution.

Given input :

A = 300, B = 360, C = 360, D = 600, VA = 10, ACCA = –30, THETA = 30

OUTPUT :

THET	PHI	BETA	VELC	VELB	ACCC	ACCB
.00	– 114.62	– 65.38	– 10.00	– 10.00	– 61.67	121.67
	114.62	65.38	– 10.00	– 10.00	121.67	– 61.67
30.00	– 144.88	– 82.70	– 8.69	– .84	101.52	181.43
	97.30	35.12	– .84	– 8.69	181.43	101.52
60.00	– 166.19	– 73.81	– 6.02	6.02	38.02	77.45
	106.19	13.81	6.02	– 6.02	77.45	38.02
90.00	174.73	– 47.86	– 8.26	12.26	– 180.18	216.18
	132.14	– 5.27	12.26	– 8.26	216.18	– 180.18
270.00	– 132.14	5.27	12.26	– 8.26	– 289.73	229.73
	– 174.73	47.86	– 8.26	12.26	229.73	– 289.73
300.00	– 106.19	– 13.81	6.02	– 6.02	– 113.57	– 1.90
	166.19	73.81	– 6.02	6.02	– 1.90	– 113.57
330.00	– 97.30	– 35.12	– .84	– 8.69	– 170.39	– 49.36
	144.88	82.70	– 8.69	– .84	– 49.36	– 176.39

25.4. Computer Aided Analysis For Slider Crank Mechanism

A slider crank mechanism is shown in Fig. 25.2 (*a*). The slider is attached to the connecting rod *BC* of length *b*. Let the crank *AB* of radius *a* rotates in anticlockwise direction with uniform

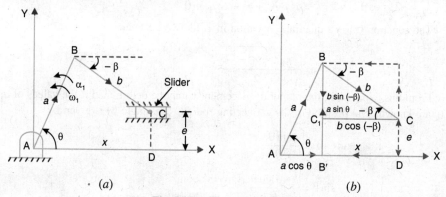

(*a*) (*b*)

Fig. 25.2 Slider crank mechanism.

angular velocity ω_1 rad/s and an angular acceleration α_1 rad/s². Let the crank makes an angle θ with the X-axis and the slider reciprocates along a path parallel to the X-axis, *i.e.* at an eccentricity $CD = e$, as shown in Fig. 25.2 (*a*).

The expressions for displacement, velocity and acceleration analysis are derived as discussed below :

1. *Displacement analysis*

For equilibrium of the mechanism, the sum of the components along X-axis and along Y-axis must be equal to zero. First of all, taking the sum of the components along X-axis, as shown in Fig. 25.2 (b), we have

$$a\cos\theta + b\cos(-\beta) - x = 0 \qquad \text{... (β in clockwise direction from X-axis is taken } -ve)$$

or
$$b\cos\beta = x - a\cos\theta \qquad \text{... (i)}$$

Squaring both sides,

$$b^2\cos^2\beta = x^2 + a^2\cos^2\theta - 2xa\cos\theta \qquad \text{... (ii)}$$

Now taking the sum of components along Y-axis, we have

$$b\sin(-\beta) + e + a\sin\theta = 0$$

or
$$-b\sin\beta + e = a\sin\theta$$

$$\therefore \qquad b\sin\beta = e - a\sin\theta \qquad \text{... (iii)}$$

Squaring both sides,

$$b^2\sin^2\beta = e^2 + a^2\sin^2\theta - 2ea\sin\theta \qquad \text{... (iv)}$$

Adding equations (ii) and (iv),

$$b^2(\cos^2\beta + \sin^2\beta) = x^2 + e^2 + a^2(\cos^2\theta + \sin^2\theta) - 2xa\cos\theta - 2ea\sin\theta$$

$$b^2 = x^2 + e^2 + a^2 - 2xa\cos\theta - 2ea\sin\theta$$

or
$$x^2 + (-2a\cos\theta)x + a^2 - b^2 + e^2 - 2ea\sin\theta = 0$$

or
$$x^2 + k_1 x + k_2 = 0 \qquad \text{... (v)}$$

where $k_1 = -2a\cos\theta$, and $k_2 = a^2 - b^2 + e^2 - 2ea\sin\theta$ ... (vi)

The equation (v) is a quadratic equation in x. Its two roots are

$$x = \frac{-k_1 \pm \sqrt{k_1^2 - 4k_2}}{2} \qquad \text{... (vii)}$$

From this expression, the output displacement x may be determined if the values of a, b, e and θ are known. The position of the connecting rod BC (i.e. angle β) is given by

$$\sin(-\beta) = \frac{a\sin\theta - e}{b}$$

or
$$\sin\beta = \frac{e - a\sin\theta}{b}$$

$$\therefore \qquad \beta = \sin^{-1}\left(\frac{e - a\sin\theta}{b}\right) \qquad \text{... (viii)}$$

Note : When the slider lies on the X-axis, *i.e.* the line of stroke of the slider passes through the axis of rotation of the crank, then eccentricity, $e = 0$. In such a case, equations (*vi*) and (*viii*) may be written as

$$k_1 = -2a\cos\theta, \quad \text{and} \quad k_2 = a^2 - b^2$$

and
$$\beta = \sin^{-1}\left(\frac{-a\sin\theta}{b}\right)$$

2. Velocity analysis

Let ω_1 = Angular velocity of the crank $AB = d\theta/dt$,

ω_2 = Angular velocity of the connecting rod $BC = d\beta/dt$, and

v_S = Linear velocity of the slider = dx/dt.

Differentiating equation (*i*) with respect to time,

$$b \times -\sin\beta \times \frac{d\beta}{dt} = \frac{dx}{dt} - a \times -\sin\theta \times \frac{d\theta}{dt}$$

or
$$-a\omega_1 \sin\theta - b\omega_2 \sin\beta - \frac{dx}{dt} = 0 \qquad \qquad \text{... (ix)}$$

Again, differentiating equation (*iii*) with respect to time,

$$b\cos\beta \times \frac{d\beta}{dt} = -a\cos\theta \times \frac{d\theta}{dt}$$

or
$$a\omega_1 \cos\theta + b\omega_2 \cos\beta = 0 \qquad \qquad \text{... (x)}$$

Multiplying equation (*ix*) by $\cos\beta$ and equation (*x*) by $\sin\beta$,

$$-a\omega_1 \sin\theta\cos\beta - b\omega_2 \sin\beta\cos\beta - \frac{dx}{dt} \times \cos\beta = 0 \qquad \qquad \text{... (xi)}$$

and
$$a\omega_1 \cos\theta\sin\beta + b\omega_2 \cos\beta\sin\beta = 0 \qquad \qquad \text{... (xii)}$$

Adding equations (*xi*) and (*xii*),

$$a\omega_1(\sin\beta\cos\theta - \cos\beta\sin\theta) - \frac{dx}{dt} \times \cos\beta = 0$$

$$a\omega_1 \sin(\beta - \theta) = \frac{dx}{dt} \times \cos\beta$$

$$\therefore \quad \frac{dx}{dt} = \frac{a\omega_1 \sin(\beta - \theta)}{\cos\beta} \qquad \qquad \text{... (xiii)}$$

From this equation, the linear velocity of the slider (v_S) may be determined.

The angular velocity of the connecting rod BC (*i.e.* ω_2) may be determined from equation (*x*) and it is given by

$$\omega_2 = \frac{-a\omega_1 \cos\theta}{b\cos\beta} \qquad \qquad \text{... (xiv)}$$

3. Acceleration analysis

Let $\quad \alpha_1$ = Angular acceleration of the crank $AB = d\omega_1 / dt$,

$\quad \alpha_2$ = Angular acceleration of the connecting rod = $d\omega_2 / dt$, and

$\quad a_S$ = Linear acceleration of the slider = d^2x / dt^2

Differentiating equation (ix) with respect to time,

$$-a\left[\omega_1 \cos\theta \times \frac{d\theta}{dt} + \sin\theta \times \frac{d\omega_1}{dt}\right] - b\left[\omega_2 \cos\beta \times \frac{d\beta}{dt} + \sin\beta \times \frac{d\omega_2}{dt}\right] - \frac{d^2x}{dt^2} = 0$$

$$-a\left[\alpha_1 \sin\theta + \omega_1^2 \cos\theta\right] - b\left[\alpha_2 \sin\beta + \omega_2^2 \cos\beta\right] - \frac{d^2x}{dt^2} = 0 \qquad \dots (xv)$$

The chain-belt at the bottom of a bulldozer provides powerful grip, spreads weight and force on the ground, and allows to exert high force on the objects to be moved.

Note : This picture is given as additional information.

Differentiating equation (x) with respect to time,

$$a\left[\omega_1 \times -\sin\theta \times \frac{d\theta}{dt} + \cos\theta \times \frac{d\omega_1}{dt}\right] + b\left[\omega_2 \times -\sin\beta \times \frac{d\beta}{dt} + \cos\beta \times \frac{d\omega_2}{dt}\right] = 0$$

$$a\left[\alpha_1 \cos\theta - \omega_1^2 \sin\theta\right] + b\left[\alpha_2 \cos\beta - \omega_2^2 \sin\beta\right] = 0 \qquad \dots (xvi)$$

Multiplying equation (xv) by $\cos\beta$ and equation (xvi) by $\sin\beta$,

$$-a\left[\alpha_1 \sin\theta\cos\beta + \omega_1^2 \cos\theta\cos\beta\right] - b\left[\alpha_2 \sin\beta\cos\beta + \omega_2^2 \cos^2\beta\right]$$

$$-\frac{d^2x}{dt^2} \times \cos\beta = 0 \qquad \dots (xvii)$$

and $\qquad a\left[\alpha_1 \cos\theta\sin\beta - \omega_1^2 \sin\theta\sin\beta\right] + b\left[\alpha_2 \cos\beta\sin\beta - \omega_2^2 \sin^2\beta\right] = 0 \qquad \dots (xviii)$

Adding equations (*xvii*) and (*xviii*),

$$a\left[\alpha_1\left(\sin\beta\cos\theta-\cos\beta\sin\theta\right)-\omega_1^2\left(\cos\beta\cos\theta+\sin\beta\sin\theta\right)\right]$$
$$-b\omega_2^2\left(\cos^2\beta+\sin^2\beta\right)-\frac{d^2x}{dt^2}\times\cos\beta=0$$

$$a\,\alpha_1\sin\left(\beta-\theta\right)-a\,\omega_1^2\cos\left(\beta-\theta\right)-b\,\omega_2^2-\frac{d^2x}{dt^2}\times\cos\beta=0$$

$$\therefore\qquad\frac{d^2x}{dt^2}=\frac{a\,\alpha_1\sin\left(\beta-\theta\right)-a\,\omega_1^2\cos\left(\beta-\theta\right)-b\,\omega_2^2}{\cos\beta}\qquad\ldots(xix)$$

From this equation, the linear acceleration of the slider (a_S) may be determined.

The angular acceleration of the connecting rod *BC* (*i.e.* α_2) may be determined from equation (*xvi*) and it is given by,

$$\alpha_2=\frac{a\left(\alpha_1\cos\theta-\omega_1^2\sin\theta\right)-b\,\omega_2^2\sin\beta}{b\cos\beta}\qquad\ldots(xx)$$

25.5. Programme for a Slider Crank Mechanism

The following is a programme in Fortran to find the velocity and acceleration in a slider crank mechanism.

```
c       PROGRAM TO FIND THE VELOCITY AND ACCELERATION IN A SLIDER
c       CRANK MECHANISM
        READ (*, *) A, B, E, VA, ACC, THA
        PI = 4 * ATAN (1.)
        TH = 0
        IH = 180/THA
        DTH = PI / IH
        DO 10 I = 1, 2 * I H
        TH = (I – 1) * DTH
        BET = ASIN (E – A * SIN (TH) ) / B)
        VS = – A * VA * SIN (TH – BET) / (COS (BET) * 1000)
        VB = – A * VA * COS (TH) / B * COS (BET)
        AC1 = A * ACC * SIN (BET – TH) – B * VB * * 2
        AC2 = A * VA * * 2 * COS (BET – TH)
        ACS = (AC1 – AC2) / (COS (BET) * 1000)
        AC3 = A * ACC * COS (TH) – A * VA * * 2 * SIN (TH)
        AC4 = B * VB * * 2 * SIN (BET)
        ACB = – (AC3 – AC4) / (B * COS (BET) )
        I F (i . EQ . 1) WRITE (*, 9)
9       FORMAT (3X,' TH', 5X,' BET', 4X,' VS,' 4X,' VB,' 4X,' ACS', 4X,' ACB')
10      WRITE (*, 8) TH * 180 / P I , BET * 180 / P I, VS, VB, ACS, ACB
8       FORMAT (6 F 8 . 2)
        STOP
        END
```

The input variables are :

   A, B, E = Length of crank *AB* (*a*), connecting rod *BC* (*b*) and offset (*e*) in mm,

       VA = Angular velocity of crank *AB* (input link) in rad/s,

     ACC = Angular acceleration of the crank *AB* (input link) in rad/s^2, and

    THA = Interval of the input angle in degrees.

The output variables are :

    THA = Angular displacement of the crank or input link *AB* in degrees,

    BET = Angular displacement of the connecting rod *BC* in degrees,

      VS = Linear velocity of the slider in m/s,

      VB = Angular velocity of the crank or input link *AB* in rad/s,

    ACS = Linear acceleration of the slider in m/s^2, and

    ACB = Angular acceleration of the crank or input link *AB* in rad/s^2.

Example 25.2. *In a slider crank mechanism, the crank AB = 200 mm and the connecting rod BC = 750 mm. The line of stroke of the slider is offset by a perpendicular distance of 50 mm. If the crank rotates at an angular speed of 20 rad/s and angular acceleration of 10 rad/s^2, find at an interval of 30° of the crank, 1. the linear velocity and acceleration of the slider, and 2. the angular velocity and acceleration of the connecting rod.*

Solution.

Given input :

     A = 200,   B = 750,   E = 50,   VA = 20,   ACC = 10,   THA = 30

OUTPUT :

T H	B E T	V S	V B	ACS	AC B
.00	3.82	.27	− 5.32	− 101.15	− .78
30.00	− 3.82	− 2.23	− 4.61	− 83.69	49.72
60.00	− 9.46	− 3.80	− 2.63	− 35.62	91.14
90.00	− 11.54	− 4.00	.00	14.33	108.87
120.00	− 9.46.	− 3.13	2.63	44.71	93.85
150.00	− 3.82	− 1.77	4.61	55.11	54.35
180.00	3.82	− .27	5.32	58.58	4.56
210.00	11.54	1.29	4.53	62.42	− 47.90
240.00	17.31	2.84	2.55	57.93	− 93.34
270.00	19.47	4.00	.00	30.28	− 113.14
300.00	17.31	4.09	− 2.55	− 21.45	− 96.14
330.00	11.54	2.71	− 4.53	− 75.44	− 52.61

25.6. Coupler Curves

    It is often desired to have a mechanism to guide a point along a specified path. The path generated by a point on the coupler link is known as a *coupler curve* and the generating point is called a *coupler point* (also known as *tracer point*). The straight line mechanisms as discussed in chapter 9 (Art. 9.3) are the examples of the use of coupler curves. In this article, we shall discuss the method of determining the co-ordinates of the coupler point in case of a four bar mechanism and a slider crank mechanism.

1. *Four bar mechanism*

Consider a four bar mechanism *ABCD* with an offset coupler point *E* on the coupler link *BC*, as shown in Fig. 25.3. Let the point *E* makes an angle α with *BC* in the anticlockwise direction and its co-ordinates are *E* (x_E, y_E).

First of all, let us find the value of *BD*, γ and β. From right angled triangle $BB_1 D$,

$$\tan \gamma = \frac{BB_1}{B_1 D} = \frac{BB_1}{AD - AB_1} = \frac{a \sin \theta}{d - a \cos \theta}$$

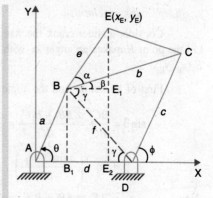

Fig. 25.3. Four bar mechainsm with a coupler point.

or $$\gamma = \tan^{-1} \left(\frac{a \sin \theta}{d - a \cos \theta} \right)$$

and $$(BD)^2 = (BB_1)^2 + (B_1 D)^2 = (BB_1)^2 + (AD - AB_1)^2$$

$$= (a \sin \theta)^2 + (d - a \cos \theta)^2$$

$$= a^2 \sin^2 \theta + d^2 + a^2 \cos^2 \theta - 2ad \cos \theta$$

$$= a^2 (\sin^2 \theta + \cos^2 \theta) + d^2 - 2ad \cos \theta$$

$$= a^2 + d^2 - 2ad \cos \theta$$

Now in triangle *DBC*,

$$\cos(\gamma + \beta) = \frac{(BD)^2 + (BC)^2 - (CD)^2}{2 BC \times BD} \qquad \text{... (cosine law of triangle)}$$

$$= \frac{f^2 + b^2 - c^2}{2bf}$$

or $$\gamma + \beta = \cos^{-1} \left(\frac{f^2 + b^2 - c^2}{2bf} \right)$$

$$\therefore \quad \beta = \cos^{-1} \left(\frac{f^2 + b^2 - c^2}{2bf} \right) - \gamma \qquad \text{... (i)}$$

Let us now find the co-ordinates x_E and y_E. From Fig. 25.3, we find that

$$x_E = AE_2 = AB_1 + B_1 E_2 = AB_1 + BE_1 \qquad \text{... ($\because B_1 E_2 = BE_1$)}$$

$$= a \cos \theta + e \cos (\alpha + \beta) \qquad \text{... (ii)}$$

and $$y_E = E_2 E = E_2 E_1 + E_1 E = B_1 B + E_1 E \qquad \text{... ($\because E_2 E_1 = B_1 B$)}$$

$$= a \sin \theta + e \sin (\alpha + \beta) \qquad \text{... (iii)}$$

From the above equations, the co-ordinates of the point *E* may be determined if *a*, *e*, θ, α and β are known.

2. Slider crank mechanism

Consider a slider crank mechanism with an offset coupler point E, as shown in Fig. 25.4. Let the point E makes an angle α with BC in the anticlockwise direction and its co-ordinates are $E(x_E, y_E)$.

First of all, let us find the angle β. From right angled triangle BC_1C,

$$\sin\beta = \frac{BC_1}{BC} = \frac{BB_1 - B_1C_1}{BC} = \frac{a\sin\theta - e_1}{b}$$

$$\therefore \quad \beta = \sin^{-1}\left(\frac{a\sin\theta - e_1}{b}\right) \qquad \dots (iv)$$

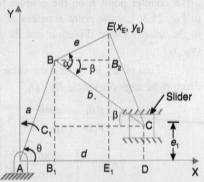

Fig. 25.4 Slider crank mechanism with coupler point.

Now
$$x_E = AE_1 = AB_1 + B_1E_1 = AB_1 + BB_2$$
$$= a\cos\theta + e\cos(\alpha - \beta) \qquad \dots (v)$$

and
$$y_E = E_1E = E_1B_2 + B_2E = B_1B + B_2E$$
$$= a\sin\theta + e\sin(\alpha - \beta) \qquad \dots (vi)$$

From the above equations, the co-ordinates of the point E may be determined, if a, b, e, e_1, θ, α and β are known.

Note : When the slider lies on the X-axis, i.e. the line of stroke of the slider passes through the axis of rotation of the crank, then eccentricity $e_1 = 0$. In such a case equation (iv) may be written as

$$\beta = \sin^{-1}\left(\frac{a\sin\theta}{b}\right)$$

25.7. Synthesis of Mechanisms

In the previous articles, we have discussed the computer-aided analysis of mechanisms, i.e. the determination of displacement, velocity and acceleration for the given proportions of the mechanism. The synthesis is the opposite of analysis. The synthesis of mechanism is the design or creation of a mechanism to produce a desired output motion for a given input motion. In other words, the synthesis of mechanism deals with the determination of proportions of a mechanism for the given input and output motion. We have already discussed the application of synthesis in designing a cam (Chapter 20) to give follower a known motion from the displacement diagram and in the determination of number of teeth on the members in a gear train (Chapter 13) to produce a desired velocity ratio.

In the application of synthesis, to the design of a mechanism, the problem divides itself into the following three parts:

Roller conveyor.
Note : This picture is given as additional information.

1. *Type synthesis*, *i.e.* the type of mechanism to be used,

2. *Number synthesis*, *i.e.* the number of links and the number of joints needed to produce the required motion, and

3. *Dimensional synthesis*, *i.e.* the proportions or lengths of the links necessary to satisfy the required motion characteristics.

In designing a mechanism, one factor that must be kept in mind is that of the accuracy required of the mechanism. Sometimes, it is possible to design a mechanism that will theoretically generate a given motion. The difference between the desired motion and the actual motion produced is known as *structural error*. In addition to this, there are errors due to manufacture. The error resulting from tolerances in the length of links and bearing clearances is known as *mechanical error*.

25.8. Classifications of Synthesis Problem

The problems in synthesis can be placed in one of the following three categories :

1. Function generation ;   2. Path generation ; and   3. Body guidance.

These are discussed as follows :

1. *Function generation.* The major classification of the synthesis problems that arises in the design of links in a mechanism is a function generation. In designing a mechanism, the frequent requirement is that the output link should either rotate, oscillate or reciprocate according to a specified function of time or function of the motion of input link. This is known as function generation. A simple example is that of designing a four bar mechanism to generate the function $y = f(x)$. In this case, x represents the motion of the input link and the mechanism is to be designed so that the motion of the output link approximates the function y.

Note : The common mechanism used for function generation is that of a cam and a follower in which the angular displacement of the follower is specified as a function of the angle of rotation of the cam. The synthesis problem is to find the shape of the cam surface for the given follower displacements.

2. *Path generation.* In a path generation, the mechanism is required to guide a point (called a tracer point or coupler point) along a path having a prescribed shape. The common requirements are that a portion of the path be a circular arc, elliptical or a straight line.

3. *Body guidance.* In body guidance, both the position of a point within a moving body and the angular displacement of the body are specified. The problem may be a simple translation or a combination of translation and rotation.

25.9. Precision Points for Function Generation

In designing a mechanism to generate a particular function, it is usually impossible to accurately produce the function at more than a few points. The points at which the generated and desired functions agree are known as *precision points* or *accuracy points* and must be located so as to minimise the error generated between these points.

The best spacing of the precision points, for the first trial, is called *Chebychev spacing*. According to Freudenstein and Sandor, the Chebychev spacing for n points in the range $x_S \leq x \leq x_F$ (*i.e.* when x varies between x_S and x_F) is given by

$$x_j = \frac{1}{2}(x_S + x_F) - \frac{1}{2}(x_F - x_S)\cos\left[\frac{\pi(2j-1)}{2n}\right] \qquad \ldots (i)$$

$$= \frac{1}{2}(x_S + x_F) - \frac{1}{2} \times \Delta x \times \cos\left[\frac{\pi(2j-1)}{2n}\right]$$

where x_j = Precision points

Δx = Range in $x = x_F - x_S$, and

$j = 1, 2, ... n$

The subscripts $_S$ and $_F$ indicate start and finish positions respectively.

The precision or accuracy points may be easily obtained by using the graphical method as discussed below.

1. Draw a circle of diameter equal to the range $\Delta x = x_F - x_S$.

2. Inscribe a regular polygon having the number of sides equal to twice the number of precision points required, *i.e.* for three precision points, draw a regular hexagon inside the circle, as shown in Fig. 25.5.

3. Draw perpendiculars from each corner which intersect the diagonal of a circle at precision points x_1, x_2, x_3.

Now for the range $1 \le x \le 3$, $x_S = 1$; $x_F = 3$, and

$\therefore \qquad\qquad \Delta x = x_F - x_S = 3 - 1 = 2$

or radius of circle, $\qquad r = \Delta x / 2 = 2/2 = 1$

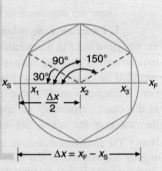

$\therefore \qquad x_2 = x_S + r = x_S + \dfrac{\Delta x}{2} = 1 + \dfrac{2}{2} = 2$

$x_1 = x_2 - r \cos 30° = x_2 - \dfrac{\Delta x}{2} \cos 30°$

$\qquad = 2 - \dfrac{2}{2} \cos 30° = 1.134$

Fig. 25.5. Graphical method for determining three precision points.

and $\qquad x_3 = x_2 + r \cos 30° = x_2 + \dfrac{\Delta x}{2} \cos 30°$

$\qquad = 2 + \dfrac{2}{2} \cos 30° = 2.866$

25.10. Angle Relationships for Function Generation

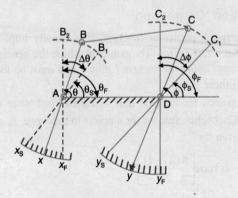

(a) Four bar mechanism.

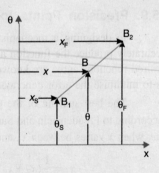

(b) Linear relationship between x and θ.

Fig. 25.6

Consider a four bar mechanism, as shown in Fig. 25.6 (*a*) arranged to generate a function $y = f(x)$ over a limited range. Let the range in x is $(x_F - x_S)$ and the corresponding range in θ is $(\theta_F - \theta_S)$. Similarly, let the range in y is $((y_F - y_S)$ and the corresponding range in ϕ is $(\phi_F - \phi_S)$.

The linear relationship between x and θ is shown in Fig. 25.6 (*b*). From the figure, we find that

$$\theta = \theta_S + \frac{\theta_F - \theta_S}{x_F - x_S}(x - x_S) \qquad \ldots (i)$$

Similarly, the linear relationship between y and ϕ may be written as

$$\phi = \phi_S + \frac{\phi_F - \phi_S}{y_F - y_S}(y - y_S) \qquad \ldots (ii)$$

An automatic filling and sealing machine.
Note : This picture is given as additional information.

For *n* points in the range, the equation (*i*) and (*ii*) may be written as

$$\theta_j = \theta_S + \frac{\theta_F - \theta_S}{x_F - x_S}(x_j - x_S) \; = \theta_S + \frac{\Delta\theta}{\Delta x}(x_j - x_S)$$

and

$$\phi_j = \phi_S + \frac{\phi_F - \phi_S}{y_F - y_S}(y_j - y_S) \; = \phi_S + \frac{\Delta\phi}{\Delta y}(y_j - y_S)$$

where

$$j = 1, 2, \ldots n,$$

$$\Delta x = x_F - x_S; \qquad \Delta\theta = \theta_F - \theta_S,$$

$$\Delta y = y_F - y_S; \qquad \text{and} \; \Delta\phi = \phi_F - \phi_S$$

Example 25.3. *A four bar mechanism is to be designed, by using three precision points, to generate the function*

$$y = x^{1.5}, \text{ for the range } 1 \le x \le 4.$$

Assuming 30° starting position and 120° finishing position for the input link and 90° starting position and 180° finishing position for the output link, find the values of x, y, θ and φ corresponding to the three precision points.

Solution : Given : $x_S = 1$; $x_F = 4$; $\theta_S = 30°$; $\theta_F = 120°$; $\phi_S = 90°$; $\phi_F = 180°$

Values of x

The three values of x corresponding to three precision points (*i.e.* for $n = 3$) according to Chebychev's spacing are given by

$$x_j = \frac{1}{2}(x_S + x_F) - \frac{1}{2}(x_F - x_S)\cos\left[\frac{\pi(2j-1)}{2n}\right], \quad \text{where } j = 1, 2 \text{ and } 3$$

$$\therefore \quad x_1 = \frac{1}{2}(1+4) - \frac{1}{2}(4-1)\cos\left[\frac{\pi(2\times1-1)}{2\times3}\right] = 1.2 \text{ Ans.} \quad \dots (\because j = 1)$$

$$x_2 = \frac{1}{2}(1+4) - \frac{1}{2}(4-1)\cos\left[\frac{\pi(2\times2-1)}{2\times3}\right] = 2.5 \text{ Ans.} \quad \dots (\because j = 2)$$

and $$x_3 = \frac{1}{2}(1+4) - \frac{1}{2}(4-1)\cos\left[\frac{\pi(2\times3-1)}{2\times3}\right] = 3.8 \text{ Ans.} \quad \dots (\because j = 3)$$

Note : The three precision points x_1, x_2 and x_3 may be determined graphically as discussed in Art. 25.9.

Values of y

Since $y = x^{1.5}$, therefore the corresponding values of y are

$$y_1 = (x_1)^{1.5} = (1.2)^{1.5} = 1.316 \text{ Ans.}$$

$$y_2 = (x_2)^{1.5} = (2.5)^{1.5} = 3.952 \text{ Ans.}$$

$$y_3 = (x_3)^{1.5} = (3.8)^{1.5} = 7.41 \text{ Ans.}$$

Note : $y_S = (x_S)^{1.5} = (1)^{1.5} = 1$ and $y_F = (x_F)^{1.5} = (4)^{1.5} = 8$

Values of θ

The three values of θ corresponding to three precision points are given by

$$\theta_j = \theta_S + \frac{\theta_F - \theta_S}{x_F - x_S}(x_j - x_S) \text{ , where } j = 1, 2 \text{ and } 3$$

$$\therefore \quad \theta_1 = 30 + \frac{120-30}{4-1}(1.2-1) = 36° \text{ Ans.}$$

$$\theta_2 = 30 + \frac{120-30}{4-1}(2.5-1) = 75° \text{ Ans.}$$

and $$\theta_3 = 30 + \frac{120-30}{4-1}(3.8-1) = 114° \text{ Ans.}$$

Values of ϕ

The three values of ϕ corresponding to three precision points are given by

$$\phi_j = \phi_S + \frac{\phi_F - \phi_S}{y_F - y_S}(y_j - y_S)$$

$\therefore$ $$\phi_1 = 90 + \frac{180 - 90}{8 - 1}(1.316 - 1) = 94.06° \text{ Ans.}$$

$$\phi_2 = 90 + \frac{180 - 90}{8 - 1}(3.952 - 1) = 127.95° \text{ Ans.}$$

and $$\phi_3 = 90 + \frac{180 - 90}{8 - 1}(7.41 - 1) = 172.41° \text{ Ans.}$$

25.11. Graphical Synthesis of Four Bar Mechanism

The synthesis of four bar mechanism consists of determining the dimensions of the links in which the output link is to occupy three specified positions corresponding to the three given positions of the input link. Fig. 25.7 shows the layout of a four bar mechanism in which the starting angle of the input link AB_1 (link 2) of known length is θ. Let θ_{12}, θ_{23} and θ_{13} be the angles between the positions B_1B_2, B_2B_3 and B_1B_3 measured anticlockwise. Let the output link DC_1 (link 4) passes through the desired positions C_1, C_2 and C_3 and ϕ_{12}, ϕ_{23} and ϕ_{13} are the corresponding angles between the positions C_1C_2, C_2C_3 and C_1C_3. The length of the fixed link (link 1) is also known. Now we are required to determine the lengths of links B_1C_1 and DC_1 (*i.e.* links 3 and 4) and the starting position of link 4 (ϕ).

The easiest way to solve the problem is based on inverting the mechanism on link 4. The procedure is discused as follows :

1. Draw AD equal to the known length of fixed link, as shown in Fig. 25.8.
2. At A, draw the input link 1 in its three specified angular positions AB_1, AB_2 and AB_3.
3. Since we have to invert the mechanism on link 4, therefore draw a line B_2D and and rotate it clockwise (in a direction opposite to the direction in which link 1 rotates) through an angle ϕ_{12} (*i.e.* the angle of the output link 4 between the first and second position) in order to locate the point B_2'.

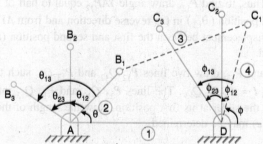

Fig. 25.7. Layout of four bar mechanism.

4. Similarly, draw another line B_3D and rotate it clockwise through an angle ϕ_{13} (*i.e.* angle of the output link between the first and third position) in order to locate point B_3'.

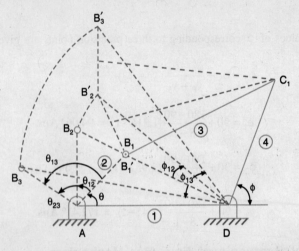

Fig. 25.8. Design of four bar mechanism (Three point synthesis).

5. Since the mechanism is to be inverted on the first design position, therefore B_1 and B_1' are coincident.

6. Draw the perpendicular bisectors of the lines $B_1'\ B_2'$ and $B_2'\ B_3'$. These bisectors intersect at point C_1.

7. Join $B_1'\ C_1$ and $C_1 D$. The figure $A B_1'\ C_1 D$ is the required four bar mechanism. Now the length of the link 3 and length of the link 4 and its starting position (ϕ) are determined.

25.12. Graphical Synthesis of Slider Crank Mechanism

Consider a slider crank mechanism for which the three positions of the crank AB (i.e. θ_1, θ_2 and θ_3) and corresponding three positions of the slider C (i.e. s_1, s_2 and s_3) are known, as shown in Fig. 25.9.

In order to synthesis such a mechanism, the following procedure is adopted.

1. First of all, draw the crank AB_1 in its initial position. If the length of crank is not specified, it may be assumed.

2. Now find the *relative poles P_{12} and P_{13} as shown in Fig. 25.10. The relative poles are obtained by fixing the link A and observing the motion of the crank AB_1 in the reverse direction. Thus, to find P_{12}, draw angle YAP_{12} equal to half of the angle between the first and second position (θ_{12}) in the reverse direction and from AY draw IP_{12} equal to half of the slider displacement between the first and second position (i.e. s_{12}). Similarly P_{13} may be obtained.

3. From P_{12} and P_{13}, draw two lines $P_{12}\ Q_{12}$ and $P_{13}\ Q_{13}$ such that $\angle AP_{12}\ I = \angle B_1 P_{12}\ Q_{12}$ and $\angle AP_{13}\ I = \angle B_1 P_{13}\ Q_{13}$. The lines $P_{12}\ Q_{12}$ and $P_{13}\ Q_{13}$ intersect at C_1, which is the location of the slider at its first position. Now the length of the connecting rod $B_1 C_1$ and the offset (e) may be determined.

---

* The relative pole is the centre of rotation of the connecting rod relative to the crank rotation and the corresponding slider displacement.

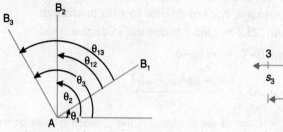

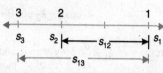

(a) Three positions of the crank.

(b) Three positions of the slider.

Fig. 25.9

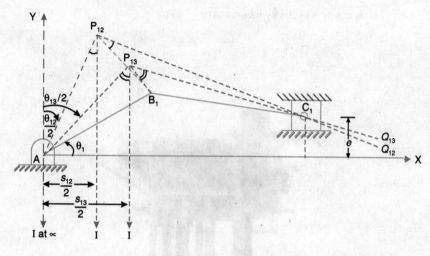

Fig. 25.10

25.13. Computer Aided (Analytical) Synthesis of Four Bar Mechanism

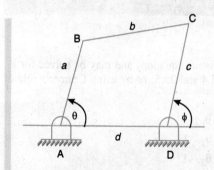

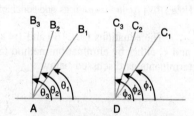

(a) Four bar mechanism.

(b) Three positions of input and output link.

Fig. 25.11

Consider a four bar mechanism as shown in Fig. 25.11.

The synthesis of a four bar mechanism, when input and output angles are specified, is discussed below :

Let the three positions *i.e.* angular displacements (θ_1, θ_2 and θ_3) of the input link AB and the three positions (ϕ_1, ϕ_2 and ϕ_3) of the output link, as shown in Fig. 25.11 (b), are known and we have to determine the dimensions a, b, c and d of the four bar mechanism.

We have discussed in Art. 25.2 that the Freudenstein's equation is

$$k_1 \cos\phi - k_2 \cos\theta + k_3 = \cos(\theta - \phi) \qquad \ldots (i)$$

where $\qquad k_1 = \dfrac{d}{a}$; $k_2 = \dfrac{d}{c}$; and $k_3 = \dfrac{a^2 - b^2 + c^2 + d^2}{2ac}$ $\qquad \ldots (ii)$

For the three different positions of the mechanism, the equation (i) may be written as

$$k_1 \cos\phi_1 - k_2 \cos\theta_1 + k_3 = \cos(\theta_1 - \phi_1) \qquad \ldots (iii)$$

$$k_1 \cos\phi_2 - k_2 \cos\theta_2 + k_3 = \cos(\theta_2 - \phi_2) \qquad \ldots (iv)$$

and $\qquad k_1 \cos\phi_3 - k_2 \cos\theta_3 + k_3 = \cos(\theta_3 - \phi_3) \qquad \ldots (v)$

An off-shore oil well.

Note : This picture is given as additional information.

The equations (iii), (iv) and (v) are three simultaneous equations and may be solved for k_1, k_2 and k_3 either by elimination method (See Examples 25.4 and 25.5) or by using Cramer's rule of determinants as discussed below :

$$\Delta = \begin{vmatrix} \cos\phi_1 & \cos\theta_1 & 1 \\ \cos\phi_2 & \cos\theta_2 & 1 \\ \cos\phi_3 & \cos\theta_3 & 1 \end{vmatrix}$$

$$\Delta_1 = \begin{vmatrix} \cos(\theta_1 - \phi_1) & \cos\theta_1 & 1 \\ \cos(\theta_2 - \phi_2) & \cos\theta_2 & 1 \\ \cos(\theta_3 - \phi_3) & \cos\theta_3 & 1 \end{vmatrix}$$

$$\Delta_2 = \begin{vmatrix} \cos\phi_1 & \cos(\theta_1-\phi_1) & 1 \\ \cos\phi_2 & \cos(\theta_2-\phi_2) & 1 \\ \cos\phi_3 & \cos(\theta_3-\phi_3) & 1 \end{vmatrix}$$

$$\Delta_3 = \begin{vmatrix} \cos\phi_1 & \cos\theta_1 & \cos(\theta_1-\phi_1) \\ \cos\phi_2 & \cos\theta_2 & \cos(\theta_2-\phi_2) \\ \cos\phi_3 & \cos\theta_3 & \cos(\theta_3-\phi_3) \end{vmatrix}$$

Now the values of k_1, k_2 and k_3 are given by

$$k_1 = \frac{\Delta_1}{\Delta}, \; k_2 = \frac{\Delta_2}{\Delta} \text{ and } k_3 = \frac{\Delta_3}{\Delta}$$

Once the values of k_1, k_2 and k_3 are known, then the link lengths a, b, c and d are determined by using equation (*ii*). In actual practice, either the value of a or d is assumed to be unity to get the proportionate values of other links.

Note : The designed mechanism may not satisfy the input and output angle co-ordination at positions other than these three positions. It is observed that a four bar mechanism can be designed precisely for five positions of the input and output links provided θ and ϕ are measured from some arbitrary reference rather than from the reference fixed link *AD*. In such cases, the synthesis equations become non-linear and some other means are required to solve such synthesis equations.

25.14. Programme to Co-ordinate the Angular Displacement of the Input and Output Links

The following is the programme in Fortran to co-ordinate the angular displacements of the input and output links.

```
C       PROGRAM TO COORDINATE ANGULAR DISPLACEMENTS OF
C       THE INPUT AND OUTPUT LINKS IN THREE POSITIONS
        READ (*, *) Q1, Q2, Q3, P1, P2, P3
        RAD = 4 * ATAN (1.0) / 180
        QA = COS (Q1 * RAD)
        QB = COS (Q2 * RAD)
        QC = COS (Q3 * RAD)
        PA = COS (P1 * RAD)
        PB = COS (P2 * RAD)
        PC = COS (P3 * RAD)
        AA = COS ( (Q1 – P1) * RAD )
        BB = COS ( (Q2 – P2) * RAD )
        CC = COS ( (Q3 – P3) * RAD )
        D = PA * (QB – QC) + QA * (PC – PB) + (PB * QC – PC * QB)
        D1 = AA * (QB – QC) + QA * (CC – BB) + (BB * QC – CC * QB)
        D2 = PA * (BB – CC) + AA * (PC – PB) + (PB * CC – PC * BB)
        D3 = PA * (QB * CC – QC * BB) + QA * (BB * PC – CC * PB) + AA * (PB * QC – PC * QB)
        A1 = D/D1
        A2 = SQRT (A1 * A1 + A3 * A3 + 1.0 – 2 * A1 * A3 * D3 / D)
        A3 = – D/D2
        WRITE (*, 1) A1, A2, A3, 1
1       FORMAT (6X, A1’, 7X,’ A2’, 7X,’ A3’ 7X,’ A4,’ / 4F8 . 2)
        STOP
        END
```

The input variables are :

Q_1, Q_2, Q_3 = Angular displacement of the input link AB in degrees,

P_1, P_2, P_3 = Angular displacement of the output link DC in degrees.

The output variables are :

A, B, C, D = Ratio of length of the links AB, BC, CD and AD respectively

Example 25.4. *Design a four bar mechanism to co-ordinate the input and output angles as follows :*

Input angles = 15°, 30° and 45° ; Output angles = 30°, 40° and 55°.

Solution. Given : $\theta_1 = 15°$; $\theta_2 = 30°$;

$\theta_3 = 45°$; $\phi_1 = 30°$; $\phi_2 = 40°$; $\phi_3 = 55°$

The Freudenstein's equation for the first position of the input and output link (*i.e.* when $\theta_1 = 15°$ and $\phi_1 = 30°$) may be written as

Grinding machine.

Note : This picture is given as additional information.

$$k_1 \cos 30° - k_2 \cos 15° + k_3 = \cos(15° - 30°)$$

or $0.866\ k_1 - 0.966\ k_2 + k_3 = 0.966$ ... (*i*)

Similarly, for the second position (*i.e.* when $\theta_2 = 30°$ and $\phi_2 = 40°$),

$$k_1 \cos 40° - k_2 \cos 30° + k_3 = \cos(30° - 40°)$$

or $0.766\ k_1 - 0.866\ k_2 + k_3 = 0.985$ ... (*ii*)

and for the third position (*i.e.* when $\theta_3 = 45°$ and $\phi_3 = 55°$),

$$k_1 \cos 55° - k_2 \cos 45° + k_3 = \cos(45° - 55°)$$

or $0.574\ k_1 - 0.707\ k_2 + k_3 = 0.985$ ... (*iii*)

Solving the three simultaneous equations (*i*), (*ii*) and (*iii*), we get

$$k_1 = 0.905 \ ; \ k_2 = 1.01 \text{ and } k_3 = 1.158$$

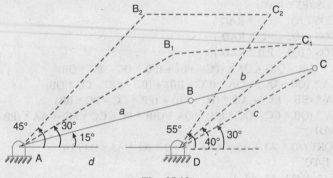

Fig. 25.12

Assuming the length of one of the links, say a as one unit, we get the length of the other links as follows :

We know that $k_1 = d/a$ or $d = k_1\ a = 0.905$ units **Ans.**

$$k_2 = d/c \text{ or } c = d/k_2 = 0.905 / 1.01 = 0.896 \text{ units } \textbf{Ans.}$$

and
$$k_3 = \frac{a^2 - b^2 + c^2 + d^2}{2ac}$$

or
$$-b^2 = k_3 \times 2ac - (a^2 + c^2 + d^2)$$
$$= 1.158 \times 2 \times 1 \times 0.896 - [1^2 + (0.896)^2 + (0.905)^2]$$
$$= 2.075 - 2.622 = -0.547 \quad \text{or} \quad b = 0.74 \text{ units } \textbf{Ans.}$$

The designed mechanism with $AB = a = 1$ unit, $BC = b = 0.74$ units ; $CD = c = 0.896$ units and $AD = d = 0.905$ units, is shown in Fig. 25.12.

Example 25.5. *Determine the proportions of four bar mechanism, by using three precision points, to generate* $y = x^{1.5}$, *where x varies between 1 and 4. Assume* $\theta_S = 30°$; $\Delta\theta = 90°$; $\phi_S = 90°$; *and* $\Delta\phi = 90°$. *Take length of the fixed link AD as 25 mm.*

Solution. Given : $x_S = 1$; $x_F = 4$; $\theta_S = 30°$; $\Delta\theta = \theta_F - \theta_S = 90°$; $\phi_S = 90°$; $\Delta\phi = \phi_F - \phi_S = 90°$; $d = 25$ mm

We have already calculated the three values of x and y for the above given data in Example 25.3. These values are :

$$x_1 = 1.2 ; \qquad x_2 = 2.5 ; \qquad \text{and} \qquad x_3 = 3.8$$
$$y_1 = 1.316 ; \qquad y_2 = 3.952 ; \qquad \text{and} \qquad y_3 = 7.41$$

The corresponding values of θ and ϕ are

$$\theta_1 = 36° ; \quad \theta_2 = 75° ; \text{ and } \theta_3 = 114°$$

$$\phi_1 = 94.06° ; \quad \phi_2 = 127.95° ; \text{ and } \phi_3 = 172.41°$$

We know that the Freudenstein's equation is

$$k_1 \cos\phi - k_2 \cos\theta + k_3 = \cos(\theta - \phi) \qquad \qquad \text{... (i)}$$

where
$$k_1 = \frac{d}{a} ; \quad k_2 = \frac{d}{c} ; \quad \text{and} \quad k_3 = \frac{a^2 - b^2 + c^2 + d^2}{2ac} \qquad \text{... (ii)}$$

Now for the three different positions of the mechanism, the equation (i) may be written three times as follows :

$$k_1 \cos 94.06° - k_2 \cos 36° + k_3 = \cos(36° - 94.06°)$$

or
$$- 0.0708 \, k_1 - 0.809 \, k_2 + k_3 = 0.529 \qquad \qquad \text{... (iii)}$$

Similarly
$$k_1 \cos 127.95° - k_2 \cos 75° + k_3 = \cos(75° - 127.95°)$$

or
$$- 0.615 \, k_1 - 0.259 \, k_2 + k_3 = 0.6025 \qquad \qquad \text{... (iv)}$$

and
$$k_1 \cos 172.41° - k_2 \cos 114° + k_3 = \cos(114° - 172.41°)$$

$$- 0.9912 \, k_1 + 0.4067 \, k_2 + k_3 = 0.5238 \qquad \qquad \text{... (v)}$$

Solving three simultaneous equations (iii), (iv) and (v), we get

$$k_1 = 0.6 ; k_2 = 0.453 ; \text{ and } k_3 = 0.12$$

Now from equation (ii),

$$a = \frac{d}{k_1} = \frac{25}{0.6} = 41.7 \text{mm} \quad \textbf{Ans.}$$

$$c = \frac{d}{k_2} = \frac{25}{0.453} = 55.2 \text{ mm} \textbf{ Ans.}$$

and

$$b = (a^2 + c^2 + d^2 - k_3 \times 2ac)^{1/2}$$

$$= \left[(41.7)^2 + (55.2)^2 + (25)^2 - 0.12 \times 2 \times 41.7 \times 55.2\right]^{1/2} = 69.7 \text{ mm} \textbf{ Ans.}$$

The designed four bar mechanism $AB_2 C_2 D$ in one position (*i.e.* for θ_2, x_2 and ϕ_2, y_2) is shown by thick lines in Fig. 25.13.

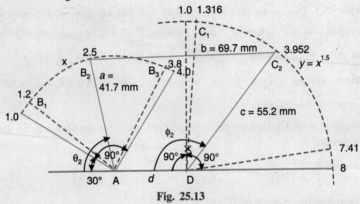

Fig. 25.13

The other two positions of the four bar mechanism may be drawn by joining $B_1 C_2$ (*i.e.* θ_1, x_1 and ϕ_1, y_1) and $B_3 C_3$ (*i.e.* θ_3, x_3 and ϕ_3, y_3).

Note : In the above example, the motion of input link and output link is taken clockwise.

Example 25.6. *Synthesize a four bar linkage, as shown in Fig. 25.14, using Freudenstein's equation to satisfy in one of its positions. The specification of position* θ, *velocity* ω *and acceleration* α *are as follows :*

$$\theta = 60°, \quad \omega_2 = 5 \text{ rad/s}; \quad \alpha_2 = 2 \text{ rad/s}^2;$$
$$\phi = 90°; \quad \omega_4 = 2 \text{ rad/s}; \quad \alpha_4 = 7 \text{ rad/s}^2.$$

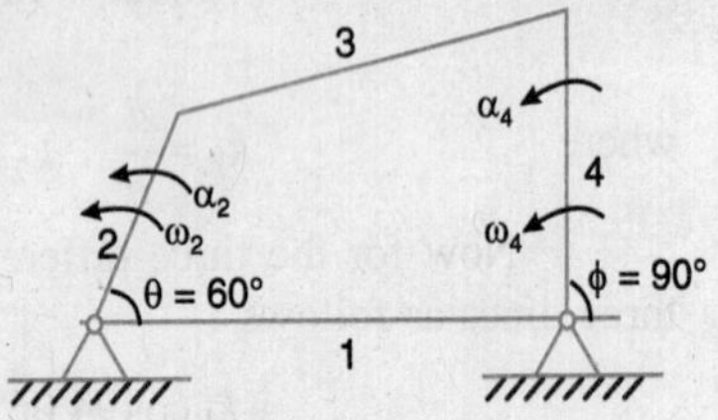

Solution : Given : $\theta = 60°$; $\omega_2 = 5$ rad/s ; $\alpha_2 = 2$ rad/s^2; $\phi = 90°$, $\omega_4 = 2$ rad/s; $\alpha_4 = 7$ rad/s^2

The four bar linkages is shown in Fig. 25.15. Let

AB = Input link = a,

BC = Coupler = b,

CD = Output link = c, and

AD = Fixed link = d.

The Freudenstein's equation is given by

$$k_1 \cos\phi - k_2 \cos\theta + k_3 = \cos(\theta - \phi) \quad ... (i)$$

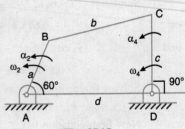

Fig. 25.14

Fig. 25.15

where $\qquad k_1 = \dfrac{d}{a}; \quad k_2 = \dfrac{d}{c}; \quad$ and $\quad k_3 = \dfrac{a^2 - b^2 + c^2 + d^2}{2ac}$

Substituting the value of θ and ϕ in equation (*i*),

$$k_1 \cos 90° - k_2 \cos 60° + k_3 = \cos(60° - 90°)$$

$$k_1 \times 0 - k_2 \times 0.5 + k_3 = 0.866$$

$$-0.5 k_2 + k_3 = 0.866 \qquad \qquad \text{... (ii)}$$

Differentiating equation (*i*) with respect to time,

$$k_1 \times -\sin\phi \times \frac{d\phi}{dt} - k_2 \times -\sin\theta \times \frac{d\theta}{dt} = -\sin(\theta - \phi) \times \frac{d(\theta - \phi)}{dt}$$

$$-k_1 \sin\phi\, \omega_4 + k_2 \sin\theta\, \omega_2 = -\sin(\theta - \phi)(\omega_2 - \omega_4) \qquad \text{... (iii)}$$

$$\dots \left(\because \frac{d\phi}{dt} = \omega_4; \text{ and } \frac{d\theta}{dt} = \omega_2 \right)$$

$$-k_1 \times \sin 90° \times 2 + k_2 \sin 60° \times 5 = -\sin(60° - 90°)\,(5 - 2)$$

$$-2k_1 + \frac{5\sqrt{3}}{2} k_2 = \frac{3}{2}$$

or $\qquad\qquad\qquad\qquad\qquad k_1 = 2.165\, k_2 - 0.75 \qquad\qquad \text{.... (iv)}$

Now differentiating equation (*iii*) with respect to time,

$$-k_1 \left[\sin\phi \times \frac{d\omega_4}{dt} + \omega_4 \cos\phi \times \frac{d\phi}{dt} \right] + k_2 \left[\sin\theta \times \frac{d\omega_2}{dt} + \omega_2 \cos\theta \times \frac{d\theta}{dt} \right]$$

$$= -\sin(\theta - \phi)\, \frac{d(\omega_2 - \omega_4)}{dt} + (\omega_2 - \omega_4) \cos(\theta - \phi) \times \frac{d(\theta - \phi)}{dt}$$

$$-k_1 \left[\sin\phi \times \alpha_4 + \omega_4^2 \cos\phi \right] + k_2 \left[\sin\theta \times \alpha_2 + \omega_2^2 \cos\theta \right]$$

$$= -\left[\sin(\theta - \phi)\, (\alpha_2 - \alpha_4) + (\omega_2 - \omega_4)^2 \cos(\theta - \phi) \right]$$

$$-k_1 \left[\sin 90° \times 7 + 2^2 \cos 90° \right] + k_2 \left[\sin 60° \times 2 + 5^2 \cos 60° \right]$$

$$= -\left[\sin(60° - 90°)\, (2 - 7) + (5 - 2)^2 \cos(60° - 90°) \right]$$

$$-k_1 (7 + 0) + k_2 (1.732 + 12.5) = -(2.5 + 7.794)$$

$$-7 k_1 + 14.232\, k_2 = -10.294$$

or $\qquad\qquad\qquad\qquad\qquad k_1 = 2.033\, k_2 + 1.47 \qquad\qquad \text{... (v)}$

From equations (*iv*) and (*v*),

$$2.165\, k_2 - 0.75 = 2.033\, k_2 + 1.47 \quad \text{or} \quad k_2 = 16.8$$

From equation (iv)

$$k_1 = 2.165k_2 - 0.75 = 2.165 \times 16.8 - 0.75 = 35.6$$

and from equation (ii),

$$k_3 = 0.5\ k_2 + 0.866 = 0.5 \times 16.8 + 0.866 = 9.266$$

Assuming the length of one of links say a as one unit, we get the length of the links as follows :

We know that $\quad k_1 = d/a$ or $\quad d = k_1 \cdot a = 35.6$ units **Ans.**

$$k_2 = d/c \quad \text{or} \quad c = d/k_2 = 35.6/16.8 = 2.12 \text{ units} \quad \textbf{Ans.}$$

and

$$k_3 = \frac{a^2 - b^2 + c^2 + d^2}{2ac} = \frac{1^2 - b^2 + (2.12)^2 + (35.6)^2}{2 \times 1 \times 2.12}$$

$$9.266 = \frac{1 - b^2 + 4.494 + 1267.36}{4.24} = \frac{1272.854 - b^2}{4.24}$$

$$b^2 = 1272.854 - 9.266 \times 4.24 = 1233.566$$

$$\therefore \qquad b = 35.12 \text{ units} \quad \textbf{Ans.}$$

Example 25.7. *Synthesize a four-bar mechanism to generate a function* $y = \sin x$ *for* $0 \le x \le 90°$. *The range of the output crank may be chosen as* $60°$ *while that of inut crank be* $120°$. *Assume three precision points which are to be obtained from Chebyshev spacing. Assume fixed link to be* 52.5 *mm long and* $\theta_1 = 105°$ *and* $\phi_1 = 66°$.

Solution. Given : $\quad x_S = 0; \quad x_F = 90°; \quad \Delta\phi = 60°; \quad \Delta\theta = 120°; \quad d = 52.5$ mm;

$\theta_1 = 105°; \quad \phi_1 = 66°$

The three values of x corresponding to three precision points (*i.e.* for n = 3), according to Chebyshev spacing are given by

$$x_j = \frac{1}{2}(x_S + x_F) - \frac{1}{2}(x_F - x_S)\cos\left[\frac{\pi(2j-1)}{2n}\right], \text{ where } j = 1, 2, 3$$

$$\therefore \qquad x_1 = \frac{1}{2}(0+90) - \frac{1}{2}(90-0)\cos\left[\frac{\pi(2 \times 1 - 1)}{2 \times 3}\right]$$

$$= 45 - 45 \cos 30° = 6° \qquad \qquad \dots (\because \ j = 1)$$

$$x_2 = \frac{1}{2}(0+90) - \frac{1}{2}(90-0)\cos\left[\frac{\pi(2 \times 2 - 1)}{2 \times 3}\right]$$

$$= 45 - 45\cos 90° = 45° \qquad \qquad \dots (\because \ j = 2)$$

and

$$x_3 = \frac{1}{2}(0+90) - \frac{1}{2}(90-0)\cos\left[\frac{\pi(2 \times 3 - 1)}{2 \times 3}\right]$$

$$= 45 - 45\cos 150° = 84°$$

Since y = sin x, therefore corresponding values of y are

$$y_1 = \sin x_1 = \sin 6° = 0.1045$$

$$y_2 = \sin x_2 = \sin 45° = 0.707$$

and
$$y_3 = \sin x_3 = \sin 84° = 0.9945$$

Also
$$y_S = \sin x_S = \sin 0° = 0$$

and
$$y_F = \sin x_F = \sin 90° = 1$$

The relation between the input angle (θ) and x is given by

$$\theta_j = \theta_S + \frac{\theta_F - \theta_S}{x_F - x_S}(x_j - x_S), \text{ where } j = 1, 2 \text{ and } 3.$$

The above expression may be written as

$$\theta_j = \theta_S + \frac{\Delta\theta}{\Delta x}(x_j - x_S)$$

The three values of θ corresponding to three precision points are given by

$$\theta_1 = \theta_S + \frac{\Delta\theta}{\Delta x} \times x_1 \qquad \qquad \dots (\because x_S = 0)\dots (i)$$

$$\theta_2 = \theta_S + \frac{\Delta\theta}{\Delta x} \times x_2 \qquad \qquad \dots (ii)$$

and
$$\theta_3 = \theta_S + \frac{\Delta\theta}{\Delta x} \times x_3 \qquad \qquad \dots. (iii)$$

From equations (*i*), (*ii*) and (*iii*),

$$\theta_2 - \theta_1 = \frac{\Delta\theta}{\Delta x}(x_2 - x_1) = \frac{120}{90}(45 - 6) = 52° \qquad \dots (iv)$$

$$\dots (\because \Delta x = x_F - x_S = 90 - 0 = 90)$$

$$\theta_3 - \theta_2 = \frac{\Delta\theta}{\Delta x}(x_3 - x_2) = \frac{120}{90}(84 - 45) = 52° \qquad \dots (v)$$

and
$$\theta_3 - \theta_1 = \frac{\Delta\theta}{\Delta x}(x_3 - x_1) = \frac{120}{90}(84 - 6) = 104° \qquad \dots (iv)$$

Since
$$\theta_1 = 105° \quad \text{(Given), therefore}$$

$$\theta_2 = \theta_1 + 52° = 105° + 52° = 157°$$

$$\theta_3 = \theta_2 + 52° = 157° + 52 = 209°$$

The relation between the output angle (ϕ) and y is given by

$$\phi_j = \phi_S + \frac{\phi_F - \phi_S}{y_F - y_S}(y_j - y_S), \text{ where } j = 1, 2 \text{ and } 3$$

This expression may be written as

$$\phi_j = \phi_S + \frac{\Delta\phi}{\Delta y}(y_j - y_S)$$

The three values of ϕ corresponding to three precision points are given by

$$\phi_1 = \phi_S + \frac{\Delta\phi}{\Delta y} \times y_1 \qquad\qquad .... (\because y_S = 0) ... (vii)$$

$$\phi_2 = \phi_S + \frac{\Delta\phi}{\Delta y} \times y_2 \qquad\qquad ... (viii)$$

and
$$\phi_3 = \phi_S + \frac{\Delta\phi}{\Delta y} \times y_3 \qquad\qquad ... (ix)$$

From equations (vii), (viii) and (ix),

$$\phi_2 - \phi_1 = \frac{\Delta\phi}{\Delta y}(y_2 - y_1) = \frac{60}{1}(0.707 - 0.1045) = 36.15° \qquad ... (x)$$

$$... (\because \Delta y = y_F - y_S = 1 - 0 = 1)$$

$$\phi_3 - \phi_2 = \frac{\Delta\phi}{\Delta y}(y_3 - y_2) = \frac{60}{1}(0.9945 - 0.707) = 17.25° \qquad ... (xi)$$

$$\phi_3 - \phi_1 = \frac{\Delta\phi}{\Delta y}(y_3 - y_1) = \frac{60}{1}(0.9945 - 0.1045) = 53.4° \qquad ... (xii)$$

Since $\phi_1 = 66°$ (Given), therefore

$$\phi_2 = \phi_1 + 36.15° = 66° + 36.15° = 102.15°$$

$$\phi_3 = \phi_2 + 17.25° = 102.15° + 17.25° = 119.40°$$

We have calculated above the three positions i.e. the angular displacements (θ_1, θ_2 and θ_3) of the input crank and the three positions (ϕ_1, ϕ_2 and ϕ_3) of the output crank. Now let us find the dimensions of the four bar mechanism.

Let a = Length of the input crank,

b = Length of the coupler,

c = Length of the output crank, and

d = Length of the fixed crank = 52.5 mm   (Given)

We know that the Freudenstein displacement equation is

$$k_1 \cos\phi - k_2 \cos\theta + k_3 = \cos(\theta - \phi) \qquad ... (xiii)$$

where $\qquad k_1 = \dfrac{d}{a}; \qquad k_2 = \dfrac{d}{c} \qquad$ and $\qquad k_3 = \dfrac{a^2 - b^2 + c^2 + d^2}{2ac}$

The equation (xiii) for the first position of input and output crank (i.e. when $\theta_1 = 105°$ and $\phi_1 = 66°$) may be written as

$$k_1 \cos\phi_1 - k_2 \cos\theta_1 + k_3 = \cos(\theta_1 - \phi_1)$$

$$k_1 \cos 66° - k_2 \cos 105° + k_3 = \cos(105° - 66°)$$

$$0.4067k_1 + 0.2588k_2 + k_3 = 0.7771 \qquad ... (xiv)$$

Similarly, for the second position (*i.e.* when $\theta_2 = 157°$ and $\phi_2 = 102.15°$),

$$k_1 \cos \phi_2 - k_2 \cos \theta_2 + k_3 = \cos(\theta_2 - \phi_2)$$

$$k_1 \cos 102.15° - k_2 \cos 157° + k_3 = \cos(157° - 102.15°)$$

$$-0.2105 k_1 + 0.9205 k_2 + k_3 = 0.5757 \qquad \qquad ...(xv)$$

and for the third position (*i.e.* when $\theta_3 = 209°$ and $\phi_3 = 119.4°$),

$$k_1 \cos \phi_3 - k_2 \cos \theta_3 + k_3 = \cos(\theta_3 - \phi_3)$$

$$k_1 \cos 119.4° - k_2 \cos 209° + k_3 = \cos(209° - 119.4°)$$

$$-0.4909 k_1 + 0.8746 k_2 + k_3 = 0.007 \qquad \qquad ... (xvi)$$

Solving the three simultaneous equations (*xiv*), (*xv*) and (*xvi*), we get

$$k_1 = 1.8; \ k_2 = 1.375 \ \text{and} \ k_3 = -0.311$$

Since the length of the fixed link (*i.e. d* = 52.5 mm) is known, therefore we get the length of other links as follows:

We know that

$$k_1 = d / a \qquad \text{or} \quad a = d / k_1 = 52.5 / 1.8 = 29.17 \text{ mm } \textbf{Ans.}$$
$$k_2 = d / c \qquad \text{or} \quad c = d / k_2 = 52.5 / 1.375 = 38.18 \text{ mm } \textbf{Ans.}$$

and

$$k_3 = \frac{a^2 - b^2 + c^2 + d^2}{2ac}$$

or

$$b^2 = a^2 + c^2 + d^2 - k_3 \times 2ac$$

$$= (29.17)^2 + (38.18)^2 + (52.5)^2 - (-0.311) \times 2 \times 29.17 \times 38.18 = 5758$$

$$\therefore \qquad b = 75.88 \text{ mm } \textbf{Ans.}$$

25.15. Least Square Technique

Most of the mechanisms are not possible to design even for five positions of the input and output links. However, it is possible to design a mechanism to give least deviation from the specified positions. This is done by using least square technique as discussed below :

We have already discussed that the Freudenstein's equation is

$$k_1 \cos \phi - k_2 \cos \theta + k_3 - \cos(\theta - \phi) = 0$$

The angles θ and ϕ are specified for a position. If θ_i and ϕ_i are the angles for *i*th position, then Freudenstein's equation may be written as

$$k_1 \cos \phi_i - k_2 \cos \theta_i + k_3 - \cos(\theta_i - \phi_i) = 0$$

Let *e* be the error which is defined as

$$e = \sum_{i=1}^{n} [k_1 \cos \phi_i - k_2 \cos \theta_i + k_3 - \cos(\theta_i - \phi_i)]^2$$

For *e* to be minimum, the partial derivatives of *e* with respect to k_1, k_2, k_3 separately must be equal to zero, *i.e.*

$$\frac{\partial e}{\partial k_1} = 0 \ ; \ \frac{\partial e}{\partial k_2} = 0, \text{ and } \frac{\partial e}{\partial k_3} = 0$$

$$\therefore \quad \frac{\partial e}{\partial k_1} = 2\sum_{i=1}^{n}[k_1\cos\phi_i - k_2\cos\theta_i + k_3 - \cos(\theta_i - \phi_i)]\cos\phi_i = 0$$

or
$$k_1\sum_{i=1}^{n}\cos^2\phi_i - k_2\sum_{i=1}^{n}\cos\theta_i\cos\phi_i + k_3\sum_{i=1}^{n}\cos\phi_i = \sum_{i=1}^{n}\cos(\theta_i - \phi_i)\cos\phi_i \qquad \dots (i)$$

Similarly,
$$\frac{\partial e}{\partial k_2} = -2\sum_{i=1}^{n}[k_1\cos\phi_i - k_2\cos\theta_i + k_3 - \cos(\theta_i - \phi_i)]\cos\theta_i = 0$$

or
$$k_1\sum_{i=1}^{n}\cos\phi_i\cos\theta_i + k_2\sum_{i=1}^{n}\cos^2\theta_i + k_3\sum_{i=1}^{n}\cos\theta_i = \sum_{i=1}^{n}\cos(\theta_i - \phi_i)\cos\theta_i \qquad \dots (ii)$$

Now
$$\frac{\partial e}{\partial k_3} = 2\sum_{i=1}^{n}[k_1\cos\phi_i - k_2\cos\theta_i + k_3 - \cos(\theta_i - \phi_i)] = 0$$

or
$$k_1\sum_{i=1}^{n}\cos\phi_i + k_2\sum_{i=1}^{n}\cos\theta_i + k_3\sum_{i=1}^{n}1 = \sum_{i=1}^{n}\cos(\theta_i - \phi_i) \qquad \dots (iii)$$

The equations (*i*), (*ii*) and (*iii*) are simultaneous, linear, non-homogeneous equations in three unknowns k_1, k_2 and k_3. These equations can be solved by using Cramer's rule.

25.16. Programme Using Least Square Technique

The following is a programme in Fortrans to find the ratio of lengths for different links by using the least square technique.

The input variables are :

J = Number of specified positions

$TH(I)$ = Angular displacements of the input link AB for $I = 1$ to J (degrees), and

$PH(I)$ = Angular displacements of the output link DC for $I = 1$ to J (degrees).

The output variables are :

A, B, C, D = Ratio of the lengths of the links AB, BC, CD and AD respectively.

```
C       PROGRAM TO COORDINATE ANGULAR DISPLACEMENT OF THE
C       INPUT AND OUTPUT LINKS IN MORE THAN THREE POSITIONS TO
C       FIND RATIO OF DIFFERENT LINKS USING LEAST SQUARE TECHNIQUE

        DIMENSION
        READ (*, *) J
        READ (*, *) (TH (I), I = 1, J), PH (I), I = 1, J)
        RAD = 4 * ATAN (1.0) / 180
        DO 10 K = 1 . J
        A1 = A1 + (COS (PH (K) * RAD ) ) * * 2
        A2 = A2 + (COS (TH (K) RAD ) ) * (COS (PH (K) * RAD ) )
        A3 = A3 + (COS (PH (K) * RAD ) )
        B1 = A2
        B2 = B2 + (COS (TH (K) * RAD ) ) * * 2
```

```
             B3 = B3 + (COS (TH (K) * RAD ) )
             P1 = A3
             P2 = B3
             P3 = J
             TT = COS ( ( TH (K) – PH (K) * RAD )
             Q1 = Q1 + TT * COS (PH (K) * RAD )
             Q2 = Q2 + TT * COS (TH (K) * RAD
10           Q3 = Q3 + TT
             D = A1 * (B2 * P3 – B3 * P2) + B1 * (P2 * A3 – P3 * A2) + P1 * (A2 * B3 – A3 * B2)
             D1 = Q1 * (B2 * P3 – B3 * P2) + B1 * (P2 * Q3 – P3 * Q2) + P1 * (Q2 * B3 – Q3 * B2)
             D2 = A1 * (Q2 * P3 – Q3 * P2) + Q1 *  (P2 * A3 – P3 * A2) + P1 * (A2 * Q3 – A3 * Q2)
             D3 = A1 * (B2 * Q3 – B3 * Q2) + B1 * (Q2 * A3 – Q3 * A2) + Q1 * (A2 * B3 – A3 * B2)
             Q = D / D1
             R = – D / D2
             P = SQRT (Q * Q + r * r + 1. – 2. * r * r * 03 / D)
             WRITE (* , 9) Q, P, r, 1.
9            FORMAT (6X, ' Q', 7X,' P', 7X,' r', 7X,' D' / 4F8 . 2)
             STOP
             END
```

25.17. Computer Aided Synthesis of Four Bar Mechanism with Coupler Point

Consider a four bar mechanism *ABCD* with a couple point *E*, as shown in Fig. 25.16, which is specified by r and γ.

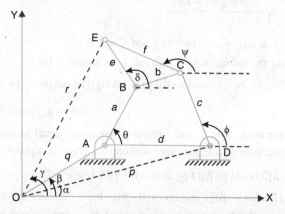

Fig. 25.16. Four bar mechanism with a couple point.

Let θ_1, θ_2 and θ_3 = Three positions of the input link *AB*,

r_1, r_2 and r_3 = Three positions of the coupler point *E* from point *O*, and

γ_1, γ_2 and γ_3 = Three angular positions of the coupler point *E* from *OX*.

The dimensions a, c, e, f and the location of points *A* and *D* specified by (q, β) and (p, α) respectively, may be determined as discussed below :

Considering the loop *OABE*, the horizontal and vertical components of vectors *q, a, e* and *r* are

$$q \cos \beta + a \cos \theta + e \cos \delta = r \cos \gamma \qquad \text{... (i)}$$

and

$$q \sin \beta + a \sin \theta + e \sin \delta = r \sin \gamma \qquad \text{... (ii)}$$

Squaring equations (i) and (ii) and adding in order to eliminate angle δ, we have

$$q[2r \cos(\gamma - \beta)] + a[2r \cos(\theta - \gamma)] + e^2 - q^2 - a^2 = r^2 + q a[2 \cos(\theta - \beta)] \qquad \text{... (iii)}$$

Let

$$q = k_1 \; ; \; a = k_2 \; ; \; e^2 - q^2 - a^2 = k_3 \; ; \text{ and } q \, a = k_4 = k_1 \, k_2 \qquad \text{... (iv)}$$

Now the equation (iii) may be written as

$$k_1[2r \cos(\gamma - \beta)] + k_2[2r \cos(\theta - \gamma)] + k_3 = r^2 + k_4[2 \cos(\theta - \beta)] \qquad \text{... (v)}$$

Since $k_4 = k_1 k_2$, therefore the equation (v) is difficult to solve for k_1, k_2, k_3 and k_4. Such type of non-linear equations can be solved easily by making them linear by some substitutions as given below :

Let

$$k_1 = l_1 + \lambda m_1 \; ; \; k_2 = l_2 + \lambda m_2 \; ; \text{ and } k_3 = l_3 + \lambda m_3 \qquad \text{... (vi)}$$

where

$$\lambda = k_4 = k_1 k_2 = (l_1 + \lambda m_1)(l_2 + \lambda m_2)$$

$$= l_1 l_2 + l_1 \lambda m_2 + \lambda m_1 l_2 + \lambda^2 m_1 m_2$$

or

$$m_1 m_2 \lambda^2 + (l_1 m_2 + l_2 m_1 - 1) \lambda + l_1 l_2 = 0$$

or

$$A \lambda^2 + B \lambda + C = 0$$

$$\therefore \qquad \lambda = \frac{-B \pm \sqrt{B^2 - 4AC}}{2A} \qquad \text{... (vii)}$$

where $A = m_1 m_2$; $B = (l_1 m_2 + l_2 m_1 - 1)$; and $C = l_1 l_2$ $\qquad$ ... (viii)

Substituting the values of k_1, k_2, k_3 and k_4 in equation (v),

$$(l_1 + \lambda m_1)[2r \cos(\gamma - \beta)] + (l_2 + \lambda m_2)[2r \cos(\theta - \gamma)] + (l_3 + \lambda m_3)$$

$$= r^2 + \lambda([2 \cos(\theta - \beta)]$$

Equating the terms with λ and without λ separately equal to zero, we get the components into two groups, one with λ and the other without λ. These components are

$$l_1[2r \cos(\gamma - \beta)] + l_2[2r \cos(\theta - \gamma)] + l_3 = r^2 \qquad \text{... (ix)}$$

and

$$m_1[2r \cos(\gamma - \beta)] + m_2[2r \cos(\theta - \gamma)] + m_3 = 2 \cos(\theta - \beta) \qquad \text{... (x)}$$

The equation (ix) for the three positions of θ, *r* and γ may be written three times as follows :

$$l_1[2r_1 \cos(\gamma_1 - \beta)] + l_2[2r_1 \cos(\theta_1 - \gamma_1)] + l_3 = r_1^2 \qquad \text{... (xi)}$$

$$l_1[2r_2 \cos(\gamma_2 - \beta)] + l_2[2r_2 \cos(\theta_2 - \gamma_2)] + l_3 = r_2^2 \qquad \text{... (xii)}$$

$$l_1[2r_3 \cos(\gamma_3 - \beta)] + l_2[2r_3 \cos(\theta_3 - \gamma_3)] + l_3 = r_3^2 \qquad \text{... (xiii)}$$

Similarly, equation (x) for the three positions of θ, *r* and γ may be written three times as follows :

$$m_1[2r\cos(\gamma_1-\beta)]+m_2[2r\cos(\theta_1-\gamma_1)]+m_3=2\cos(\theta_1-\beta) \qquad \ldots (xiv)$$

$$m_1[2r\cos(\gamma_2-\beta)]+m_2[2r\cos(\theta_2-\gamma_2)]+m_3=2\cos(\theta_2-\beta) \qquad \ldots (xv)$$

$$m_1[2r\cos(\gamma_3-\beta)]+m_2[2r\cos(\theta_3-\gamma_3)]+m_3=2\cos(\theta_3-\beta) \qquad \ldots (xvi)$$

The equations (xi), (xii) and $(xiii)$ are three linear equations in l_1, l_2, l_3. Similarly, equations (xiv), (xv) and (xvi) are three linear equations in m_1, m_2 and m_3. Assuming a suitable value of β, the values of l_1, l_2, l_3 and m_1, m_2, m_3 may be determined by using elimination method or Cramer's rule.

Knowing the values of l_1, l_2, l_3 and m_1, m_2, m_3, we can find the value of λ from equation (vii). Now the values of k_1, k_2 and k_3 are determined from equation (vi) and hence q, a and e are known from equation (iv). Using equation (i) or (ii), we can find the three valves of δ *i.e.* δ_1, δ_2 and δ_3. From equation (i), we have

$$e\cos\delta=r\cos\gamma-q\cos\beta-a\cos\theta$$

$$\therefore \qquad \delta_1=\cos^{-1}\left[\frac{r_1\cos\gamma_1-q\cos\beta-a\cos\theta_1}{e}\right] \qquad \ldots (xvii)$$

Similarly, $\qquad \delta_2=\cos^{-1}\left[\dfrac{r_2\cos\gamma_2-q\cos\beta-a\cos\theta_2}{e}\right] \qquad \ldots (xviii)$

and $\qquad \delta_3=\cos^{-1}\left[\dfrac{r_3\cos\gamma_3-q\cos\beta-a\cos\theta_3}{e}\right] \qquad \ldots (xix)$

Thus by considering the loop *OABE*, we can find the values of q, a, e, β and δ.

Now considering the loop *ODCE* in order to find p, c, f, α and ψ. The horizontal and vertical components of vectors p, c, f and r are

$$p\cos\alpha+c\cos\phi+f\cos\psi=r\cos\gamma \qquad \ldots (xx)$$

and $\qquad p\sin\alpha+c\sin\phi+f\sin\psi=r\sin\gamma \qquad \ldots (xxi)$

Since these equations are similar to equations (i) and (ii), therefore we shall proceed in the similar way as discussed for loop *OABE*.

Squaring equations (xx) and (xxi) and adding in order to eliminate angle ϕ, we have

$$p[2r\cos(\gamma-\alpha)]+f[2r\cos(\psi-\gamma)]+c^2-p^2-f^2=r^2+pf[2\cos(\psi-\alpha)] \qquad \ldots (xxii)$$

Let $\qquad p=k_5 \, ; f=k_6 \, ; c^2-p^2-f^2=k_7$ and $pf=k_8=k_5k_6 \qquad \ldots (xxiii)$

Now equations $(xxii)$ may be written as

$$k_5[2r\cos(\gamma-\alpha)]+k_6[2r\cos(\psi-\gamma)]+k_7=r^2+k_8[2\cos(\psi-\alpha)] \qquad \ldots (xxiv)$$

The equation $(xxiv)$ is a non-linear equation and can be solved easily by making it linear by some substitutions as given below :

Let $\qquad k_5=l_5+\lambda_1 m_5 \, ; k_6=l_6+\lambda_1 m_6 \, ;$ and $k_7=l_7+\lambda_1 m_7 \qquad \ldots (xxv)$

where $\qquad \lambda_1=k_8=k_5k_6=(l_5+\lambda_1 m_5)(l_6+\lambda_1 m_6)$

$$=l_5l_6+l_5\lambda_1 m_6+\lambda_1 m_5 l_6+\lambda_1^2 m_5 m_6$$

or $\qquad m_5 m_6 \lambda_1^2+(l_5 m_6+l_6 m_5-1)\lambda_1+l_5 l_6=0$

or
$$D\lambda_1^2 + E\lambda_1 + F = 0$$

∴
$$\lambda_1 = \frac{-E \pm \sqrt{E^2 - 4DF}}{2D}$$ ... (xxvi)

where $D = m_5 m_6$; $E = (l_5 m_6 + l_6 m_5 - 1)$; and $F = l_5 l_6$ ... (xxvii)

Substituting the values of k_5, k_6, k_7 and k_8 in equation (xxiv),

$$(l_5 + \lambda_1 m_5)[2r\cos(\gamma - \alpha)] + (l_6 + \lambda_1 m_6)[2r\cos(\psi - \gamma)] + l_7 + \lambda_1 m_7$$

$$= r^2 + \lambda_1[2\cos(\psi - \alpha)]$$

Equating the terms with λ and without λ separately equal to zero, we get the components into two groups, one with λ and the other without λ. These components are

$$l_5[2r\cos(\gamma - \alpha)] + l_6[2r\cos(\psi - \gamma)] + l_7 = r^2$$ ... (xxviii)

and
$$m_5[2r\cos(\gamma - \alpha)] + m_6[2r\cos(\psi - \gamma)] + m_7 = 2\cos(\psi - \alpha)$$ ... (xxix)

The equation (xxviii) for the three positions of r, γ and ψ may be written three times as follows :

$$l_5[2r_1\cos(\gamma_1 - \alpha)] + l_6[2r_1\cos(\psi_1 - \gamma_1)] + l_7 = r_1^2$$ ... (xxx)

$$l_5[2r_2\cos(\gamma_2 - \alpha)] + l_6[2r_2\cos(\psi_2 - \gamma_2)] + l_7 = r_2^2$$ ... (xxxi)

$$l_5[2r_3\cos(\gamma_3 - \alpha)] + l_6[2r_3\cos(\psi_3 - \gamma_3)] + l_7 = r_3^2$$ ... (xxxii)

Similarly, equation (xxix) for the three positions of r, γ and ψ may be written three times as follows :

$$m_5[2r_1\cos(\gamma_1 - \alpha)] + m_6[2r_1\cos(\psi_1 - \gamma_1)] + m_7 = 2\cos(\psi_1 - \alpha)$$ ... (xxxiii)

$$m_5[2r_2\cos(\gamma_2 - \alpha)] + m_6[2r_2\cos(\psi_2 - \gamma_2)] + m_7 = 2\cos(\psi_2 - \alpha)$$ .. (xxxiv)

$$m_5[2r_3\cos(\gamma_3 - \alpha)] + m_6[2r_3\cos(\psi_3 - \gamma_3)] + m_7 = 2\cos(\psi_3 - \alpha)$$ ... (xxxv)

The equations (xxx), (xxxi) and (xxxii) are three linear equations in l_5, l_6 and l_7. Similarly, equations (xxxiii), (xxxiv) and (xxxv) are linear equations in m_5, m_6 and m_7. Assuming a suitable value of α, the values of l_5, l_6, l_7 and m_5, m_6, m_7 may be determined by using elimination method or Cramer's rule.

Knowing the values of l_5, l_6, l_7 and m_5, m_6, m_7, we can find the value of λ_1 from equation (xxvi). Now the values of k_5, k_6 and k_7 are determined from equation (xxv) and hence p, f and c are known from equation (xxiii).

Assuming the value of ψ_1, the corresponding values of ψ_2 and ψ_3 may be calculated as follows :

Since the angular displacements of the coupler link *BCE* is same at the points *B* and *C*, therefore

$$\psi_2 - \psi_1 = \delta_2 - \delta_1$$

or
$$\psi_2 = \psi_1 + (\delta_2 - \delta_1)$$ ... (xxxvi)

Similarly,
$$\psi_3 = \psi_1 + (\delta_3 - \delta_1)$$ ... (xxxvii)

If the mechanism is to be designed for more than three positions of the input link *AB* and the same number of positions of the couple point *E*, then the least square technique is used. The error function from equations (*ix*) and (*x*) are defined as

$$e_1 = \sum [l_1 \{2r\cos(\gamma-\beta)\} + l_2 \{2r\cos(\theta-\gamma)\} + l_3 - r^2]^2 \qquad \dots (xxxviii)$$

and

$$e_2 = \sum [m_1 \{2r\cos(\gamma-\beta)\} + m_2 \{2r\cos(\theta-\gamma)\} + m_3 - 2\cos(\theta-\beta)]^2 \qquad \dots (xxxix)$$

An aircraft assembling plant.
Note : This picture is given as additional information.

For e_1 and e_2 to be minimum, the partial derivatives of e_1 with respect to l_1, l_2, l_3 and partial derivatives of e_2 with respect to m_1, m_2, m_3 separately must be equal to zero, *i.e.*

$$\left. \begin{array}{l} \dfrac{\partial e_1}{\partial l_1} = 0 \; ; \; \dfrac{\partial e_1}{\partial l_2} = 0 \; ; \; \dfrac{\partial e_1}{\partial l_3} = 0 \\[3mm] \dfrac{\partial e_2}{\partial m_1} = 0 \; ; \; \dfrac{\partial e_2}{\partial m_2} = 0 \; ; \; \dfrac{\partial e_2}{\partial m_3} = 0 \end{array} \right] \qquad \dots (xxxx)$$

and

First consider when $\dfrac{\partial e_1}{\partial l_1} = 0$,

$$\sum_1^n 2 \left[l_1 2r\cos(\gamma-\beta) + l_2 2r\cos(\theta-\gamma) + l_3 - r^2 \right] 2r\cos(\gamma-\beta) = 0$$

or

$$l_1 \sum_1^n [2r\cos(\gamma-\beta)]^2 + l_2 \sum_1^n [2r\cos(\theta-\gamma)][2r\cos(\gamma-\beta)]$$

$$+ l_3 \sum_1^n [2r\cos(\gamma-\beta)] = \sum_1^n [2r\cos(\gamma-\beta)]r^2 \qquad \dots (xxxxi)$$

Similarly, for $\dfrac{\partial e_1}{\partial l_2} = 0$,

$$l_1 \sum_1^n [2r\cos(\gamma-\beta)][2r\cos(\theta-\gamma)] + l_2 \sum_1^n [2r\cos(\theta-\gamma)]^2$$

$$+ l_3 \sum_1^n [2r\cos(\theta-\gamma)] = \sum_1^n [2r\cos(\theta-\gamma)]r^2 \qquad \dots (xxxxii)$$

and for $\quad \dfrac{\partial e_1}{\partial l_3} = 0, \; l_1 \sum_{1}^{n} [2r\cos(\gamma-\beta)] + l_2 \sum_{1}^{n} [2r\cos(\theta-\gamma)] + l_3 \sum_{1}^{n} 1 = \sum r^2 \qquad$ ... (*xxxiii*)

The above three equations can be solved by using Cramer's rule to find l_1, l_2 and l_3.

In the similar way as discussed above, for $\quad \dfrac{\partial e_2}{\partial m_1} = 0$

$$m_1 \sum_{1}^{n} [2r\cos(\gamma-\beta)]^2 + m_2 \sum_{1}^{n} [2r\cos(\theta-\gamma)][2r\cos(\gamma-\beta)]$$

$$+ m_3 \sum_{1}^{n} [2r\cos(\gamma-\beta)] = \sum_{1}^{n} [2r\cos(\theta-\beta)][2r\cos(\gamma-\beta)] \quad \text{... (\textit{xxxiv})}$$

Similarly, for $\quad \dfrac{\partial e_2}{\partial m_2} = 0,$

$$m_1 \sum_{1}^{n} [2r\cos(\gamma-\beta)] + [2r\cos(\theta-\gamma)] + m_2 \sum_{1}^{n} [2r\cos(\theta-\gamma)]^2$$

$$+ m_3 \sum_{1}^{n} [2r\cos(\theta-\gamma)] = \sum_{1}^{n} [2r\cos(\theta-\beta)][2r\cos(\theta-\gamma)] \quad \text{... (\textit{xxxv})}$$

and for $\quad \dfrac{\partial e_2}{\partial m_3} = 0,$

$$m_1 \sum_{1}^{n} [2r\cos(\gamma-\beta)] + m_2 \sum_{1}^{n} [2r\cos(\theta-\gamma)] + m_3 \sum_{1}^{n} 1 = \sum [2r\cos(\theta-\gamma)] \quad \text{... (\textit{xxxvi})}$$

The above three equations can be solved by using Cramer's rule to find m_1, m_2 and m_3.

Knowing the values of l_1, l_2, l_3 and m_1, m_2, m_3, we can find the value of λ from equation (*vii*) and k_1, k_2, k_3 from equation (*vi*). Thus q, a and e are determined. Now $\delta_1, \delta_2, \delta_3$ may be determined by using equation (*i*) or (*ii*).

The values of p, c and f are obtained by solving equation (*xxiv*) in the similar way as discussed earlier.

25.18. Synthesis of Four Bar Mechanism For Body Guidance

Consider the three positions of a rigid planer body containing the points A and B as shown in Fig. 25.17 (*a*). The four bar mechanism for body guidance, considering the three positions of the body, may be designed graphically as discussed below.

1. Consider the three positions of the points A and B such as A_1, A_2, A_3 and B_1, B_2, B_3 as shown in Fig. 25.17 (*a*).

2. Find the centre of a circle which passes through three points A_1, A_2, A_3. This is obtained by drawing the perpendicular bisectors of the line segments $A_1 A_2$ and $A_2 A_3$. Let these bisectors intersect at O_A. It is evident that a rigid link $A\,O_A$ pinned to the body at point A and pinned to the ground at point O_A will guide point A through its three positions A_1, A_2 and A_3.

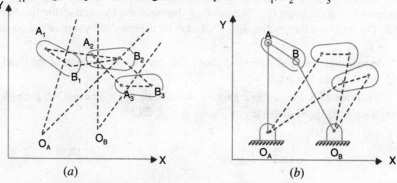

Fig. 25.17. Four bar mechanism for body guidance.

3. Similarly, find the centre O_B of a circle which passes through three points B_1, B_2, B_3. It is evident that a rigid link $B\,O_B$ pinned to the body at point B and pinned to the ground at point O_B will guide point B through its three positions B_1, B_2 and B_3.

4. The above construction forms the four bar mechanism $O_A\,ABO_B$ which guides the body through three specified positions. Fig. 25.17 (*b*) shows a four bar mechanism in these three positions.

The points O_A and O_B may be determined analytically as discussed below :

Consider the three positions of the point A such as A_1, A_2, A_3. Let the co-ordinates of these points are A_1 (x_1, y_1) ; A_2 (x_2, y_2) and A_3 (x_3, y_3). Let the co-ordinates of the point O_A are (x, y). Now we know that

Distance between points A_1 and O_A,

$$A_1 O_A = [(x_1 - x)^2 + (y_1 - y)^2]^{1/2} \qquad \text{... (i)}$$

Similarly, distance between points A_2 and O_A,

$$A_2 O_A = [(x_2 - x)^2 + (y_2 - y)^2]^{1/2} \qquad \text{... (ii)}$$

and distance between points A_3 and O_A,

$$A_3 O_A = [(x_3 - x)^2 + (y_3 - y)^2]^{1/2} \qquad \text{... (iii)}$$

For the point O_A to be the centre of a circle passing through the points A_1, A_2 and A_3, the distances $A_1 O_A$, $A_2 O_A$ and $A_3 O_A$ must be equal. In other words,

$$A_1 O_A = A_2 O_A = A_3 O_A$$

Now considering $A_1 O_A = A_2 O_A$, we have

$$\left[(x_1 - x)^2 + (y_1 - y)^2\right]^{1/2} = \left[(x_2 - x)^2 + (y_2 - y)^2\right]^{1/2} \qquad \text{... (iv)}$$

Similarly, considering $A_2 O_A = A_3 O_A$, we have

$$\left[(x_2 - x)^2 + (y_2 - y)^2\right]^{1/2} = \left[(x_3 - x)^2 + (y_3 - y)^2\right]^{1/2} \qquad \text{... (v)}$$

Squaring both sides of the equations (*iv*) and (*v*) and simplifying, we get the following two equations in the unknowns x and y.

$$2x(x_2 - x_1) + 2y(y_2 - y_1) + (x_1^2 - x_2^2) + (y_1^2 - y_2^2) = 0 \qquad \text{... (vi)}$$

and $$2x(x_3 - x_2) + 2y(y_3 - y_2) + (x_2^2 - x_3^2) + (y_2^2 - y_3^2) = 0 \qquad \text{... (vii)}$$

The equations (*vi*) and (*vii*) are simultaneous equations and may be solved to find the co-ordinates *x*, *y* of the point O_A. This point O_A becomes the location of the fixed pivot guiding the point A. The length of the guiding link O_AA may be determined by any of the equations (*i*), (*ii*) or (*iii*).

In the similar way, as discussed above, we can find the location of the fixed pivot point O_B and the length of the link O_BB.

Example 25.8. *Synthesize a four bar mechanism to guide a rod AB through three consecutive positions A_1B_1, A_2B_2 and A_3B_3 as shown in Fig. 25.18.*

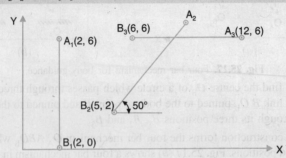

Fig. 25.18

Solution : In order to synthesize a four bar mechanism, we shall use the graphical method as discussed below :

1. Join points A_1, A_2 and A_2, A_3. Draw the perpendicular bisectors of line segments A_1A_2 and A_2A_3 to intersect at O_A, as shown in Fig. 25.19. It is evident that a rigid link O_AA_1 pinned to the body at point A_1 and pinned to the ground at point O_A will guide point A_1 through its three positions.

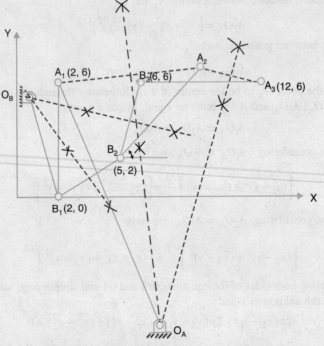

Fig. 25.19

2. Similarly, join points B_1, B_2 and B_2, B_3. Draw the perpendicular bisectors of line segments B_1B_2 and B_2B_3 to intersect at O_B as shown in Fig. 25.19. It is evident that a rigid link O_BB_1 pinned to the body at point B_1 and pinned to the ground at point O_B will guide point B, through its three positions.

3. From above we see that the points O_A and O_B are the required fixed points and $O_A A_1 B_1 O_B$ is one position of the four bar mechanism. The other two positions of the mechanism will be $O_A A_2 B_2 O_B$ and $O_A A_3 B_3 O_B$.

25.19. Analytical Synthesis for Slider Crank Mechanism

A slider crank mechanism is shown in Fig. 25.20. In the synthesis problem of the slider crank mechanism, the displacement (s) of the slider C has to co-ordinate with the crank angle (θ) in a specified manner. For example, consider that the displacement of the slider is proportional to crank angle over a given interval, *i.e.*

$$s - s_S = C(\theta - \theta_S), \text{ for } \theta_S \leq \theta \leq \theta_F \qquad \ldots (i)$$

where $\qquad C$ = Constant of proportionality, and

$\qquad\qquad s$ = Displacement of the slider when crank angle is θ.

The subscripts $_S$ and $_F$ denote starting and finishing positions.

The synthesis of a slider crank mechanism for three precision points is obtained as discussed below.

The three positions of the crank (θ_1, θ_2 and θ_3) may be obtained in the similar way as discussed in Art. 25.10 and the corresponding three positions of the slider (s_1, s_2 and s_3) are obtained from the given condition as in equation (i). Now the dimensions a, b and c may be determined as discussed below :

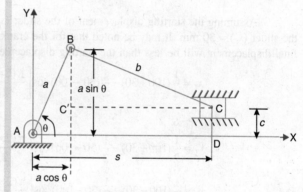

Fig. 25.20. Slider crank mechanism.

In a right angled triangle $BC'C$,

$$BC = b; \ BC' = a\sin\theta - c \ , \text{ and } \ CC' = s - a\cos\theta$$

$\therefore \qquad$
$$b^2 = (BC')^2 + (CC')^2 = (a\sin\theta - c)^2 + (s - a\cos\theta)^2$$

$$= a^2\sin^2\theta + c^2 - 2ac\sin\theta + s^2 + a^2\cos^2\theta - 2sa\cos\theta$$

$$= a^2 + c^2 - 2ac\sin\theta + s^2 - 2as\cos\theta$$

or $\qquad$
$$2as\cos\theta + 2ac\sin\theta + b^2 - a^2 - c^2 = s^2$$

$$k_1 s\cos\theta + k_2 \sin\theta - k_3 = s^2 \qquad \ldots (ii)$$

where $\qquad k_1 = 2a \ ; \ k_2 = 2ac \text{ and } k_3 = a^2 - b^2 + c^2 \qquad \ldots (iii)$

For the three different positions of the mechanism *i.e.* for $(\theta_1, \theta_2\, \theta_3)$ and (s_1, s_2, s_3), the equation (*ii*) may be written as

$$k_1\, s_1 \cos\theta_1 + k_2 \sin\theta_1 - k_3 = s_1^2 \qquad\qquad\qquad \dots (iv)$$

$$k_1\, s_2 \cos\theta_2 + k_2 \sin\theta_2 - k_3 = s_2^2 \qquad\qquad\qquad \dots (v)$$

$$k_1\, s_3 \cos\theta_3 + k_2 \sin\theta_3 - k_3 = s_3^2 \qquad\qquad\qquad \dots (vi)$$

The equations (*iv*), (*v*) and (*vi*) are three simultaneous equations and may be solved for three unknowns k_1, k_2 and k_3. Knowing the values of k_1, k_2 and k_3, the lengths a, b and c may be obtained from equations (*iii*).

Example 25.9. *Synthesize a slider crank mechanism so that the displacement of the slider is proportional to the square of the crank rotation in the interval $45° \le \theta \le 135°$. Use three precision points with Chebyshev's spacing.*

Solution : Given. $\theta_S = 45°$; $\theta_F = 135°$

First of all, let us find the three precision points (*i.e.* x_1, x_2 and x_3). We know that

$$x_j = \frac{1}{2}(x_S + x_F) - \frac{1}{2}(x_F - x_S)\cos\left[\frac{\pi(2j-1)}{2n}\right] \; ; \; \text{where} \; j = 1, 2 \text{ and } 3$$

Assuming the starting displacement of the slider (s_S) = 100 mm and final displacement of the slider (s_F) = 30 mm. It may be noted that for the crank rotating in anticlockwise direction, the final displacement will be less than the starting displacement.

$$\therefore \qquad x_1 = \frac{1}{2}(100+30) - \frac{1}{2}(30-100)\cos\left[\frac{\pi(2\times1-1)}{2\times3}\right] = 95.3 \text{ mm.}$$

$$\dots (\because \quad x_S = s_S \; ; \; x_F = s_F \text{ and } n = 3)$$

$$x_2 = \frac{1}{2}(100+30) - \frac{1}{2}(30-100)\cos\left[\frac{\pi(2\times2-1)}{2\times3}\right] = 65 \text{ mm}$$

and $$x_3 = \frac{1}{2}(100+30) - \frac{1}{2}(30-100)\cos\left[\frac{\pi(2\times3-1)}{2\times3}\right] = 34.7 \text{ mm}$$

The corresponding three values of θ are given by

$$\theta_j = \theta_S + \frac{\theta_F - \theta_S}{x_F - x_S}(x_j - x_S) \; ; j = 1, 2, \text{ and } 3$$

$$\therefore \qquad \theta_1 = 45 + \frac{135-45}{30-100}(95.3-100) = 51.04°$$

$$\theta_2 = 45 + \frac{135-45}{30-100}(65-100) = 90°$$

and $$\theta_3 = 45 + \frac{135-45}{30-100}(34.7-100) = 128.96°$$

Since it is given that the displacement of the slider (s) is proportional to the square of the crank rotation (θ), therefore, for the displacement from initial position (s_S) to s when crank rotates from initial position (θ_S) to θ, we have

A belt-conveyor that can transport small components.
Note : This picture is given as additional information.

$$s - s_S = C(\theta - \theta_S)^2 \qquad \ldots (\theta \text{ is expressed in degrees})$$

$$\therefore \qquad C = \frac{s - s_S}{(\theta - \theta_S)^2} = \frac{30 - 100}{(135 - 45)^2} = \frac{-7}{810} \qquad \ldots (\text{Taking } s = s_F \text{ ; and } \theta = \theta_F)$$

Now the three positions for the slider displacement (s) corresponding to the three positions of the crank angle (θ) are given by

$$s_1 = s_S + C(\theta_1 - \theta_S)^2 = 100 - \frac{7}{810}(51.4 - 45)^2 = 99.7 \text{ mm}$$

$$s_2 = s_S + C(\theta_2 - \theta_S)^2 = 100 - \frac{7}{810}(90 - 45)^2 = 82.5 \text{ mm}$$

$$s_3 = s_S + C(\theta_3 - \theta_S)^2 = 100 - \frac{7}{810}(128.96 - 45)^2 = 39.08 \text{ mm}$$

Now the three equations relating the (θ_1, s_1), (θ_2, s_2) and (θ_3, s_3) are written as

$$k_1 \times 99.7 \cos 51.04° + k_2 \sin 51.04° - k_3 = (99.7)^2$$

or $\qquad\qquad 62.7 k_1 + 0.7776 k_2 - k_3 = 9940 \qquad\qquad \ldots (i)$

Similarly, $k_1 \times 82.5 \cos 90° + k_2 \sin 90° - k_3 = (82.5)^2$

or $\qquad\qquad k_2 - k_3 = 6806 \qquad\qquad \ldots (ii)$

and $\qquad k_1 \times 39.08 \cos 128.96° + k_2 \sin 128.96° - k_3 = (39.08)^2$

or $\qquad\qquad -24.57 k_1 + 0.776 k_2 - k_3 = 1527 \qquad\qquad \ldots (iii)$

The equations (i), (ii) and (iii) are three simultaneous equations in three unknowns k_1, k_2 and k_3. On solving, we get

$$k_1 = 96.4 \text{ ; } \quad k_2 = 13\ 084 \text{ ; and } k_3 = 6278$$

We know that $\quad k_1 = 2a$, or $\quad a = k_1 / 2 = 96.4 / 2 = 48.2 \text{ mm Ans.}$

$$k_2 = 2a.c \text{ or } \quad c = k_2 / 2a = 13\ 084 / 2 \times 48.2 = 135.7 \text{ mm Ans.}$$

and $\qquad\qquad k_3 = a^2 - b^2 + c^2$

$$b^2 = a^2 + c^2 - k_3 = (48.2)^2 + (135.7)^2 - 6278 = 14\ 460$$

or $\qquad\qquad b = 120.2 \text{ mm Ans.}$

EXERCISES

1. In a four bar mechanism *PQRS*, the link *PS* is fixed. The length of the links are : *PQ* = 62.5 mm ; *QR* = 175 mm ; *RS* = 112.5 mm and *PS* = 200 mm. The crank *PQ* rotates at 10 rad/s clockwise. Find the angular velocity and angular acceleration of the links *QR* and *RS* for the values of angle *QPS* at an interval of 60°.

2. In a slider crank mechanism, the crank *AB* = 100 mm and the connecting rod *BC* = 300 mm. When the crank is at 120° from the inner dead centre, the crank shaft has a speed of 75 rad/s and an angular acceleration of 1200 rad/s² both clockwise. Find at an interval of 60° 1. the linear velocity and acceleration of the slider, and 2. the angular velocity and angular acceleration of the rod, when

(a) the line of stroke of the slider is offset by 30 mm, and

(b) the line of stroke of the slider is along the axis of rotation of the crank.

3. A mechanism is to be designed to generate the function

$$y = x^{0.8}$$

for the range $1 \le x \le 3$, using three precision points. Find the three values of x and y.

[Ans. 1.134, 2, 2.866 ; 1.106, 1.741, 2.322]

4. Determine the three precision positions of input and output angles for a mechanism to generate a function

$$y = x^{1.8}$$

when x varies from 1 to 5, using Chebyshev's spacing. Assume that the initial values for the input and output crank are 30° and 90° respectively and the difference between the final and initial values for the input and output cranks are each equal to 90°.

[Ans. 36°, 75°, 94.48°; 91.22°, 144.57°, 181.22°]

5. Synthesize a four bar linkage using Freudenstein's equation to generate the function $y = x^{1.8}$ for the interval $1 \le x \le 5$. The input crank is to start from $\theta_S = 30°$ and is to have a range of 90°. The output follower is to start at $\phi_S = 0°$ and is to have a range of 90°. Take three accuracy points at x = 1, 3 and 5.

6. A four bar function generator is used to generate the function $y = 1/x$ for $1 \le x \le 3$ between the input angle of a crank and the angle the follower makes with the frame. Find the three precision points from Chebyshev's spacing if the initial values of input angle (i.e. crank angle) and output angle (i.e. follower angle) are 30° and 200° respectively. The difference between the final and initial values of the crank and follower angles are each equal to 90°.

7. Synthesize a four bar linkage that will generate a function $y = x^{1.2}$ for the range $1 \le x \le 5$. Take three precision points : $\theta_S = 30°$; $\phi_S = 60°$ and $\Delta\theta = \Delta\phi = 90°$, where θ_S and ϕ_S represent respectively the initial angular positions of the input and output crank; $\Delta\theta$ and $\Delta\phi$ are respectively the ranges of the angular movements of the input and output crank.

8. Synthesize a four bar mechanism to generate the function $y = \log x$, where x varies between 1 and 10. Use three accuracy points with Chebyshev's spacing. Assume $\theta_S = 45°$; $\theta_F = 105°$; $\phi_S = 135°$ and $\phi_F = 225°$. Take the length of the smallest link equal to 50 mm.

9. Synthesize a four bar mechanism to move the rod AB as shown in Fig. 25.21, through the positions 1, 2 and 3. The end points A and B are used as moving pivot points.

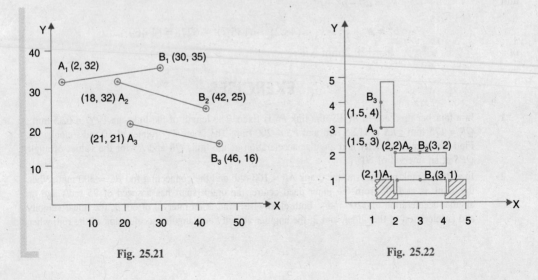

Fig. 25.21

Fig. 25.22

10. Design a four bar mechanism to guide the door in and out with little rotation until it clears the surrounding structure, after which it swings fully open to one side. The three positions of such a door under going this type of motion is shown in Fig. 25.22. The points A and B are used as moving pivots that guides the body through the three positions.

DO YOU KNOW ?

1. Explain Freudenstein's method of three point synthesis of mechanisms.
2. Derive the expressions for displacement, velocity and acceleration of a four bar mechanism.
3. What do you understand by coupler curves ? Describe the method of obtaining the co-ordinates of a coupler point in a slider crank mechanism.
4. Explain synthesis of mechanism with examples. What do you understand by
   (a) Type synthesis ;   (b) Number synthesis ; and   (c) dimensional synthesis.
5. Describe the classifications of synthesis problem.
6. Write an expression for determining the precision points.
7. Discuss the method of determining the angles for input and output link in a four bar mechanism for function generation.
8. Describe the method of designing a four bar mechanism as a function generation.

OBJECTIVE TYPE QUESTIONS

1. The analysis of mechanism deals with
   (a) the determination of input and output angles of a mechanism
   (b) the determination of dimensions of the links in a mechanism
   (c) the determination of displacement, velocity and acceleration of the links in a mechanism
   (d) none of the above

2. The synthesis of mechanism deals with
   (a) the determination of input and output angles of a mechanism
   (b) the determination of dimensions of the links in a mechanism
   (c) the determination of displacement, velocity and acceleration of the links in a mechanism
   (d) none of the above

3. The three precision points in the range $1 \leq x \leq 3$ are
   (a) 1.1, 2, 2.6   (b) 1.6, 2.5, 2.95
   (c) 1.134, 2, 2.866   (d) 1.341, 2 , 2.686

4. For a four bar mechanism, as shown in Fig. 25.23 the Freudenstein's equation is

   (a) $k_1 \cos\theta + k_2 \cos\phi + k_3 = \cos(\theta - \phi)$

   (b) $k_1 \cos\theta - k_2 \cos\phi + k_3 = \cos(\theta - \phi)$

   (c) $k_1 \cos\phi + k_2 \cos\theta + k_3 = \cos(\theta - \phi)$

   (d) $k_1 \cos\phi - k_2 \cos\theta + k_3 = \cos(\theta - \phi)$

   where $k_1 = \dfrac{d}{a}$; $k_2 = \dfrac{d}{c}$; $k_3 = \dfrac{a^2 - b^2 + c^2 + d^2}{2ac}$

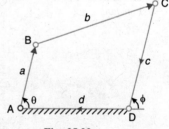

Fig. 25.23

ANSWERS

1. (c)   2. (b)   3. (c)   4. (d)

26

Automatic Control

Features

26.1. Introduction

The automatic control of system (or machine) is a very accurate and effective means to perform desired function by the system in which the human operator is replaced by a device thereby relieving the human operator from the job thus saving physical strength. The automatic control systems are also called as *self-activated systems. The* centrifugally actuated ball governor which controls the throttle valve to maintain the constant speed of an engine is an example of an automatically controlled system.

The automatic control systems are very fast, produces uniform and quality products. It reduces the requirement of human operators thus minimising wage bills.

26.2. Terms used in Automatic Control of Systems

The following terms are generally used in automatic control of systems :

1. *Command.* The result of the act of adjustment, *i.e.* closing a valve, moving a lever, pressing a button etc., is known as command.

2. *Response.* The subsequent result of the system to the command is known as response.

3. *Process control.* The automatic control of variables *i.e.* change in pressure, temperature or speed etc. in machine is termed as process control.

4. *Process controller.* The device which controls a process is called a process controller.

5. *Regulator.* The device used to keep the variables at a constant desired value is called as regulator.

6. *Kinetic control.* The automatic control of the displacement or velocity or acceleration of a member of a machine is called as kinetic control.

7. *Feed back.* It is defined as measuring the output of the machine for comparison with the input to the machine.

8. *Error detector.* A differential device used to measure the actual controlled quantity and to compare it continuously with the desired value is called an error detector. It is also known as *deviation sensor.*

9. *Transducer.* It is a device to

A rail-track maintenance machine.
Note : This picture is given as additional information.

change a signal which is in one physical form to a corresponding signal in another physical form. A Bourdon tube is an example of transducer because it converts a pressure signal into a displacement, thereby facilitating the indication of the pressure on a calibrated scale. The other examples of transducer are a loud speaker (because it converts electrical signal into a sound) and a photo-electric cell (because it converts a light signal into an electric signal). Similarly, the primary elements of all the many different forms of thermometers are transducers.

10. *Amplification.* It is defined as increasing the amplitude of the signal without affecting its waveform. For example, an error detector itself has insufficient power output to actuate the correcting mechanism and hence the error signal has to be amplified. This is generally done by employing mechanical or hydraulic or pneumatic amplifying elements like levers, gears and venturimeters etc.

26.3. Types of Automatic Control System

The automatic control systems are of the following two types :

1. *Open-loop or unmonitored system.* When the input to a system is independent of the output from the system, then the system is called an open-loop or unmonitored system. It is also called as a **calibrated system.** Most measuring instruments are open-loop control systems, as for the same input signal, the readings will depend upon things like ambient temperature and pressure. Following are the examples of open-loop system :

(*a*) A simple Bourdon tube pressure gauge commonly used for measuring pressure.

(*b*) A simple carburettor in which the air-fuel ratio adjusted through venturi remains same irrespective of load conditions.

(*c*) In traffic lights system, the timing of lights is preset irrespective of intensity of traffic.

2. *Closed-loop or monitored system.* When output of a system is measured and is continuously compared with the required value, then it is known as **closed-loop or monitored system.** In this system, the output is measured and through a feedback transducer, it is sent to an error detector which detects any error in the output from the required value thus adjusting the input in a way to get the required output. Following are the examples of a closed-loop system :

(*a*) In a traffic control system, if the flow of traffic is measured either by counting the number of vehicles by a person or by counting the impulses due to the vehicles passing over a pressure pad and then setting the time of signal lights.

(b) In a thermostatically controlled water heater, whenever the temperature of water heater rises above the required point, the thermostate senses it and switches the water heater off so as to bring the temperature down to the required point. Similarly, when the temperature falls below the required point, the thermostate switches on the water heater to raise the temperature of water to the required point.

26.4. Block Diagrams

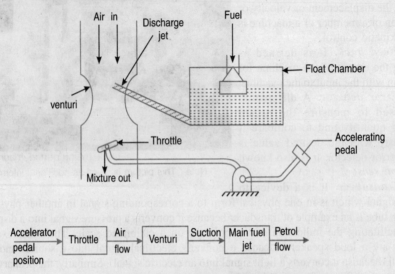

Fig. 26.1. Block diagram of a single carburettor.

The block diagrams are used to study the automatic control systems in a simplified way. In this, the functioning of a system is explained by the interconnected blocks where each block represents a labelled rectangle and is thought of as a block box with a definite function. These blocks are connected to other blocks by lines with arrow marks in order to indicate the sequence of events that are taking place. Fig. 26.1 shows the diagram of a simple carburettor. The reduction of a control system to a block diagram greatly facilitates the analysis of the system performance or response.

26.5. Lag in Response

We know that response is the subsequent result of the system to the command. In any control system, there is a delay in response (output) due to some inherent cause and it becomes difficult to measure the input and output simultaneously. This delay in response is termed as *lag in response.* For example, in steam turbines, with the sudden decrease in load, the hydraulic relay moves in the direction to close the valve. But unless the piston valve ports are made with literally zero overlap, there would be some lag in operation, since the first movement of the piston valve would not be sufficient to open the ports. This lag increases the probability of unstable operation.

26.6 Transfer Function

The transfer function is an expression showing the relation between output and the input to each unit or block of a control system. Mathematically,

$$\text{Transfer function} = \theta_o / \theta_i$$

where θ_o = Output signal of the block of a system, and

            θ_i = Input signal to the block of a system.

Thus, the output from an element may be obtained by multiplying the input signal with the transfer function.

Note : From the transfer function of the individual blocks, the equation of motion of system can be formulated.

26.7 Overall Transfer Function

In the previous article, we have discussed the transfer function of a block. A control system actually consists of several such blocks which are connected in series. The overall transfer function of the series is the product of the individual transfer function. Consider a block diagram of any control system represented by the three blocks as shown in Fig. 26.2.

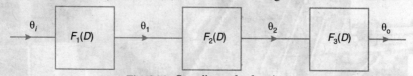

Fig. 26.2. Overall transfer function.

Thus, if F_1 (D), F_2 (D), F_3 (D) are individual transfer functions of three blocks in series, then the overall transfer function of the system is given as

$$\frac{\theta_o}{\theta_i} = \frac{\theta_1}{\theta_i} \times \frac{\theta_2}{\theta_1} \times \frac{\theta_o}{\theta_2} = F_1(D) \times F_2(D) \times F_3(D) = KG(D)$$

where K = Constant representing the overall amplification or gain, and

$G(D)$ = Some function of the operator D.

Note: The above equation is only true if there is no interaction between the blocks, that is the output from one block is not affected by its connection to the subsequent blocks.

26.8. Transfer Function for a System with viscous Damped Output

Consider a shaft, which is used to position a load (which may be pulley or gear) as shown in Fig. 26.3. The movement of the load is resisted by a viscous damping torque.

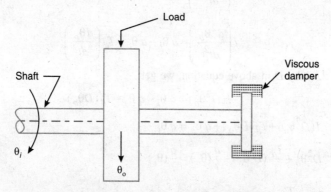

Fig. 26.3. Transfer function for a system with viscous damped output.

Let θ_i = Input signal to the shaft,

θ_o = Output signal of the shaft,

q = Stiffness of the shaft,

I = Moment of Inertia of the load, and

T_d = Viscous damping torque per unit angular velocity.

After some time t,

Twist in the shaft $\qquad = \theta_i - \theta_o$

∴ Torque transmitted to the load $\qquad = q(\theta_i - \theta_o)$

We also know that damping torque $\quad = T_d \omega_0 = T_d \left(\dfrac{d\theta_o}{dt}\right) \qquad \dots (\because \omega_0 = d\theta_o / dt)$

Material being moved via-belt conveyor.
Note : This picture is given as additional information.

According to Newton's Second law, the equation of motion of the system is given by

$$I\left(\frac{d^2\theta_o}{dt^2}\right) = q\,(\theta_i - \theta_o) - T_d\left(\frac{d\theta_o}{dt}\right) \qquad \dots (i)$$

or

$$I\left(\frac{d^2\theta_o}{dt^2}\right) = q\,\theta_i - q\,\theta_o - T_d\left(\frac{d\theta_o}{dt}\right)$$

Replacing d/dt by D in above equation, we get

$$I(D^2\theta_o) = q\,\theta_i - q\,\theta_o - T_d(D\theta_o)$$

or

$$I(D^2\theta_o) + T_d(D\theta_o) + q\,\theta_o = q\,\theta_i$$

$$D^2\theta_o + \frac{T_d}{I}(D\,\theta_o) + \frac{q}{I}(\theta_o) = \frac{q}{I}(\theta_i)$$

$$D^2\theta_o + \frac{T_d}{I}(D\,\theta_o) + (\omega_n)^2\theta_o = (\omega_n)^2\theta \qquad \dots (ii)$$

where $\qquad \omega_n$ = Natural frequency of the shaft = $\sqrt{\dfrac{q}{I}}$

Also we know that viscous damping torque per unit angular velocity,

$$T_d = 2I\xi\omega_n \quad \text{or} \quad T_d / I = 2\xi\omega_n$$

where $\qquad \xi$ = Damping factor or damping ratio.

The equation (*ii*) may now be written as

$$D^2\theta + 2\xi\omega_n(D\theta_o) + (\omega_n)^2\theta_o = (\omega_n)^2\theta_i$$

or

$$[D^2 + 2\xi\omega_n D + (\omega_n)^2]\theta_o = (\omega_n)^2\theta_i$$

∴ Transfer function $= \dfrac{\theta_o}{\theta_i} = \dfrac{(\omega_n)^2}{D^2 + 2\xi\omega_n D + (\omega_n)^2}$

$$= \dfrac{1}{T^2D^2 + 2\xi TD + 1}$$

where T = Time constant = $1/\omega_n$

Note: The time constant (T) may also be obtained by dividing the periodic time (t_d) of the undamped natural oscillations of the system by 2π. Mathematically,

$$T = \frac{t_d}{2\pi} = \frac{2\pi}{\omega_n} \times \frac{1}{2\pi} = \frac{1}{\omega_n} \qquad \dots \left(\because t_d = \frac{2\pi}{\omega_n} \right)$$

Example 26.1. *The motion of a pointer over a scale is resisted by a viscous damping torque of magnitude 0.6 N-m at an angular velocity of 1 rad/s. The pointer, of negligible inertia, is mounted on the end of a relatively flexible shaft of stiffness 1.2 N-m/rad, and this shaft is driven through a 4 to 1 reduction gear box. Determine its overall transfer function.*

If the input shaft to the gear box is suddenly rotated through 1 completed revolution, determine the time taken by the pointer to reach a position within 1 percent of its final value.

Solution. Given:

$T_d = 0.6/1 = 0.6$ N-ms/rad;

$q = 1.2$ N-m/rad

The control system along with its block diagram is shown in Fig 26.4 (*a*) and (*b*) respectively.

1. Overall transfer function

Since the inertia of the pointer is negligible, therefore the torque generated by the twisting of the shaft has only to overcome the damping torque.

Therefore

$$q(\theta_1 - \theta_o) = T_d(d\theta_o/dt)$$

where θ_1 = Output from the gear box.

∴ $q\theta_1 - q\theta_o = T_d(D\theta_o)$ ... ($\because d/dt = D$)

or $(q + T_d D)\theta_o = q\theta_1$

∴ $\dfrac{\theta_o}{\theta_1} = \dfrac{q}{q + T_d D} = \dfrac{1}{1 + (T_d/q)D} = \dfrac{1}{1 + TD}$ ...(*i*)

where T = Time constant = $T_d/q = 0.6/1.2 = 0.5$ s

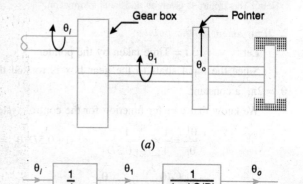

(*a*)

(*b*)

Fig. 26.4

Substituting this value in equation (i), we get

$$\frac{\theta_0}{\theta_1} = \frac{1}{1+0.5D}$$

We know that overall transfer function for the control system is

$$\frac{\theta_o}{\theta_i} = \frac{\theta_1}{\theta_i} \times \frac{\theta_2}{\theta_1} = \frac{1}{4} \times \frac{1}{(1+0.5D)} \quad \text{Ans.} \qquad \dots \left[\because \theta_1/\theta_i = \frac{1}{4}\text{(Given)}\right]$$

Aircraft engine is being assembled.

Note : This picture is given as additional information.

2. *Time taken by the pointer*

Let t = Time taken by the pointer.

Since the input shaft to the gear box is rotated through 1 complete revolution, therefore $\theta_i = 2\pi$, a constant.

We know that transfer function for the control system is

$$\frac{\theta_o}{\theta_i} = \frac{1}{4} \times \frac{1}{(1+0.5D)} \quad \text{or} \quad (1+0.5D)\,\theta_o = \frac{\theta_i}{4}$$

$$\therefore \qquad 0.5\left(\frac{d\theta_o}{dt}\right) + \theta_o = \frac{\theta_i}{4} \qquad\qquad \dots (\because D \equiv d/dt)$$

Substituting $\theta_i = 2\pi$ in the above equation, we get

$$0.5\left(\frac{d\theta_o}{dt}\right) + \theta_o = \frac{2\pi}{4} = \frac{\pi}{2}$$

or $$0.5\left(\frac{d\theta_o}{dt}\right) = \frac{\pi}{2} - \theta_o$$

Separating the variables, we get

$$\frac{d\theta}{\pi - \theta_o} = 2\,dt$$

Integrating the above equation, we get

$$-\log_e\left(\frac{\pi}{2}-\theta_o\right)=2t+\text{constant} \qquad \ldots (ii)$$

Applying initial conditions to the above equation *i.e.* when $t = 0$, $\theta_o = 0$, we get

$$\text{constant} = -\log_e\left(\frac{\pi}{2}\right)$$

Substituting the value of constant in equation (*i*),

$$-\log_e\left(\frac{\pi}{2}-\theta_o\right)=2t-\log_e\left(\frac{\pi}{2}\right)$$

or

$$\log_e\left(\frac{\pi}{2}-\theta_o\right)=-2t+\log_e\left(\frac{\pi}{2}\right)$$

∴

$$\frac{\pi}{2}-\theta_o=e^{-2t}\times\frac{\pi}{2}$$

or

$$\frac{\pi/2-\theta_o}{\pi/2}=e^{-2t}$$

i.e

$$\theta_o=\frac{\pi}{2}(1-e^{-2t}) \qquad \ldots (iii)$$

The curve depicted by above equation is shown in Fig. 26.5 and is known as *simple exponential time delay curve.*

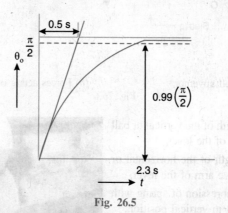

Fig. 26.5

The output θ_o will be within 1 percent of its final value when $\theta_0 = 0.99(\pi/2)$. Substituting this value in equation (*iii*), we get

$$0.99\left(\frac{\pi}{2}\right)=\frac{\pi}{2}\left(1-e^{-2t}\right)$$

$$0.99 = 1 - e^{-2t} \quad \text{or} \quad e^{-2t} = 0.01$$

∴

$$2t = \log_e 100 = 4.6 \quad \text{or} \quad t = 2.3\text{s} \textbf{ Ans.}$$

26.9. Transfer Function of a Hartnell Governor

Consider a Hartnell governor* as shown in Fig. 26.6 (*a*). The various forces acting on the governor are shown in Fig. 26.6 (*b*).

Let m = Mass of the ball

M = mass of the sleeve,

r = Radius of rotation of the governor in mid position,

Δr = Change in radius of rotation,

ω = Angular speed of rotation in mid position,

$\Delta \omega$ = Change in angular speed of rotation,

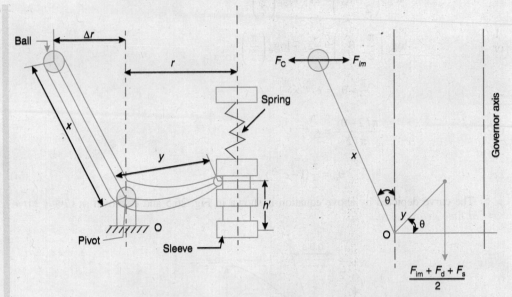

(*a*) Hartnell governor. (*b*) Forces acting on a Hartnell governor.

Fig. 26.6

x = Length of the vertical or ball arm of the lever,

y = Length of the horizontal or sleeve arm of the lever,

h = compression of spring with balls in vertical position,

h' = Displacement of the sleeve,

s = Stiffness of the spring,

c = Damping coefficient *i.e.* damping force per unit velocity, and

ξ = Damping factor.

Bucket conveyor

Note : This picture is given as additional information.

---

* For details on Hartnell governor, refer chapter 18, Art. 18.8.

The various forces acting on the governor at the given position are as follows :
1. Centrifugal force due to ball mass,

$$F_c = m(r + \Delta r)(\omega + \Delta\omega)^2$$

$$= m\left(r + \frac{x}{y}(h')\right)(\omega + \Delta\omega)^2$$

2. Inertia force of the balls, $\qquad F_{im} = m\left(\frac{x}{y}\right)\left(\frac{d^2h'}{dt^2}\right)$

3. Inertia force of the sleeve mass, $\qquad F_{iM} = M\left(\frac{d^2h'}{dt^2}\right)$

4. Damping force, $\qquad F_d = c\left(\frac{dx}{dt}\right)$

5. Spring force, $\qquad F_s = s(h + h')$

It is assumed that the load on the sleeve, weight of the balls and the friction force are negligible as compared to the inertia forces. Now, taking moments about the fulcrum O, considering only one half of the governor,

$$m\left(r + \frac{x}{y}h'\right)(\omega + \Delta\omega)^2 x = m \times \frac{x}{y}\left(\frac{d^2h'}{dt^2}\right)x + \frac{1}{2} \times M\left(\frac{d^2h'}{dt^2}\right)y$$

$$+ \frac{1}{2} \times c\left(\frac{dh'}{dt}\right)y + \frac{1}{2} \times s(h + h')y$$

Neglecting the product of small terms, we get

$$mr\omega^2 x + m \times \frac{x}{y} \times h'\omega^2 x + 2mr\omega(\Delta\omega)x$$

$$= \frac{mx^2}{y}\left(\frac{d^2h'}{dt^2}\right) + \frac{1}{2} \times M\ y\left(\frac{d^2h'}{dt^2}\right) + \frac{1}{2} \times c\ y\left(\frac{dh'}{dt}\right) + \frac{1}{2} \times s\ y(h + h')$$

$$...(i)$$

Also, we know that at equilibrium position,

$$mr\omega^2 x = \frac{1}{2} \times s\ h\ y$$

Now the equation (i) may be written as

$$\frac{1}{2} \times s\ h\ y + m \times \frac{x}{y} \times h'\omega^2 x + 2mr\ \omega(\Delta\omega)x = \frac{mx^2}{y}(D^2h') + \frac{1}{2}My(D^2h') + \frac{1}{2}c\ y(Dh')$$

$$+ \frac{1}{2}sy(h + h') \qquad ... (\because d/dt = D)$$

or $$\left(\frac{mx^2}{y}+\frac{1}{2}My\right)D^2h'+\left(\frac{1}{2}\times cy\right)Dh'+\left(\frac{1}{2}sy-\frac{mx^2}{y}\times D^2\right)h'=2mr\,\omega(\Delta\omega)x$$

Multiplying the above equation throughout by $2y$, we get

$$(2mx^2+My^2)D^2h'+(c\,y^2)dh'+(sy^2-2mx^2\omega^2)h'=4mr\,\omega(\Delta\omega)x\,y$$

$$(2mx^2+My^2)\left(D^2+\frac{cy^2}{2mx^2+My^2}+\frac{sy^2-2mx^2\omega^2}{2mx^2+My^2}\right)h'=4mr\,\omega(\Delta\omega)xy$$

or $$\left(D^2+\frac{cy^2}{2mx^2+My^2}\times D+\frac{sy^2-2mx^2\omega^2}{2mx^2+My^2}\right)h'=\frac{4mr\omega(\Delta\omega)xy}{2mx^2+My^2}$$

or $$D^2+2\xi\omega_n D+(\omega_n^2)h'=\frac{4mr\,\omega(\Delta\omega)xy}{2mx^2+My^2}$$

$\therefore$ $$h'=\frac{4mr\omega(\Delta\omega)xy}{2mx^2+My^2}\times\frac{1}{D^2+2\xi\omega_n D+(\omega_n)^2}$$

where $$2\xi\,\omega_n=\frac{cy^2}{2mx^2+My^2}$$

ξ = Damping factor, and

$$\omega_n=\text{Natural frequency}=\sqrt{\frac{sy^2-2mx^2\omega^2}{2mx^2+My^2}}$$

Thus, transfer function for the Hartnell governor,

$$=\frac{\text{Output signal}}{\text{Input signal}}=\frac{\text{Displacement of sleeve }(h')}{\text{Change in speed }(\Delta\omega)}$$

$$=\frac{4mr\,\omega xy}{2mx^2+My^2}\times\frac{1}{D^2+2\,\xi\omega_n D+(\omega_n)^2}$$

26.10. Open-Loop Transfer Function

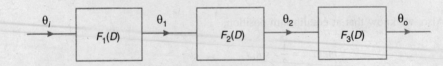

Fig. 26.7. Open loop control system.

$$\theta_i \quad \boxed{KG(D)} \quad \theta_o$$

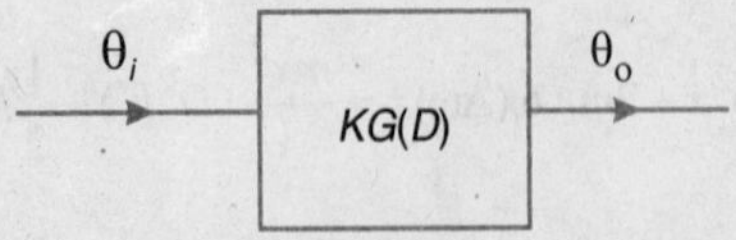

Fig. 26.8 Simplified open loop control system.

The open loop transfer function is defined as the overall transfer function of the forward path elements. Consider an open loop control system consisting of several elements having individual transfer function such $F_1(D)$, $F_2(D)$, $F_3(D)$ as shown in Fig. 26. 7. Thus

Open loop transfer function $= \dfrac{\theta_o}{\theta_i} = \dfrac{\theta_1}{\theta_i} \times \dfrac{\theta_2}{\theta_1} \times \dfrac{\theta_o}{\theta_2}$

$$= F_1(D) \times F_2(D) \times F_3(D) = KG(D)$$

The simplified block diagram of open loop transfer function is shown in Fig. 26.8.

26.11. Closed - Loop Transfer Function

The closed loop transfer function is defined as the overall transfer function of the entire control system. Consider a closed loop transfer function consisting of several elements as shown in Fig. 26.9.

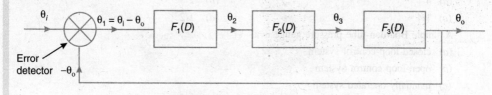

Fig 26.9 Closed-loop transfer function.

Now, for the forward path element, we know that

$$\frac{\theta_o}{\theta_1} = \frac{\theta_o}{\theta_i - \theta_o} = K \, G(D)$$

where $\qquad K \, G(D) = F_1(D) \times F_2(D) \times F_3(D)$

On rearranging, we get

$$\theta_o = K \, G \, (D)\theta_i - K \, G \, (D)\theta_o$$

or $\qquad [1 + K \, G \, (D)] \, \theta_o = K \, G \, (D)\theta_i$

$\therefore \qquad \dfrac{\theta_o}{\theta_i} = \dfrac{K \, G(D)}{1 + K \, G(D)} = \dfrac{\text{Open loop } TF}{1 + \text{Open loop } TF}$

The above expression shows the transfer function for the closed-loop control system.

Thus the block diagram may be further simplified as shown in Fig. 26.10, where the entire system is represented by a single block.

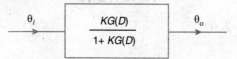

Fig. 26.10. Simplified closed-loop system.

EXERCISES

1. Define the following terms:
   (*a*) Response
   (*c*) Regulator
   (*b*) Process control
   (*d*) Transducer
2. What do you understand by open-loop and closed loop control system? Explain with an example.
3. Discuss the importance of block diagrams in control systems.

4. Draw the block diagrams for the following control systems:

   (a) A simple carburettor,

   (b) A thermostatically controlled electric furnace.

5. What is a transfer function ?

OBJECTIVE TYPE QUESTIONS

1. The device used to keep the variables at a constant desired value is called a

   (a) process controlled   (b) regulator

   (c) deviation sensor   (d) amplifier

2. The transfer function of a 4 to 1 reduction gear box is

   (a) 4   (b) 2

   (c) 1/4   (d) 1/2

3. A simple Bourdon tube pressure gauge is a

   (a) closed-loop control system

   (b) open-loop control system

   (c) manually operated system

   (d) none of the above

4. The overall transfer function of three blocks connected in series is

   (a) $\dfrac{F_1(D) \times F_2(D)}{F_3(D)}$ (b) $\dfrac{F_1(D) \times F_3(D)}{F_2(D)}$

   (c) $F_1(D) \times F_2(D) \times F_3(D)$ (d) $\dfrac{1}{F_1(D) \times F_2(D) \times F_3(D)}$

   where $F_1(D)$, $F_2(D)$ and $F_3(D)$ are the individual transfer functions of the three blocks.

5. The transfer function for a closed-loop control system is

   (a) $\dfrac{K\,G(D)}{1 + K\,G(D)}$ (b) $K\,G(D)[1 + KG(D)]$

   (c) $\dfrac{1 + K\,G(D)}{KG(D)}$ (d) $\dfrac{K\,G(D)}{1 - K\,G(D)}$

ANSWERS

1. (b)   2. (c)   3. (b)   4. (c)   5. (a)

INDEX

A

Absolute units of force, 26

Absorption dynamometers, 763

Acceleration diagram for a link, 174
— in the slider crank mechanism, 176
— of the reciprocating parts in engines, 576
— of a point on a link, 175
— of a particle moving along a circular path, 19
— moving with S.H.M., 73

Ackerman steering gear, 245

Addendum circle, 387

Addition of vectors, 7

Amplitude, 75

Angle of advance, 616
— contact, determination of, 341
— friction, 261
— obliquity, 387
— repose, 262

Angular acceleration, 18
— of the connecting rod, 525
— of the driven shaft, 249
— displacement, 17
— momentum, 25
— velocity, 18

Analytical method for inertia torque, 552

Angle relationship for function generation, 1020

Application of Kutzbach criterion to plane mechanisms, 103

Approximate analytical method for velocity and acceleration of the piston, 523
— crank positions at admission, cut-off, release and compression, 618
— straight line motion mechanisms, 236

Arc of contact of a gear, 388
— length of, 397
— recess of a gear, 388

Automatic control, 1050

Axode, 120

B

Backlash, 388

Balancing of rotating masses, 833

Band brake, simple, 741
— and block brake, 750

Beam engine, 106

Belt drive, 326
— velocity ratio of, 330
— transmission dynamometers, 767
— with idler pulleys, 329

Bennett's construction, 519

Bevel gears, 384

Bevis-Gibson flash light torsion dynamometer, 770

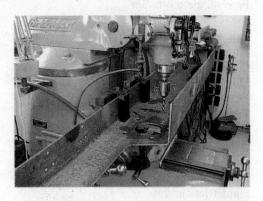

H

N

O

P

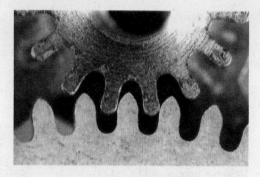

T